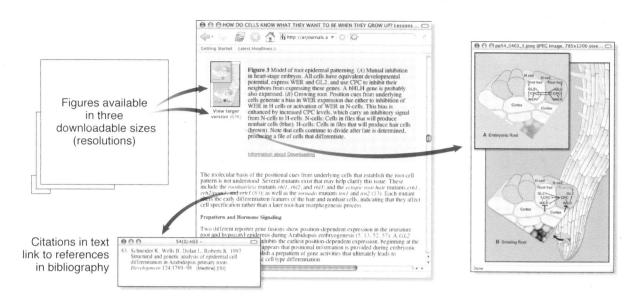

Figures available in three downloadable sizes (resolutions)

Citations in text link to references in bibliography

References in Annual Reviews chapter bibliography link out to sources of cited articles online

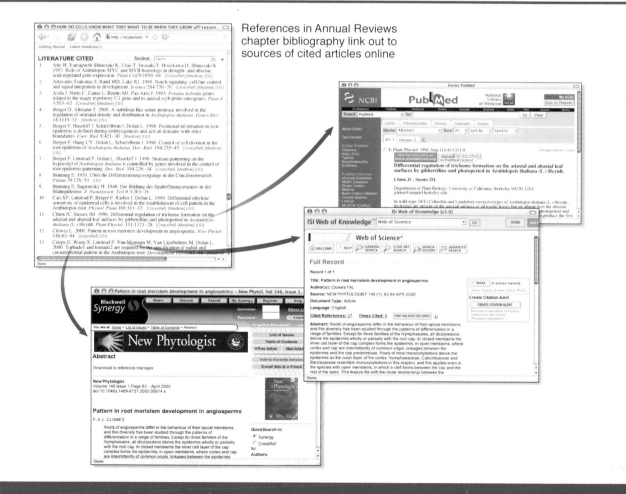

Ethel K. Smith Library

Wingate University
Wingate, North Carolina 28174

Annual Review of
Plant Biology

Annual Review of Plant Biology

Volume 57, 2006

Sabeeha Merchant, *Editor*
University of California, Los Angeles

Winslow R. Briggs, *Associate Editor*
Carnegie Institution of Washington, Stanford, California

Vicki L. Chandler, *Associate Editor*
University of Arizona

www.annualreviews.org • science@annualreviews.org • 650-493-4400

Annual Reviews
4139 El Camino Way • P.O. Box 10139 • Palo Alto, California 94303-0139

Annual Reviews
Palo Alto, California, USA

International Standard Serial Number: 1543-5008
International Standard Book Number: 0-8243-0657-0
Library of Congress Catalog Card Number: 50-13143

TYPESET BY TECHBOOKS, FALLS CHURCH, VA
PRINTED AND BOUND BY QUEBECOR WORLD BOGOTA

Contents

**Annual Review
of Plant Biology**

Volume 57, 2006

INDEXES

ERRATA

An online log of corrections to *Annual Review of Plant Biology* chapters (if any, 1977 to
the present) may be found at http://plant.annualreviews.org/

Related Articles

Sarah P. Gibbs

Looking at Life: From Binoculars to the Electron Microscope

Sarah P. Gibbs

Department of Biology, McGill University, Montreal, Quebec H3A 1B1, Canada;
email: chezgibbs@aol.com

Annu. Rev. Plant Biol.
2006. 57:1–17

The *Annual Review of
Plant Biology* is online at
plant.annualreviews.org

doi: 10.1146/
annurev.arplant.57.032905.105413

First published online as a
Review in Advance on
November 8, 2005

1543-5008/06/0602-
0001$20.00

Contents

EARLY YEARS

I was born on May 25, 1930, in Boston's Lying-In Hospital. The only detail Mother ever told me about my birth, and she told me often, was how glorious the apple blossoms were when Dad drove her over Belmont Hill en route to the hospital. My mother was a great lover of the out-of-doors. We would leave our dinners cold on the table and rush outside to see a magnificent sunset. On our many drives to the country, Mother would make Dad pull over to admire a spectacular view. In the fall she exclaimed over every red sugar maple. An eclipse was not to be missed. So even as a very young child, I learned to look admiringly at the world around me.

In reading other botanists' chapters, I have noticed how many have come from farming or working class families and have often been the first generation to go to college. I came from privilege. Mother's father, Willard Converse Hill, was a remarkable man, a descendant of George Washington's first cousin. He was related to a number of distinguished Americans: King Carter, an early governor of Virginia, Admiral Byrd, and the Senators Byrd. Grandpa became an insurance broker. After the Chelsea fire of 1908 bankrupted his firm, he joined another brokerage and was soon made a partner. The firm prospered and he became a rich man. He married Clara Laycock, who attended Boston University, unusual for a woman born in 1870. Grandpa doted on his only daughter Edith and spoiled her rotten, giving her a Crosby cat boat as her graduation present from Smith College. When she married my father, he built her a large beautiful house next door to his house in Lexington. My father, Winthrop Harold Bowker, was a shy but brilliant man, who graduated second in his class from Harvard's School of Engineering. His professors wanted him to stay on for a Ph.D., but he chose to work for the New England Telephone and Telegraph Company, where he rose to be second in command under the Chief Engineer. He had a wry sense of humor, bemoaning

that he was fated to be always second, never first. When asked, "Where did Sally get her brains?" he would reply, "From her mother. I still have mine."

Dad was the son of a doctor, Everett M. Bowker, who grew up in Machias, Maine, and came south to attend Harvard Medical School. Unfortunately, he died young of a heart attack in 1923, leaving his widow, Lucy Griggs Bowker, a large gloomy house in Brookline and three sons to support her and their two younger sisters. Most of Everett Bowker's patients were the poor of Roxbury, and he did not collect his fees. Grandma Bowker was furious when Dad left home to marry my mother five years later. Her oldest son Phil, a Massachusetts state senator, was the dutiful son and did not marry until he was 50.

Being born to privilege had definite advantages for a woman scientist. Although I didn't have any role model of a married woman who worked outside the home, the women all had well-to-do husbands to support them, and I assumed I would, too. And I knew that in a bind, there was always family money. Thus, I could start graduate school with no support in hand; later, when I looked for jobs, I could simply accept the low salary offered, as long as the job gave me the freedom to pursue my own research.

Coming from a prosperous family does not mean that I came from a happy one. My mother was the dominant force in my life. She was smart, energetic, completely unaware of other people's feelings, and extremely controlling. To my friends' delight, she gave my sister Ann and me fantastic birthday and Halloween parties with wonderful treasure hunts complete with rhyming clues. Everyone said she was a remarkable woman. Those who knew her best said my father was a saint to put up with her. I was middle-aged before I realized she was mentally ill. A psychiatrist has told me she was unipolar manic. One minute she'd be in a state of feverish excitement, the next she'd flash into a terrible rage. Ann and I took the brunt of her anger. She screamed at us daily and pummeled us often. My sister fought back, but I was cowed and took whatever she doled out. I was a timid, fearful child, trying to stay out of Mother's way, but always attracted back by her dynamism. I adored my tall handsome gentle father who never even raised his voice against us. Early in the marriage, he gave up arguing with Mother and meekly followed her orders, but more and more he absented himself from the house in the evening, serving as an air-raid warden in the Second World War and later as Town Selectman for many years. The only thing I was ever allowed to do alone with my father was to row out to the boat and bring it in to the dock. There Mother and a host of friends and relatives would be waiting for a day's excursion across the bay to Marion or a fishing expedition off Scraggy Neck.

LOOKING AT BIRDS

At age 13, I made one of the best decisions of my life. I would obtain the Girl Scout badge on Birds. I knew a few birds, robins and the bluebirds, which nested outside my bedroom window in Lexington. At Grandpa's summer house on Cape Cod, I could identify herring gulls, common terns, kingfishers, and great blue herons. But nothing prepared me for the whole new world I was about to enter. Mrs. Devereux, a kindly woman and accomplished birder, was a volunteer resource person for the Scouts. At her insistence, my parents bought me my first binoculars, a second-hand pair of 7 × 35s, an excellent choice, and *A Field Guide to the Birds* by Roger Tory Peterson. And I was off. I was Mrs. Devereux's only pupil, and I bicycled to her house almost daily. Birding quickly became my grand passion, and I am as passionate about it now as I was then. From Mrs. Devereux, I graduated to the Brookline Bird Club, which ran weekly field trips to all the best birding spots around Boston. I'd get up very early on a Saturday morning and go by bus and trolley to Boston's North Station where the group met. It was wartime, so we went by train to Ipswich or Newburyport and then walked all day along the marshes to the coast. I have seldom been happier. Not only was I seeing all sorts of exciting birds (nine snowy owls on one winter's trip), but for the first time, I'd gotten away from Mother. The trip from Lexington to Newburyport for a 14-year-old was as big an adventure as a trip to the Galapagos for a 40-year-old. Mother did not approve. Girl Scouts were all right, but the Brookline birders were not fit company for her teenage daughter: a few scraggly boys, older men, one or two married couples, a number of aging spinsters. Where was I going to find a husband there? My mother's goals for me were to be popular with the boys, marry well, have three or four children, and devote myself to them. For every Saturday bird trip I went on, I could not go on another until I had been to a dreary dance with a boy she approved of.

UNDERGRADUATE YEARS AT CORNELL UNIVERSITY

My passion for birds gave me my first scientific goal. I would proudly announce to my high school classmates that I was going to be an ornithologist and study birds in Mexico. But I did not intend to go alone. I planned to marry an ornithologist and write books with him. And that was pretty much how my life unfolded in the next few years.

My love of birds nixed Mother's plans for me to follow her footsteps and go to Smith College. Cornell was the place to go for ornithology. In April of my junior year at Lexington High School, Mother drove me to Ithaca, New York, for an interview with a young admissions officer, Robert Storandt. It is hard to imagine now, but Mother went to the interview, too. She and Mr. Storandt did virtually all the talking. Mr. Storandt suggested I apply for a Cornell National Scholarship, which I did and won one. It was a princely sum, $4800, which covered four years' tuition (read this and weep, $600 a year) and room and board (also $600 a year). But the checks were sent to my parents. Even after I was married and living in an apartment, I still had to ask them for my scholarship money. As a reward for winning the scholarship, my parents gave me $100 to buy a more powerful pair of binoculars. I made my way to downtown Boston, and bought a second-hand pair of 10 × 50 German binoculars, a souvenir brought back from the war by a U.S. soldier.

My years at Cornell were paradise. I enrolled in the College of Arts and Sciences and majored in zoology, but took a host of courses in the College of Agriculture, three courses in ornithology, vertebrate taxonomy, ichthyology, general botany and plant taxonomy, entomology and insect taxonomy, and basic genetics. I took genetics in the fall of 1951, but DNA was not mentioned. I learned a huge amount about the natural world, but no math or physics and only a watered-down chemistry course for Ag students and an uninspiring organic chemistry course. The fact that I took no course in physiology or biochemistry probably explains why I have remained a visual, largely descriptive, scientist all my life.

My social life at Cornell revolved around Jordani, a club of naturalists with a wonderful professor, Howie Evans of the Vet School, as our faculty advisor. We had Friday night meetings and field trips almost every weekend. All my good friends, many of whom I am still in touch with today, were Jordani members. I estimate over 80% of Jordani members went on to do Ph.D.s, and many became leaders in their field.

Looking back at my undergraduate years, I try to remember if I did anything particularly creative. Certainly not in my science courses, although I frequently got the top mark in the class. I diligently took copious notes and studied hard, and once I knew my notes and the textbook, I did the very unimaginative thing of reading another elementary textbook on the subject. This meant I picked up basic facts the professor thought he had covered but hadn't. (All my professors were men, of course.) During my freshman year, I took World History with Professor Fox. This was a very difficult course for me as it required voluminous amounts of reading. I prepared for the exams by asking myself broad general questions and preparing carefully reasoned answers using a wide range of examples. I was usually able to use large parts of one or more of these syntheses in the exams. On the basis of my exam answers, Professor Fox called me into his office in June and said I had been selected to be one of an experimental group of eight or ten students who would take no formal courses at Cornell, but would read on their own and be tutored by individual professors. He was very surprised when I said I was majoring in zoology and declined his offer. What a different life I would have had if I'd accepted! I am a klutz with machines (and the electron microscope is a very temperamental one). Often, in sheer frustration that the scope had broken down once again, I would think I should have accepted Dr. Fox's offer. Then I would only have to read, think, and write, and I would never again have to cope with another broken machine.

The most imaginative thing I did as an undergraduate was to form a girls' basketball team. At that time Cornell had no girls' intercollegiate basketball team. Almost all women's sports were intramural, with sorority teams playing dormitory teams. Freshman year I was rushed by Delta Gamma, which had a superb basketball team, but I did not receive a bid. That fall I took basketball as my gym elective, and there was a group of terrific players in the class. My dorm team was dreadful, so I convinced the best players in my gym class to form a team, which I modestly named Sally's Sneakers. We promptly won the intramural championship, taking the gigantic silver cup away from Delta Gamma the year it would have become permanently theirs. We won the cup the next two years, but by our senior year, half of us were married and Sally's Sneakers disbanded.

To my mother's and my delight, I found at Cornell a very intelligent and handsome husband, Bob Gibbs, who was as avid a birdwatcher as I was. We married in June, 1951, at the end of my junior and his senior year. Then we headed to Woods Hole, Massachusetts, where Bob had a job at the Aquarium and I taught birds and insects at the Children's School of Science, a job I loved and would do another four summers.

LOOKING AT CELLS

As a high school senior, I had studied the Cornell catalog and read the descriptions of the required courses for a zoology major: introductory zoology, comparative anatomy, histology and organology, and embryology. I liked the sound of all of them except histology: the study of tissues such as epithelia, muscle, and nerve, and organs like liver, kidney, and lungs—how dreadfully dull it sounded! But it turned out to be the most amazing of all my Cornell science courses. For the first time I was seeing a whole new world with a simple compound microscope. The course was very well taught by William Wimsatt and his graduate students. His technicians prepared a set of 100 slides for each student. In the lab we stained the slides, then studied them in detail. I was amazed at the beauty and complexity of the tissues and organs I saw, striated and cardiac muscle, the retina, the kidney—how astonishing they all were!

When I graduated from Cornell in 1952 at the top of my class, not a single professor asked me to do graduate work with him. Young men with stellar undergraduate records were being flown all over the country by universities like Cal Tech and Harvard. Bob had started his Ph.D. in ichthyology, so I, like most other graduate student wives, started on my Ph.T. (putting hubby through). I decided to do a Master's degree with a major in zoology and a minor in education so I could support Bob by teaching high school science. I asked my favorite professor, Perry Gilbert, who had taught me comparative anatomy, if I could be his graduate student. The first project he suggested did not work out, and I had already gravitated to Wimsatt's active lab where his technicians taught me how to fix, embed, and cut tissues. Dr. Gilbert then suggested I study the buccal gland of the lake lamprey. This small gland secretes an anticoagulant, which allows lampreys to suck the blood of fishes. Dr. Gilbert got me mature feeding lampreys from local fishermen. And when the lampreys came up the streams, which drained into Lake Cayuga, to spawn and die, it was easy to wade in the water and simply pick up breeding or dying lampreys. I have never been squeamish. I studied the histology of the gland throughout the life cycle of the lamprey, including its embryological development during the larval stage. I wrote my Master's thesis in the spring and summer of 1954. To my dismay, Gilbert tore my first draft to pieces and taught me how to write a scientific thesis, a huge gift, for after that no professor had to help me write a thesis or a paper.

With my Master's degree and new teaching qualifications in hand, I promptly went looking for a teaching job. But so many Cornell professors and graduate students had wives who were teachers that there wasn't a vacant high school teaching position within a hundred-mile radius of Ithaca. Thus I became a technician for Marcus Singer, a new zoology professor, and stained a dog's brain. The large slides had been prepared at Harvard, and all I had to do was stain them. It was mindless, tedious work. I decided this was the time to have a baby. My daughter, Betsy Gibbs, was born July 4, 1955, by far the best part of my mother's agenda for me to date.

LOOKING AT ALGAE

Six weeks later, Bob had finished his Ph.D., and the three of us headed off to Plattsburgh State Teacher's College in upstate New York, where Bob had a job replacing a professor on sabbatical. The less said about our year there the better, but I was content being the good stay-at-home mother I had been programmed to be. However, to keep my sanity, I took calculus three afternoons a week. By Christmas, Bob had landed a research position at Woods Hole Oceanographic Institution, and I joyfully started preparing a new course in earth science to teach at the Children's School of Science the following summer.

In the fall of 1956, I decided to look for a half-time technician's job at the Marine Biological Laboratory (MBL). Albert Szent-Györgyi had a world-famous lab there, but he didn't need a technician. There were only three other scientists working at MBL that winter; I read the descriptions of their research. I liked Ralph Lewin's amusing description of his experiments on mating in *Chlamydomonas*, walked up to his office, and asked if he could use a part-time technician. I had no idea this simple action would change the rest of my research life. Lewin hired me on the spot simply because I was pretty, but he soon realized I was also intelligent, and he treated me like a graduate student. Monday afternoons I had to transfer Ralph's numerous algal cultures and Fridays I had to wash dishes, but Tuesdays through Thursdays, I could work on any research problem I chose. Even at that early date, MBL had an electron microscope (EM) run by an excellent microscopist, Del Philpott, and I decided I wanted to look at the flagella of *Chlamydomonas* and those of the paralyzed mutants of *C. moewusii* Ralph had made during his Ph.D. at Yale. Even though my first attempts at fixation were very poor, once again I was fascinated by the new world I was getting my first glimpse of. Under Ralph's tutelage, I was doing research at the forefront of biology, and I loved it. Being a helpmate to my husband had lost its luster, and I decided to apply to Harvard University to do a Ph.D. Ralph recommended that I work with Kenneth Thimann, and I went to see him in November 1957. He said he'd accept me as his graduate student, provided Radcliffe admitted me. I replied, "I'll get into Radcliffe all right." My sassy rudeness should have warned Thimann he wasn't going to like me.

By chance my husband landed an assistant professorship at Boston University to begin January 1958. I had been accepted by Radcliffe, and I was able to start my Ph.D. immediately because I had a husband to support me. Also, I was confident I could win a Na-

tional Science Foundation Fellowship to start in the fall term of 1958. (I did, one of only six botanists in the country to do so.) I had a brief meeting with Thimann when I arrived. He set up my courses and my graduate research problem, to determine if auxin affected the growth of the alga *Acetabularia*, and promptly left to spend the spring semester in India.

I took an exciting, eclectic mix of courses my first term at Harvard, the best being biochemistry lab, taught by Norman Krinsky, and electron microscopy, taught by a young assistant professor, George Chapman. However, I was shocked and dismayed at how slowly *Acetabularia* grew.

In June, Bob and I returned for one last summer in Woods Hole. Without any input from Thimann, I decided to take the MBL summer course on the algae. It was a superb course taught by Harold Bold and Richard Starr with Annette Coleman as demonstrator. Ralph Lewin's collection had been mostly of green algae. In this course, I saw examples of almost all the classes of algae. We had wonderful field trips to the best collecting spots, including a trip to Penikese, the island where Agassiz had founded MBL many years earlier. We collected over 60 species of red, green, and brown seaweeds, which we took back to the lab and mounted on herbarium sheets. Those six weeks I spent looking at algae in all their amazing diversity were to shape my scientific thinking for the rest of my life.

However, I did not fare well when I returned to Thimann's lab in the fall. In our first research conference, I told Thimann how discouraged I was by *Acetabularia*'s slow growth. "I could have a baby between each experiment." I told him I had talked with an *Acetabularia* expert from Germany who was in Woods Hole that summer, and he had warned me that I would never be able to get the alga bacteria-free and, worse, that growth in *Acetabularia* was too irregular to see an auxin effect even if there were one. At the end of our interview, Thimann asked me where I wanted to be in 10 years. I replied, "Just where you are, Professor Thimann." He was appalled by my flippancy and my absurd aspiration to be a professor at Harvard. That night I wrote a detailed research plan, proposing to look at pyrenoid and chloroplast ultrastructure in the different classes of algae, and left it with Thimann's secretary in the morning. I said if I made no progress on my research in six months, I would return to the *Acetabularia* problem. By noon, I had a brief note in my mailbox from Thimann telling me I would have to find another supervisor, preferably, but not necessarily, at Harvard. The note concluded, and I still remember his words verbatim after all these years: "This decision arises not just from the nature of the research problem, but from the realization that our attitudes towards graduate studies have nothing in common." I had to go to microbiology lab that afternoon, where soon everyone had seen Thimann's letter and commiserated with me. After the lab, I walked up to George Chapman's office and asked if I could be his graduate student. After a brief phone call to Thimann, "He says you are in a hurry to be through," he welcomed me warmly to his lab. My career as an electron microscopist had begun.

LOOKING AT CHLOROPLASTS

Harvard Years

My interest in chloroplasts had been piqued when I first saw the pyrenoid of *Chlamydomonas*. I thought this large prominent structure was the cell's nucleus. Lewin assured me it was part of the chloroplast, made conspicuous by the shell of starch grains surrounding it, and that no one knew what it did. During my first term at Harvard, I had futilely tried to isolate pyrenoids as my project in the biochemistry lab course. It would be years before I tried to be a biochemist again. Now that I was officially Chapman's student, I was determined to look at pyrenoid structure in all the classes of algae I could. I was able to grow or collect 24 pyrenoid-containing species of algae belonging to eight different classes. I soon discovered that pyrenoids in all algae were basically the same. They were a region of the chloroplast that contained a dense, finely granular material and where the thylakoids were reduced in number or even completely absent. It would be another decade before Holdsworth (11) showed that this dense material was the abundant Calvin cycle enzyme, Rubisco. I quickly became fascinated by the ultrastructure of the chloroplast itself, for the thylakoids displayed an amazing variety of configurations in the different algal classes, from single thylakoids in red algae, to loosely associated pairs in cryptomonads, to loose triplets in brown algae, to bands of tightly appressed thylakoids in the other classes (2, 3). In the different classes, the thylakoid bands often took distinctive paths. These observations made a beautiful thesis and produced six papers, five of them in 1962, which astonished the phycological world. The phycologists were also delighted that each class of algae had a characteristic chloroplast ultrastructure, confirming their taxonomies. This was not surprising since the algae had been classified mainly on the basis of their chloroplast pigments. No one suspected then that basing algal taxonomy on their chloroplasts was almost the worst cell structure they could have chosen.

I did make one completely unexpected discovery, that in a number of algal classes the chloroplasts are surrounded by four, not two, membranes (4). I called the extra two membranes the outer envelope of the chloroplast. Ben Bouck (1) saw ribosomes on the cytoplasmic surface of the outermost membrane and named the two membranes chloroplast endoplasmic reticulum (ER), the name that stuck. It would take me 17 more years before I realized what the presence of these extra membranes meant.

That I, working alone, could see and describe so many new structures in only three years of work was due almost entirely to George Chapman's expertise and his selfless dedication to his many students. George had eight or nine graduate students working in his lab. Most were working for other professors, only a few were working on his research. Electron microscopy was a very difficult technique in the late 1950s. George made the scope's apertures by hand, and we all learned to cut sections on the ultramicrotome he had built. He taught us all how to correct astigmatism (hours of work in those days), but often it was only George who could get the microscope working properly. It is thanks to Chapman that we all succeeded.

Also, my three years working with Ralph Lewin had taught me how to grow algae, and Bold's course had taught me where to collect the seaweeds I wanted. Ralph gave me a number of his algal stocks, as did another Woods Hole mentor, Bob Guillard. A quick trip to Seymour Hutner at Pace University in New York netted me *Ochromonas danica*. Unlike higher plants, most algae synthesize chlorophyll in the dark. *Euglena gracilis* was the notable exception, but so many people were working on *Euglena*, I feared I'd be scooped if I studied chloroplast development in *Euglena*. *Ochromonas*, a small unicellular Chrysophyte alga that grows like a weed (one division every nine hours), would become my alga of choice when I started doing experiments on, as well as looking at, chloroplasts.

My last year at Harvard (1962) was a tumultuous one. The day after I defended my thesis on November 1, 1961, I started a National Institutes of Health postdoc with Bill Sistrom working on a photosynthetic bacterium, *Rhodospirillum molischianum*. Too late, I had the type of supervisor I should have had much earlier. Bill designed each of my experiments, taught me the techniques himself, and was so interested in my results, he stood behind me as I read the optical density of bacteriochlorophyll on a spectrophotometer. But I knew that it was more important that I write the five papers on my thesis first. These I did at night. I was in terrible conflict. I did just manage to send off the last paper to the *Journal of Cell Biology* (5) before I entered Massachusetts General Hospital with what was diagnosed as rheumatoid arthritis, but was

probably a first attack of multiple sclerosis (MS). I was prescribed three months of complete bed rest. Calamities often come in threes. Before the year was out, my father died an agonizing death from kidney cancer, and my husband and I divorced.

Edinburgh Years

The only way I knew how to live was as a wife and marry again I did, to Ronald Poole, an Englishman I'd met when he was a Fulbright fellow in Thimann's lab. Fortunately, following this husband led me to an excellent academic career! When I married Ron, he was a lecturer in Jack Dainty's Biophysics Department at the University of Edinburgh. This was a superb department in one of the world's most beautiful cities. I took my NIH postdoctoral fellowship to the Department of Bacteriology. Just as I was finishing my *Rhodospirillum* studies, I saw an ad in *Nature*. C.H. Waddington was hiring four independent researchers to staff his new Epigenetics Research Group. Not knowing he had already selected the four young men he wanted to hire, I hastily put in an application. In our interview, Waddington told me that one of the men he had hired could not come for a few years, and he would like to offer me the position until then. But there was one small problem. He could not offer me the salary (£1500) advertised in *Nature*, for he had a senior woman in his department who was only making £1000 a year. I said, "That's fine with me, Professor Waddington. I am hoping to have a baby, and when I do, I'll take four months off." To my great joy, on April 13, 1964, my son, Christopher Poole, was born. Wad sent me his warmest congratulations.

Waddington was an excellent supervisor to have. All four of us pursued completely independent research problems. I happily returned to chloroplasts. By late 1963, it was known that both chloroplasts and mitochondria possessed DNA. The dense 18-nm particles I'd earlier seen in chloroplasts and pointed out their similarity to Palade particles (yes, that's what ribosomes were first called), I now confidently called chloroplast ribosomes. In the next few years, mitochondrial ribosomes would be discovered and characterized. In my field, the hot new technique, both literally and figuratively, was electron microscopic autoradiography. I gratefully learned the technique from Joe Jacob in the Institute of Animal Genetics and would continue to use it for the next decade. I designed my big experiment to determine if chloroplast and mitochondrial RNA (almost all of which could be safely assumed to be ribosomal RNA) were synthesized without a lag as would happen if they were coded for by organelle DNA. Labeled RNA in animal cells was known to appear in the cytoplasm only after a considerable lag period, since cytoplasmic ribosomes are synthesized in the nucleus. I chose greening cells of *Ochromonas danica* for my study because the number of chloroplast ribosomes increases markedly (10-fold) during chloroplast development. Thus, I labeled cells of *Ochromons* at two stages of greening with tritiated uridine for a short and a long interval. Some labeled cells I fixed and embedded by standard techniques. Others I fixed by a more time-consuming method and embedded in water-soluble medium, so sections could be digested with RNase prior to autoradiography. It was dawn when I put the last cells in embedding medium. I remember my exhilaration driving home and how glorious the Pentland Hills were in the early morning light. The experiment showed what I predicted, that chloroplasts and mitochondria synthesize their own ribosomal RNA. But it would take me more than three years before I finished this one experiment, and by then I was on another continent and had a new job!

McGill Years

In early July 1965, Ron, Betsy, one-year-old Chris, and I embarked on the Empress of Canada for Montreal. Ron had been appointed assistant professor in the Department of Botany at McGill University. I had not been interviewed, but I was promised that an assistant professorship would be created for me in a year, and it was. The brand new Stewart Biology Building had been built with a ground floor suite of seven rooms especially designed for electron microscopy. All three biology departments, Botany, Genetics, and Zoology, wanted the new electron microscopist, and especially the suite of rooms, to be in their department; thus, I was appointed in all three departments. The first year, each department chipped in $1000 from technician funds to create a half-time salary for me. "Sally, you will be glad to work half-time so you can get your house furnished and your curtains hung." But I promptly got to work on my research full time. Skip Sheldon in the Pathology Department let me use his EM and generously paid all my darkroom expenses, and Joe Jacob, back in Edinburgh, developed my grids at appropriate intervals and mailed them to me. Without these two men, my three-year experiment would have gone down the drain. The next April, the National Research Council (NRC) awarded me the largest equipment grant they had ever awarded, the magnificent sum of $60,000, enough to buy the best EM and all the accessory equipment. I also received a good three-year grant for my own research. The reason I, before I was even officially on the academic staff, received such a large equipment grant was that there had been money in the Stewart Biology Building funds for an EM, but it had been usurped by the Dean of Medicine. He promised to repay it if I did not get a grant for a microscope from the NRC, where he was a distinguished committee member. When McGill appointed me an assistant professor in September 1966, I had already ordered a Philips EM 200, found a bright young Ph.D. student, Tiiu Slankis, and employed an excellent technician, Peter Lea. Peter would do most of the work of installing all the EM equipment and designing my research/teaching lab in the adjacent large, but unfinished, room I had promptly acquired. It would be another 10 years before my curtains were hung.

Coming to McGill when I was just learning the technique of autoradiography was fortuitous. C.P. Leblond, who had invented the technique, was chairman of McGill's Anatomy Department. Every year he invited me to give a seminar, and he was on the committee that promoted me to full professor after only eight years in the ranks. At my first seminar I showed that chloroplasts and mitochondria like the nucleolus were heavily labeled with H^3-uridine after a 30-minute labeling time, whereas the cytoplasm only became labeled after two hours. This strongly suggested that both chloroplast and mitochondria synthesize their own RNA, although it was troubling that I had to use 30 minutes as my short labeling interval. EM sections are so thin, it is very difficult to get enough radioactivity into them. Leblond asked me if I labeled the cells for only 5 minutes, would all the silver grains be localized only over the chloroplast DNA? I snappily retorted, "I'd love to do that experiment, Professor Leblond, but even with a 30-minute labeling period, I had to expose my sections for 6 months. If I only labeled for 5 minutes, I'd have to wait 3 years before developing the grids!" But that night I couldn't get Leblond's question out of my mind. Maybe the labeled RNA, presumably largely ribosomal, would be nearer the chloroplast DNA at 30 minutes than it would be after the two-hour labeling period. My biophysicist husband doubted this, calculating that a 18-nm chloroplast ribosome would diffuse to the center of the chloroplast in minutes. Chloroplast DNA in *Ochromonas* is localized in a single nucleoid, which encircles the periphery of the chloroplast. Thus, with a simple transparent measuring device I made, it was easy to measure the distance of each silver grain from the chloroplast nucleoid in the more than 500 electron micrographs I had. Also, I could be absolutely certain there was no unseen chloroplast DNA lurking just above or below the level of the section. To my astonishment, after 30 minutes, the labeled RNA was concentrated over (28%) or near the chloroplast DNA, and at two hours, labeled RNA was randomly dis-

tributed throughout the chloroplast (6, 7). I could not have gotten better morphological proof that chloroplast DNA codes for chloroplast RNA, and it was all thanks to Leblond's question.

I did one more experiment before turning over all lab work to my graduate students and postdocs. This experiment was so intricate and time-consuming that no one else ever did a similar one. When I began neither the size nor kinetic complexity of chloroplast DNA was known. My first thought when I realized that the chloroplast DNA of *Ochromonas* was localized in a single peripheral nucleoid was that the chloroplast might contain a single DNA molecule. Because the single chloroplast of *Ochromonas* divides just prior to mitosis and cell division, I would label one strand of chloroplast DNA and show à la Meselson and Stahl that after a chase of one generation, the number of chloroplasts labeled would be cut in half, and cut in half again each succeeding generation. I labeled light-grown cells of *Ochromonas* with tritiated thymidine for three hours (0.36 generations), and prepared autoradiographs of the cells at 0, 1.0, 2.2, and 3.3 generations in unlabeled medium. To know whether the cell's chloroplast was labeled or not, it was necessary to do this at the light microscope level and cut serial sections through entire chloroplasts. Slides of 10–12 serial 1-μm sections were prepared and dipped in photographic emulsion. It took an average of 7 sections to traverse an entire chloroplast (range 4 to 11). After the slides were developed and stained, I confess I hired a talented undergraduate, Rose Mak, to do the analysis. She would select a large cluster of cells, number each one, draw each cell in detail, then draw the cluster in each successive section. By this method she could follow each individual cell. She chose only those cells in which the entire chloroplast was sectioned and then counted the total number of silver grains over the chloroplast. For each variable, Rose analyzed 60 to 80 chloroplasts. Our results were the exact opposite of what I predicted. After the three-hour labeling period, every chloroplast was labeled. After 1.0, 2.2, and 3.3 generations of chase in cold medium, every cell's chloroplast was also labeled, with total mean labeling cutting in half each generation. At each generation, the numbers of grains per chloroplast followed a Poisson distribution, indicating equal labeling of all progeny chloroplasts. I calculated that the chloroplast of *Ochromonas* contained at least 10 segregating DNA molecules. This is the paper I am most proud of because it was a complex experiment combining math and statistics with meticulous observations. My husband quickly showed me my first calculations were off by a factor of two, and I gratefully gave him coauthorship (9).

Graduate students. I have been lucky and during my 33-year career at McGill have worked with a grand group of graduate students and postdoctoral fellows. I liked to have two (occasionally three) graduate students and a postdoctoral fellow in my lab, plus an EM technician whose salary the department paid. Most readers will be surprised that in my years at McGill, I only graduated 5 Ph.D. students and 12 M.Sc. students and had a total of 6 postdoctoral fellows. I discovered early that bright men did not want to do a Ph.D. under a woman professor, but very intelligent women had no such qualms. Thus, in my lab, the professor was female, all the graduate students and postdoctoral fellows were female, and the technicians were male, and I completely reversed the sex roles of a typical scientific laboratory. Late in my career, I did have two M.Sc. students and one Ph.D. student who were male. Of course the women I trained also faced many obstacles in pursuing an academic career, so my chapter won't be studded with the names of students and postdocs who are so eminent that many readers will recognize them. But I am very proud of my students. Even my M.Sc. students got a good paper out of their thesis. And all have led interesting and rewarding lives, two as physicians, several as research associates with eminent men. Among the others, there is a scientific illustrator, a flourishing translator, a director of research grants, an ethics counselor for a medical faculty, a scientific writer, and the founder of a very successful business, now happily retired. Two recent graduates, two of the nicest people I know, are working as technicians while raising two sons each. Of my postdoctoral fellows, only two have careers in academia, Rose Ann Cattolico, a professor at the University of Seattle, and Geneviève Bricheux, at the Université de Clermont-Ferrand II. A third, Marcelle Gillott, ran an EM Center at the University of Milwaukee, when she was tragically killed in a freak accident 10 years ago. Two recent Ph.D. students, who were my most independent and creative students, are pursuing research careers at universities: Martha Ludwig at the University of Western Australia and Mike McKay at Bowling Green State University in Ohio.

Teaching. Research did not come easily to me. I was a careful plodder, a perfectionist, and as I've already said, a klutz with machines. But I am a born teacher. Like many basically shy people, I come alive on a stage. I love every minute of teaching. I am not a fluent speaker, but I am interesting, and I try above all to be clear. I ask a lot of questions. And on my best days, I can be hilarious. You can't plan jokes ahead of time, you play on your Freudian slips, and I make lots of them, and you have to be willing to make a complete fool of yourself!

I don't like to be told what to teach. I like to develop a subject in my own way, from the original literature, using textbooks only for background information. Thus I was fortunate to be appointed at McGill in an area where no one was teaching. In the 1960s, a junior electron microscopist, male or female, was often expected to do EM research for other staff members. Several professors wanted me to do research for them. I told them that what I would do was teach their graduate students to do electron microscopy. Thus, the first course I set up was "Techniques in Electron Microscopy," open to six graduate students who had problems they wanted to pursue at the EM level. The first year the course officially met one afternoon a week for both terms, but this meant Tiiu, Peter, and I were at the beck and call of six eager students all year. After that, the course met all day, every day, for the month of September. This worked superbly. McGill classes then did not begin until mid-September. All lectures and instructions in techniques were finished in the first two weeks. The last two weeks, the students could teach their labs or go to other courses, and sign up for the scope, microtomes, or darkroom around the clock. Their final project was a set of 20 micrographs mounted and labeled as for a journal with accompanying figure legends. There was no time for them to write a paper. It was a wonderful course. I was as excited as the students to see their cells and learned a lot, too. Do you know what a rumposome is? At the end of the course, I'd throw a big party at my house. I taught this course every year until the late 1980s, when the Philips EM 200 died. By then my new scope and all my EM equipment had become a departmental EM Center, run by a Ph.D. or later a super tech, who would not allow a class of students to be taught on the new scope. And since electron microscopy had entered its terminal decline by then, student demand for the course had fallen sharply.

For my lecture course, I developed an advanced cell biology course, "The Ultrastructural Basis of Cell Function." I gave this course every year of my career except the seven years I gave the cell biology lectures in the large (800-student) introductory course. Yes, I even enjoyed giving those lectures. My advanced course over the years became more molecular and less structural, but it kept the same weekly format, two lectures and after two introductory EM labs, student seminars. The seminars, I told the students, were teaching exercises and would be marked one half for clarity and one half for interest and humor. The students were incredibly inventive and gave wonderful seminars. The coffee, tea, and homemade brownies I served at the break added to everyone's enjoyment.

When I arrived at McGill, the Botany Department had a phycologist, Mel Goldstein, who gave a popular algae course, so I never taught in the field of my own research. Instead, I kept up to date on the literature of cell biology. The big meeting I attended regularly was the annual meeting of the American Society for Cell Biology. This helped my research immensely. One colleague joked, "All Sally needs to do original research is to take the latest technique invented on animal cells and apply it to the algae." This was certainly true of the beautiful technique of EM immunocytochemistry, in which thin sections are labeled with antibody and the antibody labeled by protein A-gold. Moise Bendayan, one of the developers of the technique, was lured to the Université de Montréal. I promptly (in 1982) hired a francophone Montrealer, Ginette Lacoste-Royal, as my postdoc. She learned the technique from Bendayan and taught it to my students. All my subsequent students used this technique, employing a wide variety of antibodies. Klutz that I am, I raised all the antibodies on the telephone!

A BOLT FROM THE BLUE

When I was in my early twenties, I heard an unforgettable lecture on "The Nature of Discoveries" by Otto Loewi at Woods Hole. Fundamental discoveries, those which change completely the way you look at the world, are not made when you are working or when you are trying to solve a particular problem, but when you are daydreaming or sleeping or on a long train trip staring out the window mesmerized by the passing landscape. Kekulé was dozing in front of a fireplace when he saw six cats form a ring and thereby discovered the shape of the benzene molecule. On Good Friday night in 1921, Otto Loewi dreamt of a simple experiment, turned on the light and wrote it down in the notebook he kept by his bed for this purpose. But the next morning he could not decipher his handwriting. All day Saturday he was in agony trying to remember the experiment, but he could not. That night he dreamt it again. This time he took no chances, he got dressed and went to his lab. From frogs he made two separate vagus-heart preparations in glass vessels. He stimulated the vagus nerve in one prep, took a drop of the fluid surrounding the heart and dropped it on the second heart. The second heart also slowed. In his words, "By sunrise Easter morning, the chemical transmission of nerve impulses was proven."

I never imagined then that when I reached the age (47) Loewi was on that momentous Easter weekend, I would have a similar flash of inspiration—a bolt from the blue that would change forever how phycologists look at the algae and lead to incontrovertible proof that an organelle of a eukaryotic cell can evolve from the reduction of a eukaryotic endosymbiont and that this has happened more than once.

It was on a sunny afternoon late in May of 1977. I had been asked to review a paper on the fine structure of mitosis in *Euglena*. I wasn't a mitosis expert, but Tiiu Slankis and I had written a paper on mitosis in *Ochromonas*, and I had a good collection of mitosis reprints. Not wanting to spend a glorious spring afternoon in my gloomy windowless office, I took all my mitosis reprints, plus my books and reprints on *Euglena*, up to the Botany tea room, a beautiful room with many tall windows and prints of flowers on the walls. As I read the submitted paper, I learned *Euglena* was even stranger than I had thought, the mitotic spindle was intranuclear, and astonishingly, the nucleolus did not disperse during mitosis, but elongated into a dumbbell and constricted into two. This I had never seen before, and I knew did not occur in green algae. *Euglena* ultrastructurally could not be more unlike green algae, yet at that time, phycologists believed the Euglenophyceae was the class of algae most closely related to green algae, simply because euglenoids were the only other algae that contained chlorophylls *a* and *b*. After an hour of reading, I pushed the papers aside and just sat in the sun, daydreaming and watching the clouds drift by. Then out of the blue, I suddenly realized that *Euglena* wasn't related to green algae at all. It just ate them for supper. Probably lots of times, for many euglenoids are phagotrophic, but one time at least a green alga escaped being digested and became established as a permanent endosymbiont, like green algae in *Paramecium bursaria* today. Because the only useful part of the green alga to *Euglena* was its chloroplast, over time the green algal endosymbiont lost everything but its chloroplast and its cell membrane, the mysterious third membrane found around all euglenoid chloroplasts today. The moment I thought of it, I was ecstatic. I knew it had to be true. It explained too many things not to be true.

As I sat there in the sunlight, more revelations came. This also explained why chloroplasts in eight other classes of algae were surrounded by two extra membranes. Seventeen years after I first discovered them, I suddenly knew what they were. The inner membrane of the chloroplast ER had evolved from the cell membrane of a eukaryotic endosymbiont (later shown to be a red alga) and the outer membrane of the chloroplast ER from the phagocytic vacuole membrane of the host cell.

I immediately started reading the literature on symbiosis. I intuitively believed that the last thing a symbiont would give up was its cell membrane. I discovered that many bacterial endosymbionts are surrounded by a phagocytic vacuole membrane, but many others lie free in the cytoplasm surrounded only by their cell membrane(s) and the cell wall. The large eukaryotic algal endosymbiont found in several dinoflagellates is surrounded by only one membrane, clearly its plasmalemma. Thus I argued that the third membrane around *Euglena* chloroplasts was derived from the cell membrane of the green algal symbiont. I also searched the EM literature for any other cell structure that might have evolved from a eukaryotic endosymbiont, but found nothing convincing. I submitted a short paper on my theory to *Nature*, which promptly rejected it.

Fortunately, the *Canadian Journal of Botany* was kinder to me and published it (8).

In my reading I found two abstracts by Dennis Greenwood. He'd seen a small body surrounded by a double membrane in the space between the chloroplast envelope and the chloroplast ER in cryptomonads, which he named a nucleomorph. So Greenwood clearly had the idea that cryptomonads had once harbored a eukaryotic cell, but he did not elaborate on it. Nonetheless, I always give him credit. More important, I immediately switched all my group to working on the cryptomonad nucleomorph. Marcelle Gillott showed that its small nucleolus-like body likely contained RNA and that its double-membraned envelope contained elliptical pores, and we argued that the symbiont was a red alga (10). A talented undergraduate, Lisa McKerracher, showed that the single nucleomorph constricted in two just prior to chloroplast and cell division (13). Martha Ludwig proved by two different techniques that the cryptomonad nucleomorph contained DNA (12). Sue Douglas, a young Canadian scientist I greatly admire, subsequently sequenced nucleomorph and nuclear ribosomal RNA genes and showed that the former treed out with red algal nuclear ribosomal RNA genes, proving the symbiont was indeed a red alga. *Nature* quickly accepted her paper!

LOOKING BACK AT LIFE

The Right Side of the Border

When I met an American colleague shortly after I arrived at McGill, he asked, "How does it feel to come back to North America to the wrong side of the border?" He was referring to what he considered Canada's pitifully small research funding and small scientific community with only a few world-class scientists. Canada suited me just fine! True, grants from the National Research Council, later called the Natural Sciences and Engineering Research Council (NSERC), were

small by U.S. standards, but the money was all yours to spend. No overhead was paid to the university, nor did you have to pay yourself a summer salary, so every penny went to supplies, grad student and postdoc salaries, and presentations at meetings. I always had enough money for a small group, which was all I wanted. NSERC is the only agency I know that funds people, not projects. You applied every three years and were limited to four pages of text, later six. You could list only your publications in the last five years. I knew as long as I had one or two publications a year (hopefully at least one in a prestigious journal), I would never lose my grant. What bliss. And what bliss also to be limited to such a short grant proposal. Major equipment was given out in separate grants, but again the proposal forms were brief, and you could apply every year. After my lab was well set up, most years I was part of a team applying for communal equipment, like autoclaves or a state-of-the-art phytotron.

I do not publish a lot and I have had some dry spells. American colleagues have told me I would never have received continuous funding in the States. And I'm sure I wouldn't have. Some of my American friends lived in constant fear that they would not get the next grant, or worse, it would be approved, but not funded. I was spared all that, as well as hours and hours writing massive grant proposals. It made my scientific life a very happy one.

That Canada's scientific community is small also suited me. I started to become well-known in the cell biology community almost from the day I arrived. Gordin Kaplan, a wonderful man, an immunologist at the University of Ottawa, came to my talk on chloroplast RNA at the Cell Biology meetings in Denver, simply to see who the new woman at McGill was. He liked what he heard and saw, and he became my biggest booster in Canada. In 1970 he nominated me to succeed him as President of the Canadian Society for Cell Biology. In my three years on the Executive Committee, I traveled across Canada and made many good friends. NSERC discovered me early and I served three three-year stints on their committees, almost a third of my career. I loved going to Ottawa the second week of February and seeing all the skaters on the canal. I served first on the committee that gave out all the postdoctoral fellowships in science in Canada, except the medical ones. Scientists in medical schools or hospitals were then supported by the Medical Research Council. From 1982 to 1985, I was on the Cell Biology and Genetics Grant Selection Committee, a most enjoyable highlight of my career. In the fall, the committee split into three groups and visited every university in a large region of the country, interviewing every applicant. During my three-year tenure, I read the grant proposal of every cell and molecular biologist and nonmedical geneticist in Canada. It was a tremendous amount of work, but I loved every minute of it, especially the wonderful camaraderie that developed during site visits and the February meetings. I even devoted most of my second and last sabbatical year to the grant committee. I offered to do extra site visiting in the fall, and I visited every department that had applied for an EM. This took me from St. Johns, Newfoundland, to Vancouver. Then after recovering from the February meetings, I flew to Paris where I worked in a lab with Claire Berkaloff and Christiane Lichtlé at École normale supérieure, a memorable three months. Late in my career I was on the committee that awarded both the graduate scholarships and postdoctoral fellowships in all the life sciences. By then, I had become quite handicapped by MS, so that this was difficult, and I did not join the group to go out in the evening, so missed out on making new friends. During the first two committees I served on, we were put up in Ottawa's magnificent Chateau Laurier. I told a small lie when I checked in. I said I'd spent my honeymoon there and had had a beautiful room facing the Parliament Buildings. Could I have such a room again? I always got it, and there are few more beautiful sights than Canada's Parliament Buildings lit up at night.

Life with Multiple Sclerosis

I have lived with multiple sclerosis for 43 years, and looking back, the best part was that for two thirds of that time, neither I nor anyone else suspected I had MS. The diagnosis of MS is one of the most dreaded in medicine and is almost always worse than the disease, since one can have minimal disability for many years. My first attack, a painful left ankle, came when I was 32, an age when MS often begins. An orthopedic surgeon was about to do an exploratory operation on the ankle, when fortunately he was stopped by a renowned rheumatoid arthritis specialist, Marian Ropes. She was a Smith classmate and friend of my mother, so she knew I might have problems. Since she sent me to a psychiatrist at McLean's, I simply assumed the problem was in my head, not my foot. In 1966, when I was newly arrived at McGill, I learned I had diabetes. I no longer have diabetes. No, I was not miraculously cured, the medical profession has simply changed the definition. After a lifetime of adhering to a diabetic diet, I now have impaired glucose tolerance. But the many minor physical annoyances of my life I blamed on diabetes. My intense fatigue after shopping or sightseeing was, I thought, due to the diabetes. Ditto my frequent trips to the toilet. My husband and children took up cross-country skiing. I didn't even bother to buy skis. I did take one of the family's ski poles and used it all winter whenever I walked down the hill to lunch at the Faculty Club or to go to Senate or other meetings on McGill's main campus. Everyone said how clever of me.

Having a dedicated woman at home also allowed me to devote all my energy to my work and not realize I was in any way limited by MS. I would arrive home at six every evening to well-cared-for children, a spotless house, the day's washing and ironing done, and potatoes baking in the oven. I did not find it strange that, even so, right after supper, I collapsed into my green lounge chair. I still feel sad that my children, especially Chris, did not get the attention they deserved. I remember vividly

Chris pounding on my arm as I lay in my chair, "Mommy, mommy, you are not listening!"

Even my chosen scientific career suited a life with MS. Except for darkroom work, all the techniques of electron microscopy are done sitting down. I loved to spend a quiet afternoon sitting in the dark at the EM, looking at cells and taking pictures. I had to stand up occasionally to change a grid or develop a film. Even when I no longer did the scope work myself, I did most of the teaching of students to use the microscope. Right up to the end of my career, I demonstrated the scope to the students in my lecture course, and sat beside them in the dark as each got their turn operating the scope and looking enthralled at the cells through the binoculars.

In 1973–1974, I spent my first sabbatical in my own lab. I had hired an excellent algal biochemist, Rose Ann Cattolico, as my postdoc, so she could teach me how to isolate chloroplast DNA. I believed I had found the perfect alga for this, *Olisthodiscus luteus*. It has many small chloroplasts and no cell wall. Under the light microscope, as the surrounding medium dried up, the cell membrane burst and the tiny chloroplasts floated away. Biochemistry requires long hours of standing on one's feet, and the isolation of algal chloroplast DNA is not easy. Rose Ann and I never succeeded, although I was very proud when I learned to spool total cell DNA. Rose Ann took *Olisthodiscus* with her to Seattle, where she soon succeeded in purifying chloroplast DNA, and with it, went on to make a number of exciting discoveries. I had learned my lesson and never again attempted to be a biochemist.

In 1982, I had an acute MS attack (I was supposedly too old to get MS, and the neurologist feared a brain tumor). Still no diagnosis, even though three years later, I lost the vision in one eye for three months, a classical MS symptom. Due to increasing difficulty walking, I was again seeing an orthopedic surgeon. Then in 1990, my sister was diagnosed with MS, and I and my regular doctor realized at once that I had it, too. Since then I have be-come progressively handicapped, and it has not been fun. I walk very slowly and painfully with a walker, and am now, alas, starting to lose the use of my right arm. I spend a lot of time looking back at life. It has been a good life, my only real regret being that I never managed to have a happy marriage. I would think it was an oxymoron if I didn't have a number of happily married friends, who like me married in college or just afterwards.

Late Life Honors

In the last 15 years, I have received several honors that have meant a great deal to me. As I progressively could do less and less due to MS, the honors consoled me that I once was able to do a lot of good work. In 1991, I was elected a Fellow of the Royal Society of Canada. Ann Oaks, who had been elected five years earlier, nominated me. I did not mind too much that that year there was a big push to elect women. I think more than 20% of the new fellows were women, most in the two academies representing humanities, social sciences, and the arts. Two years later, I was elected a Fellow of the American Association for the Advancement of Science. I received a lot more publicity for that, for Canadians, unjustifiably, feel that their own institutions are inferior to American ones. But most unexpected of all and most delightful was receiving the 2003 Gilbert Morgan Smith Medal for research on algae, plus a prize of $20,000 from the National Academy of Sciences. Once again a woman had nominated me, Beth Gantt, who had won the medal herself in 1994. By then I was not well enough to travel to the April award ceremony in Washington. Instead, the Academy presented me the medal on August 9, 2003, at their beautiful summer headquarters overlooking Quisset harbor in Woods Hole. I was vacationing at our family's Cape house nearby. Members of my family and several of my Woods Hole friends came to the ceremony plus about 30 staff and academy members who were there for committee meetings. The same format was followed as in Washington.

Bruce Alberts, the President of the Academy, paid tribute to Gilbert Smith and presented Alex Glazer, who described my discovery of secondary endosymbiosis. After receiving the medal, I gave a brief speech of thanks emphasizing how my career had started there in Woods Hole on the September afternoon I walked into Ralph Lewin's office. Everyone said how much nicer this ceremony was than the Washington one and that they should do it again. That August day was a perfect end to a long and happy life in science. A few days later, half the world away in a small city in southern China, a three-day-old baby girl was found wrapped in a blue blanket at the eastern gate of a city park. A large part of the $20,000 prize money made its way to China and to a U.S. adoption agency, and in June 2004, my son Christopher and his wife Carolann went to China and brought that beautiful baby girl, Sophie Mei Poole, home to Pasadena. I like to think that Gilbert Smith would have been pleased to know that his generosity had played such a large part in putting an abandoned baby girl from China on the road to a long and happy life in America.

LITERATURE CITED

1. Bouck GB. 1965. Fine structure and organelle associations in brown algae. *J. Cell Biol.* 26:523–37
2. Gibbs SP. 1960. The fine structure of *Euglena gracilis* with special reference to the chloroplasts and pyrenoids. *J. Ultrastruct. Res.* 4:127–48
3. Gibbs SP. 1962. The ultrastructure of the chloroplasts of algae. *J. Ultrastruct. Res.* 7:418–35
4. Gibbs SP. 1962. Nuclear envelope–chloroplast relationships in algae. *J. Cell Biol.* 14:433–44
5. Gibbs SP. 1962. Chloroplast development in *Ochromonas danica*. *J. Cell Biol.* 15:343–61
6. Gibbs SP. 1967. Synthesis of chloroplast RNA at the site of chloroplast DNA. *Biochem. Biophys. Res. Commun.* 28:653–57
7. Gibbs SP. 1968. Autoradiographic evidence for the *in situ* synthesis of chloroplast and mitochondrial RNA. *J. Cell Sci.* 3:327–40
8. Gibbs SP. 1978. The chloroplasts of *Euglena* may have evolved from symbiotic green algae. *Can. J. Bot.* 56:2883–89
9. Gibbs SP, Poole RJ. 1973. Autoradiographic evidence for many segregating DNA molecules in the chloroplast of *Ochromonas danica*. *J. Cell Biol.* 59:318–28
10. Gillott MA, Gibbs SP. 1980. The cryptomonad nucleomorph: its ultrastructure and evolutionary significance. *J. Phycol.* 558–68
11. Holdsworth RH. 1971. The isolation and partial characterization of the pyrenoid protein of *Eremosphaera viridis*. *J. Cell Biol.* 51:499–513
12. Ludwig M, Gibbs SP. 1985. DNA is present in the nucleomorph of cryptomonads: further evidence that the chloroplast evolved from a eukaryotic endosymbiont. *Protoplasma* 127:9–20
13. McKerracher L, Gibbs SP. 1982. Cell and nucleomorph division in the alga *Cryptomonas*. *Can. J. Bot.* 11:2440–52

MicroRNAs and Their Regulatory Roles in Plants

Matthew W. Jones-Rhoades,[1] David P. Bartel,[1] and Bonnie Bartel[2]

[1] Whitehead Institute for Biomedical Research, Department of Biology, Massachusetts Institute of Technology, and Howard Hughes Medical Institute, Cambridge, Massachusetts 02142; email: dbartel@wi.mit.edu

[2] Department of Biochemistry and Cell Biology, Rice University, Houston, Texas 77005; email: bartel@rice.edu

Annu. Rev. Plant Biol. 2006. 57:19–53

The *Annual Review of Plant Biology* is online at plant.annualreviews.org

doi: 10.1146/ annurev.arplant.57.032905.105218

First published online as a Review in Advance on January 30, 2006

1543-5008/06/0602-0019$20.00

Key Words

noncoding RNAs, post-transcriptional gene regulation, plant development, RNA silencing

Abstract

MicroRNAs (miRNAs) are small, endogenous RNAs that regulate gene expression in plants and animals. In plants, these ~21-nucleotide RNAs are processed from stem-loop regions of long primary transcripts by a Dicer-like enzyme and are loaded into silencing complexes, where they generally direct cleavage of complementary mRNAs. Although plant miRNAs have some conserved functions extending beyond development, the importance of miRNA-directed gene regulation during plant development is now particularly clear. Identified in plants less than four years ago, miRNAs are already known to play numerous crucial roles at each major stage of development—typically at the cores of gene regulatory networks, targeting genes that are themselves regulators, such as those encoding transcription factors and F-box proteins.

Contents

INTRODUCTION

Multicellular organisms depend on complex networks of gene regulatory pathways. MicroRNAs (miRNAs), which went unnoticed until recently, are key components of these networks. Initially discovered as regulators of developmental timing in *Caenorhabditis elegans* (67, 114), miRNAs are now known to play a variety of important regulatory roles in both plants and animals.

MicroRNAs are short, endogenously expressed, nontranslated RNAs that are processed by Dicer-like proteins from stem-loop regions of longer RNA precursors (**Figure 1**, reviewed in 13). MicroRNAs are chemically and functionally similar to small interfering RNAs (siRNAs, see Small Interfering RNAs sidebar), which can mediate the related phenomena of RNA interference (RNAi), post-transcriptional gene silencing (PTGS), and transcriptional gene silencing (TGS). Like miRNAs, siRNAs are processed by the Dicer RNaseIII family of enzymes, but instead of deriving from local stem-loop structures, siRNAs are processed from long, double-stranded precursors (either from much longer stems or from bimolecular duplexes). Both miRNAs and siRNAs are incorporated into silencing complexes that contain Argonaute proteins, wherein they can guide repression of target genes.

Although miRNAs are deeply conserved within both the plant and animal kingdoms, there are substantial differences between the two lineages with regard to the mechanism and scope of miRNA-mediated gene regulation; several of these differences have been instrumental in the rapid increase in understanding of plant miRNA biology. Plant miRNAs are highly complementary to conserved target mRNAs, which allows fast and confident bioinformatic identification of plant miRNA targets (53, 116). As expected from this extensive complementarity to their targets, plant miRNAs guide cleavage of their targets, an activity readily assayed in vitro and in vivo, which allows facile confirmation of predicted targets (55, 79, 128). In addition, *Arabidopsis* is a genetically tractable model organism, which enables study of the genetic pathways that underlie miRNA-mediated regulation and the phenotypic consequences of perturbing miRNA-mediated gene regulation. In this review, we describe the flurry of exciting results revealing the biological functions of these tiny riboregulators that have been made possible by the convergence of these factors.

GENOMICS OF PLANT MICRORNAs

MicroRNA Gene Discovery: Cloning

MicroRNAs have been discovered using three basic approaches: direct cloning, forward genetics, and bioinformatic prediction followed by experimental validation. The most direct method of miRNA discovery is to isolate and clone small RNAs from biological samples, and several groups have used this approach to identify small plant RNAs (78, 92, 107, 115, 125, 127, 143). The cloning methods were adapted from those first used to identify large numbers of animal miRNAs (62, 64) and involve isolating small RNAs, ligating adaptor oligonucleotides, reverse transcription, amplification, and sequencing. Some protocols incorporate methods to enrich for Dicer cleavage products (i.e., molecules with 5' phosphates and 3' hydroxyls) and to concatemerize the short cDNAs so that several can be identified in a single sequencing read (64). The initial cloning experiments in *Arabidopsis* identified 19 miRNAs, which fell into 15 families (78, 92, 107, 115), although the hundreds of other small RNAs also cloned, which included degradation fragments and endogenous siRNAs, sometimes complicated classification of the miRNAs. Subsequent cloning experiments have expanded our knowledge of small RNAs in *Arabidopsis* (127, 141, 142),

SMALL INTERFERING RNAs

siRNAs were first observed in plants (47), and in *Arabidopsis*, most small RNAs are siRNAs (78, 115, 127, 141, 142). They are implicated in a variety of processes, including defense against viruses, establishment of heterochromatin, silencing of transposons and transgenes, and post-transcriptional regulation of mRNAs (reviewed in 15). MicroRNAs and siRNAs have much in common (**Figure 1**). Both are 20–24 nucleotides long and processed from longer RNA precursors by Dicer-like ribonucleases (19, 44, 47, 48, 52, 67, 147a), and both are incorporated into ribonucleoprotein silencing complexes in which the small RNAs, through their base-pairing potential, guide target gene repression (37, 48, 67, 96a, 138, 147a).

The fundamental difference between the two small RNA classes is the nature of their precursors; siRNAs are processed from long, double-stranded RNAs (37, 147a), whereas miRNAs are processed from single RNA molecules that include an imperfect stem-loop secondary structure (62, 64, 66, 115). Several additional characteristics distinguish most miRNAs from most siRNAs. Many miRNAs are conserved between related organisms, whereas most endogenously expressed siRNAs are not (62, 64, 66, 115). Many (but not all) siRNAs target the gene from which they are derived or very closely related genes. In contrast, miRNAs regulate genes unrelated to loci encoding the miRNAs. In fact, the imperfect base pairing in the miRNA precursor stem-loop may help prevent the miRNA locus from undergoing silencing by the miRNA that it encodes. Finally, although the proteins required for siRNA and miRNA biogenesis are related and sometimes overlap, the genetic requirements for miRNA and siRNA function are partially distinct in many organisms. For example, many *Arabidopsis* siRNAs require RNA-dependent RNA polymerases for their biogenesis, whereas miRNAs do not (17, 31, 97, 142). Moreover, most *Arabidopsis* miRNAs are processed by *DICER-LIKE1* (*DCL1*) (61, 107, 115), one of four Dicer-like genes in *Arabidopsis* (117), whereas many endogenous siRNAs require *DCL3* or *DCL4* (41, 141a, 142, 146a).

Oryza sativa (rice) (125, 126), and *Populus trichocarpa* (cottonwood) (81), and new, high-throughput sequencing methods have recently been employed to dramatically expand the depth of small RNA cloning coverage in *Arabidopsis* (80a).

MicroRNA Gene Discovery: Genetics

Although miRNAs were first discovered through forward genetic screens in round worms (67, 114), no miRNA gene fami-lies have been discovered by this method in plants, and miRNA involvement in plant mutant phenotypes was not inferred until after cloning experiments had established that plant genomes contained numerous miRNAs

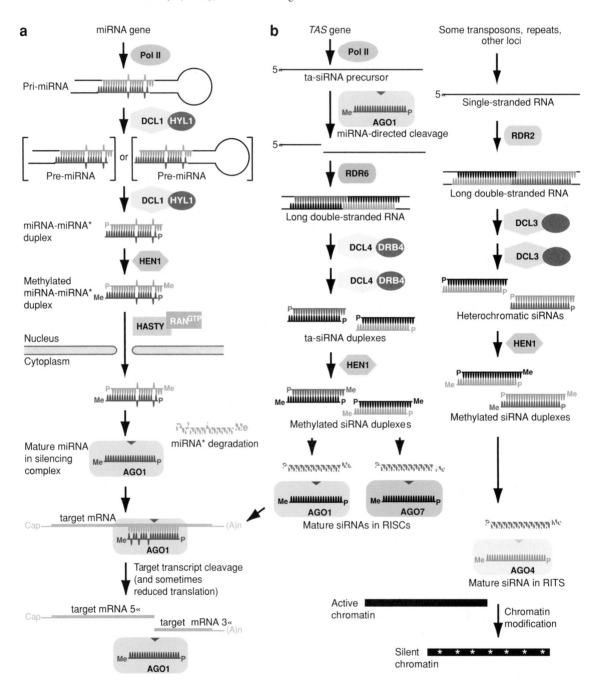

(107, 115, 116). To date, only a single plant miRNA loss-of-function allele has been identified in forward genetic screens; *early extra petals1* is caused by a transposon insertion ~160 bp upstream of the predicted *MIR164c* stem-loop, and results in flowers with extra petals (9).

The fact that loss-of-function miRNA mutants have been recovered so rarely using forward genetics may reflect small target size for mutagenesis coupled with redundancy; nearly all evolutionarily conserved plant miRNAs are encoded by gene families (**Table 1**). Family members are likely to have overlapping functions, buffering against loss at any single miRNA locus. Overexpression screens can circumvent redundancy limitations. At least three plant miRNAs, *miR319* (also known as *miR-JAW*), *miR172* (also known as *EAT*), and *miR166*, were isolated in overexpression screens for dominant mutants with developmental abnormalities (6, 59, 103, 139). Mutations in miRNA target sites, which can prevent the entire family of miRNAs from repressing a target gene, can also circumvent redundant functions of miRNA family members. The dominant mutations in the HD-ZIP genes *PHB*, *PHV*, and *REVOLUTA* (*REV*) in *Arabidopsis* and *ROLLED LEAF1* (*RLD1*) in maize result in adaxialization of leaves and/or vasculature (89, 90, 100, 148) and are all caused by mutations in miR166 complementary sites (39, 54, 87, 116, 148).

MicroRNA Gene Discovery: Bioinformatics

In both plants and animals, cloning was the initial means of large-scale miRNA discovery (62, 64, 66, 115). However, cloning is biased toward RNAs that are expressed highly and broadly. MicroRNAs expressed at low levels or only in specific cell types or in response to certain environmental stimuli are more difficult to clone. Sequence-based biases in cloning procedures might also cause certain miRNAs to be missed. Because of these limitations, bioinformatic approaches to identify miRNAs have provided a useful complement to cloning.

A straightforward use of bioinformatics has been to find homologs of known

MicroRNA (miRNA): 20- to 24-nucleotide silencing RNA processed from a stem-loop region of a longer transcript by Dicer-like enzymes

Dicer-like (DCL) proteins: RNaseIII-like enzymes that process siRNAs from long double-stranded RNA precursors or miRNAs from local stem-loop secondary structures of primary transcripts

Small interfering RNA or short interfering RNA (siRNA): silencing RNA, typically 20 to 24 nucleotides in length, processed from long double-stranded RNA by Dicer-like enzymes

RNA interference (RNAi): the phenomenon by which exogenous double-stranded RNA directs the post-transcriptional silencing of homologous genes

Argonaute (AGO) proteins: members of a protein family that contain a PAZ small RNA-binding domain and a Piwi RNase H-like domain

---

Figure 1

RNA-silencing pathways in plants. (*a*) A model for microRNA (miRNA) biogenesis in *Arabidopsis*. Following transcription, the pri-miRNA is processed by DCL1, perhaps with the aid of HYL1 and other factors, to a miRNA:miRNA* duplex with 5′ phosphates (P) and two-nucleotide 3′ overhangs. Pre-miRNAs, which are readily detectable in animals, appear to be short-lived in plants (*brackets*). The 3′ sugars of the miRNA:miRNA* duplex are methylated (Me) by HEN1, presumably within the nucleus. The miRNA is exported to the cytoplasm by HST, probably with the aid of additional factors. The mature, methylated miRNA is incorporated into a silencing complex that can include AGO1, and the miRNA* is degraded. Complex maturation is depicted after nucleocytoplasmic export, but might occur before. Within the silencing complex, the miRNA is capable of targeting complementary RNAs for cleavage by AGO1, and perhaps also for translational repression. (*b*) Models for biogenesis of trans-acting small interfering RNAs (ta-siRNA; *left*) and heterochromatic siRNAs (*right*) in *Arabidopsis*. Other endogenous siRNAs and siRNAs from transgenes or viral RNA are generated through similar or partially overlapping pathways. Long double-stranded RNA, generated through the action of RNA-dependent RNA polymerases (RDRs), is iteratively processed by Dicer-like (DCL) proteins to yield multiple siRNA duplexes. The phase of the ta-siRNA duplexes can be set by miRNA-directed cleavage of the *TAS* transcript. One strand from each siRNA duplex is stably incorporated into a silencing complex [RNA-induced silencing complex (RISC) or RNAi-induced transcriptional silencing (RITS) complex], and the other is degraded. siRNAs in RISCs guide cleavage of complementary RNAs, whereas those in RITS complexes are associated with the establishment or maintenance of heterochromatin. Pol IV is involved in heterochromatic siRNA production in plants, either transcribing the genomic DNA to produce the single-stranded RNA or transcribing the double-stranded RNA to amplify the single-stranded RNA (49a, 54a, 101a).

Table 1 MicroRNA gene families conserved in plants

miRNA family	(reference)	*Arabidopsis*	*Oryza*	*Populus*
miR156	(115)	12	12	11
miR159/319	(78, 92, 103, 107, 115)	6	8	15
miR160	(115)	3	6	8
miR162	(115)	2	2	3
miR164	(115)	3	5	6
miR166	(115)	9	12	17
miR167	(78, 107, 115)	4	9	8
miR168	(115)	2	2	2
miR169	(115)	14	17	32
miR171	(78, 115)	4	7	10
miR172	(107)	5	3	9
miR390	(2, 127, 141)	3	1	4
miR393	(53, 127)	2	2	4
miR394	(53)	2	1	2
miR395	(53)	6	19	10
miR396	(53)	2	5	7
miR397	(53, 127)	2	2	3
miR398	(53, 127)	3	2	3
miR399	(53, 127)	6	11	12
miR408	(127)	1	1	1
miR403	(127)	1	0	2
miR437	(125)	0	1*	0
miR444	(125)	0	1*	0
miR445	(125)	0	9*	0
Total		92	127	169

All known miRNA families that are conserved between more than one plant species are listed together with the number of genes identified in the sequenced genomes. Rice miRNA families that have orthologs in maize but do not appear to have orthologs in the eudicots (*Arabidopsis* and *Populus*) are marked with an asterisk. The following families contain miRNA genes annotated with more than one number: miR156 (miR156 and miR157), miR159/319 (miR159 and miR319), miR166 (miR165 and miR166), miR171 (miR170 and miR171), and miR390 (miR390 and miR391).

miRNAs, both within the same genome and in the genomes of other species (62, 64, 66, 108, 115). A more difficult challenge is to identify miRNAs unrelated to previously known miRNAs. This was first accomplished for vertebrate, nematode, and fly miRNAs, using algorithms that search for conservation of sequence and secondary structure (i.e., miRNA stem-loop precursors) between species, searching for patterns that are characteristic of miRNAs (63, 72, 74). Although these methods identified numer-ous potential animal miRNAs, many of which were subsequently confirmed experimentally, they have not been directly useful in finding plant miRNAs because of the longer and more heterogeneous secondary structures of plant miRNA stem-loops.

To address this need, several groups devised bioinformatic approaches specific to plant miRNA identification (2, 22, 53, 137). Like algorithms for identifying animal miRNAs, these approaches use conservation of secondary structure as a filter, but are necessarily more relaxed in terms of allowed structures. Some approaches take advantage of the high complementarity of plant miRNAs to target messages, implementing the requirement that the candidate has conserved complementarity to mRNAs (2, 53). This additional filter has been useful for distinguishing authentic plant miRNAs from false positives and recently has been extended to mammalian miRNA gene prediction (140).

The Conserved MicroRNAs in Plants

In aggregate, cloning, genetics, and bioinformatics have resulted in the annotation of 118 potential miRNA genes in *Arabidopsis* (miR-Base, release 7.0) (43). These 118 loci can be grouped into 42 families, with each family composed of stem-loops with the potential to produce identical or highly similar mature miRNAs. Twenty-one families represented by 92 genes are clearly conserved in species beyond *Arabidopsis* (**Table 1**; miRBase, release 7.0). These families are somewhat expanded in the other sequenced plant genomes, *Oryza sativa* (rice), and *Populus trichocarpa* (cottonwood), where they are represented by 116 and 169 potential miRNA genes, respectively (**Table 1**). The number of members per family in a genome ranges from 1 to 32. With the exception of the miR-430 family, which is represented by a cluster of ~80 loci in zebrafish (42), and a related family, which is represented by a cluster of 43 loci in human (18), animal miRNAs typically fall into smaller families that have much more diverse members; metazoan family members sometimes share only a common 5′ seed region (13). In plants, the number of members in each family correlates among examined species; certain families contain numerous members in all three species (e.g., miR156, miR166, miR169), whereas others consistently contain only a few genes (e.g., miR162, miR168, miR394) (**Table 1**). Although it is unclear why a plant would need, for example, 12 genes encoding miR156, this correlation suggests functional significance of the various miRNA family sizes.

Twenty miRNA families identified to date are highly conserved between all three sequenced plant genomes: *Arabidopsis*, *Oryza sativa*, and *Populus trichocarpa* (**Table 1**). Several additional miRNA families are conserved only within specific lineages; miR403 is present in the eudicots *Arabidopsis* and *Populus* but absent from the monocot *Oryza* (127), and three families identified by cloning in *Oryza* are conserved in other monocots such as maize, but are not evident in either sequenced eudicot (125). Within each family, the mature miRNA is always located on the same arm of the stem-loop (5′ or 3′), as would be expected if the genes share common ancestry (**Figure 2**). Although the sequence of the mature miRNA and, to a lesser extent, the segment on the opposite arm of the hairpin to which it pairs, are highly conserved between members of the same miRNA family (both within and between species), the sequence, secondary structure, and length of the intervening "loop" region can be highly divergent among family members (**Figure 2**). The pattern of pairing and nonpairing nucleotides within the mature miRNA is often conserved between homologous miRNA stem-loops from different species (**Figure 2**). The significance of the conserved mismatches is unknown; perhaps they help guide DCL1 to cleave at the appropriate positions along the stem-loop.

Most efforts to clone small RNAs in plants have focused on the eudicot *Arabidopsis* or the monocot *Oryza*, and bioinformatic methods have focused on miRNAs conserved between these two species. These flowering plants diverged from each other ~145 million years ago (27). Growing evidence shows that many angiosperm miRNA families, and their complementary sites in target mRNAs, are conserved in more basal land plants. A cDNA containing a miR166 stem-loop has been cloned from the lycopod *Selaginella kraussiana*, and a miR159 stem-loop is present in an expressed sequence tag (EST) from the moss *Physcomitrella patens* (40, 53). Furthermore, a survey of miRNA expression

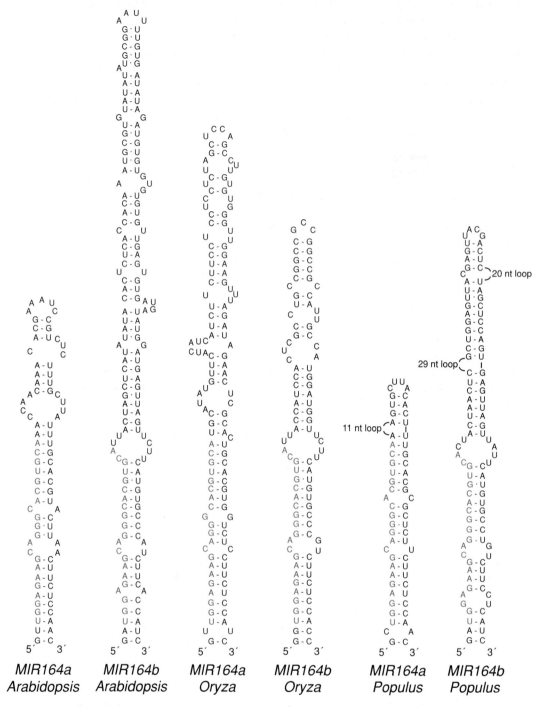

Figure 2

Representative miR164 stem-loops from *Arabidopsis*, *Oryza*, and *Populus*. Segments corresponding to the mature miRNAs are shown in red.

using microarray technology revealed at least 11 miRNA families with detectable expression in gymnosperms; at least two (miR160 and miR390) are detectable in moss (7). Ten miRNA families have conserved target sites in ESTs from gymnosperms or more basal plants (53), and five miRNA families (miR160, miR166, miR167, miR171, and miR172) in gymnosperms, ferns, lycopods, or mosses direct cleavage of target mRNAs that are homologous to the verified *Arabidopsis* targets (7, 40). More recently, direct cloning of small RNAs from moss has identified several additional homologs of Arabidopsis miRNAs (5a). Some of the deeply conserved miRNA families regulate development in *Arabidopsis* and are necessary for processes such as proper specification of floral organ identity (miR172) or leaf polarity (miR166). It is interesting that these miRNAs regulate homologous mRNAs in basal plants that have very different reproductive structures and leaf morphology, leading to the speculation that these miRNAs are parts of ancient, conserved regulatory modules underlying seemingly different developmental outcomes (7).

Nonconserved MicroRNAs and the Challenges of Definitive MicroRNA Classification

Although most annotated miRNAs are conserved throughout flowering plants (**Table 1**), others are found only in a single sequenced genome, and thus could be of a more recent evolutionary origin. The extended homology between some nonconserved miRNA precursors and target genes provides strong evidence that some of these potentially "young" miRNAs arose from duplications of target gene segments (4). Although several nonconserved miRNAs, including miR161, miR163, miR173, miR447, miR475, and miR476, are known to direct cleavage of target transcripts (3, 4, 81, 125, 132), it is difficult to confidently predict targets for many because it is not possible to use complementary site

conservation as a filter against false-positive target predictions.

In fact, it is difficult to be confident that all annotated nonconserved miRNAs are miRNAs rather than siRNAs. The established minimal standard for miRNA annotation is a small RNA with detectable expression and the potential to form a stem-loop when joined to flanking genomic sequence (5). In practice, these requirements are too loose to definitively categorize many small RNAs cloned from plants. Many plant siRNAs are detectable on blots (109, 133, 142), and hundreds of thousands of non-miRNA genomic sequences can be predicted to fold into secondary structures that resemble structures of plant miRNA precursors (53). Therefore, without conservation of both sequence and secondary structure, it is difficult to be confident that a given cloned RNA originated from a stem-loop (i.e., is a miRNA) rather than from a double-stranded RNA (i.e., is a siRNA). In fact, many of the thousands of small RNAs cloned from *Arabidopsis* (46, 80a) would probably meet the literal requirements for annotation as miRNAs. A few of these sequences might be miRNAs, but others that meet the literal criteria probably are not.

The challenges for annotating nonconserved small RNAs cloned from plants are illustrated by three related small silencing RNAs that were originally annotated as miRNAs but turned out to be among the founding members of the *trans*-acting siRNAs (ta-siRNAs) (109, 133). As is typical of plant miRNAs, these ta-siRNAs direct cleavage of mRNA targets, are detected on northern blots, and require many of the same proteins as do miRNAs for their accumulation. Although these three silencing RNAs also fall within predicted stem-loop structures, the predicted hairpins are not as extensively paired as plant miRNAs and in two cases are not part of the optimal fold of this genomic region. Current evidence supports a model in which these small RNAs are generated by the sequential DCL4-mediated cleavage of a long double-stranded product of RDR6—a model in which

Trans-acting siRNA (ta-siRNA): siRNA that negatively regulates mRNA distinct from and unrelated to the locus from which the siRNA is encoded

the predicted stem-loops are fortuitous and unrelated to the biogenesis of the ta-siRNAs (41, 109, 133, 141a, 146a). For these and other ta-siRNAs, the cleavage occurs at ~21-nt increments in essentially a single register (3, 133). This register appears to be determined by miRNA-directed cleavage of the ta-siRNA precursor, which explains why all the proteins needed for miRNA biogenesis and function are also needed for ta-siRNA accumulation (3).

The challenge in confidently identifying miRNAs is not limited to small cloned RNAs; informatic predictions face even greater difficulties. For example, recent bioinformatic screens for miRNAs conserved between *Arabidopsis* and *Oryza* (22, 137) yielded dozens of miRNA gene candidates that had not been reported in previous cloning and bioinformatic efforts. Most *Arabidopsis* genes conserved with rice, a monocot, would be expected to also be present in other eudicots. Indeed, members of each of the 20 miRNA families listed in **Table 1** that are conserved in *Arabidopsis* and *Oryza* are also found in ESTs from other plant species and in the genome of *Populus*, a recently sequenced eudicot (53). However, none of the newly reported informatic candidates (i.e., those not listed in **Table 1**) are found in the sequenced ESTs from other species or in the *Populus* genome (M.W. Jones-Rhoades, unpublished), raising questions as to whether any of these candidates identified based on their putative conservation between *Arabidopsis* and *Oryza* are bona fide miRNAs. Probing for nine of these newly reported candidates (miR413 – 420 and miR426) gave weak apparent hybridization signals on northern blots (137), thereby providing experimental evidence for expression, as required for classifying conserved stem-loops as miRNA genes. However, their apparent absence in genomes outside of *Arabidopsis* and *Oryza*, the observation that these putative miRNAs are generally less paired within their stem-loops than is typical of plant miRNAs with more experimental support (141; M.W. Jones-Rhoades, unpublished), the ab-

sence of confirmed targets of these miRNAs, and the possibility of false-positive detection on northern blots all suggest that these sequences might be bioinformatic false positives rather than bona fide miRNAs. In sum, confident annotation of poorly conserved miRNAs in plants appears to require evidence more stringent than that originally specified in the annotation guidelines (5). (See Potential Guidelines for Confident miRNA Annotation sidebar.)

Although it appears that most miRNAs that are broadly conserved among flowering plants are now identified and experimentally validated (53; **Table 1**), the challenges and ambiguities for classifying nonconserved miRNAs preclude meaningful estimates of the total number of miRNA genes in *Arabidopsis* and other plant genomes. It is possible to imagine that miRNAs in each species have escaped detection because they are both nonconserved and expressed in only a few cells or conditions. As high-throughput sequencing is applied to miRNA identification, additional nonconserved miRNAs will undoubtedly be revealed.

MICRORNA BIOGENESIS

Transcription of MicroRNA Precursors

Because plant miRNAs are primarily found in genomic regions not associated with protein-coding genes (115), it appears that most, if not all, plant miRNAs are produced from their own transcriptional units. This contrasts with animal miRNAs, which sometimes appear to be processed from introns of protein-coding genes (14). Plant miRNA genes are occasionally clustered near each other in the genome, suggesting transcription of multiple miRNAs from a single primary transcript [e.g., the miR395 cluster (44a, 53)], but this polycistronic arrangement of miRNA genes appears far less frequently in plants than in animals (13). Northern, EST, and mapping evidence indicate that plant miRNA primary transcripts (sometimes called pri-miRNAs), as in animals, are longer than needed to encompass the miRNA stem-loops (6, 53, 103, 141). At least some of these pri-miRNA transcripts appear to be spliced, polyadenylated (6, 61), and capped (141). Two rice miRNAs are contained within transcripts that contain exon junctions within the presumptive stem-loop precursor, implying that in these cases, splicing is a prerequisite for Dicer recognition (125). The observations that plant pri-miRNAs can be over 1 kb in length, that they are usually preceded by typical TATA box motifs, and that they can undergo canonical splicing, polyadenylation, and capping, indicates RNA polymerase II is probably responsible for transcribing most plant miRNAs (141), as appears to be the case for many animal miRNAs (13, 69). Relatively little is known about the regulation of miRNA transcription in plants, but there is no reason to suspect that this regulation would differ from that of protein-coding transcripts.

MicroRNA Processing and Export

A central step in miRNA maturation is excising the mature miRNA from the pri-miRNA by RNaseIII-type endonucleases, such as Dicer (**Figure 1*a***). This processing has important differences between plants and animals. In animals, miRNAs are processed from the pri-miRNA by a pair of enzymes in a stepwise manner. Drosha, a nuclear-localized RNaseIII enzyme, makes the initial cuts (one on each arm of the stem-loop) in the pri-miRNA to liberate the miRNA stem-loop, the "pre-miRNA," from the flanking sequence of the pri-miRNA (68). After export to the cytoplasm, Dicer makes a second set of cuts, separating the miRNA, duplexed with its near reverse complement, the miRNA*, from the loop region of the pre-miRNA (68). The resulting miRNA/miRNA* duplex typically has two-nucleotide 3′ overhangs (74), similar to the overhangs of siRNA duplexes produced by Dicer from long double-stranded RNA (19, 37, 38).

POTENTIAL GUIDELINES FOR CONFIDENT miRNA ANNOTATION

Confident annotation of poorly conserved miRNAs in plants appears to require evidence more stringent than that originally specified in the annotation guidelines (5). First, it seems reasonable to require that the extent of pairing within the precursor stem-loop resembles that of the conserved miRNAs. Plant miRNA stem-loops generally have no more than 7 unpaired nucleotides in the 25 nucleotides centered on the miRNA, of which no more than 3 are consecutive and no more than 2 are without a corresponding unpaired nucleotide in the miRNA*, and they have analogous pairing constraints for the 25 nucleotides centered on the miRNA*. Nearly all (96%) of the hundreds of conserved miRNA genes listed in **Table 1** fulfill these criteria, and there is little reason to suspect that authentic nonconserved miRNAs would not. Second, expression evidence would ideally include evidence that expression depends on miRNA pathway genes (such as DCL1) but does not depend on genes unique to the ta-siRNA pathway (such as RDR6 or DCL4) or heterochromatic siRNA pathway (such as RDR2 or DCL3). This second criterion is currently more difficult to satisfy in plants other than *Arabidopsis* because other species do not have mutants defective in the silencing pathways, although RNAi can be used to deplete miRNA pathway genes (75a). For these other species, high-throughput sequencing (yielding hundreds of thousands of reads per sample) is often sufficiently thorough to identify both the miRNA and miRNA* segments (**Figure 1*a***). The cloning of candidates representing both strands of the miRNA duplex to the exclusion of other small RNAs from the locus, whereby the cloned RNAs are positioned within a predicted hairpin such that they are paired with two-nucleotide 3′ overhangs, is diagnostic of a miRNA locus. Another tractable criterion would be evidence of silencing function, for example, detection of cleavage fragments of predicted miRNA targets that end precisely at the nucleotide expected for miRNA-directed cleavage (79). This functional criterion, which has now been satisfied for virtually all the confidently identified *Arabidopsis* miRNAs, was recently used to provide strong support for the authenticity of nonconserved miRNAs in *Oryza* (126) and *Populus* (81). Although the possibility remains that relying on this functional criterion would occasionally annotate other silencing RNAs (such as ta-siRNAs) as miRNAs, this possibility would be largely avoided with stringent adherence to the pairing criterion described above. Moreover, at the end of the day, evidence that a small RNA guides RNA cleavage, be it siRNA or miRNA, would provide the most useful biological information.

In plants, DCL1 is required for miRNA accumulation, yet processing intermediates do not appear to overaccumulate in DCL1 mutants, suggesting that DCL1 has the Drosha-like activity responsible for the first set of cuts (61, 107, 115). None of the other three Dicer-like enzymes in *Arabidopsis* is required for miRNA biogenesis (41, 142), suggesting that DCL1 also makes the second set of cuts. Supporting the idea that DCL1 has both Drosha and Dicer functions in plant miRNA maturation is the observation that in plants the two sets of cuts that liberate the miRNA/miRNA* duplex both occur in the nucleus, which is the predominant location of DCL1 (104, 106, 142). RNAs corresponding to the pre-miRNAs of animals are detected only rarely for plant miRNAs, suggesting that both sets of cleavage events happen in rapid succession. The scarcity of detected pre-miRNAs might also indicate that the initial set of cuts is frequently proximal to the loop rather than the base of the stem-loop, although the recent detection of the miR168 pre-miRNA-like intermediate in *Arabidopsis* indicates that some pri-miRNAs can be cut first at the base of the stem-loop (H. Vaucheret, A.C. Mallory, D.P. Bartel, unpublished).

Although there can be some length heterogeneity at both the 5′ and 3′ ends of plant miRNAs, it is clear that DCL1 cuts preferentially at specific positions in the miRNA stem-loop precursor that result in accumulation of the appropriate mature miRNA (115). The mechanism by which DCL1 recognizes where to cut is largely a mystery. As would be expected from the diversity of miRNA sequences, the secondary structure rather than the primary sequence appears to be most important within the miRNA region of the stem-loop, in that functional miRNAs are still produced when substitutions are made within the miRNA, provided that compensatory changes on the other arm of the stem-loop are introduced to maintain the same pattern of paired and unpaired residues (105, 131). However, the resulting artificial miRNA can be of a slightly different length, indicating that primary sequence or geometry of the mismatched residues plays a role in determining the cleavage sites (131). This recognition appears to involve the dsRNA-binding domain of DCL1 because the dcl1–9 allele, which disrupts the dsRNA-binding domain, cuts the miR163 stem-loop at aberrant positions (61). In addition, the *HYPONASTIC LEAVES1* (*HYL1*) (80) gene product probably collaborates with DCL1 during substrate recognition and subsequent functions. Metazoan Dicer-like (DCL) proteins each appear to partner with dsRNA-binding proteins, which can help recognize cleavage substrates and help load the silencing RNA into the silencing complex. A family of five dsRNA-binding proteins may play this role in *Arabidopsis* (50). Genetic, molecular, and biochemical evidence all indicate that HYL1 is the member of this family that preferentially partners with DCL1 during miRNA biogenesis (49, 50, 132).

In addition to *DCL1* and *HYL1*, *HUA ENHANCER1* (*HEN1*) is also important for miRNA maturation. Mutations in *HEN1* result in 3′-end uridylation of miRNAs and siRNAs, which apparently leads to reduced miRNA accumulation and function (23, 71a, 107, 143). HEN1 contains a methyltransferase domain, and can methylate miRNA/miRNA* duplexes in vitro (147). The 3′-terminal nucleotides of endogenous miRNAs are methylated on their 2′ hydroxyl groups in wild-type plants, but not in *hen1* mutants or in animals (36a, 147) (M. Axtell & D.P. Bartel, unpublished). End-methylation of miRNAs does not enhance silencing activity in vitro (112) and instead appears to protect the 3′ ends of silencing RNAs from uridylation and associated destabilization (71a).

After DCL1-mediated cleavage and HEN1-mediated methylation, most miRNA molecules exit the nucleus and enter the cytoplasm (**Figure 1a**). This export into the cytoplasm is facilitated by *HASTY* (*HST*), a member of the importin β family of nucleocytoplasmic transporters (21). A similar pathway exists in animals; Exportin-5, the mammalian HST ortholog, exports pre-miRNA hairpins from the nucleus to the cytoplasm (82, 146). *hst* mutants have reduced accumulation of most, but not all, miRNAs, suggesting that HST is important for miRNA export, but that other components or pathways can substitute (106). As pre-miRNAs appear to be very short-lived in plants, it is likely that HST transports either miRNA/miRNA* duplexes or single-stranded miRNAs after they are fully excised by DCL1. Northern blot analysis suggests that miRNAs are primarily single stranded in the nucleus (106), suggesting either that a fraction of functional miRNAs are located within the nucleus or that miRNAs are already single stranded before transport to the cytoplasm by HST. It is unknown whether plant miRNAs are already associated with components of the silencing complex when transported to the cytoplasm, or if transport occurs before loading into the silencing complex.

MicroRNA Incorporation into the Silencing Complex

The miRNA-programmed silencing complex is often referred to as an RNA-induced silencing complex (RISC) to emphasize the functional parallels between the miRNA-programmed silencing complex and the siRNA-programmed complex that mediates RNAi (48, 79, 128). MicroRNAs are processed from their pri-miRNA precursors as duplexes, still paired with their miRNA* strands. However, cloning and expression data indicate that the miRNA strand of this duplex accumulates to much higher levels in vivo than does the miRNA* (74, 115). This accumulation asymmetry is achieved by preferential loading of the miRNA strand into the silencing complex, where it is protected from degradation, whereas the miRNA* strand is preferentially excluded from the silencing complex and consequentially subject to degradation (**Figure 1***a*).

Key insight into the asymmetry of RISC loading came from bioinformatic and biochemical studies of functional siRNA du-

plexes. The siRNA duplex strand with less stable 5′ end pairing is selectively loaded into RISC, where it guides silencing, whereas the strand with the more stable 5′ end pairing is excluded from RISC (57, 119). These two strands of the siRNA duplex are called the guide and passenger strands and are analogous to the miRNA and miRNA* strands, respectively. Most miRNA/miRNA* duplexes also appear to have energetic asymmetry; the 5′ ends of most miRNAs are less stably paired than are the 5′ ends of the corresponding miRNA*s (57, 119). The mechanism by which the silencing RNA is incorporated as a single strand into the silencing complex is not fully known, but a model is emerging for siRNA incorporation into RISC, based primarily on biochemical studies in *Drosophila*: The asymmetry of an siRNA duplex is first sensed by the Dicer2–R2D2 heterodimer, wherein R2D2 is the dsRNA-binding-domain protein that partners with Dicer2. R2D2 binds the end of the duplex that is more stably paired, and Dicer binds the other end (130). Dicer2-R2D2 then loads the siRNA duplex into the Argonaute protein such that the guide strand of the siRNA directs Argonaute-catalyzed cleavage of the passenger strand (87a). Cleavage of the passenger strand facilitates its dissociation, thereby liberating the guide strand to pair to target transcripts and direct their cleavage. An analogous mechanism involving DCL1 and HYL1 might operate to load the plant miRNAs into AGO1 to form plant RISCs. Whether passenger-strand cleavage is important for plant miRNA RISC assembly is not known; cleavage-assisted loading is less important for siRNAs with mismatches to the passenger strand and appears to be bypassed altogether for miR-1 (87a), which has many mismatches to its miRNA* strand at its 5′ end. Even in this bypass scenario, the observation that plant miRNAs follow the asymmetry trends seen for siRNAs implies a function for DCL1 and HYL1 in RISC loading, which raises the question of whether plant RISC maturation occurs in the nucleus, the predominant site of DCL1 and HYL1

RNA-induced silencing complex (RISC): originally defined as the ribonucleoprotein complex that cleaves messenger RNAs during RNAi, RISC is now frequently used to refer to any silencing complex that includes an Argonaute protein and an siRNA or miRNA guide strand

proteins, or whether it occurs in the cytoplasm, where these proteins are less abundant but might still be present.

The final product of the miRNA/siRNA biogenesis pathway is a single-stranded RNA incorporated into a silencing complex (**Figure 1**). There are several varieties of these silencing complexes that vary at least partially in their composition and function; apart from the RISC mediating PTGS, a related silencing complex important for chromatin modification and TGS is typically referred to as an RNAi-induced transcriptional silencing (RITS) complex (134). A central component of all these silencing complexes is a member of the Argonaute protein family. Argonaute proteins, which have been implicated in a broad range of RNAi-related mechanisms, contain two conserved regions, the PAZ and Piwi domains (25). The PAZ domain appears to be an RNA-binding domain (75, 122, 144), and the Piwi domain has structural and functional similarity to RNase H enzymes (76, 123). Many organisms contain multiple members of the Argonaute family; in some cases, there is evidence for functional diversification of the different Argonautes. For example, only 1 of 4 mammalian Argonautes, Ago2, can mediate RNA cleavage in vitro (76). *Arabidopsis* contains 10 Argonaute proteins, 4 of which have been investigated genetically. AGO4 is involved in targeting some transposons and inverted-repeat transgenes for DNA methylation (149, 150). *PNH/ZLL/AGO10* and *ZIPPY/AGO7* are required for proper development (51, 83, 98, 99), but the mechanism by which they act is not known. AGO7 has been linked to the function of some ta-siRNAs, in that the *ago7* phenotype resembles that of *rdr6* and *sgs3*, two genes needed for ta-siRNA biogenesis (109, 133) (**Figure 1b**), and levels of messages targeted by *TAS3* (but not *TAS1*) ta-siRNAs are elevated in *ago7* (3, 109, 133). *AGO1* is the only Argonaute gene known to be required for miRNA function in *Arabidopsis*. *Arabidopsis* AGO1 binds miRNAs and catalyzes target cleavage in vitro (16, 112), and *ago1* mutants

have elevated levels of miRNA targets in vivo (131). A null allele of *AGO1* shows a sharp decrease in accumulation of most miRNAs compared to wild type, presumably because miRNAs are less stable before they enter the silencing complex than after (131).

Plant MicroRNA Expression

Transcription, processing, and RISC incorporation together determine mature miRNA levels found in a cell. Some miRNAs are among the most abundant RNAs; individual animal miRNAs are present at up to 10,000–50,000 copies per cell (74). Although the expression levels of plant miRNAs have not been similarly quantified, it is clear that many are abundantly expressed. Certain miRNAs have been cloned hundreds of times, and most are readily detectable by Northern blot (46, 115). More recently, microarray technology was adapted to rapidly survey expression profiles of plant miRNAs (7). Some miRNAs are broadly expressed, whereas others are expressed most strongly in particular organs or developmental stages (7, 115). More precise data on the localization of a few plant miRNAs have come from in situ hybridization (29, 54, 58) or from miRNA-responsive reporters (105). Little is known about the transcriptional or post-transcriptional regulation of miRNA expression, although expression patterns of miRNA promoter reporter constructs have been described for miR160 (136) and miR171 (105). Levels of several miRNAs are responsive to phytohormones or growth conditions; miR159 levels are enhanced by gibberellin (1), miR164 is transiently induced by certain auxin treatments (45), and miR393 levels are increased by a variety of stresses (127). The dependence of miR395 and miR399 levels on growth conditions is particularly striking. A regulator of sulfate-assimilation enzymes and sulfate transporters (2, 3, 53), miR395 is undetectable in plants grown on standard medium, but induced over 100-fold in sulfate-starved plants (53). Similarly, miR399 is strongly and specifically induced in plants grown on low-phosphate medium (40a).

MECHANISMS OF MICRORNA FUNCTION

MicroRNA-Directed RNA Cleavage

Small silencing RNAs regulate gene expression by three basic mechanisms: RNA cleavage, translational repression, and transcriptional silencing. Directing target cleavage is the best-understood mode of action used by small RNAs to regulate gene expression. In this mechanism, the small silencing RNAs guide the Argonaute component of RISC to cleave ("slice") a single phosphodiester bond within complementary RNA molecules. The cleavage fragments are then released, freeing the RISC to recognize and cleave another transcript.

Plant miRNAs have been implicated in both target cleavage and translational repression. Lines of evidence indicating that plant miRNAs generally guide the cleavage of complementary or nearly complementary mRNAs are as follows: MicroRNA-guided slicer activity is present in wheat germ and *Arabidopsis* lysates (112, 128). Many miRNA targets are expressed at higher levels in plants that have impaired miRNA function as the result of mutations in the miRNA pathway (e.g., *hen1*, *ago1*, and *hyl1*) (23, 131, 132). Similarly, the expression of certain viral suppressors of RNA silencing causes overaccumulation of miRNA target messages (26, 28, 36, 55, 86), whereas overexpression of miRNAs can cause reduction of target messages (1, 40a, 45, 59, 103, 118, 136, 139). These results imply that miRNAs negatively regulate stability of their targets. Moreover, the 3′ cleavage products of many miRNA targets are detectable in vivo, either by Northern blot (55, 79, 84, 124) or 5′ RACE (3, 28, 53, 55, 79, 84, 85, 87, 103, 125, 132, 143). The fragments mapped by 5′ RACE correspond to cleavage between the target nucleotides that pair to nucleotides 10 and 11 of the miRNA—precisely the position expected for RISC-mediated cleavage (38, 79). The "slicer" activity guided by the miRNAs appears to reside in the Piwi domains of certain Argonaute proteins (76, 123), including *Arabidopsis* AGO1 (16, 112).

Additional Mechanisms of MicroRNA-Directed Repression

RISC-mediated cleavage does not explain all the repression attributed to silencing RNAs, particularly in animals, in which endogenous targets are only rarely subject to this type of cleavage (145). The first miRNAs identified, the *lin-4* and *let-7* RNAs, regulate the expression of heterochronic genes that are critical for timing certain cell divisions in *C. elegans* larval development (67, 95, 114, 121, 138). The original experiments with *lin-4* RNA and two of its targets, *lin-14* and *lin-28*, indicated that *lin-4* RNA repressed the amount of target proteins without a substantial decrease in the amount of target mRNA, and it was generally thought that the same would be true for most metazoan miRNA targets, including *lin-41*, a target of *let-7* (102, 121, 138). However, a recent report describes substantial decreases in *lin-14*, *lin-28*, and *lin-41* mRNA levels, which could largely explain the repression previously reported at the protein level (8). These results from worms are consistent with previous cell-culture experiments showing that introducing a miRNA into mammalian cells can reduce the levels of ~100 mRNAs targeted by the miRNA (73). The nonextensive miRNA:target pairing and the nature of the target degradation fragments suggest that mRNA destabilization observed in worms and mammalian cell culture does not occur through the slicer mechanism (8, 73). Although these findings show that transcript destabilization plays more of a role in metazoan miRNA action than previously appreciated, evidence from reporter assays continues to implicate translational repression as a component of miRNA-directed repression, in that partial complementarity to silencing RNAs (or tethering Argonaute proteins to mRNAs by some other means) can decrease protein output of mRNAs without corresponding decreases in message levels (34, 35, 110, 111).

What then might be the mechanism of silencing when the miRNA:target pairing is not sufficient to trigger efficient RISC-mediated cleavage? A potential clue came with the observation that Argonaute proteins and miRNA targets are localized to cytoplasmic foci known as Processing bodies (P bodies), which are sites for storage and degradation of mRNAs (77, 120). This suggests that miRNA binding directs the message to the P body, where it can be sequestered from the translation machinery and destabilized (77, 120). Whether this repression appears as translation repression or message destabilization or a combination of the two would depend on the message and its relative degradation kinetics outside the P body.

In plants, the degree of repression apart from RISC-mediated cleavage is unknown, but is likely less than that seen in animals. RISC-mediated cleavage is an important component of the repression for every plant target examined, as expected from the extensive complementarity between these targets and the plant miRNAs. The original experiments investigating repression of APETALA2 (AP2) showed that miR172 appears to affect accumulation of target protein but not that of target mRNA (6, 29). More recent experiments revealed that RISC-mediated mRNA cleavage represents a large component of miR172-directed AP2 repression, but that the *AP2* message remains relatively constant because of compensatory transcriptional activation triggered by lower AP2 protein (118). Nonetheless, in addition to RISC-catalyzed cleavage, an important component of repression operates at the level of translation (or nacsient protein destabilization). The same could be true for many other established plant targets. Assessing the extent of miRNA-directed translational repression in plants awaits additional cases in which target proteins, rather than only target mRNAs, are monitored in response to changing miRNA levels.

Small RNA-Directed Transcriptional Silencing

Segments of transcriptionally silent DNA, known as heterochromatic regions, are associated with certain covalent modifications of DNA and histones. Evidence from several organisms has demonstrated that small RNAs are important for establishing and/or maintaining these heterochromatic modifications. In fission yeast, Dicer produces small RNAs corresponding to heterochromatic repeats (113), and deletion of Dicer or Argonaute disrupts heterochromatin silencing (135). This transcriptional repression involves the RITS complex, which, like RISC, contains Argonaute and a single-stranded Dicer-produced siRNA, as well as Chp1 and Tas3, proteins that are not thought to be present in RISC (96, 101, 134). Small RNAs also guide repressive modifications of DNA and histones in plants (reviewed in 88). For example, *AGO4* is required for siRNA-guided transcriptional silencing of the *SUPERMAN* gene and the maintenance of transcriptional repression triggered by inverted repeats (149, 150).

Do miRNAs guide transcriptional silencing in plants? Recent evidence raises the possibility that they might (10). Dominant mutations within the miR166 complementary sites of *PHABULOSA* (*PHB*) and *PHAVOLUTA* (*PHV*) mRNAs result in abnormal leaf development (90) that correlates with reduced miR166-guided mRNA cleavage (87). Curiously, these *phb* and *phv* mutations also correlate with reduced DNA methylation within the coding region of the mutant alleles (10). This reduced methylation occurs only in *cis*; in heterozygous plants, only the mutant copy of *PHB* is affected, whereas the wild-type copy is not (10). Because the miRNA complementary site in these mRNAs spans an exon junction, miR166 is presumably not able to interact with the genomic DNA, suggesting that interaction between miR166 and the nascent, but spliced, *PHB* mRNA somehow results in local DNA methylation (10). Although intriguing, the functional significance of this methylation change is not yet clear. Whereas methylated promoter regions are often associated with transcriptional silencing (reviewed in 91) the observed methylation in *PHB* and *PHV* is near the 3′ end of the coding regions (10), and it is unknown what effect this methylation is having on *PHB* or *PHV* transcription. Further, it is not known if reduced miRNA complementarity generally correlates with reduced target gene methylation.

REGULATORY ROLES OF PLANT MICRORNAs

Identification of Plant MicroRNA Targets

The challenge in miRNA target prediction has been to capture most of the regulatory targets without bringing in too many false predictions. Progress has been made on this front in animals, particularly in the past year (24, 60, 70), but this was more than three years after the abundance of miRNAs in animals was first discovered. In contrast to the delay in animals, the high degree of complementarity between *Arabidopsis* miRNAs and their target mRNAs allowed the confident prediction of targets soon after the discovery of the plant miRNAs themselves (116), at a time when only three targets were known for animal miRNAs. The first clue to the general paradigm for miRNA target recognition in plants came from mapping miR171 to the genome. This miRNA has four matches in the *Arabidopsis* genome: one is located between protein-coding genes and has a predicted stem-loop structure, whereas the other three are all antisense to *SCARECROW-LIKE* (*SCL*) genes and lack stem-loop structures, leading to the idea that the intergenic locus produces a miRNA that guides the cleavage of the complementary *SCL* mRNAs (78, 115).

Although other *Arabidopsis* miRNAs are not perfectly complementary to mRNAs, most are nearly so. An initial genome-wide screen for miRNA targets identified mRNAs containing ungapped, antisense alignments to miRNAs with 0–3 mismatches, a level of complementarity highly unlikely to occur by chance (116). Using this cutoff, targets were predicted for 11 out of 13 miRNA families known at the time, comprising 49 target genes in total (116). For conserved miRNAs, more sensitive predictions allowing gaps and more mismatches can be made by identifying cases where homologous mRNAs in *Arabidopsis* and *Oryza* each have complementarity to the same miRNA family (53). Moreover, including EST information in addition to annotated genes has yielded additional targets, which include ta-siRNA precursors (3).

Because plant miRNAs affect stability of their targets, mRNA expression arrays can be used in genome-wide screens for miRNA targets. For example, expression array data showed that five mRNAs encoding TCP transcription factors are downregulated in plants overexpressing miR319 (103). Expression arrays may be especially useful in identifying miRNA targets that have been missed by bioinformatic approaches, i.e., targets with more degenerate or nonconserved complementarity that are nonetheless subject to miRNA-guided cleavage or destabilization (73). Such an experiment has been done for four plant miRNAs, carefully examining the expression profiles of plants overexpressing each miRNA (118). Perhaps surprisingly, no new direct targets were identified beyond those found previously through bioinformatics. Two new target candidates were found, but evidence for miRNA-guided cleavage of these targets was not detected by 5′ RACE in wild-type plants, suggesting that these mRNAs may only be cleaved in plants that ectopically express miRNAs (118).

The Scope of MicroRNA-Mediated Regulation in Plants

The observation that the expression-array experiment did not reveal new targets (118) suggests that most cleavage targets have already been found for known plant miRNAs. Nonetheless, other types of targets might be missed both in the informatic predictions and in the array experiment. For example, targets repressed only at the level of translation would not be detected in the array experiment, and if such targets had less extensive complementary to the miRNAs, like that observed for many of the metazoan targets, they also would not be confidently predicted with the computational methods previously applied to plants. One approach for finding such targets would be to apply methods that have successfully detected metazoan targets above the noise of false predictions (24, 60, 70, 71). These methods search for conserved Watson-Crick complementarity between the 3′ UTRs and the 5′ seed region of the miRNA, a region that is also most important for miRNA target recognition in plants (87). However, applying the animal methods to plants has not yielded more predictions than expected by chance (M.W. Jones-Rhoades, unpublished data), suggesting that such animal-like target recognition is relatively rare, or might not even exist in plants, which again supports the notion that most targets for the known plant miRNAs have been found.

Many predicted miRNA targets encode regulatory proteins, suggesting that plant miRNAs are master regulators. The 21 miRNA families conserved in eudicots (*Arabidopsis* and *Populus*) have 95 confirmed or confidently predicted conserved targets in *Arabidopsis* (**Tables 2** and **3**). Sixty-five (68%) of these encode transcription factors, pointing to a role for miRNAs at the core of gene regulatory networks (**Table 2**). These transcription-factor targets have a remarkable propensity to be involved in developmental patterning or stem cell identity, leading to the proposal that many plant miRNAs function during differentiation to clear regulatory gene transcripts responsible for previous expression programs, thereby facilitating more rapid and robust transitions to new expression programs (116). Such miRNA-assisted reprogramming provides an attractive alternative to mechanisms in which regulatory genes have constitutively unstable messages.

Among the non-transcription factor targets (**Table 3**), six (6%) encode F-box proteins or ubiquitin-conjugating enzymes implicated in targeting selected proteins for proteasomal degradation, indicating a role for miRNAs in regulating protein stability. *DCL1* and *AGO1* are also miRNA targets, suggesting that plant miRNAs play a role in tuning their own biogenesis and function. Other conserved miRNA targets, such as ATP-sulfurylases, superoxide dismutases, and laccases have less clear regulatory roles, and although in vivo miRNA-mediated cleavage has been shown for many of these targets, the biological significance of their regulation by miRNAs is not yet known.

All 20 miRNA families that are conserved among *Arabidopsis*, *Populus*, and *Oryza* have complementary sites in target RNAs that also are conserved in all three species (**Tables 2** and **3**). Although these miRNAs may have additional nonconserved targets, this target-site conservation suggests that these miRNAs play similar roles in different plant species. Indeed, mutations in class III HD-ZIP target genes that reduce miR166 complementarity in *Arabidopsis* and maize confer similar phenotypes (54, 90, 116). However, the expansion of certain miRNA families and target classes in different species suggests that some of these families may have species-specific roles. For example, the miR397 family is complementary to 26 putative laccase mRNAs in *Populus*, whereas it has comparable complementarity to only three in *Arabidopsis*. Laccases are speculated to be involved in lignification (11), a process that may be more critical in woody plants such as *Populus* than in the herbaceous *Arabidopsis*.

Experimental Confirmation of Plant MicroRNA Targets

A growing number of plant miRNA targets predicted through bioinformatics have been experimentally confirmed. One means of confirmation uses *Agrobacterium* infiltration to observe miRNA-dependent cleavage of

Table 2 Transcription-factor targets of plant miRNAs

miRNA family	Target family	A.t.	O.s.	P.t.	Confirmed targets	Confirmation method
miR156	SBP (116)	11	9	16	SPL2, SPL3, SPL4, SPL10 (3, 28, 55, 133)	5′ RACE
miR159/319	MYB (107, 116)	8	6	5	MYB33, MYB65 (1, 93, 103)	5′ RACE, Agro-infiltration, miRNA-resistant target
miR159/319	TCP (103)	5	4	7	TCP2, TCP3, TCP4, TCP10, TCP24 (103)	5′ RACE, miRNA-resistant target
miR160	ARF (116)	3	5	9	ARF10, ARF16, ARF17 (3, 55, 84, 136)	5′ RACE, in vitro cleavage, Agro infiltration, miRNA-resistant target
miR164	NAC (116)	6	6	6	CUC1, CUC2, NAC1, At5g07680, At5g61430 (45, 55, 65, 85)	5′ RACE, in vitro cleavage, Agro infiltration, miRNA-resistant target
miR166	HD-ZIPIII (116)	5	4	9	PHB, PHV, REV, ATHB-8, ATHB-15 (39, 59, 87, 128, 139)	5′ RACE, in vitro cleavage, miRNA-resistant target
miR167	ARF (107, 116)	2	4	7	ARF6, ARF8 (3, 55)	5′ RACE
miR169	HAP2 (116)	8	7	9	At1g17590, At1g72830, At1g54160, At3g05690, At5g06510 (53)	5′ RACE
miR171	SCL (78, 115)	3	5	9	SCL6-III, SCL6-IV (55, 79)	5′ RACE, Agro infiltration
miR172	AP2 (107)	6	5	6	AP2, TOE1, TOE2, TOE3 (6, 29, 55)	5′ RACE, miRNA-resistant target
miR393	bZIP* (53)	1	1	1	At1g27340 (53)	5′ RACE
miR396	GRF (53)	7	9	9	GRL1, GRL2, GRL3, GRL7, GRL8, GRL9 (53)	5′ RACE
miR444	MADS (125)	0	1	0	Os02g49840 (125)	5′ RACE
Total		65	66	93		

Predicted and confirmed targets of *Arabidopsis* miRNAs that encode known or suspected transcription factors are listed. For each target family, the number of predicted target genes in each of three plant species with sequenced genomes (A.t., *Arabidopsis thaliana*; O.s., *Oryza sativa*; P.t., *Populus trichocarpa*) is indicated. To be counted, a potential target must contain a complementary site to at least one member of the indicated miRNA family with a score of 3 or less (as described in 53), with the exception of the bZIP family (marked with an asterisk), for which some targets with more relaxed complementarity were included. Abbreviations: SBP, SQUAMOSA-promoter binding protein; ARF, AUXIN RESPONSE FACTOR; SCL, SCARECROW-LIKE; GRF, GROWTH REGULATING FACTOR.

targets in *Nicotiana benthiama* leaves (55, 79). Another assays endogenous miRNA-mediated cleavage activity in wheat-germ lysate (84, 87, 128). Perhaps the most useful method of miRNA target validation uses 5′ RACE to detect in vivo products of miRNA-mediated cleavage (3, 28, 53, 55, 79, 84, 85, 87, 103, 125, 132, 143). An adaptor oligonucleotide is ligated to the 5′ end of the uncapped 3′ portion of a cleaved miRNA target, followed by reverse transcription and PCR with a gene-specific primer (79). Sequencing the resulting PCR product reveals the precise position of target cleavage, expected to be between nucleotides that pair to positions 10 and 11 of the miRNA (38). This method is particularly useful because, unlike the infiltration or in vitro methods, 5′ RACE detects miRNA-directed mRNA cleavages that occur endogenously in the plant, a necessary prerequisite for biological relevance. Analysis of the biological significance of the miRNA-mediated

Table 3 Non-transcription-factor targets of plant miRNAs

miRNA family	Target family	A.t.	O.s.	P.t.	Confirmed targets	Confirmation method
miR161	PPR (116)	9	0	0	At1g06580 (4, 133)	5′ RACE
miR162	Dicer (143)	1	1	1	DCL1 (143)	5′ RACE
miR163	SAMT (107, 116)	5	0	0	At1g66690, At1g66700, At1g66720, At3g44860 (4)	5′ RACE
miR168	ARGONAUTE (116)	1	6	2	AGO1 (131, 133)	5′ RACE, miRNA-resistant target
miR173	ta-siRNA (3)	4	0	0	TAS1a, TAS1b, TAS1c, TAS2 (3)	5′ RACE
miR390	ta-siRNA (3)	1	2	3	TAS3 (3)	5′ RACE
miR390	receptor-like kinase (125)	4	15	21	Os02g10100 (125)	5′ RACE
miR393	F-box (53, 127)	4	2	5	TIR1, ABF1, ABF2, ABF3, At3g23690 (53)	5′ RACE
miR394	F-box (53)	1	1	2	At1g27340 (53)	5′ RACE
miR395	APS (53)	3	1	2	APS1, APS4 (53)	5′ RACE
miR395	SO$_2$ transporter (2)	1	2	3	AST68 (3)	5′ RACE
miR396	Rhodenase (53)	1	1	1		
miR397	Laccase (53, 127)	3	15	26	At2g29130, At2g38080, At5g60020 (53)	5′ RACE
miR398	CSD* (53)	2	2	2	CSD1, CSD2 (53)	5′ RACE
miR398	CytC oxidase(53, 127)	1	1	0	At3g15640 (53)	5′ RACE
miR399	PO$_4$ transporter (53)	1	4	4		
miR399	E2-UBC (127)	1	1	2	At2g33770 (3)	5′ RACE
miR403	ARGONAUTE (3)	1	0	1	AGO2 (3)	5′ RACE
miR408	Laccase (118)	3	2	3	At2g30210 (81, 118)	5′ RACE
miR408	Plantacyanin (127)	1	3	1	Os03g15340 (125)	5′ RACE
miR436	Unknown (125)	0	1	0	Os12g42390 (125)	5′ RACE
miR447	2-PGK (3)	1	0	0	At5g60760 (3)	5′ RACE
miR475	PPR (81)	0	0	24	4 PPR genes (81)	5′ RACE
miR476	PPR (81)	0	0	20	1 PPR gene (81)	5′ RACE
Total		49	60	123		

Predicted and confirmed targets of *Arabidopsis* miRNAs that do not encode known or suspected transcription factors are listed. For each target family, the number of predicted target genes in each of three plant species with sequenced genomes (*A.t.*, *Arabidopsis thaliana*; *O.s.*, *Oryza sativa*; *P.t.*, *Populus trichocarpa*) is indicated. To be counted, a potential target must contain a complementary site to at least one member of the indicated miRNA family with a score of 3 or less (as described in 53), with the exception of CSD (marked with an asterisk), for which some targets with more relaxed complementarity were included. Nonconfirmed target families are listed only if they score well in all three species. Abbreviations: SAMT, SAM-dependant methyl transferase; APS, ATP-sulfurylase; CSD, COPPER SUPEROXIDE DISMUTASE; E2-UBC, E2 ubiquitin-conjugating protein; ta-siRNA, *trans*-acting short interfering RNA; 2-PGK, 2-phophoglycerate kinase.

regulation of that target can be explored by using reverse genetic approaches. As summarized below, these approaches are revealing the in vivo relevance of a growing number of miRNA-target interactions.

Regulatory Roles of Plant MicroRNAs

The first evidence that small RNAs play roles in plant development came from mutants impaired in small RNA biogenesis or function.

Indeed, several genes central to miRNA function, including *DCL1*, *AGO1*, *HEN1*, and *HYL1*, were first identified in plants based on the developmental consequences of their mutations even before they were known to be important for small RNA biogenesis or function. Multiple groups isolated *dcl1* mutants; the most severe mutations result in early embryonic arrest, and even partial loss-of-function mutants result in pleiotropic defects, including abnormalities in floral organogenesis, leaf morphology, and axillary meristem initiation (reviewed in 117). *ago1*, *hen1*, *hyl1*, and *hst* mutants all have pleiotropic developmental defects that overlap with those of hypomorphic *dcl1* plants (20, 30, 80, 94, 129). In addition, plants that express certain viral inhibitors of small RNA processing or function, such as HC-Pro and P19, exhibit developmental defects reminiscent of *dcl1* mutants (26, 28, 36, 55, 86). Although many or all of these developmental defects may result from impaired miRNA activity, they may also reflect disruption of other pathways in which these genes act, such as in the generation and function of siRNAs. However, in contrast to mutations in genes needed for miRNA biogenesis, mutations in genes required for the accumulation of various siRNAs, such as *AGO4*, *RDR6*, *DCL2*, *DCL3*, and *DCL4* (Figure 1*b*), result in few, if any, developmental abnormalities (31, 41, 97, 132, 141a, 142, 146a, 149), with the only severe abnormalities appearing stochastically after several generations, consistent with the loss of epigenetic modifications (41). This distinction suggests that disrupting miRNA-based regulation has more severe immediate consequences than does disrupting siRNA-based regulation.

Mutations that impair a fundamental step in miRNA biogenesis result in misregulation of numerous miRNA targets (23, 132), making it difficult to assign the observed phenotypes to any particular miRNA family. Fortunately, the ease with which transgenic *Arabidopsis* can be generated has allowed investigation of particular miRNA/target interactions through two reverse genetic strategies. The first is to make transgenic plants that overexpress a miRNA, typically under the control of the strong 35S promoter (**Table 4**; **Figure 3**). This approach can potentially downregulate all mRNAs targeted by the overexpressed miRNA. The second strategy is to make transgenic plants that express a miRNA-resistant version of a miRNA target, in which silent mutations have been introduced into the miRNA complementary site that disrupt miRNA-mediated regulation without altering the encoded protein product (**Table 5**; **Figure 4**). For seven miRNA families that have been investigated in vivo by these strategies,

Table 4 Consequences of miRNA overexpression

miRNA	Target family	Consequences of overexpression
miR156	SPL transcription factors	Increased leaf initiation, decreased apical dominance, delayed flowering time (118)
miR159	MYB transcription factors	Male sterility, delayed flowering time (1)
miR319	TCP transcription factors	Uneven leaf shape and curvature, late flowering (103)
miR160	ARF transcription factors	Agravitropic roots with disorganized root caps, increased lateral rooting (136)
miR164	NAC domain transcription factors	Organ fusion (65, 85), reduced lateral rooting (45)
miR166	HD-ZIP transcription factors	Seedling arrest, fasciated apical meristems, female sterility (59, 139)
miR172	AP2-like transcription factors	Early flowering, lack of petals, transformation of sepals to carpels (6, 29)
miR399	Ubiquitin-conjugating enzyme	Phosphate accumulation (40a)

Figure 3

A sampling of phenotypes resulting from microRNA (miRNA) overexpression in *Arabidopsis*. Each panel depicts wild type (*left*) compared to a corresponding specimen from a miRNA-overexpressing plant (*right*). (*a*) miR156-overexpressing plants have increased leaf initiation and decreased apical dominance, resulting in dramatically bushier plants. Images reprinted from Reference 118, copyright 2005 by Elsevier. (*b*) The stamens of miR164-overexpressing plants are frequently fused together rather than distinct (*arrows* denote point of stamen separation). This phenotype is similar to that of loss-of-function mutants in miR164 targets *CUC1* and *CUC2*. Images reprinted from Reference 85, copyright 2004 by Elsevier. (*c*) The outer floral organ whorls of miR172-overexpressing flowers are transformed into carpeloid tissue rather than having four sepals and four petals. This phenotype is similar to that of loss-of-function mutants in miR172 target *AP2*. Images reprinted with permission from Reference 29, copyright 2004, AAAS. (*d*) The *jaw-D* mutant phenotype, which includes severely affected leaf morphology, results from miR319 overexpression (103). Images copyright by Nature Publishing Group, used with permission. (*e*) Plants overexpressing miR166 have decreased stature and fertility (*top*) and fasciated, enlarged inflorescence stems (*inset*) with highly abnormal vasculature (*bottom*) (59). Images copyright by Blackwell Publishing, used with permission. (*f*) miR159a-overexpressing plants have reduced male fertility and altered anther morphology. Images reprinted from Reference 118, copyright 2005 by Elsevier. (*g*) miR160-overexpressing plants have disorganized root tips and fewer starch granules (*purple staining*) (136). Images copyright by American Society of Plant Biologists, used with permission.

Table 5 Consequences of disrupting miRNA-mediated regulation of specific targets

miRNA family or subfamily	miRNA-resistant target	Promoter	Phenotype
miR159	*MYB33*	35S	Upwardly curled leaves (103)
miR159	*MYB33*	Endogenous	Upwardly curled leaves, reduced stature, shortened petioles (93)
miR319	*TCP4*	Endogenous and 35S	Arrested seedlings, fused cotyledons, lack of SAM (103)
miR319	*TCP2*	35S	Long hypocotyls, reduced stature, and apical dominance (103)
miR160	*ARF16*	Endogenous and 35S	Fewer lateral roots, small plants with reduced fertility, increased basal expression of auxin-induced genes (136)
miR160	*ARF17*	Endogenous	Extra and lobed cotyledons, short roots with decreased branching, small plants with reduced fertility, altered basal expression of auxin-induced genes (84)
miR164	*CUC1*	Endogenous	Short petioles, aberrant leaf shape, extra petals, missing sepals (85)
miR164	*CUC2*	Inducible and 35S	Aberrant leaf shape, extra petals, increased sepal separation (65)
miR164	*NAC1*	35S	Increased number of lateral roots (45)
miR166	*REV*	Endogenous	Radialized vasculature, strands of leaf tissue attached to stem (39)
miR166	*PHB*	35S	Adaxialized leaves, ectopic meristems (87)
miR168	*AGO1*	Endogenous	Curled leaves, disorganized phyllotaxy, reduced fertility (131)
miR172	*AP2*	35S	Late flowering, excess of petals and stamens (29)
miR399	*UBC*	35S	Reduced response to low phosphate (40a)

perturbing miRNA-mediated regulation results in abnormal development. Taken together, these studies confirm that miRNAs are key regulators of many facets of *Arabidopsis* development.

One of the best-studied families of miRNA targets is the class III HD-ZIP transcription factor family. The importance of miR166 for the proper regulation of this gene class is underscored by the large number of dominant gain-of-function alleles that map to the miR166 complementary sites of HD-ZIP mRNAs (39, 54, 89, 90, 148). Dominant *phb* and *phv* mutations adaxialize leaves and overaccumulate *phb* or *phv* mRNA (89, 90), whereas dominant *rev* mutations result in radialized vasculature (39, 148). Similarly, mutations within the miR166 complementary site of the maize HD-ZIP gene *RLD1* adaxialize leaf primordia and cause overaccumulation of *rld1* mRNA (54). All of these gain-of-function HD-ZIP mutations isolated through forward genetics change the amino acid sequence of the conserved START domain. Before the discovery of miR166 it was hypothesized that the

HD-ZIP mutant phenotypes resulted from the loss of negative regulatory interaction mediated by the START domain (90), but after the discovery of miR166 and realization that the mutations map to the miRNA complementary site, it was hypothesized that the phenotypes resulted from the loss of miRNA-directed repression (116). Transgenic plants expressing an miR166-resistant version of *PHB* or *REV* with unaltered coding potential resemble the respective gain-of-function mutants, whereas transgenic plants containing additional wild-type copies of these genes have essentially wild-type phenotypes (39, 87) (**Figure 4***b*). This demonstrates that changing the RNA sequence, rather than the amino acid sequence, is sufficient to account for the developmental abnormalities observed in HD-ZIP gain-of-function mutants, indicating that the disrupted regulatory interaction is mediated at the RNA level rather than via the encoded protein.

miR172-mediated regulation of *APETALA2* (*AP2*) and related *AP2*-like genes is needed for proper specification of

Figure 4

Phenotypes of transgenic *Arabidopsis* expressing miRNA-resistant targets. Each panel depicts a control plant, either wild type or a plant expressing a miRNA-sensitive transgene (*left*), compared to a plant expressing a miRNA-resistant transgene (*right*). (*a*) Plants expressing miR159-resistant *MYB33* have reduced stature and upwardly curled leaves (93). Images copyright of American Society of Plant Biologists, used with permission. (*b*) Plants expressing miR166-resistant *PHB* have radialized, reduced leaves with adaxial characteristics all around the circumference of the leaf (87). Images copyright of EMBO, used with permission. (*c*) Seedlings expressing a wild-type *ARF17* transgene have two cotyledons (*asterisks*) and two emerging true leaves (*arrowheads*), whereas miR160-resistant *ARF17* seedlings have up to four cotyledons, with a leaf emerging between each pair of cotyledons (84). Images copyright of American Society of Plant Biologists, used with permission. (*d*) Flowers expressing a wild-type *CUC1* transgene have the expected four sepals (*S, top*) and four petals (*bottom*), whereas flowers expressing a miR164-resistant *CUC1* transgene often display two sepals (*top*) and six petals (*bottom*). Images reprinted from Reference 85, copyright 2005 by Elsevier. (*e*) miR172-resistant *AP2* transgenic flowers have variable numbers of floral organs; this flower has numerous petals and lacks inner whorl organs. Images reprinted with permission from Reference 29, copyright 2004, AAAS.

organs during flower development (6, 29). Plants that overexpress miR172 have floral defects that resemble *ap2* loss-of-function mutants, such as the absence of petals and sepal transformation into carpels (6, 29) (**Figure 3c**). As described above, these plants provide evidence that plant miRNAs can direct translation repression in addition to mRNA cleavage (6, 29, 118).

Although most miRNA families appear to target a single class of targets, the miR159/319 family regulates both MYB and TCP transcription factors (103, 116). Overexpression of miR319, which specifically downregulates *TCP* mRNAs, results in plants with uneven leaf shape and delayed flowering time (103) (**Figure 3d**). Expression of miR319-resistant *TCP4* results in aberrant seedlings that arrest with fused cotyledons and without forming apical meristems (103). Overexpression of miR159a specifically reduces *MYB* mRNA accumulation and results in male sterility (1, 118) (**Figure 3f**), whereas plants that express miR159-resistant *MYB33* have upwardly curled leaves, reduced stature, and shortened petioles (93, 103) (**Figure 4a**). Thus, miR159a and miR319, which differ at only three nucleotides, are related miRNAs that can target unrelated mRNAs (103).

The signaling pathway that mediates responses to the phytohormone auxin is particularly densely packed with miRNA regulation. For example, miR393 targets mRNAs encoding TIR1 and three closely related F-box proteins (53, 127). These F-box proteins are auxin receptors (32, 33, 56) that target short-lived repressors of ARF transcriptional activators for ubiquitin-mediated degradation in response to auxin. Intriguingly, not only the receptors, but also at least seven of the 23 *Arabidopsis ARF* mRNAs are either directly or indirectly subject to miRNA-mediated regulation (**Table 2**). miR167 targets *ARF6* and *ARF8*; miR160 targets *ARF10*, *ARF16*, and *ARF17* (55, 116), and miR390 directs cleavage of *TAS3*, leading to the production of ta-siRNAs that target *ARF3* and *ARF4* mRNAs (3). Freeing *ARF17* or *ARF16* from miR160 regulation results in dramatic morphological changes and alters basal levels of auxin-induced transcripts (84, 136) (**Figure 4c**). The deep conservation of some of these miRNAs (miR160 and miR390 are detectable in moss, one of the most evolutionarily basal land plants) implies that miRNAs have been modulating auxin signaling since very early in the development of multicellularity in plants (7). Beyond influencing auxin signaling, miRNAs are likely to aid in signal integration. For example, miR164 targets *CUC1*, *CUC2*, and *NAC1*, and perturbing this regulation disrupts root, leaf, and flower development (45, 65, 85) (**Figures 3b** and **4d**).

In addition to the miRNAs that target transcription factors, two miRNA families target genes central to miRNA biogenesis and function; miR162 targets *DCL1* (143), and miR168 targets *AGO1* (116, 131). Moreover, although the biological and biochemical roles of *Arabidopsis* AGO2 are not known, it is intriguing that *AGO2* mRNA is targeted by miR403 (3). miRNA targeting of *DCL1* and *AGO1* suggests a feedback mechanism whereby miRNAs negatively regulate their own activity. Curiously, although plants expressing miR168-resistant *AGO1* overaccumulate *AGO1* mRNA as expected, they also overaccumulate numerous other miRNA targets and exhibit developmental defects that overlap with those of *dcl1*, *hen1*, and *hyl1* loss-of-function mutants (131). This suggests that a large overabundance of AGO1 inhibits, rather than promotes, RISC activity (131). In any case, the fact that miR162 and miR168 family members also target *DCL* and *AGO* family members in *Oryza* and *Populus* (**Table 3**) suggests an important in vivo role for this regulation.

Protein-coding messages are not the only targets of plant miRNAs. At least two miRNAs, miR173 and miR390, target precursors of a special class of siRNAs, the transacting siRNAs (ta-siRNAs) (3). Unlike most siRNAs, which target loci closely related to the loci encoding them, ta-siRNAs direct cleavage of targets encoded at distinct loci (109, 133), thereby acting similarly to plant miRNAs (reviewed in 12). ta-siRNAs are encoded by *TAS* genes (**Figure 1b**). The miRNA complementarity sites in *TAS* transcripts are in register with the 21-nucleotide ta-siRNAs derived from the locus (3), suggesting a model in which *TAS* transcripts undergo miRNA-directed cleavage prior to reverse transcription by the RDR6 RNA-dependent RNA polymerase, producing a double-stranded RNA that is processed by DCL4 into 21-nucleotide siRNAs (3, 41, 109, 133, 141a, 146a). Some of these siRNAs go on to direct cleavage of target mRNAs, including those encoding a subset of ARF transcription factors and several proteins of unknown function (3, 109, 133).

MICRORNAs: PLANTS VERSUS ANIMALS

As understanding of miRNA genomics and function in plants and animals has grown, so has the realization that there are numerous differences between the kingdoms in the ways miRNAs are generated and carry out their regulatory roles. Indeed, the evolutionary relationship between plant and animal miRNAs is unclear. Did the last common ancestor of plants and animals possess miRNAs from which modern miRNAs descended, or did the plant and animal lineages independently adapt conserved RNAi machinery (including Dicer and Argonaute) to use endogenously expressed stem-loop RNAs as transregulators of other genes? Although miRNAs are deeply conserved within each kingdom (7, 40, 108), no miRNA family is known to be conserved between kingdoms. Moreover, there are several kingdom-specific differences in miRNA biogenesis. For example, the stem-loop precursors of plant miRNAs are markedly longer and more variable than their animal counterparts (115). Furthermore, the cellular localization of miRNA processing appears to differ between plant miRNAs, which are entirely processed within the nucleus (104, 106, 142), and animal miRNAs, which are sequentially processed in the nucleus and cytoplasm (68). Perhaps most interestingly, the scope and mode of regulation carried out by miRNAs appears to be drastically different between the two kingdoms. Most plant miRNAs guide the cleavage of target mRNAs (53, 55, 79, 128), and the predicted targets of *Arabidopsis* miRNAs, which comprise less than 1% of protein-coding genes, are highly biased toward transcription factors and other regulatory genes (53, 116). Although at least some animal miRNAs guide cleavage of endogenous targets (145), most appear to act through other mechanisms. Furthermore, the analysis of conserved, reverse-complementary matches to the 5′ seed regions of animal miRNAs suggests that a large percentage (20–30% or more) of animal protein-coding genes are conserved miRNA targets (24, 60, 70, 140). With these striking differences in biogenesis and function, we speculate that miRNAs arose at least twice, once in early plants and once in early animals. Perhaps in both lineages, and each in its unique way, the availability of this post-transcriptional layer of gene regulation enabled the emergence of more robust and specialized gene expression programs, thereby facilitating the emergence of the many cell types and developmental programs needed to build a complex plant or animal.

SUMMARY POINTS

1. MicroRNAs are endogenously expressed, ~21-nucleotide RNAs that do not encode proteins. A miRNA is initially expressed as a precursor RNA containing an imperfect stem-loop, from which a miRNA/miRNA* duplex is excised by DCL1. The miRNA strand of this duplex is subsequently incorporated into a silencing complex, where it guides targeting of complementary RNAs.

2. Plant miRNA genes are generally not located within protein-coding genes but comprise their own RNA polymerase II-dependent transcriptional units.

3. Plant miRNAs occur in gene families, each family contains 1–32 loci within a single genome, each potentially encoding identical or nearly identical mature miRNAs. At least 20 miRNA families are broadly conserved in flowering plants, and many are conserved to more deeply diverged plant lineages. In addition, there are an unknown number of lineage- and species-specific miRNA families.

4. Plant miRNAs primarily have been discovered through direct cloning and sequencing of small cellular RNAs or through comparative genomics. Only a handful of mutations at miRNA loci have been identified in genetic screens.

5. Nearly all plant miRNAs are highly complementary to target mRNAs, which the miRNAs repress through directed RNA cleavage and perhaps other mechanisms. The majority of known plant miRNA targets encode transcription factors or other regulatory proteins, such as components of the ubiquitin and RNAi pathways. Some miRNAs guide the cleavage of ta-siRNA precursors.

6. Bioinformatic approaches have identified targets for nearly all plant miRNAs. Several experimental methods have been used to confirm miRNA-target interactions and explore the biological significance of miRNA-mediated regulation.

7. Plant miRNAs are high-level regulators of gene expression that affect numerous aspects of plant biology, especially developmental patterning. Mutants impaired in miRNA biogenesis exhibit severe, pleiotropic abnormalities, and plants that overexpress particular miRNAs or express miRNA-resistant versions of particular miRNA targets exhibit a wide array of unusual phenotypes.

ACKNOWLEDGMENTS

We thank M.J. Axtell, A.C. Mallory, R. Rajagopalan, and H. Vaucheret for helpful discussions and colleagues for permission to reprint images. Plant miRNA research in the authors' labs is supported by the National Institutes of Health (R24-GM069512), the G. Harold and Leila Y. Mathers Charitable Foundation, and the Robert A. Welch Foundation (C-1309). David Bartel is an investigator of the Howard Hughes Medical Institute.

LITERATURE CITED

1. Achard P, Herr A, Baulcombe DC, Harberd NP. 2004. Modulation of floral development by a gibberellin-regulated microRNA. *Development* 131:3357–65

2. Adai A, Johnson C, Mlotshwa S, Archer-Evans S, Manocha V, et al. 2005. Computational prediction of miRNAs in *Arabidopsis thaliana*. *Genome Res.* 15:78–91

3. Allen E, Xie Z, Gustafson AM, Carrington JC. 2005. microRNA-directed phasing during trans-acting siRNA biogenesis in plants. *Cell* 121:207–21

4. Allen E, Xie Z, Gustafson AM, Sung GH, Spatafora JW, Carrington JC. 2004. Evolution of microRNA genes by inverted duplication of target gene sequences in *Arabidopsis thaliana*. *Nat. Genet.* 36:1282–90

5. Ambros V, Bartel B, Bartel DP, Burge CB, Carrington JC, et al. 2003. A uniform system for microRNA annotation. *RNA* 9:277–79

5a. Arazi T, Talmor-Neiman M, Stav R, Riese M, Huijser P, Baulcombe DC. 2005. Cloning and characterization of micro-RNAs from moss. *Plant J.* 43:837–48

6. Aukerman MJ, Sakai H. 2003. Regulation of flowering time and floral organ identity by a microRNA and its *APETALA2-like* target genes. *Plant Cell* 15:2730–41

7. Axtell MJ, Bartel DP. 2005. Antiquity of microRNAs and their targets in land plants. *Plant Cell* 17:1658–73

8. Bagga S, Bracht J, Hunter S, Massirer K, Holtz J, et al. 2005. Regulation by let-7 and lin-4 miRNAs results in target mRNA degradation. *Cell* 122:553–63

9. Baker CC, Sieber P, Wellmer F, Meyerowitz EM. 2005. The *early extra petals1* mutant uncovers a role for microRNA miR164c in regulating petal number in Arabidopsis. *Curr. Biol.* 15:303–15

10. Bao N, Lye KW, Barton MK. 2004. MicroRNA binding sites in Arabidopsis class III HD-ZIP mRNAs are required for methylation of the template chromosome. *Dev. Cell* 7:653–62

11. Bao W, O'Malley DM, Whetten R, Sederoff RR. 1993. A laccase associated with lignification in Loblolly Pine xylem. *Science* 260:672–74

12. Bartel B. 2005. MicroRNAs directing siRNA biogenesis. *Nat. Struct. Mol. Biol.* 12:569–71

13. Bartel DP. 2004. MicroRNAs: genomics, biogenesis, mechanism, and function. *Cell* 116:281–97

14. Baskerville S, Bartel DP. 2005. Microarray profiling of microRNAs reveals frequent coexpression with neighboring miRNAs and host genes. *RNA* 11:241–47

15. Baulcombe D. 2004. RNA silencing in plants. *Nature* 431:356–63

16. Baumberger N, Baulcombe DC. 2005. Arabidopsis ARGONAUTE1 is an RNA slicer that selectively recruits microRNAs and short interfering RNAs. *Proc. Natl. Acad. Sci. USA* 102:11928–33

17. Beclin C, Boutet S, Waterhouse P, Vaucheret H. 2002. A branched pathway for transgene-induced RNA silencing in plants. *Curr. Biol.* 12:684–88

18. Bentwich I, Avniel A, Karov Y, Aharonov R, Gilad S et al. 2005. Identification of hundreds of conserved and nonconserved human microRNAs. *Nat. Genet* 37:766–70

19. Bernstein E, Caudy AA, Hammond SM, Hannon GJ. 2001. Role for a bidentate ribonuclease in the initiation step of RNA interference. *Nature* 409:363–66

20. Bohmert K, Camus I, Bellini C, Bouchez D, Caboche M, Benning C. 1998. *AGO1* defines a novel locus of Arabidopsis controlling leaf development. *EMBO J.* 17:170–80

21. Bollman KM, Aukerman MJ, Park MY, Hunter C, Berardini TZ, Poethig RS. 2003. HASTY, the *Arabidopsis* ortholog of exportin 5/MSN5, regulates phase change and morphogenesis. *Development* 130:1493–504

22. Bonnet E, Wuyts J, Rouze P, Van de Peer Y. 2004. Detection of 91 potential conserved plant microRNAs in *Arabidopsis thaliana* and *Oryza sativa* identifies important target genes. *Proc. Natl. Acad. Sci. USA* 101:11511–16

23. Boutet S, Vazquez F, Liu J, Beclin C, Fagard M, et al. 2003. *Arabidopsis HEN1*: a genetic link between endogenous miRNA controlling development and siRNA controlling transgene silencing and virus resistance. *Curr. Biol.* 13:843–48

24. Brennecke J, Stark A, Russell RB, Cohen SM. 2005. Principles of microRNA-target recognition. *PLoS Biol.* 3:e85

25. Carmell MA, Xuan Z, Zhang MQ, Hannon GJ. 2002. The Argonaute family: tentacles that reach into RNAi, developmental control, stem cell maintenance, and tumorigenesis. *Genes Dev.* 16:2733–42

26. Chapman EJ, Prokhnevsky AI, Gopinath K, Dolja VV, Carrington JC. 2004. Viral RNA silencing suppressors inhibit the microRNA pathway at an intermediate step. *Genes Dev.* 18:1179–86

27. Chaw SM, Chang CC, Chen HL, Li WH. 2004. Dating the monocot-dicot divergence and the origin of core eudicots using whole chloroplast genomes. *J. Mol. Evol.* 58:424–41

28. Chen J, Li WX, Xie D, Peng JR, Ding SW. 2004. Viral virulence protein suppresses RNA silencing-mediated defense but upregulates the role of microRNA in host gene expression. *Plant Cell* 16:1302–13

29. Chen X. 2004. A microRNA as a translational repressor of *APETALA2* in *Arabidopsis* flower development. *Science* 303:2022–25

30. Chen X, Liu J, Cheng Y, Jia D. 2002. *HEN1* functions pleiotropically in *Arabidopsis* development and acts in C function in the flower. *Development* 129:1085–94

31. Dalmay T, Hamilton A, Rudd S, Angell S, Baulcombe DC. 2000. An RNA-dependent RNA polymerase gene in Arabidopsis is required for posttranscriptional gene silencing mediated by a transgene but not by a virus. *Cell* 101:543–53

32. Dharmasiri N, Dharmasiri S, Estelle M. 2005. The F-box protein TIR1 is an auxin receptor. *Nature* 435:441–45

33. Dharmasiri N, Dharmasiri S, Weijers D, Lechner E, Yamada M, et al. 2005. Plant development is regulated by a family of auxin receptor F box proteins. *Dev. Cell* 9:109–19

34. Doench JG, Petersen CP, Sharp PA. 2003. siRNAs can function as miRNAs. *Genes Dev.* 17:438–42

35. Doench JG, Sharp PA. 2004. Specificity of microRNA target selection in translational repression. *Genes Dev.* 18:504–11

36. Dunoyer P, Lecellier CH, Parizotto EA, Himber C, Voinnet O. 2004. Probing the microRNA and small interfering RNA pathways with virus-encoded suppressors of RNA silencing. *Plant Cell* 16:1235–50

36a. Ebhardt HA, Thi EP, Wang MB, Unrau PJ. 2005. Extensive 3′ modification of plant small RNAs is modulated by helper component-proteinase expression. *Proc. Natl. Acad. Sci. USA* 102:13398–403

37. Elbashir SM, Lendeckel W, Tuschl T. 2001. RNA interference is mediated by 21- and 22-nucleotide RNAs. *Genes Dev.* 15:188–200

38. Elbashir SM, Martinez J, Patkaniowska A, Lendeckel W, Tuschl T. 2001. Functional anatomy of siRNAs for mediating efficient RNAi in *Drosophila melanogaster* embryo lysate. *EMBO J.* 20:6877–88

39. Emery JF, Floyd SK, Alvarez J, Eshed Y, Hawker NP, et al. 2003. Radial patterning of *Arabidopsis* shoots by class III HD-ZIP and KANADI genes. *Curr. Biol.* 13:1768–74

40. Floyd SK, Bowman JL. 2004. Gene regulation: ancient microRNA target sequences in plants. *Nature* 428:485–86

40a. Fujii H, Chiou TJ, Lin SI, Aung K, Zhu JK. 2005. A miRNA involved in phosphate-starvation response in *Arabidopsis. Curr. Biol.* 15:2038–43

41. Gasciolli V, Mallory AC, Bartel DP, Vaucheret H. 2005. Partially redundant functions of Arabidopsis DICER-like enzymes and a role for DCL4 in producing trans-acting siRNAs. *Curr. Biol.* 15:1494–500

42. Giraldez AJ, Cinalli RM, Glasner ME, Enright AJ, Thomson JM, et al. 2005. MicroRNAs regulate brain morphogenesis in zebrafish. *Science* 308:833–38

43. Griffiths-Jones S. 2004. The microRNA registry. *Nucleic Acids Res.* 32: D109–11

44. Grishok A, Pasquinelli AE, Conte D, Li N, Parrish S, et al. 2001. Genes and mechanisms related to RNA interference regulate expression of the small temporal RNAs that control *C. elegans* developmental timing. *Cell* 106:23–34

44a. Guddeti S, Zhang de C, Li AL, Leseberg CH, Kang H, et al. 2005. Molecular evolution of the rice miR395 gene family. *Cell Res.* 15:631–38

45. Guo HS, Xie Q, Fei JF, Chua NH. 2005. MicroRNA directs mRNA cleavage of the transcription factor *NAC1* to downregulate auxin signals for Arabidopsis lateral root development. *Plant Cell* 17:1376–86

46. Gustafson AM, Allen E, Givan S, Smith D, Carrington JC, Kasschau KD. 2005. ASRP: the Arabidopsis Small RNA Project Database. *Nucleic Acids Res.* 33:D637–40

47. Hamilton AJ, Baulcombe, DC. 1999. A novel species of small antisense RNA in post-transcriptional gene silencing. *Science* 286:950–52

48. Hammond SM, Bernstein E, Beach D, Hannon GJ. 2000. An RNA-directed nuclease mediates post-transcriptional gene silencing in Drosophila cells. *Nature* 404:293–96

49. Han MH, Goud S, Song L, Fedoroff N. 2004. The *Arabidopsis* double-stranded RNA-binding protein HYL1 plays a role in microRNA-mediated gene regulation. *Proc. Natl. Acad. Sci. USA* 101:1093–98

49a. Herr AJ, Jensen MB, Dalmay T, Baulcombe DC. 2005. RNA polymerase IV directs silencing of endogenous DNA. *Science* 308:118–20

50. Hiraguri A, Itoh R, Kondo N, Nomura Y, Aizawa D, et al. 2005. Specific interactions between Dicer-like proteins and HYL1/DRB-family dsRNA-binding proteins in *Arabidopsis thaliana*. *Plant Mol. Biol.* 57:173–88

51. Hunter C, Sun H, Poethig RS. 2003. The Arabidopsis heterochronic gene *ZIPPY* is an *ARGONAUTE* family member. *Curr. Biol.* 13:1734–39

52. Hutvagner G, McLachlan J, Pasquinelli AE, Balint E, Tuschl T, Zamore PD. 2001. A cellular function for the RNA-interference enzyme Dicer in the maturation of the let-7 small temporal RNA. *Science* 293:834–38

53. Jones-Rhoades MW, Bartel DP. 2004. Computational identification of plant micro-RNAs and their targets, including a stress-induced miRNA. *Mol. Cell* 14:787–99

54. Juarez MT, Kui JS, Thomas J, Heller BA, Timmermans MC. 2004. microRNA-mediated repression of *rolled leaf1* specifies maize leaf polarity. *Nature* 428:84–88

54a. Kanno T, Huettel B, Mette MF, Aufsatz W, Jaligot E, et al. 2005. Atypical RNA polymerase subunits required for RNA-directed DNA methylation. *Nat. Genet.* 37:761–65

55. Kasschau KD, Xie Z, Allen E, Llave C, Chapman EJ, et al. 2003. P1/HC-Pro, a viral suppressor of RNA silencing, interferes with Arabidopsis development and miRNA function. *Dev. Cell* 4:205–17

56. Kepinski S, Leyser O. 2005. The Arabidopsis F-box protein TIR1 is an auxin receptor. *Nature* 435:446–51

57. Khvorova A, Reynolds A, Jayasena SD. 2003. Functional siRNAs and miRNAs exhibit strand bias. *Cell* 115:209–16

58. Kidner CA, Martienssen RA. 2004. Spatially restricted microRNA directs leaf polarity through ARGONAUTE1. *Nature* 428:81–84

59. Kim J, Jung JH, Reyes JL, Kim YS, Kim SY, et al. 2005. microRNA-directed cleavage of *ATHB15* mRNA regulates vascular development in Arabidopsis inflorescence stems. *Plant J.* 42:84–94

60. Krek A, Grun D, Poy MN, Wolf R, Rosenberg L, et al. 2005. Combinatorial microRNA target predictions. *Nat. Genet.* 37:495–500

61. Kurihara Y, Watanabe Y. 2004. Arabidopsis micro-RNA biogenesis through Dicer-like 1 protein functions. *Proc. Natl. Acad. Sci. USA* 101:12753–58

62. Lagos-Quintana M, Rauhut R, Lendeckel W, Tuschl T. 2001. Identification of novel genes coding for small expressed RNAs. *Science* 294:853–58

63. Lai EC, Tomancak P, Williams RW, Rubin GM. 2003. Computational identification of Drosophila microRNA genes. *Genome Biol.* 4:R42

64. Lau NC, Lim LP, Weinstein EG, Bartel DP. 2001. An abundant class of tiny RNAs with probable regulatory roles in *Caenorhabditis elegans*. *Science* 294:858–62

65. Laufs P, Peaucelle A, Morin H, Traas J. 2004. MicroRNA regulation of the CUC genes is required for boundary size control in *Arabidopsis* meristems. *Development* 131:4311–22

66. Lee RC, Ambros V. 2001. An extensive class of small RNAs in *Caenorhabditis elegans*. *Science* 294:862–64

67. Lee RC, Feinbaum RL, Ambros V. 1993. The *C. elegans* heterochronic gene *lin-4* encodes small RNAs with antisense complementarity to *lin-14*. *Cell* 75:843–54

68. Lee Y, Ahn C, Han J, Choi H, Kim J, Yim J, et al. 2003. The nuclear RNase III Drosha initiates microRNA processing. *Nature* 425:415–19

69. Lee Y, Kim M, Han J, Yeom KH, Lee S, et al. 2004. MicroRNA genes are transcribed by RNA polymerase II. *EMBO J.* 23:4051–60

70. Lewis BP, Burge CB, Bartel DP. 2005. Conserved seed pairing, often flanked by adenosines, indicates that thousands of human genes are microRNA targets. *Cell* 120:15–20

71. Lewis BP, Shih IH, Jones-Rhoades MW, Bartel DP, Burge CB. 2003. Prediction of mammalian microRNA targets. *Cell* 115:787–98

71a. Li J, Yang Z, Yu B, Liu J, Chen X. 2005. Methylation protects miRNAs and siRNAs from a 3′-end uridylation activity in Arabidopsis. *Curr. Biol.* 15:1501–7

72. Lim LP, Glasner ME, Yekta S, Burge CB, Bartel DP. 2003. Vertebrate microRNA genes. *Science* 299:1540

73. Lim LP, Lau NC, Garrett-Engele P, Grimson A, Schelter JM, et al. 2005. Microarray analysis shows that some microRNAs downregulate large numbers of target mRNAs. *Nature* 433:769–73

74. Lim LP, Lau NC, Weinstein EG, Abdelhakim A, Yekta S, et al. 2003. The microRNAs of *Caenorhabditis elegans*. *Genes Dev.* 17:991–1008

75. Lingel A, Simon B, Izaurralde E, Sattler M. 2003. Structure and nucleic-acid binding of the Drosophila Argonaute 2 PAZ domain. *Nature* 426:465–69

75a. Liu B, Li P, Li X, Liu C, Cao S, et al. 2005. Loss of function of *OsDCL1* affects microRNA accumulation and causes developmental defects in rice. *Plant Physiol.* 139:296–305

76. Liu J, Carmell MA, Rivas FV, Marsden CG, Thomson JM, et al. 2004. Argonaute2 is the catalytic engine of mammalian RNAi. *Science* 305:1437–41

77. Liu J, Valencia-Sanchez MA, Hannon GJ, Parker R. 2005. MicroRNA-dependent localization of targeted mRNAs to mammalian P-bodies. *Nat. Cell Biol.* 7:719–23

78. Llave C, Kasschau KD, Rector MA, Carrington JC. 2002. Endogenous and silencing-associated small RNAs in plants. *Plant Cell* 14:1605–19

79. Llave C, Xie Z, Kasschau KD, Carrington JC. 2002. Cleavage of *Scarecrow-like* mRNA targets directed by a class of *Arabidopsis* miRNA. *Science* 297:2053–56

80. Lu C, Fedoroff N. 2000. A mutation in the Arabidopsis *HYL1* gene encoding a dsRNA binding protein affects responses to abscisic acid, auxin, and cytokinin. *Plant Cell* 12:2351–66

80a. Lu C, Tej SS, Luo S, Haudenschild CD, Meyers BC, Green PJ. 2005. Elucidation of the small RNA component of the transcriptome. *Science* 309:1525–26

81. Lu S, Sun YH, Shi R, Clark C, Li L, Chiang VL. 2005. Novel and mechanical stress-responsive microRNAs in *Populus trichocarpa* that are absent from Arabidopsis. *Plant Cell* 17:2186–203

82. Lund E, Guttinger S, Calado A, Dahlberg JE, Kutay U. 2004. Nuclear export of microRNA precursors. *Science* 303:95–98

83. Lynn K, Fernandez A, Aida M, Sedbrook J, Tasaka M, et al. 1999. The *PIN-HEAD/ZWILLE* gene acts pleiotropically in *Arabidopsis* development and has overlapping functions with the *ARGONAUTE1* gene. *Development* 126:469–81

84. Mallory AC, Bartel DP, Bartel B. 2005. MicroRNA-directed regulation of Arabidopsis *AUXIN RESPONSE FACTOR17* is essential for proper development and modulates expression of early auxin response genes. *Plant Cell* 17:1360–75

85. Mallory AC, Dugas DV, Bartel DP, Bartel B. 2004. MicroRNA regulation of NAC-domain targets is required for proper formation and separation of adjacent embryonic, vegetative, and floral organs. *Curr. Biol.* 14:1035–46

86. Mallory AC, Reinhart BJ, Bartel D, Vance VB, Bowman LH. 2002. A viral suppressor of RNA silencing differentially regulates the accumulation of short interfering RNAs and micro-RNAs in tobacco. *Proc. Natl. Acad. Sci. USA* 99:15228–33

87. Mallory AC, Reinhart BJ, Jones-Rhoades MW, Tang G, Zamore PD, et al. 2004. MicroRNA control of *PHABULOSA* in leaf development: importance of pairing to the microRNA 5′ region. *EMBO J.* 23:3356–64

87a. Matranga C, Tomari Y, Shin C, Bartel DP, Zamore PD. 2005. Passenger-strand cleavage facilitates assembly of siRNA into Ago2-containing RNAi enzyme complexes. *Cell* 123:607–20

88. Matzke M, Aufsatz W, Kanno T, Daxinger L, Papp I, et al. 2004. Genetic analysis of RNA-mediated transcriptional gene silencing. *Biochim. Biophys. Acta* 1677:129–41

89. McConnell JR, Barton MK. 1998. Leaf polarity and meristem formation in Arabidopsis. *Development* 125:2935–42

90. McConnell JR, Emery J, Eshed Y, Bao N, Bowman J, Barton MK. 2001. Role of PHABULOSA and PHAVOLUTA in determining radial patterning in shoots. *Nature* 411:709–13

91. Mette MF, Aufsatz W, Kanno T, Daxinger L, Rovina P, et al. 2005. Analysis of double-stranded RNA and small RNAs involved in RNA-mediated transcriptional gene silencing. *Methods Mol. Biol.* 309:61–82

92. Mette MF, van der Winden J, Matzke M, Matzke AJ. 2002. Short RNAs can identify new candidate transposable element families in Arabidopsis. *Plant Physiol.* 130:6–9

93. Millar AA, Gubler F. 2005. The Arabidopsis *GAMYB-like* genes, *MYB33* and *MYB65*, are microRNA-regulated genes that redundantly facilitate anther development. *Plant Cell* 17:705–21

94. Morel JB, Godon C, Mourrain P, Beclin C, Boutet S, et al. 2002. Fertile hypomorphic *ARGONAUTE (ago1)* mutants impaired in post-transcriptional gene silencing and virus resistance. *Plant Cell* 14:629–39

95. Moss EG, Lee RC, Ambros V. 1997. The cold shock domain protein LIN-28 controls developmental timing in *C. elegans* and is regulated by the lin-4 RNA. *Cell* 88:637–46

96. Motamedi MR, Verdel A, Colmenares SU, Gerber SA, Gygi SP, Moazed D. 2004. Two RNAi complexes, RITS and RDRC, physically interact and localize to noncoding centromeric RNAs. *Cell* 119:789–802

96a. Mourelatos Z, Dostie J, Paushkin S, Sharma A, Charroux B, et al. 2002. miRNPs: a novel class of ribonucleoproteins containing numerous microRNAs. *Genes Dev.* 16:720–28

97. Mourrain P, Beclin C, Elmayan T, Feuerbach F, Godon C, et al. 2000. Arabidopsis *SGS2* and *SGS3* genes are required for posttranscriptional gene silencing and natural virus resistance. *Cell* 101:533–42

98. Moussian B, Haecker A, Laux T. 2003. *ZWILLE* buffers meristem stability in *Arabidopsis thaliana*. *Dev. Genes Evol.* 213:534–40

99. Moussian B, Schoof H, Haecker A, Jurgens G, Laux T. 1998. Role of the *ZWILLE* gene in the regulation of central shoot meristem cell fate during Arabidopsis embryogenesis. *EMBO J.* 17:1799–809

100. Nelson JM, Lane B, Frecling M. 2002. Expression of a mutant maize gene in the ventral leaf epidermis is sufficient to signal a switch of the leaf's dorsoventral axis. *Development* 129:4581–89

101. Noma K, Sugiyama T, Cam H, Verdel A, Zofall M, et al. 2004. RITS acts in cis to promote RNA interference-mediated transcriptional and post-transcriptional silencing. *Nat. Genet* 36:1174–80

101a. Onodera Y, Haag JR, Ream T, Nunes PC, Pontes O, Pikaard CS. 2005. Plant nuclear RNA polymerase IV mediates siRNA and DNA methylation-dependent heterochromatin formation. *Cell* 120:613–22

102. Olsen PH, Ambros V. 1999. The lin-4 regulatory RNA controls developmental timing in *Caenorhabditis elegans* by blocking LIN-14 protein synthesis after the initiation of translation. *Dev. Biol.* 216:671–80

103. Palatnik JF, Allen E, Wu X, Schommer C, Schwab R, et al. 2003. Control of leaf morphogenesis by microRNAs. *Nature* 425:257–63

104. Papp I, Mette MF, Aufsatz W, Daxinger L, Schauer SE, et al. 2003. Evidence for nuclear processing of plant micro RNA and short interfering RNA precursors. *Plant Physiol.* 132:1382–90

105. Parizotto EA, Dunoyer P, Rahm N, Himber C, Voinnet O. 2004. In vivo investigation of the transcription, processing, endonucleolytic activity, and functional relevance of the spatial distribution of a plant miRNA. *Genes Dev.* 18:2237–42

106. Park MY, Wu G, Gonzalez-Sulser A, Vaucheret H, Poethig RS. 2005. Nuclear processing and export of microRNAs in *Arabidopsis*. *Proc. Natl. Acad. Sci. USA* 102:3691–96

107. Park W, Li J, Song R, Messing J, Chen X. 2002. CARPEL FACTORY, a Dicer homolog, and HEN1, a novel protein, act in microRNA metabolism in *Arabidopsis thaliana*. *Curr. Biol.* 12:1484–95

108. Pasquinelli AE, Reinhart BJ, Slack F, Martindale MQ, Kuroda MI, et al. 2000. Conservation of the sequence and temporal expression of let-7 heterochronic regulatory RNA. *Nature* 408:86–89

109. Peragine A, Yoshikawa M, Wu G, Albrecht HL, Poethig RS. 2004. *SGS3* and *SGS2/SDE1/RDR6* are required for juvenile development and the production of *trans*-acting siRNAs in *Arabidopsis*. *Genes Dev.* 18:2368–79

110. Pillai RS, Artus CG, Filipowicz W. 2004. Tethering of human Ago proteins to mRNA mimics the miRNA-mediated repression of protein synthesis. *RNA* 10:1518–25

111. Pillai RS, Bhattacharyya SN, Artus CG, Zoller T, Cougot N, et al. 2005. Inhibition of translational initiation by let-7 microRNA in human cells. *Science* 309:1573–76

112. Qi Y, Denli AM, Hannon GJ. 2005. Biochemical specialization within *Arabidopsis* RNA silencing pathways. *Mol. Cell* 19:421–28

113. Reinhart BJ, Bartel DP. 2002. Small RNAs correspond to centromere heterochromatic repeats. *Science* 297:1831

114. Reinhart BJ, Slack FJ, Basson M, Pasquinelli AE, Bettinger JC, et al. 2000. The 21-nucleotide let-7 RNA regulates developmental timing in *Caenorhabditis elegans*. *Nature* 403:901–6

115. Reinhart BJ, Weinstein EG, Rhoades MW, Bartel B, Bartel DP. 2002. MicroRNAs in plants. *Genes Dev.* 16:1616–26

116. Rhoades MW, Reinhart BJ, Lim LP, Burge CB, Bartel B, Bartel DP. 2002. Prediction of plant microRNA targets. *Cell* 110:513–20

117. Schauer SE, Jacobsen SE, Meinke DW, Ray A. 2002. DICER-LIKE1: blind men and elephants in Arabidopsis development. *Trends Plant Sci.* 7:487–91

118. Schwab R, Palatnik JF, Riester M, Schommer C, Schmid M, Weigel D. 2005. Specific effects of microRNAs on the plant transcriptome. *Dev. Cell* 8:517–27

119. Schwarz DS, Hutvagner G, Du T, Xu Z, Aronin N, Zamore PD. 2003. Asymmetry in the assembly of the RNAi enzyme complex. *Cell* 115:199–208

120. Sen GL, Blau HM. 2005. Argonaute 2/RISC resides in sites of mammalian mRNA decay known as cytoplasmic bodies. *Nat. Cell Biol.* 7:633–36

121. Slack FJ, Basson M, Liu Z, Ambros V, Horvitz HR, Ruvkun G. 2000. The *lin-41* RBCC gene acts in the *C. elegans* heterochronic pathway between the *let-7* regulatory RNA and the LIN-29 transcription factor. *Mol. Cell* 5:659–69

122. Song JJ, Liu J, Tolia NH, Schneiderman J, Smith SK, Martienssen RA, et al. 2003. The crystal structure of the Argonaute2 PAZ domain reveals an RNA binding motif in RNAi effector complexes. *Nat. Struct. Biol.* 10:1026–32

123. Song JJ, Smith SK, Hannon GJ, Joshua-Tor L. 2004. Crystal structure of Argonaute and its implications for RISC slicer activity. *Science* 305:1434–37

124. Souret FF, Kastenmayer JP, Green PJ. 2004. AtXRN4 degrades mRNA in Arabidopsis and its substrates include selected miRNA targets. *Mol. Cell* 15:173–83

125. Sunkar R, Girke T, Jain PK, Zhu JK. 2005. Cloning and characterization of microRNAs from rice. *Plant Cell* 17:1397–411

126. Sunkar R, Girke T, Zhu JK. 2005. Identification and characterization of endogenous small interfering RNAs from rice. *Nucleic Acids Res.* 33:4443–54

127. Sunkar R, Zhu JK. 2004. Novel and stress-regulated microRNAs and other small RNAs from Arabidopsis. *Plant Cell* 16:2001–19

128. Tang G, Reinhart BJ, Bartel DP, Zamore PD. 2003. A biochemical framework for RNA silencing in plants. *Genes Dev.* 17:49–63

129. Telfer A, Poethig RS. 1998. *HASTY*: a gene that regulates the timing of shoot maturation in *Arabidopsis thaliana*. *Development* 125:1889–98

130. Tomari Y, Matranga C, Haley B, Martinez N, Zamore PD. 2004. A protein sensor for siRNA asymmetry. *Science* 306:1377–80

131. Vaucheret H, Vazquez F, Crete P, Bartel DP. 2004. The action of *ARGONAUTE1* in the miRNA pathway and its regulation by the miRNA pathway are crucial for plant development. *Genes Dev.* 18:1187–97

132. Vazquez F, Gasciolli V, Crete P, Vaucheret H. 2004. The nuclear dsRNA binding protein HYL1 is required for microRNA accumulation and plant development, but not posttranscriptional transgene silencing. *Curr. Biol.* 14:346–51

133. Vazquez F, Vaucheret H, Rajagopalan R, Lepers C, Gasciolli V, et al. 2004. Endogenous trans-acting siRNAs regulate the accumulation of Arabidopsis mRNAs. *Mol. Cell* 16:69–79

134. Verdel A, Jia S, Gerber S, Sugiyama T, Gygi S, et al. 2004. RNAi-mediated targeting of heterochromatin by the RITS complex. *Science* 303:672–76

135. Volpe TA, Kidner C, Hall IM, Teng G, Grewal SI, Martienssen RA. 2002. Regulation of heterochromatic silencing and histone H3 lysine-9 methylation by RNAi. *Science* 297:1833–37

136. Wang JW, Wang LJ, Mao YB, Cai WJ, Xue HW, Chen XY. 2005. Control of root cap formation by microRNA-targeted auxin response factors in Arabidopsis. *Plant Cell* 17:2204–16

137. Wang XJ, Reyes JL, Chua NH, Gaasterland T. 2004. Prediction and identification of *Arabidopsis thaliana* microRNAs and their mRNA targets. *Genome Biol.* 5:R65

138. Wightman B, Ha I, Ruvkun G. 1993. Posttranscriptional regulation of the heterochronic gene *lin-14* by *lin-4* mediates temporal pattern formation in *C. elegans*. *Cell* 75:855–62

139. Williams L, Grigg SP, Xie M, Christensen S, Fletcher JC. 2005. Regulation of *Arabidopsis* shoot apical meristem and lateral organ formation by microRNA *miR166g* and its *AtHD-ZIP* target genes. *Development* 132:3657–68

140. Xie X, Lu J, Kulbokas EJ, Golub TR, Mootha V, et al. 2005. Systematic discovery of regulatory motifs in human promoters and 3′ UTRs by comparison of several mammals. *Nature* 434:338–45

141. Xie Z, Allen E, Fahlgren N, Calamar A, Givan SA, Carrington JC. 2005. Expression of Arabidopsis *MIRNA* genes. *Plant Physiol.* 138:2145–54

141a. Xie Z, Allen E, Wilken A, Carrington JC. 2005. DICER-LIKE 4 functions in trans-acting small interfering RNA biogenesis and vegetative phase change in *Arabidopsis thaliana*. *Proc. Natl. Acad. Sci. USA* 102:12984–89

142. Xie Z, Johansen LK, Gustafson AM, Kasschau KD, Lellis AD, et al. 2004. Genetic and functional diversification of small RNA pathways in plants. *PLoS Biol.* 2:E104

143. Xie Z, Kasschau KD, Carrington JC. 2003. Negative feedback regulation of *Dicer-Like1* in *Arabidopsis* by microRNA-guided mRNA degradation. *Curr. Biol.* 13:784–89

144. Yan KS, Yan S, Farooq A, Han A, Zeng L, Zhou MM. 2003. Structure and conserved RNA binding of the PAZ domain. *Nature* 426:468–74

145. Yekta S, Shih IH, Bartel DP. 2004. MicroRNA-directed cleavage of *HOXB8* mRNA. *Science* 304:594–96

146. Yi R, Qin Y, Macara IG, Cullen BR. 2003. Exportin-5 mediates the nuclear export of pre-microRNAs and short hairpin RNAs. *Genes Dev.* 17:3011–16

146a. Yoshikawa M, Peragine A, Park MY, Poethig RS. 2005. A pathway for the biogenesis of *trans*-acting siRNAs in *Arabidopsis*. *Genes Dev.* 19:2164–75

147. Yu B, Yang Z, Li J, Minakhina S, Yang M, et al. 2005. Methylation as a crucial step in plant microRNA biogenesis. *Science* 307:932–35

147a. Zamore, PD, Tuschl, T, Sharp, PA, Bartel, DP. 2000. RNAi: double-stranded RNA directs the ATP-dependent cleavage of mRNA at 21 to 23 nucleotide intervals. *Cell* 101:25–33

148. Zhong R, Ye ZH. 2004. *Amphivasal vascular bundle 1*, a gain-of-function mutation of the *IFL1/REV* gene, is associated with alterations in the polarity of leaves, stems and carpels. *Plant Cell Physiol.* 45:369–85

149. Zilberman D, Cao X, Jacobsen SE. 2003. *ARGONAUTE4* control of locus-specific siRNA accumulation and DNA and histone methylation. *Science* 299:716–19

150. Zilberman D, Cao X, Johansen LK, Xie Z, Carrington JC, Jacobsen SE. 2004. Role of *Arabidopsis ARGONAUTE4* in RNA-directed DNA methylation triggered by inverted repeats. *Curr. Biol.* 14:1214–20

Chlorophyll Degradation During Senescence*

S. Hörtensteiner

Institute of Plant Sciences, University of Bern, CH-3013 Bern, Switzerland;
email: shorten@ips.unibe.ch

Annu. Rev. Plant Biol.
2006. 57:55–77

The *Annual Review of
Plant Biology* is online at
plant.annualreviews.org

doi: 10.1146/
annurev.arplant.57.032905.105212

1543-5008/06/0602-
0055$20.00

First published online as a
Review in Advance on
January 30, 2006

*Dedicated to Prof.
Bernhard Kräutler on the
occasion of his 60th
birthday.

Key Words

catabolite, cell death, chlorophyll breakdown, detoxification,
nitrogen economy

Abstract

The catabolic pathway of chlorophyll (Chl) during senescence and
fruit ripening leads to the accumulation of colorless breakdown products (NCCs). This review updates an earlier review on Chl breakdown published here in 1999 (69). It summarizes recent advances
in the biochemical reactions of the pathway and describes the characterization of new NCCs and their formation inside the vacuole.
Furthermore, I focus on the recent molecular identification of three
chl catabolic enzymes, chlorophyllase, pheophorbide a oxygenase
(PAO), and red Chl catabolite reductase (RCCR). The analysis of Chl
catabolic mutants demonstrates the importance of Chl breakdown
for plant development and survival. Mutants defective in PAO or
RCCR develop a lesion mimic phenotype, due to the accumulation
of breakdown intermediates. Thus, Chl breakdown is a prerequisite
to detoxify the potentially phototoxic pigment within the vacuoles
in order to permit the remobilization of nitrogen from Chl-binding
proteins to proceed during senescence.

Contents

Chl: chlorophyll

NCC: nonfluorescent chlorophyll catabolite

Gerontoplast: a senescence-specific form of chloroplasts, which is characterized by reduced volume, extensive losses of thylakoid and stromal components, but increased amount and density of plastoglobules. Gerontoplasts have an intact envelope membrane.

INTRODUCTION

The average number of yearly reports on chlorophyll (Chl) breakdown has increased from below 1 in the 1950s up to 14.4 since the new millennium, indicating an increasing recognition of the biological relevance of this pathway within the plant science community. The year 1991 is a milestone, because it marks the elucidation of the structure of a final product of Chl breakdown, a nonfluorescent Chl catabolite (NCC) (59). This major breakthrough revolutionized research on Chl breakdown, which only four years earlier had been apostrophized a "biological enigma" (36). From the structures of NCCs (e.g., 73) and from work on mutants that are impaired in Chl degradation (e.g., 125), reactions could be predicted and characterized, and intermediates of breakdown identified. **Figure 1** summarizes our present knowledge of this pathway.

The reactions can be divided into early steps that are common to all plants, followed by species-specific modification of Chl breakdown products. In addition, transfer of catabolites from senescent chloroplasts (gerontoplasts) to the vacuole is mediated by ATP-dependent transport systems. Four enzymes are necessary to degrade Chl to a colorless, blue-fluorescing intermediate (pFCC). Chl is first dephytylated to chlorophyllide (Chlide) by chlorophyllase (CLH) and, subsequently, a metal chelating substance (MCS) removes Mg. The product, pheophorbide (Pheide) *a*, is then converted to pFCC in a two-step reaction by Pheide *a* oxygenase (PAO) and red Chl catabolite reductase (RCCR). pFCC undergoes several modifications (R_1-R_3 in **Figure 1**) before catabolites are finally stored inside the vacuole in the form of NCCs.

The most important recent progress includes the cloning of three of the enzymes, CLH, PAO, and RCCR. The characterization of mutants defective in Chl catabolic genes has shed new light on the regulation of Chl breakdown and explains its importance for plant development and survival, i.e., detoxification of the potent phototoxin Chl during senescence. The recent elucidation of new NCC structures, as well as chemical and biochemical investigations aiming at their formation, prove earlier ideas about these late steps in Chl breakdown. Modifications found in NCCs occur at the FCC level and FCC-NCC conversion is catalyzed by the acidic vacuolar pH. Chl breakdown is tightly connected with the dismantling of pigment-protein complexes and the degradation of Chl-binding proteins. Recent investigations have started to tackle the fate of Chl-binding proteins during senescence. This review summarizes these new findings and concepts, and provides a minimal description of the known biochemical reactions and catabolites.

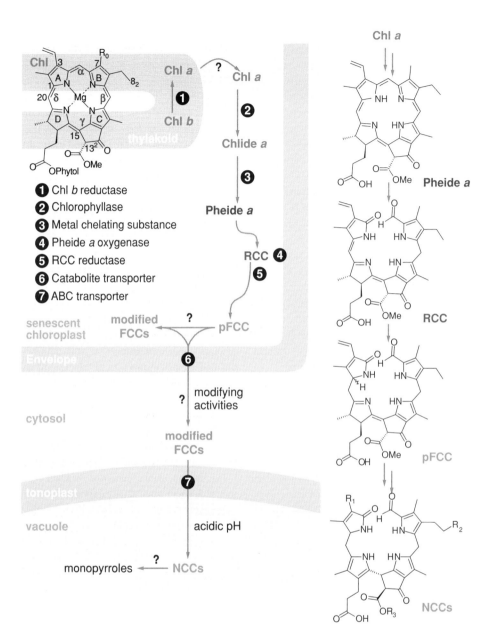

Figure 1

Topographical model
of the Chl
breakdown pathway
of higher plants and
chemical structures
of Chl and of Chl
catabolites. Putative
(enzymatic) reactions
are indicated with a
question mark.
Pyrrole rings (*A–D*),
methine bridges
(α-δ), and relevant
carbon atoms are
labeled in Chl (*top
left*). R_0 = CH_3, Chl
a; R_0 = CHO, Chl
b. R_1-R_3 in NCCs
indicate
modifications as
outlined in **Table 1**.

THE CHL DEGRADATION PATHWAY

Reactions on Green Pigments

Chlorophyllase. CHL catalyzes the conversion of Chl to Chlide and phytol. It acts preferentially on Chl *a* (6), but also accepts Chl *b* and pheophytins as substrates (see 39 and references therein). Surprisingly, cloning CLH

genes (50, 122) (see below) revealed highly soluble proteins as deduced from the amino acid composition, raising questions as to the suggested localization of CLH at the inner envelope of chloroplasts (11, 71, 107). Related to this is a remarkable functional (in vitro) latency of CLH activity, which persists during Chl breakdown in senescent leaves (69). In contrast, recombinant CLHs expressed in

FCC: fluorescent
chlorophyll
catabolite

CLH: chlorophyll
hydrolase =
chlorophyllase

MCS: metal chelating substance

Pheide: pheophorbide

PAO: pheophorbide *a* oxygenase

RCCR: red chlorophyll catabolite reductase

Chlide: chlorophyllide

Plastoglobules: globular osmiophilic structures present in all types of plastids, with a proposed role in lipid metabolism. Their abundance and size increase during chloroplast to gerontoplast transition.

Rieske-center: coordination site for a Fe_2S_2 cluster containing a conserved Cys-X-His and a Cys-X-X-His box, present in some components of electron transport chains and in some oxygenases

Escherichia coli are active in the absence of detergents and did not require glycosylation (6, 50, 122), a feature of CLHs that had been inferred from their binding to concanavalin A (121).

The localization of CLH distinct from the thylakoid membrane is rationalized on the basis of a need for a spatial separation of CLH from its substrates; therefore, entry of the substrates into the pathway requires a specific transport of Chl from the thylakoids to the envelope (69). Members of the family of water-soluble Chl proteins (WSCPs), which can remove Chl from pigment-protein complexes (95), had been proposed to function in this delivery system, but recently a role for WSCPs as pigment carriers during Chl biosynthesis was suggested instead (85). Alternatively, plastoglobules could be the hypothesized delivery vehicles. Their size and abundance increase during senescence, and plastoglobules contain a defined set of proteins (53), among them are Chl *a/b* binding proteins, and significant quantities of Chl (33). Plastoglobules are often tightly associated with the chloroplast envelope (33), indicating a role related to envelope function.

Mg-dechelation. Reports on activities that catalyze a release of Mg^{2+} from Chlide were conflicting in the past (69). Two types of activities were distinguished that either were associated with a heat-stable low-molecular weight compound or were catalyzed by a protein. The low-molecular weight compound was tentatively named MCS (formerly Mg-dechelating substance) (97). In contrast, a constitutive Mg-dechelatase enzyme was described, which was associated with chloroplast membranes (126). The discrepancy between these two activities was explained by the possibility that MCS could merely represent a cofactor (chelator) of Mg-dechelatase, which is active on its own. Recent attempts from the Shioi lab (61, 102, 103) readdressed the issue: Mg dechelating proteins only act on the frequently used artificial substrate chlorophyllin, but not on Chlide, whereas

MCS removes Mg^{2+} from both substrates. Properties of the two activities differ significantly, particularly with respect to inhibition by chelators, and MCS could not be extracted from Mg-dechelatase-containing fractions. The sizes of MCS compounds are different in *Chenopodium album* (<400 Da) and strawberry (2180 ± 20 Da), and they differ in their sensitivity to treatment with proteinase K (13, 102). We can conclude that Mg^{2+}-removal from Chlide is most probably catalyzed by different kinds of low-molecular weight compounds whose structure is not known. Elucidation of their molecular nature is an important prerequisite to understand the mechanism of MCS deducing their origin.

Chlorophyll Cycle

In the photosystems, Chl *b* is a component of antenna complexes and occurs at variable ratios to Chl *a*. Despite this, all but one of the NCCs identified so far from vascular plants are derivatives of Chl *a*. An explanation for this is found in the exclusive specificity of PAO for Pheide *a*, and consequently conversion to the *a*-form is a prerequisite of Chl *b* breakdown via PAO. Furthermore, senescence of barley leaves in the presence of D_2O leads to the formation of Chl catabolites that are specifically labeled in their 7-methyl group, indicating that they are derived from Chl *b* (23). A cycle of reactions that is able to interconvert Chl(ide) *a* and *b* was recently described (for a review see 92). The oxidative half of the cycle acts mainly on dephytylated pigments (92) and is catalyzed by Chlide *a* oxygenase, a Rieske-type iron sulfur oxygenase (80, 108). By its action, the C7 methyl group of Chlide *a* is oxidized to formyl by two successive hydroxylations, followed by the spontaneous loss of water (80). In contrast, *b* to *a* conversion occurs on both Chlide or Chl with C7-hydroxy Chl(ide) *a* as a stable intermediate. The two consecutive reductions are catalyzed by different enzymes, an NADPH-dependent Chl(ide) *b* reductase and a ferredoxin-dependent hydroxyl-Chl(ide) *a* reductase. (92). Neither the enzymes nor the genes of these reductases have been molecularly identified so far. Although an alternative role for Chl(ide) b reductase in protochlorophyllide b to protochlorophyllide a reduction during de-etiolation was suggested recently (86), the requirement of the reductive reactions of the Chl(ide) cycle for Chl b degradation is substantiated by a marked increase of chl(ide) b reductase activity during dark-induced senescence of barley leaves (96). Chl(ide) b reductase is the only enzyme of Chl breakdown that localizes to the thylakoid membrane (**Figure 1**), qualifying it as the first enzyme of Chl b degradation (see Chl Breakdown and Nitrogen Economy, below).

Loss of Green Color: PAO and RCCR

The identification of Pheide a and FCCs as intermediates of Chl breakdown allowed the establishment of an in vitro assay in which Pheide a is converted to pFCC (45). This was a prerequisite for the biochemical elucidation of this important step in Chl breakdown, which is responsible for the loss of visible color. pFCC formation from Pheide a requires the activity of two enzymes, PAO and RCCR, and proceeds via an unstable intermediate, RCC (90). Biochemical properties of the two enzymes and of the in vitro PAO/RCCR assay have been reviewed already (39, 43, 58, 60, 69); hence, I focus on new aspects of the reaction.

PAO. PAO is an Fe-dependent monooxygenase located at the envelope membrane of gerontoplasts. Electrons required to drive the redox cycle of PAO are supplied from reduced ferredoxin. PAO activity was originally shown to be strictly limited to senescence, although recent investigations using improved assay conditions show that low PAO activity is present before the onset of senescence (83, 84, 89). PAO has an intriguing specificity for Pheide a, with Pheide b inhibiting in a competitive manner. The recent identi-

AUTUMNAL LEAF COLORATION

A spectacular phenomenon associated with leaf senescence of deciduous trees is autumnal leaf coloration. While Chl is progressively degraded, carotenoids are retained to variable degrees depending on species and environmental factors. Carotenoids, together with newly synthesized red anthocyanins and dark-colored oxidation products of phenolics, define the polychromatic beauty of autumnal trees. Chemical structures and pathways for anthocyanin biosynthesis during senescence are well established, but additional factors, such as changes in vacuolar pH, considerably influence anthocyanin-derived colors in autumn leaves.

The biological function of leaf coloration is poorly understood. Explanations pointing to either ecological or physiological strategies have been proposed. The so-called "autumn signaling hypothesis" implies that bright leaf colors are a signal to potential insect predators about the tree's defense capabilities, i.e., trees are believed to pretend to be well defended, although the opposite is true during senescence. Other authors are critical of this hypothesis and favor instead physiological explanations involving a protective role of dissipation of excess energy as photosynthesis declines during senescence. Alternative functions could be as antioxidants or osmolytes. For a recent review on this topic see Reference 81.

fication of At-NCC-3, which is hydroxylated at $C7^1$ (84), may disprove this specificity. Although the mechanism of its formation has not been elucidated, At-NCC-3 could be assumed to derive from Chl b that entered the catabolic pathway through PAO/RCCR before complete reduction to Chl(ide) a in the Chl cycle. Consequently, we could hypothesize that PAO is able to accept C7-hydroxy Pheide a as substrate. In *Chlorella protothecoides*, a PAO-like monooxygenase has been identified (15) that is more unspecific, causing the occurrence of both Chl a- and Chl b-derived degradation products (20, 48).

RCCR. RCCR is a soluble protein of chloroplasts, but in young *Arabidopsis* seedlings is also associated with mitochondria (66). Reduction of the C20/C1 double bond of RCC is catalyzed by RCCR in an intriguing

RCC: red chlorophyll catabolite

Tautomerization: formation of structural isomers, mostly by intramolecular movement of protons

stereospecific manner: Depending on the source of RCCR, one of two C1 isomers of pFCC (74, 75) is formed in the PAO/RCCR assay. Thus, with *Arabidopsis* RCCR, for example, pFCC-1 is formed, whereas pFCC-2 occurs with the tomato enzyme (44). Screening the RCCR activities of more than 60 plant species indicated that, within a family, all genera and species produce the same isomer (44). Identification of genes encoding RCCR (see below) allowed a search for domains that define RCCR stereospecificity. For this, chimeric RCCRs composed of portions of the *Arabidopsis* and the tomato proteins were expressed in *E. coli*. It turned out that an exchange in the *Arabidopsis* RCCR of Phe_{218} to Val was sufficient to change the specificity of the protein from pFCC-1 to pFCC-2 production (I. Anders, S. Aubry, and S. Hörtensteiner, unpublished). In planta, the stereospecificity of RCCR defines the C1-configuration of respective NCCs. Thus, *Hv*-NCC-1 and *So*-NCC-2 are C1 isomers (77); at the same time, barley and spinach RCCR produce pFCC-1 and pFCC-2, respectively (44).

Like PAO, RCCR is ferredoxin dependent, but appears to lack a metal or flavin cofactor, indicating that electrons are directly transferred from ferredoxin to RCC (58). This was interpreted to ascribe a role to RCCR as a "chaperone" rather than a catalytic reductase (40, 58). Despite the absence of RCCR in the *Arabidopsis acd2-2* mutant (66) (see below), FCCs and NCCs accumulate during dark-induced senescence in the mutant; some catabolites occur simultaneously in both C1 isomeric forms (A. Pružinská & S. Hörtensteiner, unpublished). This indicates loss of stereospecificity in the mutant, and hence the presence of an unknown, nonselective reducing activity. Note that RCC is reduced to pFCC by electrochemical means (78). Taken together, these findings asked questions about the role of RCCR in Chl breakdown. Nevertheless, after complementation of *acd2-2* with chimeric RCCR constructs that exhibit different stereospecificity,

NCC formation follows the C1 specificity of the respective RCCR (A. Pružinská, I. Anders, and S. Hörtensteiner, unpublished). This indicates a true involvement for RCCR. RCCR could be required to mediate an efficient interaction between RCC (still bound to PAO) and ferredoxin, thereby enabling a fast, regio-, and stereoselective reduction to pFCC.

Structures of NCCs

Since the last review on Chl breakdown in this series (69), 14 new NCCs from tobacco, *Arabidopsis*, spinach, and maize have been structurally characterized (8–10, 77). In addition, improved extraction and spectroscopic procedures have enabled the identification of additional, low abundant NCCs in species that had been analyzed earlier, such as *Bn*-NCC-4 (8) and *Cj*-NCC-2, from *Cercidiphyllum japonicum* (76). Except for *At*-NCC-3 (84) (**Table 1**), all NCCs structurally analyzed so far are derived from Chl *a* and share a common basic tetrapyrrolic structure (**Figure 1**). They differ from each other by modifications of peripheral side chains, which are restricted to three positions (R_1-R_3 in **Figure 1**) and which can occur separately or simultaneously in a given NCC (**Table 1**). Given the fact that NCCs derive from pFCC, which occur in two isomeric forms, NCCs fall into two stereochemical groups.

Reactions on pFCC

The diversity of NCCs found in different species allows one to draw a series of reactions in Chl breakdown that occur after the (common) formation of pFCC. Six reactions can be distinguished: dihydroxylation of the vinyl group of pyrrole A (R_1 in **Figure 1**), hydroxylation at $C8^2$, followed by glucosylation and/or malonylation (R_2), $C13^2$ demethylation (R_3), and finally, tautomerization of FCCs to NCCs. Except for the $C8^2$-hydroxylation and tautomerization, which are reactions common to all investigated species, other side chain modifications

Table 1   Structures of NCCs from higher plants

Name[a]	R_1^b	R_2^b	R_3^b	C1-chemistry[c]	Identity with	Reference
At-NCC-1	vinyl	*O*-glucosyl	H	1	*Bn*-NCC-2	(84)
At-NCC-2	vinyl	OH	H	1	*Bn*-NCC-3	(84)
At-NCC-3	vinyl	OH[d]	H	1	—	(84)
At-NCC-4	vinyl	*O*-glucosyl[d]	CH_3	1	—	(84)
At-NCC-5	vinyl	H	H	1	*Bn*-NCC-4	(84)
Bn-NCC-1	vinyl	*O*-malonyl	H	1	—	(73)
Bn-NCC-2	vinyl	*O*-glucosyl	H	1	*At*-NCC-1	(73)
Bn-NCC-3	vinyl	OH	H	1	*At*-NCC-2	(73)
Bn-NCC-4	vinyl	H	H	1	*At*-NCC-5	(8)
Cj-NCC-1	vinyl	OH	CH_3	2	*So*-NCC-4	(14)
Cj-NCC-2	vinyl	H	CH_3	2		(76)
Hv-NCC-1	dihydroxyethyl	OH	CH_3	1		(59)
Lo-NCC-1	vinyl	OH	CH_3	nd		(49)
Ls-NCC-1	vinyl	OH	CH_3	nd		(49)
Nr-NCC-1	vinyl	*O*-glucosyl-malonyl	CH_3	2		(10)
Nr-NCC-2	vinyl	*O*-glucosyl	CH_3	2	*Zm*-NCC-2	(10)
So-NCC-1	dihydroxyethyl	OH	H	2		(9)
So-NCC-2	dihydroxyethyl	OH	CH_3	2		(77)
So-NCC-3	vinyl	OH	H	2		(9)
So-NCC-4	vinyl	OH	CH_3	2	*Cj*-NCC-1	(9)
So-NCC-5	vinyl	H	CH_3	2		(9)
Zm-NCC-1	dihydroxyethyl	*O*-glucosyl	CH_3	2		(8)
Zm-NCC-2	vinyl	*O*-glucosyl	CH_3	2	*Nr*-NCC-2	(8)

[a]A nomenclature for NCCs (and FCCs) has been defined (26) in which a prefix indicates the plant species and a suffix number indicates decreasing polarity on reversed-phase HPLC. *At, Arabidopsis thaliana; Bn, Brassica napus; Cj, Cercidiphyllum japonicum; Hv, Hordeum vulgare; Lo, Liquidambar orientalis; Ls, Liquidambar styraciflua; Nr, Nicotiana rustica; So, Spinacia oleracea; Zm, Zea mays*

[b]R_1-R_3 indicate residues at C3, $C8^2$, and $C13^2$ side positions, respectively, of NCCs as shown in **Figure 1**.

[c]C1 stereochemistry refers to the type of pFCC, i.e., pFCC-1 or pFCC-2, formed in the respective species; nd, not determined.

[d]In *At*-NCC-3, the site of hydroxylation is indicated to be $C7^1$ (rather than $C8^2$); in *At*-NCC-4, the site of attachment of the glucose moiety is not yet defined (S. Moser, T. Müller, S. Hörtensteiner, and B. Kräutler, unpublished).

occur in a species-specific manner. Most of these reactions were described in the preceding review by Matile et al. (69), and progress has been made mainly on demethylation and tautomerization.

Demethylation. An activity that is responsible for demethylation of the $C13^2$ carboxymethyl group of Pheide has been described as pheophorbidase. Due to the presence of high acetone concentrations in assays, the free carboxyl group was spontaneously lost and, consequently, pyropheophorbide was identified as the final product of the reaction (98). Pheophorbidase is present in Chenopodiaceae and Brassicaceae species, but absent from barley (104). This distribution matches the occurrence of $C13^2$-demethylated NCCs (9, 59, 73), indicating that pheophorbidase could be responsible for their formation. The placement of pheophorbidase in the cytosol (98) is difficult to explain: Demethylation at the level of Pheide, i.e., before conversion to pFCC, would require an unlikely transport of pigments out of and back into the plastid. It can be argued that the native substrates of pheophorbidase are FCCs rather then Pheide. *Raphanus sativus* pheophorbidase has been purified to near homogeneity (104), and the corresponding DNA was recently cloned (Y. Shioi, personal communication). Pheophorbidase is absent from *Chlamydomonas reinhardtii*, but an activity that catalyzes the removal of the entire carboxymethyl group without a demethyl intermediate is found in this green alga (16, 104). This enzyme may explain the identification of pyro forms of Chl in green algae (134), but its presence also raises the question of the origin of degradation products in *Chlorella* containing a free carboxyl group (20).

Tautomerization. FCCs have been described as intermediary Chl catabolites, which ultimately are converted to NCCs. This tautomerization results in the complete deconjugation of the four pyrrole units. Vacuolar localization of NCCs (37, 68) and analogy to the tautomerization chemistry of hydroporphyrins (21) suggest a nonenzymatic reaction under acid conditions (57, 69). Indeed, at acidic pH, pFCC-2 rapidly converts to the respective NCC (76). The mechanism involved is proposed to be a two-step protonation/deprotonation reaction that leads to the formation of an instable NCC, in which the $C13^2$ side group and pyrrole D are *cis* to each other. This NCC isomerizes to the final product, establishing a *trans* configuration of C15 and $C13^2$ (**Figure 1**) (76).

Do NCCs Fragment Further?

In some species, the amounts of accumulating NCCs account for all catabolized Chl (73, 84). This indicates that NCCs represent the final catabolites of Chl breakdown (39, 69). This view may be too simple, because in some instances, such as tobacco and spinach, NCC concentrations are highest in moderately senescent leaves, but decrease again at later stages of senescence (S. Hörtensteiner, unpublished). This is corroborated by a few recent reports, indicating a degradation of Chl beyond the stage of NCCs. Thus, a derivative of *Hv*-NCC-1 was described in which the

formyl group attached to pyrrole B is absent (63). Shioi and coworkers (105, 106) identified monopyrrolic oxygenation products of Chl, such as ethylmethyl maleimide and haematinic acid, during leaf senescence in barley and radish. Whether these Chl catabolites are the products of a specific (common) pathway or whether they represent products of unspecific oxidation reactions that may occur after loss of the integrity of the senescent tissue, i.e., after cell death, remains to be shown.

Catabolite Transporters and Topology of Chl Breakdown

Transport of Chl catabolites from senescing chloroplasts to the vacuole has been inferred from vacuolar localization of NCCs (37, 68). A primary active transport system for a NCC, *Bn*-NCC-1, has been described in barley vacuoles, but surprisingly, the transporter exhibited a particularly high affinity for a FCC (37). This is now corroborated by the finding of a nonenzymatic tautomerization most likely catalyzed by the acidic vacuolar sap (76) and implies that FCCs rather than NCCs are the natural substrates for Chl catabolite transport across the tonoplast. Although two members of the multidrug resistance–associated protein (MRP) subfamily of ATP binding cassette (ABC) transporters, AtMRP2 and AtMRP3, are capable of transporting NCCs after expression in yeast (64, 119), the molecular identity of the in vivo transport system remains unknown. AtMRP4 localizes to the plasma membrane (54), and other members of the MRP clade may also be at the plasma membrane rather than the tonoplast (E. Martinoia, personal communication). More than 120 ABC transporters are encoded in the *Arabidopsis* genome (94). Many of them accept a wide range of substrates (64, 119) and may have overlapping functions. Therefore, it is likely that different transports are involved in FCC import into the vacuole.

Export of a modified FCC from isolated gerontoplasts is coupled to the hydrolysis of ATP (70), but neither the nature of the transport system at the plastid envelope nor the structure of the exported FCC has been elucidated so far. Chloroplast proteomics (e.g., 22) as well as in silico prediction of transport proteins localized at the inner envelope (56) may enable the identification of candidate transporters. Notably, knockout mice that are deficient in the breast cancer resistance protein 1 (BCRP1) show a porphyria-like phenotype, which is due to the accumulation in their blood system of Pheide *a*, a dietary product of Chl breakdown, and protoporphyrin IX (51). BCRP1, an ABC-type transporter, has Pheide *a* transport capacity and, in addition, is required for detoxification from the bile of a RCC-like compound (J.W. Jonker, A.H. Schinkel, S. Aubry, and S. Hörtensteiner, unpublished). Plant homologues of BCRP1 are likely candidates for Chl catabolite export from plastids.

GENES AND MUTATIONS

Chlorophyllase

CLH has been purified repeatedly and obtained from different sources (39). Yet N-terminal and internal amino acid sequences were obtained and determined only for the enzymes purified from *Citrus sinensis* (CsCLH1) (120) and *C. album* (CaCLH) (121). *CLH* genes have been isolated from *Citrus* (50), *C. album* (122), *Arabidopsis* (*AtCLH1* and *AtCLH2*) (122), wheat (*TaCLH1*) (4), *Gingko biloba*, and *Brassica oleracea* (110). Both phylogenetic analysis (110) and biochemical characterization (121) predict that CLHs cluster into two groups. Expression of members of one group (AtCLH1 and CsCLH1) is regulated by methyl jasmonate (MeJA) and ethylene, respectively, whereas AtCLH2 and CaCLH genes, in the second group, are constitutively expressed at a low level (50, 122). The overall sequence identity between CLHs is rather low (31–42%), but they contain some common characteristics, including a conserved serine lipase motif (107, 110), which was shown by site-directed mutagenesis to be indispensi-

ble for in vitro activity (123). A charge-relay mechanism similar to other carboxylesterases was proposed (4). Although CLHs were indicated to be membrane localized (11, 71), the absence of predicted transmembrane domains from cloned CLHs suggests that they are not intrinsic membrane proteins. Furthermore, the various sequences identified indicate different localization, either inside (e.g., AtCLH2) or outside (AtCLH1 and CaCLH) the plastid (122). It was hypothesized that an additional extraplastidic pathway for Chl breakdown might exist (107). The finding of a "mass exodus" from the chloroplast of Chl-containing globules during senescence supported this idea (33). These data implied a role for CLH, together with unknown oxidative activities, in Chl degradation in a pathway that is located inside the vacuole (107). Subcellular localization experiments and analysis of CLH mutants are required to elucidate the in vivo role(s) of CLHs. Notably, alteration of AtCLH1 levels by sense or antisense gene expression changed the Chl-to-Chlide ratio in leaves and flowers, but a senescence-related Chl breakdown phenotype was not evident (6, 52). Furthermore, not all of the predicted CLHs might hydrolyze Chl in vivo: Besides Chl, recombinant TaCLH1, but not AtCLH1, also efficiently cleaved the ester bonds of other synthetic hydrophobic esters, such as *p*-nitrophenyl decanoate (4, 6).

Pheophorbide *a* Oxygenase

The biochemical properties of PAO have been investigated intensively, but attempts to purify the protein by means of classical protein purification have largely failed (46, 128; S. Hörtensteiner, unpublished). Based on the characteristics of PAO, candidate genes of *Arabidopsis* were identified in a functional genomics approach. Among these candidates was *Accelerated cell death* (*ACD*) *1* (At3g44880), which after expression in *E. coli* exhibited PAO activity with properties similar to native PAO (83). ACD1/AtPAO is the ortholog of lethal leaf spot 1 in maize (27, 131). The in vivo

BCRP1: breast cancer resistance protein 1

ACD: accelerated cell death

role of these proteins as PAO was demonstrated by the analysis of respective mutants. Maize *lls1* and an *Arabidopsis* knockout line in At3g44880, *pao1*, retain Chl during dark-induced senescence (83, 84). Furthermore, they do not accumulate colorless catabolites and are devoid of PAO activity. Both mutants show a light-dependent cell death phenotype in leaves, which is due to the accumulation of Pheide *a* (83, 84).

In *Arabidopsis*, *PAO* is a single copy gene and AtPAO belongs to a small family of Rieske-type iron-sulfur oxygenases (28). Besides PAO, two other Rieske-type oxygenases are involved in Chl metabolism, i.e., Chlide *a* oxygenase (80) and a proposed protochlorophyllide *a* oxygenase (87). Like other Rieske-type oxygenases, the plant proteins require ferredoxin as the source of electrons (45, 108). PAO-like proteins are highly conserved in plants and have been found in the genomes of oxygenic, but not anoxygenic, photosynthetic prokaryotes (29, 83; S. Hörtensteiner, unpublished). This indicates that the capacity to degrade Chl to colorless—and hence nonphototoxic—catabolites coevolved with oxygenic photosynthesis.

Red Chlorophyll Catabolite Reductase

RCCR has been purified by conventional protein purification methods (91, 129) and has been cloned from barley and *Arabidopsis* using amino acid sequence information obtained from the purified barley protein (129). Functional identity with native RCCR was confirmed after expression of *AtRCCR* in *E. coli*, and a recombinant 35-kDa precursor protein was, after import into isolated chloroplasts, cleaved to mature AtRCCR with a size of 31 kDa (129). In *Arabidopsis*, the enzyme is encoded by a single gene (At4g37000) and is identical to ACD2 (66). RCCR is a novel protein, but is distantly related to a family of bilin reductases. These include phytochromobilin synthase, catalyzing the last step in phytochrome chromophore

biosynthesis from biliverdin in higher plants, and different bilin reductases of photosynthetic bacteria required for phytobilin biosynthesis (25, 55). These enzymes are stereospecific, exclusively producing the product Z-isomers. Although the overall sequence identity is rather low, several amino acid residues are highly conserved, indicating a role in protein structure or catalysis (25). Among these is a Phe residue, which in At-RCCR corresponds to the Phe_{218} that is required for maintaining the stereospecificity of pFCC production (see above; I. Anders, S. Aubry, and S. Hörtensteiner, unpublished). RCCR is widely distributed within higher plants (129), but *RCCR* genes are not readily identifiable in the genomes of *C. reinhardtii* or of photosynthetic prokaryotes (25; S. Hörtensteiner, unpublished). This explains the identification in green algae of RCC-like compounds, which as final products of Chl breakdown are excreted into the medium (20, 41). It is possible that the evolution of *RCCR* genes was a prerequisite for land colonization by terrestrial plants: Disposal had to be developed to render red Chl catabolites into colorless ones that could be accumulated safely inside the vacuole.

Mutants in RCCR were originally isolated as *acd2* mutants that exhibit a light-dependent cell death phenotype with spontaneous spreading lesions (31). RCC was suggested to be responsible for the observed phenotype (66) and, indeed, RCC accumulates during dark-induced senescence in *acd2-2* leaves (A. Pružinská & S. Hörtensteiner, unpublished).

Chlorophyll Catabolic Mutants

Mutants and genetic variations in which senescence is apparently delayed by visible retention of Chl have been identified in a number of species. These so-called stay-green mutants can be classified into four groups, differing in the physiological and biochemical properties causing the phenotype (113). In Type C stay-greens, Chl retention is uncoupled from other senescence processes, which proceed normally, and thus most likely represent mutants that have a defect in a catalytic or regulatory gene of Chl breakdown. The best characterized among these is the *sid* locus of *Festuca pratensis* (118). *sid* has been transferred from the originally identified *Festuca* mutant, Bf 993, into *Lolium* species by introgression, and *Festulolium* hybrids show the same characteristics as the original *Festuca* mutant, i.e., retention of Chl, significant reduction of PAO activity, and accumulation of Chlides and Pheide *a* during senescence (89). Repeated backcrossing has reduced the size of the introgressed segments and enabled the localization of the mutated gene by genomic in situ hybridization (112, 114). This strategy has allowed the subsequent molecular tagging of the *sid* locus by searching for *Festuca*-specific polymorphisms in the *Lolium* background. Hence, amplified fragment length polymorphism markers closely flanking *sid* at 0.6 and 1.3 centiMorgans, respectively, have been identified (72). Close synteny of the *Festuca* genome with the sequenced rice genome (72) provides an additional tool for producing molecular markers at the *sid* locus and enabling the cloning of *sid*.

A biochemical lesion in PAO activity has also been shown for stay-green mutants in pea and bean (5, 116), but neither for these, nor for other Type C stay-greens, such as pepper *cl* (19), soybean *cytC* and $d_1d_1d_2d_2$ (34, 65), or tomato *gf* (3), have the affected genes been identified. Nevertheless, the recessive stay-green locus *sgr*(t) of rice was mapped on the long arm of chromosome 9 (12). The corresponding *Sgr* gene was recently cloned (GenBank accession no. AY850134) and highly related sequences were identified in other plant species (J.-W. Yu, S.-Y. Park, J. Li, J.-S. Park, H.-J. Koh, and N.-C. Paek, unpublished). The deduced SGR gene products have a length of 261–295 amino acids and contain a predicted chloroplast transit peptide. *Arabidopsis* SGR1 (At4g22920) is specifically expressed during senescence (S. Hörtensteiner, unpublished), but a function for SGR has not

been elucidated so far. Molecular mapping of pepper *CL* and tomato *GF* on homologous chromosomes indicated mutation of orthologous genes in the two species. Furthermore, *CL*, *PAO*, and three *CLH* genes of tomato mapped on different chromosomes, implying that *CL/GF* corresponds to another catabolic or regulatory gene of the pathway (19).

SIGNIFICANCE OF CHL BREAKDOWN

Regulation of Chl Degradation

CLH. The term senescence syndrome refers to a developmental process that describes leaf senescence– or fruit ripening–associated structural changes, such as chloroplast to gerontoplast or chromoplast transition, as well as biochemical processes, such as degradation of macromolecules including Chl (99). Hormones are involved in regulating the syndrome, hence it is not overly surprising that Chl catabolic gene expression is under hormonal control. Ethylene and MeJA, known to accelerate senescence in many species (99), enhance CLH activity (17, 107). *AtCLH1* mRNA levels increase by MeJA treatment (122), and in *Citrus*, *CLH1* expression is highly upregulated by ethylene (50). Other CLH genes, like *AtCLH2*, are not hormonally controlled (6, 110, 122). *AtCLH1* was originally identified as a coronatine- and wound-induced gene, *CORI1* (7), and expression was quickly induced after tissue damage by necrotrophic organisms (52). It was concluded that AtCLH1 pays a role in regulating plant defense pathways through detoxification of free Chl occurring upon tissue damage, thus preventing the accumulation of reactive oxygen species (52).

Pheide *a* oxygenase. Regulation of PAO has been inferred from biochemical data that show senescence-specific activity of PAO (45, 83, 125), and regulation at the posttranscriptional level has been suggested (83). A recent detailed comparison of *PAO* expression,

Introgression: interspecific backcrossing program for substitution of a target gene from one species for the equivalent gene in another species. The presence or absence of the target gene in a backcross individual of progeny generated either by selfing or by crossing to the donor parent can be determined, e.g., in a phenotypic assay or by marker assistance

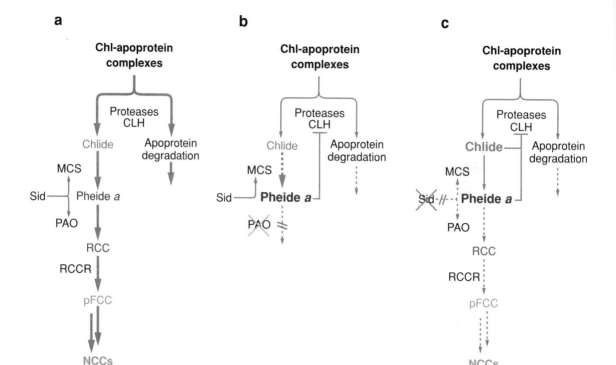

Figure 2

Proposed model for regulation of Chl breakdown in wild-type (*a*) and Chl breakdown mutants (*b*, *c*). The scheme was constructed based on data available from mutants defective in *PAO* (*b*) (83, 84) and *Sid* (*c*) (89, 125). Thickness of arrows represents relative flux of metabolites, and the font size represents relative changes in catabolite amounts and enzyme activities, respectively. For further explanations and details, see text.

LHCII:
light-harvesting complex of photosystem II

PAO protein abundance, and activity during *Arabidopsis* leaf development and senescence indicates that PAO is mainly (or exclusively) regulated at the level of de novo enzyme synthesis. *PAO* mRNA and PAO protein are present at low levels in presenescent leaves, but are highly enriched during senescence (84). Like *AtCLH1* (7), *PAO* is up-regulated rapidly upon wounding (131). In PAO mutants, as well as in stay-green mutants that are affected in PAO activity, Chl is largely retained during senescence (83, 84, 89, 125), implying that a blockage at the level of PAO inhibits Chl breakdown. Note that retention of Chl in these mutants is accompanied by retention of Chl-binding proteins, such as proteins of the light-harvesting complex of photosystem II (LHCII), but not of soluble plastid proteins (5, 83, 117). It can be assumed that a feedback mechanism exists in which initiation of breakdown is inhibited by breakdown intermediates, such as Pheide *a* (**Figure 2**). Whether such a mechanism directly affects CLH, the first catabolic enzyme, or e.g., proteases that might be responsible for dismantling of Chl-apoprotein complexes (111), remains to be shown. Whereas Pheide *a* is the only Chl catabolite that accumulates in PAO mutants, Chlide is found in *sid* mutants (89, 125), indicating that they are not affected in the structural gene of PAO. More likely, Sid induces PAO expression/activation, but it could modulate MCS as well (**Figure 2**).

Besides expression during leaf senescence, *AtPAO* is highly expressed in flowers and siliques (84), but both PAO transcripts and protein are also detectable in etiolated leaves and in roots (28, 84, 131). This is in contrast to *Arabidopsis* CLH genes, which are apparently not expressed in roots (6). Microarray analysis using the Genevestigator tool (135) indicates upregulation of PAO in response to various stress conditions, such as osmotic stress and pathogen infection (S. Hörtensteiner, unpublished) coinciding with Chl breakdown under these conditions (115). Thus, it can be assumed that the PAO pathway of Chl breakdown is activated not only during senescence, but probably under any conditions that are linked to massive degradation of Chl.

RCCR. Like *PAO*, *RCCR* is expressed in roots and RCCR activity can be detected in root extracts and etiolated leaves (91, 129), which raises questions about the role of Chl catabolic enzymes in nongreen tissues. It will be interesting to see whether PAO or RCCR mutants, for example, exhibit a root phenotype.

Analyses of mRNA abundance, protein levels, and activity demonstrated that, in contrast to PAO, RCCR is not regulated during senescence (66, 84, 129). A survey of microarray data confirms rather constant *RCCR* expression throughout *Arabidopsis* development and under stress conditions (S. Hörtensteiner, unpublished).

Chl Breakdown and Cell Death

Lesion mimic mutants have been identified in many different species, and in *Arabidopsis* more than 35 lesion mimic mutants are known. The majority of these belong to the group of so-called initiation mutants, which presumedly are blocked in a pathway for initiation of programmed cell death (PCD). In contrast, propagation mutants are assumed to be defective in a mechanism that suppresses PCD (62). In some lesion mimic mu-

tants, like *les22* of maize (47), and transgenics with defects in Chl biosynthetic steps (32), cell death is triggered by the accumulation of photoreactive porphyrins. Light is required for lesion formation in these mutants.

Likewise, mutations in or antisense expression of *PAO* and *RCCR* induces lesion mimic phenotypes (27, 28, 30, 31, 66, 83, 84, 100, 109), and in the case of PAO mutants, accumulation of Pheide *a* was unequivocally demonstrated to induce cell death (83, 84, 109). Strikingly, a lesion mimic phenotype does not occur in *sid* mutants, although these mutants also accumulate Pheide *a* (115). In *acd2-2*, RCC accumulates during senescence and contents of RCC correlate with the progression of cell death (A. Pružinská & S. Hörtensteiner, unpublished). Despite this, treatment of leaves or isolated protoplasts with protoporphyrin IX, but not with Pheide *a*, induced cell death in the mutant, and RCCR overexpressing lines were more resistant than the wild type at high protoporphyrin IX concentrations (132). Increased cell death was also observed after oxyfluorfen treatment, which inhibits protoporphyrinogen oxidase and causes the accumulation of protoporphyrin IX (A. Pružinská & S. Hörtensteiner, unpublished). It remains to be shown which pigments are responsible in vivo for the lesion mimic phenotype of *acd2*.

The mechanism by which cell death is executed in Chl catabolic mutants has not been elucidated so far. Yao et al. (132) showed that for *Arabidopsis*, changes in the mitochondrial membrane potential play an important role in PCD, and because of the localization of RCCR in chloroplasts, communication between these two organelles was implied as a prerequisite for cell death execution in *acd2*. In the case of the conditional *Arabidopsis flu* mutant, light absorption by protochlorophyllide that accumulates in the dark causes the production of singlet oxygen (79). Singlet oxygen induces a cell death–signaling pathway with EXECUTER1 as an (early) component, which is different from

Lesion mimic mutants: mutants developing necrotic lesions in the absence of pathogens, thereby mimicking the symptoms of fungal and bacterial diseases

PCD: programmed cell death

PCD programs induced by other reactive oxygen species (127). The role of EXECUTER1 has not been elucidated, but its wide distribution suggests a function common to all plants. It can be argued that light absorption by Pheide *a* or RCC/protoporphyrin IX in respective Chl catabolic mutants might induce the EXECUTER1-dependent pathway as well. Double mutants between *ex1* and *pao1* or *acd2* will answer this question in the future.

In summary, it can be concluded that functional biosynthesis and breakdown of Chl are vitally important for plant development and plant survival in order to prevent the accumulation of phototoxic intermediates. Both pathways have to be tightly regulated and PAO has a major role for Chl degradation. As has been proposed for Chl biosynthesis (18), it is likely that Chl catabolic enzymes are arranged in high-molecular weight complexes, thereby minimizing the risk of release and photoactivation of intermediates. In favor of this idea are biochemical data indicating an interaction of PAO and RCCR, and metabolic channeling of RCC (39, 69, 90).

A number of reports describe in vitro Chl oxidizing (bleaching) activities, mainly catalyzed by peroxidases in the presence of H_2O_2 and a phenolic compound (for a recent review see 130). These form $C13^2$-hydroxy Chl, which has also been found in naturally degreening sources (39, 130). Fluorescent and bilirubin-like catabolites were identified recently as in vitro products of Chl peroxidation (1), but chemical structures have not been elucidated. Furthermore, neither in vivo occurrence of these catabolites, nor a role of Chl bleaching activities within living cells, has unequivocally been demonstrated (42). A Chl bleaching activity of peroxidases, which are often associated with vacuoles (130), may be restricted to cell autolysis, i.e., after transition of individual cells from life to death, as determined by the rupture of the vacuolar membrane (67). This concept would explain bleaching of Chl in *pao* and *acd2* leaf lesions despite the absence of an active PAO pathway, but may also be responsible for the disappearance of Chl in other instances of PCD.

Chl Breakdown and Nitrogen Economy

One mole of Chl contains four moles of nitrogen, but Chl contributes only about 2% of cellular nitrogen (82). Hence, degradation to and disposal of colorless tetrapyrroles during senescence is the minimum effort plants require for remobilizing the some 20% of cellular nitrogen fixed in Chl apoproteins. Chl is required for stabilization of Chl-binding proteins (38); similarly, it is reasonable to believe that removal of Chl is a prerequisite for the degradation of Chl-associated proteins. Alternatively, proteases specifically synthesized or activated during senescence could be active first, thereby destabilizing the complexes and liberating Chl. In Bf 993, LHCII is not degraded, although it undergoes some proteolytic cleavage, which was assumed to remove an N-terminal region facing the stroma (115). This points to an interplay between proteolytic and Chl catabolic activities during senescence. Chl(ide) *b* reductase could play a critical role. In Chl *b*-less mutants, LHCII apoproteins are synthesized, but the lack of Chl *b* causes their fast turnover (35). Likewise, in vitro LHCII assembly requires the presence of Chl *b* in stoichiometric rates (38). It is possible that senescence-specific activation/synthesis of the thylakoid-localized Chl(ide) *b* reductase lowers the amount of Chl *b* of individual Chl-protein complexes. This may destabilize the complexes, make them accessible for proteases, and cause a release of Chl.

Except for the D1 protein of the PS II reaction center, proteases responsible for degradation of Chl-binding proteins are largely unknown. D1 has a rapid turnover rate not only under photoinhibitory conditions, but also during senescence (88). A prevailing dogma is that degradation of D1 occurs in two steps, an initial cleavage into two fragments, followed by complete degradation. Members of two types of chloroplast-localized proteases, DegP and FtsH, have been shown to catalyze these reactions (for a recent review see 2). In contrast, our knowledge of the degradation of LHCII is still rather limited. Serine/cysteine-type proteases are involved in its degradation during high light acclimation (e.g., 124) and a chloroplast-localized glutamyl endopeptidase was identified, which cleaves a N-terminal peptide of defined length from the LHCII subunit, Lhcb1 (24). An (isolated) report describes a zinc-binding metalloprotease acting toward Lhcb3 (133). The activity was integrally associated with thylakoid membranes, but susceptibility of Lhcb3 for proteolytic attack required the removal of unknown protective factors in a senescence-dependent manner. As judged from the enzymatic properties, members of the FtsH family, nine of which are chloroplast-localized in *Arabidopsis* (93), are good candidates for this activity.

CONCLUSIONS

As anticipated by Matile et al. in 1999 (69), the past seven years have been a time of accelerated progress for research on Chl breakdown as it reached the molecular level. What comes next? Besides the challenge to discover still unknown Chl catabolite-modifying activities, we have to uncover regulators that are required to induce and control Chl breakdown. Chl is believed to turn over rather fast at the steady-state level (111), but neither the mechanisms involved nor the factors that define a switch from turnover to massive degradation during senescence have been elucidated. Furthermore, the identification of porphyrin-based intracellular signaling systems (60a, 101) points to the importance of pigment carriers and transports, and raises the question: To what extent are Chl catabolites involved in the control of plant development?

SUMMARY POINTS

1. The pathway of chlorophyll breakdown consists of four common steps that lead to the formation of a primary fluorescent tetrapyrrolic intermediate, followed by mostly species-specific modifications of tetrapyrrole side chains. Finally, fluorescent catabolites are excreted into the vacuole, where they nonenzymatically tautomerize to the final nonfluorescent catabolites.

2. Genes for three of the common enzymes, chlorophyllase, pheophorbide *a* oxygenase, and red chlorophyll catabolite reductase, were recently identified.

3. Mutants in pheophorbide *a* oxygenase and red chlorophyll catabolite reductase develop a light-dependent cell death phenotype, due to the accumulation of photodynamic breakdown intermediates.

4. Breakdown of chlorophyll qualifies as a detoxification mechanism during senescence, which is vitally important for plant development and survival.

5. The distribution of chlorophyll catabolic genes among photosynthetic organisms indicates that chlorophyll breakdown coevolved with oxygenic photosynthesis, which suggests that evolution of red chlorophyll catabolite reductase was a prerequisite for land colonization of plants.

6. Except for senescence-specific induction of pheophorbide *a* oxygenase gene expression, regulation of chlorophyll breakdown is poorly understood.

7. Retention of chlorophyll-binding proteins in mutants affected in chlorophyll breakdown demonstrates a close interconnection between chlorophyll and apoprotein degradation during senescence.

ACKNOWLEDGMENTS

I would like to thank Helen Ougham and Howard Thomas (IGER, Wales) for critical reading of the manuscript. My work on Chl breakdown is supported by grants from the Swiss National Science Foundation and by the National Center of Competence in Research (NCCR) Plant Survival, research program of the Swiss National Science Foundation.

LITERATURE CITED

1. Adachi M, Nakabayashi K, Azuma R, Kurata H, Takahashi Y, Shimokawa K. 1999. The ethylene-induced chlorophyll catabolism of radish (*Raphanus sativus* L.) cotyledons: production of colorless fluorescent chlorophyll catabolite (FCC) *in vitro*. *J. Jpn. Soc. Hortic. Sci.* 68:1139–45

2. Adam Z, Clarke AK. 2002. Cutting edge of chloroplast proteolysis. *Trends Plant Sci.* 7:451–56

3. Akhtar MS, Goldschmidt EE, John I, Rodoni S, Matile P, Grierson D. 1999. Altered patterns of senescence and ripening in *gf*, a stay-green mutant of tomato (*Lycopersicon esculentum* Mill.). *J. Exp. Bot.* 50:1115–22

4. Arkus KAJ, Cahoon EB, Jez JM. 2005. Mechanistic analysis of wheat chlorophyllase. *Arch. Biochem. Biophys.* 438:146–55

5. Bachmann A, Fernández-López J, Ginsburg S, Thomas H, Bouwcamp JC, et al. 1994. *Stay-green* genotypes of *Phaseolus vulgaris* L.: chloroplast proteins and chlorophyll catabolites during foliar senescence. *New Phytol.* 126:593–600

6. Benedetti CE, Arruda P. 2002. Altering the expression of the chlorophyllase gene *ATH-COR1* in transgenic Arabidopsis caused changes in the chlorophyll-to-chlorophyllide ratio. *Plant Physiol.* 128:1255–63

7. Benedetti CE, Costa CL, Turcinelli SR, Arruda P. 1998. Differential expression of a novel gene in response to coronatine, methyl jasmonate, and wounding in the *Coi1* mutant of *Arabidopsis*. *Plant Physiol.* 116:1037–42

8. Berghold J. 2005. *Chemische und biochemische Untersuchungen zum Chlorophyllabbau*. PhD thesis. Univ. Innsbruck, Innsbruck. 194 pp.

9. Berghold J, Breuker K, Oberhuber M, Hörtensteiner S, Kräutler B. 2002. Chlorophyll breakdown in spinach: on the structure of five nonfluorescent chlorophyll catabolites. *Photosynth. Res.* 74:109–19

10. Berghold J, Eichmüller C, Hörtensteiner S, Kräutler B. 2004. Chlorophyll breakdown in tobacco: on the structure of two nonfluorescent chlorophyll catabolites. *Chem. Biodivers.* 1:657–68

11. Brandis A, Vainstein A, Goldschmidt EE. 1996. Distribution of chlorophyllase among components of chloroplast membranes in *Citrus sinensis* organs. *Plant Physiol. Biochem.* 34:49–54

12. Cha KW, Lee YJ, Koh HJ, Lee BM, Nam YW, Paek NC. 2002. Isolation, characterization, and mapping of the stay green mutant in rice. *Theor. Appl. Genet.* 104:526–32

13. Costa ML, Civello PM, Chaves AR, Martinez GA. 2002. Characterization of Mg-dechelatase activity obtained from *Fragaria* x *ananassa* fruit. *Plant Physiol. Biochem.* 40:111–18

14. Curty C, Engel N. 1996. Detection, isolation and structure elucidation of a chlorophyll *a* catabolite from autumnal senescent leaves of *Cercidiphyllum japonicum*. *Phytochemistry* 42:1531–36

15. Curty C, Engel N, Gossauer A. 1995. Evidence for a monooxygenase-catalyzed primary process in the catabolism of chlorophyll. *FEBS Lett.* 364:41–44

16. Doi M, Inage T, Shioi Y. 2001. Chlorophyll degradation in a *Chlamydomonas reinhardtii* mutant: an accumulation of pyropheophorbide *a* by anaerobiosis. *Plant Cell Physiol.* 42:469–74

17. Drazkiewicz M. 1994. Chlorophyllase: occurrence, functions, mechanism of action, effects of external and internal factors. *Photosynthetica* 30:321–31

18. Eckhardt U, Grimm B, Hörtensteiner S. 2004. Recent advances in chlorophyll biosynthesis and breakdown in higher plants. *Plant Mol. Biol.* 56:1–14

19. Efrati A, Eyal Y, Paran I. 2005. Molecular mapping of the *chlorophyll retainer* (*cl*) mutation in pepper (*Capsicum* spp.) and screening for candidate genes using tomato ESTs homologous to structural genes of the chlorophyll catabolism pathway. *Genome* 48:347–51

20. Engel N, Curty C, Gossauer A. 1996. Chlorophyll catabolism in *Chlorella protothecoides*. 8. Facts and artefacts. *Plant Physiol. Biochem.* 34:77–83

21. Eschenmoser A. 1988. Vitamin B12. Experiments concerning the origin of its molecular structure. *Angew. Chem. Int. Ed. Engl.* 27:5–40

22. Ferro M, Salvi D, Riviere-Rolland H, Vermat T, Seigneurin-Berny D, et al. 2002. Integral membrane proteins of the chloroplast envelope: identification and subcellular localization of new transporters. *Proc. Natl. Acad. Sci. USA* 99:11487–92

23. Folley P, Engel N. 1999. Chlorophyll *b* to chlorophyll *a* conversion precedes chlorophyll degradation in *Hordeum vulgare* L. *J. Biol. Chem.* 274:21811–16

24. Forsberg J, Strom J, Kieselbach T, Larsson H, Alexciev K, et al. 2005. Protease activities in the chloroplast capable of cleaving an LHCII N-terminal peptide. *Physiol. Plant.* 123:21–29

25. Frankenberg N, Mukougawa K, Kohchi T, Lagarias JC. 2001. Functional genomic analysis of the HY2 family of ferredoxin-dependent bilin reductases from oxygenic photosynthetic organisms. *Plant Cell* 13:965–78

26. Ginsburg S, Matile P. 1993. Identification of catabolites of chlorophyll porphyrin in senescent rape cotyledons. *Plant Physiol.* 102:521–27

27. Gray J, Close PS, Briggs SP, Johal GS. 1997. A novel suppressor of cell death in plants encoded by the *Lls1* gene of maize. *Cell* 89:25–31

28. Gray J, Janick-Bruckner D, Bruckner B, Close PS, Johal GS. 2002. Light-dependent death of maize *lls1* cells is mediated by mature chloroplasts. *Plant Physiol.* 130:1894–907

29. Gray J, Wardzala E, Yang M, Reinbothe S, Haller S, Pauli F. 2004. A small family of LLS1-related non-heme oxygenases in plants with an origin amongst oxygenic photosynthesizers. *Plant Mol. Biol.* 54:39–54

30. Greenberg JT, Ausubel FM. 1993. *Arabidopsis* mutants compromised for the control of cellular damage during pathogenesis and aging. *Plant J.* 4:327–41

31. Greenberg JT, Guo A, Klessig DF, Ausubel FM. 1994. Programmed cell death in plants: a pathogen-triggered response activated coordinately with multiple defense functions. *Cell* 77:551–63

32. Grimm B. 1998. Novel insights in the control of tetrapyrrole metabolism of higher plants. *Curr. Opin. Plant Biol.* 1:245–50

33. Guiamét JJ, Pichersky E, Noodén LD. 1999. Mass exodus from senescing soybean chloroplasts. *Plant Cell Physiol.* 40:986–92

34. Guiamet JJ, Tyystjarvi E, Tyystjarvi T, John I, Kairavuo M, et al. 2002. Photoinhibition and loss of photosystem II reaction centre proteins during senescence of soybean

leaves. Enhancement of photoinhibition by the 'stay-green' mutation *cytG*. *Physiol. Plant.* 115:468–78

35. Harrison MA, Nemson JA, Melis A. 1993. Assembly and composition of the chlorophyll *a-b* light-harvesting complex of barley (*Hordeum vulgare* L.): immunochemical analysis of chlorophyll *b*-less and chlorophyll *b*-deficient mutants. *Photosynth. Res.* 38:141–51

36. Hendry GAF, Houghton JD, Brown SB. 1987. Chlorophyll degradation. A biological enigma. *New Phytol.* 107:255–302

37. Hinder B, Schellenberg M, Rodoni S, Ginsburg S, Vogt E, et al. 1996. How plants dispose of chlorophyll catabolites. Directly energized uptake of tetrapyrrolic breakdown products into isolated vacuoles. *J. Biol. Chem.* 271:27233–36

38. Horn R, Paulsen H. 2004. Early steps in the assembly of light-harvesting chlorophyll *a/b* complex - Time-resolved fluorescence measurements. *J. Biol. Chem.* 279:44400–6

39. Hörtensteiner S. 1999. Chlorophyll breakdown in higher plants and algae. *Cell. Mol. Life Sci.* 56:330–47

40. Hörtensteiner S. 2004. The loss of green color during chlorophyll degradation - a prerequisite to prevent cell death? *Planta* 219:191–94

41. Hörtensteiner S, Chinner J, Matile P, Thomas H, Donnison IS. 2000. Chlorophyll breakdown in *Chlorella protothecoides*: characterization of degreening and cloning of degreening-related genes. *Plant Mol. Biol.* 42:439–50

42. Hörtensteiner S, Feller U. 2002. Nitrogen metabolism and remobilization during senescence. *J. Exp. Bot.* 53:927–37

43. Hörtensteiner S, Kräutler B. 2000. Chlorophyll breakdown in oilseed rape. *Photosynth. Res.* 64:137–46

44. Hörtensteiner S, Rodoni S, Schellenberg M, Vicentini F, Nandi OI, et al. 2000. Evolution of chlorophyll degradation: the significance of RCC reductase. *Plant Biol.* 2:63–67

45. Hörtensteiner S, Vicentini F, Matile P. 1995. Chlorophyll breakdown in senescent cotyledons of rape, *Brassica napus* L.: enzymatic cleavage of phaeophorbide *a in vitro*. *New Phytol.* 129:237–46

46. Hörtensteiner S, Wüthrich KL, Matile P, Ongania K-H, Kräutler B. 1998. The key step in chlorophyll breakdown in higher plants. Cleavage of pheophorbide *a* macrocycle by a monooxygenase. *J. Biol. Chem.* 273:15335–39

47. Hu G, Yalpani N, Briggs SP, Johal GS. 1998. A porphyrin pathway impairment is responsible for the phenotype of a dominant disease lesion mimic mutant of maize. *Plant Cell* 10:1095–105

48. Iturraspe J, Engel N, Gossauer A. 1994. Chlorophyll catabolism. Isolation and structure elucidation of chlorophyll *b* catabolites in *Chlorella protothecoides*. *Phytochemistry* 35:1387–90

49. Iturraspe J, Moyano N, Frydman B. 1995. A new 5-formylbilinone as the major chlorophyll *a* catabolite in tree senescent leaves. *J. Org. Chem.* 60:6664–65

50. Jakob-Wilk D, Holland D, Goldschmidt EE, Riov J, Eyal Y. 1999. Chlorophyll breakdown by chlorophyllase: isolation and functional expression of the *Chlase1* gene from ethylene-treated *Citrus* fruit and its regulation during development. *Plant J.* 20:653–61

51. Jonker JW, Buitelaar M, Wagenaar E, van der Valk MA, Scheffer GL, et al. 2002. The breast cancer resistance protein protects against a major chlorophyll-derived dietary phototoxin and protoporphyria. *Proc. Natl. Acad. Sci. USA* 99:15649–54

52. Kariola T, Brader G, Li J, Palva ET. 2005. Chlorophyllase 1, a damage control enzyme, affects the balance between defense pathways in plants. *Plant Cell* 17:282–94

Together with Reference 122, this paper describes the first cloning of an enzyme of chlorophyll breakdown, chlorophyllase.

Demonstration of the phototoxicity of pheophorbide *a* in mammals. The results point to the possible identity of chlorophyll catabolite transporters in plants.

53. Kessler F, Schnell D, Blobel G. 1999. Identification of proteins associated with plastoglobules isolated from pea (*Pisum sativum* L.) chloroplasts. *Planta* 208:107–13

54. Klein M, Geisler M, Suh SJ, Kolukisaoglu HU, Azevedo L, et al. 2004. Disruption of *AtMRP4*, a guard cell plasma membrane ABCC-type ABC transporter, leads to deregulation of stomatal opening and increased drought susceptibility. *Plant J.* 39:219–36

55. Kohchi T, Mukougawa K, Frankenberg N, Masuda M, Yokota A, Lagarias JC. 2001. The Arabidopsis HY2 gene encodes phytochromobilin synthase, a ferredoxin-dependent biliverdin reductase. *Plant Cell* 13:425–36

56. Koo AJK, Ohlrogge JB. 2002. The predicted candidates of Arabidopsis plastid inner envelope membrane proteins and their expression profiles. *Plant Physiol.* 130:823–36

57. Kräutler B. 2002. Unravelling chlorophyll catabolism in higher plants. *Biochem. Soc. Trans.* 30:625–30

58. Kräutler B. 2003. Chlorophyll breakdown and chlorophyll catabolites. In *The Porphyrin Handbook, Vol. 13*, ed. KM Kadish, KM Smith, R Guilard, pp. 183–209. Amsterdam: Elsevier Sci.

59. Kräutler B, Jaun B, Bortlik K-H, Schellenberg M, Matile P. 1991. On the enigma of chlorophyll degradation: the constitution of a secoporphinoid catabolite. *Angew. Chem. Int. Ed. Engl.* 30:1315–18

60. Kräutler B, Matile P. 1999. Solving the riddle of chlorophyll breakdown. *Acc. Chem. Res.* 32:35–43

60a. Kropat J, Oster U, Rüdiger W, Beck CF. 1997. Chlorophyll precursors are signals of chloroplast origin involved in light induction of nuclear heat-shock genes. *Proc. Natl. Acad. Sci. USA* 94:14168–72

61. Kunieda T, Amano T, Shioi Y. 2005. Search for chlorophyll degradation enzyme, Mg-dechelatase, from extracts of *Chenopodium album* with native and artificial substrates. *Plant Sci.* 169:177–83

62. Lorrain S, Vailleau F, Balaqué C, Roby D. 2003. Lesion mimic mutants: keys for deciphering cell death and defense pathways in plants? *Trends Plant Sci.* 8:263–71

63. Losey FG, Engel N. 2001. Isolation and characterization of a urobilinogenoidic chlorophyll catabolite from *Hordeum vulgare* L. *J. Biol. Chem.* 276:27233–36

64. Lu Y-P, Li Z-S, Drozdowicz Y-M, Hörtensteiner S, Martinoia E, Rea PA. 1998. AtMRP2, an *Arabidopsis* ATP binding cassette transporter able to transport glutathione S-conjugates and chlorophyll catabolites: functional comparisons with AtMRP1. *Plant Cell* 10:267–82

65. Luquez VM, Guiamet JJ. 2002. The stay green mutations *d1* and *d2* increase water stress susceptibility in soybeans. *J. Exp. Bot.* 53:1421–28

66. Mach JM, Castillo AR, Hoogstraten R, Greenberg JT. 2001. The Arabidopsis-accelerated cell death gene ACD2 encodes red chlorophyll catabolite reductase and suppresses the spread of disease symptoms. *Proc. Natl. Acad. Sci. USA* 98:771–76

67. Matile P. 1997. The vacuole and cell senescence. In *Advances in Botanical Research*, ed. JA Callow, pp. 87–112. New York: Academic

68. Matile P, Ginsburg S, Schellenberg M, Thomas H. 1988. Catabolites of chlorophyll in senescing barley leaves are localized in the vacuoles of mesophyll cells. *Proc. Natl. Acad. Sci. USA* 85:9529–32

69. Matile P, Hörtensteiner S, Thomas H. 1999. Chlorophyll degradation. *Annu. Rev. Plant Physiol. Plant Mol. Biol.* 50:67–95

70. Matile P, Schellenberg M, Peisker C. 1992. Production and release of a chlorophyll catabolite in isolated senescent chloroplasts. *Planta* 187:230–35

A comprehensive review on chlorophyll breakdown and the basis for the present updating review.

71. Matile P, Schellenberg M, Vicentini F. 1997. Localization of chlorophyllase in the chloroplast envelope. *Planta* 201:96–99

72. Moore BJ, Donnison IS, Harper JA, Armstead IP, King J, et al. 2005. Molecular tagging of a senescence gene by introgression mapping of a stay-green mutation from *Festuca pratensis*. *New Phytol.* 165:801–6

73. Mühlecker W, Kräutler B. 1996. Breakdown of chlorophyll: constitution of nonfluorescing chlorophyll-catabolites from senescent cotyledons of the dicot rape. *Plant Physiol. Biochem.* 34:61–75

74. Mühlecker W, Kräutler B, Moser D, Matile P, Hörtensteiner S. 2000. Breakdown of chlorophyll: a fluorescent chlorophyll catabolite from sweet pepper (*Capsicum annuum*). *Helv. Chim. Acta* 83:278–86

75. Mühlecker W, Ongania K-H, Kräutler B, Matile P, Hörtensteiner S. 1997. Tracking down chlorophyll breakdown in plants: elucidation of the constitution of a 'fluorescent' chlorophyll catabolite. *Angew. Chem. Int. Ed. Engl.* 36:401–4

76. **Oberhuber M, Berghold J, Breuker K, Hörtensteiner S, Kräutler B. 2003. Breakdown of chlorophyll: A nonenzymatic reaction accounts for the formation of the colorless "nonfluorescent" chlorophyll catabolites. *Proc. Natl. Acad. Sci. USA* 100:6910–15**

77. Oberhuber M, Berghold J, Mühlecker W, Hörtensteiner S, Kräutler B. 2001. Chlorophyll breakdown - on a nonfluorescent chlorophyll catabolite from spinach. *Helv. Chim. Acta* 84:2615–27

78. Oberhuber M, Kräutler B. 2002. Breakdown of chlorophyll: electrochemical bilin reduction provides synthetic access to fluorescent chlorophyll catabolites. *Chembiochemisty* 3:104–7

79. op den Camp RG, Przybyla D, Ochsenbein C, Laloi C, Kim C, et al. 2003. Rapid induction of distinct stress responses after release of singlet oxygen in Arabidopsis. *Plant Cell* 15:2320–32

80. Oster U, Tanaka R, Tanaka A, Rudiger W. 2000. Cloning and functional expression of the gene encoding the key enzyme for chlorophyll *b* biosynthesis (CAO) from *Arabidopsis thaliana*. *Plant J.* 21:305–10

81. Ougham HJ, Morris P, Thomas H. 2005. The colors of autumn leaves as symptoms of cellular recycling and defenses against environmental stresses. In *Current Topics in Developmental Biology, Vol 66*, ed. GP Schatten, pp. 135–60. Amsterdam: Elsevier Sci.

82. Peoples MB, Dalling MJ. 1988. The interplay between proteolysis and amino acid metabolism during senescence and nitrogen allocation. In *Senescence and Aging in Plants*, ed. LD Noodén, AC Leopold, pp. 181–217. San Diego: Academic

83. **Pružinská A, Anders I, Tanner G, Roca M, Hörtensteiner S. 2003. Chlorophyll breakdown: pheophorbide *a* oxygenase is a Rieske-type iron-sulfur protein, encoded by the *accelerated cell death 1* gene. *Proc. Natl. Acad. Sci. USA* 100:15259–64**

84. Pružinská A, Tanner G, Aubry S, Anders I, Moser S, et al. 2005. Chlorophyll breakdown in senescent Arabidopsis leaves: characterization of chlorophyll catabolites and of chlorophyll catabolic enzymes involved in the de-greening reaction. *Plant Physiol.* 139:52–63

85. Reinbothe C, Satoh H, Alcaraz JP, Reinbothe S. 2004. A novel role of water-soluble chlorophyll proteins in the transitory storage of chorophyllide. *Plant Physiol.* 134:1355–65

86. Reinbothe S, Pollmann S, Reinbothe C. 2003. *In situ* conversion of protochlorophyllide b to protochlorophyllide *a* in barley - Evidence for a novel role of 7-formyl reductase in the prolamellar body of etioplasts. *J. Biol. Chem.* 278:800–6

Convincing evidence that conversion of fluorescent chlorophyll catabolites to nonfluorescent ones occurs inside the vacuole and is catalyzed nonenzymatically by the acidic vacuolar pH.

Molecular identification of the key enzyme of chlorophyll breakdown, pheophorbide *a* oxygenase, a Rieske-type iron-sulfur enzyme.

87. Reinbothe S, Quigley F, Gray J, Schemenewitz A, Reinbothe C. 2004. Identification of plastid envelope proteins required for import of protochlorophyllide oxidoreductase A into the chloroplast of barley. *Proc. Natl. Acad. Sci. USA* 101:2197–202

88. Roberts DR, Thompson JE, Dumbroff EB, Gepstein S, Mattoo AK. 1987. Differential changes in the synthesis and steady-state levels of thylakoid proteins during bean leaf senescence. *Plant Mol. Biol.* 9:343–53

89. Roca M, James J, Pružinská A, Hörtensteiner S, Thomas H, Ougham H. 2004. Analysis of the chlorophyll catabolism pathway in leaves of an introgression senescence mutant of *Lolium temulentum. Phytochemistry* 65:1231–38

90. Rodoni S, Mühlecker W, Anderl M, Kräutler B, Moser D, et al. 1997. Chlorophyll breakdown in senescent chloroplasts. Cleavage of pheophorbide *a* in two enzymic steps. *Plant Physiol.* 115:669–76

91. Rodoni S, Vicentini F, Schellenberg M, Matile P, Hörtensteiner S. 1997. Partial purification and characterization of red chlorophyll catabolite reductase, a stroma protein involved in chlorophyll breakdown. *Plant Physiol.* 115:677–82

92. Rüdiger W. 2002. Biosynthesis of chlorophyll *b* and the chlorophyll cycle. *Photosynth. Res.* 74:187–93

93. Sakamoto W, Zaltsman A, Adam Z, Takahashi Y. 2003. Coordinated regulation and complex formation of YELLOW VARIEGATED1 and YELLOW VARIEGATED2, chloroplastic FtsH metalloproteases involved in the repair cycle of photosystem II in Arabidopsis thylakoid membranes. *Plant Cell* 15:2843–55

94. Sanchez-Fernandez R, Davies TGE, Coleman JOD, Rea PA. 2001. The *Arabidopsis thaliana* ABC protein superfamily, a complete inventory. *J. Biol. Chem.* 276:30231–44

95. Satoh H, Nakayama K, Okada M. 1998. Molecular cloning and functional expression of a water-soluble chlorophyll protein, a putative carrier of chlorophyll molecules in cauliflower. *J. Biol. Chem.* 273:30568–75

96. Scheumann V, Schoch S, Rüdiger W. 1999. Chlorophyll *b* reduction during senescence of barley seedlings. *Planta* 209:364–70

97. Shioi Y, Tomita N, Tsuchiya T, Takamiya K. 1996. Conversion of chlorophyllide to pheophorbide by Mg-dechelating substance in extracts of *Chenopodium album. Plant Physiol. Biochem.* 34:41–47

98. Shioi Y, Watanabe K, Takamiya K. 1996. Enzymatic conversion of pheophorbide *a* to a precursor of pyropheophorbide *a* in leaves of *Chenopodium album. Plant Cell Physiol.* 37:1143–49

99. Smart CM. 1994. Gene expression during leaf senescence. *New Phytol.* 126:419–48

100. Spassieva S, Hille J. 2002. A lesion mimic phenotype in tomato obtained by isolating and silencing an *Lls1* homologue. *Plant Sci.* 162:543–49

101. Strand Å, Asami T, Alonso J, Ecker JR, Chory J. 2003. Chloroplast to nucleus communication triggered by accumulation of Mg-protoporphyrin IX. *Nature* 421:79–83

102. Suzuki T, Kunieda T, Murai F, Morioka S, Shioi Y. 2005. Mg-dechelation activity in radish cotyledons with artificial and native substrates, Mg-chlorophyllin *a* and chlorophyllide *a. Plant Physiol. Biochem.* 43:459–64

103. Suzuki T, Shioi Y. 2002. Re-examination of Mg-dechelation reaction in the degradation of chlorophylls using chlorophyllin *a* as substrate. *Photosynth. Res.* 74:217–23

104. Suzuki Y, Doi M, Shioi Y. 2002. Two enzymatic reaction pathways in the formation of pyropheophorbide *a. Photosynth. Res.* 74:225–33

105. Suzuki Y, Shioi Y. 1999. Detection of chlorophyll breakdown products in the senescent leaves of higher plants. *Plant Cell Physiol.* 40:909–15

106. Suzuki Y, Tanabe K, Shioi Y. 1999. Determination of chemical oxidation products of chlorophyll and porphyrin by high-performance liquid chromatography. *J. Chromatogr. A.* 839:85–91

107. Takamiya K, Tsuchiya T, Ohta H. 2000. Degradation pathway(s) of chlorophyll: What has gene cloning revealed? *Trends Plant Sci.* 5:426–31

108. Tanaka A, Ito H, Tanaka R, Tanaka NK, Yoshida K, Okada K. 1998. Chlorophyll *a* oxygenase (*CAO*) is involved in chlorophyll *b* formation from chlorophyll *a*. *Proc. Natl. Acad. Sci. USA* 95:12719–23

109. Tanaka R, Hirashima M, Satoh S, Tanaka A. 2003. The *Arabidopsis-accelerated cell death* gene *ACD1* is involved in oxygenation of pheophorbide *a*: Inhibition of pheophorbide *a* oxygenase activity does not lead to the "stay-green" phenotype in *Arabidopsis*. *Plant Cell Physiol.* 44:1266–74

110. Tang L, Okazawa A, Itoh Y, Fukusaki E, Kobayashi A. 2004. Expression of chlorophyllase is not induced during autumnal yellowing in *Ginkgo biloba*. *Z. Naturforsch. C* 59:415–20

111. Thomas H. 1997. Chlorophyll: a symptom and a regulator of plastid development. *New Phytol.* 136:163–81

112. Thomas H, Evans C, Thomas HM, Humphreys MW, Morgan G, et al. 1997. Introgression, tagging and expression of a leaf senescence gene in *Festulolium*. *New Phytol.* 137:29–34

113. Thomas H, Howarth CJ. 2000. Five ways to stay green. *J. Exp. Bot.* 51:329–37

114. Thomas H, Morgan WG, Thomas AM, Ougham HJ. 1999. Expression of the stay-green character introgressed into *Lolium temulentum* Ceres from a senescence mutant of *Festuca pratensis*. *Theor. Appl. Genet.* 99:92–99

115. Thomas H, Ougham H, Hörtensteiner S. 2001. Recent advances in the cell biology of chlorophyll catabolism. In *Advances in Botanical Research*, ed. JA Callow, pp. 1–52. San Diego: Academic

116. Thomas H, Schellenberg M, Vicentini F, Matile P. 1996. Gregor Mendel's green and yellow pea seeds. *Bot. Acta* 109:3–4

117. Thomas H, Smart CM. 1993. Crops that stay green. *Ann. Appl. Biol.* 123:193–219

118. Thomas H, Stoddart L. 1975. Separation of chlorophyll degradation form other senescence processes in leaves of a mutant genotype of medow fescue (*Festuca pratensis* L.). *Plant Physiol.* 56:438–41

119. Tommasini R, Vogt E, Fromenteau M, Hörtensteiner S, Matile P, et al. 1998. An ABC transporter of *Arabidopsis thaliana* has both glutathione-conjugate and chlorophyll catabolite transport activity. *Plant J.* 13:773–80

120. Trebitsh T, Goldschmidt EE, Riov J. 1993. Ethylene induces *de novo* synthesis of chlorophyllase, a chlorophyll degrading enzyme, in *Citrus* fruit peel. *Proc. Natl. Acad. Sci. USA* 90:9441–45

121. Tsuchiya T, Ohta H, Masuda T, Mikami B, Kita N, et al. 1997. Purification and characterization of two isozymes of chlorophyllase from mature leaves of *Chenopodium album*. *Plant Cell Physiol.* 38:1026–31

122. Tsuchiya T, Ohta H, Okawa K, Iwamatsu A, Shimada H, et al. 1999. Cloning of chlorophyllase, the key enzyme in chlorophyll degradation: finding of a lipase motif and the induction by methyl jasmonate. *Proc. Natl. Acad. Sci. USA* 96:15362–67

123. Tsuchiya T, Suzuki T, Yamada T, Shimada H, Masuda T, et al. 2003. Chlorophyllase as a serine hydrolase: identification of a putative catalytic triad. *Plant Cell. Physiol.* 44:96–101

124. Tziveleka LA, Argyroudi-Akoyunoglou JH. 1998. Implications of a developmental-stage-dependent thylakoid-bound protease in the stabilization of the light-harvesting

Together with
Reference 76, first
molecular cloning
of chlorophyllase,
the initial enzyme
of chlorophyll
breakdown.

pigment-protein complex serving photosystem II during thylakoid biogenesis in red kidney bean. *Plant Physiol.* 117:961–70

125. Vicentini F, Hörtensteiner S, Schellenberg M, Thomas H, Matile P. 1995. Chlorophyll breakdown in senescent leaves: identification of the biochemical lesion in a *stay-green* genotype of *Festuca pratensis* Huds. *New Phytol.* 129:247–52

126. Vicentini F, Iten F, Matile P. 1995. Development of an assay for Mg-dechelatase of oilseed rape cotyledons, using chlorophyllin as the substrate. *Physiol. Plant.* 94:57–63

127. Wagner D, Przybyla D, op den Camp R, Kim C, Landgraf F, et al. 2004. The genetic basis of singlet oxygen-induced stress responses of *Arabidopsis thaliana*. *Science* 306:1183–85

128. Wüthrich K. 1999. *Purification of chlorophyll-catabolic enzymes: molecular cloning of a red chlorophyll catabolite reductase gene.* PhD thesis. Univ. Zürich, Zürich. 84 pp.

129. Wüthrich KL, Bovet L, Hunziker PE, Donnison IS, Hörtensteiner S. 2000. Molecular cloning, functional expression and characterisation of RCC reductase involved in chlorophyll catabolism. *Plant J.* 21:189–98

130. Yamauchi N, Funamoto Y, Shigyo M. 2004. Peroxidase-mediated chlorophyll degradation in horticultural crops. *Phytochem. Rev.* 3:221–28

131. Yang M, Wardzala E, Johal GS, Gray J. 2004. The wound-inducible *Lls1* gene from maize is an orthologue of the *Arabidopsis Acd1* gene, and the LLS1 protein is present in non-photosynthetic tissues. *Plant Mol. Biol.* 54:175–91

132. Yao N, Eisfelder BJ, Marvin J, Greenberg JT. 2004. The mitochondrion - an organelle commonly involved in programmed cell death in *Arabidopsis thaliana*. *Plant J.* 40:596–610

133. Zelisko A, Jackowski G. 2004. Senescence-dependent degradation of Lhcb3 is mediated by a thylakoid membrane-bound protease. *J. Plant Physiol.* 161:1157–70

134. Ziegler R, Blaheta A, Guha N, Schönegge B. 1988. Enzymatic formation of pheophorbide and pyropheophorbide during chlorophyll degradation in a mutant of *Chlorella fusca* SHIRIA et KRAUS. *J. Plant Physiol.* 132:327–32

135. Zimmermann P, Hirsch-Hoffmann M, Hennig L, Gruissem W. 2004. GENEVESTIGATOR. Arabidopsis microarray database and analysis toolbox. *Plant Physiol.* 136:2621–32

This paper describes the cloning of red chlorophyll catabolite reductase, catalyzing the fourth reaction in chlorophyll breakdown.

An important bioinformatics tool that allows a fast and comprehensive analysis of gene expression patterns throughout chosen environmental conditions, growth stages, or organs is described. Data are based on a large number of Affimetrix GeneChip array experiments.

RELATED RESOURCE

Thomas H, Stoddart JL. 1980. Leaf senescence. *Annu. Rev. Plant Physiol.* 31:83–111

Quantitative Fluorescence Microscopy: From Art to Science

Mark Fricker,[1] John Runions,[2] and Ian Moore[1]

[1] Department of Plant Sciences, University of Oxford, Oxford, OX1 3RB England;
email: mark.fricker@plants.ox.ac.uk, ian.moore@plants.ox.ac.uk

[2] School of Biological and Molecular Sciences, Oxford Brookes University, Oxford,
OX3 0BP England; email: jrunions@brookes.ac.uk

Annu. Rev. Plant Biol.
2006. 57:79–107

The *Annual Review of
Plant Biology* is online at
plant.annualreviews.org

doi: 10.1146/
annurev.arplant.57.032905.105239

First published online as a
Review in Advance on
January 30, 2006

1543-5008/06/0602-
0079$20.00

Key Words

confocal scanning laser microscopy, green fluorescent protein,
biosensors, cameleon, live-cell imaging

Abstract

A substantial number of elegant experimental approaches have been
developed to image the distribution and dynamics of DNA, mRNA,
proteins, organelles, metabolites, and ions in living plant cells. Although the human brain can rapidly assimilate visual information,
particularly when presented as animations and movies, it is much
more challenging to condense the phenomenal amount of data
present in three-, four-, or even five-dimensional images into statistically useful measurements. This review explores a range of in
vivo fluorescence imaging applications in plants, with particular emphasis on where quantitative techniques are beginning to emerge.

Contents

INTRODUCTION

The widespread use of intrinsically fluorescent proteins (IFPs) and greater availability of advanced microscope systems have dramatically increased routine use of microscopy in plant research. This review focuses on live-cell imaging techniques, with emphasis on where the discipline is shifting from qualitative to quantitative analysis. Quantitative analyses require significantly more rigor in experimental design and methodology than comparable qualitative assessments, but are of increasing importance if results are to be compared statistically and meaningfully between different laboratories, and are essential to develop mathematical simulations of the underlying processes. This has a direct bearing on the extent it will be possible to integrate imaging information efficiently within systems biology.

LIFE IN THE NUCLEUS

The plant nucleus can be irregular, with extensive convoluted grooves and invaginations (19), and can become distorted during rapid movement, particularly in root hairs (18, 132). However, within the nucleus, evidence from fixed tissues suggests chromosomes and key processes such as replication, transcription, and mRNA processing are spatially organized (77). Recently, tools were developed to visualize the dynamics of these processes. Thus, discrete regions of chromosomes can be tagged by inserting a concatenated target sequence, such as the *lac* operator, and visualized following binding of green fluorescent protein (GFP) fused to the appropriate DNA-binding domain (LacI) (62) (**Figure 1a**). Quantifying fluorescent spot number and amount of DNA from DAPI staining provides information on the level of endoreduplication and the degree of chromatid coherence (62, 63). The intranuclear chromatin diffusion coefficient (D) can be quantified from the spot dynamics, whereas movement relative to other loci describes the local confinement volume within each chromosome territory. These measures vary between different cell types. Thus D was ~twofold lower in epidermal versus stomatal guard cells, whereas the confinement volume was sixfold greater (63). The origin of these differences is not known, but may reflect epigenetic mechanisms influencing differential gene expression in the two cell types (63) or even biophysical effects of different turgor pressure. Although tagged loci provide new insights into intranuclear dynamics, they have drawbacks. Whereas chromosome painting using fluorescence in situ hybridization (FISH) shows that most chromosomes are randomly distributed, with slight preferential association of chromosomes carrying nucleolar organizer regions (NORs) (106), tagged loci have a higher than expected association with each other and with endogenous heterochromatin (105). Despite this caveat, in vivo tagging would be useful to test predictions from simulation models based on D and the rate of directed telomere movement during "bouquet" formation in meiotic cells (15).

Intranuclear dynamics have also been observed for GFP-tagged splicing factors. During transcription, splicing factors are recruited to spliceosomes from storage sites (interchromatin granule clusters) that appear as speckles in the nucleus. The number of speckles varies between different cell types, and their intensity varies inversely with transcriptional activity (29, 32). Speckles appear to move within a constrained volume, but can also bud, fuse, assemble, and disassemble (29, 32). Movement is abolished by blocking transcription and cannot arise simply from diffusion (32). An increasing number of proteins not directly involved in mRNA processing also cluster in intranuclear speckles (82, 94, 144), but the functional significance of this localization is not known.

QUANTITATIVE IMAGING OF GENE EXPRESSION

Recent advances in genomic technologies have enabled simultaneous measurement of thousands of gene expression profiles with increasing quantitative precision from progressively smaller tissue samples (89). However, there is often little correlation between levels of mRNA and expressed protein, necessitating parallel high-throughput proteome analysis, which currently requires much larger tissue samples. Conversely, when expression has been monitored for individual cells in a notionally homogeneous population, considerable variation in expression capacity (19a), and an extraordinary range of expression profiles have been reported, encapsulated as "the myth of the average cell" (79). Increased spatial resolution is possible with laser micro-dissection of single cells or micro-sampling (89), or by imaging following in situ hybridization or in situ polymerase chain reaction (107), but these techniques are difficult to convert to a high-throughput format suitable for time-resolved analysis of different cell types during development or in response to environmental stimuli.

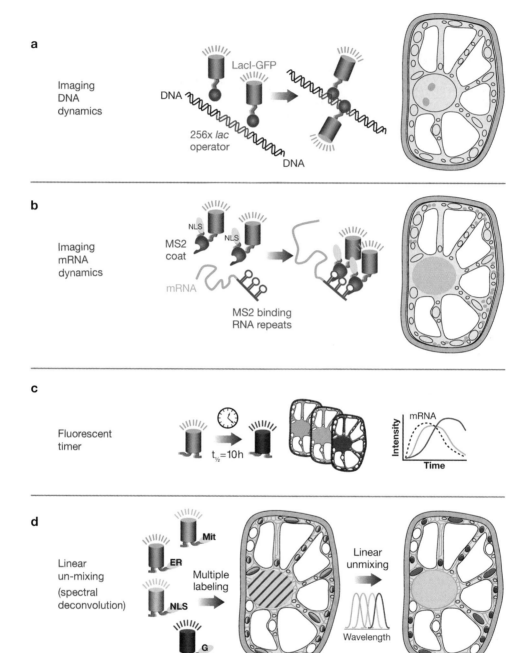

Figure 1

Schematic representations of the quantitative imaging techniques described in this review. Intrinsically fluorescent proteins (*cylinders*) are color coded to represent their characteristic emission peak and the relative levels of emission are shown by the lines above. Targeting sequences are shown in yellow. High-intensity laser illumination is indicated by lightning symbols and normal excitation by wavy arrows. The clock symbol represents a passage of time. NLS, nuclear localization sequence; ER, endoplasmic reticulum; G, Golgi; Mit, mitochondria.

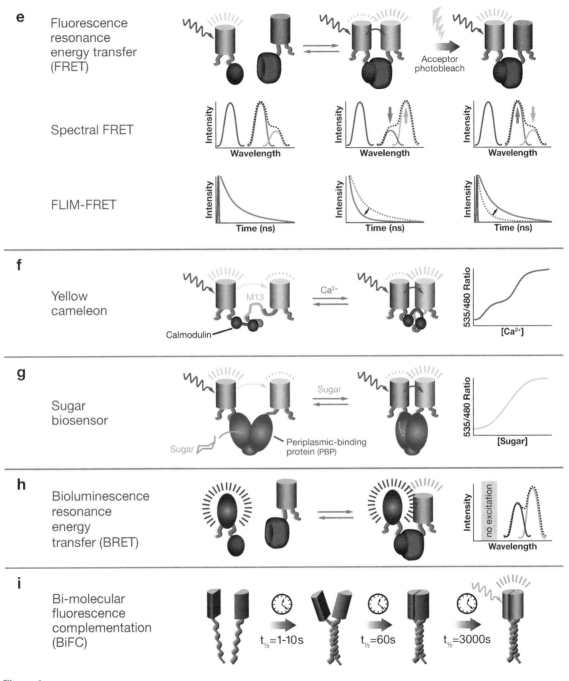

e Fluorescence resonance energy transfer (FRET)

Acceptor photobleach

Spectral FRET

Intensity / Wavelength | Intensity / Wavelength | Intensity / Wavelength

FLIM-FRET

Intensity / Time (ns) | Intensity / Time (ns) | Intensity / Time (ns)

f Yellow cameleon

M13

Ca²⁺

Calmodulin

535/480 Ratio / [Ca²⁺]

g Sugar biosensor

Sugar

Sugar — Periplasmic-binding protein (PBP)

535/480 Ratio / [Sugar]

h Bioluminescence resonance energy transfer (BRET)

no excitation

Intensity / Wavelength

i Bi-molecular fluorescence complementation (BiFC)

$t_{1/2}=1\text{-}10s$ $t_{1/2}=60s$ $t_{1/2}=3000s$

Figure 1

(*Continued*)

j

Fluorescence
correlation
spectroscopy
(FCS)

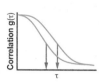

Movement of IFPs in and out of the illumination volume gives fluctuations in intensity.
The decay of the auto-correlation function for these fluctuations is related to their diffusional mobility.

---

k

Fluorescence
recovery after
photobleaching
(FRAP)

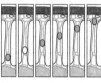

Bleached proteins move out of the region of interest and are replaced by other fluorescent proteins,
leading to a recovery in the signal, in this case representing ER to Golgi traffic.

---

l

Fluorescence
localization after
photobleaching
(FLAP)

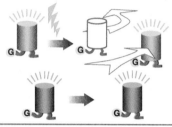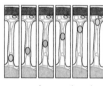

A second marker that is not bleached
makes it easier to follow FRAP in moving organelles.

---

m

Photoactivation

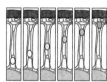

Photoactivatable IFPs require a pulse of high-intensity blue or UV light to become
fluorescent, but then 'highlight' the marked organelle.

---

n

Photoswitching
or photoconversion

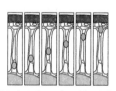

Photoswitchable IFPs are already visible, but alter color with a pulse of high-intensity blue or
UV light, again making it easier to follow moving organelles.

Figure 1

(Continued)

In Vivo Imaging of mRNA Localization and Dynamics

Recently, tools were developed to follow mRNA dynamics by adding a stem-loop aptamer sequence to the mRNA that is recognized by a coexpressed fluorescently tagged partner (10). For example, a GFP fusion with the bacteriophage MS2 coat protein can be used to visualize concatenated repeats of the 19-base pair (bp) MS2-binding

RNA sequence (**Figure 1b**). This confirmed that specific mRNA molecules are localized to endoplasmic reticulum (ER) subdomains and revealed that tagged-RNA particle movement is actin based (50). In situ hybridization shows that other specific transcripts are also spatially localized (100), and in *Acetabularia*, 6 out of 12 mRNAs examined showed cytoskeleton-dependent asymmetric distribution (135), suggesting mRNA localization may be widespread. The aptamer-partner system might allow more systematic investigation of this phenomenon. The tagging approach is also useful for plant viruses that do not tolerate insertion of additional reporter sequences (147), and may even be adaptable to track non-cell-autonomous movement of small RNA molecules (146).

In Vivo Imaging of Promoter Activity

Promoter-GFP constructs are widely used to monitor promoter activity from individual cells to plants under field conditions (48), although quantitation in vivo may require correction for light absorption by endogenous plant pigments (149). Even with notionally constitutive promoters, a mosaic pattern of expression can occur (7), and reproducible expression may require matrix attachment regions (MARs) flanking the promoter-GFP (49) or mutants defective in post-transcriptional gene silencing (14a) to reduce local gene silencing events.

Unmodified GFP is less useful to quantify transient expression as the fluorescent signal reflects both promoter activity and fluorophore maturation, which gives a lag before fluorescence is detectable. Likewise, the stability of GFP ($t_{1/2} > 24$ h) obscures any reduction in promoter activity. Promoter-luciferase constructs are regarded as better reporters for transient expression as the light output more closely matches the level and timing of mRNA changes (45, 144a). More rapid GFP turnover can be achieved by adding protein- or mRNA-destabilizing elements that reduce the half life to ~3 h (136). Such approaches have been used for luciferase and β-glucuronidase in plants (143), but have not yet been applied to GFP.

An alternative method to analyze transient gene expression uses the DsRed "timer" fluorescent protein that slowly matures from a green to a red fluorescent form, distinguishing changes in gene expression by color (91, 129). Thus, immediately following gene induction, the signal is exclusively green, steady-state expression gives a defined G/R ratio (depending on the precise imaging configuration), and a decrease in expression shifts the ratio increasingly toward the red (**Figure 1c**).

PROTEIN LOCATION, LEVEL, AND TURNOVER

Fluorescent-Protein Fusions

In-frame fusions with IFPs are straightforward to generate, compared to immunoprobes, and greatly facilitate visualization of intracellular protein distribution and dynamics. Ideal IFP tags should be nondimerizing monomers without any targeting motifs that fold efficiently and can tolerate N- or C-terminal fusions. They should have high molar extinction coefficients, quantum efficiency, and photostability that are insensitive to the local environment. Suitable monomeric IFPs spanning the entire visible spectrum have been isolated from different species, or generated by ingenious rational design and molecular evolution (131).

Tagging Traumas

IFP fusions have provided significant insights into a number of developmental and physiological processes, including subcellular organization of metabolic pathways into metabolons (1, 41), dissection of non-cell autonomous protein (NCAP) movement through the phloem (123), movement of transcription factors in meristems (96), or screening localization of unknown proteins (31). Despite the power of this approach, it is important to validate that the pattern observed for the fusion protein reflects the true behavior of the native target. There is high confidence if the fusion protein, driven from its own promoter, complements a null mutant and the distribution pattern is confirmed by alternative techniques, such as immunocytochemistry (96). These stringent criteria have become an almost *de facto* requirement in tractable genetic organisms, such as yeast. In the next few years they will become the accepted standard in plants. In contrast, tagging with the IFP and driving expression of the fusion protein from a strong promoter can generate artifacts ranging from protein aggregation, steric interference in targeting or complex formation, saturation of normal transport and targeting pathways, and generation of phenotypes resulting from overexpression of the protein. Even when targeting is not impaired, IFP tagging can generate dominant inhibitory alleles, particularly when the tagged protein is involved in protein-protein interactions.

For example, actin can be visualized in vivo by binding of GFP-mTalin (70). However, labeling has a major impact on actin organization (65). GFP-Fimbrin is less disruptive (120), but high levels of expression still give stunted phenotypes (138) and disrupt organelle dynamics (J. Runions, unpublished data). Rab GTPases can be localized as IFP fusions (71, 121a, 131b), but some IFP tags generate a dominant-negative phenotype with similar sorting defects as untagged dominant-negative point mutants (71). In assays of subcellular targeting or transport, it is important that the IFP tag has no intrinsic sorting information. This is not always the case and the effect is species and cell-type dependent. Thus, in tobacco epidermis, a secreted mRFP1 marker is transported exclusively along the default secretory pathway while an equivalent GFP marker also appears in the vacuole, suggesting GFP contains a weak vacuolar sorting determinant (148), similar to the situation in yeast. Conversely, in tobacco BY2 suspension culture cells, mRFP1

also accumulates in vacuoles (145). In other cases, overexpression of IFP-tagged proteins, such as the vacuolar sorting receptor BP80, appears to compete with endogenous receptors, causing sorting defects (22).

More subtle errors can arise from the different properties of each IFP. For example, EYFP (pK_a 7.0) is more sensitive to quenching in acidic compartments than other IFPs, making them less obvious when labeled with EYFP compared to an identical GFP construct (148). This could lead to significant misinterpretation of the intracellular distribution of certain fusion proteins. On the positive side, the pH sensitivity of YFP can be used to infer whether particular protein loops or termini are cytoplasmic or extracellular (127). Although GFP fluorescence is less sensitive to pH, blue-light-dependent conformational changes in GFP make it a target for degradation by vacuolar proteinases at acidic pH, leading to a loss in signal in tissues exposed to the light (128). Whether comparable light-dependent degradation occurs for other IFPs is not yet known.

Protein Concentration Controls

Almost no reports attempt to calibrate IFP expression levels against appropriate standards, but rely on subjective comparisons of relative expression levels ("dim" or "bright"). A notable exception is the recent work in yeast that combined quantitative imaging of YFP-fusion proteins, driven from their endogenous promoters, with either quantitative immunoblotting or flow cytometric analysis (143a). Of greater concern is the absence of proper reference images to relate the apparent expression level to the amount of protein in different cell types. For example, the visual impression of uniform gene expression is deceptive and skewed to regions with higher net cytoplasmic density (meristems, vascular tissue, and stomatal guard cells). Protein concentration controls are routinely used when running gels and we advocate equivalent controls should be used when imaging tissues (e.g., 37).

Low-Molecular Weight Genetically Encoded Tags

A variety of much smaller fluorescent tags have been developed to label proteins in vivo that circumvent potential steric interference associated with IFP fusions (61). Thus, the small tetra-cysteine peptide motif (Cys-Cys-Pro-Gly-Cys-Cys) binds fluorescent bis-arsenical ligands with high affinity ($\sim 10^{-11}$ M) to give a fluorescent complex (47). Three fluorescent ligands, with different spectra based on xanthene (CHoXAsH), fluorescein (FlAsH), or resorufin (ReAsH), are now commercially available (Invitrogen, Lumio™ series). The ligands are applied as membrane-permeant complexes with 1,2-ethanedithiol (EDT). Once in the cell, the tetracysteine hairpin displaces the EDT to generate a minimally disrupted fluorescent fusion protein. As an example, a tubulin-TetCys fusion rescues yeast cells lacking tubulin, whereas GFP-tubulin is unable to functionally complement the mutant (5).

Under high levels of illumination, these fluorophores produce singlet oxygen capable of inactivating proteins in the immediate vicinity, in a process termed chromophore-assisted light inactivation (CALI) (130). This could provide a novel means to knockdown specific tagged proteins with a high degree of spatial and temporal resolution.

Multichannel Imaging in Plants

The range of IFPs available has dramatically increased possibilities for multiple labeling and colocalization analysis in vivo (64). To provide unambiguous results, it is essential that the signals from the different spectral variants can be unequivocally isolated, either through minimizing bleed-through between different channels (64) or by spectral deconvolution (linear unmixing). Bleed-through can be reduced by rapid switching between different excitation/emission combinations at millisecond intervals to avoid movement artifacts. Although enhanced GFP is brighter and excited efficiently at 488 nm, the spectral properties of the Haseloff mGFP5 variant are better suited to separate GFP and yellow fluorescent protein (YFP) using line switching with 458/514-nm excitation.

Spectral Imaging and Linear Unmixing

A number of imaging systems now implement simultaneous or sequential collection of several spectrally distinct channels to give a stack of wavelength (lambda, λ) images (150). Even if fluorophores (or autofluorescence) have a high degree of spectral overlap, their individual contributions can be extracted by linear unmixing of the spectrum recorded at each pixel using appropriate reference spectra (9, 150) (see **Figures 1d; 2a,b**). Protocols have been developed to optimize the number of channels and their bandwidth needed to separate particular fluorophores (98). Linear unmixing is only possible if signals from the individual channels are within the dynamic range of the instrument. This can be difficult to achieve, particularly in multiple-construct transient expression systems. Using the FMDV 2A peptide (48a) or internal ribosome entry sites (IRES) (144a) to generate stoichiometric quantities of two polypeptides from a single transcript may be advantageous in this respect (**Figure 2c–e**).

Quantitative Colocalization Analysis

Colocalization describes the extent that two (or more) probes occur at the same physical location in the cell. Before colocalization can be quantified, it is essential that spectral bleed-through is eliminated, pinholes are aligned, and images are properly registered and not affected by chromatic aberration (142). Threshold values are chosen to remove background, ideally using objective criteria (20). Pearson's coefficient or the overlap coefficient provide a single measure of colocalization. However, it is more informative to analyze the proportion of each probe contributing to the colocalized pixels as separate coefficients (81). Even with confocal and multiphoton systems, the blurring associated with the point spread function (psf) can give erroneous superposition of adjacent objects and intermediate values of colocalization. De-convolution of the three-dimensional (3D) image prior to colocalization analysis reduces these artifacts and improves quantitation (78). Furthermore, the significance of the coefficients can be assessed by comparison with an expected random

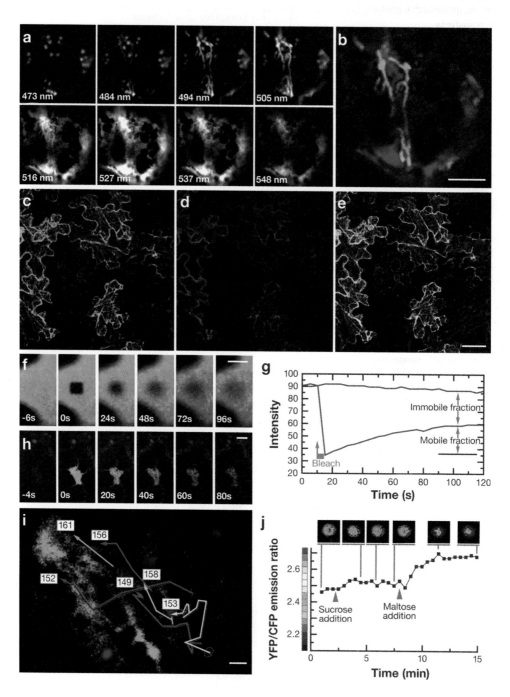

pattern obtained by repeatedly randomizing the pixel distribution in one of the channels (20). Despite the availability of appropriate software and the widespread use of multiple labeling experiments purporting to assess colocalization, quantitative analysis (1) is still rare in plant systems.

number of other live-cell techniques, such as fluorescence (or Förster) resonance energy transfer (FRET), bioluminescence resonance energy transfer (BRET), fluorescence correlation spectroscopy (FCS), or bi-molecular fluorescence complementation (BiFC), can provide this information.

PROTEIN-PROTEIN INTERACTIONS

Although colocalization is a prerequisite for two molecular species to interact, it cannot readily be used to demonstrate that physical association has occurred. Fortunately, a

Fluorescence Resonance Energy Transfer

FRET describes the radiationless transfer of energy from a donor fluorophore to an adjacent acceptor fluorophore that has significant spectral overlap and appropriate orientation

---

Figure 2

Quantitative imaging of protein levels and dynamic processes in plants. (*a*, *b*) Linear unmixing of signals from cyan fluorescent protein (CFP), green fluorescent protein (GFP), and yellow fluorescent protein (YFP). Spectral images in 10.7-nm bands centered on the wavelengths indicated (*a*) were collected using the Zeiss LSM510 META detector system from epidermal cells of the lower epidermis of *Nicotiana tabacum* four days after infiltration with three different *Agrobacterium* strains containing plasmids that express ST-ECFP to label Golgi, GFP targeted to mitochondria, and YFP-HDEL to label the ER. The considerable spectral overlap between the signals from each organelle was resolved using linear unmixing with reference spectra collected under identical conditions (*b*). Scale bar = 5 μm. (*c*, *d*) Stoichiometric expression of GFP and YFP using the FMDV 2A peptide. Images were collected from epidermal cells of the lower epidermis of *Nicotiana tabacum* four days after infiltration with *Agrobacterium* containing a single construct expressing cytoplasmic YFP and endoplasmic reticulum (ER)-targeted mGFP5 linked by the FMDV 2A peptide. Cleavage between the IFPs released two separate fluorescent proteins and the signals were separated by rapid line switching between ex 458 nm, em 475–525 nm (*c*), and ex 514 nm, em 535–590 nm (*d*). At low inoculum densities, there is considerable variation in expression between different cells in the epidermis, yet the ratio of the two fluorescent proteins remains almost constant in the merged image (*e*) (M. Samalova & I. Moore, unpublished data). Autofluorescence from chloroplasts was imaged at >650 nm (coded in *blue*). (*f*, *g*) Measurement of plasma membrane protein mobility using fluorescence recovery after photobleaching (FRAP). LTI6B-GFP marks the plasma membrane of *Arabidopsis* leaf epidermal cells, shown here as a single paradermal optical section (*f*). A high-intensity laser pulse was used to bleach a rectangular region at t = 0 s. Movement of fluorescent protein from adjacent areas gave a recovery in signal over time (*f*, *g*) that was analyzed to give the fraction of mobile molecules and the half time for recovery ($t_{1/2}$ 27.9s) (J. Runions, unpublished data). Scale bar = 20 μm. (*h*) Measurement of ER protein mobility using photoactivatable GFP (PA-GFP). Calnexin was PA-GFP localized to the ER membrane (weakly labeled in *red* with a second marker), but gave very little fluorescence with excitation at 488 nm until it was activated with a high-intensity pulse of short wavelength light (405 nm) at t = 0 s. The highly localized increase in fluorescence subsequently dissipated as the calnexin dispersed through the ER (112). Scale bar = 2 μm. (*i*) Tracking movement of Golgi bodies in leaf epidermal cells of *Nicotiana*. Golgi bodies (*red*) were imaged in confocal time series and automated tracking software was used to measure their movement patterns (*numbered, colored lines*). The ER membrane was highlighted with photoactivated GFP (*green*) (112). Scale bar = 1 μm. (*j*) Measurement of maltose uptake in yeast using a fluorescence resonance energy transfer (FRET)-based sensor. Intracellular maltose concentrations were imaged with a genetically encoded sensor that incorporated a hinged maltose-binding element between CFP and YFP. Uptake of maltose, but not sucrose, into the cytoplasm resulted in a conformational change in the hinged segment and an increase in FRET, measured as a change in the YFP/CFP emission ratio. The pseudo color-coded images show the relative increase in the YFP/CFP ratio. Adapted from Reference 33 with permission.

(**Figure 1e**). FRET efficiency falls off with the inverse sixth power of the fluorophore separation. The distance at which energy transfer is reduced by 50% (the Förster radius) is around 3–6 nM for common donor-acceptor pairs (39, 55). FRET can be detected spectrally as a decrease (quenching) of donor emission with commensurate increase in sensitized acceptor emission, or as a decrease in the fluorescence lifetime (τ) of the donor fluorophore, measured using fluorescence lifetime imaging microscopy (FLIM). Quantitative measurements, particularly of steady-state protein association, need controls to accommodate background, auto-fluorescence, bleedthrough, photobleaching, and different environmental sensitivity of the fluorophores (39, 55). FLIM-FRET can be determined just from the donor fluorescence lifetime (58), although the extent of protein-protein interaction still depends on the stoichiometry of the interacting partners. The most common, but irreversible, control to validate that FRET really occurs is to bleach the acceptor and measure the resulting increase in donor fluorescence intensity or lifetime.

The range of molecular interactions probed by FRET is increasing slowly and includes dimerization of transcription factors (58, 64) or receptors (113, 116), formation of lipid domains (134), interactions between subunits in a single functional protein complex (66) or "metabolons" (1), complexes of plastid division proteins (81a), and association of regulatory or signaling proteins (8, 11, 82, 117). One of the biggest problems in FRET measurements is reproducible control of tagged-protein stoichiometry, which may also benefit from application of the FMDV 2A peptide (48a) or IRES (144a) technology. In some cases it may be advantageous to use a luminescent donor, such as luciferase, and BRET (125, 126) (**Figure 1b**). BRET avoids problems with autofluorescence, photobleaching, direct acceptor excitation, or triggering light-dependent signaling pathways, but has lower spatial resolution than FRET.

Bi-Molecular Fluorescence Complementation

FCS provides an alternative means to characterize fluorophore mobility, concentration, and interaction in vivo (114). FCS works by measuring the time series of fluctuations in signal as fluorescent molecules move in and out of a small excitation volume, typically achieved with stationary confocal or multiphoton optics (**Figure 1j**). The decrease in the autocorrelation function of the time series provides a measure of the diffusion coefficient of the fluorophore. Thus, the cytoplasmic concentration of GFP driven from a 35S promoter was measured as 0.1-1 μM and the cytoplasmic diffusion coefficient as $4 \pm 2 \times 10^{-7}$ cm^2 s^{-1} (69). Diffusion of single GFP molecules and larger aggregates were quantified in chloroplast stromules, with some evidence of active transport, possibly along a "plastoskeleton" (69). FCS has also been used to measure the location, accumulation, and mobility of fluorescently tagged Nod factors in membranes and the cell wall from very low-bulk concentrations (42). Although complex formation does affect the diffusion coefficient measured by FCS, fluorescence cross-correlation spectroscopy (FCCS) between two fluorescently tagged species provides a more sensitive measure of protein-protein interaction (68).

Fluorescence Correlation Spectroscopy

BiFC may provide a simpler test for protein interaction in vivo. Potential interacting partners are tethered to specific nonfluorescent fragments of IFPs. If the partners bind, the fragments associate to form a bi-molecular complex capable of reconstituting fluorescence (**Figure 1i**). Complex formation is essentially irreversible, which prevents imaging of changes in protein association state, but captures weak or transiently interacting partners. Very high levels of expression of the IFP fragments can yield nonspecific interaction (137), and not all permutations of C or N tagging are effective (13), probably because of steric constraints on the interacting partners. In plants, BiFC has been used to assess homo- or heterodimerization of transcription factors (27, 137), chromodomain proteins (13), 14-3-3 proteins (137), complex formation between plastid division proteins (81a), and the α and β subunits of protein farnesyltransferase (13). Other BiFC strategies use reconstitution of fragments from murine dihydrofolate reductase (mDHFR) that bind a fluorescein-conjugated inhibitor, methotrexate, with high affinity (124). The authors followed decreases as well as increases in fluorescence (124). This implies that mDHFR complex formation is reversible or turns over on a timescale of hours, unlike BiFC with IFPs. If this is a general feature of the mDHFR system it may provide a dynamic readout of protein-protein interactions rather than just a cumulative response.

MEASURING PROTEIN AND ORGANELLE DYNAMICS

Quantitation of Organelle Motility

There is a long history in microscopical measurements of organelle motility using phase and Nomarski imaging. Fluorescent labeling of organelles provides greater contrast that facilitates quantitative tracking of various organelles including nuclei (132), Golgi bodies (97, 112, 145), peroxisomes (83), and microtubules (26, 119). Although much plant work has used manual tracking from 2D time-lapse images, several algorithms have been developed for (semi-)automated tracking in 4D (40). For example, Runions et al. (112) tracked hundreds of mRFP-tagged Golgi bodies to determine their average velocity and track profile characteristics (**Figure 2i**).

Measurement of Protein Dynamics Using Photobleaching or Photoactivation

During time-lapse imaging, fluorophore in a defined region of interest (ROI) can be bleached by high-intensity illumination. Fluorescence recovery after photobleaching (FRAP) occurs as unbleached fluorophore moves back into the bleached area (**Figures 1k,2f**) and provides a measure of the rate of movement and the underlying movement mechanism (122). If the goal is to determine total connectivity within an extended membrane system, such as the ER, continuous bleaching of the ROI will eventually drain signal from all connected compartments (139), termed fluorescence loss in photobleaching (FLIP).

FRAP is useful at various levels from exchange between cells or organelles (75, 139), diffusion of proteins within membranes (**Figure 2f,g**) or organelles (112, 139), down to protein turnover in complexes (32). For example, Hush et al. (57) first employed FRAP in plants using carboxyfluorescein-labeled tubulin to study microtubule dynamics. Subsequently, FRAP revealed microtubule translocation through treadmilling in cortical arrays (119) and dynamic interactions with microtubule-associated proteins (MAPs) (16). Whereas FRAP or FLIP are straightforward between fairly static structures, such as chloroplasts connected by stromules (75), it is technically more difficult if the target protein or organelle is moving, not least because it becomes invisible immediately after the bleach. To aid in localization post-bleach, a second fluorophore can be introduced to the target that remains visible throughout the time course (14, 21, 139), termed fluorescence localization after photobleaching (FLAP) (**Figure 1l**).

Photoactivation

As an alternative strategy, Patterson & Lippincott-Schwartz (104) developed photoactivatable (PA) GFP to fluorescently highlight proteins in targeted subcellular regions or organelles. PA-GFP shows a 100-fold increase in fluorescence after a brief pulse of irradiation with near UV (104) (**Figure 1m**). PA-GFP works in plants and has been targetted to Golgi bodies and peroxisomes and used to follow ER dynamics (112) (**Figure 2b**). Recently, the first photoactivatable red fluorescent protein (PA-mRFP1-1) was developed (133), although it currently has a relatively low extinction coefficient and quantum efficiency, and requires prolonged UV exposure for activation.

Photoactivation has the converse problem to FRAP. The absence of signal prior to irradiation makes it difficult to find cells or organelles expressing PA-GFP. One solution is to use double labeling, similar to FLAP. An alternative strategy is to use IFPs that are fluorescent initially, but shift color upon intense illumination (photoswitching or photoconversion) (**Figure 1n**). This provides a reference image of the entire labeled structure, while following the dynamics of a selected portion. For example, Kaede gives a 200-fold increase in green-to-red emission following photoconversion with (ultra-)violet illumination. As the native Kaede protein is a tetramer, it is not appropriate as a fusion tag, but may be used for organelle tracking (4) and has been used to probe transient fusion and fission events of mitochondria (6). More recently, several monomeric photoswitchable fluorescent proteins suitable for tagging were developed, including photoswitchable cyan fluorescent protein (PS-CFP) that gives a 1,500-fold increase in green-to-cyan fluorescence following (ultra-)violet excitation (17) and EosFP (142a) and KikGR (131a), which both shift from green-to-red fluorescence with (ultra-)violet irradiation. Although there are no full papers reporting the use of these photoswitchable proteins in plants, preliminary data indicate they are expressed in a functional form and can be photoconverted effectively (16a).

Under low O_2 levels, S65T GFP from *Aequori victoria* can be converted to a red fluorescing form with high-intensity illumination at normal excitation wavelengths, and has been used to show luminal continuity of mitochondria in anaerobic *Saccharomyces cerevisiae* (60). This technique may even be useful to assess onset of anoxia for any GFP-labeled specimen on the microscope.

QUANTITATIVE MORPHOLOGY AND DEVELOPMENTAL STUDIES

Three-Dimensional Measurement of Cell and Organelle Size

Confocal, multiphoton, or wide-field deconvolution imaging can all sample 3D volumes, facilitating quantitative analysis of morphology (**Figure 3a,b**). Volume measurements using intensity-based segmentation require correction for depth-dependent signal attenuation and z-axis distortion (36, 44, 121, 142) (**Figure 3c–f**) and are sensitive to the segmentation threshold used. Surface-area measurements also depend on the "granularity" of the voxel dimensions and sampling noise. 3D segmentation using deformable meshes that grow to fill cell volumes are reported to give more robust results that are less sensitive to noise (52).

An alternative approach is to use stereology to quantify geometrical properties (number, length, surface area, or volume) by counting interactions with randomly positioned sampling probes. Points probes are used to measure volumes, lines to measure surface areas, planes to measure lengths, and volumes to count numbers (56, 72). Stereological techniques work particularly well for volume measurements from confocal datasets (72, 86, 88) (**Figure 3g–j**).

Even when cellular objects approach the 3D dimensions of the point-spread function (psf), their "true" volume can be estimated using 3D model-based approaches that incorporate a measured psf (12). Meckel et al. (84) used a simplifying 2D (x,y) Gaussian model to analyze populations of vesicles in guard cells, on the assumption that these objects are spherical.

Quantitation of Morphology and Lineage at the Tissue Level

Confocal z-series of fixed and cleared specimens are useful to study patterns of cell division and elongation during development (52) (**Figure 3a,b**). Recently, techniques for 4D in vivo confocal imaging of the surface layers of intact meristems were developed using combinations of FM dyes, IFP markers, and spectral unmixing (43, 52a, 110, 110a). 3D and 4D imaging of larger intact structures is also possible using optical coherence microscopy (OCM) (54, 111) or optical projection tomography (OPT) (118; E. Coen & K. Lee, personal communication). OCM is an interference technique based on back-scattered light, whereas OPT can be used in either transmission or fluorescence mode (118). In theory, OPT could be used with the many fluorescent lineage markers available, including those developed for constitutive or inducible transgene activation. Relatively precise spatial and temporal cell marking is also possible through local heat activation by repeated laser scanning of a heat-shock promoter that drives expression of *Ac* transposase. This removes a *Ds1* element inserted between the 35S promoter and H2B-YFP, which then marks nuclei in the targeted cells and the lineage of their progeny (74) (**Figure 3k**).

IMAGING IONS AND METABOLITES

Genetically Encoded Ca^{2+} Sensors

Tsien and colleagues pioneered construction of genetically encoded ion sensors using FRET with the development of the cameleon probes for Ca^{2+} (93). FRET probes retain the highly desirable ratioable properties of the best chemical Ca^{2+} dyes, but are introduced by transformation rather than potentially damaging microinjection. They are relatively photostable, nontoxic, and are not sequestered by cellular detoxification systems. Furthermore, their sensitivity can be adjusted by modifying the ligand-binding sequence and they can be targeted to different subcellular compartments.

In the yellow cameleons, CFP and YFP are linked by calmodulin (CaM) and the M13-CaM-binding peptide from myosin light-chain kinase (**Figure 1f**). On binding Ca^{2+}, the CaM alters its conformation, binds to M13, and brings the fluorophores together with an increase in FRET (93). Most confocal systems do not have an appropriate blue (432-nm) excitation source. However, it may be possible to use the common Ar-ion 458-nm line and recover changes in FRET by spectral unmixing (59).

YC2 has a biphasic Ca^{2+} response with K'_d values of 70 nM and 11 μM. The K'_d values do not vary with pH, Mg^{2+}, and ionic strength at physiological levels, probably as the CaM-based sensor is naturally tailored to operate in a cytoplasmic milieu. This should make cameleon measurements more accurate than ratiometric dyes (93). For comparison, K'_d values for Indo-1 and Fura-2 increase 2-4-fold in vivo in animal cells. The corresponding shifts in plants are less clear as reliable in vivo calibrations are difficult (109). Introducing mutations in the Ca^{2+}-binding domains give the YC3 series (E104Q), with a single K'_d (4.4 μM), or the YC4 series (E31Q), with a lower affinity K'_d (700 μM), which are suitable to measure Ca^{2+} in ER (93).

Set against these benefits, cameleon expression levels are low, perhaps a few micromolar, and the relative ratio change (RRC) for a full response is only ~1.6–1.8. Furthermore, EYFP is quenched by mild acidification (pK_a 6.9) and Cl$^-$ ions (K'_d 110 mM), and the CaM-M13 linker may interact with endogenous CaM or CaM-binding proteins. The pH sensitivity has been reduced (pK_a 6.1) by introducing mutations in EYFP (V68L and Q69K) to give YC2.1, YC3.1, and YC4.1 (92), which are the only cameleons so far used in plants (3, 59, 140). The YC2.3, YC3.3, and YC4.3 series use Q69M YFP (citrine), which lowers the pK_a further to 5.7, removes the Cl$^-$ sensitivity, and gives better folding (46). However, the most significant recent breakthrough is inclusion of circularly permuted Venus-YFP, which increases the RRC by 600% by altering the dipole orientation between the CFP and YFP couple (95).

Cameleons in Plants

Allen et al. (3) first generated stable *Arabidopsis* plants expressing YC2.1 and measured Ca²⁺ dynamics in guard cells in response to

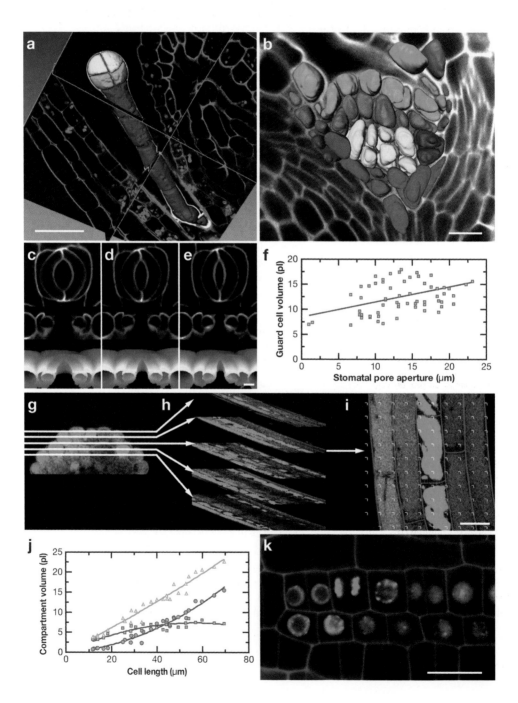

a range of stimuli and in different mutant backgrounds. YC2.1 has also been expressed in pollen tubes of *Lilium longiflorum* and *Nicotiana tabacum* (140), and YC3.1 in pollen tubes and stigmatic papillae of *Arabidopsis* (59). In general, results with the cameleons are comparable to previous reports with ratiometric probes. For example, cameleons report oscillating, tip-high Ca^{2+}-gradients in pollen tubes that are similar in magnitude to those reported with ratiometric dyes (e.g., 108). Likewise, localized repetitive transients were observed during pollen germination on stigmatic papillae (59), similar to those reported using microinjected Calcium Green-1 dextran (24). In stomatal guard cells, there is much more information on Ca^{2+} responses, and some interesting quantitative and qualitative differences, albeit derived from different species.

Comparison of Cameleon Measurements with Dye Measurements in Stomatal Guard Cells

Quantitatively, resting $[Ca^{2+}]_{cyt}$ in YC2.1-expressing *Arabidopsis* guard cells is 5–10-fold lower than that typically reported with ratiometric dyes. YC2.1 values may be more reliable because of the stability of the K'_d in cells and also because potentially disruptive iontophoretic microinjection is not needed. Qualitatively, all YC2.1 responses in wild-type *Arabidopsis* reveal transient spikes or oscillations, often with a delay following the stimulus and running on after the closing response has been triggered.

Interpretation of some YC2.1 results has been challenged (109), particularly those from experiments switching between hyperpolarizing (0.1 mM KCl) and depolarizing (100 mM

Figure 3

Quantitative imaging three-dimensional (3D) morphology in plants. (*a, b*) 3D reconstruction following intensity-based segmentation of confocal optical sections. High-contrast staining techniques were used to differentiate the cell wall from cell lumen, which were then filled and rendered to create a surface representation of cells and tissues. Cellular relationships were studied by rotating and slicing the reconstructions (J. Runions, unpublished data). (*a*) An eight-cell *Arabidopsis* embryo and suspensor within the ovule. Scale bar = 20 μm. (*b*) Vegetative shoot apical meristem of a mature *Arabidopsis* embryo. Scale bar = 20 μm. (*c–e*) 4D measurement of guard cell volume changes during ABA-induced stomatal closure. The cell wall in epidermal strips of *Commelina communis* was labeled with primulin and time-lapse 3D images collected with excitation at 442 nm. Images are presented as median (*x,y*) and (*x,z*) sections and as a height-coded projection, following correction for depth-dependent attenuation and intensity-based segmentation (142). The luminal volume was measured by seed filling the segmented volumes. Scale bar = 10 μm. (*f*) Represents the relationship between guard cell lumenal volume and stomatal pore aperture (J. Wood, M.D. Fricker & N.S. White, unpublished data). (*g–i*) Compartment volume measurements in *Arabidopsis* roots using stereological techniques. Stereology is a robust statistical method for morphological measurements and was used to determine changes in cytoplasmic and vacuolar volumes during elongation of trichoblasts in *Arabidopsis* roots using the Cavalieri estimator. 3D images were collected by two-photon laser-scanning microscopy following fluorescent labeling and vacuolar sequestration of glutathione (*green*) and cell walls with propidium iodide (*red*). (*g, h*) Uniform random sections (*h*) were overlaid with a point grid (*i*) and the cytoplasm, vacuole, and cell wall volumes were determined as a function of intersection with the grid (38, 86). Scale bar = 10 μm. (*j*) Shows the resultant relationship between cytoplasmic (*blue*), vacuolar (*red*), and total cell volume (*green*) for trichoblast cells in the elongation zone. (*k*) Light-activated lineage marking of cells in the *Arabidopsis* root epidermis. Local heating, generated by repeated laser scanning, was used to activate a heat-shock promoter driving expression of *Ac* transposase. The *Ac* transposase removed a *Ds* element from between the promoter and histone H2B-YFP gene allowing its expression (74). This change was heritable and marked nuclei of all cells derived from the initial event, enabling investigation of tissue origins and cell division patterns. Scale bar = 10 μm.

KCl) buffers to impose Ca^{2+} oscillations (2). Plieth (109) generated almost identical ratio changes using this protocol in plants expressing either the Cl^--responsive Clomeleon indicator (73, 80) or the Ca^{2+}-indicator YC2.1. As Clomeleon does not contain the CaM-M13 Ca^{2+}-sensing linker, the implication is that some, if not all, of the YC2.1 response reflects changes in $[Cl^-]_{cyt}$ and pH, rather than $[Ca^{2+}]_{cyt}$. However, YC2.1 lacks the H148Q substitution used in Clomeleon, and only shows a slight shift in pK_a from 6.0 to 6.1 in the presence of Cl^- (46). Even a substantial drop in $[Cl^-]_{cyt}$ from $\sim$150 mM to 0 mM, combined with cytoplasmic alkalinization from pH 7 to pH 8, would only give a 10–15% increase in YFP fluorescence in YC2.1 (46). As CFP is not affected, this would give a similar shift in the ratio value, irrespective of the prevailing $[Ca^{2+}]_{cyt}$. The magnitude of the Ca^{2+} spikes is much greater than these estimates, suggesting the potential for misinterpretation of these responses would be slight. Nevertheless, a Cl^- contribution to the lower plateau values might overestimate the level of apparent $[Ca^{2+}]_{cyt}$. Furthermore, the change in $[Cl^-]_{cyt}$ measured with Clomeleon (109) highlights the many other potential consequences of the Ca^{2+}-clamp protocol on guard cell physiology.

Why Are Oscillations Not Always Observed with Ratiometric Dyes?

In contrast to YC2.1, calcium responses measured with ratiometric dyes during stomatal closure have shown general increases of varying rate, magnitude, and duration, or occasionally no change at all, rather than just oscillations. This has a bearing on the current debate on whether information is encoded in the amplitude, frequency, or both of the Ca^{2+} signature or whether increases in $[Ca^{2+}]_{cyt}$ simply act as a chemical switch (53, 109, 115).

YC2.1 and ratiometric dyes differ in their intracellular concentration and rate of diffusion. The concentration of microinjected dye

($<$50 μM) is unlikely to buffer $[Ca^{2+}]_{cyt}$ directly. However, the rate of Ca^{2+}-dye diffusion may be sufficiently fast to dissipate localized Ca^{2+} gradients. In contrast, YC2.1, which diffuses more slowly, may report localized Ca^{2+} increases more faithfully. Messerli et al. (85) suggested a similar explanation for the higher estimated Ca^{2+}-gradient in pollen tubes measured with aequorin compared to ratiometric probes. There is some evidence for localized $[Ca^{2+}]$ elevations or waves using imaging (99), which might hint at spatial localization of the Ca^{2+} response. However, such measurements are prone to error and require careful masking of low-intensity signals, subtraction of both general background and structured auto-fluorescence, spatial and temporal filtering, and sufficiently high spatiotemporal resolution. Unfortunately, the areas that show the most interesting changes have the worst signal-to-noise, signal-to-background, and signal-to-auto-fluorescence ratios, and are the most prone to specimen and organelle movement artifacts and optical aberrations. This is a general problem in most plant cells in comparison with animal cells, as they tend to have a very thin layer of cytoplasm around the cell periphery and very active cytoplasmic movements.

The Spectre of Light-Induced Reactive Oxygen Species Generation and Artifactual Ca^{2+} Oscillations

A more worrying scenario is the converse explanation, namely that Ca^{2+} oscillations and spikes are actually artifacts triggered by the measurement process itself, particularly as $\sim$30% of control experiments also show spontaneous oscillations and spikes without any stimulus. In chondrocytes, Ca^{2+} transients with a similar period (5 min) to those in guard cells are triggered by reactive oxygen species (ROS) produced by dye excitation (67). Producing ROS by strong dye illumination is sufficient to prevent progression through mitosis in plant cells (28) and may be a widespread problem in physiological measurements. The illumination intensity at the specimen and total irradiation dose are rarely measured or reported in plant experiments. However, rates of photobleaching provide an indication of ROS production and can be assessed if the original wavelength traces are included in the results.

Fluorescence Resonance Energy Transfer-Based Metabolite Sensors

The cameleon concept has inspired the development of genetically encoded FRET-based sensors for other metabolites. Frommer and coworkers exploited the substrate-induced conformation change in bacterial periplasmic-binding proteins (PBPs) to construct sensors for maltose (33) (**Figures 1g, 2j**), glucose (34, 35), ribose (76), and glutamate (101). Unlike most measurements of metabolites, these sensors report concentration directly from specific cellular compartments. As reaction rates and enzyme kinetics are concentration dependent, this should provide a much better understanding of the control of metabolism in vivo. Sensitivity can be altered by mutations in the binding site and sensors can be targeted to other compartments, such as the ER (M. Fehr & W. Frommer, personal communication). The ratio change for these sensors is very small (R_{max}-R_{min} < 0.4 or R_{max}/R_{min} < 0.2). However, recent improvements include replacing EYFP with Venus (25, 101) and modifying the linker length and site of chromophore insertion to improve dipole-dipole coupling thus giving a ~twofold increase in RRC (25). Other PBP-based FRET sensors for sugars, amino acids, sulphate, and phosphate have already been synthesized using chemical coupling of fluorescent dyes (23). Incorporating the appropriate binding modules into the genetically encoded FLIP sensors should yield equivalent transgenic probes. These sensors can be expressed in plants (34), but metabolite measurements have not yet been reported.

Imaging Metabolites with Reactive Probes

In contrast to reversible binding exemplified by the cameleons, biosensors, and ratiometric ion probes, it is possible to image some metabolites, such as glutathione, ROS, or NO, following reaction in vivo to give a fluorescent product. The fluorescent signal is a cumulative measure of the amount of target molecule that reacts and is usually irreversible. Thus, reports that show decreases in fluorescence suggest interference by other processes, such as photobleaching, sequestration in a low-pH environment that quenches the fluorescence, and leakage to the medium or dye destruction by detoxification systems. If the dyes work with high efficiency, they should deplete the target molecule and interfere with the downstream pathways. For example, glutathione (GSH) concentrations can be measured in vivo following GST-catalyzed conjugation to monochlorobimane (MCB) to give a fluorescent glutathione-bimane (GSB) adduct (88). The GSB formed is transferred to the vacuole by GS-X conjugate pumps. Protocols have been developed to measure cytoplasmic GSH concentration $[GSH]_{cyt}$ in a variety of cell types (37, 38, 51, 86, 87), although imaging deep within tissues requires correction for depth-dependent attenuation (37, 51). The assay can also be used to quantify the activity of the GSH-based detoxification pathway (38) and as an indirect assay for other factors that affect GSH levels such as heavy metals, herbicides, or even explosive compounds (87, 90). The assay depletes the level of GSH and thus perturbs the system under study during the measurement. In some cases this can be used advantageously to follow the capacity of the system to respond to GSH depletion (87). Although knowledge of the total GSH pool is useful, it is perhaps more important to monitor the redox poise (GSH/GSSG ratio). Until recently this was only possible by destructive sampling and chemical analysis. However, introduction of a pair of cysteine residues (N149C and S202C) in YFP (rxYFP) confers reversible redox-dependent changes in fluorescence (102, 103). rxYFP can be expressed in plants (P. Mullineaux, unpublished data) and is sensitive to shifts in redox state (M.D. Fricker & P. Mullineaux, unpublished data).

CONCLUSIONS

The clear drive in biology at present is to combine the predominantly reductionist approaches of the past century with the high-throughput screening technologies of this decade to provide a complete, systematic analysis. Systems biology has two components. Biologists have tended to focus on the experimental technologies used to generate vast quantities of gene, protein, and, more recently, metabolite profiles. There is a growing awareness that sophisticated data analysis tools are required to deal with these data, reflected in the rapidly expanding field of bioinformatics. What is appreciated far less is that the test of our understanding of any system at this level of complexity will be the extent to which the essential features can be captured in a mathematical model, which demands quantitative input (141). Although current "-omics" technologies excel at resolving relative amounts of different molecular species (transcripts, proteins, or metabolites), they have very poor spatial and temporal resolution. Conversely, quantitative live-cell imaging is capable of measuring amounts, concentrations, or interactions and how these change in space and time with tissue, cell, and subcellular resolution, but can typically only measure a limited, and rather restrictive, number of species simultaneously. Maximizing our understanding will require careful balancing of the strengths and weaknesses of each approach. Thus, although we envisage important roles for imaging both in setting up the precepts for model development and as a challenging environment to validate the subsequent mathematical formalization, considerable thought will be needed on how to integrate imaging effectively within systems biology. By its very nature, microscope-based imaging can only analyze a very small proportion of an individual plant and only a limited number of individuals in a population. Procedures are needed to ensure that sampling is unbiased at every level in the sampling hierarchy. Furthermore, imaging lacks an agreed standardized format for collecting, reporting, and archiving data; there are few curated and publically accessible image databases; most data is only described in qualitative terms, not least because routine quantitative analysis tools are only just beginning to become widely available, and most studies do not attempt calibration measurements with standard references (151, 152, 13a). With the explosive rise in the popularity of imaging, now would be a good time to establish appropriate guidelines to maximize the long-term value of imaging data.

ACKNOWLEDGMENTS

We would like to thank numerous colleagues for illuminating discussions during preparation of this review and apologize to the large number of authors whose work we were unable to cite fully. Research in the authors' laboratories has been supported by BBSRC (43/P19284, 43/C13425, BBS/B/03904, REI20537), NERC (GR3/12946 and NER/A/S/2002/882), EPSRC (GR/S63090/01), EU Framework 6 (STREP No. 12999), Oxford University Research Infrastructure Fund, and the University Dunston Bequest.

LITERATURE CITED

1. Achnine L, Blancaflor EB, Rasmussen S, Dixon RA. 2004. Colocalization of L-phenylalanine ammonia-lyase and cinnamate 4-hydroxylase for metabolic channeling in phenylpropanoid biosynthesis. *Plant Cell* 16:3098–109

2. Allen GJ, Chu SP, Harrington CL, Schumacher K, Hoffmann T, et al. 2001. A defined range of guard cell calcium oscillation parameters encodes stomatal movements. *Nature* 411:1053–57

3. Allen GJ, Kwak JM, Chu SP, Llopis J, Tsien RY, et al. 1999. Cameleon calcium indicator reports cytoplasmic calcium dynamics in *Arabidopsis* guard cells. *Plant J.* 19:735–47

4. Ando R, Hama H, Yamamoto-Hino M, Mizuno H, Miyawaki A. 2002. An optical marker based on the UV-induced green-to-red photoconversion of a fluorescent protein. *Proc. Natl. Acad. Sci. USA* 99:12651–56

5. Andresen M, Schmitz-Salue R, Jakobs S. 2004. Short tetracysteine tags to beta-tubulin demonstrate the significance of small labels for live cell imaging. *Mol. Biol. Cell* 15:5616–22

6. Arimura S, Yamamoto J, Aida GP, Nakazono M, Tsutsumi N. 2004. Frequent fusion and fission of plant mitochondria with unequal nucleoid distribution. *Proc. Natl. Acad. Sci. USA* 101:7805–8

7. Bastar M-T, Luthar Z, Skof S, Bohanec B. 2004. Quantitative determination of mosaic GFP gene expression in tobacco. *Plant Cell Rep.* 22:939–44

8. Benvenuto G, Formiggini F, Laflamme P, Malakhov M, Bowler C. 2002. The photomorphogenesis regulator DET1 binds the amino-terminal tail of histone H2B in a nucleosome context. *Curr. Biol.* 12:1529–34

9. Berg RH. 2004. Evaluation of spectral imaging for plant cell analysis. *J. Microsc.* 214:174–81

10. Bertrand E, Chartrand P, Schaefer M, Shenoy SM, Singer RH, Long RM. 1998. Localization of ASH1 mRNA particles in living yeast. *Mol. Cell.* 2:437–45

11. Bhat RA, Miklis M, Schmelzer E, Schulze-Lefert P, Panstruga R. 2005. Recruitment and interaction dynamics of plant penetration resistance components in a plasma membrane microdomain. *Proc. Natl. Acad. Sci. USA* 102:3135–40

12. Bornfleth H, Saetzler K, Eils R, Cremer C. 1998. High-precision distance measurements and volume-conserving segmentation of objects near and below the resolution limit in three-dimensional confocal fluorescence microscopy. *J. Microsc.* 189:118–36

13. Bracha-Drori K, Shichrur K, Katz A, Oliva M, Angelovici R, et al. 2004. Detection of protein-protein interactions in plants using bimolecular fluorescence complementation. *Plant J.* 40:419–27

13a. Brakenhoff GJ, Wurpel GWH, Jalink K, Oomen L, Brocks L, Zwier JM. 2005. Characterization of sectioning fluorescence microscopy with thin uniform fluorescent layers: Sectioned Imaging Property or SIPcharts. *J. Microsc.* 219:122–32

14. Brandizzi F, Snapp EL, Roberts AG, Lippincott-Schwartz J, Hawes C. 2002. Membrane protein transport between the endoplasmic reticulum and the Golgi in tobacco leaves is energy dependent but cytoskeleton independent: evidence from selective photobleaching. *Plant Cell* 14:1293–309

14a. Butaye KMJ, Goderis IJWM, Wouters PFJ, Pues JM-TG, Delaure SL, et al. 2004. Stable high-level transgene expression in *Arabidopsis thaliana* using gene silencing mutants and matrix attchment regions. *Plant J.* 39:440–49

15. Carlton PM, Cowan CR, Cande WZ. 2003. Directed motion of telomeres in the formation of the meiotic bouquet revealed by time course and simulation analysis. *Mol. Biol. Cell* 14:2832–43

16. Chang HY, Smertenko AP, Igarashi H, Dixon DP, Hussey PJ. 2005. Dynamic interaction of NtMAP65-1a with microtubules in vivo. *J. Cell Sci.* 118:3195–201

16a. Chapman S, Oparka KJ, Roberts AG. 2005. New tools for *in vivo* fluorescence tagging. *Curr. Opin. Plant Biol.* 8:565–73

17. Chudakov DM, Verkhusha VV, Staroverov DB, Souslova EA, Lukyanov S, Lukyanov KA. 2004. Photoswitchable cyan fluorescent protein for protein tracking. *Nat. Biotechnol.* 22:1435–39

18. Chytilova E, Macas J, Sliwinska E, Rafelski SM, Lambert GM, Galbraith DW. 2000. Nuclear dynamics in *Arabidopsis thaliana*. *Mol. Biol. Cell* 11:2733–41

19. Collings DA, Carter CN, Rink JC, Scott AC, Wyatt SE, Allen NS. 2000. Plant nuclei can contain extensive grooves and invaginations. *Plant Cell* 12:2425–40

19a. Colman-Lerner A, Gordon A, Serra E, Chin T, Renekov O, et al. 2005. Regulated cell-to-cell variation in a cell-fate decision system. *Nature* 437:699–706

20. Costes SV, Daelemans D, Cho EH, Dobbin Z, Pavlakis G, Lockett S. 2004. Automatic and quantitative measurement of protein-protein colocalization in live cells. *Biophys. J.* 86:3993–4003

21. daSilva LL, Snapp EL, Denecke J, Lippincott-Schwartz J, Hawes C, Brandizzi F. 2004. Endoplasmic reticulum export sites and Golgi bodies behave as single mobile secretory units in plant cells. *Plant Cell* 16:1753–71

22. daSilva LL, Taylor JP, Hadlington JL, Hanton SL, Snowden CJ, et al. 2005. Receptor salvage from the prevacuolar compartment is essential for efficient vacuolar protein targeting. *Plant Cell* 17:132–48

23. de Lorimier RM, Smith JJ, Dwyer MA, Looger LL, Sali KM, et al. 2002. Construction of a fluorescent biosensor family. *Protein Sci.* 11:2655–75

24. Dearnaley JD, Levina NN, Lew RR, Heath IB, Goring DR. 1997. Interrelationships between cytoplasmic Ca^{2+} peaks, pollen hydration and plasma membrane conductances during compatible and incompatible pollinations of *Brassica napus* papillae. *Plant Cell Physiol.* 38:985–99

25. Deuschle K, Okumoto S, Fehr M, Looger LL, Kozhukh L, Frommer WB. 2005. Construction and optimization of a family of genetically encoded metabolite sensors by semi-rational protein engineering. *Prot. Sci.* 14:2304–14

26. Dhonukshe P, Gadella TW Jr. 2003. Alteration of microtubule dynamic instability during preprophase band formation revealed by yellow fluorescent protein-CLIP170 microtubule plus-end labeling. *Plant Cell* 15:597–611

27. Diaz I, Martinez M, Isabel-LaMoneda I, Rubio-Somoza I, Carbonero P. 2005. The DOF protein, SAD, interacts with GAMYB in plant nuclei and activates transcription of endosperm-specific genes during barley seed development. *Plant J.* 42:652–62

28. Dixit R, Cyr R. 2003. Cell damage and reactive oxygen species production induced by fluorescence microscopy: effect on mitosis and guidelines for non-invasive fluorescence microscopy. *Plant J.* 36:280–90

29. Docquier S, Tillemans V, Deltour R, Motte P. 2004. Nuclear bodies and compartmentalization of pre-mRNA splicing factors in higher plants. *Chromosoma* 112:255–66

30. Deleted in proof

31. Escobar NM, Haupt S, Thow G, Boevink P, Chapman S, Oparka K. 2003. High-throughput viral expression of cDNA-green fluorescent protein fusions reveals novel subcellular addresses and identifies unique proteins that interact with plasmodesmata. *Plant Cell* 15:1507–23

32. Fang Y, Hearn S, Spector DL. 2004. Tissue-specific expression and dynamic organization of SR splicing factors in Arabidopsis. *Mol. Biol. Cell* 15:2664–73

33. Fehr M, Frommer WB, Lalonde S. 2002. Visualization of maltose uptake in living yeast cells by fluorescent nanosensors. *Proc. Natl. Acad. Sci. USA* 99:9846–51

34. Fehr M, Lalonde S, Ehrhardt DW, Frommer WB. 2004. Live imaging of glucose homeostasis in nuclei of COS-7 cells. *J. Fluoresc.* 14:603–9

35. Fehr M, Lalonde S, Lager I, Wolff MW, Frommer WB. 2003. In vivo imaging of the dynamics of glucose uptake in the cytosol of COS-7 cells by fluorescent nanosensors. *J. Biol. Chem.* 278:19127–33

36. Franks PJ, Buckley TN, Shope JC, Mott KA. 2001. Guard cell volume and pressure measured concurrently by confocal microscopy and the cell pressure probe. *Plant Physiol.* 125:1577–84

37. Fricker MD, May M, Meyer AJ, Sheard N, White NS. 2000. Measurement of glutathione levels in intact roots of Arabidopsis. *J. Microsc.* 198:162–73

38. Fricker MD, Meyer AJ. 2001. Confocal imaging of metabolism in vivo: pitfalls and possibilities. *J. Exp. Bot.* 52:631–40

39. Gadella TW Jr, van der Krogt GN, Bisseling T. 1999. GFP-based FRET microscopy in living plant cells. *Trends Plant Sci.* 4:287–91

40. Gerlich D, Mattes J, Eils R. 2003. Quantitative motion analysis and visualization of cellular structures. *Methods* 29:3–13

41. Giege P, Heazlewood JL, Roessner-Tunali U, Millar AH, Fernie AR, et al. 2003. Enzymes of glycolysis are functionally associated with the mitochondrion in *Arabidopsis* cells. *Plant Cell* 15:2140–51

42. Goedhart J, Hink MA, Visser AJ, Bisseling T, Gadella TW Jr. 2000. In vivo fluorescence correlation microscopy (FCM) reveals accumulation and immobilization of Nod factors in root hair cell walls. *Plant J.* 21:109–19

43. Grandjean O, Vernoux T, Laufs P, Belcram K, Mizukami Y, Traas J. 2004. In vivo analysis of cell division, cell growth, and differentiation at the shoot apical meristem in *Arabidopsis*. *Plant Cell* 16:74–87

44. Gray JD, Kolesik P, Høj PB, Coombe BG. 1999. Technical advance: confocal measurement of the three-dimensional size and shape of plant parenchyma cells in a developing fruit tissue. *Plant J.* 19:229–36

45. Greer LF 3rd, Szalay AA. 2002. Imaging of light emission from the expression of luciferases in living cells and organisms: a review. *Luminescence* 17:43–74

46. Griesbeck O, Baird GS, Campbell RE, Zacharias DA, Tsien RY. 2001. Reducing the environmental sensitivity of yellow fluorescent protein. Mechanism and applications. *J. Biol. Chem.* 276:29188–94

47. Griffin BA, Adams SR, Tsien RY. 1998. Specific covalent labeling of recombinant protein molecules inside live cells. *Science* 281:269–72

48. Halfhill MD, Millwood RJ, Rufty TW, Weissinger AK, Stewart CN. 2003. Spatial and temporal patterns of green fluorescent protein (GFP) fluorescence during leaf canopy development in transgenic oilseed rape, *Brassica napus* L. *Plant Cell Rep.* 22:338–43

48a. Halpin C, Cooke SE, Barakate A, El Amrani A, Ryan MD. 1999. Self-processing 2A-polyproteins—a system for co-ordinate expression of multiple proteins in transgenic plants. *Plant J.* 17:453–59

49. Halweg C, Thompson WF, Spiker S. 2005. The Rb7 matrix attachment region increases the likelihood and magnitude of transgene expression in tobacco cells: a flow cytometric study. *Plant Cell* 17:418–29

50. Hamada S, Ishiyama K, Choi SB, Wang C, Singh S, et al. 2003. The transport of prolamine RNAs to prolamine protein bodies in living rice endosperm cells. *Plant Cell* 15:2253–64

51. Hartmann TN, Fricker MD, Rennenberg H, Meyer AJ. 2003. Cell-specific measurement of cytosolic glutathione in poplar leaves. *Plant Cell Environ.* 26:965–75

52. Haseloff J. 2003. Old botanical techniques for new microscopes. *Biotechniques* 34:1174–82

52a. Heisler MG, Ohno C, Das P, Sieber P, Reddy GV, et al. 2005. Patterns of auxin transport and gene expression during primordium development revealed by live imaging of the *Arabidopsis* inflorescence meristem. *Curr. Biol.* 15:1899–1911

53. Hetherington AM, Brownlee C. 2004. The generation of Ca^{2+} signals in plants. *Annu. Rev. Plant Biol.* 55:401–27

54. Hettinger JW, de la Pena Mattozzi M, Myers WR, Williams ME, Reeves A, et al. 2000. Optical coherence microscopy. A technology for rapid, in vivo, non-destructive visualization of plants and plant cells. *Plant Physiol.* 123:3–16

55. Hink MA, Bisseling T, Visser AJ. 2002. Imaging protein-protein interactions in living cells. *Plant Mol. Biol.* 50:871–83

56. Howard CV, Reed MG. 1998. *Unbiased Stereology: Three-Dimensional Measurement in Microscopy.* Oxford: BIOS Sci. Publ.

57. Hush JM, Wadsworth P, Callaham DA, Hepler PK. 1994. Quantification of microtubule dynamics in living plant cells using fluorescence redistribution after photobleaching. *J. Cell Sci.* 107:775–84

58. Immink RG, Gadella TW Jr, Ferrario S, Busscher M, Angenent GC. 2002. Analysis of MADS box protein-protein interactions in living plant cells. *Proc. Natl. Acad. Sci. USA* 99:2416–21

59. Iwano M, Shiba H, Miwa T, Che FS, Takayama S, et al. 2004. Ca^{2+} dynamics in a pollen grain and papilla cell during pollination of *Arabidopsis*. *Plant Physiol.* 136:3562–71

60. Jakobs S, Schauss AC, Hell SW. 2003. Photoconversion of matrix targeted GFP enables analysis of continuity and intermixing of the mitochondrial lumen. *FEBS Lett.* 554:194–200

61. Johnsson N, Johnsson K. 2003. A fusion of disciplines: chemical approaches to exploit fusion proteins for functional genomics. *Chembiochem* 4:803–10

62. Kato N, Lam E. 2001. Detection of chromosomes tagged with green fluorescent protein in live Arabidopsis thaliana plants. *Genome Biol.* 2: research0045.1–10

63. Kato N, Lam E. 2003. Chromatin of endoreduplicated pavement cells has greater range of movement than that of diploid guard cells in *Arabidopsis thaliana*. *J. Cell Sci.* 116:2195–201

64. Kato N, Pontier D, Lam E. 2002. Spectral profiling for the simultaneous observation of four distinct fluorescent proteins and detection of protein-protein interaction via fluorescence resonance energy transfer in tobacco leaf nuclei. *Plant Physiol.* 129:931–42

65. Ketelaar T, Anthony RG, Hussey PJ. 2004. Green fluorescent protein-mTalin causes defects in actin organization and cell expansion in *Arabidopsis* and inhibits actin depolymerizing factor's actin depolymerizing activity in vitro. *Plant Physiol.* 136:3990–98

66. Kluge C, Seidel T, Bolte S, Sharma SS, Hanitzsch M, et al. 2004. Subcellular distribution of the V-ATPase complex in plant cells, and in vivo localisation of the 100 kDa subunit VHA-a within the complex. *BMC Cell Biol.* 5:29

67. Knight MM, Roberts SR, Lee DA, Bader DL. 2003. Live cell imaging using confocal microscopy induces intracellular calcium transients and cell death. *Am. J. Physiol.* 284:C1083–89

68. Kohl T, Haustein E, Schwille P. 2005. Determining protease activity in vivo by fluorescence cross-correlation analysis. *Biophys. J.* 89:2770–82

69. Kohler RH, Schwille P, Webb WW, Hanson MR. 2000. Active protein transport through plastid tubules: velocity quantified by fluorescence correlation spectroscopy. *J. Cell Sci.* 113:3921–30

70. Kost B, Spielhofer P, Chua NH. 1998. A GFP-mouse talin fusion protein labels plant actin filaments in vivo and visualizes the actin cytoskeleton in growing pollen tubes. *Plant J.* 16:393–401

71. Kotzer AM, Brandizzi F, Neumann U, Paris N, Moore I, Hawes C. 2004. AtRabF2b (Ara7) acts on the vacuolar trafficking pathway in tobacco leaf epidermal cells. *J. Cell Sci.* 117:6377–89

72. Kubínová L, Janáček J, Guilak F, Opatrny Z. 1999. Comparison of several digital and stereological methods for estimating surface area and volume of cells studied by confocal microscopy. *Cytometry* 36:85–95

73. Kuner T, Augustine GJ. 2000. A genetically encoded ratiometric indicator for chloride: capturing chloride transients in cultured hippocampal neurons. *Neuron* 27:447–59

74. Kurup S, Runions J, Köhler U, Laplaze L, Hodge S, Haseloff J. 2005. Marking cell lineages in living tissues. *Plant J.* 42:444–53

75. Kwok EY, Hanson MR. 2004. GFP-labelled Rubisco and aspartate aminotransferase are present in plastid stromules and traffic between plastids. *J. Exp. Bot.* 55:595–604

76. Lager I, Fehr M, Frommer WB, Lalonde S. 2003. Development of a fluorescent nanosensor for ribose. *FEBS Lett.* 553:85–89

77. Lam E, Kato N, Watanabe K. 2004. Visualizing chromosome structure/organization. *Annu. Rev. Plant Biol.* 55:537–54

78. Landmann L. 2002. Deconvolution improves colocalization analysis of multiple fluorochromes in 3D confocal data sets more than filtering techniques. *J. Microsc.* 208:134–47

79. Levsky JM, Singer RH. 2003. Gene expression and the myth of the average cell. *Trends Cell Biol.* 13:4–6

80. Lorenzen I, Aberle T, Plieth C. 2004. Salt stress-induced chloride flux: a study using transgenic Arabidopsis expressing a fluorescent anion probe. *Plant J.* 38:539–44

81. Manders EMM, Verbeek FJ, Aten JA. 1993. Measurement of co-localization of objects in dual-colour confocal images. *J. Microsc.* 169:375–82

81a. Maple J, Aldridge C, Møller SG. 2005. Plastid division is mediated by combinatorial assembly of plastid division proteins. *Plant J.* 43:811–23

82. Mas P, Devlin PF, Panda S, Kay SA. 2000. Functional interaction of phytochrome B and cryptochrome 2. *Nature* 408:207–11

83. Mathur J, Mathur N, Hulskamp M. 2002. Simultaneous visualization of peroxisomes and cytoskeletal elements reveals actin and not microtubule-based peroxisome motility in plants. *Plant Physiol.* 128:1031–45

84. Meckel T, Hurst AC, Thiel G, Homann U. 2004. Endocytosis against high turgor: intact guard cells of *Vicia faba* constitutively endocytose fluorescently labelled plasma membrane and GFP-tagged K-channel KAT1. *Plant J.* 39:182–93

85. Messerli MA, Creton R, Jaffe LF, Robinson KR. 2000. Periodic increases in elongation rate precede increases in cytosolic Ca^{2+} during pollen tube growth. *Dev. Biol.* 222:84–98

86. Meyer AJ, Fricker MD. 2000. Direct measurement of glutathione in epidermal cells of intact *Arabidopsis* roots by two-photon laser scanning microscopy. *J. Microsc.* 198:174–81

87. Meyer AJ, Fricker MD. 2002. Control of demand-driven biosynthesis of glutathione in green Arabidopsis suspension culture cells. *Plant Physiol.* 130:1927–37

88. Meyer AJ, May MJ, Fricker M. 2001. Quantitative in vivo measurement of glutathione in Arabidopsis cells. *Plant J.* 27:67–78

89. Meyers BC, Galbraith DW, Nelson T, Agrawal V. 2004. Methods for transcriptional profiling in plants. Be fruitful and replicate. *Plant Physiol.* 135:637–52

90. Mezzari MP, Walters K, Jelinkova M, Shih MC, Just CL, Schnoor JL. 2005. Gene expression and microscopic analysis of *Arabidopsis* exposed to chloroacetanilide herbicides and explosive compounds. A phytoremediation approach. *Plant Physiol.* 138:858–69

91. Mirabella R, Franken C, van der Krogt GN, Bisseling T, Geurts R. 2004. Use of the fluorescent timer DsRED-E5 as reporter to monitor dynamics of gene activity in plants. *Plant Physiol.* 135:1879–87

92. Miyawaki A, Griesbeck O, Heim R, Tsien RY. 1999. Dynamic and quantitative Ca^{2+} measurements using improved cameleons. *Proc. Natl. Acad. Sci. USA* 96:2135–40

93. Miyawaki A, Llopis J, Heim R, McCaffery JM, Adams JA, et al. 1997. Fluorescent indicators for Ca^{2+} based on green fluorescent proteins and calmodulin. *Nature* 388:882–87

94. Moriguchi K, Suzuki T, Ito Y, Yamazaki Y, Niwa Y, Kurata N. 2005. Functional isolation of novel nuclear proteins showing a variety of subnuclear localizations. *Plant Cell* 17:389–403

95. Nagai T, Yamada S, Tominaga T, Ichikawa M, Miyawaki A. 2004. Expanded dynamic range of fluorescent indicators for Ca^{2+} by circularly permuted yellow fluorescent proteins. *Proc. Natl. Acad. Sci. USA* 101:10554–59

96. Nakajima K, Sena G, Nawy T, Benfey PN. 2001. Intercellular movement of the putative transcription factor SHR in root patterning. *Nature* 413:307–11

97. Nebenführ A, Gallagher LA, Dunahay TG, Frohlick JA, Mazurkiewicz AM, et al. 1999. Stop-and-go movements of plant Golgi stacks are mediated by the acto-myosin system. *Plant Physiol.* 121:1127–42

98. Neher R, Neher E. 2004. Optimizing imaging parameters for the separation of multiple labels in a fluorescence image. *J. Microsc.* 213:46–62

99. Ng CKY, McAinsh MR. 2003. Encoding specificity in plant calcium signalling: Hotspotting the ups and downs and waves. *Ann. Bot.* 92:477–85

100. Okita TW, Choi SB. 2002. mRNA localization in plants: targeting to the cell's cortical region and beyond. *Curr. Opin. Plant Biol.* 5:553–59

101. Okumoto S, Looger LL, Micheva KD, Reimer RJ, Smith SJ, Frommer WB. 2005. Detection of glutamate release from neurons by genetically encoded surface-displayed FRET nanosensors. *Proc. Natl. Acad. Sci. USA* 102:8740–45

102. Østergaard H, Henriksen A, Hansen FG, Winther JR. 2001. Shedding light on disulfide bond formation: engineering a redox switch in green fluorescent protein. *EMBO J.* 20:5853–62

103. Østergaard H, Tachibana C, Winther JR. 2004. Monitoring disulfide bond formation in the eukaryotic cytosol. *J. Cell Biol.* 166:337–45

104. Patterson GH, Lippincott-Schwartz J. 2002. A photoactivatable GFP for selective photolabeling of proteins and cells. *Science* 297:1873–77

105. Pecinka A, Kato N, Meister A, Probst AV, Schubert I, Lam E. 2005. Tandem repetitive transgenes and fluorescent chromatin tags alter local interphase chromosome arrangement in Arabidopsis thaliana. *J. Cell Sci.* 118:3751–58

106. Pecinka A, Schubert V, Meister A, Kreth G, Klatte M, et al. 2004. Chromosome territory arrangement and homologous pairing in nuclei of Arabidopsis thaliana are predominantly random except for NOR-bearing chromosomes. *Chromosoma* 113:258–69

107. Pesquet E, Barbier O, Ranocha P, Jauneau A, Goffner D. 2004. Multiple gene detection by in situ RT-PCR in isolated plant cells and tissues. *Plant J.* 39:947–59

108. Pierson ES, Miller DD, Callaham DA, Van AJ, Hackett G, Hepler PK. 1996. Tip-localized calcium entry fluctuates during pollen tube growth. *Dev. Biol.* 174:160–73

109. Plieth C. 2005. Calcium: just another regulator in the machinery of life? *Ann. Bot.* 96:1–8

110. Reddy GV, Heisler MG, Ehrhardt DW, Meyerowitz EM. 2004. Real-time lineage analysis reveals oriented cell divisions associated with morphogenesis at the shoot apex of *Arabidopsis thaliana*. *Development* 131:4225–37

110a. Reddy GV, Meyerowitz EM. 2005. Stem-cell homeostasis and growth dynamics can be uncoupled in the *Arabidopsis* shoot apex. *Science* 310:663–67

111. Reeves A, Parsons RL, Hettinger JW, Medford JI. 2002. In vivo three-dimensional imaging of plants with optical coherence microscopy. *J. Microsc.* 208:177–89

112. Runions J, Brach T, Kuhner S, Hawes C. 2005. Photoactivation of GFP reveals protein dynamics within the endoplasmic reticulum membrane. *J. Exp. Bot.* 50:43–50

113. Russinova E, Borst JW, Kwaaitaal M, Cano-Delgado A, Yin Y, et al. 2004. Heterodimerization and endocytosis of Arabidopsis brassinosteroid receptors BRI1 and AtSERK3 (BAK1). *Plant Cell* 16:3216–29

114. Schwille P, Haupts U, Maiti S, Webb WW. 1999. Molecular dynamics in living cells observed by fluorescence correlation spectroscopy with one- and two-photon excitation. *Biophys. J.* 77:2251–65

115. Scrase-Field SAMG, Knight MR. 2003. Calcium: just a chemical switch? *Curr. Opin. Plant Biol.* 6:500–6

116. Shah K, Gadella TW Jr, van Erp H, Hecht V, de Vries SC. 2001. Subcellular localization and oligomerization of the *Arabidopsis thaliana* somatic embryogenesis receptor kinase 1 protein. *J. Mol. Biol.* 309:641–55

117. Shah K, Russinova E, Gadella TW Jr, Willemse J, De Vries SC. 2002. The *Arabidopsis* kinase-associated protein phosphatase controls internalization of the somatic embryogenesis receptor kinase 1. *Genes Dev.* 16:1707–20

118. Sharpe J, Ahlgren U, Perry P, Hill B, Ross A, et al. 2002. Optical projection tomography as a tool for 3D microscopy and gene expression studies. *Science* 296:541–45

119. Shaw SL, Kamyar R, Ehrhardt DW. 2003. Sustained microtubule treadmilling in *Arabidopsis* cortical arrays. *Science* 300:1715–18

120. Sheahan MB, Staiger CJ, Rose RJ, McCurdy DW. 2004. A green fluorescent protein fusion to actin-binding domain 2 of *Arabidopsis* fimbrin highlights new features of a dynamic actin cytoskeleton in live plant cells. *Plant Physiol.* 136:3968–78

121. Shope JC, DeWald DB, Mott KA. 2003. Changes in surface area of intact guard cells are correlated with membrane internalization. *Plant Physiol.* 133:1314–21

121a. Sohn EJ, Kim ES, Zhao M, Kim SJ, Kim H, et al. 2003. Rha1, an Arabidopsis Rab5 homolog, plays a critical role in the vacuolar trafficking of soluble cargo proteins. *Plant Cell* 15:1057–70

122. Sprague BL, McNally JG. 2005. FRAP analysis of binding: proper and fitting. *Trends Cell Biol.* 15:84–91

123. Stadler R, Wright KM, Lauterbach C, Amon G, Gahrtz M, et al. 2005. Expression of GFP-fusions in Arabidopsis companion cells reveals non-specific protein trafficking into sieve elements and identifies a novel post-phloem domain in roots. *Plant J.* 41:319–31

124. Subramaniam R, Desveaux D, Spickler C, Michnick SW, Brisson N. 2001. Direct visualization of protein interactions in plant cells. *Nat. Biotechnol.* 19:769–72

125. Subramanian C, Kim BH, Lyssenko NN, Xu X, Johnson CH, von Arnim AG. 2004. The Arabidopsis repressor of light signaling, COP1, is regulated by nuclear exclusion: mutational analysis by bioluminescence resonance energy transfer. *Proc. Natl. Acad. Sci. USA* 101:6798–802

126. Subramanian C, Xu Y, Johnson CH, von Arnim AG. 2004. In vivo detection of protein-protein interaction in plant cells using BRET. *Methods Mol. Biol.* 284:271–86

127. Swarup R, Kargul J, Marchant A, Zadik D, Rahman A, et al. 2004. Structure-function analysis of the presumptive Arabidopsis auxin permease AUX1. *Plant Cell* 16:3069–83

128. Tamura K, Shimada T, Ono E, Tanaka Y, Nagatani A, et al. 2003. Why green fluorescent fusion proteins have not been observed in the vacuoles of higher plants. *Plant J.* 35:545–55

129. Terskikh A, Fradkov A, Ermakova G, Zaraisky A, Tan P, et al. 2000. "Fluorescent timer": protein that changes color with time. *Science* 290:1585–88

130. Tour O, Meijer RM, Zacharias DA, Adams SR, Tsien RY. 2003. Genetically targeted chromophore-assisted light inactivation. *Nat. Biotechnol.* 21:1505–8

131. Tsien RY. 2005. Building and breeding molecules to spy on cells and tumors. *FEBS Lett.* 579:927–32

131a. Tsutsui H, Karasawa S, Shimizu H, Nukina N, Miyawaki A. 2005. Semi-rational engineering of a coral fluorescent protein into an efficient highlighter. *EMBO Rep.* 6:233–38

131b. Ueda T, Uemura T, Sato MH, Nakano A. 2004. Functional differentiation of endosomes in Arabidopsis cells. *Plant J.* 40:783–89

132. Van Bruaene N, Joss G, Thas O, Van Oostveldt P. 2003. Four-dimensional imaging and computer-assisted track analysis of nuclear migration in root hairs of *Arabidopsis thaliana*. *J. Microsc.* 211:167–78

133. Verkhusha VV, Sorkin A. 2005. Conversion of the monomeric red fluorescent protein into a photoactivatable probe. *Chem. Biol.* 12:279–85

134. Vermeer JE, Van Munster EB, Vischer NO, Gadella TW Jr. 2004. Probing plasma membrane microdomains in cowpea protoplasts using lipidated GFP-fusion proteins and multimode FRET microscopy. *J. Microsc.* 214:190–200

135. Vogel H, Grieninger GE, Zetsche KH. 2002. Differential messenger RNA gradients in the unicellular alga *Acetabularia acetabulum*. Role of the cytoskeleton. *Plant Physiol.* 129:1407–16

136. Voon DC, Subrata LS, Baltic S, Leu MP, Whiteway JM, et al. 2005. Use of mRNA- and protein-destabilizing elements to develop a highly responsive reporter system. *Nucleic Acids Res.* 33:e27

137. Walter M, Chaban C, Schutze K, Batistic O, Weckermann K, et al. 2004. Visualization of protein interactions in living plant cells using bimolecular fluorescence complementation. *Plant J.* 40:428–38

138. Wang YS, Motes CM, Mohamalawari DR, Blancaflor EB. 2004. Green fluorescent protein fusions to *Arabidopsis fimbrin* 1 for spatio-temporal imaging of F-actin dynamics in roots. *Cell Motil. Cytoskeleton* 59:79–93

139. Ward TH, Brandizzi F. 2004. Dynamics of proteins in Golgi membranes: comparisons between mammalian and plant cells highlighted by photobleaching techniques. *Cell. Mol. Life Sci.* 61:172–85

140. Watahiki MK, Trewavas AJ, Parton RM. 2004. Fluctuations in the pollen tube tip-focused calcium gradient are not reflected in nuclear calcium levels: a comparative analysis using recombinant yellow cameleon calcium reporter. *Sex. Plant Reprod.* 17:125–30

141. Westerhoff HV, Palsson BO. 2004. The evolution of molecular biology into systems biology. *Nat. Biotechnol.* 22:1249–52

142. White NS, Errington RJ, Fricker MD, Wood JL. 1996. Aberration control in quantitative imaging of botanical specimens by multidimensional fluorescence microscopy. *J. Microsc.* 181:99–116

142a. Wiedenmann J, Ivanchenko S, Oswald F, Schmitt F, Röcker C, et al. 2004. EosFP, a fluorescent marker protein with UV-inducible green-to-red fluorescence conversion. *Proc. Natl. Acad. Sci. USA* 101:15905–10

143. Worley CK, Ling R, Callis J. 1998. Engineering in vivo instability of firefly luciferase and *Escherichia coli* beta-glucuronidase in higher plants using recognition elements from the ubiquitin pathway. *Plant Mol. Biol.* 37:337–47

143a. Wu J-Q, Pollard TD. 2005. Counting cytokinesis proteins globally and locally in fission yeast. *Science* 310:310–14

144. Yamaguchi R, Nakamura M, Mochizuki N, Kay SA, Nagatani A. 1999. Light-dependent translocation of a phytochrome B-GFP fusion protein to the nucleus in transgenic *Arabidopsis*. *J. Cell Biol.* 145:437–45

144a. Yamamoto YY, Tsuhara Y, Gohda K, Suzuki K, Matsui M. 2003. Gene trapping of the *Arabidopsis* genome with a firefly luciferase reporter. *Plant J.* 35:273–83

145. Yang YD, Elamawi R, Bubeck J, Pepperkok R, Ritzenthaler C, Robinson DG. 2005. Dynamics of COPII vesicles and the Golgi apparatus in cultured *Nicotiana tabacum* BY-2 cells provides evidence for transient association of Golgi stacks with endoplasmic reticulum exit sites. *Plant Cell* 17:1513–31

146. Yoo BC, Kragler F, Varkonyi-Gasic E, Haywood V, Archer-Evans S, et al. 2004. A systemic small RNA signaling system in plants. *Plant Cell* 16:1979–2000

147. Zhang F, Simon AE. 2003. A novel procedure for the localization of viral RNAs in protoplasts and whole plants. *Plant J.* 35:665–73

148. Zheng H, Camacho L, Wee E, Batoko H, Legen J, et al. 2005. A Rab-E GTPase mutant acts downstream of the Rab-D subclass in biosynthetic membrane traffic to the plasma membrane in tobacco leaf epidermis. *Plant Cell* 17:2020–36

149. Zhou X, Carranco R, Vitha S, Hall TC. 2005. The dark side of GFP. *New Phytol.* 168:313–21

150. Zimmermann T, Rietdorf J, Pepperkok R. 2003. Spectral imaging and its applications in live cell microscopy. *FEBS Lett.* 546:87–92

151. Zucker RM, Price O. 2001. Evaluation of confocal microscopy system performance. *Cytometry* 44:273–94

152. Zucker RM, Price OT. 2001. Statistical evaluation of confocal microscopy images. *Cytometry* 44:295–308

Control of the Actin Cytoskeleton in Plant Cell Growth

Patrick J. Hussey,[1] Tijs Ketelaar,[2] and Michael J. Deeks[1]

[1]The Integrative Cell Biology Laboratory, School of Biological and Biomedical Sciences, University of Durham, Science Laboratories, Durham DH1 3LE, United Kingdom; email: p.j.hussey@durham.ac.uk

[2]Laboratory of Plant Cell Biology, Wageningen University, 6703 BD Wageningen, The Netherlands

Annu. Rev. Plant Biol. 2006. 57:109–25

The *Annual Review of Plant Biology* is online at plant.annualreviews.org

doi: 10.1146/ annurev.arplant.57.032905.105206

First published online as a Review in Advance on January 30, 2006

1543-5008/06/0602-0109$20.00

Key Words

morphogenesis, Suppressor of Cyclic AMP Receptor (SCAR), Rho of Plants (ROP)

Abstract

Plant cells grow through increases in volume and cell wall surface area. The mature morphology of a plant cell is a product of the differential rates of expansion between neighboring zones of the cell wall during this process. Filamentous actin arrays are associated with plant cell growth, and the activity of actin-binding proteins is proving to be essential for proper cell morphogenesis. Actin-nucleating proteins participate in cell expansion and cell plate formation whereas the recycling of actin monomers is required to maintain actin dynamics and controlled growth. Coordination of actin-binding protein activity and other aspects of cytoskeletal behavior during cell development maintains cohesive cell expansion. Emerging plant signaling networks are proving to be powerful regulators of morphology-shaping cytoskeletal activity, and in this review we highlight current research in actin network regulation.

Contents

INTRODUCTION

Plant cell growth is a coordinated irreversible increase in plasma membrane and cell wall surface area. The building blocks for cell growth are Golgi-derived vesicles, which consist of cell wall matrix materials surrounded by membrane. These Golgi-derived vesicles are delivered to the cellular location where growth occurs, where they fuse with the plasma membrane and deposit their contents into the cell wall. Due to the inability of cell wall matrix to move within the cell wall, growth is limited to sites of exocytosis (51). In plant cells, different types of cell growth have been defined: isodiametrical growth, anisotropic, intercalary or diffuse growth, and tip growth. Isodiametrical-growing cells expand equally over their whole surface, resulting in a ball-shaped cell. Anisotropic expand-

ing cells restrict growth to large but defined areas, creating elongated and sometimes more complicated cell morphologies. Examples of these cell types are leaf pavement cells that form interlocking lobes and trichomes that exhibit several developmental stages where some parts of the cell expand over a large surface area to form complex branching patterns. In tip-growing cells, expansion occurs over a small area of the cell surface, which results in tubular, elongated cells.

The eukaryote actin cytoskeleton plays a pivotal role in many cellular processes that together regulate cell growth and morphology. Specifically in the case of plant cell growth, filamentous actin (F-actin) coordinates cytoplasmic streaming and guides growth materials to zones of exocytosis (88) although not all actin-dependent vesicle trafficking is coupled to growth (74a). In several plant cell types, such as root hairs and leaf pavement cells, evidence is accumulating for dynamic fine F-actin configurations that localize to cell surface areas undergoing expansion (29, 31, 71). Fine F-actin has been hypothesized to deliver, filter, and retain cell wall matrix containing Golgi-derived vesicles to the plasma membrane area where exocytosis occurs (71) and has been demonstrated in some cell types to determine the cell surface area where growth takes place (50). The formation of F-actin arrays depends on the biochemical interactions of actin monomers and actin-binding proteins (ABPs). Studying the role of actin and ABPs in plant cell growth has consequently provided insights into the biochemistry of the plant actin cytoskeleton. In this review we summarize the experiments that have identified the functions of actin during plant cell growth, and describe the genetic and biochemical evidence for the role of plant ABPs in coordinating F-actin formation to achieve cell expansion. Additionally, the genetic and physical interactions of ABPs with regulatory proteins can be placed into a signaling network to describe the plant morphogenetic pathways that lead to the actin cytoskeleton.

Exocytosis: delivery of vesicles and their contents to the external environment via fusion with the plasma membrane

F-actin: filamentous actin (actin polymer)

Cytoplasmic streaming: the active movement of vesicles and organelles through the cytoplasm

ABP: actin-binding protein

DEFINING THE ROLE OF ACTIN IN PLANT CELL GROWTH

A productive method to investigate the function of the actin cytoskeleton in cellular processes and plant development is to depolymerize the actin cytoskeleton and analyze the consequences. There are two classes of commonly used actin-depolymerizing drugs: the latrunculins and the cytochalasins. Latrunculin forms a high-affinity 1:1 complex with monomeric actin [globular actin (G-actin)], preventing incorporation into filamentous actin (19). The lack of available G-actin for polymerization changes the equilibrium between G-actin and F-actin so that F-actin depolymerizes. Cytochalasins inhibit polymerization by capping free barbed ends, thus preventing the addition of G-actin to actin filaments (13), leading to net-depolymerization. In tip-growing pollen tubes and root hair cells, the consequences of treatment with actin-depolymerizing drugs have been carefully analyzed. In both cell types, growth is inhibited when low concentrations of actin-depolymerizing drugs are applied (31, 47, 50, 71). At still lower concentrations of actin-depolymerizing drugs, the expanding apex of tip-growing cells swells. This root hair swelling is concentration dependent to a concentration of 0.1 μM of cytochalasin D (50). Surprisingly, the amount of available data concerning the consequences of actin depolymerization on intercalary cell growth is limited. Plants grown in medium complemented with a high concentration of latrunculin B (10 μM) for two weeks show little alteration in cell division organization, but cell elongation is reduced dramatically (4). A two-day treatment of *Arabidopsis* roots with cytochalasin B causes root cells to swell radially (6).

Observations made using pharmaceuticals can be compared to the phenotypes of actin mutants. Mutations of the *Arabidopsis ACT7* actin gene cause a reduction in the total amount of F-actin in vegetative tissue (32). Consequently, germination is delayed and less efficient, and root growth is retarded and wavy. In plants homozygous for the most severe mutant alleles, root apical cells are not organized in straight files with oblique cell-cell junctions (32). Mutations of *ACT2* (*act2-1*; *deformed root hairs* (*der*) *1–1* to *1–3*) cause phenotypes restricted to root hair positioning and growth (69, 79). Although overexpression of *ACT2* under its own promoter does not cause any strong defects, overexpression of *ACT1* under the *ACT2* promoter causes dwarfed plants and morphological changes in most organs, which correlates with a strong increase in actin polymerization and bundling (46). These data show that plant actin isoforms must vary in their biochemical properties, and both the expression levels of actin genes and their developmental context are important during plant development to achieve cell expansion.

In trichomes, the effects of actin depolymerization during different developmental stages of individual cell expansion have been studied in detail. Trichomes are structures that extend from the surface of many aerial organs. *Arabidopsis* leaf trichomes are unicellular, highly polarized, and consist of a stalk with an average of three branches. The relatively consistent size and spacing of branches makes leaf trichomes a powerful morphogenetic model. Treatment with cytochalasin or latrunculin disrupts trichome morphogenesis: The first stages of trichome development (stalk elongation and branch initiation) take place normally (66, 86); however, during later developmental stages, actin depolymerization causes branches to swell, twist, or abort. For distortion to occur, the location of exocytosis must be altered by actin depolymerization, not just inhibited (83). This suggests that during certain types of intercalary growth F-actin guides rather than drives the zones of cell expansion.

ACTIN-BINDING PROTEINS IN PLANTS

In all eukaryote cells, F-actin configuration and actin dynamics are determined by the actions of numerous ABPs. The actions of different classes of ABPs regulate aspects

G-actin: globular actin (actin monomer)

Barbed end: An actin polymer has two ends; the barbed (+) end and the pointed (−) end. The barbed end has a higher affinity for monomers and grows at a greater rate

Bundling: the parallel or antiparallel close alignment of individual actin filaments to form an actin cable

Intercalary growth: relatively unfocused insertion of new cell wall material within a defined area of plant cell wall, resulting in "diffuse" growth, as opposed to the highly focused process of tip growth

of actin biochemistry including nucleation, bundling, filament capping, fragmentation, and monomer availability; other ABPs are involved in transport along actin filaments or use actin as a scaffold. Below, we discuss the functions of ABPs in actin organization and plant development.

Actin Nucleators

Actin nucleation is the formation of a new actin filament from G-actin. It can occur spontaneously when the G-actin concentration is high. However, despite high concentrations of G-actin in living cells, G-actin is prevented from nucleating spontaneously by actin-sequestering proteins such as profilin, and chaotic spontaneous nucleation is unlikely to be responsible for F-actin formation in vivo. Recently, specialized actin-nucleating proteins were found to play essential roles in actin-dependent plant growth processes.

The Arp2/3 Complex

In animals, protists, and fungi the activated Arp2/3 complex nucleates actin by promoting barbed-end actin assembly while capping the pointed end. The complex attaches itself to the flanks of existing filaments and initiates a new F-actin branch at an angle of 70° relative to the parent filament. The Arp2/3 complex consists of seven subunits [Arp2, Arp3, ArpC1/p41, ArpC2/p31, ArpC3/p21, ArpC4/p20, and ArpC5/p16 (39)]. Homologs of all Arp2/3 complex subunits are present in plants (64), but to date there is no in vitro biochemical evidence that a plant Arp2/3 complex nucleates actin filaments in a similar fashion to other eukaryote Arp2/3 complexes. However, components of the *Arabidopsis* Arp2/3 complex can complement mutations of yeast homologs, and vice versa, inferring the existence of a plant complex (25, 59). In addition, mutations in the plant Arp2/3 complex can be complemented with mammalian subunits (65).

Three "distorted" class mutants have been shown to encode subunits of the Arp2/3 complex: *wurm* is a mutant of the Arp2 subunit, *distorted1* is a mutant of the Arp3 subunit, and *crooked* represents the ArpC5/p16 subunit (59, 61, 64, 65). The most dramatic phenotype can be observed in trichomes, which develop a distorted morphology highly similar to that caused by actin-depolymerizing drugs, indicating that these mutant phenotypes are generated by defects in the actin cytoskeleton (66, 86). Besides defects in trichome development, root hair growth under certain conditions is disturbed in Arp2/3 mutants (64, 65). The root hair phenotype varies from wavy growth to a widened diameter to root hairs with multiple tips. Also, less pronounced interlocking of lobes between leaf pavement cells and the curling of hypocotyl epidermal cells during periods of rapid elongation in Arp2/3 mutants have been reported (64, 65).

The changes in actin organization, caused by mutations in Arp2/3 complex subunits, have best been studied in trichomes. Using the GFP-mTalin probe, Mathur et al. (64, 65) show severe, localized aggregations of actin. Using immunolocalization and phalloidin staining, the Szymanski group (25, 59) concludes that the actin filaments failed to localize as coherent populations that are aligned with the long axis of the cell. In addition they show that the amount of actin in the core of trichome branches, compared to the total amount of actin (core and cortical actin together), is reduced in Arp2/3 complex mutants. From these descriptions it can be concluded that the actin organization in Arp2/3 mutant trichomes differs somewhat when alternative actin visualization techniques are used.

A functioning Arp2/3 complex is essential in yeast where deletion of several subunits is lethal (93). The Arp2/3 complex is also essential in *C. elegans* (82) and *Drosophila* (43, 100). In mammalian cells, RNAi inhibition of the Arp2/3 complex inhibits cell growth (37). In contrast, plants only develop several subtle, tissue-specific, developmental defects, as discussed above. Also, the loss of total F-actin content appears to be far less severe in plants compared to animal and protist cells. This points to a less pronounced role of the Arp2/3 complex in the biochemistry of plant actin nucleation than in other eukaryotic organisms.

Formins

Formins represent a second major group of actin nucleators that stimulate de novo actin nucleation and extension from the barbed end. Paradoxically, fungal and animal formins partially cap the growing barbed end (56, 76, 102), yet in some cases can accelerate monomer incorporation at the barbed end beyond the limits of free diffusion (80).

Unlike the putative plant Arp2/3 complex, plant formins have been studied to some extent in vitro. Four plant formins (AtFH1, AtFH4, AtFH5, and AtFH8) have been shown to nucleate purified actin, and allow extension from the barbed end of filaments (44, 70, 96, 20a). Like other formins, the plant formins appear to bind to the barbed end of F-actin, inhibit actin depolymerization from the barbed end, and partially protect the barbed end from other proteins that otherwise would terminate barbed-end growth. The study of the biochemistry of plant formins is complicated by several factors including the division of plant formins into two large and distinct clades, the absence of recognizable autoinhibition domains that are found in animal and yeast formins, and the direct tethering of group I formins to lipid membranes. The 21 plant formins are divided by sequence similarity and domain organization into groups I and II (20, 21), but only group I formins have been studied in vitro. The divergence between groups I and II extends to the residues predicted to make contact with actin monomers, suggesting that group II formins may have a very distinct biochemistry. Also, few in vitro studies have included longer fragments containing transmembrane domains and putative control regions that might influence the interactions between plant formins and actin.

When overexpressed in tobacco pollen tubes, the actin-nucleating domains of group I formin AtFH1 increase the number of actin cables (18), indicating that group I plant formins can induce actin polymerization in vivo. Pollen tubes transformed with less than 1 μg of full-length *AtFH1* transgene show an initial increase in growth rate followed by subsequent growth inhibition as F-actin cables begin to accumulate (18). In root hairs, overexpression of full-length AtFH8 can induce the accumulation of fine F-actin and the disruption of tip growth (96). Expression of the N terminus of AtFH4 without the actin-nucleating C terminus also disrupts root hair growth (20a). The overexpression of AtFH1, AtFH4, and AtFH8 shows that formins have the potential to affect growth through F-actin formation, but the actual function of most plant formins remains unknown. So far only one isoform, AtFH5, has been reported to have any null phenotype (44). Interestingly, this is a reduction in the rate of cell wall formation, supporting the hypothesis that plant formins within a natural context participate in growth processes.

AtFH: *Arabidopsis thaliana* formin homolog

Gelsolin

A gelsolin-like protein that can nucleate actin polymerization from monomers has been identified in poppy pollen tubes (40). Gelsolin can tightly cap barbed ends in vitro, and only allows extension from the pointed end of filaments (40). The pointed end has distinct biochemical properties to the barbed end, and the action of proteins such as profilin are likely to inhibit pointed-end growth within a plant cell. Gelsolin also severs actin filaments and blocks the assembly of profilin-actin complex onto actin filament ends and enhances profilin-mediated actin depolymerization. The localization and function of gelsolin have not been investigated in vivo.

Heterodimeric Capping Protein

Heterodimeric capping protein binds tightly to the barbed end of actin filaments. Like gelsolin, the barbed-end binding affinity of plant capping protein allows it to act as a nucleator that facilitates pointed-end elongation (41). The elongation rate of filaments in vitro is significantly slowed by a combination of capping protein and profilin, as capping protein blocks barbed-end growth and profilin actin is unable to associate with the pointed end (41). In animals, capping protein dramatically alters F-actin arrays generated by Arp2/3 complex activity (10), and it remains to be seen whether plant capping protein function is required for plant Arp2/3 complex-dependent growth processes.

To date, the number of varieties of actin-nucleating proteins in plants is unknown, and other classes of actin nucleators may yet be identified. F-actin severing proteins can conceivably produce a significant contribution of free F-actin ends for plant actin polymerization. Future work will reveal additional insight into the regulation of free barbed and pointed-end generation in plants and how these processes contribute to plant development.

Other ABPs that Affect Cell Growth: Profilin

Profilin specifically binds G-actin. When bound to profilin, G-actin cannot incorporate at the pointed ends of actin filaments or nucleate, whereas incorporation at the barbed ends continues at the normal rate (75). The sequestering action of proteins like profilin allows cells to maintain high levels of actin monomers without risking spontaneous nucleation or filament extension. In some plant cells actin exists at a 1:1 molar concentration with profilin (31). Because pollen grains are packed with such a high concentration, profilin is a major antigen responsible for pollen allergies. Formins are designed to exploit actin monomers bound to profilin, and the presence of profilin greatly influences formin biochemistry (56, 80). Five isoforms of profilin have been identified in the *Arabidopsis* genome, and the biochemical proper-

ties of profilin vary from isoform to isoform in Maize (54). In pollen tubes and Tradescantia stamen hair cells, profilin is evenly distributed throughout the cytoplasm, although some of the profilin accumulates in the nucleus of Tradescantia stamen hair cells for unknown reasons (38, 89, 90). Transgenic plants overexpressing PFN-1 have longer roots and root hairs that are twice as long as wild-type hairs (78). An increase in the amount of growth, but no change in cell shape, suggests that profilin does not play a role in spatially restricting actin turnover. It is not clear whether the growth rate or the duration of the growth period is increased in these lines. When expression of profilin was inhibited by antisense RNA expression, a variety of developmental changes were found, including an overall dwarf phenotype with short hypocotyls and early flowering. The dwarf phenotype is caused by the development of shorter and more isodiametrically shaped cells (78). This indicates that a minimum amount of profilin-bound monomeric actin has to be available for proper cell expansion.

ADF/cofilin

ADF/cofilin binds both to G- and F-actin and enhances actin dynamics by severing actin filaments and increasing the depolymerization from the pointed end (14, 35). The activity of plant ADF is influenced by several factors. Phosphorylation of Ser-6 decreases the activity of plant ADF (85) and undoes the localization of overexpressed GFP-ADF to actin filaments (16). In contrast to animals, phosphorylation of plant ADF is regulated by a calmodulin-like domain protein kinase (CDPK) (2, 85). The activity of ADF is also inhibited by phosphatidylinositol 4,5-bisphosphate (PIP2) or phosphatidylinositol 4-monophosphate (PIP) binding (35). Finally, the activity of ADF is pH dependent. At high pH (8.0), ADF severs actin filaments, whereas it binds F-actin at a lower pH (6.0) (36). Dong et al. (23) tested the consequences of overexpression and inhibition of the ADF1 gene in *Arabidopsis*. Overexpression of ADF causes irregular cellular and tissue morphogenesis and reduces the growth of cells and organs (23). In contrast, ADF inhibition results in a delay in flowering and stimulated cell expansion, as well as organ growth (23). The actin cytoskeleton was visualized with the live cell actin probe GFP-mTalin. When ADF1 was overexpressed, this revealed the disappearance of thick actin cables in different cell types. ADF1 inhibition caused an induction of actin cable formation. Although it should be kept in mind that GFP-mTalin has been shown to compete for binding places on F-actin with ADF and thus inhibits the activity of the latter (49), it is likely that an increase in actin polymerization when ADF is inhibited and a decrease in actin polymerization when ADF is overexpressed occur.

In tip-growing cells, ADF plays an important role in regulating actin dynamics. In root hairs, ADF overexpression leads to a highly irregular F-actin organization and the disappearance of thick bundles of actin, resulting in an increase in the radial root hair diameter, whereas underexpression inhibits root hair growth (23). In pollen tubes, a different response is observed: Overexpression of ADF inhibits pollen tube growth in a dose-dependent manner (16). Differences between the biochemical properties of pollen and vegetative ADFs have been found, which may cause these contrasting responses (1).

AIP1

Plant Actin Interacting Protein 1 (AIP1), a protein also conserved in yeast and animals, enhances the activity of the lily pollen-specific ADF1 in vitro in a synergistic manner (1). The activity of this ADF isoform in the absence of AIP1 is remarkably low, and it is not phosporylated, even though the conserved Ser-6 is present (1). When at an equimolar concentration, AIP1 enhances the activity of LiADF1 in vitro by nearly three times (1). Upon the expression of AIP1 RNAi species and the subsequent reduction of endogenous

AIP1 protein levels, *Arabidopsis* leaves, roots, shoots, and root hairs fail to expand normally (48). These cell expansion defects are fatal in lines where AIP1 expression is inhibited strongly. The actin organization in intercalary growing cells and root hairs is severely disrupted. Thick bundles of actin appear in the cytoplasm of intercalary growing cells, and (unlike control root hairs) F-actin cables are observed in the root hair tip (48). If AIP1 solely enhances the activity of ADF, a similar phenotype would be expected in ADF-inhibited plants (see previous section), but this is not the case. Even though actin bundling has been reported in both situations (23, 48), ADF inhibition stimulates cell expansion and organ growth whereas AIP1 underexpression inhibits these processes. Further characterization of the ADF-AIP1 biochemical relationship is required to understand these phenotypic contrasts. The possibility exists that the functions of plant AIP1 may extend beyond the stimulation of ADF activity.

CAP

In yeast, Cyclase Associated Protein (CAP) is a subunit of the cAMP-generating adenylyl cyclase complex. CAP interacts with the actin cytoskeleton in many eukaryotic species and inhibits actin polymerization in vitro by sequestering monomeric actin (27, 33). In *Arabidopsis*, a CAP homolog was successfully used to pull down actin and vice versa from cytoplasmic extracts (5), which might indicate a direct interaction with plant actin. Overexpression of the *Arabidopsis* CAP homolog resulted in a lower level of fluorescence in Bright Yellow 2 (BY-2) Tobacco tissue culture cells stained with fluorescent phalloidin, from which the authors conclude that CAP induces actin depolymerization. BY-2 cells overexpressing AtCAP are inhibited from entering mitosis. Overexpression of CAP in *Arabidopsis* induces growth defects such as size reduction of leaves and petioles caused by decreased cell size and cell number. *Arabidopsis* plants overexpressing profilin isoform PFN1 do not show

AIP1: actin interacting protein 1

CAP: cyclase associated protein

growth inhibition, but instead some cell types show excessive expansion (78). Therefore, the actin-sequestering role of AtCAP cannot be entirely equivalent to that of profilin. Recent work has shown that the S. cerevisiae homolog of CAP prevents actin monomer addition to the barbed end of F-actin whereas profilin prevents monomer addition to the pointed end (67). S. cerevisiae CAP also appears to enhance actin turnover mediated by ADF and profilin (3). Plant CAP is therefore likely to play a unique biochemical role in cytoskeletal organization and plant development.

Actin-Bundling Proteins

Plants possess at least three classes of actin-bundling proteins: villins (42, 91, 99), fimbrins (55, 57, 68), and elongation factor-1α (36). Villin bundles actin filaments in a unipolar fashion (97) and localizes to actin cables in pollen tubes (91, 98) and root hairs (87). In root hairs, microinjection of an antibody raised against villin causes unbundling of F-actin (52, 87) and migration of the nucleus toward the apex of growing root hairs (52). Although villin-mediated actin bundling reinforces F-actin against depolymerization by ADF, plant villins do not appear to posses other activities of proteins from the villin/gelsolin family (these include actin nucleation, capping, depolymerization, and filament severing) (42). The activity of plant villin isoforms can either be sensitive (99) or insensitive (42) to the concentration of calcium ions.

Fimbrins are actin filament cross-linkers that are calcium concentration independent (57), localize to actin filaments (55), and protect actin filaments against profilin-induced depolymerization (57). Fimbrin has two actin-binding domains. The second domain, fused to GFP, is used for in vivo visualization of the actin cytoskeleton in plant cells (48, 84, 92).

Elongation Factor-1α (EF-1α) is a protein with a dual function. It binds aminoacyl-tRNA to the ribosome, but it also binds to actin and bundles it, while inhibiting incorpo-

ration of monomeric actin at low pH (36). The activity of EF-1α is enhanced by ADF (36). Lopez-Valenzuela et al. (63a) show that during maize endosperm development, the actin-bundling properties of EF-1a differ.

Actin-bundling activity is shared by several different families of plant ABPs, but much remains to be discovered concerning the functions of actin-bundling proteins in vivo and their importance during plant development.

SIGNALING TO ACTIN

A striking example of the coordinated power of ABPs comes from the in vitro reconstitution of actin-based motility. This requires the unpolarized biochemical activity of profilin and ADF to maintain a pool of free G-actin, and the polar stimulation of the Arp2/3 complex to produce localized F-actin (74). In a plant cell the formation of F-actin arrays must require the coordinated activation and/or repression of a variety of ABPs in time and space. Recent developments have begun to identify signaling systems that orchestrate this activity in developing plant cells (see **Figure 1**). The function of small GTPases in cytoskeletal control is currently receiving wide attention.

ROPs

In tip-growing cells and leaf epidermal pavement cells, Rho of Plants (ROP) GTPases are involved in regulating cell expansion and localize to sites of tip growth and intercalary growth (15, 17, 29, 45, 72). In addition, ROPs localize to developing cell plates and cross walls (72) and to Golgi bodies (17), as well as particpate in endocytosis (11). The animal, protist, and fungal homologs of ROPs (the RHOs, RACs, and CDC42) are major regulators of the actin cytoskeleton.

Overexpression of constitutively active ROP (CA-rop) leads to the production of root hairs with multiple tips and isodiametric swelling. Dominant negative forms of ROP (DN-rop) cause inhibition of cell growth (45, 72). In both cases, changes in the actin

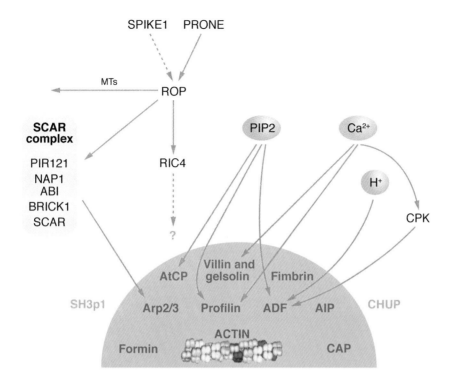

Figure 1

Major known control pathways to the plant actin cytoskeleton. Proteins within the red zone have been proven to alter actin biochemistry directly whereas ABPs within the yellow zone (CHUP and SH3p1) bind actin but with unknown effects (58, 73). SPIKE1 (77) and the PRONE family (9) are ROP GTPase exchange factors with the potential to stimulate ROP activity.

configuration correlate with defects in cell growth. Root hairs expressing DN-rop2 have a reduced amount of fine F-actin in comparison to wild-type hairs, whereas in hairs expressing CA-rop2 a dense network of fine F-actin is present (45). Molendijk et al. (72) show that the polar ROP signaling occurs before root hair growth initiates, indicating that ROPs may serve as a polarity marker. Once root hair growth is initiated, ROPs localize to the expanding root hair tip. Changes in the actin cytoskeleton and cell expansion have also been reported in pollen tubes when ROPs are overexpressed (17, 30). Excessive fine F-actin accumulates in the apical region and a thick band of transverse F-actin is formed in the subapex, which correlates with a switch from polar growth to isodiametrical swelling (30). Overexpression of GTPase-activating protein (RopGAP1) (30), and injection of antibodies against Rop1 (63), caused a similar decrease in the amount of apical fine F-actin and growth inhibition. During the early expansion phase of leaf pavement cells, the location of fine F-

actin formation and cell expansion are determined by ROP proteins. Expression of CA-rop2 leads to expansion over the whole cell surface, which correlates with the formation of cortical fine F-actin over the whole cell surface. In contrast, expression of DN-rop2 leads to inhibition of growth and a decrease in the amount of cortical fine F-actin (29). These observations resemble observations made in root hairs and pollen tubes: At the membrane surface where expansion takes place, ROPs are activated and fine F-actin is formed.

RICs: Effectors of ROP

RICs are CRIB motif-containing proteins that interact with the active (GTP-bound) form of ROP isoforms (94). Different classes of RICs have been identified that activate antagonizing pathways in pollen tube and leaf pavement cell growth. In pollen tubes, Rop1 interacts directly with Ric3 and Ric4 (34, 94). Both Ric3 and Ric4 cause growth depolarization when overexpressed (34, 94). Ric4

RIC: ROP interacting CRIB motif protein

CRIB: Cdc42/Rac interactive binding protein

SCAR: suppressor
of Cyclic AMP
Receptor

stimulates the formation of F-actin in the pollen tube apex (34). Ric3 overexpression leads to an increased cytoplasmic calcium concentration in the apex of growing pollen tubes that disassembles fine F-actin (34). Combined overexpression of both Ric3 and Ric4 does not cause changes in pollen tube growth, indicating that the balance between Ric3 and Ric4 activity is critical (34).

In leaf epidermal cells, a similar mechanism that requires balanced levels of two counteracting Rics is essential for the intercalation of adjoining cells (28). Leaf epidermal cells adhere together by forming a series of interlocking lobes. GTP-bound Rop2 and Rop4 activate Ric4, which in turn induces local assembly of cortical F-actin in zones of growth that become lobes (28). Simultaneously, Rop2 and Rop4 inhibit Ric1 (28). Ric1 promotes the formation of organized cortical microtubules and in turn inhibits the formation of a growing lobe and Rop2/4 activation. This interrelationship between actin, microtubules, and the cell wall during plant cell expansion has been recently reviewed by Smith and Oppenheimer (85a). Through the local changes in Rop2/4 activity, indentations and outgrowths are formed by the two counteracting pathways of Ric1 and Ric4 (28).

The components of the ROP pathway downstream of Ric4 that effect changes to the actin cytoskeleton remain to be identified, but this pathway appears to be a major component in the regulation of localized growth.

The SCAR Complex

The SCAR complex is an effector of Rac cytoskeletal reorganization in animals and protists, and recent work has identified homologs of SCAR complex components in plants (7, 8, 12, 22, 24, 62, 81, 101, 103). Yeast-2-hybrid assays and in vitro pull-down experiments have demonstrated binary interactions between these plant protein homologs that are equivalent to those characterized in the mammalian complex (7, 8, 24, 26, 101). One member of the putative plant complex, PIR121,

binds the active form of ROP2 (7) whereas plant SCAR, another component, can activate the Arp2/3 complex in vitro and bind G-actin (8, 22, 26). Null mutants of components PIR121 and NAP1 phenocopy the knockouts of the Arp2/3 complex, showing almost an identical distortion of trichomes and other epidermal cell types. This indicates that the SCAR complex is required to activate the Arp2/3 complex. To date, mutant alleles of only one isoform of *Arabidopsis* SCAR (SCAR2) have been found to exhibit a phenotype (8, 101). This again resembles that of other Arp2/3 pathway knockouts, but is less severe, indicating that other SCAR isoforms or other classes of Arp2/3 regulators may perform similar functions to SCAR2 via the SCAR complex.

CONCLUDING REMARKS

Accumulating evidence points toward the importance of a subpopulation of dynamic F-actin in growth processes. The morphogenesis of different cell types appears reliant on the activities of different subsets of ABPs: Pollen growth is insensitive to Arp2/3 mutations but is sensitive to manipulation of profilin or ADF, whereas trichome growth is so dependent on Arp2/3 activity that Arp2/3 null mutants resemble the effects of total actin depolymerization. Many plant ABPs have been studied in biochemical assays in vitro, but their precise role in plant growth is uncharacterized. Very fundamental questions concerning how actin influences growth remain to be answered: How do actin filaments guide vesicles? Do polymerizing actin filaments exert forces against membranes, and if so, which ones? How much of the influence of actin filaments on growth is through the organization of other systems such as the microtubule cytoskeleton?

Some of these questions might be answered in part by discovering how and where ABPs are manipulated within a plant cell. The recent developments in the understanding of ROP effectors has added support to the role of ROPs in signaling to the plant cytoskeleton. Activated ROP localizes to zones of growth and F-actin dynamicity. One intact pathway from GTPase signaling to F-actin formation is beginning to emerge from the plant SCAR complex, although the biological significance of the ROP2-PIR121 interaction remains to be proven. Still to be considered are the actions of other signaling systems such as phospholipids and calcium ions. Both affect the activities of muiltiple ABPs, and it has been suggested that both systems are downstream of ROP signaling (53, 60). However, lessons from the study of animal signaling pathways to the cytoskeleton show that ABP control is often dependent upon multiple pathways with extensive cross talk and self-regulation.

SUMMARY POINTS

1. In plant cells, growth is limited to sites of exocytosis and coincides with local fine F-actin arrays.

2. Actin and the Arp2/3 complex govern the locations of cell growth in *Arabidopsis* leaf trichome cells, but unlike other eukaryotes, the plant Arp2/3 complex is not essential for life.

3. Plant formins nucleate F-actin that grows from the barbed end in vitro and are involved in plant growth processes in vivo.

4. Capping protein and gelsolin also have the potential to nucleate filaments, but these grow from the pointed end only.

5. Profilin prevents spontaneous nucleation and chaotic polymerization by sequestering G-actin, whereas capping protein potentially controls the availability of growing F-actin barbed ends.

6. Recycling actin monomers through the actions of ADF and AIP1 maintains actin dynamics and has complex effects on plant growth.

7. ROP GTPases promise to be the focus of a signaling network that controls multiple cytoskeletal processes, including F-actin formation and cell morphogenesis.

8. RIC proteins are ROP effectors that act differentially to regulate actin and microtubules during cell morphogenesis.

9. The plant SCAR complex regulates the Arp2/3 complex and is possibly a ROP effector.

LITERATURE CITED

1. Allwood EG, Anthony RG, Smertenko AP, Reichelt S, Drobak BK, et al. 2002. Regulation of the pollen-specific actin-depolymerizing factor LlADF1. *Plant Cell* 14:2915–27
2. Allwood EG, Smertenko AP, Hussey PJ. 2001. Phosphorylation of plant actin-depolymerising factor by calmodulin-like domain protein kinase. *FEBS Lett.* 499:97–100
3. Balcer HI, Goodman AL, Rodal AA, Smith E, Kugler J, et al. 2003. Coordinated regulation of actin filament turnover by a high-molecular-weight Srv2/CAP complex, cofilin, profilin, and Aip1. *Curr. Biol.* 13:2159–69
4. Baluska F, Jasik J, Edelmann HG, Salajová T, Volkmann D. 2001. Latrunculin B-induced plant dwarfism: Plant cell elongation is F-actin-dependent. *Dev. Biol.* 231:113–24
5. Barrero RA, Umeda M, Yamamura S, Uchimiya H. 2002. Arabidopsis CAP regulates the actin cytoskeleton necessary for plant cell elongation and division. *Plant Cell* 14:149–63

6. Baskin TI, Bivens NJ. 1995. Stimulation of radial expansion in Arabidopsis roots by inhibitors of actomyosin and vesicle secretion but not by various inhibitors of metabolism. *Planta* 197:514–21

7. Basu D, El-Assal Sel D, Le J, Mallery EL, Szymanski DB. 2004. Interchangeable functions of Arabidopsis PIROGI and the human WAVE complex subunit SRA1 during leaf epidermal development. *Development* 131:4345–55

8. Basu D, Le J, El-Essal Sel D, Huang S, Zhang C, et al. 2005. DISTORTED3/SCAR2 is a putative Arabidopsis WAVE complex subunit that activates the Arp2/3 complex and is required for epidermal morphogenesis. *Plant Cell* 17:502–24

9. Berken A, Thomas C, Wittinghofer A. 2005. A new family of RhoGEFs activates the Rop molecular switch in plants. *Nature* 436:1176–80

10. Blanchoin L, Amann KJ, Higgs HN, Marchand JB, Kaiser DA, Pollard TD. 2000. Direct observation of dendritic actin filament networks nucleated by Arp2/3 complex and WASP/Scar proteins. *Nature* 404:1007–11

11. Bloch D, Lavy M, Efrat Y, Efroni I, Bracha-Drori K, et al. 2005. Ectopic expression of an activated RAC in Arabidopsis disrupts membrane cycling. *Mol. Biol. Cell* 16:1913–27

12. Brembu T, Winge P, Seem M, Bones AM. 2004. NAPP and PIRP encode subunits of a putative wave regulatory protein complex involved in plant cell morphogenesis. *Plant Cell* 16:2335–49

13. Brown SS, Spudich JA. 1979. Cytochalasin inhibits the rate of elongation of actin filament fragments. *J. Cell Biol.* 83:657–62

14. Carlier MF, Laurent V, Santolini J, Melki R, Didry D, et al. 1997. Actin depolymerizing factor (ADF/cofilin) enhances the rate of filament turnover: implication in actin-based motility. *J. Cell Biol.* 136:1307–22

15. Chen CY, Cheung AY, Wu HM. 2003. Actin-depolymerizing factor mediates Rac/Rop GTPase-regulated pollen tube growth. *Plant Cell* 15:237–49

16. Chen CY, Wong EI, Vidali L, Estavillo A, Hepler PK, et al. 2002. The regulation of actin organization by actin-depolymerizing factor in elongating pollen tubes. *Plant Cell* 14:2175–90

17. Cheung AY, Chen CY, Tao LZ, Andreyeva T, Twell D, Wu HM. 2003. Regulation of pollen tube growth by Rac-like GTPases. *J. Exp. Bot.* 54:73–81

18. Cheung AY, Wu HM. 2004. Overexpression of an Arabidopsis formin stimulates supernumerary actin cable formation from pollen tube cell membrane. *Plant Cell* 16:257–69

19. Coué M, Brenner SL, Spector I, Korn ED. 1987. Inhibition of actin polymerization by latrunculin A. *FEBS Lett.* 213:316–18

20. Cvrckova F, Novotny M, Pickova D, Zarsky V. 2004. Formin homology 2 domains occur in multiple contexts in angiosperms. *BMC Genomics* 5:44

20a. Deeks MJ, Cvrckova F, Machesky LM, Mikitova V, Ketelaar T, et al. 2005. Arabidopsis group Ie formins localize to specific cell membrane domains, interact with actin-binding proteins and cause defects in cell expansion upon aberrant expression. *New Phytol.* 168:529–40

21. Deeks MJ, Hussey PJ, Davies B. 2002. Formins: intermediates in signal-transduction cascades that affect cytoskeletal reorganization. *Trends Plant Sci.* 7:492–98

22. Deeks MJ, Kaloriti D, Davies B, Malho R, Hussey PJ. 2004. Arabidopsis NAP1 is essential for Arp2/3-dependent trichome morphogenesis. *Curr. Biol.* 14:1410–14

23. Dong CH, Xia GX, Hong Y, Ramachandran S, Kost B, Chua NH. 2001. ADF proteins are involved in the control of flowering and regulate F-actin organization, cell expansion, and organ growth in Arabidopsis. *Plant Cell* 13:1333–46

24. El-Assal Sel D, Le J, Basu D, Mallery EL, Szymanski DB. 2004. Arabidopsis GNARLED encodes a NAP125 homolog that positively regulates ARP2/3. *Curr. Biol.* 14:1405–9

25. El-Din El-Assal S, Le J, Basu D, Mallery EL, Szymanski DB. 2004. DISTORTED2 encodes an ARPC2 subunit of the putative Arabidopsis ARP2/3 complex. *Plant J.* 38:526–38

26. Frank M, Egile C, Dyachok J, Djakovic S, Nolasco M, et al. 2004. Activation of Arp2/3 complex-dependent actin polymerization by plant proteins distantly related to Scar/WAVE. *Proc. Natl. Acad. Sci. USA* 101:16379–84

27. Freeman NL, Chen Z, Horenstein J, Weber A, Field J. 1995. An actin monomer binding activity localizes to the carboxyl-terminal half of the *Saccharomyces cerevisiae* cyclase-associated protein. *J. Biol. Chem.* 270:5680–85

28. Fu Y, Gu Y, Zheng Z, Wasteneys G, Yang Z. 2005. Arabidopsis interdigitating cell growth requires two antagonistic pathways with opposing action on cell morphogenesis. *Cell* 120:687–700

29. Fu Y, Li H, Yang Z. 2002. The ROP2 GTPase controls the formation of cortical fine F-actin and the early phase of directional cell expansion during Arabidopsis organogenesis. *Plant Cell* 14:777–94

30. Fu Y, Wu G, Yang Z. 2001. Rop GTPase-dependent dynamics of tip-localized F-actin controls tip growth in pollen tubes. *J. Cell Biol.* 152:1019–32

31. Gibbon BC, Kovar DR, Staiger CJ. 1999. Latrunculin B has different effects on pollen germination and tube growth. *Plant Cell* 11:2349–63

32. Gilliland LU, Pawloski LC, Kandasamy MK, Meagher RB. 2003. Arabidopsis actin gene ACT7 plays an essential role in germination and root growth. *Plant J.* 33:319–28

33. Gottwald U, Brokamp R, Karakesisoglou I, Schleicher M, Noegel AA. 1996. Identification of a cyclase-associated protein (CAP) homologue in *Dictyostelium discoideum* and characterization of its interaction with actin. *Mol. Biol. Cell* 7:261–72

34. Gu Y, Fu Y, Dowd P, Li S, Vernoud V, et al. 2005. A Rho family GTPase controls actin dynamics and tip growth via two counteracting downstream pathways in pollen tubes. *J. Cell Biol.* 169:127–38

35. Gungabissoon RA, Jiang CJ, Drobak BK. 1998. Interaction of maize actin-depolymerising factor with actin and phosphoinositides and its inhibition of plant phospholipase C. *Plant J.* 16:689–96

36. Gungabissoon RA, Khan S, Hussey PJ. 2001. Interaction of elongation factor 1 alpha from Zea mays (ZmEF-1 alpha) with F-actin and interplay with the maize actin severing protein, ZmADF3. *Cell Motil. Cytoskel.* 49:104–11

37. Harborth J, Elbashir SM, Bechert K, Tuschl T, Weber K. 2001. Identification of essential genes in cultured mammalian cells using small interfering RNAs. *J. Cell Sci.* 114:4557–65

38. Hepler PK, Vidali L, Cheung AY. 2001. Polarized cell growth in higher plants. *Annu. Rev. Cell Dev. Biol.* 17:159–87

39. Higgs HN, Pollard TD. 2001. Regulation of actin filament network formation through ARP2/3 complex: activation by a diverse array of proteins. *Annu. Rev. Biochem.* 70:649–76

40. Huang S, Blanchoin L, Chaudhry F, Franklin-Tong VE, Staiger CJ. 2004. A gelsolin-like protein from Papaver rhoeas pollen (PrABP80) stimulates calcium-regulated severing and depolymerization of actin filaments. *J. Biol. Chem.* 279:23364–75

41. Huang S, Blanchoin L, Kovar DR, Staiger CJ. 2003. Arabidopsis capping protein (AtCP) is a heterodimer that regulates assembly at the barbed ends of actin filaments. *J. Biol. Chem.* 278:44832–42

42. Huang S, Robinson RC, Gao LY, Matsumoto T, Brunet A, et al. 2005. Arabidopsis VILLIN1 generates actin filament cables that are resistant to depolymerization. *Plant Cell* 17:486–501

43. Hudson AM, Cooley L. 2002. A subset of dynamic actin rearrangements in Drosophila requires the Arp2/3 complex. *J. Cell Biol* 156:677–87

44. Ingouff M, Fitz Gerald JN, Guerin C, Robert H, Sorensen MB, et al. 2005. Plant formin AtFH5 is an evolutionarily conserved actin nucleator involved in cytokinesis. *Nat. Cell Biol.* 7:374–80

45. Jones MA, Shen JJ, Fu Y, Li H, Yang Z, Grierson CS. 2002. The Arabidopsis Rop2 GTPase is a positive regulator of both root hair initiation and tip growth. *Plant Cell* 14:763–76

46. Kandasamy MK, McKinney EC, Meagher RB. 2002. Functional nonequivalency of actin isovariants in Arabidopsis. *Mol. Biol. Cell* 13:251–61

47. Ketelaar T. 2002. *Spatial Organisation of Cell Expansion by the Cytoskeleton.* Wageningen: Wageningen Univ.

48. Ketelaar T, Allwood EG, Anthony R, Voigt B, Menzel D, Hussey PJ. 2004. The actin-interacting protein AIP1 is essential for actin organization and plant development. *Curr. Biol.* 14:145–49

49. Ketelaar T, Anthony RG, Hussey PJ. 2004. Green fluorescent protein-mTalin causes defects in actin organization and cell expansion in Arabidopsis and inhibits actin depolymerizing factor's actin depolymerizing activity in vitro. *Plant Physiol.* 136:3990–98

50. Ketelaar T, de Ruijter NC, Emons AM. 2003. Unstable F-actin specifies the area and microtubule direction of cell expansion in Arabidopsis root hairs. *Plant Cell* 15:285–92

51. Ketelaar T, Emons AM. 2001. The cytoskeleton in plant cell growth: lessons from root hairs. *New Phytol.* 152:409–18

52. Ketelaar T, Faivre-Moskalenko C, Esseling JJ, de Ruijter NC, Grierson CS, et al. 2002. Positioning of nuclei in Arabidopsis root hairs: an actin-regulated process of tip growth. *Plant Cell* 14:2941–55

53. Kost B, Lemichez E, Spielhofer P, Hong Y, Tolias K, et al. 1999. Rac homologues and compartmentalized phosphatidylinositol 4,5-bisphosphate act in a common pathway to regulate polar pollen tube growth. *J. Cell Biol.* 145:317–30

54. Kovar DR, Drobak BK, Staiger CJ. 2000. Maize profilin isoforms are functionally distinct. *Plant Cell* 12:583–98

55. Kovar DR, Gibbon BC, McCurdy DW, Staiger CJ. 2001. Fluorescently-labeled fimbrin decorates a dynamic actin filament network in live plant cells. *Planta* 213:390–95

56. Kovar DR, Kuhn JR, Tichy AL, Pollard TD. 2003. The fission yeast cytokinesis formin Cdc12p is a barbed end actin filament capping protein gated by profilin. *J. Cell Biol.* 161:875–87

57. Kovar DR, Staiger CJ, Weaver EA, McCurdy DW. 2000. AtFim1 is an actin filament crosslinking protein from Arabidopsis thaliana. *Plant J.* 24:625–36

58. Lam BC, Sage TL, Bianchi F, Blumwald E. 2001. Role of SH3 domain-containing proteins in clathrin-mediated vesicle trafficking in Arabidopsis. *Plant Cell* 13:2499–512

59. Le J, El-Assal Sel D, Basu D, Saad ME, Szymanski DB. 2003. Requirements for Arabidopsis ATARP2 and ATARP3 during epidermal development. *Curr. Biol.* 13:1341–47

60. Li H, Lin Y, Heath RM, Zhu MX, Yang Z. 1999. Control of pollen tube tip growth by a Rop GTPase-dependent pathway that leads to tip-localized calcium influx. *Plant Cell* 11:1731–42

61. Li S, Blanchoin L, Yang Z, Lord EM. 2003. The putative Arabidopsis arp2/3 complex controls leaf cell morphogenesis. *Plant Physiol.* 132:2034–44

62. Li Y, Sorefan K, Hemmann G, Bevan MW. 2004. Arabidopsis NAP and PIR regulate actin-based cell morphogenesis and multiple developmental processes. *Plant Physiol.* 136:3616–27

63. Lin Y, Yang Z. 1997. Inhibition of pollen tube elongation by microinjected anti-Rop1Ps antibodies suggests a crucial role for Rho-type GTPases in the control of tip growth. *Plant Cell* 9:1647–59

63a. Lopez-Valenzuela JA, Gibbon BC, Hughes PA, Dreher TW, Larkins BA. 2003. eEF1A isoforms change in abundance and actin-binding activity during maize endosperm development. *Plant Physiol.* 133:1285–95

64. Mathur J, Mathur N, Kernebeck B, Hulskamp M. 2003. Mutations in actin-related proteins 2 and 3 affect cell shape development in Arabidopsis. *Plant Cell* 15:1632–45

65. Mathur J, Mathur N, Kirik V, Kernebeck B, Srinivas BP, Hulskamp M. 2003. Arabidopsis CROOKED encodes for the smallest subunit of the ARP2/3 complex and controls cell shape by region specific fine F-actin formation. *Development* 130:3137–46

66. Mathur J, Spielhofer P, Kost B, Chua N. 1999. The actin cytoskeleton is required to elaborate and maintain spatial patterning during trichome cell morphogenesis in *Arabidopsis thaliana*. *Development* 126:5559–68

67. Mattila PK, Quintero-Monzon O, Kugler J, Moseley JB, Almo SC, et al. 2004. A high-affinity interaction with ADP-actin monomers underlies the mechanism and in vivo function of Srv2/cyclase-associated protein. *Mol. Biol. Cell* 15:5158–71

68. McCurdy DW, Kim M. 1998. Molecular cloning of a novel fimbrin-like cDNA from *Arabidopsis thaliana*. *Plant Mol. Biol.* 36:23–31

69. McKinney EC, Ali N, Traut A, Feldmann KA, Belostotsky DA, et al. 1995. Sequence-based identification of T-DNA insertion mutations in Arabidopsis: actin mutants act2-1 and act4-1. *Plant J.* 8:613–22

70. Michelot A, Guerin C, Huang S, Ingouff M, Richard S, et al. 2005. The formin homology 1 domain modulates the actin nucleation and bundling activity of Arabidopsis FORMIN1. *Plant Cell* 17:2296–13

71. Miller DD, de Ruijter NCA, Bisseling T, Emons AMC. 1999. The role of actin in root hair morphogenesis: studies with lipochito-oligosaccharide as a growth stimulator and cytochalasin as an actin perturbing drug. *Plant J.* 17:141–54

72. Molendijk AJ, Bischoff F, Rajendrakumar CS, Friml J, Braun M, et al. 2001. *Arabidopsis thaliana* Rop GTPases are localized to tips of root hairs and control polar growth. *EMBO J.* 20:2779–88

73. Oikawa K, Kasahara M, Kiyosue T, Kagawa T, Suetsugu N, et al. 2003. Chloroplast unusual positioning1 is essential for proper chloroplast positioning. *Plant Cell* 15:2805–15

74. Pantaloni D, Le Clainche C, Carlier MF. 2001. Mechanism of actin-based motility. *Science* 292:1502–6

74a. Parton RM, Fischer-Parton S, Trewavas AJ, Watahiki MK. 2003. Pollen tubes exhibit regular periodic membrane trafficking events in the absence of apical extension. *J. Cell Sci.* 116:2707–19

75. Pollard TD, Blanchoin L, Mullins RD. 2000. Molecular mechanisms controlling actin filament dynamics in nonmuscle cells. *Annu. Rev. Biophys. Biomol. Struct.* 29:545–76

76. Pruyne D, Evangelista M, Yang C, Bi E, Zigmond S, et al. 2002. Role of formins in actin assembly: nucleation and barbed-end association. *Science* 297:612–15

77. Qiu JL, Jilk R, Marks MD, Szymanski D. 2002. The *Arabidopsis SPIKE1* gene is required for normal cell shape control and tissue development. *Plant Cell* 14:101–18

78. Ramachandran S, Christensen HE, Ishimaru Y, Dong CH, Chao-Ming W, et al. 2000. Profilin plays a role in cell elongation, cell shape maintenance, and flowering in Arabidopsis. *Plant Physiol.* 124:1637–47

79. Ringli C, Baumberger N, Diet A, Frey B, Keller B. 2002. ACTIN2 is essential for bulge site selection and tip growth during root hair development of Arabidopsis. *Plant Physiol.* 129:1464–72

80. Romero S, Le Clainche C, Didry D, Egile C, Pantaloni D, Carlier MF. 2004. Formin is a processive motor that requires profilin to accelerate actin assembly and associated ATP hydrolysis. *Cell* 119:419–29

81. Saedler R, Zimmermann I, Mutondo M, Hulskamp M. 2004. The *Arabidopsis KLUNKER* gene controls cell shape changes and encodes the AtSRA1 homolog. *Plant Mol. Biol.* 56:775–82

82. Sawa M, Suetsugu S, Sugimoto A, Miki H, Yamamoto M, Takenawa T. 2003. Essential role of the C. elegans Arp2/3 complex in cell migration during ventral enclosure. *J. Cell Sci.* 116:1505–18

83. Schwab B, Mathur J, Saedler R, Schwarz H, Frey B, et al. 2003. Regulation of cell expansion by the *DISTORTED* genes in Arabidopsis thaliana: actin controls the spatial organization of microtubules. *Mol. Genet. Genomics* 269:350–60

84. Sheahan MB, Staiger CJ, Rose RJ, McCurdy DW. 2004. A green fluorescent protein fusion to actin-binding domain 2 of Arabidopsis fimbrin highlights new features of a dynamic actin cytoskeleton in live plant cells. *Plant Physiol.* 136:3968–78

85. Smertenko AP, Jiang CJ, Simmons NJ, Weeds AG, Davies DR, Hussey PJ. 1998. Ser6 in the maize actin-depolymerizing factor, ZmADF3, is phosphorylated by a calcium-stimulated protein kinase and is essential for the control of functional activity. *Plant J.* 14:187–93

85a. Smith LG, Oppenheimer DG. 2005. Spatial control of cell expansion by the plant cytoskeleton. *Annu. Rev. Cell Dev. Biol.* 21:271–95

86. Szymanski DB, Marks MD, Wick SM. 1999. Organized F-actin is essential for normal trichome morphogenesis in Arabidopsis. *Plant Cell* 11:2331–47

87. Tominaga M, Yokota E, Vidali L, Sonobe S, Hepler PK, Shimmen T. 2000. The role of plant villin in the organization of the actin cytoskeleton, cytoplasmic streaming and the architecture of the transvacuolar strand in root hair cells of Hydrocharis. *Planta* 210:836–43

88. Valster AH, Pierson ES, Valenta R, Hepler PK, Emons AMC. 1997. Probing the plant actin cytoskeleton during cytokinesis and interphase by profilin microinjection. *Plant Cell* 9:1815–24

89. Valster AH, Vidali L, Hepler PK. 2003. Nuclear localization of profilin during the cell cycle in *Tradescantia virginiana* stamen hair cells. *Protoplasma* 222:85–95

90. Vidali L, Hepler PK. 1997. Characterization and localization of profilin in pollen grains and tubes of *Lilium longiflorum. Cell Motil. Cytoskeleton* 36:323–38

91. Vidali L, Yokota E, Cheung AY, Shimmen T, Hepler PK. 1999. The 135kDa actin-bundling protein from *Lilium longiflorum* pollen is the plant homologue of villin. *Protoplasma* 209:283–91

92. Wang YS, Motes CM, Mohamalawari DR, Blancaflor EB. 2004. Green fluorescent protein fusions to Arabidopsis fimbrin 1 for spatio-temporal imaging of F-actin dynamics in roots. *Cell Motil. Cytoskeleton* 59:79–93

93. Winter DC, Choe EY, Li R. 1999. Genetic dissection of the budding yeast Arp2/3 complex: a comparison of the in vivo and structural roles of individual subunits. *Proc. Natl. Acad. Sci. USA* 96:7288–93

94. Wu G, Gu Y, Li S, Yang Z. 2001. A genome-wide analysis of Arabidopsis Rop-interactive CRIB motif-containing proteins that act as Rop GTPase targets. *Plant Cell* 13:2841–56

95. Yamaguchi H, Lorenz M, Kempiak S, Sarmiento C, Coniglio S, et al. 2005. Molecular mechanisms of invadopodium formation: the role of the N-WASP-Arp2/3 complex pathway and cofilin. *J. Cell Biol.* 168:441–52

96. Yi K, Guo C, Chen D, Zhao B, Yang B, Ren H. 2005. Cloning and functional characterization of a formin-like protein (AtFH8) from Arabidopsis. *Plant Physiol.* 138:1071–82

97. Yokota E, Shimmen T. 1999. The 135-kDa actin-bundling protein from lily pollen tubes arranges F-actin into bundles with uniform polarity. *Planta* 209:264–66

98. Yokota E, Takahara K, Shimmen T. 1998. Actin-bundling protein isolated from pollen tubes of lily. Biochemical and immunocytochemical characterization. *Plant Physiol.* 116:1421–29

99. Yokota E, Vidali L, Tominaga M, Tahara H, Orii H, et al. 2003. Plant 115-kDa actin-filament bundling protein, P-115-ABP, is a homologue of plant villin and is widely distributed in cells. *Plant Cell Physiol.* 44:1088–99

100. Zallen JA, Cohen Y, Hudson AM, Cooley L, Wieschaus E, Schejter ED. 2002. SCAR is a primary regulator of Arp2/3-dependent morphological events in *Drosophila*. *J. Cell Biol.* 156:689–701

101. Zhang X, Dyachok J, Krishnakumar S, Smith LG, Oppenheimer DG. 2005. IRREGULAR TRICHOME BRANCH1 in Arabidopsis encodes a plant homolog of the actin-related protein2/3 complex activator scar/WAVE that regulates actin and microtubule organization. *Plant Cell* 17:2314–26

102. Zigmond SH, Evangelista M, Boone C, Yang C, Dar AC, et al. 2003. Formin leaky cap allows elongation in the presence of tight capping proteins. *Curr. Biol.* 13:1820–23

103. Zimmermann I, Saedler R, Mutondo M, Hulskamp M. 2004. The *Arabidopsis GNARLED* gene encodes the NAP125 homolog and controls several actin-based cell shape changes. *Mol. Genet. Genomics* 272:290–96

RELATED RESOURCES

Staiger CJ. 2000. Signaling to the actin cytoskeleton in plants. *Annu. Rev. Plant Physiol. Plant Mol. Biol.* 51:257–88

Wasteneys GO, Galway ME. 2003. Remodeling the cytoskeleton for growth and form: an overview with some new views. *Annu. Rev. Plant Biol.* 54:691–722

Welch MD, Mullins RD. 2002. Cellular control of actin nucleation. *Annu. Rev. Cell Dev. Biol.* 18:247–88

Responding to Color: The Regulation of Complementary Chromatic Adaptation

David M. Kehoe and Andrian Gutu

Department of Biology, Indiana University, Bloomington, Indiana 47405;
email: dkehoe@indiana.edu, agutu@indiana.edu

Annu. Rev. Plant Biol.
2006. 57:127–50

The *Annual Review of Plant Biology* is online at
plant.annualreviews.org

doi: 10.1146/
annurev.arplant.57.032905.105215

Key Words

light regulation, signal transduction, phytochrome photoreceptors,
redox regulation, light harvesting, cyanobacteria

Abstract

The acclimation of photosynthetic organisms to changes in light
color is ubiquitous and may be best illustrated by the colorful process of complementary chromatic adaptation (CCA). During CCA,
cyanobacterial cells change from brick red to bright blue green, depending on their light color environment. The apparent simplicity
of this spectacular, photoreversible event belies the complexity of
the cellular response to changes in light color. Recent results have
shown that the regulation of CCA is also complex and involves at least
three pathways. One is controlled by a phytochrome-class photoreceptor that is responsive to green and red light and a complex two-
component signal transduction pathway, whereas another is based
on sensing redox state. Studies of CCA are uncovering the strategies
used by photosynthetic organisms during light acclimation and the
means by which they regulate these responses.

Contents

INTRODUCTION

Photosynthetic organisms harvest energy and information from light. Complex regulatory systems efficiently modify light-harvesting structures and cellular processes to accommodate changes in ambient light information, specifically in wavelength distribution (color) and intensity. One of the best studied examples of this is a process called complementary chromatic adaptation (CCA), a response to changes in ambient light color that is found in many freshwater, marine, and soil cyanobacterial species. The most spectacular consequence of CCA is the massive restructuring of the photosynthetic light-harvesting antennae, or phycobilisomes (PBS), which are responsible for providing light energy primarily to photosystem II reaction centers. This review focuses on recent developments in understanding CCA regulation as it influences PBS biogenesis and other cellular processes. Because a number of excellent reviews exist on the structural and functional aspects of PBS (49, 70, 97), this article provides information on PBS only as it pertains to CCA.

When last reviewed in the *Annual Reviews* series (53), CCA had been clearly defined at the level of changes in PBS structure and initial information on its regulation had been obtained (21). In the past decade, significant progress was made in understanding CCA regulatory mechanisms and identifying cellular processes in addition to PBS structural modifications that are controlled by CCA. Focusing primarily on the model organism *Fremyella diplosiphon* UTEX 481 (also called *Calothrix* or *Tolypothrix* sp. PCC 7601), a freshwater filamentous species, we examine the developing definition of CCA and describe the responses known to occur during this process. We discuss the two photosensory systems found to control CCA. We also describe a regulatory mechanism that activates gene expression in green light and apparently coordinates the transcription of PBS-related genes in many cyanobacteria, including some that are not capable of CCA. Finally, we review how CCA studies are providing insights into the coordination of gene expression, including light-harvesting apoprotein and chromophore biosynthetic enzyme genes.

The Evolving Concept of Complementary Chromatic Adaptation

There is a rich history of scientific inquiry into the process of CCA (105). The term

CCA:
complementary
chromatic adaptation

"complementary chromatic adaptation" was initially used by both Engelmann and his student Gaidukov, but with slightly different meanings (36, 37, 47, 48). Englemann proposed that the variations in the vertical distribution of pigments in marine macroalgal communities correlated with the changes in the spectral distribution of light throughout the water column. He predicted that the color of the pigments synthesized by each species was complementary to its ambient light color. Although subsequent studies did not support this proposal (30, 88, 89, 94), they led to the demonstration by Gaidukov in 1902 that the cyanobacterium *Oscillatoria sancta* was blue green when grown in orange light and red when grown in green light. This color change was due to changes in the levels of two light-harvesting proteins that are synthesized by the organism (**Figure 1**) (10). Phycocyanin (PC) accumulates in red light and phycoerythrin (PE) accumulates in green light (**Figure 2a**). Ever since its discovery, this change in pigmentation has been considered to be the defining feature of CCA. Thus, CCA can only occur in cyanobacterial species that make both PC and PE, although not all such species are capable of this process (104). It is noteworthy that although red macroalgae also use PBS for light harvesting (49, 53), none are known to undergo CCA.

From a current genetic perspective and our present understanding of CCA and its regulation, the phrase "complementary chromatic adaptation" is a misnomer, because "adaptation" involves fundamental changes in the genetic composition of an organism that may allow it to better exploit a specific ecological niche. All available information on CCA and its regulation suggest that the immediate changes occurring during this response are the result of changes at the level of gene expression rather than genome structure. Thus, "complementary chromatic adaptation" can be strictly defined as an "acclimation" response, although historical usage of the word "adaptation" weighs against renaming this process. In addition, viewed over a longer time

period, cyanobacterial species that undergo CCA must have accumulated the structural and regulatory genes needed for this response, and such genes are likely to either be absent or have other roles in species that do not undergo CCA. In this context, developing the capacity to carry out the acclimation process we call CCA can be considered an adaptation, perhaps increasing fitness for those cyanobacterial species that exploit environments with significant variations in light color. It would be interesting to test this hypothesis.

The understanding of CCA progressed in the 1950s and 1960s through the work of Fujita & Hattori, who generated action spectra and demonstrated that in the soil cyanobacterium *Tolypothrix tenuis* (PCC 7101), CCA was controlled by a photoreversible pigment(s) that responded to green (~540 nm) and red (~640 nm) light (44–46, 54, 55). Exposures of only a few minutes of either light color were sufficient to direct whether PE or PC was produced. The responses were insensitive to photosynthesis inhibitors. These results suggested that CCA was controlled by a photoreceptor rather than via photosynthesis or another cellular process. This process was also photoreversible, responsive only to the final light treatment that was given. Thus, CCA shared features with plant responses that were controlled by a class of red/far-red light photoreversible photoreceptors called the phytochromes (98). Photobiological studies later showed that CCA and phytochrome regulation differed in several ways besides their action spectra. Most notably, the CCA system(s) remained fully in one state or the other in darkness, depending on the final light treatment (79). In addition, there was

Figure 1

The color phenotypes of *F. diplosiphon* filaments grown on agar plates and fully acclimated to green light (*left*) and red light (*right*). The accumulation of different pigmented proteins into phycobilisome (PBS) rods renders the cells brick red or blue green.

Phycobilisomes (PBS): water-soluble supermolecular complexes found in cyanobacteria and red algae that are associated with thylakoid membranes and efficiently harvest light energy to drive photosynthesis

UTEX: University of Texas Culture Collection

PCC: Pasteur Culture Collection

PC: phycocyanin

PE: phycoerythrin

no detectable dark reversion or destruction of the photoreceptor(s), as occurs in some phytochrome responses. Additional action spectra conducted in the 1970s and 1980s using *F. diplosiphon*, *T. tenuis*, and *Synechocystis*

sp. PCC 6701 supported the results of Hattori and Fujita by demonstrating that CCA was maximally responsive to light in the green and red regions of the spectrum in these species as well (35, 56, 84, 106, 112).

There have been two important refinements in our understanding of the general pigmentation changes during the CCA response. The first described variation that exists in the CCA regulation of PE and PC abundance between strains (104). Within species that produce both PE and PC, three response groups were defined. Group I strains, which made up about 27% of the total, were not capable of CCA because they altered neither PE nor PC abundance in response to changing light colors. Group II strains comprised 16% of the total. These had elevated PE levels in green light but did not vary PC levels in response to green-red light shifts. The remaining 57% were group III strains, which varied both PE and PC, increasing PE in green light and PC in red light. The second refinement, identified by studies of CCA in *T. tenuis*, *F. diplosiphon*, *Nostoc* sp. MAC, *Synechocystis* sp. PCC 6701, and

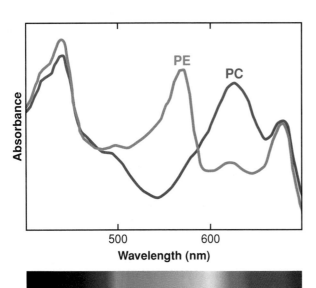

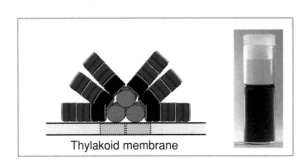

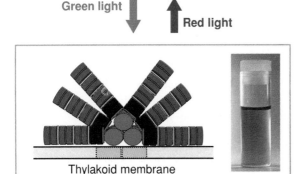

Figure 2

(*a*) Whole-cell absorption spectra of *F. diplosiphon* cells grown in green and red light. The phycoerythrin (PE) and phycocyanin (PC) absorption peaks are indicated. The remaining peaks in the blue and red regions represent absorption by chlorophyll *a* and carotenoids. (*b*) Red and green light induced structural changes in an *F. diplosiphon* phycobilisome (PBS) and the corresponding extracted phycobiliproteins. The water-soluble PBS associates with photosystem II reaction centers (*green rectangles*) and consists of a tricylindrical core (*light blue*) and the outwardly oriented rods. The PBS structural unit is a hexamer (discs consisting of stacked pairs of cylindrical trimers when viewed on end), allophycocyanin (AP) (*light blue*) in the core, and constitutive PC (*dark blue*), inducible PC (*medium blue*), and/or PE (*pink*) in the rods. Linker proteins (*gray*) serve as scaffolds. Green rectangles represent photosystem II reaction centers. This model was derived using ultrastructural and biochemical data (6, 13, 52, 93).

Phormidium sp. C86, was the finding that a range of species-dependent structural changes in PBS morphology occurred in cyanobacteria during CCA (13, 82, 83, 93, 113).

Over time it has become clear that many additional cellular responses are affected by shifts between green and red light, including changes in cell and filament architecture (7, 9), cell differentiation states (32, 66), and the abundance of many RNAs and proteins that do not encode PBS components (51, 101). These results showed that far more occurs during CCA than a simple change in pigmentation, the definition originally used for this response. Defining CCA and its regulation has become even more complex with the finding that CCA responses affecting PBS composition are photoreceptor controlled in *F. diplosiphon* (62, 110), while other green-red light responses are regulated through the redox state of the photosynthetic electron transport chain (17, 32). Further complicating matters, studies have identified green-red light-controlled, photoreversible developmental responses in cyanobacteria that are not known to change their PBS pigment ratios, such as *Nostoc muscorum* and *Nostoc commune* 584 (66, 92).

We propose that any green-red light photoreversible response occurring in a cyanobacterial strain that is capable of decreasing its PC:PE ratio in green light and increasing this ratio in red light be considered a "CCA response." This includes responses that do not directly affect PBS biogenesis or change the color of the cell, as well as rapid and transient responses such as state transitions (18). It is important to note that our definition distinguishes between the same green-red light–controlled response if it occurs in two different species, one that alters its PC:PE ratio in response to green and red light and the other that does not. In the former strain, this is a CCA response, but is not considered a CCA response in the latter. Finally, we propose that any process through which a species alters the composition of its light-harvesting antenna in response to colors of light other than green and red, or the ratio of pigmented proteins other than PC and PE, as in some marine *Synechococcus* strains (85), be referred to as "chromatic adaptation" or (likely more accurately) "chromatic acclimation."

CELLULAR RESPONSES DURING COMPLEMENTARY CHROMATIC ADAPTATION

Changes in Phycobilisome Structure and Gene Expression

The changes in the ratio of PC to PE in *F. diplosiphon* during CCA (**Figure 1**) are typical of group III species (104) and lead to the synthesis of PBS with absorption characteristics that are optimized to capture the most abundant wavelength(s) of ambient light in the green-to-red region of the spectrum. This is because PE most efficiently absorbs green light, whereas PC absorbs red light most effectively (**Figure 2a**). Although no selective advantage has yet been demonstrated for species capable of CCA in environments with variable ratios of green and red light, a correlation has been found between such an environment and the prevalence of CCA-capable species (87). The structural and color differences in PBS from *F. diplosiphon* grown in red and green light are shown in **Figure 2b**. The structures presented in this figure represent the extremes of the CCA response; intermediate levels of accumulation of these proteins occur under light containing both green and red wavelengths. The thorough characterization of PBS components and corresponding genes, and the analysis of their expression in green and red light, have been the cornerstones of current studies on CCA regulation and are discussed below.

The two major substructures within a *F. diplosiphon* PBS are the core and rods, six of which emanate from the core (**Figure 2b**). These PBS may contain various combinations of three major types of chromophore-carrying proteins called phycobiliproteins: PE [absorption maximum (A_{max}) = 565 nm], PC

Action spectrum: identification of the wavelengths of the light spectrum that are the most effective in eliciting a given cellular response

Phytochrome: a class of proteins containing a covalently attached bilin chromophore that are present in prokaryotes and eukaryotes and act as photoreceptors. Phytochromes undergo photoreversible changes in conformation that regulate their activity.

RNA: ribonucleic acid

A_{max}: absorption maximum

AP: allophycocyanin

INTEGRATING NUTRIENT AND LIGHT COLOR INFORMATION

F. diplosiphon possesses an unexpected and fascinating aspect of PBS biogenesis. The PBS structures described in this review make up an important part of the CCA response when nutrients are not limiting in the environment. However, under sulfur-limiting conditions in red light, RNA from the red light–inducible *cpc2* operon is virtually undetectable. In its place, a third PC-encoding operon called *cpcB3A3H3I3D3* (*cpc3*) is expressed (73, 74). Thus far, no other conditions are known to lead to the accumulation of *cpc3* transcripts. Analysis of the amino acid sequences of the α and β subunits of this low sulfur-inducible form of PC (PC$_s$ or PC3) demonstrated that they did not contain any methionines and only possessed the four cysteines required for covalent attachment of the PCB chromophores (74). This was the first identification of a molecular response to nutrient limitation that entailed the production of alternative proteins containing less of the limiting nutrient. Such responses may be widespread among organisms capable of oligotrophy or otherwise under nutrient stress (90). For example, yeast exposed to cadmium produce large amounts of glutathione for detoxification, placing severe demands on cellular sulfur supplies. In turn, cells have a proteome-wide response that involves replacing abundant, sulfur-rich proteins with sulfur-depleted isozymes (38). In the future, it will be of great interest to explore the mechanisms used by *F. diplosiphon* to integrate its CCA response with this sulfur-limitation response.

PC$_c$ or PC1:
constitutive
phycocyanin

PC$_i$ or PC2:
inducible
phycocyanin

(A$_{max}$= 620 nm), and allophycocyanin (AP) (A$_{max}$= 650 nm). Each of these form unique disc-like structures of six monomers stacked as two cylindrical trimers, with each monomer consisting of an α and β subunit (49, 52, 103). Discs are connected by linker proteins, which are predominantly not chromophorylated (39, 40, 58, 59, 68, 107) and also attach rods to the core and the core to the thylakoid membrane.

AP is found within the core. Its α and β subunits are encoded by the *apcA1B1* genes (29, 59). The genes encoding the core-linker protein (*apcC*) and the core-membrane linker (*apcE*) are located near the *apcA1B1* genes (58). Both transcript and protein levels from

these genes do not significantly change during CCA.

The core-proximal disc of each rod consists of a type of PC called "constitutive PC" (PC$_c$ or PC1), which is encoded by *cpcB1A1* (27, 29, 59, 73). Both transcripts and the corresponding protein from this operon are equally abundant in green and red light.

The core-distal regions of the rods are the sites of changes during CCA in this species. During growth in green light, up to three separate discs of PE may be present (**Figure 2b**) (13, 93). The β and α subunits of PE are encoded by the *cpeBA* operon (71). The PE discs associate with each other and the core-proximal portion of the rod through the action of three PE linkers, which are encoded by *cpeCDE* (39, 40). Although the *cpeBA* and *cpeCDE* operons are not closely linked in the *F. diplosiphon* genome, it has been shown that both are highly and rapidly upregulated after cells are switched from red to green light (39). During red-light growth, the outer two discs of the PBS rods contain a second form of PC known as "inducible PC" (PC$_i$ or PC2) (27, 28, 68, 103). The β and α subunits of this phycobiliprotein are encoded by the *cpcB2A2* genes, which are cotranscribed with three corresponding linker proteins that are encoded by the *cpcH2I2D2* genes. This large transcription unit (*cpcB2A2H2I2D2*), whose expression is highly and continuously upregulated in red light, will be called "*cpc2*."

Morphological, Developmental, and Nonphycobilisome Gene Responses

In *F. diplosiphon*, the cellular response during CCA is extensive. Under red light, cells are smaller and more rounded than during growth in fluorescent (green) light. Also, mean filament length is approximately 10 times less in red light due to the conversion of approximately 20% of the cells to necridia, sites of programmed cell death (7, 8, 9). The synthesis of hormogonia is CCA regulated in *F. diplosiphon*. Hormogonia are short, differentiated, motile filaments that develop pili and gas vesicles. They are resistant to adverse environmental conditions and appear to play a role in dispersal and survival (91, 103). This transient developmental stage typically exists for 72 to 96 hours and is stimulated by red light and inhibited by green light (32, 108). CCA also affects the growth rate of *F. diplosiphon* cells grown with glucose in darkness. A daily five-minute green-light exposure depresses the dark growth rate by up to 50%, and this effect can be reversed by brief irradiation with red light (34).

The above findings suggest that there are many changes in protein abundance during CCA in addition to those involved in the restructuring of PBS. Several studies have confirmed this. Protein-labeling experiments demonstrated that the abundance of several unidentified membrane-associated polypeptides changes during CCA (51). Such changes were further delineated by two-dimensional gel electrophoresis results demonstrating that the abundance of at least 80 soluble proteins changes significantly during CCA (101).

Many CCA-regulated genes in *F. diplosiphon* that do not encode PBS structural proteins have also been identified. During red light–induced hormogonia formation, transcripts from the *gvpABC* operon, which encodes several gas vesicle components, increase significantly in *F. diplosiphon* (31–33). DNA microarray studies have identified 17 genes that were not previously known to be CCA regulated (101). The expression of three, *tspO*-like, *nblA1*, and *orf114*, are five- to sevenfold more highly expressed in cells acclimated to green light than in cells acclimated to red light. *nblA1* had not been previously identified as green-light activated (69). The roles of the proteins encoded by these genes are unknown, although they are contiguous with the *cpeBA* operon in this organism (101). Another gene revealed by microarray studies to be upregulated under green light was *chlL*, encoding a subunit of the light-independent form of protochlorophyllide reductase. This enzyme carries out the penultimate step in chlorophyll *a* biosynthesis

(43). Cyanobacteria also produce a second, evolutionarily unrelated type of protochlorophyllide reductase whose enzymatic activity is red-light dependent. The fact that a gene encoding a subunit of the light-independent form of this enzyme is upregulated in green light is interesting because it appears to reveal another facet of the CCA strategy used by *F. diplosiphon* to acclimate to green-light environments. Because the light-dependent form of protochlorophyllide reductase cannot function efficiently in green light, this species apparently increases the production of the light-independent form in order to continue to synthesize chlorophyll *a* at a sufficient level for sustained growth in green light.

The expression of genes encoding chromophore biosynthesis enzymes is also CCA regulated in *F. diplosiphon*. These findings were based on years of research on the synthesis of bilins in cyanobacteria, algae, and plants (5), and the identification of bilin biosynthetic enzymes in cyanobacteria. These enzymes convert biliverdin IXα to phycocyanobilin (PCB), the PC and AP chromophore, and phycoerythrobilin (PEB), the PE chromophore (42). PEB is synthesized by two oxidoreductases, PebA and PebB, which are encoded by *pebAB* in cyanobacteria (1, 42). The expression of this operon in *F. diplosiphon* is highly upregulated during growth in green light through a mechanism similar to that controlling the *cpeBA* expression (see below) (1). The gene encoding the PCB biosynthesis enzyme, *pcyA* (42), was cloned from *F. diplosiphon* and its expression was examined. *pcyA* RNA abundance was fivefold higher under red-light growth than green light, and the *pcyA* and *cpc2* promoters share a DNA direct repeat that may be involved in CCA regulation (R.M. Alvey & D.M. Kehoe, unpublished results; see below). However, unlike for *cpc2*, significant *pcyA* transcript levels are still present in green light. This finding is consistent with the requirement for PCB production in green light, because this chromophore is attached to both PC_c and AP, which are present in PBS during growth in green as well as red light.

DNA:
deoxyribonucleic acid

PEB:
phycoerythrobilin

PCB:
phycocyanobilin

Redox regulation: control of cellular processes though sensing and responding to the relative reduction or oxidation state of specific molecules

THE REGULATION OF COMPLEMENTARY CHROMATIC ADAPTATION

Redox- and Photoreceptor-Based Control Mechanisms

CCA responses in *F. diplosiphon* are responsive to the redox state of photosynthetic electron transport chain and to at least one, and perhaps multiple, photoreceptors that are maximally sensitive to green and red light (17, 56, 62, 79, 84, 96, 110, 112). The redox state of the plastoquinone pool reportedly controls the cellular differentiation of green-light-acclimated cells. When such cells are maintained in green light, the relatively reduced plastoquinone pool inhibits the production of hormogonia and promotes heterocyst (specialized nitrogen-reducing cells) differentiation. Shifting these cells to red light partially oxidizes the plastoquinone pool, leading to inhibition of heterocyst development and the production of hormogonia (17). Although it has not been tested, the oxidation of the plastoquinone pool should be transient in red light, with the pool becoming highly reduced by the time the cells are completely acclimated and the PBS are able to optimally excite photosystem II. This control mechanism is not the central element of the CCA regulatory pathway(s) that controls PBS biogenesis, but there is a link between this redox-based system and such pathways because PBS-encoding genes are transiently downregulated during the differentiation of hormogonia (17, 32). Currently, nothing is known about the pathways or components controlling redox-based CCA responses in *F. diplosiphon*.

The most thoroughly defined CCA regulation mechanism is that controlling the expression of genes encoding PBS components. It is at least in part photoreceptor controlled (17, 62, 79, 96, 110). The expression of *pebAB* and *pcyA* are also regulated by the same photoreceptor-based pathway(s) (1; R.M. Alvey & D.M. Kehoe, unpublished results). Given the many cellular responses controlled by CCA, it is possible that both redox- and photoreceptor-based control mechanisms jointly control a large number of responses, perhaps in a manner similar to the genes encoding PBS components during hormogonium differentiation (17, 32).

Why might cells use both redox- and photoreceptor-based systems to control CCA? One possibility becomes apparent when the process of CCA is considered from a temporal perspective. Then, for red- versus green-light growth, CCA can be regarded most simply as consisting of two separate but potentially overlapping phases. The "acclimation state" is the period immediately after a shift in light color, when the photosynthetic efficiency of the cells is suboptimal, especially in the excitation of photosystem II. This inefficiency is due to the poor overlap between the light-absorption characteristics of the existing rod phycobiliproteins and the color distribution of the ambient light (16, 32). This transient state exists for days both for red light–grown cells shifted to green light and vice versa, and in both cases reduces photosynthetic efficiency by approximately 40% (16). In both light conditions these decreases probably lower the extent of the reduction of the plastoquinone pool, although the degree of such a drop might be greater in cells shifted to red light because this wavelength is capable of oxidizing the plastoquinone pool by driving photosystem I activity. [For simplicity, we will not consider the many other cellular parameters (14) that affect the redox state of the plasoquinone pool here.] So far, this effect has only been demonstrated experimentally for green light–grown cells that were shifted to red light (17). Thus, transient CCA responses occurring during the acclimation state could be primarily controlled by sensing the extent of oxidation of the plastoquinone pool, possibly with additional control of these responses through photoreceptor-based mechanisms. The second phase, the "steady state," is attained when the cells have optimized PBS composition for absorption of the ambient light color. Because the photosynthetic efficiency (as measured by oxygen evolution) of *F. diplosiphon* steady-state cells in red light is essentially the same as for steady-state cells in green light (16), and in both situations the PBS composition is optimized for providing energy to photosystem II, it is likely that the plastoquinone pool is equally highly reduced under both light colors. In such a state, the redox state of the plastoquinone pool would not provide any information to the cell regarding ambient light color. Therefore, the longer-term CCA responses that persist during the steady state would be predominantly photoreceptor controlled.

Efforts to uncover CCA regulatory mechanisms to date have focused on the steady-state period and, not surprisingly, only photoreceptor-based regulatory components have been isolated thus far. The one exception to this is a DNA binding protein named RcaD, which has been proposed to function in the acclimation phase (see below) (77), and the mechanism controlling RcaD activity is unknown. However, in the future, microarray analyses will allow many genes that are controlled by CCA exclusively or predominantly during the acclimation phase to be identified. Subsequent studies of the regulation of such genes will add significantly to our overall understanding of CCA regulation.

Transcriptional and Post-Transcriptional Control of Complementary Chromatic Adaptation

The level(s) at which CCA is regulated in *F. diplosiphon* has been analyzed through the use of inhibitors of transcription and translation and by reporter gene studies, focusing primarily on the control of the expression of PBS components. These have shown that CCA regulation of PC_i and PE synthesis is predominantly at the transcriptional level for *cpc2* and *cpeBA* (19, 51, 78). The level at which *cpeCDE* is controlled has not yet been estab-

lished. Inhibitor studies indicated that *cpc2* and *cpeBA* regulation is quite complex. Protein synthesis is required for de novo induction of *cpc2* during acclimation to red light and of *cpeBA* during acclimation to green light, but is not needed to maintain the expression of these operons once steady-state CCA is reached (80). In addition, the rapid rate of loss of *cpc2* mRNA after a switch from red to green light depends both on the cessation of transcription, which is not dependent on protein synthesis, and an increase in the transcript degradation rate, which is protein synthesis dependent. The decline in *cpeBA* mRNA after a red- to green-light shift is not protein synthesis dependent and is apparently not an active process. Taken together, these results show that although CCA regulation of PBS gene expression is primarily transcriptional, the regulatory mechanisms controlling these responses are complex and significantly different for *cpc2* versus *cpeBA*.

The changes in RNA levels of PBS components after an inductive light treatment are, in most cases, relatively rapid. *cpc2* RNA reaches a maximum level two hours after a shift from green to red light and drops to undetectable levels two hours after a shift from red to green light (78). *cpeCDE* and *cpeBA* RNA reaches a maximum level approximately 8 hours after a red- to green-light shift, and although *cpeCDE* RNA declines to background levels by four hours after a shift from green to red light, *cpeBA* RNA takes more than 14 hours to drop to undetectable levels (39, 78). PE and PC protein levels (as measured by absorbance) changed much more slowly, both requiring approximately seven days to fully shift between the red- and green-light steady states at light intensities of 15 μmol photons $m^{-2} s^{-1}$ (L. Li & D.M. Kehoe, unpublished results). This is not surprising because PBS have been estimated to comprise more than 60% of the total soluble protein (7, 8), and at least PE is not actively degraded in *F. diplosiphon* after a switch from green to red light (7). Whether PC is more actively degraded in green light than in red light in *F. diplosiphon* is unknown,

kDa: kilodalton

although the time required for complete pigmentation shifts argues against this possibility. However, active degradation of PC in green light in *T. tenuis* has been suggested (81).

Other levels of regulation are likely to be important in controlling CCA. For example, there is an antisense RNA that is made within the *gvpABC* operon that is upregulated after the red-light induction of hormogonia in *F. diplosiphon* (31). However, the function of this RNA has not yet been established.

The Photoreceptor–Controlled Rca System

Significant improvements in the genetic and molecular tools available for working with *F. diplosiphon* have been provided by (*a*) the isolation of the shortened filament, colony-forming strain SF33 (also called Fd33) (26), (*b*) the development of vectors such as pPL2.7 (22) and pJFC62603 (23), (*c*) the ability to transform *F. diplosiphon* via electroporation and conjugation (22, 26, 64), (*d*) the creation of plasmid, cosmid, and phage libraries (23, 62, 64), and (*e*) allelic exchange technology (15, 23, 75, 77). In addition, many *F. diplosiphon* mutants have been generated by the development of a Tn5 transposition system (25), homologous recombination (23, 75, 77), or the isolation of spontaneous mutants caused by mobilization of endogenous DNA elements (1, 4, 6, 11, 21, 24, 61, 62, 63, 96). Some of these mutants have structural defects directly or indirectly affecting their PBS. Others contain lesions in regulatory components controlling PBS biogenesis. The analysis and complementation of many of these mutants lead to the identification of at least two light-response pathways controlling PBS synthesis during CCA. The first is the regulator for complementary chromatic adaptation (Rca) (100) system, which is a complex, photoreceptor-based two-component regulatory system (62, 86, 110). Thus far, four Rca components have been isolated and further studied.

The photoreceptor controlling the Rca pathway is named RcaE (62). RcaE is a soluble, histidine kinase-class protein of approximately 74 kDa that contains a phytochrome-class chromophore-binding domain within its N-terminal half, a central PER-ARNT-SIM (PAS) domain (109), and a C-terminal kinase domain (**Figure 3**). It was the first of a large class of prokaryotic phytochrome-class photoreceptors to be isolated (60, 76, 111), and is unique because instead of controlling red/far-red light photoreversible responses, as do all known plant phytochromes (65), it controls the green-red photoreversible process of CCA. RcaE contains a cysteine at position 198, which is the location equivalent to the cysteine responsible for bilin chromophore binding in plant phytochromes (62). Deleting this cysteine in RcaE leads to the loss of the bilin chromophore that is covalently attached in vivo (110), strongly implicating this residue as the chromophore attachment site. The type of bilin chromophore bound by RcaE in vivo is not known. Attempts to correctly attach either PCB or the plant phytochrome chromophore phytochromobilin to RcaE, either in vitro or in *Escherichia coli* cells producing these bilins, were unsuccessful (110). RcaE may lack the ability to covalently attach a chromophore autocatalytically, as do all other known prokaryotic and eukaryotic phytochromes, and may need a separate enzyme to catalyze that process.

rcaE null mutants contain intermediate levels of *cpc2*, *cpeCDE*, and *cpeBA* RNAs and PC and PE in both red and green light, giving them a nearly black phenotype (1, 62, 96, 110). This phenotype suggests that RcaE may be active in both red and green light. Specifically, it may act as a kinase in red light and a phosphatase in green light, because *rcaE* mutants with DNA insertions in the C-terminal kinase domain have a high PE:PC ratio and are phenotypically red in both red and green light (63). Similar mutations in other sensor histidine kinases resulted in truncated receptors with constitutive phosphatase activity and no kinase activity (3, 20). This

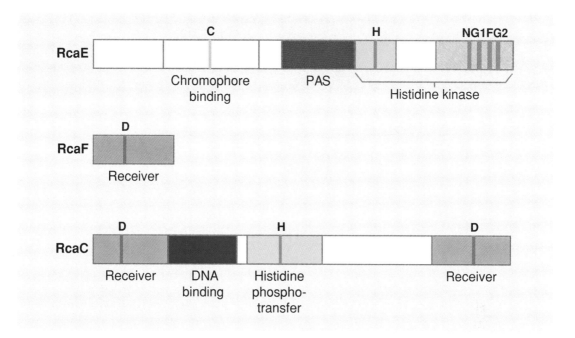

Figure 3

Structures of the regulator for complementary chromatic adaptation (Rca) components controlling steady-state responses. The putative chromophore-binding cysteine (C) and phosphorylation site histidine (H) are shown. N, G1, F, and G2 are blocks of conserved sequence found in ATPase domains of histidine kinases. RcaF contains a putative phosphorylation site aspartate (D), as do each of the receiver domains of RcaC. The histidine (H) consensus phosphorylation site of the histidine-containing phosphotransfer (HPt) domain is also shown. The nomenclature and domain structures were derived using ExPASy proteomic server tools (50).

suggests that the predominantly dephosphorylated state of the Rca pathway results in a red phenotype, which occurs in green light, whereas the predominantly phosphorylated state leads to the blue-green phenotype seen in red light. This hypothesis is supported by analysis of *F. diplosiphon* lines containing a mutant form of RcaE lacking the histidine predicted to be the site of phosphorylation. Such lines, which presumably lack the ability to phosphorylate downstream components of the Rca pathway, are red during growth in both red and green light (L. Li & D.M. Kehoe, unpublished results).

Genetic studies have placed a small response regulator called RcaF (**Figure 3**) immediately after RcaE in this pathway (**Figure 4**) (63). *rcaF* is located immediately 3′ of *rcaE* in the *F. diplosiphon* genome and these genes are likely to be cotranscribed. RcaF is predicted to consist of 124 amino acids and is comprised of a single receiver domain that contains the aspartate and lysine residues typically found in such modules. The lack of functional RcaF results in a red mutant phenotype during growth in both red and green light, further supporting the hypothesis that the Rca pathway is more highly phosphorylated in red light than in green light.

RcaC is a second response regulator that acts in this pathway, apparently after RcaF (**Figure 4**) (21, 63). At 73 kDa, it is larger than most response regulators and contains four identified domains (**Figure 3**). There are two receiver modules, one at the N terminus and the other at the C terminus. Each of these contains the conserved aspartate and lysine residues typically present in such domains,

N terminus: amino terminus

C terminus: carboxyl terminus

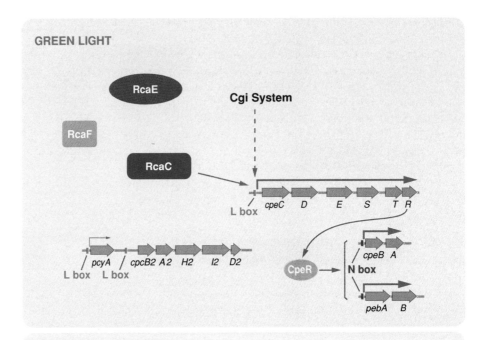

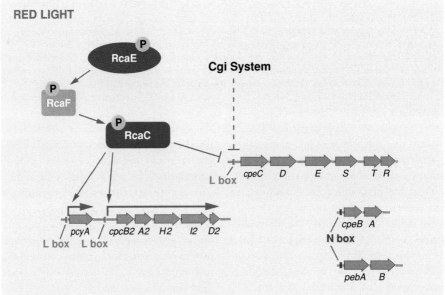

Figure 4

The current model of steady-state complementary chromatic adaptation (CCA) regulation. The expression of the *cpeCDESTR* operon is asymmetrically dependent on the Rca and control of green light induction (Cgi) systems. Cgi control is indicated by dashed lines because it is unknown whether it activates or represses (or both) the expression of this operon. RcaE may act as a phosphatase in green light (not shown, see text). The mechanisms by which these components operate have not been established. The extent of transcription is indicated by the presence and thickness of red arrows. The locations of L and N boxes (see text for description of these) are indicated. The color of the cells during growth in each light condition is indicated by the large colored boxes.

including aspartates 51 and 576, which are the likely sites of reversible phosphorylation in these domains during CCA. Contiguous with the N-terminal input domain is an OmpR-class DNA-binding domain. Such DNA-binding domains are unique because they typically bind to short, direct repeat sequences. Although a number of short, direct repeats are present in many CCA-regulated promoters of *F. diplosiphon*, binding by RcaC has not yet been demonstrated for any of these. Adjacent to the DNA-binding domain is a histidine-containing phosphotransfer (HPt) domain, a region that acts within a complex type of two-component system called a multistep phosphorelay (2). This domain contains a histidine at position 316 that is predicted to be the site of reversible phosphorylation during CCA (63). Also, although not shown in **Figure 3**, RcaC contains an incomplete third receiver domain between the HPt domain and the C-terminal receiver domain (A. Gutu & D.M. Kehoe, unpublished results). RcaC is the founding and best studied member of a large group of cyanobacterial response regulators with related, multidomain architectures (67). In an *rcaC* null mutant, *cpc2* RNA is undetectable whereas *cpeCDE* and *cpeBA* transcripts are present at levels found in wild-type cells during growth in green light. Such mutants are phenotypically red during growth in both red and green light (21, 63, 67). In vivo studies of site-directed mutant forms of RcaC demonstrated that CCA is primarily controlled through histidine 316 and aspartate 51, whereas aspartate 576 plays a relatively minor role and may serve some other role, for example, to integrate other cellular signals. The phenotype of an aspartate 51 to glutamate 51 mutant (which mimics a constitutively phosphorylated aspartate) is blue green, whereas the phenotype of an aspartate 51 to asparagine 51 mutant (which mimics the constitutively unphosphorylated form of the aspartate) is red (67). These data further support the hypothesis that the Rca system is predominantly phosphorylated in red light and nonphosphorylated in green light (**Figure 4**), and suggest that the primary route of phosphoryl group flow through RcaC during CCA regulation is from histidine 316 to aspartate 51.

RcaC abundance is approximately six times higher in red-light steady-state cells than in green-light steady-state cells (67), a somewhat surprising result because RcaE levels do not change under these two light conditions (110). The reason for this RcaC abundance change is currently unknown.

RcaD was identified in partially purified *F. diplosiphon* protein extracts as a protein capable of shifting the electrophoretic mobility of the *cpc2* promoter and protecting two regions (Box1, centered at −176, and Box2, centered at −255) of this promoter from DNase I degradation (99). The binding activity is red-light specific and is lost after alkaline phosphatase treatment. Each of these boxes contained a direct repeat of the sequence 5′TGTAAC3′. However, a separate promoter deletion analysis showed that these two regions are not necessary for red-light activation of *cpc2* expression and used electrophoretic gel mobility shift assays to detect binding activity to Box1 in protein extracts from both red and green light–grown cells (19). Although the reason for the discrepancy in DNA-binding activities between these two studies is unknown, it is clear that Box1 and Box2 are not needed for the *cpc2* steady-state CCA response. Using biochemical approaches, RcaD was purified and *rcaD* was cloned (77). A 60–amino acid region in the N-terminal half of the predicted RcaD sequence showed some similarity to E2 proteins of papillomavirus, whereas the C-terminal half was somewhat similar to the sliding clamp of the DNA polymerase III β-subunit. An *rcaD* mutant was created by allelic exchange. No obvious effect on CCA was observed for cells in red- or green-light steady states, but the induction kinetics of several operons encoding PBS components appeared to be altered. From these data it was concluded the RcaD may play a role in coordinating the expression of several operons in red light, perhaps during the acclimation state.

HPt:
histidine-containing phosphotransfer domain

Several other proteins have been identified or isolated and given Rca designations, although no compelling evidence has been provided for their roles in CCA regulation. RcaA binds specifically to a direct repeat within the *cpeBA* promoter that is highly conserved within the *cpeBA* promoters of other cyanobacterial species (100) (see below). Binding activity to the same region of the *cpeBA* promoter was also detected by a second group, who named the binding protein PepB (phycoerythrin promoter-binding protein) (95). Because functional studies have not yet been conducted for the *cpeBA* promoter, it remains unclear whether or not RcaA/PepB regulates CCA. RcaB is also a *cpeBA* promoter-binding protein that was detected only in protein extracts from green light–grown cells (100). It binds downstream of −38 relative to the transcription start site, but its precise binding site could not be determined. RcaB has not been isolated, nor have further studies been carried out on its role in CCA regulation. *rcaG* was identified during the cloning of *rcaD* as the open reading frame (ORF) immediately downstream of and apparently cotranscribed with *rcaD* (77). RcaG has limited similarity to papillomavirus E2 protein and no known role in CCA regulation.

RNA blot analyses using *rca* mutants have demonstrated that the Rca pathway controls the expression of both red and green light–induced genes in *F. diplosiphon* (**Figure 4**). Steady-state CCA regulation of the *cpc2* operon is completely lost in both *rcaE* (1, 96) and *rcaC* (67) null mutants. These results suggest that no additional CCA regulatory pathway(s) controls *cpc2* expression in this organism during steady-state growth, although it cannot be ruled out that another pathway(s) exists but requires the Rca pathway to operate. If this is the case, it must integrate into the Rca pathway at RcaE, because CCA regulation of *cpc2* expression is lost when either RcaC or RcaE is absent. The steady-state CCA responsiveness of another gene that is upregulated in red light, *pcyA*, also appears to be solely under the control of the Rca system, because *rcaE*,

rcaF, and *rcaC* mutants all fail to CCA regulate the expression of this gene (R.M. Alvey & D.M. Kehoe, unpublished results). Thus, all evidence to date suggests that the Rca system is the sole pathway controlling the CCA response for PBS genes that are upregulated during steady-state growth in red light.

Several studies have shown that the Rca system also controls the steady-state CCA expression of the green light–responsive operons *cpcCDE* and *cpeBA* (1, 67, 96) and *pebAB* (1). These investigations also revealed a second CCA regulatory system that controls the light responsiveness of these operons (see below).

The Cgi System and Its Interaction with the Rca System: Evolutionary Implications

Unlike the known red light–activated genes in *F. diplosiphon*, many green light–activated genes are controlled by at least two systems, the Rca pathway and one that we provisionally call the Cgi (control of green light induction) system. The possibility that a second pathway existed was revealed by photobiology experiments in the 1980s (79), and additional evidence that it affected PE synthesis was provided by studies of double mutants (61). Direct confirmation of the pathway came from analyses of the light responsiveness of *cpeCDE* and *cpeBA* transcript levels in an *rcaE* null mutant (1, 96) and an *rcaC* null mutant (67). These studies demonstrated that the normal 20- to 30-fold green-light increase in RNA abundance from each of these operons is reduced to two- to threefold in *rcaE* and *rcaC* mutants. The main reason for the tenfold decrease in green-light responsiveness in these mutants is because they accumulate close to 10 times more *cpeCDE* and *cpeBA* transcripts in red light than wild-type cells. However, they also only accumulate approximately 80% of the wild-type levels of these transcripts in green light. These results demonstrated that there are two effects of the Rca system on CCA regulation of *cpeCDE* and *cpeBA*. It significantly lowers *cpeCDE* and *cpeBA* transcript levels in red light and slightly increases them in green light. This discovery is significant because it provides important clues to the unsolved puzzle of how these two pathways interact mechanistically.

Although these results clearly demonstrate that two light-responsive systems control the CCA responses of PBS genes and confirm previous suggestions (61, 79), the way in which these systems share the regulation of CCA is surprising and unexpected because it is asymmetrical (**Figure 4**). To date, no components of the Cgi system have been identified or isolated. Therefore, it is unclear whether or not it is a photoreceptor-based system, although this might be expected given that it controls steady-state CCA responses.

The finding that two regulatory systems asymmetrically control CCA does not only offer important insights into the differences in the control of red and green light–induced genes. It also provides the foundation for a hypothesis to explain the molecular basis for the differences between the pathways controlling CCA in group II versus group III chromatic adapting species (104). We propose that group II species provide CCA control of PE synthesis without light color regulating PC synthesis by utilizing the Cgi system but not the Rca system. In support of this possibility, it is noteworthy that in group II strains, PE synthesis never stops completely in red light (104), a phenotype consistent with the elevated *cpeCDE* and *cpeBA* RNA levels measured in *rcaE* and *rcaC* mutants grown in red light (1, 67, 96). We further propose that group III strains, in which CCA controls both PE and PC abundance, exert their additional control of CCA by using both the Rca and Cgi systems, which not only brings PC under CCA control but also increases the regulation of *cpeCDE* and *cpeBA* by further dampening their expression in red light and slightly boosting it in green light. This hypothesis will provide a fascinating link between CCA physiology and the molecular aspects of two signal transduction pathways if it is correct. It can

be tested by analyzing group II and III strains for components of the Rca and Cgi pathways once components of the Cgi system have been identified. The ability to carry out group II or group III CCA does not seem to be strongly correlated with the generic assignments for these strains (12, 103). However, this finding may be in part due to poor strain assignments, because at least in one case (for *Tolypothrix*) the refinement of these assignments led to a better correlation between clusters of genetically related strains and the type of CCA (57). As the Cgi pathway is uncovered and more cyanobacterial genomes are sequenced, it also may be possible to establish whether group II strains were derived from group III strains by the loss of the Rca system, or if group III strains arose from group II strains through the acquisition of the Rca pathway, or if both events occurred.

Coordination of Genes Activated by Green Light

There is a question that has persisted since the discovery that the *cpeCDE* and *cpeBA* operons are both upregulated by green light: How is this coordinate regulation achieved? Promoter analyses failed to uncover any unique, shared DNA sequence elements (39, 72, 100). This question has been partly answered by the identification of a small activator called CpeR, which is required for the expression of *cpeBA* but not *cpeCDE* (23, 96). Mutants lacking functional CpeR therefore belong to a class of mutants called "green mutants," in which PC levels are normally regulated but PE fails to accumulate regardless of the ambient light color (6, 11, 24, 25, 103). *cpeR* is located downstream of the *cpeCDE* genes and two additional genes named *cpeS* and *cpeT* in the *F. diplosiphon* genome. This discovery led to the suggestion that, in green light, *cpeR* is cotranscribed with *cpeCDE* and *cpeST* and forms a regulatory circuit that operates through the serial expression of two operons, first *cpeCDESTR*, then *cpeBA* (**Figure 4**) (23). This proposal requires that the *cpeCDESTR* genes are actually

6His: six histidine

cotranscribed, an idea that was supported but not proven by the detection of a RNA species that extended from *cpeE* to *cpeR* using reverse transcription polymerase chain reaction amplification (23). We have recently used RNA transcript blot analysis to detect a very low abundance transcript that encompasses all the genes within *cpeCDESTR*, providing support for this hypothesis (R.P. Bezy & D.M. Kehoe, unpublished results).

CpeR has an estimated molecular mass of 14 kDa, lacks any obvious membrane-spanning domains, and its function has not yet been firmly established. It was noted to share sequence similarity to members of the PP2C class of protein serine/threonine phosphatases (96). However, recent studies of *E. coli*-produced CpeR containing a six-histidine tag at its N-terminal end (6His-CpeR) determined that this fusion protein can bind a 100–base pair region of the *cpeBA* promoter that contains the RcaA/PepB binding site (see below) and the first 20 base pairs of the *cpeBA* transcribed sequence. In electrophoretic mobility shift assay experiments, two separate 6His-CpeR-DNA complexes were detected (J.G. Cobley, personal communication). These data suggest that RcaA/PepB and CpeR may be the same protein.

Is CpeR part of the CCA regulatory system, or does it simply provide a mechanism for coordinating the expression of genes involved in the biosynthesis of PE-containing PBS? CpeR homologs have been identified only in cyanobacteria that synthesize PE, but one of these (*Synechococcus* WH8102) is apparently incapable of CCA (23), making it unlikely that CpeR is exclusively a CCA regulatory component. Among the additional genes that were recently found to be upregulated by green light in *F. diplosiphon* (1, 101), the expression *pebAB* and several of the highly induced genes identified in microarray studies are CpeR-dependent (1; E.L. Stowe-Evans & D.M. Kehoe, unpublished results). The promoters of each of these genes contain the same or similar direct repeat as is found within the RcaA/PepB-binding site in

the *cpeBA* promoter (see below), further supporting a functional role for this repeat in the green-light responses of these promoters. Taken together, these data suggest that CpeR not only synchronizes transcript accumulation of the *cpeCDE* and *cpeBA* operons in green light but also acts as a more global activator, possibly serving to coordinate the expression of genes encoding proteins directly or indirectly involved in PBS biosynthesis in green light (102). If this hypothesis is correct, then CpeR should only be considered a CCA regulatory component in situations where it has been brought under CCA control, such as has presumably occurred in both group II and III species. The discovery of CpeR and its role in *F. diplosiphon* has moved the *cpeCDE-STR* operon into a position of increased importance in the CCA regulatory scheme. Not only does the green-light induction of many genes depend on its proper CCA control of *cpeR* expression, but this operon is also the likely integration site of the Rca and Cgi pathways and thus also important for the coordination of red- and green-light transcriptional responses in *F. diplosiphon*. This possibility is discussed further in the next section. We know little about how CCA regulates *cpeCDESTR* expression, however, because promoter studies have primarily focused on *cpeBA* and *cpc2*.

Promoter Studies, DNA-Binding Activities, and Coordination of Red- and Green-Light Responses

Substantial information concerning the mechanisms of CCA regulation has come from analyses of *F. diplosiphon* CCA-responsive promoters. Such work has already been described for *cpc2* promoter binding by RcaD, along with its cloning and analysis (see above) (77, 99) and for CpeR (see previous section). Investigations of the *cpeBA*, *pebAB*, and *pcyA* promoters, as well as additional studies of the *cpc2* promoter, are discussed below.

Two studies have examined *cpeBA* promoter DNA-binding activities using partially purified protein extracts from red and green light–grown cells. As mentioned above, RcaB was detected using EMSAs, but its binding site could not be determined by DNase I footprinting (100). In the same study, DNase I footprinting was used to demonstrate that RcaA bound to the direct repeat 5′TTGTTA3′, separated by four base pairs, that is present from –66 to –45 of the *cpeBA* promoter, and we refer to as the "N box" (**Figure 4**). RcaA-binding activity was only present in protein extracts from cells grown in green light and was lost after treating the extract with alkaline phosphatase, suggesting that phosphorylation was required for binding activity. As also noted above, DNA-binding studies carried out by another group using EMSAs and in vivo and in vitro footprinting approaches showed binding activity of PepB to the RcaA-binding site within *cpeBA* (95). However, PepB-binding activity was detected in partially purified protein extracts from both red and green light–grown cells. Because it is likely that RcaA and PepB are the same protein, the difference in their binding characteristics remains to be resolved. Even though no functional study has yet examined the role of the N box in regulating *cpeBA* expression, it is also highly conserved within the promoters of *pebAB* in *F. diplosiphon* (1) and several additional CpeR-regulated, green-light activated genes (101; E.L. Stowe-Evans & D.M. Kehoe, unpublished results). This, along with the report that CpeR binds to this region of the *cpeBA* promoter (J.G. Cobley, personal communication), suggests that the N box is important for the coordination of CCA transcriptional regulation, directly or indirectly, by CpeR.

Using a series of *cpc2* promoter fusions to the *gus* reporter gene, a functional study clearly showed that the red-light response element of this promoter was between −76 and +25 (19). Removing additional 5′ sequences resulted in the complete loss of promoter activity. The 13–base pair direct repeat 5′AAATTTGCACAAA3′, overlapping by two base pairs, was identified from −36 to −11 within this promoter and suggested

to bind an activator. Such direct repeats were noted to be bound by OmpR-class transcription factors. Although no DNA-binding protein has yet been demonstrated to bind to this site, it is possible that RcaC, which contains an OmpR-class DNA-binding domain (**Figure 3**), might be this protein. In the same study, EMSAs detected specific DNA-binding activity to the region of *cpc2* from −76 to +25 that was present only in partially purified protein extracts from red light–grown cells. This activity was competed away by a 5- to 10-fold molar excess of an unlabeled *cpc2* DNA fragment from −37 to +25, further implicating this direct repeat in CCA regulation.

Recent studies of the *pcyA* and *cpeCDESTR* promoter regions provide additional evidence that at least the core of this 13-mer repeat is involved in CCA regulation. The core sequence 5′TTGCACA3′, repeated once and separated by four base pairs, is present in the *pcyA* and *cpc2* promoters in the same orientation and at virtually the same distance upstream from the red light–dependent transcription start sites (R.M. Alvey & D.M. Kehoe, unpublished results). We named this repeat the "L box" (**Figure 4**). The L box is also present within the *cpeCDESTR* promoter, although it is centered at approximately −78, is in the opposite orientation, and contains a single base pair change in the upstream repeat (**Figure 4**) (R.M. Alvey & D.M. Kehoe, unpublished results). The L box is the first direct repeat that has been found exclusively in both red and green light–responsive promoters. It will be exciting to determine what, if any, role the L box plays in the control and coordination of CCA transcriptional responses in *F. diplosiphon*.

CONCLUDING REMARKS

Our understanding of the process of CCA has grown from an initial perception that involved only changes in the ratio of light-harvesting pigments into an appreciation of CCA as a complex, integrated cellular response that likely affects nearly every aspect of cellular morphology and physiology. CCA may be thought of as an extreme, but relatively common, mechanism through which cyanobacteria efficiently acclimate to changing light color conditions in soil, freshwater, and marine environments. It is also becoming clear that the regulation of CCA involves multiple, intertwined signaling pathways that are controlled both by the redox state of the plastoquinone pool and one or more photoreceptor(s), and that these are finely and differentially coordinated over time. In addition, because a prokaryotic phytochrome-class photoreceptor governs the CCA response, the large body of knowledge that has accumulated concerning CCA and its regulation over the past four decades has made it the best model system for studying the signal transduction mechanisms through which prokaryotic phytochromes function. The study of CCA regulation is contributing significantly to a major goal in photosynthesis research, which is to achieve a detailed understanding of the mechanisms through which photosynthetic organisms acclimate to changing environmental conditions, especially light.

SUMMARY POINTS

1. CCA regulates a wide range of cellular processes in addition to changes in PBS structure.

2. Both photoreceptor and redox sensing systems regulate cellular responses during CCA.

3. At least two regulatory pathways, the Rca and Cgi systems, control the transcription of light-responsive genes, especially those encoding proteins involved in PBS biogenesis.

4. The coordinate regulation of green light–activated genes occurs through the production of a small activator called CpeR.

ACKNOWLEDGMENTS

We dedicate this review to the memory of Professor Yoshihiko Fujita, a pioneer whose outstanding research on CCA set the standard for all who followed him. We wish to thank those who provided us with results prior to publication, including Richard Alvey, John Cobley, Ryan Bezy, Lina Li, and Emily Stowe-Evans. We also thank Elizabeth Gantt for valuable discussions and her important perspectives, the members of the Kehoe laboratory and Bettina Kehoe for their helpful comments on the manuscript, and the NSF, USDA, NIH, and Indiana University for the financial support that has allowed us to contribute to the progress that has been made in unraveling the regulation of CCA. This work was supported by the NSF under Grant No. MCB-0519433 to D.M.K.

LITERATURE CITED

1. Alvey RM, Karty JA, Roos E, Reilly JP, Kehoe DM. 2003. Lesions in phycoerythrin chromophore biosynthesis in *Fremyella diplosiphon* reveal coordinated light regulation of apoprotein and pigment biosynthetic enzyme gene expression. *Plant Cell* 15:2448–63

2. Appleby JL, Parkinson JS, Bourret RB. 1996. Signal transduction via the multi-step phosphorelay: not necessarily a road less traveled. *Cell* 86:845–48

3. Atkinson MR, Ninfa AJ. 1993. Mutational analysis of the bacterial signal-transducing protein kinase/phosphatase nitrogen regulator II (NRII or NtrB). *J. Bacteriol.* 175:7016–23

4. Balabas BE, Montgomery BL, Ong LE, Kehoe DM. 2003. CotB is essential for complete activation of green light-induced genes during complementary chromatic adaptation in *Fremyella diplosiphon*. *Mol. Microbiol.* 50:781–93

5. Beale SI. 1993. Biosynthesis of phycobilins. *Chem. Rev.* 93:785–802

6. Beguin S, Guglielmi G, Rippka R, Cohen-Bazire G. 1985. Chromatic adaptation in a mutant of *Fremyella diplosiphon* incapable of phycoerythrin synthesis. *Biochimie* 67:109–17

7. Bennett A, Bogorad L. 1973. Complementary chromatic adaptation in a filamentous blue-green alga. *J. Cell. Biol.* 58:419–35

8. Bogorad L. 1975. Phycobiliproteins and complementary chromatic adaptation. *Annu. Rev. Plant Physiol.* 26:369–401

9. Bogorad L, Gendel SM, Haury JF, Koller K-P. 1982. Photomorphogenesis and complementary chromatic adaptation in *Fremyella diplosyphon*. In Proceedings of the Special FEBS Meeting on Cell Function and Differentiation, ed. GC Papageorgiou, L Packer, pp. 119–26. Athens, Greece, April 25–29

10. Boresch K. 1922. Die komplementäre chromatic Adaptation. *Arch. Protistenkd.* 44:1–70

11. Bruns BU, Briggs WR, Grossman AR. 1989. Molecular characterization of phycobilisome regulatory mutants of *Fremyella diplosiphon*. *J. Bacteriol.* 171:901–8

12. Bryant DA. 1982. Phycoerythrocyanin and phycoerythrin: properties and occurrence in cyanobacteria. *J. Gen. Microbiol.* 128:835–44

13. Bryant DA, Guglielmi G, Tandeau de Marsac N, Castets AM, Cohen-Bazire G. 1979. The structure of cyanobacterial phycobilisomes: a model. *Arch. Microbiol.* 123:113–27

14. Buchanan BB, Balmer Y. 2005. Redox regulation: a broadening horizon. *Annu. Rev. Plant. Biol.* 56:187–220

15. Cai YP, Wolk CP. 1990. Use of a conditionally lethal gene in *Anabaena* sp. strain PCC 7120 to select for double recombinants and to entrap insertion sequences. *J. Bacteriol.* 172:3138–45

16. Campbell D. 1996. Complementary chromatic adaptation alters photosynthetic strategies in the cyanobacterium *Calothrix*. *Microbiology* 142:1255–63

17. Campbell D, Houmard J, Tandeau de Marsac N. 1993. Electron transport regulates cellular differentiation in the filamentous cyanobacterium *Calothrix*. *Plant Cell* 5:451–63

18. Campbell D, Hurry V, Clarke AK, Gustafsson P, Oquist G. 1998. Chlorophyll fluorescence analysis of cyanobacterial photosynthesis and acclimation. *Microbiol. Mol. Biol. Rev.* 62:667–83

19. Casey ES, Grossman AR. 1994. In vivo and in vitro characterization of the light-regulated *cpcB2A2* promoter of *Fremyella diplosiphon*. *J. Bacteriol.* 176:6362–74

20. Cavicchioli R, Schroder I, Constanti M, Gunsalus RP. 1995. The NarX and NarQ sensor-transmitter proteins of *Escherichia coli* each require two conserved histidines for nitrate-dependent signal transduction to NarL. *J. Bacteriol.* 177:2416–24

21. Chiang GG, Schaefer MR, Grossman AR. 1992. Complementation of a red-light-indifferent cyanobacterial mutant. *Proc. Natl. Acad. Sci. USA* 89:9415–19

22. Chiang GG, Schaefer MR, Grossman AR. 1992. Transformation of the filamentous cyanobacterium *Fremyella diplosiphon* by conjugation or electroporation. *Plant Physiol. Biochem.* 30:315–25

23. Cobley JG, Clark AC, Weerasurya S, Queseda FA, Xiao JY, et al. 2002. CpeR is an activator required for expression of the phycoerythrin operon (*cpeBA*) in the cyanobacterium *Fremyella diplosiphon* and is encoded in the phycoerythrin linker-polypeptide operon (*cpeCDESTR*). Mol. Microbiol. 44:1517–31

24. Cobley JG, Miranda RD. 1983. Mutations affecting chromatic adaptation in the cyanobacterium *Fremyella diplosiphon*. *J. Bacteriol.* 153:1486–92

This study identified CpeR and provided a model for the serial regulation of *cpeCDE* and *cpeBA* operons.

25. Cobley JG, Seneviratne L, Drong L, Thounaojam M, Oda JF, Carroll J. 1999. Transposition of Tn5 derivatives in the chromatically adapting cyanobacterium, *Fremyella diplosiphon*. In *The Phototrophic Prokaryotes*, ed. G Peschek, W Löffelhardt, G Schmetterer, pp. 443–51. New York: Kluwer Acad./Plenum

26. Cobley JG, Zerweck E, Reyes R, Mody A, Seludo-Unson JR, et al. 1993. Construction of shuttle plasmids which can be efficiently mobilized from *Escherichia coli* into the chromatically adapting cyanobacterium, *Fremyella diplosiphon*. *Plasmid* 30:90–105

27. Conley PB, Lemaux PG, Grossman AR. 1988. Molecular characterization and evolution of sequences encoding light-harvesting components in the chromatically adapting cyanobacterium *Fremyella diplosiphon*. *J. Mol. Biol.* 199:447–65

28. Conley PB, Lemaux PG, Grossman AR. 1985. Cyanobacterial light-harvesting complex subunits encoded in two red-light induced transcripts. *Science* 230:550–53

29. Conley PB, Lemaux PG, Lomax TL, Grossman AR. 1986. Genes encoding major light-harvesting polypeptides are clustered on the genome of the cyanobacterium *Fremyella diplosiphon*. *Proc. Natl. Acad. Sci. USA* 83:3924–28

30. Crossett RN, Drew EA, Larkum AWD. 1965. Chromatic adaptation in benthic marine algae. *Nature* 207:547–48

31. Csiszar K, Houmard J, Damerval T, Tandeau de Marsac N. 1987. Transcriptional analysis of the cyanobacterial *gvpABC* operon in differentiated cells: occurrence of an antisense RNA complementary to three overlapping transcripts. *Gene* 60:29–37

32. Damerval T, Guglielmi G, Houmard J, Tandeau de Marsac N. 1991. Hormogonium differentiation in the cyanobacterium *Calothrix* - a photoregulated developmental process. *Plant Cell* 3:191–201

33. Damerval T, Houmard J, Guglielmi G, Csiszar K, Tandeau de Marsac N. 1987. A developmentally regulated *gvpABC* operon is involved in the formation of gas vesicles in the cyanobacterium *Calothrix* 7601. *Gene* 54:83–92

34. Diakoff S, Scheibe J. 1975. Cultivation in the dark of blue-green alga *Fremyella diplosiphon*. A photoreversible effect of green and red light on growth rate. *Physiol. Plant.* 34:125–28

35. Diakoff S, Scheibe J. 1973. Action spectra for chromatic adaptation in *Tolypothrix tenuis*. *Plant Physiol.* 51:382–85

36. Engelmann TW. 1902. Untersuchungen über die qualitativen Beziehungen zwieschen Absorbtion des Lichtes und Assimilation in Pflanzenzellen. I. Das Mikrospectraphotometer, ein Apparat zur qualitativen Mikrospectralanalyse. II. Experimentelle Grundlangen zur Ermittelung der quantitativen Beziehungen zwischen Assimilationsenergie und Absorptiongrösse. III. Bestimmung der Vertheilung der Energie im Spectrum von Sonnenlicht mittels Bacterien-methode und quantitativen Mikrospectralanalyse. *Bot. Z.* 42:81–105

37. Engelmann TW. 1883. Farbe und Assimilation. I. Assimilation findet nur in den farbstoffhaltigen Plasmatheilchen statt. II Näherer Zusammenhang zwischen Lichtabsorbtion und Assimilation. III. Weitere folgerungen. *Bot. Z.* 41:1–29

38. Fauchon M, Lagniel G, Aude JC, Lombardia L, Soularue P, et al. 2002. Sulfur sparing in the yeast proteome in response to sulfur demand. *Mol. Cell.* 9:713–23

39. Federspiel NA, Grossman AR. 1990. Characterization of the light-regulated operon encoding the phycoerythrin-associated linker proteins from the cyanobacterium *Fremyella diplosiphon*. *J. Bacteriol.* 172:4072–81

40. Federspiel NA, Scott L. 1992. Characterization of a light-regulated gene encoding a new phycoerythrin-associated linker protein from the cyanobacterium *Fremyella diplosiphon*. *J. Bacteriol.* 174:5994–98

41. Deleted in proof

42. Frankenberg N, Mukougawa K, Kohchi T, Lagarias JC. 2001. Functional genomic analysis of the HY2 family of ferredoxin-dependent bilin reductases from oxygenic photosynthetic organisms. *Plant Cell* 13:965–78

43. Fujita Y, Bauer CE. 2003. The light-independent protochlorophyllide reductase: a nitrogenase-like enzyme catalyzing a key reaction for greening in the dark. In *The Porphyrin Handbook*, Vol. 13, ed. KM Kadish, KM Smith, R Guilard, pp. 109–56. San Diego, CA: Elsevier Sci.

44. Fujita Y, Hattori A. 1960. Effect of chromatic lights on phycobilin formation in a blue-green alga, *Tolypothrix tenuis*. *Plant Cell Physiol.* 1:293–303

45. Fujita Y, Hattori A. 1960. Formation of phycoerythrin in pre-illuminated cells of *Tolypothrix tenuis* with special reference to nitrogen metabolism. *Plant Cell Physiol.* 1:281–92

46. Fujita Y, Hattori A. 1962. Photochemical interconversion between precursors of phycobilin chromoproteids in *Tolypothrix tenuis*. *Plant Cell Physiol.* 3:209–20

47. Gaiducov N. 1903. Die Farbenveränderung bei den Prozessen der komplementären chromatischen Adaptation. *Ber. Deutsch. Bot. Ges.* 21:517–22

48. Gaiducov N. 1902. Über den Einfluss farbigen Lichtes auf die Färbung lebender Oscillarien. *Abh. Preuss. Akad. Wiss.* 5:1–36

49. Gantt E. 1981. Phycobilisomes. *Annu. Rev. Plant Physiol.* 32:327–47

50. Gasteiger E, Gattiker A, Hoogland C, Ivanyi I, Appel RD, Bairoch A. 2003. ExPASy: the proteomics server for in-depth protein knowledge and analysis. *Nucleic Acids Res.* 31:3784–88

51. Gendel S, Ohad I, Bogorad L. 1979. Control of phycoerythrin synthesis during chromatic adaptation. *Plant Physiol.* 64:786–90

52. Glazer AN. 1982. Phycobilisomes: structure and dynamics. *Annu. Rev. Microbiol.* 36:173–98

53. Grossman AR, Bhaya D, Apt KE, Kehoe DM. 1995. Light-harvesting complexes in oxygenic photosynthesis: diversity, control, and evolution. *Annu. Rev. Genet.* 29:231–88

54. Hattori A, Fujita Y. 1959. Effect of pre-illumination on the formation of phycobilin pigments in a blue-green alga, *Tolypothrix tenuis*. *J. Biochem.* 46:1259–61

55. Hattori A, Fujita Y. 1959. Formation of phycobilin pigments in a blue-green alga, *Tolypothrix tenuis*, as induced by illumination with colored lights. *J. Biochem.* 46:521–24

56. Haury JF, Bogorad L. 1977. Action spectra for phycobiliprotein synthesis in a chromatically adapting cyanophyte, *Fremyella diplosiphon*. *Plant Physiol.* 60:835–39

57. Herdman M, Castenholzh RW, Rippka R. 2001. Form genus III. *Tolypothrix* Kützing 1843. In *Bergey's Manual of Systematic Bacteriology*, ed. DR Boone, RW Castenholzh, pp. 587–89. New York: Springer

58. Houmard J, Capuano V, Colombano MV, Coursin T, Tandeau de Marsac N. 1990. Molecular characterization of the terminal energy acceptor of cyanobacterial phycobilisomes. *Proc. Natl. Acad. Sci. USA* 87:2152–56

59. Houmard J, Capuano V, Coursin T, Tandeau de Marsac N. 1988. Genes encoding core components of the phycobilisome in the cyanobacterium *Calothrix* sp. strain PCC 7601: occurrence of a multigene family. *J. Bacteriol.* 170:5512–21

60. Hughes J, Lamparter T. 1999. Prokaryotes and phytochrome. The connection to chromophores and signaling. *Plant Physiol.* 121:1059–68

61. Kahn K, Mazel D, Houmard J, Tandeau de Marsac N, Schaefer MR. 1997. A role for *cpeYZ* in cyanobacterial phycoerythrin biosynthesis. *J. Bacteriol.* 179:998–1006

62. Kehoe DM, Grossman AR. 1996. Similarity of a chromatic adaptation sensor to phytochrome and ethylene receptors. *Science* 273:1409–12

This study, along with Ref. 110, identified the first CCA photoreceptor, which was also the first identified prokaryotic phytochrome-class protein.

63. Kehoe DM, Grossman AR. 1997. New classes of mutants in complementary chromatic adaptation provide evidence for a novel four-step phosphorelay system. *J. Bacteriol.* 179:3914–21

64. Kehoe DM, Grossman AR. 1998. Use of molecular genetics to investigate complementary chromatic adaptation: advances in transformation and complementation. *Meth. Enzymol.* 297:279–90

65. Kendrick RE, Kronenberg GHM. 1994. *Photomorphogenesis in Plants*. Dordrecht: Kluwer-Martinus Nijhoff. 828 pp.

66. Lazaroff N, Schiff J. 1962. Action spectrum for developmental photo-induction of blue-green alga *Nostoc muscorum*. *Science* 137:603–4

67. Li L, Kehoe DM. 2005. *In vivo* analysis of the roles of conserved aspartate and histidine residues within a complex response regulator. *Mol. Microbiol.* 55:1538–52

68. Lomax TL, Conley PB, Schilling J, Grossman AR. 1987. Isolation and characterization of light-regulated phycobilisome linker polypeptide genes and their transcription as a polycistronic mRNA. *J. Bacteriol.* 169:2675–84

69. Luque I, Ochoa de Alda JAG, Richaud C, Zabulon G, Thomas JC, Houmard J. 2003. The NblAI protein from the filamentous cyanobacterium *Tolypothrix* PCC 7601: regulation of its expression and interactions with phycobilisome components. *Mol. Microbiol.* 50:1043–54

70. MacColl R. 1998. Cyanobacterial phycobilisomes. *J. Struct. Biol.* 124:311–34

71. Mazel D, Guglielmi G, Houmard J, Sidler W, Bryant DA, Tandeau de Marsac N. 1986. Green light induces transcription of the phycoerythrin operon in the cyanobacterium *Calothrix* 7601. *Nucleic Acids Res.* 14:8279–90

72. Mazel D, Houmard J, Castets AM, Tandeau de Marsac N. 1990. Highly repetitive DNA sequences in cyanobacterial genomes. *J. Bacteriol.* 172:2755–61

73. Mazel D, Houmard J, Tandeau de Marsac N. 1988. A multigene family in *Calothrix* sp. PCC 7601 encodes phycocyanin, the major component of the cyanobacterial light-harvesting antenna. *Mol. Gen. Genet.* 211:296–304

74. Mazel D, Marliere P. 1989. Adaptive eradication of methionine and cysteine from cyanobacterial light-harvesting proteins. *Nature* 341:245–48

75. Montgomery BL, Casey ES, Grossman AR, Kehoe DM. 2004. AplA, a member of a new class of phycobiliproteins lacking a traditional role in photosynthetic light harvesting. *J. Bacteriol.* 186:7420–28

76. Montgomery BL, Lagarias JC. 2002. Phytochrome ancestry: sensors of bilins and light. *Trends Plant. Sci.* 7:357–66

77. Noubir S, Luque I, Ochoa de Alda JAG, Perewoska I, Tandeau de Marsac N, Cobley JG, Houmard J. 2002. Co-ordinated expression of phycobiliprotein operons in the chromatically adapting cyanobacterium *Calothrix* PCC 7601: a role for RcaD and RcaG. *Mol. Microbiol.* 43:749–62

78. Oelmüller R, Conley PB, Federspiel N, Briggs WR, Grossman AR. 1988. Changes in accumulation and synthesis of transcripts encoding phycobilisome components during acclimation of *Fremyella diplosiphon* to different light qualities. *Plant Physiol.* 88:1077–83

79. Oelmüller R, Grossman AR, Briggs WR. 1988. Photoreversibility of the effect of red and green light-pulses on the accumulation in darkness of mRNAs coding for phycocyanin and phycoerythrin in *Fremyella diplosiphon*. *Plant Physiol.* 88:1084–91

80. Oelmüller R, Grossman AR, Briggs WR. 1989. Role of protein synthesis in regulation of phycobiliprotein mRNA abundance by light quality in *Fremyella diplosiphon*. *Plant Physiol.* 90:1486–91

81. Ohki K, Fujita Y. 1991. Complementary chromatic adaptation in the cyanobacterium, *Tolypothrix tenuis*: location of phycoerythrin newly synthesized by green illumination. *Plant Cell Physiol.* 32:483–88

82. Ohki K, Fujita Y. 1992. Photoregulation of phycobilisome structure during complementary chromatic adaptation in the marine cyanophyte *Phormidium* sp. C86. *J. Phycol.* 28:803–8

83. Ohki K, Gantt E, Lipschultz CA, Ernst MC. 1985. Constant phycobilisome size in chromatically adapted cells of the cyanobacterium *Tolypothrix tenuis*, and variation in *Nostoc* sp. *Plant Physiol.* 79:943–48

84. Ohki K, Watanabe M, Fujita Y. 1982. Action of near UV and blue light on the photocontrol of phycobiliprotein formation; a complementary chromatic adaptation. *Plant Cell Physiol.* 23:651–56

85. Palenik B. 2001. Chromatic adaptation in marine *Synechococcus* strains. *Appl. Environ. Microbiol.* 67:991–94

86. Parkinson JS. 1995. Genetic approaches for signalling pathways and proteins. In *Two-Component Signal Transduction*, ed. JA Hoch, TJ Silhavy, pp. 9–23. Washington, DC: ASM Press

87. Postius C, Neuschaefer-Rube O, Haid V, Boger P. 2001. N_2-fixation and complementary chromatic adaptation in non-heterocystous cyanobacteria from Lake Constance. *FEMS Microbiol. Ecol.* 37:117–25

88. Ramus J. 1983. A physiological test of the theory of complementary chromatic adaptation. II. Brown, green and red seaweeds. *J. Phycol.* 19:173–78

89. Ramus J, van der Meer JP. 1983. A physiological test of the theory of complementary chromatic adaptation. I. Color mutants of a red seaweed. *J. Phycol.* 19:86–91

90. Raven JA, Andrews M, Quigg A. 2005. The evolution of oligotrophy: implications for the breeding of crop plants for low input agricultural systems. *Ann. Appl. Biol.* 146:261–80

91. Rippka R, Deruelles J, Waterbury JB, Herdman M, Stanier RY. 1979. Generic assignments, strain histories and properties of pure cultures of cyanobacteria. *J. Gen. Microbiol.* 111:1–61

92. Robinson BL, Miller JH. 1970. Photomorphogenesis in blue-green alga *Nostoc commune* 584. *Physiol. Plant.* 23:461–72

93. Rosinski J, Hainfeld JF, Rigbi M, Siegelman HW. 1981. Phycobilisome ultrastructure and chromatic adaptation in *Fremyella diplosiphon*. *Ann. Bot.* 47:1–12

94. Saffo MB. 1987. New light on seaweeds. *Bioscience* 37:654–64

95. Schmidt-Goff CM, Federspiel NA. 1993. *In vivo* and *in vitro* footprinting of a light-regulated promoter in the cyanobacterium *Fremyella diplosiphon*. *J. Bacteriol.* 175:1806–13

96. Seib LO, Kehoe DM. 2002. A turquoise mutant genetically separates expression of genes encoding phycoerythrin and its associated linker peptides. *J. Bacteriol.* 184:962–70

97. Sidler WA. 1994. Phycobilisome and phycobiliprotein structures. In *The Molecular Biology of Cyanobacteria*, ed. DA Bryant, pp. 139–216. Dordrecht: Kluwer Acad.

98. Siegelman HW, Hendricks SB. 1965. Purification and properties of phytochrome: a chromoprotein regulating plant growth. *Fed. Proc.* 24:863–67

99. Sobczyk A, Bely A, Tandeau de Marsac N, Houmard J. 1994. A phosphorylated DNA-binding protein is specific for the red-light signal during complementary chromatic adaptation in cyanobacteria. *Mol. Microbiol.* 13:875–85

100. Sobczyk A, Schyns G, Tandeau de Marsac N, Houmard J. 1993. Transduction of the light signal during complementary chromatic adaptation in the cyanobacterium *Calothrix*

This study identified CpeR and provided proof of a second light-responsive CCA regulatory system.

sp. PCC 7601: DNA-binding proteins and modulation by phosphorylation. *EMBO J.* 12:997–1004

101. Stowe-Evans EL, Ford J, Kehoe DM. 2004. Genomic DNA microarray analysis: identification of new genes regulated by light color in the cyanobacterium *Fremyella diplosiphon*. *J. Bacteriol.* 186:4338–49

102. Stowe-Evans EL, Kehoe DM. 2004. Signal transduction during light-quality acclimation in cyanobacteria: a model system for understanding phytochrome-response pathways in prokaryotes. *Photochem. Photobiol. Sci.* 3:495–502

103. Tandeau de Marsac N. 1983. Phycobilisomes and complementary chromatic adaptation in cyanobacteria. *Bull. Inst. Pasteur* 81:201–54

104. Tandeau de Marsac N. 1977. Occurrence and nature of chromatic adaptation in cyanobacteria. *J. Bacteriol.* 130:82–91

105. Tandeau de Marsac N. 2003. Phycobiliproteins and phycobilisomes: the early observations. *Photosynth. Res.* 76:197–205

106. Tandeau de Marsac N, Castets AM, Cohen-Bazire G. 1980. Wavelength modulation of phycoerythrin synthesis in *Synechocystis* sp. 6701. *J. Bacteriol.* 142:310–14

107. Tandeau de Marsac N, Cohen-Bazire G. 1977. Molecular composition of cyanobacterial phycobilisomes. *Proc. Natl. Acad. Sci. USA* 74:1635–39

108. Tandeau de Marsac N, Mazel D, Damerval T, Guglielmi G, Capuano V, Houmard J. 1988. Photoregulation of gene expression in the filamentous cyanobacterium *Calothrix* sp. PCC 7601: light-harvesting complexes and cell differentiation. *Photosynth. Res.* 18:99–132

109. Taylor BL, Zhulin IB. 1999. PAS domains: internal sensors of oxygen, redox potential, and light. *Microbiol. Mol. Biol. Rev.* 63:479–506

110. Terauchi K, Montgomery BL, Grossman AR, Lagarias JC, Kehoe DM. 2004. RcaE is a complementary chromatic adaptation photoreceptor required for green and red light responsiveness. *Mol. Microbiol.* 51:567–77

111. Vierstra RD. 2003. Cyanophytochromes, bacteriophytochromes, and plant phytochromes: light-regulated kinases related to bacterial two-component regulators. In *Histidine Kinases in Signal Transduction*, ed. M Inouye, R Dutta, pp. 273–95. San Diego, CA: Academic

112. Vogelmann TC, Scheibe J. 1978. Action spectra for chromatic adaptation in the blue-green alga *Fremyella diplosiphon*. *Planta* 143:233–39

113. Westermann M, Wehrmeyer W. 1995. A new type of complementary chromatic adaptation exemplified by *Phormidium* sp. C86: changes in the number of peripheral rods and in the stoichiometry of core complexes in phycobilisomes. *Arch. Microbiol.* 164:132–41

This study identified the three regulatory groups within strains of cyanobacteria potentially capable of CCA.

Seasonal Control of Tuberization in Potato: Conserved Elements with the Flowering Response

Mariana Rodríguez-Falcón,[1,2] Jordi Bou,[1] and Salomé Prat[1]

[1] Departamento Genética Molecular de Plantas, Centro Nacional de Biotecnología-CSIC. Campus Universidad Autónoma de Madrid, 28049 Madrid, Spain; email: sprat@cnb.uam.es

[2] Instituto de Biología Vegetal y Biotecnología, Universidad de Talca, Talca, Chile

Annu. Rev. Plant Biol. 2006. 57:151–80

The *Annual Review of Plant Biology* is online at plant.annualreviews.org

doi: 10.1146/ annurev.arplant.57.032905.105224

1543-5008/06/0602- 0151$20.00

Key Words

day length, gibberellin, tuberization transition, stolon meristem, potato tuber development

Abstract

Fluctuations in day length determine the time to flower in many plants and in potato are critical to promote differentiation of tubers. Day length is perceived in the leaves and under inductive conditions these synthesize a systemic signal that is transported to the underground stolons to induce tuber development. Flowering tobacco shoots grafted into potato stocks promote tuberization in the stocks, indicating that the floral and tuber-inducing signals might be similar. We describe recent progress in the identification of the molecular mechanisms underlying day-length recognition in potato. Evidence has been obtained for a conserved function of the potato orthologs of the CONSTANS (CO) and FLOWERING LOCUS T (FT) proteins in tuberization control under short days (SDs). These observations indicate that common regulatory pathways are involved in both flowering and tuberization photoperiodic responses in plants.

Contents

INTRODUCTION

Tuberization is a developmental process unique to some *Solanum* species, which under favorable conditions differentiate specialized underground propagation organs or tubers. Tubers are modified underground stems, with very short swollen internodes and scale leaves subtending the dormant axillary buds or tuber "eyes." They serve a double function to the plant, as a storage organ and as a vegetative propagation system. After a winter period of dormancy or rest, dormant axillary buds reactivate and grow out to produce a plant that is genetically identical to the mother plant, tubers thus serving as perennation organs to these annual species.

Potato tubers accumulate large amounts of starch, are low in fat, and have a protein content as high as cereals, with the added advantage of a more equilibrated composition in essential amino acids. A medium-sized potato tuber, in addition, provides about half the daily adult requirement of vitamin C. Due to these nutritional properties and ease of propagation, potato is currently the fourth most important food crop in the world, after cereals. It is used on a large scale in the chip and fries food industry, or in a processed form to obtain starch and alcohol, with the annual production of tubers approaching 300 million tons.

Tubers form in the subapical region of underground stem-like structures or stolons that develop at the base of the main stem. Under noninductive conditions, stolons grow as horitzontal stems and, if exposed to sufficient light, they become green and emerge from the soil to form a new shoot. During this process, the stolon acquires all the characteristics of a main stem, forming roots and new leaves and eventually flowering. Under low temperature or short day conditions, however, elongation growth of the stolon ceases and the tip begins to swell to form a tuber. Swelling is correlated with an expansion and radial cell division of the cells located in the pith and cortex of the subapical part of the stolon, and subsequent random cell division and expansion of the cells in the perimedullary region contribute to tuber bulking (142). These changes in cell division are accompanied by a switch in the developmental program of the stolon subapical meristem cells to a tuber fate. Meristem growth becomes determinate, and cell division ceases after a few rounds. The mechanism of sucrose unloading changes from apoplastic to symplastic, and this is accompanied by a decline in cell wall invertase activity and a dramatic increase in the activity of the sucrose synthase and fructokinase enzymes (8, 136). During the rapid growth phase, tubers accumulate large amounts of storage compounds, mainly in the form of starch and proteins (i.e., patatin and proteinase inhibitors), which serve as a source of energy to the future plant (94). Regulatory routes leading to starch biosynthesis have been extensively studied in potato, and current knowledge on these pathways is summarized in excellent reviews (31, 35, 36).

In its natural habitat, differentiation of potato tubers occurs in autumn to early winter, depending on the potato genotype. These newly formed tubers undergo a period of inactivity or endodormancy, which is characterized by the absence of bud growth even if tubers are exposed to conditions favorable to sprouting. Such a period of physiological rest lasts for a few months and assures survival of the plant during the cool winter temperatures. Tuber sprouting is desired in potatoes that will be used as tuber seeds, but unwanted during storage, because it reduces the post-harvest life of tubers and decreases their nutritional quality. Endogenous factors determining this economically important trait are just beginning to be uncovered and have been extensively discussed in different reviews published on this subject (117, 120, 138).

DAY-LENGTH CONTROL AND GENOTYPE

Potato was brought to cultivation in the highlands of South America near the equator. In these equatorial high-altitude regions, day length remains close to 12 h (SD conditions) and temperatures are low at night. Wild Andean varieties (*Solanum tuberosum* ssp. *andigena*) are adapted to these conditions and are unable to tuberize or do so very poorly when grown under the higher temperatures of lowland tropics or the longer summer days of temperate zones. Modern cultivated potatoes derive from Chilean landraces (*Solanum tuberosum* ssp. *tuberosum*) grown in the low-

lands of southern Chile and therefore are more adapted to the longer summer days of the temperate regions of Europe and North America. Repeated selection for tuberization under long days (LDs) would have favored these clones over the less-adapted Andean varieties, and Chilean landraces would have become the predominant modern breeding stock. *Tuberosum* potatoes give very low yields in the highland tropics because, under the cool temperatures and SD conditions characteristic of these regions, tubers are formed very early, before shoot growth can support a good tuber yield (30). Such a trend toward prevailing short or longer days for induction is characteristic of all *andigena* or *tuberosum* species, although there are substantial genetic differences within each group.

Short days, cool temperatures, and low rates of nitrogen supply promote tuberization, whereas tuber formation is delayed by long days, high temperatures, and nitrogen-rich fertilizers, conditions that are noninductive for tuberization (29, 75, 83). Among these environmental conditions, day length has been the most intensively investigated because of its critical effect on tuberization. SDs induce tuber formation in all potato varieties, although there is considerable variation in the degree to which this environmental cue is required for induction (118). Modern potatoes were subjected to iterative selection for early tuberization, and tuber transition in these cultivars is relatively independent of day length. However, wild potato species such as *S. tuberosum* ssp. *andigena* or *S. demissum* are strictly dependent on SDs for tuber formation (30, 76). These species tuberize only under SDs (8 h light) and do not produce tubers when grown under LD conditions (16 h light) or SDs supplemented with a night break (NB) or pulse of light in the night period (SD+NB). The inhibitory effect of a 15-min pulse of light given in the middle of the night (NB) demonstrates that it is the overall length of the night period (long nights), rather than that of the day (SDs), that induces tuber formation in these plants (**Figure 1**).

SD: short day

LD: long day

NB: night break

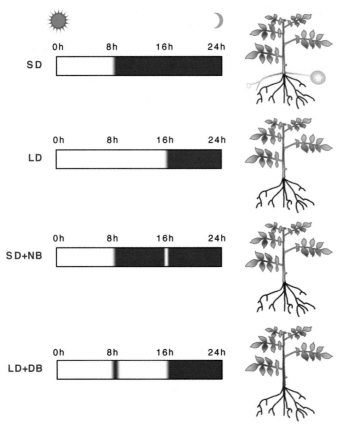

DAY LENGTH IS PERCEIVED IN THE LEAVES

Evidence demonstrating that the principal site of perception of the photoperiodic signal is in the leaf was obtained from grafting studies in *andigena* potatoes (20, 38). When leaves of *andigena* plants grown under inductive (8 h light) conditions were grafted onto noninduced stocks (16 h light), tubers were formed in the stock plants, whereas stocks grafted with noninduced leaves did not produce tubers. This demonstrates that inductive conditions are sensed in the leaf but not in the stolons, leading to the hypothesis that, in response to the photoperiodic signal, the leaves produce a tuberization stimulus that is transported across the graft union to the noninduced stock, where it induces tuberization.

Tuber induction is associated with several morphological changes in the plant (30). Leaves become larger, thinner, and a paler green, and acquire a flatter angle to the stem. Axillary branching is suppressed, flower buds abort more frequently, and senescence is accelerated, coinciding with the rapid growth phase of the tubers. Such alterations in morphology, together with transmission of the inducing signal across a graft, led to the belief that the stimulus was of hormonal nature. Several hormones, i.e., gibberellin (100, 143), cytokinin (56, 86), jasmonic and tuberonic acids (70, 130) or abscisic acid (83, 143), reportedly play a role in tuberization, and changes in the endogenous levels of these hormones could be correlated with the tuberization onset. However, as discussed below, effects of many of these hormones are likely exerted directly at the level of the stolon, and these growth regulators then play a role in tuberization transition, but are not involved in the production of the inducing stimulus derived from the leaves.

Analysis of gene expression during tuber growth has been hampered by the lack of synchronicity of the tuberization process. To overcome this problem, in vitro tuberization systems based on single-node stem cuttings were developed, in which tuber formation can

Figure 1

Day-length control of tuberization in andigena potatoes. *Andigena* species are strictly dependent on short days (SDs) (8–10 h light) for tuberization and do not tuberzize under long days (LDs) (14–16 h light). Like in other SD species, the overall length of the night period rather than that of the day determines the tuberization response. Interruption of long nights with a pulse of light inhibits tuber formation, whereas interruption of long days with a dark pulse has no effect. Response to night break (NB) enables growth of induced (SD) and noninduced (SD+NB) plants under identical culture conditions except for a 15-min light interruption in the middle of the night.

Temperature is also an important environmental factor for tuberization. High temperatures inhibit tuber formation, whereas low temperatures promote tuber growth. A strong day-length response is observed at elevated temperatures, whereas day-length control is less prominent at lower temperatures (118, 129). This indicates that these environmental cues converge at some point, possibly by controlling a common component of the day-length pathway.

be synchronously induced in response to day length (29) or high levels of sucrose in the media (56). Single-node cuttings taken from noninduced plants will develop axillary shoots when buried in soil and kept humid, whereas formation of a stolon, a tuber subtended by a stolon, or a sessile tuber is observed in leaf cuttings taken from plants grown under shorter photoperiods, depending on the strength of induction. Tuberization is uniformly induced and swelling is observed within 4–5 days of cutting which makes these a useful tool in tuberization studies (29).

Synchronized tuber induction is also observed in stem-node cuttings cultured in vitro in high (8%) sucrose medium (27, 34), such an in vitro tuberization system is being widely used for production of virus-free certified seed potatoes or propagation of stock cultures. Microtubers obtained in vitro show identical changes in the activities of enzymes involved in sucrose unloading and starch biosynthesis to those observed in field-grown tubers (7, 10, 133), and are therefore a valuable model system in tuberization research. However, although a day-length response is still observed in potato plantlets cultured in high sucrose (56, 112), photoperiodic control is not as strict as in soil-cultured plants, as tuberization is also observed in continuous light. Therefore, these in vitro systems are not useful for studying tuberization control by day length, and *andigena* species are more suitable for these studies. In these species, stolons develop under noninductive LD or SD+NB conditions, but differentiation of these stolons into tubers is not observed unless plants are transferred to SDs. Transfer to inductive SD conditions induces a synchronous growth of tubers, with tuber swelling observed after 8–12 days of transfer to SDs. These plants offer an excellent model system in which to study production of the mobile-inducing signal derived from the leaves, and development of stable transgenic lines for both up or downregulated gene expression has substantially contributed to our understanding of the molecular mechanisms underlying production of the mobile-inducing signal in these cultivars. Here we focus on recent discoveries concerning the inhibitory function of gibberellins (GAs) on tuberization and the involvement of a conserved CONSTANS/ FLOWERING LOCUS T (FT) pathway in SD-dependent control of tuber formation. An emerging topic of this work is that despite divergence of the flowering and tuberization responses, plants rely on the same signal transduction components to synchronize these two distinct developmental transition processes to seasonal changes in day length. Hence, it is feasible that similarly conserved day length–related pathways regulate other seasonal responses such as leaf abscission in fall, bud dormancy, or annual rings of cambial activity in trees.

GA: gibberellin

FT: flowering locus T

PHY: phytochrome

DAY-LENGTH DURATION IS SENSED BY THE LIGHT RECEPTOR PHYTOCHROME

Red light (R) is most effective for interrupting long nights. A far red light (FR) pulse given immediately after the pulse of red light reverses the inhibitory effect of the R night break (13), indicating that length of the night is sensed by phytochromes. In potato, two phytochrome-encoding genes (PHYA and PHYB) have been characterized (52, 53). Of these, only PHYB stably accumulates in green leaves, and is thus likely involved in sensing day-length duration. By transforming *andigena* plants with an antisense construct for this gene, we showed that PHYB does play a crucial role in day-length perception and in regulation of the SD pathway of tuberization. Plants in which PHYB expression is downregulated are almost day-length insensitive and tuberize very early under LD, SD+NB, or SD conditions (59). These lines actually behave as though they are strongly induced to tuberize, forming sessile tubers that are directly attached to the main stem. These observations are consistent with a regulatory model in which PHYB functions under noninductive SD+NB or LD conditions

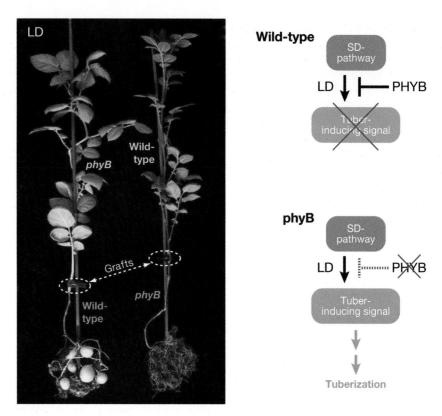

Figure 2

PHYB represses tuber induction in long days (LDs). Day length is perceived by phytochromes. PHYA resets the endogenous rhythm and PHYB senses the length of the day and night intervals. Plants in which PHYB expression is downregulated (*phyB*) show a constitutive activation of the short day (SD)-dependent tuberization pathway and are day-length insensitive. When these plants are grafted to wild-type stocks, they induce tuber formation under LDs in the stock, providing evidence for constitutive production of the tuberization stimulus in the leaves. The reverse graft of a wild-type scion into the *phyB* stock does not tuberize in LDs because production of the graft transmissible signal is repressed under noninductive conditions in wild-type leaves.

to repress a SD regulatory pathway promoting tuber formation. This inducing pathway is constitutively activated in the *phyB* mutants, and these plants then tuberize under any day-length condition. In line with this observation, *phyB* scions grafted onto wild-type plants induced the wild-type stocks to tuberize in LDs, whereas tuber formation is not observed in reciprocal grafts of wild-type scions onto *phyB* stocks (61). This agrees with constitutive production of the tuberization stimulus in these leaves, and the idea that PHYB represses synthesis of this stimulus under noninductive conditions (**Figure 2**).

Evidence for a function of PHYA in day-length control was also obtained in antisense lines with reduced levels of expression of this photoreceptor (54). A 6-h extension of the day with FR+R light caused a delay in tuber formation in wild-type plants, but not in antisense *PHYA* lines, providing evidence for a role of this light-labile photoreceptor in day-length perception. Exposure to 5 h FR or FR+R light at the end of the night, before transfer to constant (free-running) light conditions, advances the phase of circadian movement of the leaves in wild-type potato or *PHYB* antisense lines but not in plants with reduced levels of PHYA accumulation. Blue light still causes a phase shift in these lines, thus showing a role for PHYA in the input to the clock but not as an integral part of the circadian clock (146). Concerted action of PHYA, PHYB, and blue light receptors then seems to mediate photoperiodic control of tuber formation, PHYA and cryptochromes having a role in setting the phase of the internal circadian rhythm, whereas PHYB would make tuberization responsive to the photoperiod by sensing the presence/absence of light during the sensitive phase of the rhythm.

Besides loss of photoperiodic control of tuberization, the antisense *phyB* lines exhibit an elongated phenotype that is reminiscent of plants treated with saturating doses of GAs. Similar to the *slender* mutants, these plants have paler leaves and very elongated internodes, indicative of either increased GA synthesis, altered feedback regulation, or a constitutive activation of the response to GAs. The *StGA20ox1* transcript encoding GA 20-oxidase was upregulated (62) and GA content was elevated in *phyB* shoots (79), which contrasts with the recognized inhibitory effect of GAs on tuberization. Nevertheless, we obtained evidence indicating that the inhibitory effects of GAs are directly exerted at the stolon level, and increased aerial levels of GAs not only do not inhibit tuberization but likely play a role in modulating production of the tuberization stimulus.

GIBBERELLINS DELAY TUBERIZATION

GAs have long been implicated in the regulation of tuber development (137). Tuber initiation is delayed by applying GA_3 (115, 143), whereas adding inhibitors of GA biosynthesis such as tetcyclacis, chlorocholine chloride, paclobutrazol, or ancymidol enhances tuber formation in stem-node cuttings (1, 42, 83, 115, 136) and in greenhouse-grown plants (12, 60). There is multiple evidence for an inhibitory function of GAs on tuber formation. First, tuber initiation is correlated with a sharp decrease in the endogenous GA_1 content in the stolon (143). Second, modifying endogenous GA levels due to overexpression or antisense inhibition of the GA 20-oxidase *StGA20ox1* gene results in delayed or advanced tuberization in SDs, showing a correlation between GA levels and tuberization onset (18). Third, the *andigena ga1* dwarf mutant, apparently blocked in the 13-hydroxylation biosynthetic step, can form tubers in LD conditions, although it requires cultivation for several months under these noninducing conditions (131). Transfer to SDs induces rapid tuberization (within three to four days) in these dwarf potatoes, indicating that although SD requirement is less severe than in wild-type plants, tuberization in these mutants is still under day-length control. This indicates two independent pathways of tuberization: a SD pathway and a GA-dependent pathway, the balance between the inducing and inhibitory effects of these pathways determining tuberization onset.

GA 20-oxidase and GA 3-hydroxylase catalyze the two last steps in the GA biosynthetic pathway, and GA 2-oxidase catalyzes degradation of bioactive GAs into inactive catabolites (47). These enzymes encode key regulatory steps for GA biosynthesis and homeostasis and thus are subjected to transcriptional feedback control by the end product GA_1 (48), and are regulated in response to day-length conditions or phytochrome (66). Studies concerning potato GA biosynthetic activities have focused mainly on these genes, as they are the best candidates to mediate the changes in GA levels observed in induced stolons. Analysis of expression of three different transcripts encoding potato GA 20-oxidase activity did not show significant differences in the levels of accumulation of any of these mRNAs in SD as compared to LD conditions (17). In LDs, an extended interval of accumulation of these mRNAs was detected during the supplementary hours of light, but transcript levels were not higher than in SDs, indicating that, in contrast to *Arabidopsis* or spinach, expression of these genes in potato is not differentially regulated by day length. Important changes in transcript levels were, however, observed for gene *StGA3ox2* encoding potato GA 3-hydroxylase (J. Bou, J.L. García-Martínez & S. Prat, submitted). In plants entrained to LD conditions, this mRNA accumulates to low levels in the stem but is abundantly expressed in the stolon. Transfer to SD conditions leads to upregulated expression of this gene in the apex and stem nodes, but to a complete repression of gene expression in the stolon, suggesting an important role of this gene in downregulated GA synthesis during tuberization transition. Microarray RNA-profiling analysis of tuber development has also identified a GA 2-oxidase transcript that is upregulated in induced stolons (69). Expression of this gene is activated very early after transfer to SD conditions, and transcript accumulation is observed before any visible swelling of the stolon, preceding accumulation of the tubulin *TUB8* mRNA (125). The *Stgan* transcript encoding a short-chain alcohol dehydrogenase was also identified in amplified fragment length polymorphism (AFLP)-based RNA-finger-printing analysis of genes that were upregulated in the induced stolons (11). Antisense lines for the *Stgan* gene show a taller growth habit and elevated levels of GAs, indicating that this steroid dehydrogenase-related gene functions in breaking down GAs through an alternative route to GA 2-oxidases (11). Changes in the GA 3-hydroxylase, GA 2-oxidase, or *Stgan* transcripts are among the earliest changes in gene expression observed during tuber differentiation. This indicates that local drop in GA_1 levels is a key event in tuberization transition. What remains to be determined is how this GA-dependent signal is integrated with the SD-inducing signal derived from the leaves.

GIBBERELLIN SYNTHESIS IN AERIAL TISSUES

To analyze further the role of potato GA 3-oxidase in tuberization, we overexpressed the *StGA3ox2* gene in *andigena* potato plants.

Transgenic lines exhibiting high levels of expression of this transgene showed a taller phenotype and increased shoot GA_1 content, which correlated with the upregulated levels of expression of the transgene. However, contrary to expectations, these lines tuberized earlier in SD conditions and showed a higher tuber yield than the untransformed controls (J. Bou, J.L. García-Martínez & S. Prat, submitted for publication). This observation appears to indicate a negative effect on tuberization of increased levels of the GA_{20} precursor, as in GA 20-oxidase overexpressers (18), but a tuberization-promotive effect of an increased rate of GA_1 synthesis in the shoot, as in the GA 3-oxidase lines. A possible explanation for this contradictory result is that GA_{20} is more active at inhibiting tuberization than GA_1, or, alternatively, that these two GAs are not equally transported to the stolon. It is possible that GA_{20} is rapidly transported throughout the plant, thus inhibiting tuber transition, whereas GA_1 remains in the vicinity of the cells where it is produced, exerting its effect mainly on these cells. Evidence for a different mobility of these two GA molecules was in fact obtained in grafting experiments with the pea *Le* and *Na* mutants, blocked respectively in the GA 3-oxidase and *ent*-kaurenoic acid oxidase biosynthetic steps (23). In these studies, *Na* scions grafted on wild-type stocks grew normally, due to efficient conversion of GA_{20}, mobilized from the wild-type stock, into bioactive GA_1 by endogenous GA 3-oxidases in the mutant. However, *Le* scions grafted on wild-type stocks remained dwarf because of the poor transport of GA_1 from the wild-type stock (95). Such a preferential transport model would actually explain the early tuberization phenotype of the 3-oxidase overexpressers, as an increased rate of GA_{20} to GA_1 conversion in these plants would bring a reduction in the concentration of GA_{20} available to be transported to the stolon.

Although it is accepted that tuberization induction in SDs correlates with a reduced rate of synthesis of bioactive GAs in the

Figure 3

Elongation of the stem observed after transfering the plants to short days (SDs), indicating an increased synthesis of GA_1 in the shoot. Transfer of *andigena* plants to SD conditions induces tuber formation but also a visible elongation of the stem. This is observed only in plants exposed to SDs (8 h), but not in plants exposed to SDs with a 15-min interruption of the night (SD+NB, noninductive conditions), and correlates with increased levels of expression of the *StGA30x2* and *PHOR1* transcripts (*green box*). pACO lines expressing the *Arabidopsis CO* gene do not show this response and tuberize very late in SDs. A constitutive elongation of the stem is observed in the *phyB* lines that are insensitive to day length and behave as though strongly induced to tuberize. Elevated levels of GA_1 were observed in these lines (*blue box*).

leaves (65, 74, 93, 100), we have consistently observed that transfer to SD conditions induces elongation of the youngest internodes of the stem (**Figure 3**). Stem growth is rapidly induced after transfer to SD conditions, and these plants show a stronger resemblance to the *phyB* antisense lines than plants kept under LDs.

The photoperiod responsive 1 (*PHOR1*) gene was identified in a search for genes show-

ing upregulated expression in SD leaves and with a possible function in tuberization control (5). *PHOR1* encodes a U-box domain protein with an arm-repeat region homologous to the *Drosophila* segment polarity gene, *armadillo*. Antisense repression of PHOR1 led to a reduction in stem length and resulted in early tuberization in SDs and partial insensitivity to applied GAs. Subcellular localization studies using a fusion to the green fluorescent

PHOR1:
photoperiod
responsive 1

SCF: Skp1 Cullin
F-box/ring-H2

gai-1:
GA-insensitive 1

protein showed that PHOR1 is localized to the cytosol but rapidly migrates to the nucleus upon treatment with GAs. PHOR1 was recently shown to exhibit E3-ligase activity and to ubiquitinate the DELLA repressor proteins to target them for degradation by the 26S proteasome (A. Espinosa, J.M. Iglesias, and S. Prat, unpublished results) in a reaction independent of that mediated by the SLEEPY1 F-box protein SCF complex (26). It is therefore possible that upregulated expression of this E3 ligase in aerial tissues functions by relieving DELLA-mediated growth restraint in response to day-length conditions, thus promoting the increase in stem growth observed in SDs. Consistent with this observation, increased levels of expression of the *StGA3ox2* transcript were observed in the apex and nodes of SD plants, suggesting an increased rate of GA_1 synthesis in the aerial tissues of these plants. Such increase in shoot GA_1 synthesis is mimicked in the GA 3-oxidase overexpresser lines, which resemble SD-induced plants by exhibiting a taller phenotype and tuberizing earlier than the controls. A similar diversion mechanism can also explain the somehow contradictory phenotype of the *phyB* antisense plants, in which a four- to sixfold increase in GA_1 content in the shoot paradoxically coexists with a strong induction to tuberize. Therefore, contrary to the general idea that GAs inhibit tuberization, our observations indicate that high levels of GAs in the stolons inhibit tuberization, whereas a high rate of GA_{20} to GA_1 conversion in the shoot would favor tuber formation, likely by lowering the levels of GA_{20} in the aerial tissues and thus transport of this precursor to the stolon.

GIBBERELLINS EXERT A LOCAL EFFECT IN THE STOLON

How do GAs regulate tuberization transition? The observation that the andigena *ga1* dwarf mutant, with a block in the 13-hydroxylation step, can form tubers in LDs seemed to point to a function of these hormones in day-length signaling (131); however, several lines of evidence, including the sharp drop in GA_1 levels in the stolon tip coinciding with the onset of tuberization (143), support a local inhibitory function of these hormones in the stolon. Evidence for a main function of GAs in repressing stolon differentiation was obtained in a recent study in which wild-type and *phyB* potato lines blocked in the GA-response pathway were obtained by expression of the *gai-1* dominant allele of *Arabidopsis* (M. Rodriguez-Falcon & S. Prat, submitted for publication). *gai-1* encodes a DELLA repressor protein with a 17 amino acid deletion within the DELLA domain that renders the protein unresponsive to GA-dependent degradation and leads to a severe dwarf phenotype that does not respond to exogenous GA (25, 88, 126). Expression of this allele caused a GA-insensitive dwarf phenotype in both genetic backgrounds, the strength of this effect being directly correlated with the levels of expression of the transgene. Although GA response was compromised, tuberization time was not affected in these transformants, which tuberized about at the same time as the respective controls, thus suggesting an independent function for both GA and day-length pathways.

GA insensitivity could not overcome the SD requirement of wild-type *andigena* plants to tuberize. After several months of culture in LD conditions, tubers were observed in the *ga1*-deficient mutant but not in the GA-insensitive *gai-1* transformants, indicating that the GA-response pathway is still required for tuberization in LDs. It is possible that increased GA_1 synthesis in aerial tissues not only is involved in diverting GA_{20} from the stolon, but also in promoting tuberization by activating one of the genes involved in tuberization control. However, such a positive control function of GAs needs further investigation.

Tubers developed by the dwarf lines were highly irregular in shape and looked more like swollen stolons than tubers. An accumulation of tuber-specific transcripts and massive amounts of starch were observed in the basal internodes subtending these tubers, thus showing unrestricted differentiation of all stolon internodes to a tuber fate. In the most severely dwarf lines, swelling of the buried stem was also observed, suggesting tuber differentiation of the whole belowground region. These results are consistent with a function of GAs in restricting tuber transition to the subapical region of the stolon, the drop in GA_1 levels at the onset of tuberization thus playing a role in defining the domain of cells that will undergo transition to a tuber fate. In the *gai-1* transformants, a block in the GA response will likely expand the domain of tuberization competence to the whole stolon and main belowground stem, as tuber differentiation is also observed in these organs.

GAs promote stolon elongation by inducing a transverse alignment of cortical microtubules to the long axis of growing cells (114). Reduced GA levels after treatment with the GA synthesis inhibitor uniconazol were reported to cause a reorientation of the stolon cell cortical microtubules to longitudinal or oblique directions, thus initiating longitudinal division of these cells and radial expansion of the tuber (33). The sharp decrease in GA levels observed in the cells located at the subapical region of the stolon is thus likely directly involved in signaling the change in the plane of cell division of these cells during differentiation to a tuber fate. However, the observation that the entire stolon and belowground stem undergo tuber fate transition in the *gai* lines would indicate an additional function of low GAs in differentiation of the cells in the subapical meristem to make them competent to respond to the tuberization-inducing signal derived from the leaf. This leads to a regulatory model in which tuber differentiation is regulated by the concerted action of two opposing signals: a GA-dependent signal that represses tuber growth and a leaf-derived signal that promotes tuber transition. How these signals are integrated at the molecular level is at present unknown. Recent identification of the rice *GIBBERELLIN INSENSITIVE DWARF1* (*GID1*) gene as a

soluble receptor for gibberellin (127) will provide a better tool for GA-response modification than the *gai* dominant allele. ESTs coding for homologs of this gene have been reported in potato and could be used to design specific RNAi constructs aimed to impair GA signalling in the stolons or the leaves, thus allowing to analyze the effects on tuber differentiation of a tissue specific block in GA perception.

THE KNOX GENES MAY SUPPRESS GIBBERELLIN ACTIVITY IN THE STOLON MERISTEM

Several studies have implicated the KNOX genes in repression of GA synthesis in the shoot apical meristem. Overexpression of the tobacco *NTH15* homeobox gene, for example, leads to a decrease in bioactive GA levels by repressing GA 20-oxidase gene expression (109, 123). The *Arabidopsis* homeobox protein SHOOTMERISTEMLESS (STM) excludes expression of the *AtGA20ox1* gene from the shoot apical meristem, as repression of GA synthesis is crucial to maintaining the indeterminate state of the meristem corpus cells (43). In potato, overexpression of the homeobox *POTH1* gene resulted in enhanced tuberization in vitro, under both SD and LD photoperiods, together with a mouse ear leaf phenotype. Accumulation of the *GA 20-oxidase1* transcript is repressed in the overexpresser lines, and GA_1 levels reduced by one half (107), suggesting a role of this KNOX regulatory protein in repression of GA synthesis. In line with this observation, GA application suppressed the leaf mouse ear phenotype of the overexpressers, giving a more wild-type leaf shape. POTH1 interacts with BEL5, a member of the BEL-1 family of TALE homeodomain proteins that is upregulated both in leaves and stolons in SDs (21). Ectopic *BEL5* expression also leads to enhanced tuber formation and decreased levels of *GA 20-oxidase1* mRNA in the stolon tips, but in contrast to POTH1 does not affect

KNOX: Knotted-like homeobox

***POTH1*:** potato homeobox 1

BEL: BEL-type homeodomain factor

leaf shape (21). Members of the KNOX/BEL families of transcription factors interact selectively, the different heterodimer combinations apparently regulating different downstream genes. In this regard, the heterodimer POTH1/BEL5 binds the *GA 20 oxidase1* gene promoter with higher affinity than the POTH1 or BEL5 homodimers and is more effective at suppressing the activity of this promoter (22). These observations reinforce the idea that the POTH1-BEL5 heterodimer may play a role in tuberization by suppressing bioactive GA synthesis in the stolon tip, thus creating a reduced GA regime favorable for meristematic activity and enabling undifferentiated cells to respond to the leaf-derived inducing signal. Generating transgenic lines with increased levels of expression of both transcription factors will be crucial to prove interaction of these homeodomain proteins in vivo and to reveal to which extent reduced GA synthesis mediates tuberization control by these regulatory factors, thus further contributing to our understanding of the mechanistic basis underlying tuber fate determination in response to low GAs.

OTHER HORMONAL SIGNALS

Besides GAs, several other phytohormones have also been implicated in tuberization. A possible role of ABA in this process, for example, was demonstrated by the higher number of tubers, earlier tuberization, and sessile tubers obtained after ABA application (83). Similar effects have been reported in vitro, with earlier tuberization and formation of sessile tubers observed in high sucrose + ABA. Application of ABA can stimulate tuber formation also in low sucrose, or in the presence of GAs, thus counteracting the inhibitory effect of these hormones (143). Tuberization, however, is not associated with an increase in the endogenous levels of ABA, as a similar decrease in ABA levels was observed in noninduced or induced stolons during development (74, 143). In line with this evidence, the ABA-deficient *droopy* mutant of *S. phureja* tuberized

normally (99), indicating that ABA synthesis is not required for induction. Thereby, it was concluded that ABA would not play a main role in tuberization and that the stimulatory effects of this hormone are due to the antagonistic effect of ABA and GAs (143).

The glucoside of 12-OH jasmonic acid (JA), tuberonic acid (TA), was isolated from shoots of potato plants induced to tuberize (70). Both JA and TA stimulate in vitro tuber formation when added to the agar medium (122, 130), and increased levels of JA were detected in the stolons at tuberization onset (2). JA itself, however, does not seem to be involved in tuberization control, as application of JA on noninduced *andigena* leaves did not induce tuberization even though it did activate wound-induced gene expression (58). Preferential accumulation of the 11-OH JA and 12-OH JA derivatives in leaflets of *S. demissum* plants grown under SD conditions led to the postulation that the respective hydroxylating enzymes are activated in SD conditions, and these hydroxylated forms are then glucosidated and transported out of the leaves to initiate tuber formation (49). However, attempts to demonstrate a causal link between these hydroxylated JAs and tuber formation have failed, as tuber formation is still observed in plants treated with the LOX inhibitor salicylhydroxamic acid (SHAM) to repress JA synthesis. Further evidence against a role of these hydroxylated JAs in tuberization control comes from the recent isolation of a gene encoding hydroxyjasmonate sulfotransferase from *Arabidopsis* (37). Characterization of this hydroxylating activity demonstrates that 12-OH JA synthesis is not restricted to tuberizing species, suggesting that hydroxylated JAs are probably involved in developmental processes other than tuber formation. These observations would exclude a function of jasmonates as components of the tuberization-inducing signal synthesized in the leaves and point more to a specific action of these compounds in the stolon (122). JAs were reported to cause a similar change in the orientation of cortical microtubules as that observed in response to the inhibitor of GA synthesis *uniconazol* (3, 81); thus high JA levels are likely to contribute to induced radial cell expansion during tuberization onset. Transcripts encoding lipoxygenase activity are upregulated during tuberization transition (9), and evidence for the involvement of a Lox1-class lipoxygenase, designated *POTLX-1*, in tuber growth was also obtained (72). Antisense lines repressed in expression of this tuber-specific 9-LOX showed a strong reduction in tuber yield, and stem-node cuttings taken from these plants failed to tuberize. Sprouts from these transgenic tubers were shorter than sprouts from the controls and developed multiple branched shoots, demonstrating an additional role of this LOX activity in sprout elongation (72).

Cytokinins (CK) have long been suggested to play a prominent role in tuberization. They are predominantly used for microtuber induction in vitro (27, 56) and promote tuberization when directly applied to isolated stolons cultured in vitro (28, 86). Attempts to induce tuber formation by applying CK to the leaves, however, have produced ambiguous results as these treatments were unable to induce tuberization in *andigena* plants grown under noninducing conditions. Also, even endogenous CK levels increase in stolon tips during induction (82) and later stages of tuber growth (85), the promotive effects of these hormones could only be observed in the presence of high (above 4%) concentrations of sucrose (86). These observations suggest that CK may function to control tuber enlargement and growth, but would not signal transition to a tuber fate. Cytokinins can activate cell division by stimulating Cyclin D expression (101) and thus may be involved in cell proliferation during the early phases of tuber growth. These hormones might also control sink strength by activating the expression of genes implicated in assimilate partitioning, such as invertases, sucrose synthase, and hexose transporter genes (103), thus pointing to a role of increased CK levels in sink identity acquisition during the storage phase of tuber growth. Evidence for a function of

CK in sink regulation was obtained in transgenic tobacco lines expressing the cytokinin *ipt* biosynthetic gene in axillary buds (40). Local overproduction of CK in these lines caused a morphological alteration characterized by the development of very short lateral branches, with small narrow-scale leaflets and swollen internodes, which accumulate large amounts of starch. Localized *ipt* expression thus appears to be sufficient to confer tuber-related identity to the cytokinin-accumulating cells, also in species that normally do not tuberize as tobacco. Increased cytokinin levels due to antisense suppression of the potato MADS box gene *POTM1* also result in increased starch accumulation and active cell division in specific regions of the meristem and the leaves (106). These observations indicate an important function of these hormones in sink-source regulation and starch accumulation, although further research is still required to dissect the exact mechanisms involved in this response. In the meantime, it is important to note that in addition to a reduction in GA levels, levels of cytokinin were elevated by four- to fivefold in the transgenic lines overexpressing the KNOX *POTH1* or *BEL5* genes (21, 107). This result implies a possible involvement of these homeodomain proteins in triggering tuber formation through a modification of both GA and cytokinin levels. KNOX activity was recently shown to activate the CK biosynthetic genes *isopentenil transferase5* and *-7* (*AtIPT5* and *AtIPT7*) and the early CK-activated gene *ARABIDOPSIS RESPONSE REGULATOR5* (*ARR5*), and to lead to a dramatic increase in CK levels (63, 144). KNOX proteins were shown as well to regulate GA catabolism, by increasing expression of the GA 2-oxidase *AtGA2ox2* and *AtGA2ox4* genes, thus preventing GA influx into the meristem and confining GA activity to the differentiating leaf primordia (63). Thereby, KNOX proteins seem to promote meristem activity by increasing CK and lowering GA activity, both high CK and low GA levels being a requisite for meristem development.

POTLX-1: potato Lox1-class lipoxygenase

CK: cytokinin

POTM1: potato MADS box 1

THE DAY-LENGTH REGULATORY PATHWAY

CO: constans

GI: gigantea

CRY: cryptocrome

Interspecific grafting experiments between tobacco and potato plants show that the flowering signal produced in the tobacco leaves is similar to or identical to the signal that induces tuberization in potato (19). In these studies, shoots of tobacco species with different photoperiodic requirements (SD, LD, or day neutral) for floral induction were grafted onto *andigena* potatoes, and tuber formation was analyzed in the potato stocks. It was clear that when scions were obtained from tobacco plants induced to flower, they induced tuberization in the potato stock, but when they were taken from nonflowering plants they did not. Identical results were obtained with LD, SD, or day-neutral tobacco species. *N. silvestrys* species induced tuberization in the potato stock only if they were exposed to LDs, whereas *N. tabacum* Mammoth induced a similar tuberization response only if it was exposed to SDs. These observations suggest that the stimulus for flowering in tobacco could be the same as the stimulus inducing tuberization in potato, and that the nature of this stimulus is equivalent in day-neutral, SD, or LD plants.

Day-Length Control of Flowering Time

The molecular mechanisms by which plants recognize day length to induce flowering have been best characterized in *Arabidopsis*. In this facultative LD plant, LDs promote flowering, whereas flowering is delayed in SDs. Mutations in the *gigantea* (*gi*), *constans* (*co*), and *flowering locus T* (*ft*) genes cause late flowering in LDs but do not affect flowering in SDs, indicating a role of these genes in the LD flowering pathway (73). *GI* encodes a large nuclear protein of unknown function, which is required for the activation of CO transcription (32, 87). *CO* expression is reduced in the *gi* mutants, and overexpression of *CO* overcomes the late-flowering phenotype of these mutants. Mutations in the *GI* gene also cause

additional defects due to faster cycling of circadian rhythms, indicating a function of this gene close to the endogenous clock. *CO* encodes a nuclear CCT domain zinc-finger protein with a central role in day-length control of flowering (97, 119). This transcription factor functions as an output to the clock and directly activates expression of the downstream floral regulator genes *FT* and *SUPPRESSOR OF OVEREXPRESSION OF CO 1* (*SOC1*, also known as *AGL20*). *FT* encodes a RAF-kinase inhibitor-like protein and *SOC1* encodes a MADS-box transcription factor, and overexpression of these genes causes extreme early flowering (14, 67, 111). They are also regulated in response to the vernalization or autonomous flowering pathways thus being proposed to function as floral integrators (46, 98, 147).

CO is cyclically expressed with a broad biphasic peak of expression in LDs. Under LDs, expression of *CO* coincides with the light at dawn and in the afternoon, causing *FT* expression and floral induction. In SDs, the *CO* peak is narrower and occurs only in the night. *FT* is then not expressed and flowering is delayed (**Figure 4**). Light regulates *CO* activity by suppressing degradation of the CO protein (128). In the dark, CO is ubiquitinated and degraded by the proteasome complex. The CRY1/CRY2 and PHYA photoreceptors stabilize the CO protein in blue light and FR light, respectively, and PHYB promotes CO degradation in R. These results explain why the cryptochrome and *phyA* mutants flower later in blue and FR light conditions, whereas the *phyB* mutant flowers earlier than wild-type plants in R, and also provide a molecular basis to the external coincidence model for day-length perception (90). This model proposes that the circadian clock generates an internally regulated rhythm controlling flowering and is sensitive to light at a particular phase of the rhythm. When the plant is exposed to light at this particular phase, flowering is induced in LD plants or delayed in SD plants.

Genetic studies in rice show that this flowering control pathway is highly conserved in

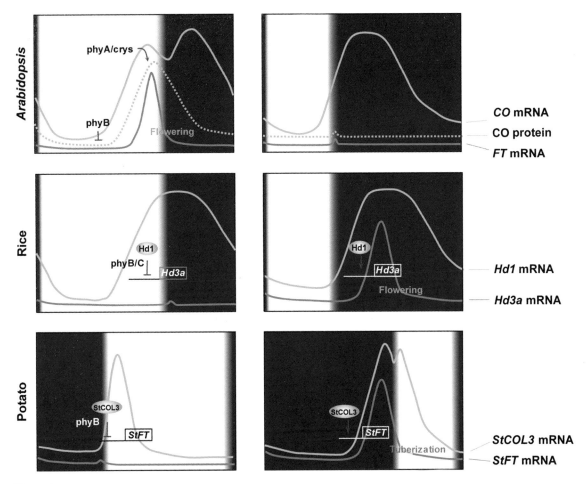

Figure 4

Diurnal rhythm of expression of the CONSTANS (CO) homolog in potato. *StCOL3* mRNA exhibits a diurnal rhythm of expression that peaks at dawn and therefore has a different phase than those of *CO/Hd1* in *Arabidopsis* and rice. *StCOL3* accumulates at the end of the night to midday under long days (LDs), and the coincidence of *StCOL3* expression with light suppresses tuberization under these conditions. In short days (SDs), *StCOL3* accumulates only during the night, and tuberization is then promoted. Hence, regulation of tuberization by *StCOL3* is reversed with respect to the light, as observed for *Hd1*. In rice, phytochrome modifies Hd1 function to inhibit expression of the *FT*-homolog *H3da*. The rice *se5* mutant defective in phytochrome activity shows early flowering irrespective of day length because Hd1 is always in the dark form. Function of PHYB might be similar in potato, with the *phyB* lines showing early tuberization under all day-length conditions. Dark areas represent the night period and light areas represent the interval of light.

this SD plant. *OsGI*, *Heading date 1* (*Hd1*, the ortholog of *CO*) and *Heading date 3a* (*Hd3a*, the ortholog of *FT*) regulate day-length-dependent flowering by acting in a genetic pathway closely related to the one described in *Arabidopsis* (44, 71, 145). However, over-expression of *OsGI* in transgenic rice causes late flowering under both SD and LD conditions. In these transgenic lines, expression of the *CO* ortholog *Hd1* is increased, but expression of *Hd3a* is suppressed (45). This suggests that regulation of the *FT* gene by *CO* is reversed in rice, and *Hd1* suppresses flowering under LD conditions. Consistent with

Hd1: Heading date 1

Hd3a: Heading date 3a

this hypothesis, loss-of-function mutations in the *Hd1* gene caused early flowering under LDs and late flowering under SDs (145), and this was correlated with an increase in *Hd3a* transcript levels in LDs but decreased levels of this transcript in SDs (71). *Hd1* shows a diurnal rhythm with a pattern similar to that of *CO* (45, 71). Under LDs, *Hd1* is expressed at high levels at the mid- to end of the day (**Figure 4**). Interaction of *Hd1* with light is dependent on phytochrome because high levels of *Hd3a* expression and early flowering in LDs is observed in the *se5* mutants, with a lesion in a heme oxygenase gene required for chromophore synthesis (57). Therefore, it was proposed that in LDs *Hd1* is expressed at the end of the day and is somehow modified by phytochrome, repressing *Hd3a* expression and inhibiting flowering. In SDs, *Hd1* is only expressed during the night when phytochrome is in an inactive form, which allows *Hd1* to induce *Hd3a* expression, thereby inducing flowering. These results demonstrate that *Arabidopsis* and rice utilize the same genetic pathways to recognize day length and promote flowering, although specific differences to these LD and SD species, involved in mediating opposite regulation of *FT* (*Hd3a*) expression by the CO and Hd1 proteins, need to be studied in further detail.

A CONSTANS Homolog is Involved in Tuberization Control

Evidence for a role of the CO protein in day-length control of tuberization was also obtained in transgenic *andigena* plants expressing the *CO* gene from *Arabidopsis* (80). Lines overexpressing the *AtCO* gene (pACO lines) were smaller than the controls and in SD conditions tuberized much later than wild-type plants. Whereas control plants started to form tubers after two weeks of transfer to SD-inducing conditions, the pACO overexpressers required more than nine weeks under SDs to tuberize, thereby demonstrating a negative effect of *AtCO* on the photoperiodic control of tuberization.

Analysis of the diurnal rhythm of expression of the *StCOL-1* gene, encoding a zinc-finger regulatory protein with homology to *CO*, showed that oscillation of this transcript was not affected in the pACO overexpresser lines. Thus, CO overexpression did not seem to affect diurnal rhythm of expression of clock-regulated genes, but did interfere with a further downstream step in day-length regulation, either by blocking the production or transport of the tuberization-inducing signal or the response of the stolons to this inductive signal. Grafting combinations of controls and pACO lines were critical to demonstrate that the negative effect of *AtCO* on tuberization is caused by an interfering function in the leaves. In these studies, wild-type scions grafted onto pACO stocks tuberized normally, but pACO scions grafted onto wild-type stocks showed a similar delay in tuber formation as that observed for the pACO lines (80). This excluded an effect of *CO* in the stolon but pointed to a specific function of the *Arabidopsis* protein in the leaves, possibly by interfering with SD function of the endogenous potato *CO* ortholog and thus with generation of the inducing signal. These findings indicate a function of *CO* in the regulation of the synthesis or the transport of this systemic inducing signal, thus showing a close association of this regulatory protein with the mobile signal produced in the leaves.

A detailed study of the pattern of expression of the *Arabidopsis CO* gene, using a promoter fusion to the GUS marker gene, showed that *CO* is expressed in the vascular tissue of the hypocotyl, the cotyledons, and the leaves and is detected at the apex and young leaves (6, 121). Expression of *CO* under control of the *AtSUC2* or *rolC* promoters driving specific expression to the phloem companion cells was able to complement the *co* mutation, but such a complementation was not observed when *CO* was directly expressed in the meristem. Interestingly, phloem expression of *CO* did not induce early flowering in the *ft* mutants, indicating that the flowering promoting effects of *CO* are mediated by *FT*.

CO was not able to move from the phloem to adjacent cells, which indicates that the non-cell autonomous flowering-promoting effects of *CO* require movement of the *FT* transcript or protein, or activation of a signaling step downstream of FT. In line with this evidence, *FT* complements the late-flowering phenotype of the *co* mutants when expressed in the phloem, but also when expressed in the meristem or meristem epidermal cells, demonstrating that either the RNA or the protein can move between cells. In transgenic lines carrying a heat shock inducible *Hsp:FT* construct, heating a single leaf was found to be as effective at inducing flowering as heating the whole plant. After 6 h of leaf induction, an increase in transgenic *FT* transcript could be detected in the shoot apex, showing that the transgenic *FT* mRNA is able to move from the leaf to the shoot apex (55). These results demonstrate that the *FT* mRNA is part of the long-distance inducing signal although they do not exclude subsequent movement of the FT protein or the possibility that FT might still induce another transcript or compound that moves together with its own transcript.

Potato might be a good model system to test long-range phloem transport of *FT* because of the larger size of phloem cells and ease of grafting experiments. Emerging evidence from transgenic studies seems to indicate that the genetic mechanisms controlling photoperiodic tuberization in potato are closely related to those mediating flowering time control in *Arabidopsis* and rice. Preliminary evidence indicates that a *GIGANTEA* homolog of potato might be implicated in photoperiodic control of tuber formation (D. Hannapel, personal communication). Three *CO* homologs also have been identified in potato, and evidence for a role in tuberization control has been obtained for one of these genes, designated *StCOL3* (N. González-Schain, S. Prat & P. Suárez-López, unpublished results). *StCOL3* is cyclically expressed with a biphasic peak of expression at the end of the night (**Figure 4**). Under SDs, *StCOL3* expression rises during the second half of the night and

is still high during the first day hours. In LDs, the peak is narrower and occurs only during the day. Hence, this transcript peaks at a different time of the day than observed for the *CO/Hd1* transcripts in *Arabidopsis* or rice. Despite such a difference in the timing of expression, StCOL3 accumulation seems to fit with a similar model as that described in rice, and tuberization is promoted when StCOL3 is expressed during the night but delayed when expression of this protein coincides with light. Therefore, it will be interesting to compare the orthologs from potato, rice, or the SD plant *Pharbitis nil* (78) with the CO *Arabidopsis* protein, and to search for conserved domains that might explain the differential regulatory function of the SD proteins.

FT Homologs May Function as Tuberization Integrators

FT is one of the targets of *CO* and functions as an integrator of the different flowering regulatory pathways. *FT* induces early flowering not only when expressed in the phloem, but also when directly expressed in the meristem cells or in the meristem epidermis (6). Grafting of tobacco shoots into potatoes showed that the flowering stimulus produced in tobacco leaves induces tuberization in the potato stock (19). Hence, an important issue is whether *FT* also plays a role at tuberization induction, as would be expected for a function of this transcript as part of the inducing stimulus. In tomato, *FT* is a member of a small gene family comprised by six genes designated as *SP* (*SELF-PRUNING*), based on the first member of the gene family to be isolated (16, 91). This gene is the ortholog of *TERMINAL FLOWER 1* (*TFL1*) and is involved in tomato sympodial growth after floral transition (91). A seventh additional *FT* homolog is found in the TIGR potato expressed sequence tag (EST) database. Phylogenetic analysis placed two of these gene homologs into the same clade as *Arabidopsis FT* and rice *Hd3a*, thus pointing to a function of these genes as orthologs of *FT*.

SP: self-prunning

A single amino acid change was recently demonstrated to be sufficient to convert the *TFL1* repressor in an activator of flowering (15, 41). This residue is always His in those members shown to have *TFL1*-like function and Tyr in those with *FT*-like function. The two potato *FT* homologs exhibit a Tyr residue in this position, consistent with a likely *FT/Hd3a* ortholog function of these genes. Expression analysis showed that one of these genes is strongly induced under SD conditions but not under LDs (A. López & S. Prat, unpublished results). Abundance of this mRNA was much higher in the *phyB* antisense lines than in wild type, and this transcript is repressed in the pACO lines, in which tuberization induction is delayed. Hence, we have observed a strong correlation between levels of expression of this transcript and tuberization induction, pointing to a function of this gene as an *FT* ortholog. These results indicate that genetic mechanisms controlling photoperiodic flowering in rice and *Arabidopsis* and tuberization in potato are closely related (**Figure 5**). Control of tuberization time by *StCOL3* is then likely mediated by regulation of *FT* activity, perhaps through a PHYB-dependent mechanism of regulation similar to that reported in rice (57). According to this model, interaction of PHYB with *StCOL3* in the presence of light would repress *FT* expression in LDs, whereas in SDs, *StCOL3* accumulates in the dark, thus activating *FT* expression. In the *phyB* mutants, PHYB is repressed and interaction with *StCOL3* in the light is abolished. These plants then accumulate the *FT* transcript and tuberize in LDs. Further studies are required to confirm this hypothetical model and to determine how *FT* expression promotes tuberization transition. The mechanism of action of these proteins was explored by means of protein-protein interaction studies in a yeast two-hybrid system, which led to identification of several interacting partners (92). One of such partners, the bZIP transcription factor FD, is expressed at the shoot apex before floral induction and forms a complex with FT that activates transcription of the floral identity gene *APETALA1* (*AP1*) (4, 141). It will be interesting to investigate whether similar transcription factors act as partners of FT in the stolon subapical meristem, and which are the possible tuber identity genes regulated by this complex.

GENE EXPRESSION DURING TUBER DEVELOPMENT

Which genes act downstream of *StFT* to trigger tuberization transition? Molecular mechanisms underlying early phases of tuber development are still poorly understood. Previous gene-expression analyses mainly focused on the later phases of tuber growth, in which starch accumulation and storage protein synthesis take place. In these studies, lipoxygenase and proteinase inhibitor transcripts, such as proteinase inhibitor I, proteinase inhibitor II, or Kunitz-type proteinase inhibitors, were abundant, raising the question of whether these inhibitors may function as storage proteins in addition to providing protection against pest attack. The major storage protein of potato tubers is patatin, which makes up to 40% of the total tuber protein. On the other hand, starch is the primary constituent of potato tubers, accounting for 80% of the tuber dry matter. Genes involved in starch synthesis and degradation are therefore abundant during the later stages of tuber growth.

More recent RNA-profiling studies of earlier stages of tuber development show a common expression profile, characterized by a strong up- or downregulation of several genes, illustrating highly coordinated pathways of transcriptional control during tuber initiation and growth (69). One of the earliest genes to be upregulated was GA 2-oxidase, as reported above. Upregulation of this gene was observed prior to visible swelling, indicating that a decrease in GA levels precedes other transcriptional changes during tuber transition. Genes involved in starch synthesis were strongly upregulated from the swelling

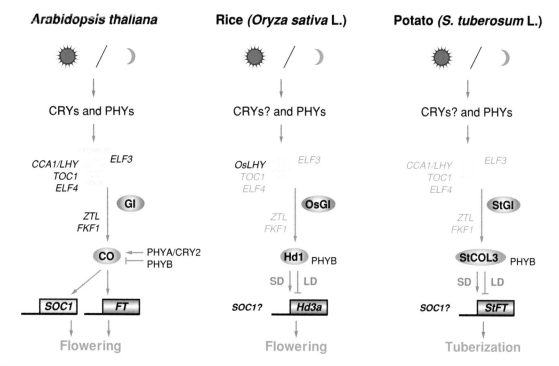

Arabidopsis thaliana   **Rice (Oryza sativa L.)**   **Potato (S. tuberosum L.)**

Figure 5

Short-day (SD) pathway controlling tuberization in potato: conservation with the day-length flowering pathways in *Arabidopsis* and rice. The circadian clock is reset by phytochromes and cryptochromes and is the central component of the day-length measuring mechanism. The clock regulates abundance of GIGANTEA (*GI*), which positively regulates transcription of the nuclear zinc-finger proteins constans (CO) and Heading date 1 (Hd1). These transcription factors in turn regulate expression of flowering locus T (FT) and Heading date 3a (H3da), two RAF-kinase inhibitor-related proteins that strongly promote flowering. CO/Hd1 activity is regulated by light in a post-transcriptional manner. Whereas CO activates transcription of *FT* in the light, Hd1 appears to activate *H3da* expression in the dark, but negatively control expression of this floral integrator in the light. Interaction of Hd1 with phytochrome appears to mediate *H3da* repression in the light. Homologs of *GI* (*StGI*), *CO* (*StCOL3*), and *FT* (*StFT*) have been identified in potato and preliminary evidence indicates that they are implicated in tuberization control. *StFT* mRNA accumulation correlates with the peak of *StCOL3* transcript during the night, suggesting a light-reversed mechanism of regulation, as reported in rice. Components of the clock autoregulatory feedback loop such as *CIRCADIAN CLOCK ASSOCIATED1* (*CCA1*), *LATE ELONGATED HYPOCOTYL* (*LHY*), *TIMING OF CAB EXPRESSION1* (*TOC1*), and *EARLY FLOWERING4* (*ELF4*) have not been characterized in potato. Genes involved in the light input to the clock, such as *EARLY FLOWERING 3* (*ELF3*) or the F-box kelch repeat proteins *FLAVIN-BINDING KELCH REPEAT F-BOX1* (*FKF1*) and *ZEITLUPE* (*ZTL*), also remain to be identified.

stage onward. Expression of genes involved in sucrose cleavage changed during the early stages of tuber development, correlating with the switch from apoplastic to symplastic sucrose unloading (8, 135). Sucrose synthase (*SUSY*) and fructokinase increased dramatically, whereas transcripts for soluble acid invertase were downregulated. Plastidic phosphoglucomutase was strongly upregulated, whereas levels of the cytosolic isoforms did not change, thereby reflecting an active import of glucose-6-phosphate into the amyloplast (124). ADP-glucose pyrophosphorylase (*AGPase*), with a key regulatory function in starch synthesis (84), and transcripts for soluble starch synthase (*SSS*), granule-bound starch synthase (*GBSS*), and starch branching enzyme (*BE*), were strongly upregulated at tuber organogenesis and further tuber development, consistent with the role of these enzymes in starch synthesis (31, 35).

In addition to a steady down- or upregulated trend, observed for genes involved in sucrose-to-starch synthesis or storage proteins, a transient change in gene expression was also detected for several additional genes (69). Such up- or downregulated peak of expression occurred at stolon swelling and tuber initiation, thus suggesting a function of these genes in cell division and cell expansion (142). Gene-expression analyses using the luciferase reporter system showed that cell division and protein storage and starch synthesis do not occur in a fixed order during tuber development (134). In vivo analyses using promoter fusions of the *AGPaseS*, the patatin *Pat21* and cell-cycle genes *cycB1* and *CDC2a*, showed that whereas induction of the *CDC2a* and *cycB1* genes always coincided with visible swelling, activation of the *AGPaseS* and *Pat21* genes was highly variable. Activation of these promoters oscillated from 4 days before to 10 days after onset of swelling, and occasionally they were also upregulated in stolons. This suggests that the signals responsible for activating starch and storage protein accumulation are different from those inducing swelling, and therefore that two independent signaling pathways are involved at the control of these genes during tuber development.

Although no clear indication of the molecular mechanisms involved in tuber transcriptional control has been obtained to date, there is no doubt that sucrose is an important metabolic signal coordinating gene expression during tuber initiation and growth. In vitro tuberization is highly dependent on sucrose (115, 143), suggesting a specific role of sucrose in triggering storage sink function. The switch from apoplastic to symplastic sucrose unloading during tuberization is correlated with a decrease in hexose and a concomi-

tant increase in sucrose levels in the stolon subapical cells. Such a rise in cellular sucrose likely mediates increased starch synthesis and storage protein gene expression in the tuberizing stolons (51, 108). Consistent with this function, genes involved in sugar metabolism and starch synthesis, including *SUSY* and *AGPase*, are activated by sucrose (84, 110), and sucrose also mediates post-translational regulation of AGPase (50), thereby providing an additional short-term level of control in starch synthesis. Sucrose also upregulates expression of the patatin and proteinase inhibitor II genes in organs different from the tubers (64, 89, 139). Tuber-specific and sucrose-inducible *cis* elements were identified in the patatin promoter (39, 68), and a DNA-binding protein designated Storekeeper (STK) was identified, which binds to these elements and apparently mediates tuber-specific and sucrose-inducible expression of this gene (148). In addition to cytokinin, high sucrose was also correlated with increased levels of expression of the cell-cycle D-type cyclin transcripts (24, 101), suggesting that sucrose signaling might also play an important role in modulating cell division and stolon swelling during tuber differentiation. Together, these observations point to a central role of sucrose in promoting storage cell differentiation and source-sink regulation, with interaction between the sugar, gibberellin, and cytokinin signal transduction pathways likely involved in such control (102).

Components involving sugar sensing and sugar signaling are starting to be unveiled. A regulatory role for hexokinase (HXK) as a glucose sensor controlling multiple plant growth and developmental responses, for example, has been demonstrated (113, 116). Isolating glucose insensitive (*gin*) mutants showed that several of these mutations were allelic to ABA signaling genes, pointing to a close interaction between the glucose and ABA signaling pathways (104). Sucrose nonfermenting 1-related protein kinases (SNF1) also function as mediators of sucrose-specific signals and are induced in response to high sucrose. Antisense potato lines with reduced levels of expression of the SNF1-related protein kinase PKIN1 showed decreased sucrose synthase gene expression and failed to induce expression of this gene in response to high sucrose, thus providing clear evidence for a role of PKIN1 in the sucrose signaling pathway regulating carbohydrate metabolism (96). Sucrose-specific signaling pathways also repress translation of the *Arabidopsis* ATB2 bZIP transcription factor, through a conserved upstream open reading frame in the 5'-UTR of the gene (105, 140). However, future studies will be required to demonstrate a function of these sugar signaling components in tuber differentiation and define how transition to a tuber fate is integrated with this sugar signaling pathway.

A pending issue is the identification of the genes conferring tuber identity. As opposed to flowering, tuber formation does not involve organogenesis. Tubers are comprised by the storing parenchyma cells, vascular bundles, and the peridermis, but there is no differentiation in specialized organs. Therefore, floral homeotic genes involved in whorl organ formation have not been identified in tubers. This, together with the observation that tuber storage proteins can accumulate in aerial organs, brought the belief that tuber formation is under less strict control than flowering. Pathways involved in day-length control tuber transition, however, are closely related to those controlling flowering. Upregulated expression of *FT*-ortholog genes was also correlated with tuberization induction, which indicates that genes acting downstream of these integrators may be directly involved in tuberization transition by promoting differentiation of stolon meristem cells to a tuber fate. Aside from a possible implication of the KNOX/BEL tandem of transcription factors, no clear clues exist about these tuber identity genes. The expression of inducible constructs for the *StFT* integrators will be instrumental to the identification of such important genes.

CONCLUSIONS AND PERSPECTIVES

Most potato varieties are tetraploid, which adds considerable difficulty to genetic studies in these plants. Transformation methods are, however, well established in cultivated and *andigena* species, and transgenic approaches substantially contributed to our understanding of the molecular mechanisms underlying day-length control of tuberization. This research has provided evidence for two main pathways of tuberization control: a GA-dependent and a SD-dependent pathway, with concerted action of these two signaling pathways regulating tuberization transition of the stolon subapical meristem cells.

GAs have long been considered inhibitory to tuberization. Modification of GA levels or block of the response to GAs by expression of the *Arabidopsis gai-1* dominant allele showed that GA signaling has a negative role in tuberization transition, by repressing differentiation of the stolon cells to a tuber fate. Another important finding was that increased levels of these hormones in the shoot were not only not detrimental to tuber formation but seemed to be required for induction. Strong tuberization induction in *phyB* lines, for example, coexist with a fourfold increase in endogenous levels of GA_1, whereas the potato *CO* overexpresser lines (pACO) show delayed tuberization in SDs, and a characteristic semidwarf phenotype indicative of a reduction in GA levels. These observations suggest some sort of cross-talk regulation between the SD and GA pathways, although further studies will be necessary to clarify the mechanisms underlying such interaction.

Evidence for a role of *CO* in tuberization transition was obtained by expression of the *Arabidopsis* gene in *andigena* potato plants. Orthologs of the *GIGANTEA*, *CO*, and *FT* genes were recently identified in potato and preliminary evidence points to a conserved role of these genes in tuberization control. Hence, regulatory pathways involved in day-length control of tuberization appear to be closely related to those controlling flowering time in *Arabidopsis* or rice. Transcription of the potato *CO* ortholog *StCOL3* peaks during the day in LDs, but accumulates in the dark in SDs. This indicates that in potato, as in rice, expression of the target *StFT* genes is repressed by *CO* in the light and induced by this regulatory protein in the dark. Thus, reverse regulation of these genes might be a general feature of SD plants and be the principal mechanism underlying differential response to day length in SD as compared to LD species. How this different regulation is generated is not yet understood. Direct comparison of the SD or LD orthologs will help to shed light on such differential mechanisms of transcriptional control.

Quantitative trait loci (QTL) analyses have identified 11 loci affecting tuberization in reciprocal backcrosses between *Solanum tuberosum* and *S. berthaultii*, a major QTL being mapped on chromosome 5 (132). The *Arabidopsis* MADS box protein *SUPPRESSOR OF OVER-EXPRESSION OF CO1* (SOC1) is another target of CO with a function as flowering time integrator (77, 111), and at least one *SOC1* homolog has been identified in potato, although the function of this homolog in tuberization control has not been tested. Sequencing of the complete tomato genome will undoubtedly aid the identification of additional flowering time homologs, and isolation of the corresponding potato orthologs is relatively straightforward due the high-nucleotide sequence conservation between tomato and potato. Hence, combining comparative genomics and reverse genetics studies should contribute in the future to our understanding of the complex genetic networks controlling tuber development in potato and to the identification of the gene targets of these genetic pathways involved in triggering stolon-to-tuber transition and thereby a function as tuber identity genes.

ACKNOWLEDGMENTS

We apologize to authors whose work we were unable to mention due to space constraints. We are indebted to David Hannapel and Paula Suárez-López for sharing results before their publication. Funding from the Spanish Ministerio de Ciencia y Tecnología and the Comunidad de Madrid is acknowledged.

LITERATURE CITED

1. Abdala G, Guiñazú M, Tizio R, Pearce DW, Pharis RP. 1995. Effect of 2-chloroethyl trimethyl ammonium chlorides on tuberization and endogenous GA$_3$ in roots of potato cuttings. *Plant Growth Regul.* 17:95–100

2. Abdala G, Castro G, Miersch O, Pearce D. 2002. Changes in jasmonate and gibberellin levels during development of potato plants (*Solanum tuberosum*). *Plant Growth Regul.* 36:121–26

3. Abe M, Shibaoka H, Yamane H, Takahashi N. 1990. Cell-cycle dependent disruption of microtubules by methyl-jasmonates in tobacco BY2 cells. *Protoplasma* 156:1–8

4. Abe M, Kobayashi Y, Yamamoto S, Daimon Y, Yamaguchi A, et al. 2005. *FD*, a bZIP protein mediating signals from the floral pathway integrator *FT* at the shoot apex. *Science* 309:1052–56

5. Amador V, Monte E, García-Martínez JL, Prat S. 2001. Gibberellins signal nuclear import of PHOR1, a photoperiod-responsive protein with homology to *Drosophila* armadillo. *Cell* 106:343–54

6. **An H, Roussot C, Suárez-López P, Corbesier L, Vincent C, et al. 2004. CON-STANS acts in the phloem to regulate a systemic signal that induces photoperiodic flowering of *Arabidopsis*. *Development* 131:3615–26**

7. Appeldoorn NJG, de Bruijn SM, Koot-Gronsveld EAM, Visser RGF, Vreugdenhil D, van der Plas LHW. 1997. Developmental changes of enzymes involved in conversion of sucrose to hexose-phosphate during early tuberisation of potato. *Planta* 202:220–26

8. **Appeldoorn NJG, Sergeeva L, Vreugdenhil D, van der Plas LHW, Visser RGF. 2002. *In situ* analysis of enzymes involved in sucrose to hexose-phosphate conversion during stolon-to-tuber transition of potato. *Physiol. Plant.* 115:303–10**

9. Bachem CWB, van der Hoeven RS, de Bruijn SM, Vreugdenhil D, Zabeau M, Visser R. 1996. Visualization of differential gene expression using a novel method of RNA fingerprinting based on AFLP: analysis of gene expression during potato tuber development. *Plant J.* 9:745–53

10. Bachem CWB, van der Hoeven RS, Lucker J, Oomen RJFJ, Casarini E, et al. 2000. Functional genomic analysis of potato tuber life-cycle. *Potato Res.* 43:297–312

11. Bachem CW, Horvath B, Trindale L, Claassens M, Davelaar E, et al. 2001. A potato tuber-expressed mRNA with homology to steroid dehydrogenases affects gibberellin levels and plant development. *Plant J.* 25:595–604

12. Bandara PMS, Tanino KK. 1995. Paclobutrazol enhances minituber production in Norland potatoes. *J. Plant Growth Regul.* 14:151–55

13. Batutis EJ, Ewing EE. 1982. Far-red reversal of red light effect during long-night induction of potato (*Solanum tuberosum* L.) tuberization. *Plant Physiol.* 69:672–74

14. Borner R, Kampmann G, Chandler J, Gleissner R, Wisman E, et al. 2000. A MADS domain gene involved in the transition to flowering in *Arabidopsis*. *Plant J.* 24:591–99

15. Bradley D, Ratcliffe O, Vincent C, Carpenter R, Coen E. 1997. Inflorescence commitment and architecture in *Arabidopsis*. *Science* 275:80–83

16. Carmel-Goren L, Liu YS, Lifschitz E, Zamir D. 2003. The *SELF-PRUNNING* gene family in tomato. *Plant Mol. Biol.* 52:1215–22

17. Carrera E, Jackson SD, Prat S. 1999. Feedback control and diurnal regulation of gibberellin 20-oxidase transcript levels in potato. *Plant Physiol.* 119:765–74

18. Carrera E, Bou J, García-Martínez JL, Prat S. 2000. Changes in GA 20-oxidase gene expression strongly affect stem length, tuber induction and tuber yield of potato plants. *Plant J.* 22:247–56

19. **Chailakhyan MKh, Yanina LI, Davedzhiyan AG, Lotova GN. 1981. Photoperiodism and tuber formation in grafting of tobacco onto potato. *Dokl. Akad. Nauk SSSR* 257:1276–80**

20. Chapman HW. 1958. Tuberization in the potato plant. *Physiol. Plant.* 11:215–24

21. Chen H, Rosin FM, Prat S, Hannapel DJ. 2003. Interacting transcription factors from the three-amino acid loop extension superclass regulate tuber formation. *Plant Physiol.* 132:1391–404

22. **Chen H, Banerjee AK, Hannapel DJ. 2004. The tandem complex of BEL and KNOX partners is required for transcriptional repression of *GA20ox1*. *Plant J.* 38:276–84**

23. Davidson SE, Elliott RC, Helliwell CA, Poole AT, Reid JB. 2003. The pea gene *NA* encodes *ent*-kaurenoic acid oxidase. *Plant Physiol.* 131:335–44

24. de Veylder L, de Almeida-Engler J, Burssens S, Manevski A, Lescure B, et al. 1999. A new D-type cyclin of *Arabidopsis thaliana* expressed during lateral root primordia formation. *Planta* 208:453–62

Phloem cell, but not SAM, expression of CO induces flowering. CO is shown not to move between cells, activating FT expression within the phloem.

The pattern of expression of enzymes involved in sucrose to hexose phosphate conversion changes notably at the onset of tuberization. Hexokinase and acid invertase are highly expressed in elongating stolons, but disappear from the swelling region at tuberization onset.

Using grafts of tobacco scions into *andigena* potato stocks, the authors demonstrate that the flowering signal produced in tobacco induces tuberization in the potato stock.

The authors describe isolation of BEL5 that specifically interacts with the potato POTH1 KNOTTED homolog and is induced in both leaves and stolons in response to SDs.

25. Dill A, Jung HS, Sun TP. 2001. The DELLA motif is essential for gibberellin-induced degradation of RGA. *Proc. Natl. Acad. Sci. USA* 98:14162–67

26. Dill A, Thomas SG, Hu J, Steber CM, Sun TP. 2004. The *Arabidopsis* F-box protein SLEEPY1 targets gibberellin signalling repressors for gibberellin-induced degradation. *Plant Cell* 16:1392–405

27. Donnelly DJ, Coleman WK, Coleman SE. 2003. Potato microtuber production and performance: a review. *Am. J. Potato Res.* 80:103–15

28. Estrada R, Zovar P, Dodds JH. 1986. Induction of *in vitro* tubers in a broad range of phenotypes. *Plant Cell Tiss. Org. Cult.* 7:3–10

29. Ewing EE, Wareing PF. 1978. Shoot, stolon, and tuber formation on potato (*Solanum tuberosum* L) cuttings in response to photoperiod. *Plant Physiol.* 61:348–53

30. Ewing EE, Struik PC. 1992. Tuber formation in potato: induction, initiation, and growth. *Hortic. Rev.* 14:89–198

31. Fernie AR, Willmitzer L, Trethewey RN. 2002. Sucrose to starch: a transition in molecular plant physiology. *Trends Plant Sci.* 7:35–41

32. Fowler S, Lee K, Onouchi H, Samach A, Richardson K, et al. 1999. *GIGANTEA*: a circadian clock-controlled gene that regulates photoperiodic flowering in *Arabidopsis* and encodes a protein with several possible membrane-spanning domains. *EMBO J.* 18:4679–88

33. Fujino K, Koda Y, Kikuta Y. 1995. Reorientation of cortical microtubules in the sub-apical region during tuberization in single-node stem segments of potato in culture. *Plant Cell Physiol.* 36:891–95

34. Garner N, Blake J. 1989. The induction and development of potato microtubers *in vitro* on media free of growth regulating substances. *Ann. Bot.* 63:663–74

35. Geigenberger P. 2003. Regulation of sucrose to starch conversion in growing potato tubers. *J. Exp. Bot.* 54:457–65

36. Geigenberger P, Stitt M, Fernie AR. 2004. Metabolic control analysis and regulation of the conversion of sucrose to starch in growing potato tubers. *Plant Cell Env.* 27:655–73

37. Gidda SK, Miersch O, Levitin A, Schmidt J, Wasternack C, Varin L. 2003. Biochemical and molecular characterization of a hydroxyjasmonate sulfotransferase from *Arabidopsis thaliana*. *J. Biol. Chem.* 278:17895–900

38. Gregory LE. 1956. Some factors for tuberization in the potato. *Ann. Bot.* 41:281–88

39. Grierson C, Du JS, de Torres-Zabala M, Beggs K, Smith C, et al. 1994. Separate *cis* sequences and *trans* factors direct metabolic and developmental regulation of a potato tuber storage protein gene. *Plant J.* 5:815–26

40. Guivarc'h A, Rembur J, Goetz M, Roitsch T, Noin M, et al. 2002. Local expression of the *ipt* gene in transgenic tobacco (*Nicotiana tabacum* L. cv. SR1) axillary buds establishes a role for cytokinins in tuberization and sink formation. *J. Exp. Bot.* 53:621–29

41. Hanzawa Y, Money T, Bradley D. 2005. A single amino acid converts a repressor to an activator of flowering. *Proc. Natl. Acad. Sci. USA* 102:7748–53

42. Harvey BMR, Crothers SH, Evans NE, Selby C. 1991. The use of growth retardants to improve microtuber formation by potato (*Solanum tuberosum* L.). *Plant Cell Tiss. Org. Cult.* 27:59–64

43. Hay A, Kaur H, Phillips A, Hedden P, Hake S, Tsiantis M. 2002. The gibberellin pathway mediates KNOTTED1-type homeobox function in plants with different body plans. *Curr. Biol.* 12:1557–65

44. Hayama R, Izawa T, Shimamoto K. 2002. Isolation of rice genes possibly involved in the photoperiodic control of flowering by a fluorescent differential display method. *Plant Cell Physiol.* 43:494–504

45. Hayama R, Yokoi S, Tamaki S, Yano M, Shimamoto K. 2003. Adaptation of pho-toperiodic control pathways produces short-day flowering in rice. *Nature* 422:719–22

46. Hayama R, Coupland G. 2003. Shedding light on the circadian clock and the photoperiodic control of flowering. *Curr. Opin. Plant Biol.* 6:13–19

47. Hedden P, Phillips AL. 2000. Gibberellin metabolism: new insights revealed by the genes. *Trends Plant Sci.* 5:523–30

48. Hedden P. 2001. Gibberellin metabolism and its regulation. *J. Plant Growth Regul.* 20:317–18

49. Helder H, Miersch O, Vreugdenhil D, Sembdner G. 1993. Occurrence of hydroxylated jasmonic acids in leaflets of *Solanum demissum* plants grown under long- and short-day conditions. *Physiol. Plant* 88:647–53

50. Hendriks JHM, Kolbe A, Gibon Y, Stitt M, Geigenberger P. 2003. ADP-glucose py-rophosphorylase is activated by posttranslational redox-modification in response to light and to sugars in leaves of *Arabidopsis* and other plant species. *Plant Physiol.* 133:838–49

51. Herbers K, Sonnewald U. 1998. Molecular determinants of sink strength. *Curr. Opin. Plant Biol.* 1:207–16

52. Heyer A, Gatz C. 1992. Isolation and characterization of a cDNA clone coding for potato type A phytochrome. *Plant Mol. Biol.* 18:535–43

53. Heyer A, Gatz C. 1992. Isolation and characterization of a cDNA clone coding for potato type B phytochrome. *Plant Mol. Biol.* 20:589–600

54. Heyer A, Mozley D, Landschütze V, Thomas B, Gatz C. 1995. Function of phytochrome A in *Solanum tuberosum* as revealed through the study of transgenic plants. *Plant Physiol.* 109:53–61

55. Huang T, Böhlenius H, Eriksson S, Parcy F, Nilsson O. 2005. The mRNA of the Ara-bidopsis gene *FT* moves from leaf to shoot apex and induces flowering. *Science* 309:1694–96

56. Hussey G, Stacey NJ. 1984. Factors affecting the formation of *in vitro* tubers of potato (*Solanum tuberosum* L) *Ann. Bot.* 53:565–78

57. Izawa T, Oikawa T, Sugiyama N, Tanisaka T, Yano M, Shimamoto K. 2002. Phytochrome mediates the external light signal to repress FT orthologs in photoperiodic flowering of rice. *Genes Dev.* 16:2006–20

58. Jackson S, Willmitzer L. 1994. Jasmonic acid spraying does not induce tuberization in short-day requiring potato species kept in non-inducing conditions. *Planta* 194:155–59

59. **Jackson SD, Heyer A, Dietze J, Prat S. 1996. Phytochrome B mediates the pho-toperiodic control of tuber formation in potato. *Plant J*. 9:159–66**

60. Jackson S, Prat S. 1996. Control of tuberization in potato by gibberellins and phytochrome B. *Physiol. Plant* 98:407–12

61. Jackson SD, James P, Prat S, Thomas B. 1998. Phytochrome B affects the levels of a graft-transmissible signal involved in tuberization. *Plant Physiol.* 117:29–32

62. Jackson SD, James PE, Carrera E, Prat S, Thomas B. 2000. Regulation of transcript levels of a potato gibberellin 20-oxidase gene by light and phytochrome B. *Plant Physiol.* 124:423–30

63. Jasinski S, Piazza P, Craft J, Hay A, Woolley L, et al. 2005. KNOX action in *Arabidopsis* is mediated by coordinate regulation of cytokinin and gibberellin activities. *Curr. Biol.* 15:1560–65

64. Johnson R, Ryan CA. 1990. Wound-inducible potato inhibitor II genes: enhancement of expression by sucrose. *Plant Mol. Biol.* 14:527–36

Overexpression of the rice *GIGANTEA* gene in transgenic rice produces late flowering under both LD and SD conditions.

The authors demonstrate a function of the light receptor PHYB in day-length control of tuberization.

65. Jones MG, Horgan R, Hall MA. 1988. Endogenous gibberellins in the potato (*Solanum tuberosum*). *Phytochemistry* 27:7–10

66. Kamiya Y, García-Martínez JL. 1999. Regulation of gibberellin biosynthesis by light. *Curr. Opin. Plant Biol.* 2:398–403

67. Kardailsky I, Shukla VK, Ahn JH, Dagenais N, Christensen SK, et al. 1999. Activation tagging of the floral inducer FT. *Science* 286:1962–65

68. Kim SY, May GD, Park WD. 1994. Nuclear protein factors binding to a class I patatin promoter region are tuber-specific and sucrose-inducible. *Plant Mol. Biol.* 26:603–15

69. Kloosterman B, Vorst O, Hall RD, Visser RGH, Bachem CW. 2005. Tuber on a chip: differential gene expression during potato tuber development. *Plant Biotech. J.* 3:505–19

70. Koda Y, Omer EA, Yoshihara T, Shibata H, Sakamura S, Okazawa Y. 1988. Isolation of a specific potato tuber-inducing substance from potato leaves. *Plant Cell Physiol.* 29:1047–51

71. Kojima S, Takahashi Y, Kobayashi Y, Monna L, Sasaki T, et al. 2002. *Hd3a*, a rice ortholog of the *Arabidopsis FT* gene, promotes transition to flowering downstream of *Hd1* under short-day conditions. *Plant Cell Physiol.* 43:1096–105

72. Kolomiets MV, Hannapel DJ, Chen H, Tymeson M, Gladon RJ. 2001. Lipoxygenase is involved in the control of potato tuber development. *Plant Cell* 13:613–26

73. Koornneef M, Hanhart CJ, van Der Veen JH. 1991. A genetic and physiological analysis of late flowering mutants in *Arabidopsis thaliana*. *Mol. Gen. Genet.* 229:57–66

74. Krauss A, Marschner H. 1982. Influence of nitrogen nutrition, daylength, and temperature on contents of gibberellic and abscisic acid and on tuberization in potato plants. *Potato Res.* 25:13–21

75. Krauss A. 1985. Interaction of nitrogen nutrition, phytohormones and tuberization. In *Potato Physiology*, ed. PH Li. pp. 209–31. London: Academic

76. Kumar D, Wareing PF. 1974. Studies on tuberization of *Solanum andigena*. II. Growth, hormones and tuberization. *New Phytol.* 73:833–40

77. Lee H, Suh SS, Park E, Cho E, Ahn JH, et al. 2000. The *AGAMOUS-LIKE 20* MADS domain protein integrates floral inductive pathways in *Arabidopsis*. *Genes Dev.* 14:2366–76

78. Liu J, Yu J, McIntosh L, Hende K and Zeevaart JAD. 2001. Isolation of a CONSTANS ortholog from Pharbitis nil and its role in flowering. *Plant Physiol.* 125:1821–30.

79. Martínez-García J, García-Martínez JL, Bou J, Prat S. 2002. The interaction of gibberellins and photoperiod in the control of potato tuberization. *J. Plant Growth Regul.* 20:377–86

80. Martínez-García JF, Virgós-Soler A, Prat S. 2002. Control of photoperiod-regulated tuberization in potato by the *Arabidopsis* flowering-time gene *CONSTANS*. *Proc. Natl. Acad. Sci. USA* 99:15211–16

81. Matsuki T, Tazaki H, Fujimori T, Hogetsu T 1992. The influences of jasmonic acid methyl ester on microtubules in potato cells and formation of potato tubers. *Biosci. Biotechnol. Biochem.* 56:1329–33

82. Mauk S, Langille AR. 1978. Physiology of tuberization in *Solanum tuberosum* L. *Plant Physiol.* 62:438–42

83. Menzel CM. 1980. Tuberization in potato at high temperatures. Responses of gibberellin and growth inhibitors. *Ann. Bot.* 46:259–65

84. Müller-Röber B, Sonnewald U, Willmitzer L. 1992. Inhibition of the ADP-glucose pyrophosphorylase in transgenic potatoes leads to sugar-storing tubers and influences tuber formation and expression of tuber storage protein genes. *EMBO J.* 11:1229–38

The authors identify transcripts induced along tuberization induction and tuber growth using a potato tuber microarray.

Expression of the *Arabidopsis CO* gene in transgenic *andigena* potatoes strongly delays tuberization in SDs. CO exerts this repression function in the leaves, thus interfering with production or transport of the tuberization stimulus to the underground stolons.

85. Obata-Sasamoto H, Suzuki H. 1979. Activities of enzymes relating to starch synthesis and endogenous levels of growth regulators in potato stolon tips during tuberization. *Physiol. Plant.* 45:320–24

86. Palmer CE, Smith OE. 1970. Effect of kinetin on tuber formation on isolated stolons of *Solanum tuberosum* L. cultured *in vitro*. *Plant Cell Physiol.* 11:303–14

87. Park DH, Somers DE, Kim YS, Choy YH, Lim HK, et al. 1999. Control of circadian rhythms and photoperiodic flowering by the *Arabidopsis GIGANTEA* gene. *Science* 285:1579–82

88. Peng J, Carol P, Richards DE, King KE, Cowling RJ, et al. 1997. The *Arabidopsis GAI* gene defines a signaling pathway that negatively regulates gibberellin responses. *Genes Dev.* 11:3194–205

89. Perl A, Aviv D, Willmitzer L, Galun E. 1991. *In vitro* tuberization in transgenic potatoes harboring β-glucuronidase linked to a patatin promoter: effect of sucrose levels and photoperiods. *Plant Sci.* 73:87–95

90. Pittendrigh CS, Minis DH. 1964. The entrainment of circadian oscillations by light and their role as photoperiodic clocks. *Am. Nat.* 98:261–322

91. Pnueli L, Carmel-Goren L, Hareven D, Gutfinger T, Alvarez J, et al. 1998. The *SELF-PRUNNING* gene of tomato regulates vegetative to reproductive switching of sympodial meristems and is the ortholog of *CEN* and *TFL1*. *Development* 125:1979–89

92. Pnueli L, Gutfinger T, Hareven D, Ben-Naim O, Ron N, et al. 2001. Tomato SP-interacting proteins define a conserved signalling system that regulates shoot architecture and flowering. *Plant Cell* 13:2687–702

93. Pont Lezica RF. 1970. Evolution des substances de type gibberellins chez la pomme de terre pendant la tuberisation, en relation avec la lingueur du jour et la temperature. *Potato Res.* 13:323–31

94. Prat S, Frommer WB, Höfgen R, Keil M, Kossman J, et al. 1990. Gene expression during tuber development in potato plants. *FEBS Lett.* 268:334–38

95. Proebsting WM, Hedden P, Lewis ML, Croker SJ, Proebsting LN. 1992. Gibberellin concentration and transport in genetic lines of pea. *Plant Physiol* 100:1354–60

96. Purcell PC, Smith AM, Halford NG. 1998. Antisense expression of a sucrose non-fermenting-1-related protein kinase sequence in potato results in decreased expression of sucrose synthase in tubers and loss of surose-inducibility of sucrose synthase transcripts in leaves. *Plant J.* 14:195–202

97. Putterill J, Robson F, Lee K, Simon R, Coupland G. 1995. The *CONSTANS* gene of *Arabidopsis* promotes flowering and encodes a protein showing similarities to zinc finger transcription factors. *Cell* 80:847–57

98. Putterill J, Laurie R, Macknight R. 2004. It's time to flower: the genetic control of flowering time. *BioEssays* 26:363–73

99. Quarrie SA. 1982. Droopy—a wilty mutant of potato deficient in abscisic-acid. *Plant Cell Environ.* 5:23–26

100. Railton ID, Wareing PF. 1973. Effects of daylength on endogenous gibberellins in leaves of *Solanum andigena*. *Physiol. Plant.* 28:88–94

101. Riou-Khamlichi C, Huntley R, Jacqmard A, Murray JA. 1999. Cytokinin activation of *Arabidopsis* cell division through a D-type cyclin. *Science* 283:1541–44

102. Roitsch T. 1999. Source-sink regulation by sugar and stress. *Curr. Opin. Plant Biol.* 2:198–206

103. Roitsch T, Ehneβ R. 2000. Regulation of source/sink relations by cytokinins. *Plant Growth Regul.* 32:359–67

104. Rolland F, Moore B, Sheen J. 2002. Sugar sensing and signaling in plants. *Plant Cell* 14:185–205

105. Rook F, Gerrits N, Kortstee A, van Kampen M, Borrias M, et al. 1998. Sucrose-specific signalling represses translation of the *Arabidopsis ATB2* bZIP transcription factor gene. *Plant J.* 15:253–63

106. Rosin FM, Hart JK, van Onckelen H, Hannapel DJ. 2003. Suppression of a vegetative MADS box gene of potato activates axillary meristem development. *Plant Physiol.* 131:1613–22

107. Rosin FM, Hart JK, Horner HT, Davies PJ, Hannapel DJ. 2003. Overexpression of a knotted-like homeobox gene of potato alters vegetative development by decreasing gibberellin accumulation. *Plant Physiol.* 132:106–17

108. Ross HA, Davies HV, Burch LR, Viola R, McRae D. 1994. Developmental changes in carbohydrate content and sucrose degrading enzymes in tuberising stolons of potato (*Solanum tuberosum* L.). *Physiol. Plant.* 90:748–56

109. Sakamoto T, Kamiya N, Ueguchi-Tanaka M, Iwahori S, Matsuoka M. 2001. KNOX homeodomain protein directly suppresses the expression of a gibberellin biosynthetic gene in the tobacco shoot apical meristem. *Genes Dev.* 15:581–90

110. Salanoubat M, Belliard G. 1989. The steady-state level of potato sucrose synthase mRNA is dependent on wounding, anaerobiosis and sucrose concentration. *Gene* 84:181–85

111. Samach A, Onouchi H, Gold SE, Ditta GS, Schwarz-Sommer Z, et al. 2000. Distinct roles of CONSTANS target genes in reproductive development of *Arabidopsis*. *Science* 288:1613–16

112. Seabrook JEA, Coleman S, Levy D. 1993. Effect of photoperiod on *in vitro* tuberization of potato (*Solanum tuberosum* L). *Plant Cell Tiss. Org. Cult.* 34:43–51

113. Sheen J, Zhou L, Jang JC. 1999. Sugars as signaling molecules. *Curr. Opin. Plant Biol.* 2:410–18

114. Shibaoka H. 1993. Regulation by gibberellins of the orientation of cortical microtubules in plant cells. *Aust. J. Plant Physiol.* 20:461–70

115. Simko I. 1994. Sucrose application causes hormonal changes associated with potato tuber induction. *J. Plant Growth Regul.* 13:73–77

116. Smeekens S. 2000. Sugar-induced signal transduction in plants. *Annu. Rev. Plant Physiol. Plant Mol. Biol.* 51:49–81

117. Sonnewald U. 2001. Control of potato tuber sprouting. *Trends Plant Sci.* 6:333–35

118. Snyder E, Ewing EE. 1989. Interactive effects of temperature, photoperiod and cultivar on tuberization of potato cuttings. *Hortic. Sci.* 24:336–38

119. Suárez-López P, Wheatley K, Robson F, Onouchi H, Valverde F, Coupland G. 2001. CONSTANS mediates between the circadian clock and the control of flowering in *Arabidopsis*. *Nature* 410:1116–20

120. Suttle JC. 2004. Involvement of endogenous gibberellins in potato tuber dormancy and early sprout growth: a critical assessment. *J. Plant Physiol.* 161:157–64

121. Takada S, Goto K. 2003. TERMINAL FLOWER2, a HETEROCHROMATIN PROTEIN1-LIKE protein of *Arabidopsis*, counteracts the activation of *FLOWERING LOCUS T* by *CONSTANS* in the vascular tissues of leaves to regulate flowering time. *Plant Cell* 15:2856–65

122. Takahashi F, Fujino K, Kikuta Y, Koda Y. 1994. Expansion of potato cells in response to jasmonic acid. *Plant Sci.* 100:3–8

123. Tanaka-Ueguchi M, Itoh H, Oyama N, Koshioka M, Matsuoka M. 1998. Over-expression of a tobacco homeobox gene, *NTH15*, decreases the expression of a gibberellin biosynthetic gene encoding *GA 20-oxidase*. *Plant J.* 15:391–400

124. Tauberger E, Fernie AR, Emmermann M, Renz A, Kossmann J, et al. 2000. Antisense inhibition of plastidial phosphoglucomutase provides compelling evidence that potato tuber amyloplasts import carbon from the cytosol in the form of glucose-6-phosphate. *Plant J.* 23:43–53

125. Taylor MA, Arif SA, Kumar A, Davies HV, Scobie LA, et al. 1992. Expression and sequence analysis of cDNAs induced during the early stages of tuberisation in different organs of the potato plant (*Solanum tuberosum* L.). *Plant Mol. Biol.* 20:641–51

126. Thomas SG, Sun TP. 2004. Update on gibberellin signaling. A tale of the tall and the short. *Plant Physiol.* 135:668–76

127. Ueguchi-Tanaka M, Ashikari M, Nakajima M, Itoh H, Katoh E, et al. 2005. *GIBBERELLIN INSENSITIVE DWARF1* encodes a soluble receptor for gibberellin. *Nature* 437:693–98

128. Valverde F, Mouradov A, Soppe W, Ravenscroft D, Samach A, Coupland G. 2004. Photoreceptor regulation of CONSTANS protein and the mechanism of photoperiodic flowering. *Science* 303:1003–6

129. vanDam J, Kooman PL, Struik PC. 1996. Effects of temperature and photoperiod on early growth and final number of tubers in potato (*Solanum tuberosum* L). *Potato Res.* 39:51–62

130. van den Berg JH, Ewing EE. 1991. Jasmonates and their role in plant growth and development, with special reference to the control of potato tuberization: a review. *Am. Potato J.* 68:781–94

131. van den Berg JH, Simko I, Davies PJ, Ewing EE, Halinska A. 1995. Morphology and [^{14}C] gibberellin A$_{12}$ metabolism in wild-type and dwarf *Solanum tuberosum* ssp. *andigena* grown under long and short photoperiods. *J. Plant Physiol.* 146:467–73

132. van den Berg JH, Ewing EE, Plaisted RL, McMurry S, Bonierbale MW. 1996. QTL analysis of potato tuberization. *Theor. Appl. Genet.* 93:307–16

133. Veramendi J, Willmitzer L, Trethewey RN. 1999. *In vitro* grown potato microtubers are a suitable system for the study of primary carbohydrate metabolism. *Plant Physiol. Biochem.* 37:693–97

134. Verhees J, van der Krol AR, Vreugdenhil D, van der Plas LHW. 2002. Characterization of gene expression during potato tuber development in individuals and populations using the luciferase reporter system. *Plant Mol. Biol.* 50:653–65

135. Viola R, Roberts AG, Haupt S, Gazzani S, Hancock RD, et al. 2001. Tuberization in potato involves a switch from apoplastic to symplastic phloem unloading. *Plant Cell* 13:385–98

136. Vreugdenhil D, Bindels P, Reinhoud P, Klocek J, Hendriks T. 1994. Use of growth retardant *tetcyclacis* for potato tuber formation in vitro. *Plant Growth Regul.* 14:257–65

137. Vreugdenhil D, Sergeeva LI. 1999. Gibberellins and tuberization in potato. *Potato Res.* 42:471–81

138. Vreugdenhil D. 2004. Comparing potato tuberization and sprouting: opposite phenomena? *Am. J. Potato Res.* 81:275–80

139. Wenzler HC, Mignery GA, Fisher LM, Park WD. 1989. Analysis of a chimeric class-I patatin-GUS gene in transgenic potato plants: high-level expression in tubers and sucrose-inducible expression in cultured leaf and stem explants. *Plant Mol. Biol.* 12:41–50

140. Wiese A, Elzinga N, Wobbes B, Smeekens S. 2004. A conserved upstream open reading frame mediates sucrose-induced repression of translation. *Plant Cell* 16:1717–29

141. Wigge PA, Kim MC, Jaeger KE, Busch W, Schmid M, et al. 2005. Integration of spatial and temporal information during floral induction in Arabidopsis. *Science* 309:1056–59

Phloem unloading changes from being predominantly apoplastic in elongating stolons to mainly symplastic during the early stages of tuberization.

142. Xu X, Vreugdenhil D, van Lammeren AAM. 1998. Cell division and cell enlargement during potato tuber formation: a comparison of *in vitro* and *in vivo* tuber development. *J. Exp. Bot.* 49:573–82

143. Xu X, van Lammeren AAM, Vermeer E, Vreugdenhil D. 1998. The role of gibberellin, abscisic acid, and sucrose in the regulation of potato tuber formation *in vitro*. *Plant Physiol.* 117:575–84

144. Yanai O, Shani E, Dolezal K, Tarkowski P, Sablowski R, Sandberg G, Samach A, Ori N. 2005. *Arabidopsis* KNOXI proteins activate cytokinin biosynthesis. *Curr. Biol.* 15:1566–71

145. Yano M, Katayose Y, Ashikari M, Yamanouchi U, Monna L, et al. 2000. Hd1, a major photoperiod sensitivity quantitative trait locus in rice, is closely related to the *Arabidopsis* flowering time gene *CONSTANS*. *Plant Cell* 12:2473–84

146. Yanovsky MJ, Izaguirre M, Wagmaister JA, Gatz C, Jackson SD, et al. 2000. Phytochrome A resets the circadian clock and delays tuber formation under long days in potato. *Plant J*. 23:223–32

147. Yanovsky MJ, Kay SA. 2003. Living by the calendar: how plants know when to flower. *Nat. Rev. Mol. Cell. Biol.* 4:265–75

148. Zourelidou M, de Torres-Zabala M, Smith C, Bevan MW. 2002. Storekeeper defines a new class of plant-specific DNA-binding proteins and is a putative regulator of patatin expression. *Plant J*. 30:489–97

The authors demonstrate a role of PHYA in circadian clock entrainment in potato.

RELATED RESOURCES

Ewing EE. 1995. The role of hormones in potato (*Solanum tuberosum* L.) tuberization. In *Plant Hormones and Their Role in Plant Growth and Development*, ed. PJ Davies. pp. 698–724. Dordrecht: Martinus Nijhoff

Fernie AR, Willmitzer L. 2001. Molecular and biochemical triggers of potato tuber development. *Plant Physiol.* 127:1459–65

Jackson SD. 1999. Multiple signaling pathways control tuber induction in potato. *Plant Physiol.* 119:1–8

Izawa T, Takahashi Y, Yano M. 2003. Comparative biology comes into bloom: genomic and genetic comparison of flowering pathways in rice and Arabidopsis. *Curr. Opin. Plant Biol.* 6:113–20

Searle I, Coupland G. 2004. Induction of flowering by seasonal changes in photoperiod. *EMBO J*. 23:1217–22

Laser Microdissection of Plant Tissue: What You See Is What You Get

Timothy Nelson, S. Lori Tausta,
Neeru Gandotra, and Tie Liu

Department of Molecular, Cellular, and Developmental Biology, Yale University,
New Haven, Connecticut 06511; email: timothy.nelson@yale.edu,
susan.tausta@yale.edu, fno.neeru@yale.edu, tie.liu@yale.edu

Annu. Rev. Plant Biol.
2006. 57:181–201

The *Annual Review of
Plant Biology* is online at
plant.annualreviews.org

doi: 10.1146/
annurev.arplant.56.032604.144138

First published online as a
Review in Advance on
February 22, 2006

1543-5008/06/0602-
0181$20.00

Key Words

plant cell type, transcript profiling, metabolite profiling,
proteomics

Abstract

Laser microdissection (LM) utilizes a cutting or harvesting laser to
isolate specific cells from histological sections; the process is guided
by microscopy. This provides a means of removing selected cells
from complex tissues, based only on their identification by microscopic appearance, location, or staining properties (e.g., immuno-
histochemistry, reporter gene expression, etc.). Cells isolated by LM
can be a source of cell-specific DNA, RNA, protein or metabolites for subsequent evaluation of DNA modifications, transcript/
protein/metabolite profiling, or other cell-specific properties that
would be averaged with those of neighboring cell types during analysis of undissected complex tissues. Plants are particularly amenable
to the application of LM; the highly regular tissue organization and
stable cell walls of plants facilitate the visual identification of most
cell types even in unstained tissue sections. Plant cells isolated by LM
have been the starting point for a variety of genomic and metabolite
studies of specific cell types.

Contents

Introduction

Virtually all of the processes we study as plant biologists are distributed nonuniformly among the cells that make up the plant body. Physiology, biochemistry, responses to the environment, defenses against pathogens, growth, and development—these and other processes rely on the distinct features, activities, and interactions of subsets of specialized cells in organs and tissues. Techniques such as immunolocalization, in situ hybridization, and histochemical staining have long revealed the cell-specific distributions of individual proteins, transcripts, and metabolites, often well correlated with localized biological processes. Until recently, with few exceptions, the same cellular resolution was not available for the comprehensive view of the entire transcriptome, proteome, and metabolome afforded by "unbiased" profiling methods. Since systems biology approaches promise to reconstruct the phenotypes of cells, tissues, organs, and organisms from combinations and inter-

actions of these cellular outputs, it is essential to capture data with cellular resolution (27, 49).

Laser microdissection (LM) is one of a growing list of methods for harvesting selected cells or cell contents in sufficient quantity and quality for profiling and other analyses of DNA, RNA, protein, or metabolites. Other cell-specific harvesting methods for plants include the direct micropipetting of cell contents (7, 8, 40, 73), fluorescence-activated sorting of protoplasts from dissociated tissues (6, 67), recovery of differentiated cells from cell culture or protoplasts (15, 17), tissue homogenization and cell fractionation (90), hand microdissection (69, 87), and (potentially) expression-based microdissection (95). All of these methods select and isolate cells from tissue context on the basis of their appearance/location, molecular markers, or other distinguishing properties. The advantages and disadvantages of some of these methods have been compared to those of LM in other reviews (9, 16, 42, 43, 47, 48). Among these, LM has the advantage that it permits the harvest of any cell target in any tissue from any plant species that can be viewed by conventional microscopy. LM does not require cell-specific markers or tags, genetic lines, or special tissue or cell properties (e.g., epidermal peels, differential size, or density through fractionation). Its relative disadvantages are that histological fixation and processing are generally required, potentially compromising the target materials (RNA, proteins, metabolites), that current instrumentation is costly, and that the number of cells that can be recovered is limited by the abundance and recognition of cellular targets in histological sections. The limited amount of RNA, protein, or metabolite that can be recovered by LM is becoming less of an issue, as methods for RNA amplification and for microanalysis of proteins and metabolites are driven to ever-greater sensitivity by the multitude of emerging small-sample and high-throughput strategies in life science research and clinical analysis.

Laser Microdissection Technology

Current LM systems use one of two strategies—laser capture microdissection (LCM) and laser cutting—each represented by a number of commercial instruments (12, 22, 62, 100, 101). Each instrument is designed around a microscope, usually with capabilities for brightfield, darkfield, and fluorescence viewing of samples. Both strategies have been used successfully on plant materials, and each has relative advantages and disadvantages.

Laser Capture Microdissection

LCM is the LM technology developed and patented at the NIH by Robert Bonner and colleagues (22), then licensed to Arcturus Bioscience, who developed the PixCell, AutoPix, and Veritas instruments. In the LCM technique, cell targets are captured from a tissue section by a "melt-stick-pull off" strategy. A human operator or target-recognition software identifies target cells in the section, above which is suspended a thermoplastic ethyl-vinyl-acetate (EVA) polymer film (commonly used for heat-sealing plastics in the food industry) that is coated on an optically clear microfuge cap (LCM cap). The EVA film is manufactured with a proprietary dye that is excited by the solid-state near-infrared (nIR) laser. When the laser is pulsed, the film is excited, expands, and sticks to the cell(s) of interest. The cell is affixed to the film by molding of the melted polymer into the porous and dehydrated surface of the sample. The size of the contact made between the film and the target can be controlled by adjusting the focus, duration, and power of the laser pulse. The user can adjust laser settings so a single pulse creates attachment sites from 4 to 90 microns in diameter, a range appropriate for the harvest of from one to several plant or animal cells. Larger targets or irregular shapes require multiple pulses. When the desired cells have been bonded to the film, the LCM cap is lifted, harvesting with it the attached cells.

The success of LCM in obtaining specific plant cells of high purity depends to a sig-

nificant degree on the optimization of histological preparation of the samples (45). Since the target cells are effectively torn away from neighboring cells, portions of undesired cells may adhere to the selected affixed cells, depending on the relative strengths of cell-to-film, cell-to-cell, and cell-to-slide contacts. The relationship of these contacts depends on tissue preparation and on the native properties of the tissue. Once histological preparation and laser parameters are optimized for a particular tissue, the indirect harvest of undesired materials from neighboring cells is rarely an issue. Plant materials appear to be particularly amenable to the LCM approach, since most tissues do not exhibit indirect harvest under any conditions, possibly because the protoplasts of selected cells can be harvested from within their walls, while unselected ones remain behind cleanly, well segregated by intervening primary and secondary walls. The separation of the protoplast away from the wall and neighboring cells can be enhanced in vacuolated plant tissue by osmotic treatments that cause plasmolysis (45), as long as there are controls for any accompanying osmotic responses in the harvested cell.

LCM has several advantages compared to other LM methods. Cells can be harvested onto the cap while preserving their spatial relationships in the original section. This simplifies the quality control (QC) inspection of LCM-isolated cells on the harvest cap, for evidence of contamination from neighboring cells. Since any such cells or fragments are not bonded to the film, they can be quickly removed by blotting with an adhesive strip or by UV laser ablation (in the Veritas instruments).

LCM is occasionally criticized as a "contact" method for cell harvest, implying that contact of the overlay EVA film with nontarget portions of the sample leads to contamination of harvested cells with the contents of undesired cells. However, the possibility of unintended contact of source tissue with the capture cap can be avoided in several ways. First, specialized high-sensitivity LCM caps

Laser pressure catapulting (LPC): proprietary method for collecting cells freed from tissue by laser cutting, using an intense defocused pulse of the cutting laser to eject them into a collection vessel

have been developed to limit contact of the LCM film only to target cells. At targets, the film is laser excited and expanded into contact, but is otherwise suspended with a 12-μm gap above the sample via standoff rails. This separation of the film from the sample gives LCM the advantage among LM technologies that most of the laser energy is absorbed by the dye-sensitized EVA film and never strikes the sample, making it unlikely that sample composition is altered by the laser. Second, a QC inspection of the harvest cap, using the microscope optics, permits detection and removal of any unintended material by blotting or ablation. Third, membrane "frame" slides are available for mounting tissue samples onto a membrane that separates the tissue from the EVA film. At harvest sites, a piece of the membrane is captured along with the cell of interest. This prevents unintended contacts of harvested cells on the cap with unharvested tissue, even if the cap is repeatedly repositioned across the tissue.

The first generation of LCM instruments (PixCell series) is manually operated. The user views the sample through the microscope or on a video monitor (12, 22), selects the target by positioning it under the laser beam site using a mechanical stage joystick, then pulses the laser with a thumb switch or foot pedal. Later instrument generations (e.g., Veritas) can perform cell harvests robotically. The operator marks the targets on multiple tissue sections and slides onscreen, after which the instrument automatically collects the targets onto the EVA film on a cap. Multiple distinct targets (e.g., different cell types) in a single tissue section can be collected robotically onto separate caps. Alternatively, targets can be identified via image-recognition software that is trained in advance by the operator to distinguish target cells. In both cases, the advance definition of targets has the advantage that it eliminates the risk of captures misguided by the user.

Emerging variations on the LCM technology, in which the film more closely con-

tacts and conforms to the sample, or in which target cells or subcellular features are marked by laser-sensitizing dyes should provide even higher capture resolutions than the 4-5-micron diameter areas that are now the practical limit for harvest of smaller cells and subcellular regions. In addition, the combination of LCM with UV laser cutting and ablation to limit and/or trim the captured target size, as in the Veritas instrument (see below), permits rapid clean harvests of smaller cells, irregular shapes, and subcellular features. This combined cut-and-capture approach can be used to harvest cells from live plant tissue, such as intact leaves.

Laser Cutting

Laser cutting relies on a cut-and-remove strategy (10, 12, 62, 82, 88, 100, 101). Laser cutting has been applied to biological tissues for over 30 years, and is not patent-protected, although there are several proprietary and patented methods for removal of the piece cut free from the tissue. Once the target is defined, it is circumscribed by a tissue-ablating UV laser beam, usually guided by computer-controlled movement of the mechanical substage on the microscope, and recovered by one of the following systems. In the laser pressure catapulting (LPC) method (PALM-Microlaser Technologies, purchased by Zeiss in 2005), the target is cut free with a UV nitrogen gas laser (337 nm), then catapulted toward a collection vessel. The catapulting comes from an intense defocused UV laser pulse that propels the sample upward. Collection of the sample onto the cap can be enhanced with oil or adhesive. In the Leica Microsystems laser microdissection (LMD) method, the biological section is in inverted orientation, and the UV-circumscribed target is ejected downward to a collection tube. In the Molecular Machines and Industries (MMI) method, the target is cut free and harvested by blotting onto an adhesive cap. In the hybrid laser-cutting/laser-capture Veritas instrument (Arcturus Biosystems), the target is cut free by a 340-nm solid-state active-switch laser and captured onto EVA film by LCM. Solid-state lasers permit a narrower cutting beam than the gas lasers, and their longer life makes it likely that all cutting instruments will eventually incorporate their use. As for all LM technologies, once the target is user- or software-defined, the cutting and harvest can be robotic.

Laser cutting has several advantages. One is the speed and efficiency of working with hydrated and thick samples, both of which present challenges for LCM. Another advantage is the avoidance of the undesired harvest of fragments of neighboring cells, since neighboring cells are laser ablated during the cutting process (12). Samples collected by laser cutting have clean user-defined boundaries. To accomplish this, however, the UV laser must strike the sample adjacent to the harvested material, raising several cautions for the subsequent analyses of macromolecules or metabolites. First, the wavelength of the UV laser (337–340 nm) is chosen to avoid protein and nucleic acid absorbance maxima, but fragmentation debris and UV damage are still potential issues, particularly for downstream analyses such as matrix-assisted laser desorption/ionization mass spectrometry (MALDI MS) that rely on controlled fragmentation (105). This may be a particular issue for cutting systems that use LPC for harvest, because the laser that cuts and ablates is the same one that propels the sample to the collection device. For the harvest of single cells, this means that UV energy is exposed both at the periphery of and directly on a significant area of the sample. This may explain the relatively small number of publications that have reported the use of this method for single-cell harvests. Second, the UV ablation of sample-adjacent cells raises the potential of contaminating sample "spray" during UV laser cutting, although no independent published studies have evaluated this (12). Any effects of UV-caused damage and neighbor cell "spray" should be greatest on the harvest of samples with small areas, such as single cells, and of less importance to the harvest of larger multicellular areas. Although laser cutting is frequently described in comparison to LCM as a "noncontact" process (10, 100), implying relative freedom from contamination with material from nonharvested cells, the risk that samples are modified by laser cutting may be just as significant as the concerns over LCM "contacts." Further independent evaluations of the effects of the LM harvesting process on sample composition are needed for both LCM and laser cutting.

Laser cutting and LCM provide different access to the harvested cells and the remaining source tissue. The laser-cutting process destroys areas of the sample immediately adjacent to the harvest. LCM leaves neighboring cells intact, permitting their subsequent harvest and analysis. This may or may not be important for a particular biological study. Most of the current laser-cutting instruments do permit some form of QC inspection of the harvested cells. Only the MMI and Arcturus systems preserve their spatial orientation from the original tissue and provide a means of editing the harvested cells. The MMI system provides this by harvesting onto an adhesive cap that contacts the entire tissue section, unless a membrane frame slide is used to separate the sample from the cap.

LM instruments and technologies are under constant development, so the potential user should consult manufacturers for the latest specifications and methods. Instrumentation centers or individual laboratories considering acquiring one should test and compare candidate systems on their own range of intended biological applications. The host of an LM system with significant use should anticipate the need for regular instrument service to maintain the alignment and function of the many complex component systems; a service contract agreement with the manufacturer is essential.

Preparation of Plant Samples for Laser Microdissection

The preparation of tissues for LM requires a balance between morphological preservation and genomic/proteomic recovery that differs from the requirements of related microscopic analytical methods such as in situ hybridization and immunolocalization, which detect specific molecules without extraction. For LM, both the sample preparation and staining must be adjusted to assure that target cells can be identified and distinguished from nontarget neighbors, and that the DNA, RNA, proteins, or metabolites to be extracted from the target cells are preserved yet fully and nondifferentially extractable. Fortunately, most plant cells can be identified without the use of histological stains.

Fixation with noncross-linking precipitative or coagulative tissue fixatives is desirable for LM of both animals and plants (31, 34, 35, 45). Although cross-linking fixatives (e.g., paraformaldehyde) can provide greater histological detail, and are often used for the preparation of animal tissues for LM, they achieve this at the expense of the extractability of molecules from the fixed tissue. The loss of some extractability may be acceptable if the aim is to evaluate the presence/absence or relative abundance of one or a few well-defined RNAs or proteins among various cell types. However, if the aim is RNA, protein, or metabolite profiling, or some other quantitative evaluation that relies on uniform recovery of entire classes of compounds, including those of low relative abundance, any interference with extraction is unacceptable. In any event, the enhanced subcellular detail resolved by cross-linking fixatives is generally unnecessary for LM cell selection and harvest from plant tissues.

Based on comparisons thus far among fixatives for plant tissues, acetone, ethanol, ethanolic acetic acid, methacarn (methanol/chloroform/acetic acid), and certain proprietary fixatives appear to achieve a good balance between preservation and extraction (30,

31, 35, 38, 45). Among these, fixation in 100% acetone may provide the greatest degree of preservation of RNA and protein for plant samples. It is also one of the fastest methods when combined with paraffin embedding, since many plant tissues can transition directly from acetone into pre-embedding medium without lengthy dehydration steps. Note, however, that any single protocol is unlikely to be optimal for all plant tissue sources, and the user should optimize fixation and processing protocols on a case-by-case basis. Recently, microwave fixation in phosphate buffer, combined with microwave treatment to accelerate tissue-processing steps through paraffin embedding, provided histological detail in *Arabidopsis* leaves that is equal or superior to conventional processing with ethanolic acetic acid fixation or proprietary fixatives, and with comparable RNA recovery and quality (35). However, this study did not compare the preservation and accelerated processing made possible by acetone fixation. Many of the steps of conventional plant histological processing, from fixation through embedding, can be greatly accelerated by automatic tissue processors that perform programs of steps with gentle agitation under pressure or vacuum (19).

LM has been performed successfully on both cryosections and paraffin sections of plant tissues (**Figure 1**). Several plant studies have demonstrated that RNA, proteins, and metabolites can be recovered from cryosections, as is routinely done for animal LM, without the extended histological preparation needed for paraffin embedding and sectioning (1, 11, 66, 80, 81). However, many plant tissues lose their histological integrity in cryosections, even with prior fixation and treatment with cryoprotectants, thus rendering the identification of target cells difficult. The issue is severe for mature tissues such as leaves that have vacuolated cells and air spaces, and less significant for tissues with densely packed, less-vacuolated cells, such as meristems and embryos. Nonetheless,

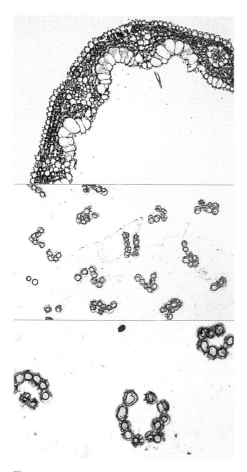

Figure 1

Laser microdissection of cells from paraffin sections of rice leaves. In the upper panel is a dry deparaffinized transverse 10-µm section of a rice leaf. In the middle panel is a field of bulliform cells captured from the adaxial surface of the leaf in the upper panel. The lower panel shows a field of bundle sheath cells captured from same leaf. Cells were captured using Pixcell IIe Laser Capture Microdissection (LCM) system (Arcturus Bioscience). Middle and lower panels are images of LCM caps.

cryosections may be the only choice if the aim is to recover small metabolites from harvested cells, because these would leach from the sample during preparative steps for paraffin sections. Cryosections can be stabilized onto a support film for LM (41).

Paraffin embedding generally preserves morphology better, and thus provides a

greater ability to identify distinct cell types (45). Fixed and dehydrated samples that are embedded in paraffin blocks can be archived and sectioned repeatedly over a period of months or longer. Once samples are embedded, conventional microtome sectioning to 8–10 microns, followed by mounting on positively charged glass slides, or on one of several types of membrane support, has been the choice of most plant LM workers using paraffin. Some workers report that yields of RNA and proteins are lower from paraffin-embedded animal tissues than from cryosections of the same material (30, 31). However, this depends on the histological preparation, and may not be the case for plant tissues and preparations. Inclusion of RNA protectants enhances the maintenance of RNA quality and quantity through the aqueous preparative steps for cryosections (46). Such protectants are probably unnecessary during postfixation preparative steps for paraffin, however, because they usually include conditions inhibitory to nucleases. One study suggests that protein recovery and preservation from LM-harvested plant cells are rendered unacceptable by fixation and preparation for paraffin sections, compared to fresh frozen cryosections (80). However, protein recovery and intactness can be excellent from plant cells LCM harvested from paraffin sections (S. Tausta & T. Nelson, unpublished observations). Additional studies of the effects of various preparative methods on recovery and preservation of RNA and protein from paraffin sections of plant tissue are needed.

Target Visualization

The highly regular organization of the cells in plant tissues, the organization of plant tissues in layers, and the stability afforded by cell walls usually make it relatively simple to identify distinct cell-type targets in plants, even when there is some deterioration in histological appearance due to the compromises in tissue preparation needed for LM. For cryosections this is particularly important, because the predictable organization of plant tissues relative to stable landmarks such as veins and sclerenchyma can overcome the loss of structural detail to guide the harvest. For paraffin sections, the LM operator has a much easier job, since even the unstained, deparaffinized, dehydrated sections required for LM usually preserve the original structure of the tissue well enough to distinguish cell types. The user should be aware, however, that the appearance of tissues in dry deparaffinized sections can differ significantly from the familiar hydrated appearance of the same tissues. Recently, methods were described for restoring some hydrated morphology to dry deparaffinized sections with a fluid overlay that is compatible with cell harvest by laser cutting and LPC (5, 61).

There are cases in which cells must be distinguished on the basis of properties not visible in an untreated sample. For example, it may be desirable to select a subset of cells expressing a particular gene, or accumulating a particular protein or virus, from a group of cells with otherwise similar appearance. The target cells (or nontarget cells) can be revealed by reporter gene expression or immunolocalization prior to LM (20, 24, 64).

This has the obvious caveat that the revealing treatment must not influence the properties of the cells to be harvested, for example by permitting RNA degradation or by skewing the RNA or protein profile of the cell. Rapid immunolocalization and other staining methods are routinely used to guide LM of animal tissues (24, 25, 29, 34, 63, 64), although not always without affecting the recovered RNA or protein. For plants, cell markers may be simplest to implement as part of a cryosectioning strategy, as they may be leached away, diffused, quenched, or otherwise rendered useless during the preparative steps for dry deparaffinized sections. However, with some optimization, many plant cell-marking strategies should be adaptable to the paraffin sections as prepared for LM. Our laboratory successfully implemented a rapid GUS-staining treatment to LM samples that does not interfere with the subsequent recovery of intact RNA (**Figure 2**). In cases in which treatments to mark target cells cause unavoidable changes to the cell, or are incompatible with histological preparation for LM, the chosen marker could be developed on reference sections to identify targets that are then harvested from untreated serial sections.

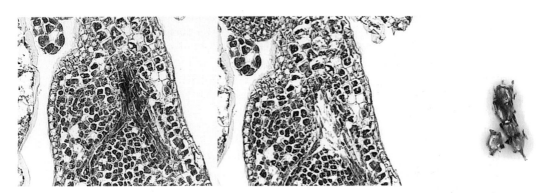

Figure 2

Capture of GUS-stained cells from a paraffin section of an *Arabidopsis* leaf. The leaf was isolated from a plant with an AtHB8-GUS transgene, which directs GUS reporter expression in developing vascular tissue. The tissue was subjected to rapid GUS staining (*green*) prior to processing for paraffin embedding. In the left panel is a dry deparaffinized section of a young leaf with blue GUS stain at developing vascular cells. The middle panel shows the same, following LCM harvest of stained cells. The right panel shows harvested GUS-stained cells on a LCM cap.

Number of Cells to Harvest

The number of cells it is necessary to harvest depends on the requirements of the subsequent analysis and on the efficiency of extraction of molecules from the particular harvested cells. Current selective LM technology makes it practical to harvest from hundreds of cells to tens of thousands of cells over the course of minutes to hours. Computer-guided harvests can be both faster per cell and extended in total duration (and thus cellular yield) compared to human-guided harvests. The efficiency of either approach depends mostly on speed of target recognition, which in turn depends on sample preparation and on the dispersal of the target in the tissue (rare or abundant, single cells or clusters, regular or irregular shapes). For planning RNA analyses starting with LM, it is useful to consider that plant and animal cells typically contain on the order of 10–100 pg of total RNA per cell (18, 106). This means that the nanogram amounts of total RNA needed for methods such as reverse transcription-polymerase chain reaction (RT-PCR) may be recovered directly from the harvest of several hundreds or thousands of cells. On the other hand, to obtain the microgram amounts of mRNA needed for microarray profiling analysis, one or two rounds of linear amplification of the RNA are required. There are many published strategies and commercial kits currently available for linear amplification of RNA, and each of these is subject to constant improvement (greater sensitivity, higher yield, longer product) (4, 50–52, 55, 60, 76, 82–85, 92, 102). Such amplification is obviously not an option for protein and metabolite analysis, but this is compensated for by the greater sensitivity of analytical methods for these compounds (3, 13, 37, 42, 59, 80, 81, 91, 105).

Considerations for Experiments Including Laser Microdissection

For any small-sample, high-sensitivity, multiple-step workflow, such as those that begin with LM and continue through RNA,

protein, or metabolite analysis, it is essential for the investigator to employ multiple steps of QC and validation with independent methods to assure that the workflow itself does not influence the cells or the materials extracted from them for analysis. For the LM steps in a workflow, the investigator should have QC means to evaluate cell purity, extraction efficiency, and degree of degradation of the extracted compounds, not only at the time preparative, harvest, and extraction steps are initially optimized, but also for ongoing data collection. The stochastic behavior of individual cells is another important issue that should be considered in experiments with small numbers of cells (18, 21, 23, 28, 43, 47, 70, 86, 96, 103). The biological activity of a tissue, even of a uniform cell type, may be the sum of cells whose individual activities (e.g., transcription of particular genes) differ significantly from the average. This biological "noise" is of most concern for studies of single cells or small groups of cells, which may require many replicates to obtain results that represent the actual distribution of individual cell behaviors. This is obviously not an issue for studies that pool hundreds or thousands of the selected cells before each analysis.

We do not evaluate here the many available methods employed subsequent to LM in various workflows, such as those for the extraction of small amounts of RNA, linear amplification of RNA, or RNA, proteomic, and metabolite profiling, because these are not unique to LM or to plant biology, and because the methods of choice are likely to have evolved by the time our review is consulted. Instead, below we describe specific examples of the incorporation of LM into plant biology studies using a variety of these workflows.

Laser Microdissection and Plant Biology

LM technology is particularly attractive for the analysis of plant phenomena. The highly structured and stereotypical nature of most plant tissues means that the identity and function of a plant cell can usually be inferred from its relative position and appearance. In many cases, cells differentiate in fixed spatial relationship to visible landmarks such as apical meristems, veins, or other differentiated cells. The distinct shapes, sizes, and densities that distinguish different cell types are preserved throughout most histological preparations, thanks largely to the cell walls that compartmentalize cells in each tissue. This is in contrast to many animal tissues, which may require histological staining to reveal differences among cell types (20, 24, 25, 34, 64).

LM should be particularly useful for the analysis of plant development. Since plant cells do not move relative to one another during development, differentiated plant cell types and their precursors can often be followed visually at a single time point in successive tissue sections or along a single section, without the need for cell-type markers such as cell-specific antibodies or reporter genes to identify them. Many developmental processes such as the proliferation and differentiation of cells from root meristems or from leaf ground cells are distributed stage-wise along a spatial gradient that can be sampled by LM at a single time point. Similarly, the specific cells that respond to environmental conditions (e.g., illumination), biotic or abiotic stresses (e.g., pathogen attack), symbiont signals, or other inputs can be visually identified and sampled by LM. If their identities are uncertain, they can be established by LM sampling of candidate cells selected by relative position alone.

The following examples should give the reader an idea of the range of plant biology investigations made possible by LM.

Transcript Analysis of Laser Microdissection-Isolated Plant Cells

Much of the application of LM to plants has been with the aim of evaluating mRNAs, through transcript profiling on microarrays, measurement of specific mRNAs by RT-PCR, evaluation of cDNA libraries, or other means.

The serial analysis of gene expression (SAGE) method should be applicable to RNA amplified from LM-isolated plant cells (14, 32, 68, 71, 98, 99). SAGE has the advantage of providing a representative library of transcripts, including transcripts that may not be represented on particular microarrays or that are missed because of incompatible 3' or 5' bias of the arrays and probes.

In one of the first plant applications of LM, Asano et al. (1) isolated RNA from ~150 phloem cells harvested by LM from cryosections of rice leaves, performed T7-based linear amplification of the RNA, and created a cDNA library to identify individual mRNAs by DNA sequencing. The library included several mRNAs previously known to be phloem specific, with a degree of redundancy in the library that presumably reflected their abundance. The cell specificity of the study was further verified by the phloem-specific in situ hybridization of a library-represented amino acid permease whose specificity had not previously been established.

Ivashikina et al. (36) isolated 150 phloem regions from 10–15-μm thick paraffin sections of *Arabidopsis* inflorescence stems using LM, and detected mRNAs for a K+ channel, sucrose carrier, and H+ pump by RT-PCR. However, they also detected the phloem-periphery marker SUC3 in their phloem harvests, suggesting some cross-contamination of their phloem cells with peripheral cell types. Because they were unable to use LM to harvest individual phloem cell types, they used enzymatic cell fractionation methods to isolate protoplasts expressing the phloem companion cell marker AtSUC2-GFP, as well as mesophyll cells not expressing the marker. The companion cell protoplasts still contained SUC3 messages, but at a lower level than mesophyll protoplasts from the periphery. The study resulted in the identification of novel phloem-specific transcripts, in particular those for K+ channels.

Nakazono et al. (66) compared transcript profiles of epidermal cells and veins that were isolated by LM from cryosections of maize leaf. Their recovery of total RNA (approximately 40 ng from >10,000 cells) suggests that a few picograms per cell were extracted. They subjected this to T7 linear amplification prior to transcript profiling on maize cDNA microarrays and found cell-specific expression of >120 novel genes.

Kerk et al. (45) verified the distinct harvest of neighboring bundle sheath and mesophyll cells by LCM from paraffin sections of maize leaves by the RT-PCR detection of cell-specific C4 pathway transcripts. The cell specificity of the same markers had been shown previously by in situ hybridizations and cell separation.

Ramsay et al. (72) measured transcripts in the giant cells induced in tomato roots four days postinfection by root-knot nematodes. These cells, which correspond to provascular cells that are induced to reenter the cell cycle, were isolated by LCM from paraffin sections and compared to neighboring uninfected cells. Using RT-PCR, they detected giant cell-specific expression of a subset of cyclin genes. They used staining with acridine orange to assure that RNA did not undergo degradation during preparative steps. In comparisons, paraffin sections were superior to cryosections for morphology and RNA recovery from these tissues. The RNA isolated from giant cells has been used to create cDNA libraries.

Liu et al. (53) used LCM on paraffin sections of the stem base of rice plants to compare pericycle cells from wild type and the *arl1* mutant, which lacks the adventitious roots that normally form in this region. Using RT-PCR, they showed that pericycle cells from the mutant expressed the pericycle-specific marker OsNAS1, but not the QHB and OsSCR markers normally expressed in pericycle cells undergoing periclinal divisions for the initiation of root primordia.

Sanders et al. (78) used LEM on paraffin sections of tobacco anthers to recover ~450 stomium cells, whose RNA was subjected to qRT-PCR to measure the abundance of two mRNAs previously shown by in situ hybridization to be stomium specific. They estimated that they represented ~1.4% and 0.4% of stomium transcripts, or approximately 7000 and 2000 molecules per stomium cell.

Casson et al. (11) used LEM on cryosections of *Arabidopsis* embryos to recover cells from apical and basal regions. They reported single excisions as small as 7.5 microns in diameter, which correspond to 5–10 cells in these embryos. After three rounds of linear amplification of extracted RNA, they identified differences in transcript profiles of the apical and basal regions, using hybridization to Affymetrix microarrays. They validated their region-specific RNA isolations by measuring several predicted RNAs by RT-PCR, and by demonstrating region-specific expression of GUS reporter fusions for genes selected from the microarray results. The study demonstrated that 65% of the genome is expressed in developing embryos and included particularly good attention to controls and to potential factors in their workflow that might bias the transcript profiles they obtained, such as 3' vs 5' bias in amplification steps and microarray design.

Jiang et al. (38) used LEM on paraffin sections of maize root caps to obtain RNA from root proximal meristem (PM), quiescent center, cap central columella, and lateral root cap. These RNAs were used in qRT-PCR experiments to measure the regional expression of selected genes that had been previously detected by microarray transcript profiling of hand-microdissected PM, quiescent center, and root cap. In this study, LM plus RT-PCR was used largely as a verification of the hand-microdissection and microarray study. Note that these two independent approaches both avoided the need to amplify the isolated RNA.

Murata & DeLuca (65) used LCM on paraffin sections of leaves of *Catharanthus roseus* (Madagascar periwinkle) to obtain RNA individually from epidermal, vascular, idioblast, laticifer, and mesophyll cells. The biosynthetic steps for anticancer dimeric alkaloids (e.g., vinblastine and vincristine) are distributed among these cell types. They used RT-PCR to establish that transcripts for several key enzymes in the pathway are epidermis specific, permitting them to use a simple carborundum abrasion method to release epidermal cell contents from intact leaves for immunological and biochemical studies of the steps.

Many other transcript-profiling and other RNA analyses of specific cell types or regions isolated by LM are now underway. Among these are transcript profiling of cells in *Arabidopsis* silique abscission zones (C. Lashbrook, personal communication), nematode-induced feeding syncytia in soybean and *Arabidopsis* roots (M. Mitchum, personal communication), powdery mildew infection sites on *Arabidopsis* leaves (M. Wildermuth, personal communication), cell types of *Arabidopsis* developing seeds (R. Day & R. Macknight, personal communication), and many others.

Cell-Type Atlases

The universal access of LM to different cell types enables the comparative and comprehensive analysis of all cell types of a particular multicellular organism, in the form of an "atlas" database (26). For such atlas resources, different cell types are collected from a common source (e.g., plants grown under defined conditions) and all cell types are subjected in parallel to transcriptional profiling, proteomic analysis, or other analysis. Users are able to consult a cellular atlas database not only to recover data sets from individual cell types, but also to make meaningful comparisons among cell types. If acquired in a statistically rigorous fashion, with attention to QC at each step in the cell preparation, harvest, and analysis workflow, the data sets from different cell types can be normalized to make cell-type-to-cell-type comparisons that should accurately reveal the relative behaviors and properties of the cells in the original body. Such cell-type

comparisons would be difficult or impossible to make in a statistically valid manner if data sets for each cell type are produced in independent projects, from plants or animals grown and sampled under varying conditions and analyzed with varying protocols (77). The comparison of cell types with the resolution of molecular profiling technology should cast new light on the number and nature of cell types in plants. Based on anatomical criteria, botanists have generally held that there are no more than a few dozen cell types in plants. The cell atlas projects may reveal distinct molecular profile patterns among anatomically similar cells that warrant the redefining of cell types. A rice cell-type atlas is currently in progress, with the goal of profiling transcripts of 135 cell types on whole-genome microarrays (laboratories of T. Nelson, X.-W. Deng & H. Zhao, unpublished data; **http://plantgenomics.biology.yale.edu/riceatlas/**). Similar transcriptional atlases are underway for several animals, including humans (26).

DNA, Chromatin Modifications, Whole Chromosomes

LM is a particularly successful tool for evaluating cell-specific DNA and chromatin characteristics, such as sequence polymorphisms and DNA methylation. DNA and chromatin are stable and of relatively fixed composition per cell, compared to RNA, protein, and metabolites, making extraction and recovery more reliable. When larger amounts are required for analysis, small amounts of DNA can be amplified (74).

LM has been applied in various ways to evaluate the contributions of sex chromosomes in *Silene*. Scutt et al. (89) used laser manipulation to isolate all *Silene* chromosomes onto a polyester membrane, then laser ablated the autosomes, and performed degenerate oligonucleotide-primed PCR (DOP-PCR) to evaluate repeat sequences and organization of the remaining sex chromosomes. Matsunaga et al. (57) used a UV laser to open a hole in a single *Silene* pollen grain and catapulted the entire genome for amplification using primer-extension-preamplification PCR (PEP-PCR). They then detected individual single-copy genes by PCR from single pollen grains. Matsunaga & Kwano (56) evaluated sex-determining genes on *Silene* Y chromosomes isolated with a UV laser. Hobza et al. (33) isolated X and Y chromosomes from *Silene* root tips using the PALM system, followed by FAST-FISH instead of ablating autosomes. Liu et al. (54) used laser optical tweezers to localize single rice chromosomes, which were then harvested with glass micropipette.

LM has been applied in a variety of animal systems to examine cell-specific DNA and chromatin modifications associated with epigenetic phenomena. For example, Ropke et al. (75) microdissected a low-grade chondroid compartment and a highly malignant compartment of the dedifferentiated chondrosarcoma tumor and examined CpG island methylation of eight tumor suppressor genes in the two cell types. Similarly, Sato et al. (79) used LCM to isolate cancerous vs. noncancerous pancreatic tissue and found a cyclin-dependent kinase inhibitor gene expression to be downregulated in cancerous pancreatic tissue through a combination of promoter hypermcthylation, histone deacetylation, and loss of maternal allele expressing CDKN1C. Bisulfite genomic sequencing has been successfully applied directly to DNA from LM-isolated cells (44). In plants, there are numerous tissue-specific epigenetic phenomena that might be explored with greater resolution via LM, such as DNA methylation of specific genes during male and female gametophyte development (2, 93, 97, 104), or the cellular distributions of microRNAs that regulate developmental patterns (39).

Proteins and Metabolites

To date, few plant studies have used LM as the starting point for protein or metabolite analysis, although such analyses have been applied to plants at the tissue or organ levels. Schad

et al. (81) used laser cutting on cryosections of *Arabidopsis* influorescence stems (without cryoprotectants) to compare metabolites extracted from vascular bundles to the remaining stem tissue. The harvest of 100 vascular bundles in cross section or five entire

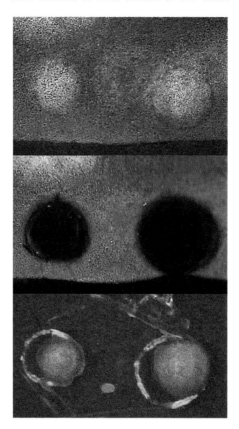

Figure 3

Laser microdissection of green fluorescent protein (GFP)-marked regions from live tobacco leaves. The top panel shows a whole mount of *Nicotiana benthamiana* leaf 24 hours after infection with the TMV::GFP virus; it is illuminated to show fluorescent infection sites. The middle panel shows the same illustration, following removal of two infection sites (approximately 1-mm and 1.3-mm diameter) by UV cutting and laser capture microdissection (LCM), using the Veritas instrument (Arcturus Bioscience). In the bottom panel are harvested live infection sites from the same sample on LCM cap. Brighter green fluorescence on edges of harvested disks is due to fluorescence of LCM film, not the tissue. (S. Tausta, N. Gandotra & S.P. Dinesh-Kumar, unpublished results)

bundleless sections provided enough material for the statistically significant analysis of 65–68 metabolites (largely acids and sugars) by GC-TOF MS. Schad et al. (80) showed that 5000 LM-isolated vascular bundle cross sections or 50 of the cryosections left after their harvest were sufficient for protein analysis by two-dimensional gel electrophoresis. About 5–10 times less material was sufficient for identifying 160–350 proteins by LC-MS/MS. As the authors note for both of these studies, although their protocol for cryosections preserved robust anatomical features such as vascular bundles in stems, the same approach is unlikely to provide adequate resolution for the harvest of specific cells from more delicate tissues. The authors of the latter study tested an alternative approach using paraffin-embedded tissue for LM, but found that their fixation protocol reduced protein extractability in a nonuniform manner. This is a relatively new analytical approach for plants, and there is still much opportunity for the optimization of LM tissue preparation and harvest methods for protein and metabolite studies.

Prospects

Laser ablation has been applied to a variety of investigations of live cells. A variation of LCM has been commercialized for harvesting selected live cells from cultures grown on membrane support (Clonis workstation, Bio-Rad). However, only recently has it become practical to use LM systems to isolate small regions of live tissues (58, 94). The solid-state UV laser beam of some LM instruments (e.g., Arcturus Veritas) is of high enough energy to cut through whole leaves or other organs. In most cases, such live-cell harvests will not be limited to a single cell type or layer. This may be acceptable if the aim is to isolate material with event or site specificity rather than cell specificity, such as pathogen infection sites or insect feeding sites. Live LM permits the viewing of GFP and other markers that may be difficult to preserve through preparative steps that include tissue fixation, or difficult to view in cryosections (**Figure 3**). The same methodology might be applied for the microdissection of plant parts for further growth in culture.

One emerging alternative to LM is expression microdissection (xMD) (95). In this method, a thermoplastic EVA film is layered directly on a tissue sample that has been sensitized by treating with a specific antibody coupled to an IR-absorbant dye. A laser rapidly scans the sample, causing bonding of cells to the film only where the antibody is present. Since the method does not rely on microscopy or image recognition, and instead relies on well-developed scanning and antibody technology, it should be far less costly than LM systems. It should also be more rapid, because a scan that takes seconds could bond hundreds of thousands or millions of cells for harvest, depending on the antibody used as sensitizing tag. The method requires a specific antibody to mark the targets for capture, so it is conceptually similar to the cell-sorting approach guided by GFP expression from cell-specific genes. Since it requires tissue treatments for antibody staining, samples may be altered too much for some kinds of analysis. The cell-type atlas resources described might be used to identify cell-specific tags for each cell that would make the xMD approach applicable to any chosen cell.

SUMMARY POINTS

1. Laser microdissection (LM) utilizes a cutting or harvesting laser to remove specific cells from histological sections; the process is guided by microscopy.

2. There are two basic LM strategies: laser capture, which bonds selected cells to a harvesting membrane, and laser cutting, which excises selected cells for recovery by one of several methods.

3. LM-harvested cells are suitable for comprehensive analysis of DNA, RNA, protein, and metabolites.

4. Tissue preparation for LM must balance the preservation of tissue morphology to aid cell selection against preservation and extraction of molecules for subsequent genomic or metabolite analysis.

5. Plants are particularly amenable to LM, thanks to the highly regular tissue organization and cell wall stability.

ACKNOWLEDGMENTS

The authors wish to thank Julia Kehr, Mary Wildermuth, Fred Sack, Michael Deyholos, Vincenzo De Luca, Lewis Feldman, Thomas Laux, Robert Day, Ueli Grossniklaus, Coralie Lashbrook, Melissa Mitchum, Marja Timmermans, and Michael Scanlon for sharing information that was in press or unpublished, and Ashi Malekafzali for helpful comments on the manuscript. The authors' work on laser microdissection is supported by a grant to Timothy Nelson from the NSF Plant Genome Program (DBI-0325821).

LITERATURE CITED

1. Asano T, Masumura T, Kusano H, Kikuchi S, Kurita A, et al. 2002. Construction of a specialized cDNA library from plant cells isolated by laser capture microdissection: toward comprehensive analysis of the genes expressed in the rice phloem. *Plant J.* 32:401–8

2. Autran D, Huanca-Mamani W, Vielle-Calzada JP. 2005. Genomic imprinting in plants: the epigenetic version of an Oedipus complex. *Curr. Opin. Plant Biol.* 8:19–25

3. Batorfi J, Ye B, Mok SC, Cseh I, Berkowitz RS, Fulop V. 2003. Protein profiling of complete mole and normal placenta using ProteinChip analysis on laser capture microdissected cells. *Gynecol. Oncol.* 88:424–28

4. Baugh LR, Hill AA, Brown EL, Hunter CP. 2001. Quantitative analysis of mRNA amplification by in vitro transcription. *Nucleic Acids Res.* 29:E29

5. Bazan V, La Rocca G, Corsale S, Agnese V, Macaluso M, et al. 2005. Laser pressure catapulting (LPC): optimization LPC-system and genotyping of colorectal carcinomas. *J. Cell. Physiol.* 202:503–9

6. Birnbaum K, Shasha DE, Wang JY, Jung JW, Lambert GM, et al. 2003. A gene expression map of the Arabidopsis root. *Science* 302:1956–60

7. Brandt S, Kehr J, Walz C, Imlau A, Willmitzer L, Fisahn J. 1999. Technical advance: a rapid method for detection of plant gene transcripts from single epidermal, mesophyll and companion cells of intact leaves. *Plant J.* 20:245–50

8. Brandt S, Kloska S, Altmann T, Kehr J. 2002. Using array hybridization to monitor gene expression at the single cell level. *J. Exp. Bot.* 53:2315–23

9. Brandt SP. 2005. Microgenomics: gene expression analysis at the tissue-specific and single-cell levels. *J. Exp. Bot.* 56:495–505

10. Burgemeister R. 2005. New aspects of laser microdissection in research and routine. *J. Histochem. Cytochem.* 53:409–12

This study is notable for the careful optimization of every step in the workflow, from tissue preparation and LM through microarray hybridization.

11. **Casson S, Spencer M, Walker K, Lindsey K. 2005. Laser capture microdissection for the analysis of gene expression during embryogenesis of Arabidopsis.** *Plant J.* **42:111–23**

12. Cornea A, Mungenast A. 2002. Comparison of current equipment. *Methods Enzymol.* 356:3–12

13. Cowherd SM, Espina VA, Petricoin EF 3rd, Liotta LA. 2004. Proteomic analysis of human breast cancer tissue with laser-capture microdissection and reverse-phase protein microarrays. *Clin. Breast Cancer* 5:385–92

14. Datson NA, van der Perk-de Jong J, van den Berg MP, de Kloet ER, Vreugdenhil E. 1999. MicroSAGE: a modified procedure for serial analysis of gene expression in limited amounts of tissue. *Nucleic Acids Res.* 27:1300–7

15. Davey MR, Anthony P, Power JB, Lowe KC. 2005. Plant protoplasts: status and biotechnological perspectives. *Biotechnol. Adv.* 23:131–71

16. Day RC, Grossniklaus U, Macknight RC. 2005. Be more specific! Laser-assisted microdissection of plant cells. *Trends Plant Sci.* 10:397–406

17. Demura T, Tashiro G, Horiguchi G, Kishimoto N, Kubo M, et al. 2002. Visualization by comprehensive microarray analysis of gene expression programs during transdifferentiation of mesophyll cells into xylem cells. *Proc. Natl. Acad. Sci. USA* 99:15794–99

18. Dixon AK, Richardson PJ, Pinnock RD, Lee K. 2000. Gene-expression analysis at the single-cell level. *Trends Pharmacol. Sci.* 21:65–70

19. Drea S, Leader DJ, Arnold BC, Shaw P, Dolan L, Doonan JH. 2005. Systematic spatial analysis of gene expression during wheat caryopsis development. *Plant Cell* 17:2172–85

20. Ehrig T, Abdulkadir SA, Dintzis SM, Milbrandt J, Watson MA. 2001. Quantitative amplification of genomic DNA from histological tissue sections after staining with nuclear dyes and laser capture microdissection. *J. Mol. Diagn.* 3:22–25

21. Elowitz MB, Levine AJ, Siggia ED, Swain PS. 2002. Stochastic gene expression in a single cell. *Science* 297:1183–86

This paper describes the first implementation of the LCM strategy.

22. **Emmert-Buck MR, Bonner RF, Smith PD, Chuaqui RF, Zhuang Z, et al. 1996. Laser capture microdissection.** *Science* **274:998–1001**

23. Fedoroff N, Fontana W. 2002. Genetic networks. Small numbers of big molecules. *Science* 297:1129–31

24. Fend F, Emmert-Buck MR, Chuaqui R, Cole K, Lee J, et al. 1999. Immuno-LCM: laser capture microdissection of immunostained frozen sections for mRNA analysis. *Am. J. Pathol.* 154:61–66

25. Fend F, Specht K, Kremer M, Quintanilla-Martinez L. 2002. Laser capture microdissection in pathology. *Methods Enzymol.* 356:196–206

26. Fraser AG, Marcotte EM. 2004. Development through the eyes of functional genomics. *Curr. Opin. Genet. Dev.* 14:336–42

27. Fraser AG, Marcotte EM. 2004. A probabilistic view of gene function. *Nat. Genet.* 36:559–64

28. Gallagher JA, Koroleva OA, Tomos DA, Farrar JF, Pollock CJ. 2001. Single cell analysis technique for comparison of specific mRNA abundance in plant cells. *J. Plant Physiol.* 158:1089–92

29. Gillespie JW, Ahram M, Best CJ, Swalwell JI, Krizman DB, et al. 2001. The role of tissue microdissection in cancer research. *Cancer J.* 7:32–39

30. Gillespie JW, Best CJ, Bichsel VE, Cole KA, Greenhut SF, et al. 2002. Evaluation of non-formalin tissue fixation for molecular profiling studies. *Am. J. Pathol.* 160:449–57

31. Goldsworthy SM, Stockton PS, Trempus CS, Foley JF, Maronpot RR. 1999. Effects of fixation on RNA extraction and amplification from laser capture microdissected tissue. *Mol. Carcinog.* 25:86–91

32. Heidenblut AM, Luttges J, Buchholz M, Heinitz C, Emmersen J, et al. 2004. aRNA-longSAGE: a new approach to generate SAGE libraries from microdissected cells. *Nucleic Acids Res.* 32:e131

33. Hobza R, Lengerova M, Cernohorska H, Rubes J, Vyskot B. 2004. FAST-FISH with laser beam microdissected DOP-PCR probe distinguishes the sex chromosomes of Silene latifolia. *Chromosome Res.* 12:245–50

34. Huang LE, Luzzi V, Ehrig T, Holtschlag V, Watson MA. 2002. Optimized tissue processing and staining for laser capture microdissection and nucleic acid retrieval. *Methods Enzymol.* 356:49–62

35. Inada N, Wildermuth MC. 2005. Novel tissue preparation method and cell-specific marker for laser microdissection of Arabidopsis mature leaf. *Planta* 221:9–16

36. Ivashikina N, Deeken R, Ache P, Kranz E, Pommerrenig B, et al. 2003. Isolation of AtSUC2 promoter-GFP-marked companion cells for patch-clamp studies and expression profiling. *Plant J.* 36:931–45

37. Jain KK. 2002. Application of laser capture microdissection to proteomics. *Methods Enzymol.* 356:157–67

38. Jiang K, Zhang S, Lee S, Tsai G, Kim K, et al. 2005. Transcription profile analyses identify genes and pathways central to root cap functions in maize. *Plant Mol. Biol.* In press

39. Jover-Gil S, Candela H, Ponce M-R. 2005. Plant microRNAs and development. *Int. J. Dev. Biol.* 49:733–44

40. Karrer EE, Lincoln JE, Hogenhout S, Bennett AB, Bostock RM, et al. 1995. In situ isolation of mRNA from individual plant cells: creation of cell-specific cDNA libraries. *Proc. Natl. Acad. Sci. USA* 92:3814–18

41. Kawamoto T. 2003. Use of a new adhesive film for the preparation of multi-purpose fresh-frozen sections from hard tissues, whole-animals, insects and plants. *Arch. Histol. Cytol.* 66:123–43

42. Kehr J. 2001. High resolution spatial analysis of plant systems. *Curr. Opin. Plant Biol.* 4:197–201

43. Kehr J. 2003. Single cell technology. *Curr. Opin. Plant Biol.* 6:617–21

44. Kerjean A, Vieillefond A, Thiounn N, Sibony M, Jeanpierre M, Jouannet P. 2001. Bisulfite genomic sequencing of microdissected cells. *Nucleic Acids Res.* 29:E106–9

45. Kerk NM, Ceserani T, Tausta SL, Sussex IM, Nelson TM. 2003. Laser capture microdissection of cells from plant tissues. *Plant Physiol.* 132:27–35

46. Kihara AH, Moriscot AS, Ferreira PJ, Hamassaki DE. 2005. Protecting RNA in fixed tissue: An alternative method for LCM users. *J. Neurosci. Methods* 148:103–7

47. Lange BM. 2005. Single-cell genomics. *Curr. Opin. Plant Biol.* 8:236–41

48. Lee JY, Levesque M, Benfey PN. 2005. High-throughput RNA isolation technologies. New tools for high-resolution gene expression profiling in plant systems. *Plant Physiol.* 138:585–90

49. Levesque MP, Benfey PN. 2004. Systems biology. *Curr. Biol.* 14:R179–80

50. Li J, Adams L, Schwartz SM, Bumgarner RE. 2003. RNA amplification, fidelity and reproducibility of expression profiling. *C. R. Biol* 326:1021–30

51. Li L, Roden J, Shapiro BE, Wold BJ, Bhatia S, et al. 2005. Reproducibility, fidelity, and discriminant validity of mRNA amplification for microarray analysis from primary hematopoietic cells. *J. Mol. Diagn.* 7:48–56

This paper discusses the issues relevant to adapting LM to plant tissues.

This review compares current methods for genomic evaluation of specific cells in plants.

52. Li Y, Li T, Liu S, Qiu M, Han Z, et al. 2004. Systematic comparison of the fidelity of aRNA, mRNA and T-RNA on gene expression profiling using cDNA microarray. *J. Biotechnol.* 107:19–28

53. Liu H, Wang S, Yu X, Yu J, He X, et al. 2005. ARL1, a LOB-domain protein required for adventitious root formation in rice. *Plant J.* 43:47–56

54. Liu X, Wang H, Li Y, Tang Y, Liu Y, et al. 2004. Preparation of single rice chromosome for construction of a DNA library using a laser microbeam trap. *J. Biotechnol.* 109:217–26

55. Luzzi V, Mahadevappa M, Raja R, Warrington JA, Watson MA. 2003. Accurate and reproducible gene expression profiles from laser capture microdissection, transcript amplification, and high density oligonucleotide microarray analysis. *J. Mol. Diagn.* 5:9–14

56. Matsunaga S, Kawano S, Michimoto T, Higashiyama T, Nakao S, et al. 1999. Semi-automatic laser beam microdissection of the Y chromosome and analysis of Y chromosome DNA in a dioecious plant, Silene latifolia. *Plant Cell Physiol.* 40:60–68

57. Matsunaga S, Schutze K, Donnison IS, Grant SR, Kuroiwa T, Kawano S. 1999. Technical advance: single pollen typing combined with laser-mediated manipulation. *Plant J.* 20:371–78

58. Mayer A, Stich M, Brocksch D, Schutze K, Lahr G. 2002. Going in vivo with laser microdissection. *Methods Enzymol.* 356:25–33

59. Melle C, Kaufmann R, Hommann M, Bleul A, Driesch D, et al. 2004. Proteomic profiling in microdissected hepatocellular carcinoma tissue using ProteinChip technology. *Int. J. Oncol.* 24:885–91

60. Meyers BC, Galbraith DW, Nelson T, Agrawal V. 2004. Methods for transcriptional profiling in plants. Be fruitful and replicate. *Plant Physiol.* 135:637–52

61. Micke P, Bjornsen T, Scheidl S, Stromberg S, Demoulin JB, et al. 2004. A fluid cover medium provides superior morphology and preserves RNA integrity in tissue sections for laser microdissection and pressure catapulting. *J. Pathol.* 202:130–38

62. Micke P, Ostman A, Lundeberg J, Ponten F. 2005. Laser-assisted cell microdissection using the PALM system. *Methods Mol. Biol.* 293:151–66

63. Mojsilovic-Petrovic J, Nesic M, Pen A, Zhang W, Stanimirovic D. 2004. Development of rapid staining protocols for laser-capture microdissection of brain vessels from human and rat coupled to gene expression analyses. *J. Neurosci. Methods* 133:39–48

64. Murakami H, Liotta L, Star RA. 2000. IF-LCM: laser capture microdissection of immunofluorescently defined cells for mRNA analysis rapid communication. *Kidney Int.* 58:1346–53

65. Murata J, De Luca V. 2005. Localization of tabersonin 16-hydroxylase and 16-OH tabersonine-16-O-methyltransferase to leaf epidermal cells defines them as a major site of precursor biosynthesis in the vindoline pathway in *Catharanthus roseus*. *Plant J.* 44:581–94

66. Nakazono M, Qiu F, Borsuk LA, Schnable PS. 2003. Laser-capture microdissection, a tool for the global analysis of gene expression in specific plant cell types: identification of genes expressed differentially in epidermal cells or vascular tissues of maize. *Plant Cell* 15:583–96

67. Nawy T, Lee J-Y, Colinas J, Wang JY, Thongrod SC, et al. 2005. Transcriptional profile of the Arabidopsis root quiescent center. *Plant Cell* 17:1908–25

68. Neilson L, Andalibi A, Kang D, Coutifaris C, Strauss JF 3rd, et al. 2000. Molecular phenotype of the human oocyte by PCR-SAGE. *Genomics* 63:13–24

69. Outlaw WH Jr, Zhang S. 2001. Single-cell dissection and microdroplet chemistry. *J. Exp. Bot.* 52:605–14

70. Ozbudak EM, Thattai M, Kurtser I, Grossman AD, van Oudenaarden A. 2002. Regulation of noise in the expression of a single gene. *Nat. Genet.* 31:69–73

71. Peters DG, Kassam AB, Yonas H, O'Hare EH, Ferrell RE, Brufsky AM. 1999. Comprehensive transcript analysis in small quantities of mRNA by SAGE-lite. *Nucleic Acids Res.* 27:e39

72. Ramsay K, Wang Z, Jones MGK. 2004. Using laser capture microdissection to study gene expression in early stages of giant cells induced by root-knot nematodes. *Methods Enzymol.* 5:587–92

73. Raps A, Kehr J, Gugerli P, Moar WJ, Bigler F, Hilbeck A. 2001. Immunological analysis of phloem sap of *Bacillus thuringiensis* corn and of the nontarget herbivore *Rhopalosiphum padi* (Homoptera: Aphididae) for the presence of Cry1Ab. *Mol. Ecol.* 10:525–33

74. Rook MS, Delach SM, Deyneko G, Worlock A, Wolfe JL. 2004. Whole genome amplification of DNA from laser capture-microdissected tissue for high-throughput single nucleotide polymorphism and short tandem repeat genotyping. *Am. J. Pathol.* 164:23–33

75. Ropke M, Boltze C, Neumann HW, Roessner A, Schneider-Stock R. 2003. Genetic and epigenetic alterations in tumor progression in a dedifferentiated chondrosarcoma. *Pathol. Res. Pract.* 199:437–44

76. Saghizadeh M, Brown DJ, Tajbakhsh J, Chen Z, Kenney MC, et al. 2003. Evaluation of techniques using amplified nucleic acid probes for gene expression profiling. *Biomol. Eng.* 20:97–106

77. Sandberg R, Ernberg I. 2005. The molecular portrait of in vitro growth by meta-analysis of gene-expression profiles. *Genome Biol.* 6:R65

78. Sanders P, Bui A, Le B, Goldberg R. 2005. Differentiation and degeneration of cells that play a major role in tobacco anther dehiscence. *Sexual Plant Reprod.* 17:219–41

79. Sato N, Matsubayashi H, Abe T, Fukushima N, Goggins M. 2005. Epigenetic down-regulation of CDKN1C/p57KIP2 in pancreatic ductal neoplasms identified by gene expression profiling. *Clin. Cancer Res.* 11:4681–88

80. **Schad M, Lipton MS, Giavalisco P, Smith RD, Kehr J. 2005. Evaluation of two-dimensional electrophoresis and liquid chromatography - tandem mass spectrometry for tissue-specific protein profiling of laser-microdissected plant samples.** *Electrophoresis* 26:2729–38

This paper provides a first example of proteomic methods as applied to plant cells isolated by LM.

81. Schad M, Mungur R, Fiehn O, Kehr J. 2005. Metabolic profiling of laser microdissected vascular bundles of Arabidopsis thaliana. *Plant Methods* 1:2

82. Scheidl SJ, Nilsson S, Kalen M, Hellstrom M, Takemoto M, et al. 2002. mRNA expression profiling of laser microbeam microdissected cells from slender embryonic structures. *Am. J. Pathol.* 160:801–13

83. Scherer A, Krause A, Walker JR, Sutton SE, Seron D, et al. 2003. Optimized protocol for linear RNA amplification and application to gene expression profiling of human renal biopsies. *Biotechniques* 34:546–50, 52–54, 56

84. Schnable PS, Hochholdinger F, Nakazono M. 2004. Global expression profiling applied to plant development. *Curr. Opin. Plant Biol.* 7:50–56

85. Schneider J, Buness A, Huber W, Volz J, Kioschis P, et al. 2004. Systematic analysis of T7 RNA polymerase based in vitro linear RNA amplification for use in microarray experiments. *BMC Genomics* 5:29

86. Schober MS, Min YN, Chen YQ. 2001. Serial analysis of gene expression in a single cell. *Biotechniques* 31:1240–42

87. Schrader J, Nilsson J, Mellerowicz E, Berglund A, Nilsson P, et al. 2004. A high-resolution transcript profile across the wood-forming meristem of poplar identifies potential regulators of cambial stem cell identity. *Plant Cell* 16:2278–92

88. Schutze K, Posl H, Lahr G. 1998. Laser micromanipulation systems as universal tools in cellular and molecular biology and in medicine. *Cell Mol. Biol. (Noisy-le-grand)* 44:735–46

89. Scutt CP, Kamisugi Y, Sakai F, Gilmartin PM. 1997. Laser isolation of plant sex chromosomes: studies on the DNA composition of the X and Y sex chromosomes of Silene latifolia. *Genome* 40:705–15

90. Sheen JY, Bogorad L. 1987. Differential expression of C4 pathway genes in mesophyll and bundle sheath cells of greening maize leaves. *J. Biol. Chem.* 262:11726–30

91. Shekouh AR, Thompson CC, Prime W, Campbell F, Hamlett J, et al. 2003. Application of laser capture microdissection combined with two-dimensional electrophoresis for the discovery of differentially regulated proteins in pancreatic ductal adenocarcinoma. *Proteomics* 3:1988–2001

92. Spiess AN, Mueller N, Ivell R. 2003. Amplified RNA degradation in T7-amplification methods results in biased microarray hybridizations. *BMC Genomics* 4:44

93. Steimer A, Schob H, Grossniklaus U. 2004. Epigenetic control of plant development: new layers of complexity. *Curr. Opin. Plant Biol.* 7:11–19

94. Stich M, Thalhammer S, Burgemeister R, Friedemann G, Ehnle S, et al. 2003. Live cell catapulting and recultivation. *Pathol. Res. Pract.* 199:405–9

95. Tangrea MA, Chuaqui RF, Gillespie JW, Ahram M, Gannot G, et al. 2004. Expression microdissection: operator-independent retrieval of cells for molecular profiling. *Diagn. Mol. Pathol.* 13:207–12

96. Tomos AD, Sharrock RA. 2001. Cell sampling and analysis (SiCSA): metabolites measured at single cell resolution. *J. Exp. Bot.* 52:623–30

97. Vielle-Calzada JP, Thomas J, Spillane C, Coluccio A, Hoeppner MA, Grossniklaus U. 1999. Maintenance of genomic imprinting at the Arabidopsis medea locus requires zygotic DDM1 activity. *Genes Dev.* 13:2971–82

98. Vilain C, Libert F, Venet D, Costagliola S, Vassart G. 2003. Small amplified RNA-SAGE: an alternative approach to study transcriptome from limiting amount of mRNA. *Nucleic Acids Res.* 31:e24

99. Vilain C, Vassart G. 2004. Small amplified RNA-SAGE. *Methods Mol. Biol.* 258:135–52

100. Westphal G, Burgemeister R, Friedemann G, Wellmann A, Wernert N, et al. 2002. Noncontact laser catapulting: a basic procedure for functional genomics and proteomics. *Methods Enzymol.* 356:80–99

101. Willenberg HS, Walters R, Bornstein SR. 2002. Use of laser microdissection in complex tissue. *Methods Enzymol.* 356:216–23

102. Wilson CL, Pepper SD, Hey Y, Miller CJ. 2004. Amplification protocols introduce systematic but reproducible errors into gene expression studies. *Biotechniques* 36:498–506

103. Xia F, Jin W, Yin X, Fang Z. 2005. Single-cell analysis by electrochemical detection with a microfluidic device. *J. Chromatogr. A* 1063:227–33

104. Xiao W, Gehring M, Choi Y, Margossian L, Pu H, et al. 2003. Imprinting of the MEA Polycomb gene is controlled by antagonism between MET1 methyltransferase and DME glycosylase. *Dev. Cell* 5:891–901

105. Xu BJ, Caprioli RM, Sanders ME, Jensen RA. 2002. Direct analysis of laser capture microdissected cells by MALDI mass spectrometry. *J. Am. Soc. Mass Spectrom.* 13:1292–97

106. Zimmerman JL, Goldberg RB. 1977. DNA sequence organization in the genome of *Nicotiana tabacum. Chromosoma* 59:227–52

Integrative Plant Biology: Role of Phloem Long-Distance Macromolecular Trafficking

Tony J. Lough[1] and William J. Lucas[2]

[1] Agrigenesis Biosciences, Auckland, New Zealand; email: T.Lough@agrigenesis.co.nz

[2] Section of Plant Biology, Division of Biological Sciences, University of California, Davis, California 95616; email: wjlucas@ucdavis.edu

Annu. Rev. Plant Biol.
2006. 57:203–32

The *Annual Review of Plant Biology* is online at
plant.annualreviews.org

doi: 10.1146/
annurev.arplant.56.032604.144145

First published online as a
Review in Advance on
January 30, 2006

1543-5008/06/0602-
0203$20.00

Key Words

information macromolecules, long-distance transport, RNA, signaling

Abstract

Recent studies have revealed the operation of a long-distance communication network operating within the vascular system of higher plants. The evolutionary development of this network reflects the need to communicate environmental inputs, sensed by mature organs, to meristematic regions of the plant. One consequence of such a long-distance signaling system is that newly forming organs can develop properties optimized for the environment into which they will emerge, mature, and function. The phloem translocation stream of the angiosperms contains, in addition to photosynthate and other small molecules, a variety of macromolecules, including mRNA, small RNA, and proteins. This review highlights recent progress in the characterization of phloem-mediated transport of macromolecules as components of an integrated long-distance signaling network. Attention is focused on the role played by these proteins and RNA species in coordination of developmental programs and the plant's response to both environmental cues and pathogen challenge. Finally, the importance of developing phloem transcriptome and proteomic databases is discussed within the context of advances in plant systems biology.

Contents

INTRODUCTION

To understand the context in which long-distance molecules function, whole-plant signaling must be viewed from the perspective of the evolutionary development of organismal complexity. As biological systems advanced from cellular to multicellular, a parallel increase in the sophistication of their signaling processes had to occur in order to allow for the integration of processes at a multicellular level (94). In this regard, retention of the cell wall by the plant kingdom imposed an interesting challenge to the development of an informational network that could operate at the multicellular/organismal level. The outcome was that, within plant tissues, coordination was achieved by a combination of cell-cell, receptor-ligand signaling systems (33, 140) and cell-to-cell communication through plasmodesmata (PD). Biogenesis, structure, and dynamics of PD have been extensively reviewed elsewhere (34, 38, 59, 92, 112, 168). The important feature of PD is that they establish continuity between the cytoplasm of neighboring cells, thereby forming a symplasmic state that allows for the local exchange of molecules and ions.

Inter-organ communication was achieved through the development of a vascular system. In this regard, it is important to note that significant differences exist between the vascular systems that evolved in the animal and plant kingdoms; however, both conform to Murray's Law of fluid dynamics (100, 105). It is an axiom that, in animals, the arteries and veins circulate blood, carrying nutrients, various signaling molecules, and a range of cell types around the body. In plants, the vascular system is comprised of the xylem and phloem conducting tissues whose mode of formation and function are strikingly different from that of animals. For the purpose of this review, the basic difference is that, except for water and ions, (macro)molecules moving in one direction in the phloem do not circulate back to their sites of origin through the xylem, i.e., the plant vascular system is noncirculatory in nature (**Figure 1**). One important consequence of this system is that, whereas the shoot apical meristem (SAM) can receive input signals from the mature regions of the plant, output signals cannot be translocated back to the lower organs, as both the xylem and phloem operate in the same direction (**Figure 1a**). (Note that hormones, such as auxin, produced in the apex move locally down the stem via a

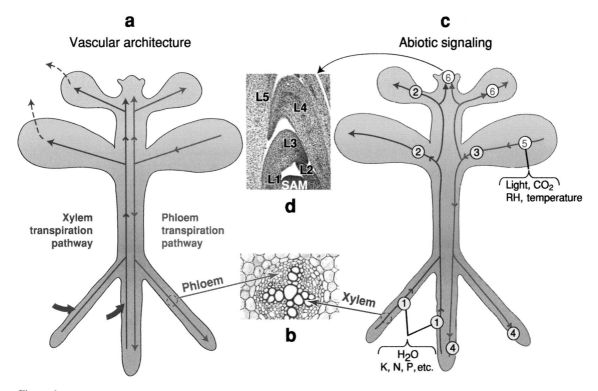

a
Vascular architecture

Xylem
transpiration
pathway

Phloem
transpiration
pathway

Phloem

Xylem

b

c
Abiotic signaling

② ⑥ ⑥

② ③ ⑤

Light, CO₂
RH, temperature

① ①

①

H₂O
K, N, P, etc.

④ ④

L5 L4

L3 L2

L1 SAM

d

Figure 1

The plant vascular system functions as the conduit for long-distance communication between distantly located organs. (*a*) Schematic illustration of the xylem and phloem, illustrating the fundamental feature that, in contrast to the animal kingdom, the flow pathway is noncirculatory in nature. (*b*) Transverse section of a root demonstrating the physical separation of the phloem and xylem tissues. Xylem conducting elements are dead at maturity, whereas the sieve tube system acts as a specialized symplasmic domain; thus, the plasma membrane of the phloem cells acts as a barrier to exchange between the two streams. (*c*) Coordination of physiological and developmental programs requires the integration of a spectrum of abiotic input signals. Root-shoot-root relay signaling: (*1*) input signal for nutrient deficiency produced in the roots is transported, via the xylem, to the shoot; (*2*) signal recognition activates a pathway located in the symplasm of the leaf; (*3*) response signal enters the phloem for delivery to the roots; (*4*) output signal adjusts the genetic program controlling nutrient uptake. Leaf-to-apex signaling: (*5*) input signal for an environmental parameter enters the phloem for transport to sink organs, including the apex; (*6*) developmental program is adjusted to optimize the morphological/anatomical/physiological features of the developing organ for the existing conditions. (*d*) Shoot apical meristem (SAM) functions in a protected environment markedly different from that experienced by mature organs. A median longitudinal section through the vegetative apex illustrates the manner in which the developing leaves (L1–L5) ensheath the SAM. Identity of the proposed long-distance signals remains to be elucidated, but current research indicates the involvement of information macromolecules.

Plasmodesmata (PD): unique plasma membrane-lined cytoplasmic channels that establish symplasmic continuity between neighboring plant cells

Shoot apical meristem (SAM): the vegetative apex of a plant is comprised of a group of stem cells that form the shoot apical meristem. These cells give rise to leaf primordia, vascular initials, axillary buds, and the stem

cell-cell transfer process.) This architectural feature most surely imposed novel challenges on the evolution of an effective long-distance communication system in plants.

The primary focus of this review is the analysis of current knowledge on the operation of the phloem as a conduit for long-distance macromolecular signaling in plants. This topic was last reviewed in this series by Oparka & Santa Cruz (113). Signaling systems, incorporating phytohormones, sugars, jasmonic acid, and similar such low molecular weight compounds have been reviewed elsewhere (31, 39, 41, 49, 90, 133, 137, 147,

157, 160). Although a number of studies have shown that transcripts (125), proteins (51), and small RNA (167) are present in the phloem translocation stream, the pressing issue facing this field is the functional significance of these molecules and the roles they play in the integration of whole-plant signaling processes.

Plasmodesmata, Protein Trafficking, and Developmental Domains

In addition to facilitating the cell-to-cell exchange of metabolites and ions, PD provide a pathway for the trafficking of macromolecules, including proteins and RNA. Proteins that move through PD are defined as non-cell-autonomous proteins (NCAPs); RNA is thought to traffic cell to cell as a ribonucleotide-protein complex (RNP). It is now well established that the local movement of NCAPs and RNPs can contribute to the establishment of cell fate and patterning in plant tissues (43, 59, 60, 77, 94, 106, 107, 132).

As this PD property is important to an understanding of how and why macromolecules are trafficked through the phloem, we will first describe an elegant illustration of this concept derived from studies on *Arabidopsis* root development. Endodermal cell fate is controlled by SHR, a putative transcription factor expressed only in the stele (107). Studies on transgenic plants expressing P_{SHR}:SHR-GFP revealed the presence of a strong fluorescent signal in the nuclei of endodermal initials, identifying it as an NCAP. As SHR-GFP did not move through PD connecting endodermal and cortical cells, it represents an excellent case of controlled NCAP trafficking, across a single cell boundary that is essential for the orchestration of cell fate (43, 107). An ever-increasing number of NCAPs are currently being shown to participate in tissue/organ development (26, 78, 124). The important question is whether NCAPs or RNPs also function to coordinate and synchronize developmental activities between distantly located organs.

PHLOEM AS A CONDUIT FOR DELIVERY OF MACROMOLECULES

Vascularization and SE-CC Properties

Evolution of the plant vascular system for long-distance delivery of nutrients relieved prior size constraints and opened new opportunities for the colonization of terrestrial habitats. A low-resistance water-conducting conduit, comprised of dead xylem tracheids and vessel elements, provides water and mineral nutrients to aerial parts of the plant. In contrast, photoassimilates (sugars) are transported within nucleate cells of vascular cryptograms and other primitive land plants. The evolutionary trend of these conducting vessels was a progression toward simplification. The nuclei of these conducting cells became reduced in gymnosperms and in angiosperms they are completely degraded, giving rise to enucleate sieve elements (SE) that form a conduit called the sieve tube system. Lacking any apparent capacity for transcription or translation, the angiosperm sieve tube system became dependent on an association with the neighboring companion cells (CCs), which are considered to provide all cellular components required for maintenance and function of the sieve tube system. As such, this obligatory association is best considered as the SE-CC complex (145, 146). A consequence of this operating system is that any macromolecule identified within the sieve tube system was probably delivered through PD from an associated CC (124).

The interconnection of local tissues to the phloem sieve tube system, through PD, established the potential for both local and long-distance macromolecular trafficking. The central question, therefore, is whether the phloem developed solely to deliver photoassimilate to heterotrophic regions of the plant, or did information molecules also become transported, in parallel, as a component of a more sophisticated control system for coordination of plant processes? The latter would allow plants to operate as unique integrated supracellular organisms.

Whole-Plant Function

Plant growth and development is the execution of genetic programs conditioned by environmental inputs. These inputs include both biotic events, for instance pathogen attack or herbivory, and abiotic, such as seasonal variation in temperature, day length, water status, and nutrient availability, etc. (**Figure 1c**). This plasticity is an adaptive response to ensure the best possible chance of completing the plant life cycle. The implication, therefore, is that meristimatic regions act in concert with environmental inputs. The question then arises as to how the SAM (plus other meristematic tissues) detects these environmental inputs to respond with an optimal pattern of growth and development.

It is important to note that, generally, the SAM is protected within a modified environment formed by ensheathing developing lateral organs (**Figure 1d**). Such an environment prevents the SAM from directly detecting variation in some inputs, e.g., ambient relative humidity, CO_2 levels, fluctuations in light intensity/wavelength and day length. Plants appear to have resolved this situation by evolving a sophisticated system that perceives environmental inputs in distant tissues and translates them into signals that are then communicated to, and acted upon, by the SAM and other meristematic regions. Ample experimental evidence exists to support this whole-plant signaling/integration hypothesis (15, 21, 41, 56, 115, 141); however, until recently, little information was available as to whether macromolecular constituents were involved in this long-distance signaling network.

ENDOGENOUS MACROMOLECULES ON THE MOVE

Phloem Proteins

Analysis of phloem exudates, principally collected from cucurbits (9, 50, 51), *Ricinus* (128),

and lupin (97), has revealed a complex population of NCAPs present in the phloem of plants. Convenient collection of milliliter quantities of phloem sap makes the cucurbits an excellent model for the analysis of phloem function. The presence of contaminating material both from the cut surface and CC contents can be excluded based on a number of findings. First, grafted plant systems utilizing taxonomically diverse rootstocks (base) and scions (grafted tissue) have been used to examine the translocation of phloem-mobile molecules, including proteins (50, 51). Detection of pumpkin stock-derived phloem sap proteins, following direct analysis of cucumber scion sieve tube contents, confirms that these molecules are mobile across a graft union (50) and, thus, are bona fide constituents of the phloem sap. Additionally, the association between the holoparasite *Cascuta reflexa* and *Nicotiana tabacum* established that macromolecular trafficking also occurs across a naturally formed graft union (57).

The diversity of proteins identified in the phloem translocation stream implicates them in a wide variety of functions. Structural components include phloem protein 1 (PP1) and phloem protein 2 (PP2) (51) that function to block damaged sieve tubes in a calcium-dependent manner (81). A complete antioxidant defense system, including thioredoxin-h, cytosolic Cu/Zn superoxide dismutase, monodehydroascobate, and peroxidase, probably operates as a protective system against reactive oxygen species (66, 155). A functional cytoskeleton system is suggested by the presence of profilin and actin in the translocation stream (128). The extensive array of proteinase inhibitors may well reflect a defense mechanism to counter probing insects (54, 166). These proteinase inhibitors may also function to protect NCAPs against proteolysis during long-distance trafficking to their target tissues, or function to regulate peptide NCAP maturation from protein precursors. The molecular chaperone, CmHsc70, may function to assist delivery of protein "cargo" into the sieve tube system (4). Finally, the

Supracellular organisms: tissues of these complex organisms consist of populations of cells, but most cells are interconnected by plasmodesmata to their nearest neighbors. As the phloem interconnects all symplasmic domains within the body of the plant, such a system of organization works above the level of the cell, hence the term supracellular

Graft union: plant tissues from a given species, termed a scion, can be transferred to the body of a different species, termed the stock, and if they are compatible the vascular tissues will form a functional graft union to allow the exchange of water and photosynthate

presence of a number of RNA-binding proteins, including CmPP16-1, CmPP16-2, and CmPSRP1, provide a foundation for protein components functioning within an RNA-based communication network (74, 163, 167).

If the phloem operates as a conduit for long-distance communication of macromolecules, then clearly this system would have evolved mechanisms for controlling NCAP/RNP entry into and exit from the sieve tubes. Evidence for the operation of such a system is afforded by studies on CmPP36 (162). For this phloem-mobile protein, the N terminus contains a predicted plasma membrane-anchoring domain and, following its cleavage, the processed form of the protein enters and moves within the phloem translocation stream. Interestingly, this ΔN-CmPP36 may maintain Fe within the phloem sap in a reduced state, in order to ensure the efficient delivery of this essential mineral nutrient to sink tissues.

Reminiscent of motifs directing nuclear targeting (134), proteins may similarly engage an NCAP pathway for efficient entry into the sieve tube system. Support for this hypothesis was obtained by detection of a sequence motif present within the C terminus of the phloem-mobile CmHsc70. Function of this motif was proven in gain-of-movement experiments in which a human Hsp70 acquired the capacity to be translocated through PD (4). Interestingly, an endoplasmic reticulum-bound NCAP pathway protein (NtNCAPP1) has the capacity to interact with some 30% of the pumpkin phloem sap proteins (89). Transgenic plants expressing an engineered dominant negative form of NCAPP1, lacking the N-terminal membrane-anchoring domain, displayed developmental changes probably reflecting selective blockage to the cell-to-cell trafficking of specific NCAPs. Collectively, these experiments support the hypothesis that protein targeting to the sieve tube system occurs by a selective, regulated mechanism (**Figure 2a**).

A selective mode of protein translocation through the sieve tube system is fur-ther illustrated by the differential movement of the NCAP, CmPP16-1, to the roots (5). Stylectomy-assisted introduction of labeled proteins was performed directly into the rice sieve tube system. Biotin-labeled probes, including the NCAPs, CmPP16-1, and CmPP16-2, were introduced directly into a SE and their subsequent translocation was monitored to distant leaf and root tissues. Relative accumulation of CmPP16-1 and CmPP16-2 was measured using a very sensitive biotin detection method. Based on these studies, it would appear that mass flow could account for the observed translocation of CmPP16-1 and CmPP16-2 to leaf tissues. However, movement to the roots seemed to involve an additional selective process resulting in preferential translocation of CmPP16-1. This property was abolished if CmPP16-1 was chromatographically purified from the other phloem sap proteins prior to its reintroduction into the sieve tube system. Interestingly, reconstitution experiments, involving CmPP16-1 and specific pumpkin phloem sap fractions, restored this selective delivery of CmPP16-1 to the roots. Immunoprecipitation experiments identified the molecular constituents associated with a CmPP16-1 complex and it will be of great interest to learn whether these proteins underlie the observed process of selective translocation to a specific sink organ.

Unregulated, diffusion-based movement across the companion cell–sieve element complex (CC-SE) PD also accounts for a proportion of proteins that enter the sieve tube system. Perhaps the best example illustrating this principle is derived from studies performed on plants in which *GFP* expression was controlled by a CC-specific promoter (65, 114). This small, cylindrical heterologous 27-kDa protein was detected in the SE and was carried in the translocation stream to sink tissues. Similar experiments involving CC expression of GFP-fusion proteins suggested that the diffusion-based molecular size exclusion limit for CC-SE PD was on the order of 50 kDa (114). Aphid stylectomy-assisted introduction of variously sized fluorescent probes, into wheat grains, provided further support that CC-SE PD permit diffusion-based unloading (40).

Post-phloem diffusion of GFP has been used to examine properties of the symplasmic pathway for the movement of nutrients and macromolecules. As GFP is not of plant origin it is unlikely to enter a selective translocation pathway. It is important to note that similar experiments based on CC-mediated expression of GFP indicate post-phloem transport and symplasmic domain establishment in the root apical meristem (136) and in cortical tissues destined to develop as root nodules (28). Collectively, these studies support the notion that some proteins can co-diffuse through CC-SE PD that are actively engaged in selective NCAP trafficking. In this case, protein diffusion is probably made possible by the increase in PD size exclusion limit(s) that takes place during selective NCAP trafficking (**Figure 2b**). A molecular mechanism may also operate to gate the CC-SE PD for the sole purpose of facilitating protein exchange by simple diffusion (94). It will be interesting to learn the relative importance of these two pathways on overall protein exchange within the phloem long-distance communication pathway.

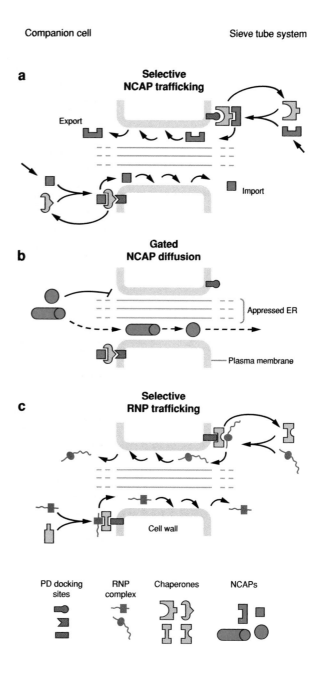

Figure 2

Potential mechanisms for the cell-to-cell trafficking of macromolecules through plasmodesmata. (*a*) Selective delivery of non-cell-autonomous proteins (NCAPs) to specific plasmodesmata (PD) docking sites is mediated by chaperones. Docking of the NCAP-chaperone complex induces dilation in a PD microchannel that allows NCAP translocation along the length of the PD. Mutations within the NCAP can prevent formation of the NCAP-chaperone complex, thereby inhibiting delivery to and/or trafficking through the PD. The model illustrates NCAP import into and export from the sieve tube system. (*b*) Dilated PD microchannels can act as a size-exclusion limit barrier to NCAP diffusion. Mutations within NCAPs that move in this manner are not expected to affect their capacity for movement. (*c*) In a process analogous to (*a*), cell-to-cell trafficking of RNA molecules into and out of the sieve tube system is mediated by RNA binding proteins in conjunction with specific chaperones. Mutations in the RNA may affect delivery to and/or translocation through PD.

Phloem mRNA and small RNA

The certainty that RNA transcripts and small RNA are present, mobile in the phloem, and likely function as information macromolecules is one of the most exciting new prospects in plant biology. Building on the foundation that mRNA encoding the plant transcription factor, *KNOTTED-1*, and many plant viruses can move between cells through PD (20, 46, 91), RNA localization experiments revealed that *SUCROSE TRANSPORTER-1 (SUT1)* RNA was present within the SE-CC complex (85). Numerous other transcripts, including transcriptional regulators, genes controlling cell fate, the cell cycle, phytohormone response, and metabolic genes were subsequently identified in the pumpkin and tomato sieve tube systems (60, 77, 125). Confirmation that these representative transcripts were phloem mobile was gained from grafting studies and RT-PCR analysis, using gene-specific primers. Additional studies based on rice (127) and barley (36) indicate that these results may well have general applicability to higher plants, at least for the angiosperms. Indeed, this mobile population of mRNA species may be quite extensive with >1500 transcripts already identified from the phloem of cucurbits (W.J. Lucas & T.J. Lough, unpublished data). The presence of these transcripts supports the notion that RNA-based signaling networks may function to control many plant processes (27, 59, 73, 74, 95, 161).

Selective translocation of RNA, via the sieve tube system, is indicated by differential localization of RNA transcripts in apical tissues and the presence of RNA-binding proteins in the phloem. Heterografted plants were once again employed to reveal that pumpkin stock–derived *CmNACP* transcripts were present in the cucumber scion meristem (125). Selectivity was confirmed by differential detection of other phloem-derived transcripts in apical tissues of the cucumber scion. A population of RNA-binding proteins, present in the phloem, suggests formation

and regulated movement of RNP complexes. The pumpkin CmPP16-1, immunologically related to movement proteins of viruses, binds mRNA, enters the sieve tube system, and translocates long distance (163). Identification of both RNA-binding proteins and cognate RNA in the phloem (52, 167) attests to the existence of numerous RNPs most likely functioning as information molecules within an RNA-based network (**Figure 2c**).

Micro (mi)RNA-mediated regulation of gene expression has been identified in both plants and animals and is currently an area of intense research activity (12, 30). A diverse and dynamic population of small RNA (19–25 nucleotides), present in phloem sap of cucurbits, *Ricinus*, *Yucca*, and lupin, suggests a potential long-distance signaling role for small RNA (167). This small RNA population includes known miRNA species, siRNA reflecting virus infection, transposon challenge, and other classes of small RNA of undefined function. The potential role played by these molecules, in response to pathogen attack, is considered in a later section.

EXOGENOUS MACROMOLECULES: HITCHING A RIDE

Viroids

A phloem-based RNA signaling network presupposes that mechanisms evolved to regulate the entry and exit of specific transcripts. Insight into the operation of such a system has been gained through studies on exogenous RNA molecules, acting as pathogenic RNAs, including both viroids and RNA viruses. Each viral RNA system recognizes the host's machinery to support replication, cell-to-cell movement, and systemic spread via the phloem (153). As viroids do not encode any proteins, they must rely on host cellular factors for all required functions of replication and movement. *Potato spindle tuber viroid* (PSTVd) has been utilized to examine the regulation of RNA trafficking in the phloem (121, 169, 170). In this study, tobacco was used for the serial maintenance of a poorly accumulating strain, PSTVd^{NT}. After a number of passages, these workers isolated a new strain, PSTVd^{NB}, that could accumulate to a much higher level when reinoculated onto tobacco. Equivalent replication levels in protoplasts suggested that relative accumulation levels might well reflect differences in the capacity of these two viroid strains to invade specific tissues.

Specific RNA sequence motifs, or zip codes, can direct the interaction with cellular factors to regulate targeted delivery of RNA (71). Evidence that such a system acts at the level of the PD has been gained through experiments in which a CC-specific promoter was used to express infectious PSTVd strains in transgenic tobacco lines. Detailed in situ RNA localization experiments performed on these lines demonstrated that the poorly accumulating strain, PSTVd^{NT}, lacked the capacity to move beyond phloem tissues. In contrast, the new mutant strain, PSTVd^{NB}, was detected in phloem, bundle sheath, and mesophyll cells. Clearly, the nucleotide changes present in the PSTVd^{NB} genome permit its viroid RNA to pass through the bundle sheath to enter the mesophyll tissues (121).

Additional insight into the presence of an endogenous mechanism aimed at regulating cell-to-cell trafficking of RNA was also provided by experiments in which both viroid strains were mechanically inoculated onto mature (source) tobacco leaves. Quite unexpectedly, both strains were capable of replicating in and moving cell-to-cell through mesophyll, bundle sheath, and phloem cells (121). This finding provided strong support for the notion that bundle sheath-mesophyll PD function as a rectifier to regulate viroid RNA movement. Mutagenesis experiments defined a bipartite motif, comprising 4 separate nucleotide changes, that was necessary and sufficient to regulate unidirectional trafficking of PSTVd. This elegant study identified what may be the first zip code essential for RNA delivery to and/or movement through PD.

Examination of the tissue-specific patterns of viroid RNA accumulation in sink organs indicated that developmental programs could influence cell-to-cell movement of macromolecules. The bundle sheath-mesophyll PD of younger (sink) but not older (source) leaves acted as a barrier for RNA trafficking (121). In addition, PSTVd was able to enter some, but not all, sink tissues (169), suggesting that simple mass flow alone does not control systemic movement. Rather, some form of selectivity appears to dictate the delivery of viroid RNA into certain sink tissues/organs. These features of viroid RNA trafficking are therefore distinct, and studies of this nature provide important insights into the dynamic capacity of plants to regulate the movement of RNA out of the phloem into surrounding tissues.

RNA Viruses

In contrast to viroids, RNA viruses encode proteins required for replication and movement. These so-called movement proteins (MPs) (93, 153) function in a manner analogous to NCAPs (89, 94), and interact with host components of the cell-to-cell translocation pathway (84). Numerous studies have demonstrated that MPs bind viral RNA, potentiate dilation of PD, and facilitate translocation of the viral RNA-MP complex to the adjacent cells (59). Transported forms of viral RNA include both virions and RNPs (46). Support for translocation of viral RNPs, both cell-to-cell and long-distance, via the phloem, is derived from analysis of plant RNA viruses that lack a functional coat protein gene (88). In these instances, viral RNA movement must be in the form of an RNP complex. An immunological relationship between CmPP16 and the MP of *Red clover necrotic mosaic virus* suggests not only functional but also distant evolutionary origins (163). This observation reinforces the premise that plant viruses can be used as powerful genetic tools to further

MP: movement protein

explore the mechanisms controlling endogenous RNA-based signaling systems.

It is generally accepted that the majority of plant viral MPs function in cell-to-
cell movement of the infectious nucleic acids
in the absence of a requirement for cognate viral sequence recognition (44). This
assertion is based on experiments including the functional rescue of RNA movement when the MP was expressed, in *cis*, in
the context of a hybrid viral genome (32,
45), or in *trans*, using transgenic plants or
cobombardment experiments (29, 101). However, reminiscent of regulated unidirectional
translocation of viroid RNA, a number of
viral systems are restricted in their movement by a defined cellular boundary. Many
phloem-limited viruses cannot traffic from
phloem parenchyma into the bundle sheath,
whereas other viruses that are unable to enter
the phloem generally cannot move from the
bundle sheath into the phloem parenchyma.
This phloem parenchyma-bundle sheath PD
boundary, which is distinct from that operating to control viroid translocation, acts as a
checkpoint for entry into and exit from the
SE-CC. Hence, the possibility exists that this
cellular boundary, within the host plant, may
require some degree of additional cognate
protein-RNA specificity to permit cell-to-cell
transport of RNA. Indeed, such a requirement
may explain why for some viruses, including
Tobacco mosaic virus and *Red clover necrotic mosaic virus*, entry into the plant vascular system
requires both the MP and capsid protein (CP)
(35, 126, 144).

Biochemical, genetic, and yeast two
hybrid-based studies have identified a number of plant genes that play a role in virus
long-distance movement (23–25, 96, 143,
158, 159). The pectin methylesterase (PME)
and cadmium-ion-induced glycine-rich protein (cdiGRP) are of special interest, as they
have been suggested to function in virus exit
from the phloem (23, 24, 143). As both PME
and cdiGRP are expressed in phloem tissues
and appear to be localized to the cell walls, the
manner in which these proteins might influ-

ence viral RNA trafficking remains obscure.
However, because cdiGRP increased callose
deposits in the phloem (143), and callose is deposited around PD (109), its mode of action
might be to limit the capacity of PD to undergo an increase in SEL; this could block the
movement of viral RNA from the phloem into
the surrounding tissues, thereby preventing
systemic spread (153). The challenge ahead
will be to discover why cdiGRP only caused a
virus-specific block to systemic movement in
tobacco.

WHOLE-PLANT SIGNALING

Flowering & Florigen

The holy grail of plant biology is the identification of the phloem-mobile stimulus
involved in floral induction. This vegetative-
to-floral transition is induced by environmental cues, with day length considered the
most important. This cue is perceived in the
mature leaves and a signal is transported in
the phloem translocation stream to the shoot
apex. Pioneering work by Chailakhyan defined this substance(s) as florigen, on the basis
that a graft-transmissible substance could induce flowering in a scion being maintained
under a noninductive photoperiod (21). Symplasmic tracers have shown that the onset of
the floral transition is highly correlated with a
transitory decrease in symplasmic connectivity between the apex and the terminal phloem,
consistent with a major change in the selectivity of communication between the body of
the plant and the vegetative meristem (47, 48).
Numerous substances, including gibberellins
(79), sucrose (14), cytokinin (70), and peptides (64), have been advanced as the florigenic
stimulus, but to date formal proof is lacking.

Molecular genetic approaches have revealed four different pathways involved in
controlling flowering time in *Arabidopsis* (13,
102). Two pathways are responsive to environmental cues, namely photoperiod and vernalization; there is also an autonomous pathway
that promotes flowering under all conditions

and, finally, a gibberellin pathway that is required to promote flowering under short-day conditions (102). Key elements involved in integrating the input signal(s) from the photoperiodic pathway are the zinc-finger protein, CONSTANS (CO) (120), and the raf-1 kinase inhibitor (RKIP)-like protein, FLOWERING LOCUS T (FT) (75, 82). Promoter GUS analyses have revealed vascular- rather than meristem-specific expression patterns for both genes, findings consistent with signaling roles for both CO and FT in floral induction (3, 138).

A signaling role for CO was confirmed using tissue-specific promoters in which *CO* expression, within CCs located in source leaves, promoted flowering in the *co* mutant background (3). Grafting studies confirmed that CO controls the production of a phloem-borne substance essential for floral induction, i.e., the ever elusive "florigen." Assignment of CO, per se, as florigen could be discounted as CC-specific expression of CO fused to GFP did not reveal a capacity of CO to traffic beyond the cells in which it was transcribed (3, 7). However, this CO-GFP fusion protein was still able to rescue flowering in the *co* mutant background.

A high probability exists that FT and/or *FT* mRNA are components of the phloem-mobile florigenic signal. Parallel experiments using tissue-specific promoters revealed a capacity for FT to promote flowering, not only through expression in CCs, but also in numerous other tissues, including those of the meristem. As activation of *FT* expression is, in itself, controlled by CO and is required to promote flowering, these results once again underscore the importance of long-distance signaling through the phloem. The capacity to induce flowering and its relatively small size make FT a good candidate as a component of the phloem-mobile stimulus.

Support for such a model is provided by the capacity of FT to induce flowering when present in cell types beyond the vasculature (3, 138). Protein-protein interactions involving (non-) phosphorylated forms of the human *FT* ortholog, RKIP, modulate outputs from the MAPK, GRK-2, and NF*k*B signaling pathways (110, 164, 165). Yeast two-hybrid studies utilizing a tomato FT homolog, *SELF PRUNING* (SP), have identified interacting proteins including a kinase (SPAK) and a G-box transcription factor (117). Taken together, these data are consistent with a model in which FT/*FT* mRNA controls floral induction by manipulating kinase signaling cascades or transcriptional events in cells associated with the phloem.

The demonstration that FT/*FT* mRNA has the capacity to traffic cell to cell, and move long-distance via the phloem, has been keenly anticipated. Indirect evidence that *FT* mRNA can move from mature (source) leaves to the SAM is provided by studies on transgenic Arabidopsis lines expressing *FT* driven by a heat shock promoter (64a). Application of a heat shock stimulus to a single source leaf induced accumulation of the transgene *FT* mRNA in both the source leaf and the shoot apex. The time course of *FT* mRNA accumulation was highly correlated with the triggering of floral induction in the apex. Importantly, delivery of the "florigenic" signal into the shoot apex causes endogenous *FT* mRNA to increase, suggestive of a positive autoregulatory loop in the "florigen" signaling pathway whereby FT, directly or indirectly, controls its own expression. It remains to be established whether FT also moves to the apex through the phloem (64a). It could well be that de novo synthesis of FT in the terminal protophloem, from the imported mRNA, initiates the signaling relay that propagates from this region of the apex to the SAM (**Figure 3**). How FT/*FT* mRNA navigates its way through the intervening tissues to enter a specific subset of cells which then give rise to the floral meristem remains a challenge for the future.

Tuberization and Tuberigen

Short-day photoperiodic induction and graft transmissibility of a signal leading to potato tuber formation indicate that parallels exist

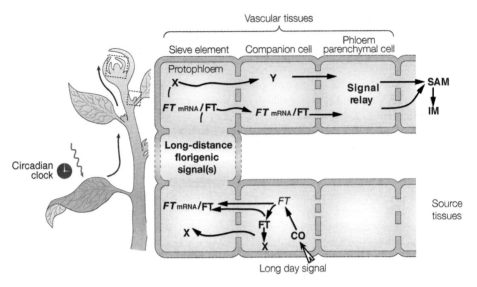

Figure 3

Photoperiodic control over floral induction requires phloem-mediated delivery of florigenic signal(s). *CONSTANS* (*CO*) expression is under photoperiodic control and occurs in the companion cells (CCs) of source leaves where it activates *FLOWERING LOCUS T* (*FT*) expression (3, 7, 138). FT and/or *FT* mRNA may serve as the florigenic stimulus that controls the shoot apical meristem (SAM) to inflorescence meristem (IM) transition (64a). Also, FT may exert control over floral induction through a kinase signaling cascade and/or a transcriptional event within the CCs that regulates entry into the phloem of an as yet unidentified molecule (X). Changes in the population of miRNA molecules, which move in the phloem (167), may serve as one component of the X → Y signal relay. One species, miR159, moves through the cucurbit phloem (167) and exerts an effect on flowering time in *Arabidopsis* (1). Alternatively, FT may serve as the signal relay through upregulation of its own expression. Arrival of FT into specific target cells of the SAM allows an interaction with a bZIP protein, FD, that triggers IM formation and initiates organ development by transcriptional activation of *APETALA1*, a floral meristem identity gene (1a, 159a).

between tuber and floral initiation (68, 118). (Note that the tuber forms at the tip of each stolon, a specialized underground stem.) Downregulation of *PhyB* impairs photoperiod perception leading to constitutive tuber formation under noninductive long-day conditions; this finding is consistent with the involvement of the photoperiodic pathway (69). Furthermore, transgenic potato plants expressing *CO* exhibit strong suppression of photoperiodic tuber induction (98). This finding is similar to the situation in the short-day plant, rice, where high levels of Hd1 (CO homolog) also suppress floral induction (58).

As with floral induction, grafting studies have shown that the tuberizing signal, termed "tuberigen," is derived from the leaves and is transported within the long-distance translocation stream (98). Experiments in which transgenic *CO*-expressing potato scions were grafted onto wild-type potato stocks resulted in a significant delay in tuber initiation in the stocks, even when plants were grown under short-day conditions. (Note that, in these studies, the scion functioned as the source of photosynthate being translocated down the plant axis to the underground stolons.) These studies confirmed that *CO* acts in the vegetative tissues and is upstream of tuberigen production. That florigen and tuberigen are components of the same signal is highlighted by tuber induction in potato-stock tissue following grafting onto photoperiodically induced tobacco scions (68). In view of the recent progress made in our understanding of the role played by the plant vasculature system in photoperiodic control of flowering, it is highly likely that ectopic expression of *CO*, under a CC-specific promoter, will result in the suppression of tuber initiation. Results of this nature would further confirm the central role of the phloem in long-distance signaling to exert photoperiodic control over tuber induction.

Resource Allocation

Do plants measure environmental inputs, allocate resources, and respond as a whole-plant system? Validation that such a signaling network operates in plants was provided by the action of mature leaves sensing environmental inputs that then influenced the characteristics of newly forming leaves (76, 87, 139). Exposing mature *Arabidopsis* leaves to either elevated CO_2 or shade conditions, while allowing newly formed leaves to develop in ambient conditions, resulted in a decrease in stomatal density compared to control plants. Reciprocal experiments confirmed the existence of systemic signals influencing leaf characteristics, such as stomatal pore length, density, epidermal cell shape, and developing leaf size (87, 139). The existence of such signals has appeal, as this offers an explanation as to how the SAM, ensheathed by antecedent leaf primordia, and therefore unable to monitor accurately ambient light and CO_2 levels, is able to produce leaves with optimal characteristics for the environment into which they will eventually emerge.

Acclimation of mature leaves to environmental conditions also appears to involve the operation of a signaling network that integrates carbon resources at the whole-plant level. Clear evidence for such a system was provided by experiments conducted on soybean plants in which individual, attached leaves were exposed to elevated CO_2 conditions (135). Rubisco levels and rates of CO_2 fixation within these leaves reflected those observed for the rest of the leaves that were exposed to ambient CO_2 levels. In the reverse situation, where individual leaves were provided ambient CO_2 levels while the rest of the soybean plant was exposed to elevated CO_2 conditions, the photosynthetic properties of the individual leaves were the same as those measured for leaves exposed to high CO_2 conditions! Although these findings implicate long-distance signaling through the phloem, the nature of the signaling molecules remains to be elucidated.

Manipulation of PD and the long-distance signaling pathway can influence carbon partitioning in plants. Expression of the TMV MP in tobacco source leaves leads to elevated levels of starch and sugars and a decrease in sugar export during the photoperiod compared to control plants (111). At the whole-plant level, expression of TMV MP causes a dramatic shift in the root-to-shoot ratio, with an ~50% decrease in root biomass in the TMV MP transgenic lines (8). Grafting experiments demonstrated that transgenic scion tissues, expressing TMV MP, induced the same change in root-to-shoot ratio when grafted onto wild-type tobacco rootstocks (8).

Involvement of the SE-CC is indicated by tissue-specific expression of TMV MP in potato, using the phloem-specific *rolC* promoter. In these transgenic potato lines, source leaves displayed elevated sugar/biomass accumulation and a concomitant reduction in the root-to-shoot dry-weight ratio (2). Of particular note is the finding that when these TMV MP transgenic potato lines were grown under short-day (tuber-inducing) conditions, tubers displayed higher dry matter partitioning (increased harvest index) as compared with control lines. Interestingly, tuber initiation is correlated with a shift from an apoplasmic to a symplasmic pathway for phloem unloading (149). It would be intriguing to learn if the observed influence of TMV MP over carbon partitioning to the tuber were due to the promotion of an endogenous long-distance signal that regulates PD properties in the tuber tissues to increase the import of photoassimilates. In any event, these changes in photoassimilate partitioning further support the notion that NCAPs, like the TMV MP, can exert long-distance effects over carbon allocation.

Expression of a pathogenesis-related maize gene, *PRms*, results in profound physiological changes to the plant. Immunolocalization and in situ hybridization studies established that PRms is an NCAP, as it was detected within PD and traffics cell to cell through parenchyma cells of the vascular cylinder, a cell type not actively transcribing *PRms* (103). Ectopic expression of *PRms*, with the *CaMV35S* promoter, resulted in a 20-fold increase in sugar export from the petiole of transgenic tobacco source leaves and an accelerated growth rate (104). Support for the notion that the phloem plays a role in these PRms-induced changes in photoassimilate partitioning was provided by the fact that PRms was detected within the CC-SE PD, in the phloem translocation stream, and in wild-type scions grafted onto *PRms* transgenic tobacco stocks (16). Elucidation of the mechanism by which PRms causes these changes in the regulation of resource allocation/growth rate, at the whole-plant level, will likely yield further insights into the operation of long-distance signaling as well as provide a means to genetically engineer plant productivity.

Nutrient Signaling

Shoots exercise regulatory control over the nitrogen acquisition activity of the root system by a feedback mechanism involving root-shoot (xylem-phloem) communication. Plants respond locally to differences in nitrogen availability by increased levels of nitrate uptake and lateral root proliferation. Split-root experiments demonstrate that regulation of this process involves not only local but also long-distance signaling. In such studies, different parts of the root mass are exposed to either high or low nitrate levels. Consistent with a whole-plant response, nitrate starvation in one part of the root is compensated for

by increased uptake from another root zone (19, 41).

The rhizobia-legume symbiotic system provides further evidence for the operation of whole-plant signaling over nodule primordia proliferation. Split-root experiments, in which nitrogen was supplied to only one part of the root biomass, clearly demonstrated an inhibition to the proliferation of nodule primordia on the untreated roots (19). The molecular components regulating this phenomenon, autoregulation of nodulation (AON), are now under intensive investigation. Soybean mutants, defective in AON, supernodulated and have increased numbers of lateral root hairs. Reciprocal grafting experiments involving these mutants and wild-type genotypes revealed that it is the leaf genotype that exerts control over the proliferation of nodule primordia. Map-based cloning led to the identification of a CLAVATA1-like gene, called *Glycine max NODULE AUTOREGULATION RECEPTOR KINASE* (*GmNARK*). As CLV1 functions as a receptor in a receptor-ligand (CLV3)-mediated signaling cascade in the *Arabidopsis* SAM (33), this homology suggests a regulatory system involving a small extracellular (xylem-mobile) ligand, sent by the root and recognized by GmNARK in the shoot.

This xylem long-distance signaling system (root-to-shoot) would function to promote phloem-mobile signals that exercise homeostatic control over nodule meristem proliferation (130). Thus, in the presence of adequate inorganic nitrogen, the xylem-borne signal would be perceived by GmNARK, which would then activate a phloem-mobile signal(s) to downregulate nodule primordia proliferation in the roots (**Figure 4**). A central role for the SE-CC in this regulatory circuit awaits the demonstration that CC-specific expression of GmNARK restores AON in a soybean null mutant background. The possibility that the SE-CC plays a more significant role in both development of the nodule primordia and integration of nodule function on whole-plant

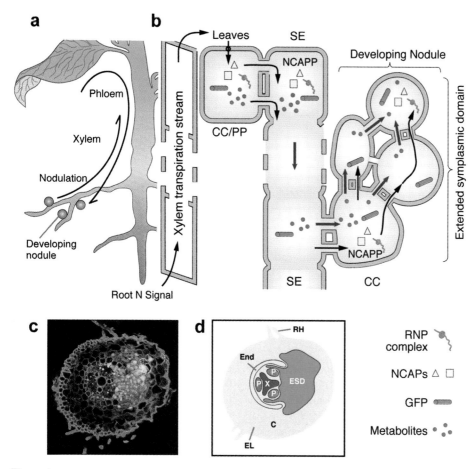

a

Phloem

Xylem

Nodulation

Developing
nodule

Root N Signal

b

Leaves

SE

NCAPP

CC/PP

Xylem transpiration stream

Developing Nodule

NCAPP

SE   CC

Extended symplasmic domain

c

d

RH

End

P
P X ESD
P

C

EL

RNP
complex

NCAPs △ □

GFP

Metabolites

Figure 4

Xylem-phloem communication network: control over nitrogen fixation in the root system of the plant. (*a*) Plants use their vascular system to exchange information on the status of mineral nutrient acquisition by the root system and the growth requirements of the vegetative organs. (*b*) A symbiotic relationship with bacteria fixes N_2 into organic nitrogen; this process occurs in the roots in special structures called nodules (129). Coordination between nodulation and nitrogen demand for growth involves signal perception by a receptor kinase (GmNARK), located in the leaves (130), and phloem delivery of a feedback signal that exerts control over nodule development. One facet of this signaling system controls the formation of special symplasmic fields of cells that contain the nodule initials (28). (*c*) Transverse section of a nodule primordium from a *Medicago truncatula* root system inoculated with *Rhizobium*. Green fluorescence represents the cell-to-cell movement of green fluorescent protein (GFP) from the sieve tube system into all cells involved in the formation of the nodule primordium. GFP was produced in source tissues using a companion cell (CC)-specific promoter. Image reproduced from Reference 28, with permission. (*d*) Schematic illustration of the symplasmic field identified by the entry of GFP from the phloem translocation stream. Abbreviations are as follows: C, cortex; EL, epidermal layer; End, endodermis; ESD, extended symplasmic domain; P, phloem; RH, root hair; X, xylem.

physiology is indicated by the establishment of a new symplasmic domain in cells destined to become the nodule meristem (28).

What is the identity of the phloem-mobile regulators that control nutrient sig-

naling? The identification of small interfering (si)RNA and micro (mi)RNA in the phloem (167) is consistent with their involvement in the integration of whole-plant growth and development. In this regard, the phloem-mobile

Me: *Mouse ears*
mutant in tomato

GAI/gai: wild-type
and mutant form of
the GIBBERELLIC
ACID
INSENSITIVE
gene

miR395, predicted to target ATP sulphory-lases (APS1, APS3 and APS4) (72), is potentially one such phloem-borne molecular regulator that acts within the whole-plant nutritional control system. APS activity is the first step leading to sulfate assimilation in the root. Accumulation of miR395 is influenced by SO_4^{2-} availability in the media to which the roots are exposed. In addition, miR395 levels are inversely proportional to the level of the target APS transcripts (72). Thus, the implication is that a shoot-derived and phloem-borne signal, miR395, regulates SO_4^{2-} uptake by modifying the level of APS expression. Experimental proof of this hypothesis would be the first demonstration of systemic control of a biological process by an miRNA mobile in the phloem translocation stream.

Leaf Architecture

Recent studies implicate a phloem long-distance RNA-based information network in the control over leaf shape. Such a system may explain, at least in part, the plasticity in leaf shape exhibited by plants. Graft transmissibility of tomato *Mouse ears* (*Me*) transcripts [*PFP-LeT6* fusion transcripts (22)] into wild-type scions was highly correlated with the appearance of the *Me* leaf developmental phenotype (77). Both the localization of *Me* transcripts, within the wild-type scion SAM, and the phenotype of the developing leaves reflect a property of the transcript to be translocated from stock to scion, through the phloem and post-phloem transport to the SAM.

A detailed analysis of *GIBBERELLIC ACID INSENSITIVE* (*GAI*) in pumpkin and tomato revealed similar functional properties of these phloem-mobile transcripts on leaf shape (60). GAI is an important negative regulator of GA signaling (116) and, thus, because GA influences a range of plant processes (122), long-distance translocation of *GAI* mRNA may fine-tune processes taking place in mature and developing organs.

Recessive loss-of-function *gai* alleles exhibit dark-green dwarfed phenotypes (83). Gain-of-function alleles, carrying mutations within the DELLA domain that is required for GA perception, result in a semidominant dwarf phenotype (116). Both *gai*-associated developmental phenotypes and transcript localization data, revealing a capacity of *Cm-GAIP* transcripts to traffic from the SE-CC into the meristem (125), implicated *GAI* as a regulator of developmental processes operating through the long-distance communication pathway. Heterologous expression of an engineered gain-of-function form of *Cm-GAIP*, carrying a mutated *DELLA* domain ($\Delta DELLA$-*gai*), induced leaf-shape phenotypes in tomato and *Arabidopsis*. Parallel grafting experiments in both plant systems revealed that the $\Delta DELLA$-*gai* transcripts had the capacity to traffic across the graft union and induce pronounced changes in leaf development. Interestingly, these phenotypes were restricted to sink regions of newly formed leaves on the scion; continued scion growth led to the restoration of wild-type leaves. This phenomenon likely reflects the influence of endogenous tomato *GAI* transcripts whose entry into the scion phloem translocation stream would dilute the influence of the stock-derived $\Delta DELLA$-*gai* transcripts, thereby restoring normal patterns of leaf development.

A developmental influence over the phloem-mediated delivery of $\Delta DELLA$-*gai* transcripts was observed in studies performed with tomato. Careful analysis of wild-type scions, grafted onto $\Delta DELLA$-*gai* stocks, failed to detect $\Delta DELLA$-*gai* transcripts in developing fruit, whereas transcripts were readily detectable within young leaves located closer to the scion apex. The basis for selectivity is likely associated with an as yet unidentified motif associated with the $\Delta DELLA$-*gai* transcript. Consistent with this notion, control grafting experiments, incorporating either *CaMV-35S*- or *Suc2*-mediated GFP expression, revealed GFP protein but not *GFP* transcripts in scion phloem/tissue. Collectively, these features indicate that, as with CmPP16-1 and PSTVd RNA, Δ*DELLA-gai* mRNA translocation is a property of the transcript itself and that mass flow consideration alone cannot account for the observed selective trafficking within the plant (60).

Pathogen Defense

Systemic response to pathogen attack includes an epigenetic process called post-transcriptional gene silencing (PTGS) that results in sequence-specific degradation of target RNA. Once again, evidence supporting a whole-plant response involves use of grafting techniques. In the seminal works of Palauqui et al. (115), spontaneously silencing plants, activated to target either nitrate reductase or nitrite reductase, when used as a rootstock, efficiently induced PTGS in non-silenced scion tissues. Transmission of the silencing state to the scion was proven by both a marked reduction in transcript accumulation and by the development of chlorosis that is associated with a loss of nitrate or nitrite reductase activity.

In another study, *Agrobacterium*-mediated transient expression was used to activate PTGS in *GFP*-expressing plants (150). Again, the silencing signal was graft transmissible and initiated PTGS in scion tissues. The persistence of fluorescence signal in symplasmically isolated guard cells confirmed a role for PD in translocation of the silencing signal (150). Establishment of PTGS was correlated with the accumulation of 19–25 nucleotide (nt) siRNA (55). The observed sequence specificity of the silencing signal implied the involvement and phloem mobility of an RNA species. Evidence is now accumulating that siRNA comprises a component of this systemic silencing signal.

Direct analysis of phloem sap has been used to test the hypothesis that the systemic silencing signal is carried by small RNA species. As virus infection induces PTGS (156), phloem sap from virus-infected plants was first examined and found to contain homologous ~21 nt siRNA (167). Cloning and sequencing of these siRNA species revealed approximately equal proportions of sense and antisense RNA, consistent with the involvement of double-stranded (ds) siRNA. Transgenic cucurbit lines expressing a viral *CP* provided further confirmation that siRNA moves in the phloem translocation stream. Here, phloem sap derived from spontaneously silencing *CP* lines revealed siRNA homologous to this transgene. Again, both sense and antisense siRNA species were identifiable by Northern blot analysis. However, RNase protection assays failed to identify a double-stranded (ds) siRNA duplex. In any event, these siRNA molecules were mobile across a graft union and, furthermore, their presence was highly correlated with induction of the silenced state within CP transgenic scion tissues.

Consistent with the concept of selective si/miRNA trafficking within an RNA-based information network, microinjection experiments demonstrated that 25 nt siRNA molecules do not move through PD by simple diffusion. Rather, the capacity of siRNA to traffic between cells appears to be mediated by a small RNA-binding protein, CmPSRP1, identified from pumpkin phloem sap. Proteins having similar properties were detected within the phloem sap of cucumber and lupin, consistent with the notion that a similar mechanism operates in all plants. Binding studies revealed that CmPSRP1 has a 1000-fold higher affinity for single-stranded (ss) siRNA over ds siRNA. Furthermore, CmPSRP1 exhibited substrate specificity in that it bound, preferentially, to small RNA molecules in the size range of 20–40 nt. In addition, microinjection experiments indicated that CmPSRP1 only mediates the trafficking of ss siRNA. Collectively, these findings are consistent with ss siRNA acting as the phloem-mobile silencing signal; however, a role for ds siRNA species should not be excluded from further consideration.

Indirect evidence in support of siRNA as the systemic silencing molecule is provided by a number of studies employing different experimental systems. For example, a positive reporter system was developed to reveal tissues in which PTGS had been activated (73, 80). Microprojectile bombardment was used to introduce specific forms of RNA and DNA homologous to the target gene. Double-stranded siRNA, but not sense or antisense ss siRNA, induced effective systemic gene silencing. In another experimental system, utilizing GUS transgenic sunflower, infiltration into the apoplasm of 21–23 nt RNA, isolated from GUS-silenced tissues, efficiently induced systemic silencing of GUS in newly developing leaves located above the point of infiltration (62). Although the mechanism by which these small RNA species may enter the symplasm remains to be elucidated, if applicable to other plants this infiltration method could provide an effective means with which to explore the events underlying systemic silencing.

Virus-encoded counter measures act directly on the capacity of the plant to utilize the systemic silencing signal (37, 119, 123, 151, 152). Systemic transmission of silencing signals is blocked by expression of the *Cucumber mosaic virus* (CMV) 2b gene, a PTGS suppressor, in vascular tissues through which the signal would otherwise be translocated (53). The inhibitory effect of the CMV 2b suggests a need for some form of relay/amplification along the phloem pathway. Use of the ds siRNA-sequestering tombusvirus-derived p19 suppressor of PTGS abolishes both local (63) and systemic PTGS (86). Collectively, these observations confirm the importance of siRNA in PTGS and are consistent with its role as the long-distance signaling agent. Clearly, these viral suppressors of PTGS have proven extremely useful in dissecting the different stages of the amplification and transmission of the PTGS signal.

Exclusion from the meristem of the systemic silencing signal (150), and most viruses

(99), is consistent with the operation of a regulatory component in the RNA-based information superhighway (74). However, such a surveillance system would have to allow for the observed selective translocation of endogenous mRNA into the meristem (60, 77, 125). Support for this hypothesis was provided through ectopic expression of a potexvirus *TGB1* gene that induced a marked change in the establishment of organ polarity; this viral gene gave rise to radially symmetric leaves (42). Expression of the TGB1 in the apex appeared to disarm the plant's surveillance system as a range of viruses were able to penetrate all the way into the SAM. Interestingly, entry of either the potexvirus or a *TGB1*-derived silencing signal into the meristem induced transgene silencing that then restored normal patterns of lateral organ development. Here, as virus entry into the plant meristem was dependent on expression of the *TGB1*, induction of PTGS removed both the transgene and the viral-derived *TGB1*, resulting in oscillating patterns of radially symmetric and normal leaves. These results provide support for the existence of a surveillance field regulating the entry of silencing signals and viral RNA into the meristem (42, 95).

"PHLOEMICS": FUNCTIONAL GENOMICS OF THE PHLOEM

Vascular Genomics

Understanding the molecular basis for the integration of long-distance communication networks will require knowledge of the cognate component parts: Identification of the appropriate genes should assist in the assignment of function. To this end, specialized expressed sequence tag (EST) databases will need to be developed to better define: (*a*) genes specifically expressed within the plant vasculature system, (*b*) mRNA and si/miRNA molecules that are mobile in the phloem, and (*c*) the full complement of proteins that operate in the long-distance signaling pathway.

A full understanding of the plant vasculature must include analysis of xylem function and the role it plays in coordinating whole-plant processes, including growth and development. Xylogenesis (61) and root-shoot feedback systems, controlling branching, nutrient sensing, and resource allocation attest to the importance of a fully integrated approach (15, 18). Recent studies to define the profile of genes active in the vasculature have been based on laser-capture microdissection of phloem-enriched cells from rice and maize (6, 108) and sequence analysis of a cDNA library derived from the "stripped" petiole vascular tissues of celery (148). Macro/microarrays have been employed to better define the slate of vasculature-associated genes. As the number of sequenced plant genomes steadily increases, eventually we will have a solid foundation for a more comprehensive analysis of a wider range of plant vascular systems. An integration of bioinformatics and vascular studies will most surely accelerate progress in this important area of plant biology.

Phloem Transcriptome Contains Both mRNA and Small RNA

Current approaches to defining phloem-mobile transcripts include profiling the mRNA population within the SE-CC complex (6, 17, 67, 148) and direct analysis of transcripts present in the phloem translocation stream (60, 125, 163). The concept of mRNA mobility and an initial characterization of the transcript profile were provided by direct analysis of phloem exudates collected from cucurbits. Based on these studies, the phloem sieve tube transcriptome appears to be comprised of >1500 different mRNA molecules (W.J. Lucas & T.J. Lough, unpublished data), plus many thousands of small RNA species (167).

Insect laser-based stylectomy-assisted extraction of rice phloem sap has been used to obtain limited amounts of mRNA (127).

Other workers have taken a glass microcapillary approach to collect the contents of CCs that were identified by GFP expression driven by a CC-specific promoter. In this case, cellular extracts were not further purified prior to RT-PCR amplification using a range of different primer sets (17). A somewhat similar approach was used to isolate CC protoplasts that were expressing GFP; in this study, RNA was extracted and a cDNA library was constructed to allow the cloning of K^+ transporters (67). Interestingly, stylectomy-based analysis of barley phloem sap revealed the presence of mRNA encoding a number of integral membrane proteins (36); the K^+ transporter, HAKT1, could not be detected, consistent with the hypothesis that the PD interconnecting the CC-SE complex mediate selective trafficking of mRNA.

Given the importance of the CC-SE complex, in both phloem transport of photoassimilates and delivery of macromolecules involved in long-distance signaling, it would seem timely to launch efforts aimed at developing complete transcriptomes for a range of plant species. Laser microdissection techniques performed on plants for which genomes have already been sequenced would probably be the most expedient strategy to adopt. Parallel analyses performed on phloem sap derived using insect stylectomy as well as from natural phloem bleeders, such as lupin, castor bean, and the cucurbits, would also serve as an invaluable resource for the development of the phloem database. In view of the positive attributes of the cucurbits, and the fact that their genome size is similar to that of *Arabidopsis*, a cucurbit-based genome sequencing project would accelerate progress in this emerging frontier.

Phloem Proteome

Direct analysis of phloem sap indicates that the phloem proteome is comprised of more than 1500 species present within the translocation stream of the angiosperms (50, 51, 89,

Phloem
transcriptome: a
database containing
sequence
information for all
RNA species,
including mRNA,
small interfering
(si)RNA, and
micro(mi)RNA,
present within the
sieve tube system

167). Development of the above-mentioned vascular and phloem transcriptomes would underpin identification of these proteins. Here, mass spectrometry approaches would allow for the efficient identification of individual proteins comprising the phloem proteome (10).

Proof of the benefits of this approach is derived from direct analysis of cucumber and pumpkin phloem sap identifying proteins contributing to stress and defense (154) and an antioxidant defense system (50, 51, 155). Comparative proteomics would allow the further identification and characterization of proteins whose entry into the phloem sieve tube system is induced by a range of inputs, including pathogen challenge, nutrient stress, etc. Lastly, this database would greatly facilitate the identification of peptide signaling components that may participate in signaling cascades associated with such processes as flowering control (64) or systemic acquired resistance (147).

FUTURE PERSPECTIVES

Recent progress in our understanding of the processes that act to control macromolecular trafficking through PD have laid the foundation for the elucidation of the various mechanisms that operate to orchestrate NCAP exchange within the phloem long-distance signaling pathway. Assignment of function for specific phloem-mobile macromolecules

has now provided compelling proof of principle for the role played by the phloem in controlling physiological, developmental, and pathogenesis-related processes at the whole-plant level. These findings ensure a bright future for continued dissection of these long-distance communication networks.

The critical next steps include development of comprehensive databases of vascular genes and phloem-mobile transcripts, small RNA, and proteins. It is only in the context of this knowledge that we will be able to understand the various control points and regulatory pathways that utilize the phloem for signal transduction. Natural next steps then include developing protein interaction maps (11, 131) and unraveling the cascades of post-translational modifications involved in regulating signal propagation and/or transduction along each specific pathway. The establishment of such phloem proteomic and transcriptome databases will provide a critical resource for the development of a systems biology approach to the study of whole-plant biology. Studies of this nature will also yield important insights into the evolution of the phloem, both as a nutrient and information macromolecule delivery system. Finally, as plants allocate their resources on a whole-organismal basis, in response to multiple inputs, understanding the molecular basis for these decisions will ultimately enhance our capacity to bioengineer agriculturally important traits.

SUMMARY POINTS

1. Evolutionary development of the plant vascular system afforded a long-distance system for the delivery of both nutrients and information molecules.

2. Plasmodesmata (PD) mediate the local (cell-to-cell) exchange of non-cell-autonomous proteins (NCAPs) and ribonucleoprotein complexes, including transcription factors and RNA involved in developmental programs.

3. A combination of the enucleate sieve tube system of the phloem and the symplasmic domains established by PD allowed the angiosperms to develop an NCAP-based signaling network to integrate environmental cues at the whole-plant level.

4. Cell biologists have now identified and characterized a broad array of proteins and RNA species contained within the phloem translocation stream. The authenticity of these macromolecules as bona fide components of the phloem sap offers support for the hypothesis that they participate in an interorgan signaling network.

5. Plant viruses and viroids evolved the capacity to utilize the properties of PD and the phloem to establish systemic infections. As such, these viral systems provide an effective means with which to dissect the molecular determinants involved in the trafficking of macromolecules into specific tissues/cell types. Recent elegant work on viroid movement identified the first RNA motif involved in RNA trafficking across a specific cellular/PD boundary.

6. Florigen and tuberigen, long sought-after signals involved in floral and tuber induction, in response to day length, move through the phloem and may be transmitted as a long-distance protein and/or RNA signaling molecule(s).

7. Resource allocation and nutrient signaling are affected by specific NCAPs of endogenous and viral origins. One such NCAP, the maize pathogenesis-related protein, PRms, orchestrates profound changes in physiology and growth, apparently by manipulating control over resource allocation.

8. A proteomic approach to the study of phloem long-distance signaling is underway; however, to be most effective, this work will require database initiatives for a number of plant species. The same situation holds for efforts to develop phloem transcriptomes. Given the utility of these databases for a range of projects, including plant systems biology, an initiative is urgently needed at the international level to coordinate such programs.

FUTURE ISSUES TO BE RESOLVED

1. There is a need to develop a comprehensive database of phloem-mobile macromolecules, including mRNA, small RNA, and proteins; ideally, this would incorporate bioinformatic analysis of a number of different plant species. This resource will be essential for future systems biology applications.

2. We need to assign function for all phloem-mobile macromolecules; this information will provide a foundation for the dissection of the component parts involved in specific interorgan signaling pathways.

3. We need to identify the macromolecular determinants responsible for phloem-mediated selective delivery of information macromolecules to target tissues. Studies on the processes involved in maintaining the enucleate sieve tube system may provide important insights into the evolution of the angiosperm phloem.

ACKNOWLEDGMENTS

Our thanks go to colleagues who provided unpublished work for inclusion in this review, to John Bowman for stimulating discussions, Judy Jernstedt for photomicrographs, and Samantha Silva for expert assistance with the art work. We apologize to all of our colleagues whose work could not be discussed due to space limitations. Work in our laboratory on plasmodesmal biology and long-distance signaling through the phloem is supported by grants from the National Science Foundation and the Department of Energy Office of Basic Energy Sciences and the New Zealand Foundation for Research Science and Technology.

LITERATURE CITED

1. Achard P, Herr A, Baulcombe DC, Harberd NP. 2004. Modulation of floral development by a gibberellin-regulated microRNA. *Development* 131:3357–65

1a. **Abe M, Kobayashi Y, Yamamoto S, Daimon Y, Yamaguchi A, et al. 2005. FR, a bZIP protein mediating signals from the floral pathway integrator FT at the shoot apex. *Science* 309:1052–56**

2. Almon E, Horowitz M, Wang HL, Lucas WJ, Zamski E, Wolf S. 1997. Phloem-specific expression of the tobacco mosaic virus movement protein alters carbon metabolism and partitioning in transgenic potato plants. *Plant Physiol.* 115:1599–607

3. **An H, Roussot C, Suarez-Lopez P, Corbesier L, Vincent C, et al. 2004. CONSTANS acts in the phloem to regulate a systemic signal that induces photoperiodic flowering of Arabidopsis. *Development* 131:3615–26**

4. Aoki K, Kragler F, Xoconostle-Cazares B, Lucas WJ. 2002. A subclass of plant heat shock cognate 70 chaperones carries a motif that facilitates trafficking through plasmodesmata. *Proc. Natl. Acad. Sci. USA* 99:16342–47

5. **Aoki K, Suzui N, Fujimaki S, Dohmae N, Yonekura-Sakakibara K, et al. 2005. Destination-selective long-distance movement of phloem proteins. *Plant Cell* 17:1801–14**

6. Asano T, Masumura T, Kusano H, Kikuchi S, Kurita A, et al. 2002. Construction of a specialized cDNA library from plant cells isolated by laser capture microdissection: toward comprehensive analysis of the genes expressed in the rice phloem. *Plant J.* 32:401–8

7. Ayre BG, Turgeon R. 2004. Graft transmission of a floral stimulant derived from *CONSTANS*. *Plant Physiol.* 135:2271–78

8. Balachandran S, Hull RJ, Vaadia Y, Wolf S, Lucas WJ. 1995. Tobacco mosaic virus movement protein-induced change in carbon partitioning originates from the mesophyll and is independent of change in plasmodesmal size exclusion limit. *Plant Cell Environ.* 18:1301–10

9. Balachandran S, Xiang Y, Schobert C, Thompson GA, Lucas WJ. 1997. Phloem sap proteins from *Cucurbita maxima* and *Ricinus communis* have the capacity to traffic cell to cell through plasmodesmata. *Proc. Natl. Acad. Sci. USA* 94:14150–55

10. Barnes A, Bale J, Constantinidou C, Ashton P, Jones A, Pritchard J. 2004. Determining protein identity from sieve element sap in *Ricinus communis* L. by quadrupole time of flight (Q-TOF) mass spectrometry. *J. Exp. Bot.* 55:1473–81

11. Barrios-Rodiles M, Brown KR, Ozdamar B, Bose R, Liu Z, et al. 2005. High-throughput mapping of a dynamic signaling network in mammalian cells. *Science* 307:1621–25

12. Bartel DP. 2004. MicroRNAs: genomics, biogenesis, mechanism, and function. *Cell* 116:281–97

13. Bastow R, Dean C. 2003. Plant sciences. Deciding when to flower. *Science* 302:1695–96

14. Bernier G, Havelange A, Houssa C, Petitjean A, Lejeune P. 1993. Physiological signals that induce flowering. *Plant Cell* 5:1147–55

In this study, molecular genetic tools were used to establish the link between FT and the steps involved in floral induction.

Heterografting experiments were used to established that CONSTANS (CO) acts non-cell-autonomously to control flowering.

These authors developed an ingenious method to demonstrate that specific phloem-mobile NCAPs can undergo selective transport to a particular target tissue.

15. Beveridge CA, Weller JL, Singer SR, Hofer JM. 2003. Axillary meristem development. Budding relationships between networks controlling flowering, branching, and photoperiod responsiveness. *Plant Physiol.* 131:927–34

16. **Bortolotti C, Murillo I, Fontanet P, Coca M, Segundo BS. 2005. Long-distance transport of the maize pathogenesis-related PRms protein through the phloem in transgenic tobacco plants.** *Plant Sci.* **168:813–21**

17. Brandt S, Kehr J, Walz C, Imlau A, Willmitzer L, Fisahn J. 1999. Technical advance: a rapid method for detection of plant gene transcripts from single epidermal, mesophyll and companion cells of intact leaves. *Plant J.* 20:245–50

18. Buhtz A, Kolasa A, Arlt K, Walz C, Kehr J. 2004. Xylem sap protein composition is conserved among different plant species. *Planta* 219:610–18

19. Caetano-Anolles G, Gresshoff PM. 1991. Plant genetic control of nodulation. *Annu. Rev. Microbiol.* 45:345–82

20. Carrington JC, Kasschau KD, Mahajan SK, Schaad MC. 1996. Cell-to-cell and long-distance transport of viruses in plants. *Plant Cell* 8:1669–81

21. Chailakyan MK. 1936. New facts in support of the hormonal theory of plant development. *C.R.(Dokl.) Acad. Sci. URSS* 13:79–83

22. Chen JJ, Janssen BJ, Williams A, Sinha N. 1997. A gene fusion at a homeobox locus: alterations in leaf shape and implications for morphological evolution. *Plant Cell* 9:1289–304

23. Chen MH, Citovsky V. 2003. Systemic movement of a tobamovirus requires host cell pectin methylesterase. *Plant J.* 35:386–92

24. Chen MH, Sheng J, Hind G, Handa AK, Citovsky V. 2000. Interaction between the tobacco mosaic virus movement protein and host cell pectin methylesterases is required for viral cell-to-cell movement. *EMBO J.* 19:913–20

25. Chisholm ST, Parra MA, Anderberg RJ, Carrington JC. 2001. Arabidopsis *RTM1* and *RTM2* genes function in phloem to restrict long-distance movement of tobacco etch virus. *Plant Physiol.* 127:1667–75

26. Cilia ML, Jackson D. 2004. Plasmodesmata form and function. *Curr. Opin. Cell Biol.* 16:500–6

27. Citovsky V, Zambryski P. 2000. Systemic transport of RNA in plants. *Trends Plant Sci.* 5:52–54

28. **Complainville A, Brocard L, Roberts I, Dax E, Sever N, et al. 2003. Nodule initiation involves the creation of a new symplasmic field in specific root cells of medicago species.** *Plant Cell* **15:2778–91**

29. Cooper B, Schmitz I, Rao AL, Beachy RN, Dodds JA. 1996. Cell-to-cell transport of movement-defective cucumber mosaic and tobacco mosaic viruses in transgenic plants expressing heterologous movement protein genes. *Virology* 216:208–13

30. Couzin J. 2002. Small RNAs make big splash. *Science* 298:2296–97

31. Curie C, Briat JF. 2003. Iron transport and signaling in plants. *Annu. Rev. Plant Biol.* 54:183–206

32. De Jong W, Ahlquist P. 1992. A hybrid plant RNA virus made by transferring the noncapsid movement protein from a rod-shaped to an icosahedral virus is competent for systemic infection. *Proc. Natl. Acad. Sci. USA* 89:6808–12

33. Dievart A, Clark SE. 2004. LRR-containing receptors regulating plant development and defense. *Development* 131:251–61

34. Ding B, Itaya A, Qi Y. 2003. Symplasmic protein and RNA traffic: regulatory points and regulatory factors. *Curr. Opin. Plant Biol.* 6:596–602

In this study, grafted plants and western analysis revealed that PRms is a phloem-mobile NCAP.

This study provides an excellent example of the development of a special symplasmic field that is established between SEs and root cells that form nodule initials.

35. Ding X, Shintaku MH, Carter SA, Nelson RS. 1996. Invasion of minor veins of tobacco leaves inoculated with tobacco mosaic virus mutants defective in phloem-dependent movement. *Proc. Natl. Acad. Sci. USA* 93:11155–60

36. Doering-Saad C, Newbury HJ, Bale JS, Pritchard J. 2002. Use of aphid stylectomy and RT-PCR for the detection of transporter mRNAs in sieve elements. *J. Exp. Bot.* 53:631–37

37. Dunoyer P, Lecellier CH, Parizotto EA, Himber C, Voinnet O. 2004. Probing the microRNA and small interfering RNA pathways with virus-encoded suppressors of RNA silencing. *Plant Cell* 16:1235–50

38. Ehlers K, Kollmann R. 2001. Primary and secondary plasmodesmata: structure, origin, and functioning. *Protoplasma* 216:1–30

39. Farmer EE, Almeras E, Krishnamurthy V. 2003. Jasmonates and related oxylipins in plant responses to pathogenesis and herbivory. *Curr. Opin. Plant Biol.* 6:372–78

40. Fisher DB, Cash-Clark CE. 2000. Sieve tube unloading and post-phloem transport of fluorescent tracers and proteins injected into sieve tubes via severed aphid stylets. *Plant Physiol.* 123:125–38

41. Forde BG. 2002. Local and long-range signaling pathways regulating plant responses to nitrate. *Annu. Rev. Plant Biol.* 53:203–24

42. Foster TM, Lough TJ, Emerson SJ, Lee RH, Bowman JL, et al. 2002. A surveillance system regulates selective entry of RNA into the shoot apex. *Plant Cell* 14:1497–508

43. Gallagher KL, Benfey PN. 2005. Not just another hole in the wall: understanding intercellular protein trafficking. *Genes Dev.* 19:189–95

44. Ghoshroy S, Lartey R, Sheng J, Citovsky V. 1997. Transport of proteins and nucleic acids through plasmodesmata. *Annu. Rev. Plant Physiol. Plant Mol. Biol.* 48:27–50

45. Giesman-Cookmeyer D, Silver S, Vaewhongs AA, Lommel SA, Deom CM. 1995. Tobamovirus and dianthovirus movement proteins are functionally homologous. *Virology* 213:38–45

46. Gilbertson RL, Lucas WJ. 1996. How do viruses traffic on the "vascular highway"? *Trends Plant Sci.* 1:260–68

47. Gisel A, Barella S, Hempel FD, Zambryski PC. 1999. Temporal and spatial regulation of symplastic trafficking during development in *Arabidopsis thaliana* apices. *Development* 126:1879–89

48. Gisel A, Hempel FD, Barella S, Zambryski P. 2002. Leaf-to-shoot apex movement of symplastic tracer is restricted coincident with flowering in *Arabidopsis*. *Proc. Natl. Acad. Sci. USA* 99:1713–17

49. Glazebrook J. 2005. Contrasting mechanisms of defense against biotrophic and necrotrophic pathogens. *Annu. Rev. Phytopathol.* 43:205–27

50. Golecki B, Schulz A, Carstens-Behrens U, Kollmann R. 1998. Evidence for graft transmission of structural phloem proteins or their precursors in heterografts of Cucurbitaceae. *Planta* 206:630–40

51. Golecki B, Schulz A, Thompson GA. 1999. Translocation of structural P proteins in the phloem. *Plant Cell* 11:127–40

52. Gomez G, Torres H, Pallas V. 2005. Identification of translocatable RNA-binding phloem proteins from melon, potential components of the long-distance RNA transport system. *Plant J.* 41:107–16

53. Guo HS, Ding SW. 2002. A viral protein inhibits the long range signaling activity of the gene silencing signal. *EMBO J.* 21:398–407

54. Haebel S, Kehr J. 2001. Matrix-assisted laser desorption/ionization time of flight mass spectrometry peptide mass fingerprints and post source decay: a tool for the identification and analysis of phloem proteins from *Cucurbita maxima* Duch. separated by two-dimensional polyacrylamide gel electrophoresis. *Planta* 213:586–93

55. Hamilton AJ, Baulcombe DC. 1999. A species of small antisense RNA in posttranscriptional gene silencing in plants. *Science* 286:950–52

56. Hannah MA, Iqbal MJ, Sanders FE. 2000. The DL system in common bean: a possible mechanism for control of root-shoot partitioning. *New Phytol.* 147:487–91

57. Haupt S, Oparka KJ, Sauer N, Neumann S. 2001. Macromolecular trafficking between *Nicotiana tabacum* and the holoparasite *Cuscuta reflexa*. *J. Exp. Bot.* 52:173–77

58. Hayama R, Coupland G. 2004. The molecular basis of diversity in the photoperiodic flowering responses of Arabidopsis and rice. *Plant Physiol.* 135:677–84

59. Haywood V, Kragler F, Lucas WJ. 2002. Plasmodesmata: Pathways for protein and ribonucleoprotein signaling. *Plant Cell* 14:S303–25

60. Haywood V, Yu TS, Huang NC, Lucas WJ. 2005. Phloem long-distance trafficking of GIBBERELLIC ACID-INSENSITIVE RNA regulates leaf development. *Plant J.* 42:49–68

This studies provides strong evidence that phloem-mobile mRNA can contribute to the regulation of developmental processes in sink tissues.

61. Hertzberg M, Aspeborg H, Schrader J, Andersson A, Erlandsson R, et al. 2001. A transcriptional roadmap to wood formation. *Proc. Natl. Acad. Sci. USA* 98:14732–37

62. Hewezi T, Alibert G, Kallerhoff J. 2005. Local infiltration of high and low molecular weight RNA from silenced sunflower (*Helianthus annuus* L.) plants trigger post transcriptional gene silencing in non-silenced plants. *Plant Biotech. J.* 3:81–89

63. Himber C, Dunoyer P, Moissiard G, Ritzenthaler C, Voinnet O. 2003. Transitivity-dependent and -independent cell-to-cell movement of RNA silencing. *EMBO J.* 22:4523–33

64. Hoffmann-Benning S, Gage DA, McIntosh L, Kende H, Zeevaart JA. 2002. Comparison of peptides in the phloem sap of flowering and non-flowering *Perilla* and lupine plants using microbore HPLC followed by matrix-assisted laser desorption/ionization time-of-flight mass spectrometry. *Planta* 216:140–47

64a. Huang T, Böhlenius H, Eriksson S, Rarcy F, Nilsson O. 2005. The mRNA of the *Arabidopsis* gene FT moves from leaf to shoot apex and induces flowering. *Science* 309:1694–96

Using a heat shock promoter, these authors demonstrated local induction of *FT* in a single *Arabidopsis* leaf resulted in *FT* mRNA delivery to the apex, floral induction, and activation of downstream genes.

65. Imlau A, Truernit E, Sauer N. 1999. Cell-to-cell and long-distance trafficking of the green fluorescent protein in the phloem and symplastic unloading of the protein into sink tissues. *Plant Cell* 11:309–22

66. Ishiwatari Y, Fujiwara T, McFarland KC, Nemoto K, Hayashi H, et al. 1998. Rice phloem thioredoxin h has the capacity to mediate its own cell-to-cell transport through plasmodesmata. *Planta* 205:12–22

67. Ivashikina N, Deeken R, Ache P, Kranz E, Pommerrenig B, et al. 2003. Isolation of At-SUC2 promoter-GFP-marked companion cells for patch-clamp studies and expression profiling. *Plant J.* 36:931–45

68. Jackson SD. 1999. Multiple signaling pathways control tuber induction in potato. *Plant Physiol.* 119:1–8

69. Jackson SD, Heyer A, Dietze J, Prat S. 1996. Phytochrome B mediates the photoperiodic control of tuber formation in potato. *Plant J.* 9:159–66

70. Jacqmard A, Detry N, Dewitte W, Van Onckelen H, Bernier G. 2002. In situ localisation of cytokinins in the shoot apical meristem of *Sinapis alba* at floral transition. *Planta* 214:970–73

71. Janssen R-P 2001. mRNA localization: message on the move. *Nat. Rev. Mol. Cell Biol.* 2:247–56

72. Jones-Rhoades MW, Bartel DP. 2004. Computational identification of plant micro-RNAs and their targets, including a stress-induced miRNA. *Mol. Cell* 14:787–99

73. Jorgensen RA. 2002. RNA traffics information systemically in plants. *Proc. Natl. Acad. Sci. USA* 99:11561–63

74. Jorgensen RA, Atkinson RG, Forster RL, Lucas WJ. 1998. An RNA-based information superhighway in plants. *Science* 279:1486–87

75. Kardailsky I, Shukla VK, Ahn JH, Dagenais N, Christensen SK, et al. 1999. Activation tagging of the floral inducer FT. *Science* 286:1962–65

76. Karpinski S, Reynolds H, Karpinska B, Wingsle G, Creissen G, Mullineaux P. 1999. Systemic signaling and acclimation in response to excess excitation energy in *Arabidopsis*. *Science* 284:654–57

77. Kim M, Canio W, Kessler S, Sinha N. 2001. Developmental changes due to long-distance movement of a homeobox fusion transcript in tomato. *Science* 293:287–89

78. Kim JY, Rim Y, Wang L, Jackson D 2005. A novel cell-to-cell trafficking assay indicates that the KNOX homeodomain is necessary and sufficient for intercellular protein and mRNA trafficking. *Genes Dev.* 19:788–793

79. King RW, Evans LT. 2003. Gibberellins and flowering of grasses and cereals: prizing open the lid of the "florigen" black box. *Annu. Rev. Plant Biol.* 54:307–28

80. Klahre U, Crete P, Leuenberger SA, Iglesias VA, Meins F. 2002. High molecular weight RNAs and small interfering RNAs induce systemic posttranscriptional gene silencing in plants. *Proc. Natl. Acad. Sci. USA* 99:11981–86

81. Knoblauch M, Peters WS, Ehlers K, van Bel AJ. 2001. Reversible calcium-regulated stopcocks in legume sieve tubes. *Plant Cell* 13:1221–30

82. Kobayashi Y, Kaya H, Goto K, Iwabuchi M, Araki T. 1999. A pair of related genes with antagonistic roles in mediating flowering signals. *Science* 286:1960–62

83. Koornneef M, Elgersma A, Hanhart CJ, Loenen-Martinet EP, Rign L, Zeevaart JAD. 1985. A gibberellin insensitive mutant of *Arabidopsis thaliana*. *Physiol. Plant.* 65:33–39

84. Kragler F, Monzer J, Xoconostle-Cazares B, Lucas WJ. 2000. Peptide antagonists of the plasmodesmal macromolecular trafficking pathway. *EMBO J.* 19:2856–68

85. Kühn C, Franceschi VR, Schulz A, Lemoine R, Frommer WB. 1997. Macromolecular trafficking indicated by localization and turnover of sucrose transporters in enucleate sieve elements. *Science* 275:1298–300

86. Lakatos L, Szittya G, Silhavy D, Burgyan J. 2004. Molecular mechanism of RNA silencing suppression mediated by p19 protein of tombusviruses. *EMBO J.* 23:876–84

87. Lake JA, Quick WP, Beerling DJ, Woodward FI. 2001. Plant development. Signals from mature to new leaves. *Nature* 411:154

88. Lazarowitz SG, Beachy RN. 1999. Viral movement proteins as probes for intracellular and intercellular trafficking in plants. *Plant Cell* 11:535–48

89. Lee JY, Yoo BC, Rojas MR, Gomez-Ospina N, Staehelin LA, Lucas WJ. 2003. Selective trafficking of non-cell-autonomous proteins mediated by NtNCAPP1. *Science* 299:392–96

90. Leyser O. 2002. Molecular genetics of auxin signaling. *Annu. Rev. Plant Biol.* 53:377–98

91. Lucas WJ. 1995. Plasmodesmata: intercellular channels for macromolecular transport in plants. *Curr. Opin. Cell Biol.* 7:673–80

92. Lucas WJ, Ding B, van der Schoot C. 1993. Plasmodesmata and the supracellular nature of plants. *New Phytol.* 125:435–76

93. Lucas WJ, Gilbertson RL. 1994. Plasmodesmata in relation to viral movement within leaf tissues. *Annu. Rev. Phytopathol.* 32:387–411

94. Lucas WJ, Lee JY. 2004. Plasmodesmata as a supracellular control network in plants. *Nat. Rev. Mol. Cell Biol.* 5:712–26

95. Lucas WJ, Yoo BC, Kragler F. 2001. RNA as a long-distance information macromolecule in plants. *Nat. Rev. Mol. Cell Biol.* 2:849–57

96. Mahajan SK, Chisholm ST, Whitham SA, Carrington JC. 1998. Identification and characterization of a locus (*RTM1*) that restricts long-distance movement of tobacco etch virus in *Arabidopsis thaliana*. *Plant J.* 14:177–86

97. Marentes E, Grusak MA. 1998. Mass determination of low-molecular-weight proteins in phloem sap using matrix-assisted laser desorption/ionization time-of-flight mass spectrometry. *J. Exp. Bot.* 49:903–11

98. Martinez-Garcia JF, Virgos-Soler A, Prat S. 2002. Control of photoperiod-regulated tuberization in potato by the *Arabidopsis* flowering-time gene *CONSTANS*. *Proc. Natl. Acad. Sci. USA* 99:15211–16

99. Matthews REF. 1991. *Plant Virology*. San Diego: Academic

100. McCulloh KA, Sperry JS, Adler FR. 2003. Water transport in plants obeys Murray's law. *Nature* 421:939–42

101. Morozov SY, Fedorkin ON, Juttner G, Schiemann J, Baulcombe DC, Atabekov JG. 1997. Complementation of a potato virus X mutant mediated by bombardment of plant tissues with cloned viral movement protein genes. *J. Gen. Virol.* 78:2077–83

102. Mouradov A, Cremer F, Coupland G. 2002. Control of flowering time: interacting pathways as a basis for diversity. *Plant Cell* 14: S111–30

103. Murillo I, Cavallarin L, San Segundo B. 1997. The maize pathogenesis-related PRms protein localizes to plasmodesmata in maize radicles. *Plant Cell* 9:145–56

104. Murillo I, Roca R, Bortolotti C, Segundo BS. 2003. Engineering photoassimilate partitioning in tobacco plants improves growth and productivity and provides pathogen resistance. *Plant J.* 36:330–41

105. Murray CD. 1926. The physiological principle of minimum work. I. The vascular system and the cost of blood volume. *Proc. Natl. Acad. Sci. USA* 12:207–14

106. Nakajima K, Benfey PN. 2002. Signaling in and out: control of cell division and differentiation in the shoot and root. *Plant Cell* 14:S265–76

107. Nakajima K, Sena G, Nawy T, Benfey PN. 2001. Intercellular movement of the putative transcription factor SHR in root patterning. *Nature* 413:307–11

108. Nakazono M, Qiu F, Borsuk LA, Schnable PS. 2003. Laser-capture microdissection, a tool for the global analysis of gene expression in specific plant cell types: identification of genes expressed differentially in epidermal cells or vascular tissues of maize. *Plant Cell* 15:583–96

109. Northcote DH, Davey R, Lay J. 1989. Use of antisera to localize callose, xylan and arabidogalactan in cell-plate, primary and secondary walls of plant cells. *Planta* 178:353–66

110. Odabaei G, Chatterjee D, Jazirehi AR, Goodglick L, Yeung K, Bonavida B. 2004. Raf-1 kinase inhibitor protein: structure, function, regulation of cell signaling, and pivotal role in apoptosis. *Adv. Cancer Res.* 91:169–200

111. Olesinski AA, Almon E, Navot N, Perl A, Galun E, et al. 1996. Tissue-specific expression of the Tobacco mosaic virus movement protein in transgenic potato plants alters plasmodesmal function and carbohydrate partitioning. *Plant Physiol.* 111:541–50

112. Oparka KJ. 2004. Getting the message across: How do plant cells exchange macromolecular complexes? *Trends Plant Sci.* 9:33–41

113. Oparka KJ, Santa Cruz S. 2000. The great escape: phloem transport and unloading of macromolecules. *Annu. Rev. Plant Physiol. Plant Mol. Biol.* 51:323–47

114. Oparka KJ, Turgeon R. 1999. Sieve elements and companion cells - traffic control centers of the phloem. *Plant Cell* 11:739–50

115. Palauqui JC, Elmayan T, Pollien J-M, Vaucheret H. 1997. Systemic acquired silencing: transgene-specific post-transcriptional silencing is transmitted by grafting from silenced stocks to non-silenced scions. *EMBO J.* 16:4738–45

116. Peng J, Carol P, Richards DE, King KE, Cowling RJ, et al. 1997. The *Arabidopsis GAI* gene defines a signaling pathway that negatively regulates gibberellin responses. *Genes Dev.* 11:3194–205

117. Pnueli L, Gutfinger T, Hareven D, Ben-Naim O, Ron N, et al. 2001. Tomato SP-interacting proteins define a conserved signaling system that regulates shoot architecture and flowering. *Plant Cell* 13:2687–702

118. Rodríguez-Falcón M, Bou J, Prat S. 2006. Seasonal control of tuberization in potato: conserved element with the flowering response. *Annu. Rev. Plant Biol.* 57:151–80

119. Pruss G, Ge X, Shi XM, Carrington JC, Bowman Vance V. 1997. Plant viral synergism: the potyviral genome encodes a broad-range pathogenicity enhancer that transactivates replication of heterologous viruses. *Plant Cell* 9:859–68

120. Putterill J, Robson F, Lee K, Simon R, Coupland G. 1995. The *CONSTANS* gene of *Arabidopsis* promotes flowering and encodes a protein showing similarities to zinc finger transcription factors. *Cell* 80:847–57

121. Qi Y, Pelissier T, Itaya A, Hunt E, Wassenegger M, Ding B. 2004. Direct role of a viroid RNA motif in mediating directional RNA trafficking across a specific cellular boundary. *Plant Cell* 16:1741–52

122. Richards DE, King KE, Ait-Ali T, Harberd NP. 2001. How gibberellin regulates plant growth and development: a molecular genetic analysis of gibberellin signaling. *Annu. Rev. Plant Physiol. Plant Mol. Biol.* 52:67–88

123. Ruiz MT, Voinnet O, Baulcombe DC. 1998. Initiation and maintenance of virus-induced gene silencing. *Plant Cell* 10:937–46

124. Ruiz-Medrano R, Xoconostle-Cázares B, Kragler F. 2004. The plasmodesmatal transport pathway for homoeotic proteins, silencing signals and viruses. *Curr. Opin. Plant Biol.* 7:641–50

125. Ruiz-Medrano R, Xoconostle-Cázares B, Lucas WJ. 1999. Phloem long-distance transport of CmNACP mRNA: implications for supracellular regulation in plants. *Development* 126:4405–19

126. Saito T, Yamanaka K, Okada Y. 1990. Long-distance movement and viral assembly of tobacco mosaic virus mutants. *Virology* 176:329–36

127. Sasaki T, Chino M, Hayashi H, Fujiwara T. 1998. Detection of several mRNA species in rice phloem sap. *Plant Cell Physiol.* 39:895–97

128. Schobert C, Gottschalk M, Kovar DR, Staiger CJ, Yoo BC, Lucas WJ. 2000. Characterization of *Ricinus communis* phloem profilin, RcPRO1. *Plant Mol Biol.* 42:719–30

129. Schultze IR, Kondorosi A. 1998. Regulation of symbiotic root nodule development. *Annu. Rev. Genet.* 32:33–57

130. Searle IR, Men AE, Laniya TS, Buzas DM, Iturbe-Ormaetxe I, et al. 2003. Long-distance signaling in nodulation directed by a CLAVATA1-like receptor kinase. *Science* 299:109–12

A seminal study providing the first demonstration that the systemic silencing signal is both graft-transmissible and sequence-specific.

This study provides the first evidence that a zip code directs selective RNA movement between plant cells.

Provides the key finding that the receptor-like kinase, Nodule Autoregulation Receptor Kinase (GmNARK), integrates signaling from the aerial parts of the plant to control nodule proliferation within the root.

131. Service RF. 2005. Proteomics. Protein chips map yeast kinase network. *Science* 307:1854–55

132. Sessions A, Yanofsky MF, Weigel D. 2000. Cell-cell signaling and movement by the floral transcription factors LEAFY and APETALA1. *Science* 289:779–82

133. Rolland F, Baena-Gonzalez E, Sheen J. 2006. Sugar sensing and signaling in plants: conserved and novel mechanisms. *Annu. Rev. Plant Biol.* 57:675–709

134. Shulga N, Roberts P, Gu Z, Spitz L, Tabb MM, et al. 1996. In vivo nuclear transport kinetics in Saccharomyces cerevisiae: a role for heat shock protein 70 during targeting and translocation. *J. Cell Biol.* 135:329–39

135. Sims DA, Luo Y, Seemann JR. 1998. Importance of leaf versus whole plant CO_2 environment for photosynthetic acclimation. *Plant Cell Environ.* 21:1189–96

136. Stadler R, Wright KM, Lauterbach C, Amon G, Gahrtz M, et al. 2005. Expression of GFP-fusions in Arabidopsis companion cells reveals non-specific protein trafficking into sieve elements and identifies a novel post-phloem domain in roots. *Plant J.* 41:319–31

137. Stitt M. 1996. Plasmodesmata play an essential role in sucrose export from leaves: a step toward an integration of metabolic biochemistry and cell biology. *Plant Cell* 8:565–71

138. Takada S, Goto K. 2003. TERMINAL FLOWER 2, an Arabidopsis homolog of HETEROCHROMATIN PROTEIN1, counteracts the activation of FLOWERING LOCUS T by CONSTANS in the vascular tissues of leaves to regulate flowering time. *Plant Cell* 15:2856–65

139. Thomas PW, Woodward FI, Quick WP. 2003. Systemic irradiance signalling in tobacco. *New Phytol.* 161:193–98

140. Torii KU. 2000. Receptor kinase activation and signal transduction in plants: an emerging picture. *Curr. Opin. Plant Biol.* 3:361–67

141. Turnbull CG, Booker JP, Leyser HM. 2002. Micrografting techniques for testing long-distance signalling in Arabidopsis. *Plant J.* 32:255–62

142. Deleted in proof

143. Ueki S, Citovsky V. 2002. The systemic movement of a tobamovirus is inhibited by a cadmium-ion-induced glycine-rich protein. *Nat. Cell Biol.* 4:478–86

144. Vaewhongs AA, Lommel SA. 1995. Virion formation is required for the long-distance movement of red clover necrotic mosaic virus in movement protein transgenic plants. *Virology* 212:607–13

145. van Bel AJE. 2003. The phloem, a miracle of ingenuity. *Plant Cell Environ.* 26:125–49

146. van Bel AJE, Ehlers K, Knoblauch M. 2002. Sieve elements caught in the act. *Trends Plant Sci.* 7:126–32

147. van Bel AJE, Gaupels F. 2004. Pathogen-induced resistance and alarm signals in the phloem. *Mol. Plant Path.* 5:495–504

148. Vilaine F, Palauqui JC, Amselem J, Kusiak C, Lemoine R, Dinant S. 2003. Towards deciphering phloem: a transcriptome analysis of the phloem of *Apium graveolens*. *Plant J.* 36:67–81

149. Viola R, Roberts AG, Haupt S, Gazzani S, Hancock RD, et al. 2001. Tuberization in potato involves a switch from apoplastic to symplastic phloem unloading. *Plant Cell* 13:385–98

150. Voinnet O, Vain P, Angell S, Baulcombe DC. 1998. Systemic spread of sequence-specific transgene RNA degradation in plants is initiated by localized introduction of ectopic promoterless DNA. *Cell* 95:177–87

151. Voinnet O, Lederer C, Baulcombe DC. 2000. A viral movement protein prevents spread of the gene silencing signal in *Nicotiana benthamiana*. *Cell* 103:157–67

This study provided the first evidence of a signaling role for CO and FT in the phloem long-distance signaling pathway.

152. Voinnet O, Pinto YM, Baulcombe DC. 1999. Suppression of gene silencing: a general strategy used by diverse DNA and RNA viruses of plants. *Proc. Natl. Acad. Sci. USA* 96:14147–52

153. Waigmann E, Ueki S, Trutnyeva K, Citovsky V. 2004. The ins and outs of nondestructive cell-to-cell and systemic movement of plant viruses. *Crit. Rev. Plant Sci.* 23:195–250

154. Walz C, Giavalisco P, Schad M, Juenger M, Klose J, Kehr J. 2004. Proteomics of curcurbit phloem exudate reveals a network of defence proteins. *Phytochemistry* 65:1795–804

155. Walz C, Juenger M, Schad M, Kehr J. 2002. Evidence for the presence and activity of a complete antioxidant defence system in mature sieve tubes. *Plant J.* 31:189–97

156. Waterhouse P, Wang M-B, Lough T. 2001. Gene silencing: an adaptive defence against viruses. *Nature* 411:834–42

157. Wendehenne D, Durner J, Klessig DF. 2004. Nitric oxide: a new player in plant signalling and defence responses. *Curr. Opin. Plant Biol.* 7:449–55

158. Whitham SA, Anderberg RJ, Chisholm ST, Carrington JC. 2000. Arabidopsis *RTM2* gene is necessary for specific restriction of tobacco etch virus and encodes an unusual small heat shock-like protein. *Plant Cell* 12:569–82

159. Whitham SA, Yamamoto ML, Carrington JC. 1999. Selectable viruses and altered susceptibility mutants in *Arabidopsis thaliana*. *Proc. Natl. Acad. Sci. USA* 96:772–77

159a. **Wigge PA, Kim MC, Jaeger KE, Busch W, Schmid M, et al. 2005. Integration of spatial and temporal information during floral induction in *Arabidopsis*. *Science* 309:1056–59**

160. Wilkinson S, Davies WJ. 2002. ABA-based chemical signalling: the co-ordination of responses to stress in plants. *Plant Cell Environ.* 25:195–210

161. Wu X, Weigel D, Wigge PA. 2002. Signaling in plants by intercellular RNA and protein movement. *Genes Dev.* 16:151–58

162. Xoconostle-Cázares B, Ruiz-Medrano R, Lucas WJ. 2000. Proteolytic processing of CmPP36, a protein from the cytochrome b(5) reductase family, is required for entry into the phloem translocation pathway. *Plant J.* 24:735–47

163. Xoconostle-Cázares B, Xiang Y, Ruiz-Medrano R, Wang HL, Monzer J, et al. 1999. Plant paralog to viral movement protein that potentiates transport of mRNA into the phloem. *Science* 283:94–98

164. Yeung K, Janosch P, McFerran B, Rose DW, Mischak H, et al. 2000. Mechanism of suppression of the Raf/MEK/extracellular signal-regulated kinase pathway by the Raf kinase inhibitor protein. *Mol. Cell Biol.* 20:3079–85

165. Yeung K, Seitz T, Li S, Janosch P, McFerran B, et al. 1999. Suppression of Raf-1 kinase activity and MAP kinase signalling by RKIP. *Nature* 401:173–77

166. Yoo BC, Aoki K, Xiang Y, Campbell LR, Hull RJ, et al. 2000. Characterization of cucurbita maxima phloem serpin-1 (CmPS-1). A developmentally regulated elastase inhibitor. *J. Biol. Chem.* 275:35122–28

167. **Yoo BC, Kragler F, Varkonyi-Gasic E, Haywood V, Archer-Evans S, et al. 2004. A systemic small RNA signaling system in plants. *Plant Cell* 16:1979–2000**

168. Zambryski P, Crawford K. 2000. Plasmodesmata: gatekeepers for cell-to-cell transport of developmental signals in plants. *Annu. Rev. Cell Dev. Biol.* 16:393–421

169. Zhu Y, Green L, Woo YM, Owens R, Ding B. 2001. Cellular basis of potato spindle tuber viroid systemic movement. *Virology* 279:69–77

170. Zhu Y, Qi Y, Xun Y, Owens R, Ding B. 2002. Movement of potato spindle tuber viroid reveals regulatory points of phloem-mediated RNA traffic. *Plant Physiol.* 130:138–46

Provides evidence that FT forms a complex with FD, a bZIP transcription factor, to activate expression of *APETALA1* in cells that will form the floral meristem.

This study demonstrated that the phloem carries a unique population of small interfering (si)- and micro-RNA species.

The Role of Root Exudates in Rhizosphere Interactions with Plants and Other Organisms

Harsh P. Bais,[5] Tiffany L. Weir,[1,2] Laura G. Perry,[2,3] Simon Gilroy,[4] and Jorge M. Vivanco[1,2]

[1]Department of Horticulture and Landscape Architecture, [2]Center for Rhizosphere Biology, and [3]Department of Forest, Rangeland, and Watershed Stewardship, Colorado State University, Fort Collins, Colorado 80523-1173
[4]Department of Biology, Pennsylvania State University, University Park, Pennsylvania 16802; email: j.vivanco@colostate.edu
[5]Department of Plant and Soil Sciences, Delaware Biotechnology Institute, Newark, Delaware 19711

Annu. Rev. Plant Biol. 2006. 57:233–66

The *Annual Review of Plant Biology* is online at plant.annualreviews.org

doi: 10.1146/ annurev.arplant.57.032905.105159

First published online as a Review in Advance on January 30, 2006

1543-5008/06/0602-0233$20.00

Key Words

allelopathy, quorum-sensing, symbiosis, antimicrobial

Abstract

The rhizosphere encompasses the millimeters of soil surrounding a plant root where complex biological and ecological processes occur. This review describes recent advances in elucidating the role of root exudates in interactions between plant roots and other plants, microbes, and nematodes present in the rhizosphere. Evidence indicating that root exudates may take part in the signaling events that initiate the execution of these interactions is also presented. Various positive and negative plant-plant and plant-microbe interactions are highlighted and described from the molecular to the ecosystem scale. Furthermore, methodologies to address these interactions under laboratory conditions are presented.

Contents

INTRODUCTION

Plant roots exude an enormous range of potentially valuable small molecular weight compounds into the rhizosphere. Some of the most complex chemical, physical, and biological interactions experienced by terrestrial plants are those that occur between roots and their surrounding environment of soil (i.e., the rhizosphere). Interactions involving plants roots in the rhizosphere include root-root, root-insect, and root-microbe interactions. Over the past decade, enormous steps have been taken toward understanding these different types of interactions (79), and recently the field of plant biology has recognized

Rhizosphere: the soil zone that surrounds and is influenced by the roots of plants

PGPB: plant growth–promoting bacteria

the importance of root exudates in mediating these biological interactions (9, 180, 187).

The rhizosphere represents a highly dynamic front for interactions between roots and pathogenic and beneficial soil microbes, invertebrates, and root systems of competitors (79). However, because plant roots are hidden belowground, many of the interesting phenomena in which they are involved have remained largely unnoticed. In particular, the role of chemical signals in mediating belowground interactions is only beginning to be understood. Chemical signaling between plant roots and other soil organisms, including the roots of neighboring plants, is often based on root-derived chemicals. The same chemical signals may elicit dissimilar responses from different recipients. Chemical components of root exudates may deter one organism while attracting another, or two very different organisms may be attracted with differing consequences to the plant. A concrete example of diverse meanings for a chemical signal is the secretion of isoflavones by soybean roots, which attract a mutualist (*Bradyrhizobium japonicum*) and a pathogen (*Phytopthora sojae*) (122). The mechanisms used by roots to interpret the innumerable signals they receive from other roots, soil microbes, and invertebrates in the rhizosphere are largely unknown.

Root-root, root-microbe, and root-insect interactions may be classified as either positive or negative associations (**Figure 1**). A third category of neutral associations also exists, but is not addressed here. Positive interactions include symbiotic associations with epiphytes and mycorrhizal fungi, and root colonization by bacterial biocontrol agents and plant growth–promoting bacteria (PGPB). Negative interactions include competition or parasitism among plants, pathogenesis by bacteria or fungi, and invertebrate herbivory. The factors that determine whether the chemical signature of a plant's root exudates will be percieved as a negative or a positive signal still require elucidation. However, accumulated evidence suggests that root exudates have a major role in determining outcomes of interactions in the rhizosphere and, ultimately, plant and soil community dynamics.

WHAT ARE ROOT EXUDATES?

In addition to accumulating biologically active chemicals, plant roots continuously produce and secrete compounds into the rhizosphere (13, 60). Root exudation includes the secretion of ions, free oxygen and water, enzymes, mucilage, and a diverse array of carbon-containing primary and secondary metabolites (17, 172). Root exudation can be broadly divided into two active processes. The first, root excretion, involves gradient-dependent output of waste materials with unknown functions, whereas the second, secretion, involves exudation of compounds with known functions, such as lubrication and defense (8, 172). Roots release compounds via at least two potential mechanisms. Root exudates are transported across the cellular membrane and secreted into the surrounding rhizosphere. Plant products are also released from root border cells and root border-like cells, which separate from roots as they grow (71, 175). Root exudates are often divided into two classes of compounds. Low-molecular weight compounds such as amino acids, organic acids, sugars, phenolics, and other secondary metabolites account for much of the diversity of root exudates, whereas high-molecular weight exudates, such as mucilage (polysaccharides) and proteins, are less diverse but often compose a larger proportion of the root exudates by mass. Root exudation clearly represents a significant carbon cost to the plant (117), and the magnitude of photosynthates secreted as root exudates varies with the type of soil, age, and physiological state of the plant, and nutrient availability (21, 23). Although the functions of most root exudates have not been determined, several compounds present in root exudates play important roles in biological processes (9, 10, 11, 98) (**Figure 2**). The following sections of this

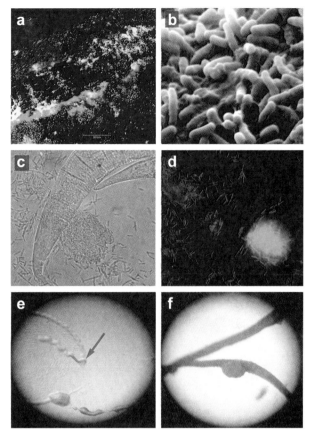

Figure 1

Plant-microbe positive and negative interactions. (*a*) Biocontrol of *Bacillus subtilis* (6051) on *Arabidopsis thaliana* roots by forming protective biofilms against gram-negative bacteria *Pseudomonas syringae* pv. *tomato* DC3000. Panel a shows the formation of aggregates or biofilm by *B. subtilis* on Arabidopsis root surface. Colonization of the root by *B. subtilis* biofilms limits the root space available for *P. syringae* to infection. Additionally, *B. subtilis*, like other gram-positive biocontrols, produces an antibacterial compound, surfactin, against *P. syringae* DC3000. (*b*) Pathogenic biofilm formation by a non-bonafide plant pathogen *Pseudomonas aeruginosa* on *A. thaliana* root surface. Panel b represents a crossover human pathogen, *P. aeruginosa*, which can infect plants under controlled conditions. *P. aeruginosa* forms pathogenic biofilm on Arabidopsis roots to exhibit full pathogenesis in a plant model. (*c–d*) Attachment of symbiont *Sinorhizobium meliloti* on *C. elegans* outer cuticle. In this unique interaction *C. elegans* acts as a vector for *S. meliloti* to transfer rhizobial inoculum to legume roots. (*e–f*) *C. elegans* feeding on the rhizobial lawn and nodule formation on host *Medicago* roots. Panels c–f represent one of the first reports to show a positive tritrophic interaction. *C. elegans*, a soil nematode, uses *S. meliloti* as food but does not digest all the bacteria. Instead the undigested *S. meliloti* and the attached bacteria on the *C. elegans* cuticle are transferred to the host plant root to complete the vector-mediated symbiosis. Additionally, plant roots also trigger *C. elegans* behavioral response by emitting volatile signals inviting nematodes to the root proximity. We kindly thank Dr. Junichiro Horiuchi for providing photos in panels c–f.

Allelopathy: the inhibition of growth in one species of plants by chemicals produced by another species

review describe the importance of root exudates in positive and negative interactions that determine plant and soil microbe growth and survival.

PLANT-PLANT INTERACTIONS MEDIATED BY ROOT EXUDATES

Resource competition, chemical interference, and/or parasitism lead to negative interactions between plants (**Figure 2**). Root exudates have the potential to influence all three mechanisms of interference. For a number of plant species, root exudates play a direct role as phytotoxins in mediating chemical interference (i.e., allelopathy). In addition, root exudates are critical to the development of associations between some parasitic plants and their hosts. Finally, root exudates may play important indirect roles in resource competition by altering soil chemistry, soil processes, and microbial populations.

Positive interactions between plants are also sometimes controlled by root exudates. In particular, some root exudates induce defense responses in neighboring plants. In some cases, the plant defenses induced by root exudates simply reduce susceptibility to pathogen infection, whereas in other cases these defenses initiate production and release of leafy volatiles that attract predators of plant enemies. In addition, effects of root exudates on soil processes and microbial populations can lead to some positive effects on neighboring plants.

Negative Plant-Plant Interactions

Allelopathy. Chemical-mediated plant-plant interference, or allelopathy, is one mechanism by which plants may gain an advantage over their competitors. Plants that produce and release potent phytotoxins can reduce the establishment, growth, or survival of susceptible plant neighbors, thus reducing competition and increasing resource availability. Plants release phytotoxins in decomposing leaf and root tissue, in leachates from live tissue, in green leafy volatiles, and in root exudates (17, 187). Plant-produced phytotoxins vary considerably in chemical structure, mode of action, and effects on plants. Different phytotoxins in root exudates affect metabolite production, photosynthesis, respiration, membrane transport, germination, root growth, shoot growth, and cell mortality in susceptible plants (47, 187). These effects on plant physiology, growth, and survival may in turn influence plant and soil community composition and dynamics.

A number of phytotoxic compounds in plant root exudates have been identified, including but not limited to 7,8-benzoflavone (*Acroptilon repens*, Russian knapweed) (164), (±)-catechin (*Centaurea maculosa*, spotted knapweed) (12), DIMBOA and DIBOA (*Triticum aestivum*, wheat) (190), juglone (*Juglans nigra*, black walnut) (89), 8-hydroxyquinoline (*Centaurea diffusa*, diffuse knapweed) (176), sorgoleone (*Sorghum* spp.) (133), and 5,7,4′-trihydroxy-3′,5′-dimethoxyflavone (*Oryza sativa*, rice) (101). These compounds share some structural

---

Figure 2

Rhizospheric chemical warfare: schematic representation of possible rhizospheric interactions mediated by root exudates. Root-mediated rhizospheric interactions are broadly classified into two categories, positive and negative interactions. Positive interactions involve root exudate-mediated interactions with plant growth–promoting Rhizobacteria (PGPR). Roots produce chemical signals that attract bacteria and induce chemotaxis. Positive interactions mediated by root exudates also include growth facilitators or growth regulator mimics that support growth of other plants and also perform cross-species signaling with rhizospheric invertebrates. Contrastingly, negative interactions mediated by root exudates involve secretion of antimicrobials, phytotoxins, nematicidal, and insecticidal compounds. The arrows in the panels indicate chemical exchange. VAM, vesicular arbuscular mycorrhizas; SARs, systemic acquired resistance.

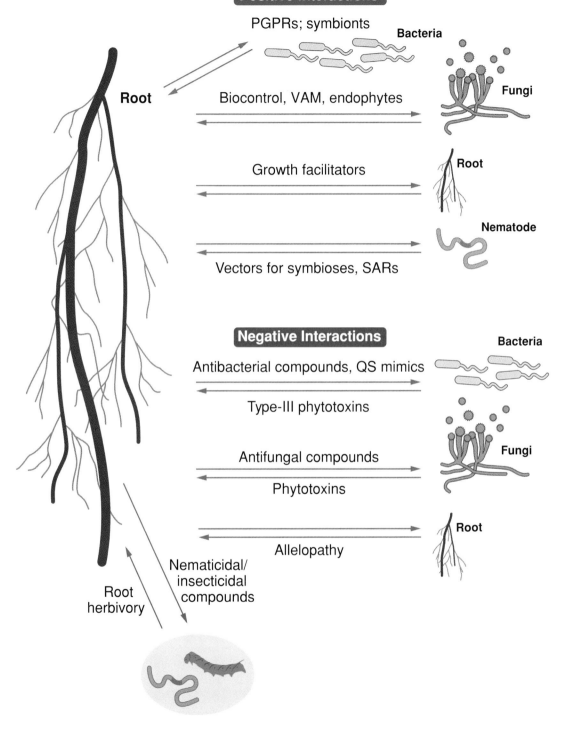

Positive Interactions

PGPRs; symbionts

Bacteria

Root

Biocontrol, VAM, endophytes

Fungi

Growth facilitators

Root

Nematode

Vectors for symbioses, SARs

Negative Interactions

Bacteria

Antibacterial compounds, QS mimics

Type-III phytotoxins

Fungi

Antifungal compounds

Phytotoxins

Root

Allelopathy

Nematicidal/
insecticidal
compounds

Root
herbivory

components, such as aromaticity (with the exception of sorgoleone), and the presence of hydroxyl and/or ketone groups. However, the structures of the compounds also vary considerably, and include flavonoids [7,8-benzoflavone, (±)-catechin, and 5,7,4′-trihydroxy-3′,5′-dimethoxyflavone], quinones (juglone and sorgoleone), quinolines (8-hydroxyquinoline), and hydroxamic acids (DIMBOA, DIBOA).

Phytotoxic root exudates can mediate negative plant-plant interactions only if present at sufficient concentrations to affect plant growth and survival. *Centaurea maculosa, C. diffusa*, and *Sorghum* spp. produce their phytotoxins at high concentrations, whereas *Juglans nigra* appears to produce lower concentrations of juglone. Young *C. maculosa* plants grown together in liquid culture can produce >80 μg ml^{-1} under standard conditions and >180 μg ml^{-1} in the presence of fungal cell wall materials (12). Soil (±)-catechin concentrations averaged 2.24 mg g^{-1} in one *C. maculosa* population (9) and 1.55 mg g^{-1} in another population (144). 8-Hydroxyquinoline soil concentrations in a *C. diffusa* population were lower than reported catechin concentrations, but still relatively high: 0.25 mg g^{-1} (176). Variation in (±)-catechin and 8-hydroxyquinoline concentrations among seasons, years, and soil types has not yet been examined. *Sorghum* spp. rhizosecrete more sorgoleone than any other compound in their root exudates (36). Agricultural species such as *S. bicolor* (sorghum) and *S. sudanese* (sudangrass) produce between 1.3 and 1.9 mg g^{-1} of sorgoleone, whereas the invasive weed *S. halepense* (johnsongrass) can rhizosecrete up to 14.8 mg g^{-1}. Sorgoleone concentrations in *Sorghum* spp. soils have not yet been reported. Juglone concentrations in soil beneath *J. nigra* trees rarely exceed 3 ug g^{-1} of soil (89), suggesting that production of juglone may be much lower than production of (±)-catechin, 8-hydroxyquinoline, and sorgoleone. However, both chemical stability and production rates determine phytotoxin concentrations in the rhizosphere. Juglone is relatively stable in soil and shows lit-

tle seasonal variation in concentration (89). In contrast, sorgoleone degrades quickly in soil (35), suggesting that continuously high production rates may be necessary to maintain phytotoxic concentrations of sorgoleone in soil. Degradation rates of (±)-catechin and 8-hydroxyquinoline in soil have not yet been determined.

The ecological relevance of phytotoxic root exudates also depends on the susceptibility of the plants with which the allelopathic plants coexist. (±)-Catechin and 8-hydroxyquinoline inhibit the growth of native North American plants in communities invaded by *Centaurea maculosa* (9, 186) and *C. diffusa* (176), respectively. In particular, (±)-catechin inhibits root growth of more than 20 North American grassland species (143). Likewise, sorgoleone, DIBOA, and 5,7,4′-trihydroxy-3′,5′-dimethoxyflavone limit the growth of weeds that coexist in agricultural systems with *Sorghum bicolor* (133), *Triticum aestivum* (114), and *Oryza sativa* (101), respectively. However, most of these experiments were conducted under laboratory, and not field, conditions. Tests applying typical soil phytotoxin concentrations under realistic conditions are necessary to evaluate with more certainty the importance of phytotoxin production to outcomes of plant-plant interference (83). An even more informative approach would involve comparisons with mutants or transgenic plants that do not produce phytotoxins. Recently, a gene involved in sorgoleone production was identified in *Sorghum bicolor* (192), perhaps providing an opportunity for a clear test of the importance of allelopathy in one species.

Many plants also produce secondary metabolites that inhibit the growth of conspecific plants (i.e., autotoxicity). Autotoxicity has been widely observed in agricultural crops and weeds, as well as in some plants that inhabit natural systems (160). Phytotoxic root exudates appear to mediate autoinhibition in at least some of these species, including *Asparagus officinalis* (garden asparagus) (131), *Cucumis sativa* (garden cucumber) (195), and *Centaurea maculosa* (spotted knapweed) (144). In many cases, plants that are allelopathic also exhibit signs of autotoxicity (160). However, only one study has identified that the same root exudate is responsible for both allelopathy and autotoxicity in a plant species. Perry et al. (144) demonstrated that ($\pm$)-catechin, the phytotoxin produced by *C. maculosa*, also inhibits *C. maculosa* seedling establishment at high concentrations. Autotoxicity may be a simple consequence of producing an allelochemical for which complete resistance is energetically expensive. Alternatively, autotoxicity may be beneficial to some plants within the population, a phenomenon termed autoinhibition. Autoinhibition may benefit adult plants or seedlings that produce autoinhibitors by reducing the establishment of intraspecific competitors in dense populations (44), or may benefit ungerminated seeds by delaying germination in areas with intense intraspecific competition, if the autoinhibitor induces seed dormancy (146).

Many allelopathic plants, however, appear to be relatively resistant to the phytotoxins they produce. Furthermore, some nonallelopathic plants are also relatively resistant to phytotoxins produced by other plants. For example, in a study of grassland species resistant to *Centaurea maculosa*'s phytotoxin, 8 of 23 species examined were more resistant to ($\pm$)-catechin than *C. maculosa* (143). Plants employ various methods to resist phytotoxins in the rhizosphere. Some plants may avoid effects of phytotoxins by sequestering the toxins in vacuoles or specialized tissues, or by secreting the phytotoxins as they are taken up (189). Other plants avoid inhibition from phytotoxins by altering the chemical structure of the toxins. For example, *Polygonella myriophylla* (Small's jointweed) avoids the effects of its own phytotoxins, hydroquinone and benzoquinone, by instead producing and releasing arbutin, a glycoside of hydroquinone (185). Microbial degradation of the glycoside allows the phytotoxins to be produced in the rhizosphere rather than in the plant. Similarly, *Zea mays* (corn) relies on *N*-glucosylation to avoid

the effects of DIMBOA, DIBOA, and BOA, phytotoxins secreted into the rhizosphere by *Triticum aestivum* (wheat) and several other grasses. BOA glucosylation occurs in incubations with *Z. mays*, forming a substantially less toxic compound (158). *Zea mays* possesses two glucosyltransferases, *BX8* and *BX9*, that act specifically on DIBOA and DIMBOA, and confer resistance to DIBOA and DIMBOA in transgenic *Arabidopsis thaliana* plants, demonstrating the importance of *BX8* and *BX9* to *Z. mays* phytotoxin resistance (179).

Nevertheless, the sensitivity of many plants to a range of plant-produced phytotoxins suggests that resistance may be energetically expensive and limited to a subset of species. Thus, negative biochemical interactions among plants may be an important factor shaping plant community structure.

Community-scale interactions: biological invasions. Over evolutionary time, plants frequently encountering allelopathic species are likely to acquire resistance to root-secreted phytotoxins. However, because phytotoxin resistance probably involves some energetic cost, plants that do not frequently encounter a phytotoxin may be unlikely to possess resistance to the toxin. Thus, transient plant species might be more sensitive to phytotoxins produced by other plants. By the same logic, phytotoxins produced by transient plants might be expected to affect a wider array of plant species than those that persist for long periods in particular plant communities. Among species that frequently associate with one another, coevolution might lead to an arms race of increasingly sophisticated allelochemicals with increasingly expensive requirements for resistance. Alternatively, coevolution in plant communities might decrease the ecological importance of direct chemical interference.

Biological invasions by exotic allelopathic plants present a unique case, in which native species in the invaded range have most likely never encountered the phytotoxins produced by the invader. As a result, these

Autotoxicity: a form of allelopathy that refers to a plant's ability to ward off competition from new growth within its own species

"novel weapons" (29) would have much larger negative effects on "naïve" native species in an invaded range than the "experienced" species in the invader's native range. The greater success of some exotic plants in their invaded ranges may be partially explained by the sensitivity of native species to the phytotoxins of the invader (9, 29, 77, 176). To date, the novel weapons hypothesis for invasion has been tested for only a few species, although the available evidence suggests that numerous other exotic invaders may also be allelopathic (36, 61, 164). The strongest evidence for the novel weapons hypothesis comes from experiments on two invaders of North American grasslands, *Centaurea diffusa* (diffuse knapweed) and *C. maculosa* (spotted knapweed). Callaway & Aschehoug (29) found that adding activated carbon to adsorb organic compounds (i.e., root exudates) in *C. diffusa* soils alleviated phytotoxic effects on neighboring grass species. Their experiments indicated that North American grassland species were significantly more inhibited by *C. diffusa* root exudates than the European grassland species with which *C. diffusa* naturally coexists. Vivanco et al. (176) applied 8-hydroxyquinoline, a phytotoxin identified in *C. diffusa* root exudates, to North American and European grassland species and also found that the North American species were significantly more susceptible to the phytotoxin, suggesting an important role of 8-hydroxyquinoline in *C. diffusa* invasions in North America. In a similar experiment, Bais et al. (9) found that North American grassland species are also more sensitive than European congeners to (±)-catechin, the phytotoxin identified in *C. maculosa* root exudates, suggesting a similar role of (±)-catechin in *C. maculosa* invasions. Finally, Prati & Bossdorf (148) found that root exudates from *Allium petiolata*, another invasive species in North America, had a significantly greater negative effect on a North American species, *Geum laciniatum*, than on a European congener, *Geum urbanum*, supporting the novel weapons hypothesis for *A. peti-*

olata invasion. However, root exudates from European *A. petiolata* populations had similar negative effects on the two congeners, indicating that *A. petiolata* phytotoxins may have important ecological effects in both the native and the invaded range.

Biological invasions may result from phytochemical effects on soil chemistry and soil microbial communities as well as from direct chemical interference (184). For example, secondary metabolites from one invasive plant, *Carduus nutans* (musk thistle), appear to inhibit nodulation and nitrogen fixation in leguminous species such as *Trifolium repens* (white clover) (182). Perhaps as a result, *T. repens* growth and survival is strongly reduced in field patches invaded by *C. nutans* (183). *C. nutans* appears to tolerate the resulting low-nitrogen conditions and benefit from the absence of competitors, re-establishing in previously invaded patches (182). In another example, secondary metabolites from *Empetrum hermaphroditum* (crowberry) inhibit symbiotic associations between *Pinus sylvestris* (Scots pine) trees and mycorrhizal fungi, thus reducing *P. sylvestris* nitrogen uptake (132). Moreover, secondary metabolites in *E. hermaphroditum* litter inhibit soil microbial and macrofaunal activity, thus reducing decomposition rates and further reducing soil nutrient availability (181). The effects of *E. hermaphroditum* secondary metabolites on soil processes, perhaps in conjunction with phytotoxic effects on forest plants (196), appear to facilitate *E. hermaphroditum* dominance and reduce tree productivity (184). Despite the strong evidence that plant secondary metabolites can affect soil processes that in turn alter plant-plant interactions, the effects of invasive plants' root exudates on soil processes in their native and invaded ranges have received little attention. More research is needed to evaluate the importance of interactions between root exudates and soil processes as mechanisms of biological invasion.

Parasitic plant-host interactions. Root exudates are essential in the development of associations between parasitic plants and their plant hosts, an association that is negative for the host and positive for the parasite. More than 4000 facultative and obligate parasitic plants have been identified to date (194). The chemical cross talk that controls the location of parasite germination and the development of physical connections between the parasite and the host is well understood for several obligate parasites, including *Striga* spp. (witchweed) and *Orobanche* spp. (broomrape) (137). Most current knowledge of the role of root exudates in parastic plants has been obtained from research on *Striga asiatica* and *S. hermonthica* (hereafter *Striga*) infestations of *Sorghum* spp.

Striga have very small seeds that can survive for only a few days after germination before forming an association with a host (137). The limited carbohydrate reserves in *Striga* seeds restrict seedling root elongation before host attachment. Thus, arranging for germination to coincide with proximity of an appropriate host root is critical to *Striga* seedling survival. To ensure that germination occurs near host roots, *Striga* seeds germinate only in the presence of sustained (10–12 h) high concentrations of germination inducers exuded into the soil by host roots (31). Germination inducers vary between different *Striga* hosts. To date, the only plant-produced *Striga* germination inducer that has been identified and characterized is sorghum xenognosin (SXSg). SXSg is highly unstable in aqueous solution (49), a useful trait for a *Striga* germination inducer because it is unlikely to persist in the soil and falsely indicate the presence of a host. However, SXSg is so unstable that it initially seemed difficult to explain how SXSg persisted and traveled in the soil in quantities sufficient to affect nearby *Striga* seeds (49). Fate & Lynn (49) provided an explanation for SXSg activity in soil by demonstrating that a compound structurally similar to SXSg, recorcinol, is released in small quantities with SXSg in sorghum root exudates and stabilizes SXSg enough to allow it to induce *Striga* germination.

Root exudates also play an integral role in *Striga* haustorial formation. Haustoria are specialized root structures in plant parasites that allow the parasites to infect host roots and form connections with host vascular tissue. The most recent evidence suggests that the chemical cross talk between *Striga* seedlings and host roots that results in haustorial formation begins with the constitutive release of hydrogen peroxide from *Striga* seedling root tips into the rhizosphere (94). Hydrogen peroxide activates host, and perhaps parasite, peroxidases that degrade host cell wall pectins, oxidatively releasing benzoquinones into the rhizosphere (92). The host benzoquinones are detected by the *Striga* seedling root, perhaps by redox activation of a receptor, and initiate haustorial formation (161). The mechanisms through which host benzoquinones induce haustorial development are not yet fully understood, but involve downregulation of a gene for one *Striga* expansin protein, and upregulation of genes for two unusual expansins, saExp1 and saExp2 (135). Expansins enable cell expansion by disrupting hydrogen bonds in cell walls (120). saExp1 and saExp2 may be important factors in the development and expansion of the unusual root cells in *Striga* haustoria.

Positive Plant-Plant Interactions

Induced herbivore resistance. Root exudates can also have positive effects in plant-plant interactions, although these have been less frequently reported. In particular, some root exudates increase herbivore resistance in neighboring plants. For example, *Elytrigia repens* (couch-grass) produces several phytotoxic compounds in its root exudates, of which one, carboline, has been identified (61). *Hordeum vulgare* (barley) treated with either *E. repens* root exudates or with carboline alone was significantly less likely to be chosen as a host by aphids than control *H. vulgare* plants. Carboline in the absence of *H. vulgare* did not repel aphids, indicating that *H. vulgare*

SXSg: sorghum xenognosin

Haustorium: a specialized absorbing structure of a parasitic plant, such as the rootlike outgrowth of the dodder, that obtains food from a host plant

responses to *E. repens* root exudates are necessary for aphid repulsion. The induction of *H. vulgare* defense responses by *E. repens* exudates may be a consequence of secondary metabolite production resulting from exposure to *E. repens* phytotoxins. Alternatively, *E. repens* may produce carboline in part for induction of its own defense responses, and has unintended effects on neighboring plants such as *H. vulgare*.

Induced herbivore defense via predator attraction. In addition to having direct effects on herbivore behavior, some root exudates induce defense responses in neighboring plants that reduce herbivore populations indirectly by attracting predators and parasites of the offending herbivore (30). For example, *V. faba* plants under attack release root exudates that induce green leafy volatile production in undamaged *V. faba* plants, which in turn attracts aphid parasitoids (42a). Similarly, *Phaseolus lunatus* (lima bean) plants under attack by spider mites produce root exudates that induce volatile production in undamaged *P. lunatus* plants, attracting predatory mites (66). Green leafy volatiles produced by plants under herbivore attack have also been shown to induce volatile production in neighboring plants, increasing the predator attraction signal (24). Thus, both root exudates and leafy volatiles can serve as signals to inform plants of herbivores nearby. Plants that have developed the ability to "eavesdrop" on the chemical status of their neighbors are more likely to be prepared for herbivore attacks, and can participate in coordinated biocontrol efforts that may substantially reduce herbivore populations. Most research on induced herbivore defense responses within plant communities has focused on volatile signals and predator behavior aboveground. Further research is needed to identify and characterize the root exudates that initiate volatile production in neighboring, undamaged plants.

Mechanisms That Influence Soil Resources

Some effects of root exudates on both positive and negative plant-plant interactions may also be mediated by indirect effects on soil resources (84, 184). Root exudation can increase or decrease soil nutrient availability by altering soil chemistry and soil biological processes. These effects can in turn influence outcomes of resource competition between plants, particularly if the root exudates alter the limiting resources. Effects of root exudates on soil resource availability may most often be strongest in the rhizosphere of the plants that produce them, providing a competitive advantage over neighboring plants that lack the same abilities. However, in some systems, root exudates may influence soil properties on a larger scale, with the potential for positive or negative effects on soil resource availability to neighboring plants. Here, we discuss two of the mechanisms through which root exudation of plant secondary metabolites can influence soil resource availability: phytosiderophore secretion and organic acid secretion.

Phytosiderophores and micronutrient availability. Some root exudates that act as metal chelators in the rhizosphere can increase the availability of metallic soil micronutrients, including iron, manganese, copper, and zinc (37). Metal chelators form complexes with soil metals, thus releasing metals that are bound to soil particles and increasing metal solubility and mobility. The best evidence that plants use chelators in root exudates to increase micronutrient availability comes from research on the effects of graminoid phytosiderophores on iron (Fe) availability. Although Fe is often relatively abundant in soil, it is also often present as insoluble Fe(III) precipitates, particularly in soils with high or neutral pH. Graminoid-secreted phytosiderophores bind to Fe(III) to form Fe(III)-phytosiderophores, which grasses can take up with substantially greater efficiency than other chelated forms of Fe (153). Phytosiderophores that have been identified include nonproteinogenic amino acids such as mugenoic and avenic acid (165). Graminoid secretion of phytosiderophores is markedly greater in Fe-deficient than Fe-sufficient plants, indicating an important role of the compounds in mitigating Fe stress. Different grasses efficiently take up Fe(III) bound to phytosiderophores produced by other species (153), suggesting that phytosiderophore secretion may increase Fe availability across graminoid communities. The evidence that rhizosecreted chelators play a similarly important role in micronutrient availability to dicots is less strong than for graminoids (88). However, many phenolics produced by dicots have the potential to form complexes with metallic micronutrients and may also increase metal availability (37).

Organic acids and phosphorus availability. Organic acids can also act as metal chelators in the rhizosphere, but are thought to have more important effects on phosphorus availability than on micronutrient availability (37). Phosphorus, like iron, is often relatively abundant in soils, but in unavailable forms. In particular, phosphorus is often bound in insoluble ferric, aluminum, and calcium phosphates, especially in soils with high pH. Organic acids such as citric, malic, and oxalic acid can form complexes with the iron or aluminum in ferric and aluminum phosphates, thus releasing plant-available phosphates into the soil (37, 118). Organic acids may also increase phosphorus availability by blocking phosphorus absorption sites on soil particles or by forming complexes with cations on soil mineral surfaces (88). Several plants increase organic acid rhizosecretion substantially in response to phosphorus deficiencies, including *Lupinus alba* (white lupine) (87, 129), *Brassica napus* (rape) (80), and *Medicago sativa* (alfalfa) (108). Among species examined for organic acid production in response to phosphorus stress, lupines exhibit the strongest trends (37). Lupines form clusters of specialized root structures, termed proteoid roots, in response to phosphorus deficiency. Mature proteoid roots appear to both increase organic acid production and decrease organic acid metabolism compared to nonproteoid roots, resulting in much higher levels of organic acid exudation (1.16 compared to 0.09 μmol h^{-1} g^{-1} in one study) (91, 129, 171). Perhaps as a result, phosphorus uptake can be as much as 50% greater in proteoid than nonproteoid lupine roots (129). However, to date, research on effects of organic acids on phosphorus availability and uptake has been conducted mainly under relatively unrealistic laboratory conditions. Further studies to determine rhizosphere concentrations of organic acids in live soil and to examine the effects of those concentrations on phosphorus solubility and uptake are needed to confirm the role of organic acids in plant responses to phosphorus stress (88). In addition, it has not yet been determined whether the high rates of organic acid secretion by lupines also increase phosphorus availability to neighboring plants.

Plant-Plant Molecular Interactions

The molecular targets of root exudates remain poorly defined. For allelochemicals, a range of cellular effects have been reported, from loss of plasma membrane integrity and ion leakage (54) to inhibition of photosynthetic and respiratory electron transport (1, 54, 141) and inhibition of cell division (3). There are very few cases where the effects of allelochemicals are proposed to be more or less direct. For example, sorgoleone likely interferes with mitochondrial electron transport by inhibiting the reduction of cytochrome c_1 by cytochrome b, a site inhibited by several hydroxyquinone analogus (178), and the photosynthetic electron transport chain by blocking oxidation of the PSII-reduced primary electron acceptor, by binding to Q_B (62). Similarly, juglone and sorgoleone inhibit plasma membrane proton pumping (72, 73), likely contributing directly to loss of membrane integrity and ion leakage. One other potential direct allelochemical effect contributing to cell death is through generation of reactive oxygen species (ROS) and subsequent oxidative damage to the target plant. Bais et al. (9) reported that catechin produced from *Centaurea maculosa* could elicit root toxicity associated with an increase in ROS production by the susceptible root. Scavenging the ROS change reduced catechin's toxicity, leading to the idea that ROS might be part of the phytoxic cascade elicited by this root exudate. Indeed, an increase in oxidative stress has been proposed as a widespread phenomenon in such allelopathic responses (9, 34, 152). Environmental stress is often linked to oxidative stress, which is countered by a plant antioxidant system including ascorbate, superoxide dismutase, catalase, and the glutathione system (4). ROS can have wide-ranging damaging effects on biology through directly modifying cellular components. One such action that may be highly relevant to allelochemical-induced toxicity is ROS-related effects on the lipid bilayer, such as lipid peroxiadation. Lipid peroxidation leads to the destruction of the polyunsaturated fatty acids that are integral to membrane integrity and transport activities across the plasma membrane. Increase in lipid peroxidation accompanies addition of aqueous allelochemical in tomato and cucumber roots (34, 147) and, as noted above, electrolyte leakage from cells is often associated with allelopathic response. It is interesting that a range of antioxidant system-related genes are induced in *Arabidopsis* treated with catechin (9). Thus, although a major pathway to plant resistance to allelochemical action is thought to be through chemical detoxification and sequestration (187), the relationship between antioxidant system and allelochemical resistance is worthy of a more in-depth study.

However, in addition to a direct role in cell mortality, ROS is also well characterized as a signaling molecule (4). For example, ROS gates signal-related ion channels (e.g., 52, 100, 140) and has critical roles in mediating hormone responses (105). These observations highlight the possibility that root exudates could act via triggering a host of signaling events within the susceptible plant. Thus, flavanoids are well characterized in animal cells as being signaling molecules (188), and in plants they act in many signaling and regulatory pathways. For example, they modulate auxin transport either directly through interactions with the transport system (26, 124) or possibly indirectly via regulating the vesicular trafficking responsible for targeting this system to the correct membrane surface (139). Similarly, flavanoids play roles in pollen germination (121), perhaps via a protein kinase signaling cascade (67). However, the molecular sites of action and signaling cascades triggered by flavanoids in general, and especially by the varied components of root exudates, are unknown. Defining potential receptors and the associated signaling systems for these exudates is an area with great potential to help elucidate how exudates yield such highly specific and yet varied responses in susceptible plants.

PLANT-MICROBE INTERACTIONS MEDIATED BY ROOT EXUDATES

Plant-microbe interactions can positively influence plant growth through a variety of mechanisms, including fixation of atmospheric nitrogen by different classes of proteobacteria (123), increased biotic and abiotic stress tolerance imparted by the presence of endophytic microbes (157), and direct and indirect advantages imparted by plant growth–promoting rhizobacteria (63) (**Figure 2**). Bacteria can also positively interact with plants by producing protective biofilms or antibiotics operating as biocontrols against potential pathogens (7), or by degrading plant- and microbe-produced compounds in the soil that would otherwise be allelopathic or even autotoxic. However, rhizosphere bacteria can also have detrimental effects on plant health and survival through pathogen or parasite infection. Secreted chemical signals from both plants and microbes mediate these complex exchanges and determine whether an interaction will be malevolent or benign.

Root colonization is important as the first step in infection by soil-borne pathogens and beneficial associations with microorganisms. The "rhizosphere effect," first described by Hiltner in 1904 (78), assumes that many microorganisms are attracted to nutrients exuded by plant roots. Hiltner observed that the number and activity of microorganisms increased in the vicinity of plant roots. However, in addition to providing a carbon-rich environment, plant roots initiate cross talk with soil microbes by producing signals that are recognized by the microbes, which in turn produce signals that initiate colonization. Motility is an important trait for competitive pathogens and beneficial microbes and enables participation in this cross talk (39, 112, 113). Chemical attraction of soil microbes to plant roots, or chemotaxis, is a well understood mechanism involved in initiating cross talk between plant roots and microbes (8). Another recently discovered mechanism involves the use of electric potentials in plant roots, produced by electrogenic ion transport at the root surface, to attract swimming zoospores of oomycete plant pathogens to plant root surfaces (174). These data also suggest that electrical signals may mask the chemical signals in mediating short-range responses of oomycete zoospores to root surfaces. It is not known whether the perception of chemotaxis or electrotaxis signals may affect the likelihood that soil microbes will act as pathogens or symbionts. Below, we describe in depth the direct and indirect positive and negative roles of root exudates in mediating plant-microbe interactions in the rhizosphere.

Positive Plant-Microbe Interactions

Nodulation of legumes by rhizobia. Rhizobia form symbiotic associations with leguminous plants by fixing atmospheric nitrogen in root nodules. Scientists have always won-

dered whether plants outside the Fabaceae family might be manipulated to form associations with rhizobia (109). However, rhizobia-legume interactions are very specific, allowing specific rhizobial strains to nodulate with specific host legumes. *Sinorhizobium meliloti* effectively nodulates species of the *Medicago*, *Melilotus*, and *Trigonella* genera, whereas *Rhizobium leguminosarum bv viciae* induces nodules in the *Pisum*, *Vicia*, *Lens*, and *Lathyrus* genera. However, not all rhizobia-legume associations are this limited. For example, Rhizobium strain NGR234 nodulates with 232 species of legumes from 112 genera tested and even nodulates with the nonlegume *Parasponia andersonii*, a member of the elm family (149). Conversely, not all members of the legume family form nodules. Of the three subfamilies of legumes, *Caesalpinoideae*, *Mimosoideae*, and *Papilionoideae*, members of the basal subfamily *Caesalpinoideae* are mainly non-nodulating. Thus, nodulation and presumably nitrogen fixation are not ubiquitous within the legume family.

The signal components largely responsible for these specific host-microbe relationships belong to a class of compounds termed flavonoids (145). More than 4000 different flavonoids have been identified in vascular plants, and a particular subset of them is involved in mediating host specificity in legumes (142). Isoflavonoids are only found in members of the legume family. Daidzein and genistein, isoflavonoids produced by soybean (*Glycine max*), effectively induce *Bradyrhizobium japonicum nod* genes, but inhibit *S. meliloti nod* gene expression. *S. meliloti nod* genes are instead induced by luteolin (145). This specificity enables rhizobia to distinguish their hosts from other legumes. The specific flavonoid not only induces *nod* gene expression, but also rhizobial chemotaxis. Nevertheless, other than the isoflavones, most flavonoids are not unique to legumes. How do soil rhizobia recognize their host and initiate the symbiosis when nonlegume plant species growing in the same area are also sources of flavonoids? Apparently,

AMF: arbuscular mycorrhizal fungi

GUS: β-glucuronidase

CHS: chalcone synthase

once the flavonoids are perceived, another level of specificity comes into play. Flavonoids are perceived as aglycones, which induce rhizobial *nod* genes by interacting with the gene product of *nodD*, a LysR-type regulator. This interaction results in a conformational change in the NodD protein that allows it to bind to *nod* box elements in the promoters of the *nod* genes (142). The concerted expression of these genes leads to the synthesis of Nod factor molecules, lipochitooligosaccharides, that usually consist of four or five β-1,4 N-acetylglucosamines, with the terminal nonreducing sugar N-acylated by a 16–18 carbon fatty acid. Nod factors can be chemically modified with acetate, sulfate, or carbamoyl groups, or can have different sugars, such as arabinose, fructose, and substituted fructose. The degree of saturation of the acyl tail may also vary (142). The assemblage of these substitutions results in a specific Nod factor that is recognized by the host legume.

Mycorrhizal associations. Unlike the selective legume-rhizobial associations, arbuscular mycorrhizal fungi (AMF) and plant roots form associations in more than 80% of terrestrial plants. This symbiotic relationship increases nutrient uptake, improving plant fitness, and in turn, the associated fungi extract lipids and carbohydrates from the host root (5, 130). Both AMF and rhizobial associations with plants derive from a common ancestral plant-microbe interaction, likely of fungal origin. This position is supported by the fact that AMF and rhizobia share conserved proteins that regulate both AMF and rhizobial associations with plants (107). AMF may recognize the presence of a compatible host through root exudates, similar to recognition by rhizobia (125, 166). Evidence for a fungal signaling molecule that induces plant gene activation was obtained from experiments by Kosuta et al. (102), in which fungal hyphae and host roots were grown in close proximity but physically separated by impenetrable membranes. In this system, a *Medicago EARLY NODULATION11* (*ENOD11*)-promoter::β-glucuronidase (GUS) fusion, which is responsive to both AMF and a rhizobial Nod-factor (90), was activated at a distance from the fungal hyphae (102). This was the first experimental evidence for a postulated fungally derived, diffusible signaling molecule.

The critical developmental step in the life cycle of mycorrhizal fungi is hyphal branching, which ensures contact with the host root and establishment of symbiosis (38). The branch-inducing factor is a plant signaling molecule that triggers hyphal morphogenesis preceding successful root colonization (25, 58). The development of an in vitro bioassay for hyphal branching in germinating spores from the genus *Gigaspora* (126) facilitated the analysis of the chemical characteristics and distribution of branching factor in the plant kingdom. Branch-inducing factor was present in root exudates of all the mycotrophic plants tested, but absent in those of nonhost plants. Flavonoids have been ruled out as branching factor candidates because root exudates of maize mutants deficient in chalcone synthase (CHS) show comparable activity to those of the wild type (25). Root exudates from phosphate (P)-limited plants are more active than those from plants with sufficient P, suggesting that the production and/or exudation of branching factor in roots is regulated by P availability (126). Recently, a sesquiterpene, which triggers hyphal branching in dormant mycorrhizal fungi, was identified from *Lotus japonicus* root exudates (2), establishing a novel role for root exudates in plant root-mycorrhizal cross talk.

As described above, mycorrhizal fungi extensively invade host root tissues upon perceiving a chemical response from the host roots. However, the spread of mycorrhizal mycelium occurs only in the root cortex, suggesting that host plants exert control over fungal proliferation, confining it to specific root tissues. Defense processes, which are triggered in response to microbial invasion, are modulated in mycorrhizal roots (56). Most host plants show remarkably little cytological reaction to appressorium formation or the first steps of root colonization (57). Some elements of plant defense response such as phenylpropanoid biosynthesis, oxidative stress-induced enzymes, and pathogenesis-related (PR) genes are activated in mycorrhizal roots. In most cases, however, these defense responses are weak, transient, or strictly localized, differing from those in plant-pathogen interactions (57). Transcripts encoding enzymes of the flavonoid biosynthetic pathway, phenylalanine ammonia lyase (PAL), and chalcone synthase (CHS), but not the defense-specific enzyme isoflavone reductase (IFR), are induced specifically in cells containing arbuscules in *M. truncatula*. This induction may reflect biosynthesis of flavonoid compounds that stimulate the growth of mycorrhizal fungi rather than production of antimicrobial phytoalexins (68, 69). Changes in the profiles of antioxidative enzymes such as superoxide dismutase (SOD), catalases, and peroxidases have also been observed in mycorrhizal roots (19, 136). A recent study by Lanfranco et al. (106) describes the cloning and characterization of a *CuZnSOD* gene from *Gigaspora margarita* and presents evidence that this gene is differentially expressed during the fungal life cycle. The study also showed that the expression levels of *G. margarita CuZnSOD* are enhanced following exposure to plant root exudates.

Plant growth–promoting bacteria. Bacteria thrive on abundant nutrients in the rhizosphere and some of these rhizobacteria provide benefits to the plant, resulting in plant growth stimulation (63). Bacteria are likely to locate plant roots through cues exuded from the root, and root exudates such as carbohydrates and amino acids stimulate PGPB chemotaxis on root surfaces (162). Root exudates also influence flagellar motility in some rhizospheric bacteria (39). To test the hypothesis that motility was induced by chemotaxis toward exudate components, *cheA* mutants, motile but defective in flagella-driven chemotaxis, were constructed in four strains of *Pseu-*

domonas fluorescens, a known PGPB (112, 113). Relative to wild-type bacteria, mutants had a strongly reduced ability to competitively colonize roots (39). Thus, chemotaxis appears to be important for competitive colonization by extracellular PGPB. The bacterial Major Outer Membrane Protein (MOMP) also plays an important role in early host recognition. MOMPs from *Azospirillum brasilense* bind to membrane-immobilized root extracts from several plant species with differing affinities. The *A. brasilense* MOMP showed stronger adhesion to extracts of cereals than extracts of legumes and tomatoes, and may act as an adhesin involved in root adsorption and cell aggregation of the bacterium (27).

Some PGPB produce phytostimulators, which directly enhance plant growth. In addition to fixing atmospheric nitrogen, *Azospirillum* spp. secrete phytohormones such as auxins, cytokinins, and gibberellins (163). There is the exciting possibility that most PGPB are capable of producing growth regulators continuously, provided that precursors of phytohormones are available in the rhizosphere. Root exudates could supply the pool of precursors for PGPBs to biotransform. An interesting report describes the mapping of sugar and amino acid availability in the root exudates of *Avena barbata* (85). The study showed the availability of tryptophan mainly near the root tip region. Tryptophan is the precursor for a major auxin, indole 3-acetic acid (33), suggesting that PGPB could exploit root exudate pools for various precursors of growth regulators.

Other rhizobacteria create "suppressive soils" by controlling plant diseases caused by soil fungi and bacteria. The mechanisms responsible for this biocontrol activity include competition for nutrients, niche exclusion, induced systemic resistance (ISR), and the production of antifungal metabolites. The biocontrol agents that are best characterized at the molecular level belong to the genus *Pseudomonas*. Most of the identified *Pseudomonas* biocontrol strains produce antifungal metabolites, of which phenazines, pyrrolnitrin,

PAL: phenylalanine ammonia lyase

IFR: isoflavone reductase

Phytoalexins: toxic compounds produced by higher plants in response to attack by pathogens and to other stresses; sometimes referred to as plant antibiotics, but rather nonspecific, having a general fungicidal and bacteriocidal action

SOD: superoxide dismutase

MOMP: Major Outer Membrane Protein

Biotransform: the transformation of a material by microbial action

ISR: induced systemic resistance

DAPG:
2,4-diacetylphloro-
glucinol

CMV: Cucumber
mosaic virus

RA: rosmarinic acid

2,4-diacetylphloroglucinol (DAPG), and py-oluteorin are most frequently detected. However, antifungal metabolites belonging to the class of cyclic lipopeptides, such as viscosinamide (127) and tensin (128), have also been discovered. Viscosinamide prevents infection of *Beta vulgaris* L. (sugarbeet) by *Pythium ultimum* (170). *Arabidopsis thaliana* ecotype Columbia plants (Col-0) treated with the PGPBs *Serattia marcescens* strain 90–166 and *Bacillus pumilus* strain SE34 developed minor disease symptoms upon infection with the Cucumber mosaic virus (CMV) (156). The study also showed that the acquired resistance in *Arabidopsis* plants to CMV by *B. pumilus* strain 90–166 is caused by adapting a signaling pathway for virus protection that is independent of salicylic acid (156). Finally, it was reported that some of the known gram-positive biocontrol PGPBs (such as *B. subtilis* 6051 strain) assist plants in evading a gram-negative plant pathogen, *Pseudomonas syringae* pv. *tomato* DC3000, by forming a protective biofilm on *A. thaliana* roots limiting pathogen access to the root surface and by producing an antimicrobial cyclic lipopeptide surfactin (7).

Negative Plant-Microbe Interactions

Antimicrobial effects. Plant root exudates substantially increase microbial activity in the rhizosphere (134). The role root exudates play in pathogenesis of root-infecting bacteria and fungi, however, has not been fully appreciated, in part because of inadequate methods available for analysis. Just as symbiotic root-microbe interactions depend on secondary metabolites in root exudates for initiation and development of beneficial associations, the survival of physically vulnerable root cells under continuous attack from pathogenic microorganisms depends on "underground chemical warfare" mediated by plant secretion of phytoalexins, defense proteins, and other as yet unknown chemicals (8, 9, 50). *Arabidopsis*, rice, corn, soybean, and the model legume *Medicago truncatula*, which have been subject to intensive sequencing efforts,

are, collectively, rich sources of antimicrobial indole, terpenoid, benzoxazinone, and flavonoid/isoflavonoid natural products. The unexplored chemodiversity of root exudates in all these genetically tractable species is an obvious place to search for novel biologically active compounds, including antimicrobials.

Bais et al. (11) identified rosmarinic acid (RA), a caffeic acid ester, in the root exudates of hairy root cultures of sweet basil (*Ocimum basilicum*) elicited using fungal cell wall extracts from *Phytophthora cinnamoni*. Basil roots also exuded RA by fungal in situ challenge with *Pythium ultimum*, and RA demonstrated potent antimicrobial activity against an array of soil-borne microorganisms, including an opportunistic plant pathogen *Pseudomonas aeruginosa* (11). Brigham et al. (22) reported that *Lithospermum erythrorhizon* hairy roots showed elicited, cell-specific production of pigmented naphthoquinones that had biological activity against soil-borne bacteria and fungi. These findings strongly suggest the importance of root exudates in defending the rhizosphere against pathogenic microorganisms.

Distinguishing between phytoalexins, which are produced in response to pathogen attack, and phytoanticipins, which are produced constitutively and prior to attack, can be difficult, because the terms describe in vivo antimicrobial activity. In most cases, local concentrations of phytoalexins have not been measured in cells that are in direct contact with invading microorganisms. One exception is a careful study of the cellular- and organ-level concentrations of different classes of phenylpropanoids in the root exudates of *A. thaliana*. Phenylpropanoid levels were significantly higher in roots that were challenged by nonhost bacterial pathogens (nonhost *Pseudomonas syringae* strains) compared to host bacterial pathogens (*P. syringae* pv. *tomato* DC3000). Bacterial pathogens capable of infecting roots and causing disease were resistant to these compounds, suggesting an important role of these compounds in defense against nonhost pathogens (6). In contrast, a recent study revealed that concentrations of indolic and phenylpropanoid secondary metabolites in *A. thaliana* roots increased upon infection with the root-pathogenic oomycete *Pythium sylvaticum* (15, 167). These results indicate that roots differ greatly from root exudates with regard to the nature and relative abundance of major soluble phenylpropanoid constituents and with regard to responses to applied biological stress. To date, only a few studies have been undertaken to gain insights into the diverse metabolic realm of antimicrobial root exudates. These recent findings outline the current direction of this field, which may lead to the discovery of novel antimicrobial compounds and to unraveling as yet unknown root-microbe interactions in the rhizosphere.

Quorum-sensing inhibitors and signal mimics. A number of studies have shown overlap in the virulence factors that are required for bacterial pathogenesis in both mammalian and plant systems (86, 150, 151). In a large number of pathogenic bacteria, initiation of the production and secretion of these virulence factors is controlled by a phenomenon described as quorum-sensing (QS). Briefly, QS is a density-dependent regulatory mechanism that was first described in the aquatic bacteria *Vibrio fischeri* as the signal-mediated induction of the *lux* genes responsible for bioluminescence (45). QS activation is mediated by small autoinducer (AI) molecules, which are responsible for cell-cell communication, and the coordinated action of many bacteria, including plant-associated bacteria. The most commonly reported type of autoinducer signals are N-acyl homoserine lactones (AHLs) (177), although half a dozen other molecules, including diketopiperazines in several gram-negative bacteria (81), a furanosyl borate diester in *Vibrio harveyi* (32), and γ-butyrolactone in *Streptomyces* (191), have also been implicated in density-dependent signaling. Typically, a basal level of AHLs are constitutively synthesized until a threshold population of bacteria has been achieved, at

which point these molecules serve as ligands to a global transcription regulator (LuxR or LuxR-like proteins) that activates many QS-controlled genes, including virulence factors. The rhizosphere contains a higher proportion of AHL-producing bacteria as compared to bulk soil, suggesting that they play a role in colonization (48). This leads to the speculation that plants could be using root-exuded compounds in the rhizosphere to take advantage of this bacterial communication system and influence colonizing communities. Discovery and characterization of these plant-secreted compounds could have important biological implications in both agriculture and medicine.

Since the discovery of penicillin, only a limited selection of new antibiotics have been discovered or synthesized for treating bacterial infections. These antibiotics work by interfering with specific metabolic events that ultimately culminate in the death of the bacteria. However, selective pressure exerted by this approach has resulted in the survival of antibiotic-resistant bacterial strains. This has created an urgent need for new strategies to control bacterial infections (74). A recent trend in drug discovery has been to search for compounds that are capable of inhibiting or interfering with QS in pathogenic bacteria. QS inhibitors may prove to be valuable treatments for bacterial infections because they decrease selective pressure by having little effect on bacterial growth and survival, while downregulating the production of antibiotic-resistant biofilms and bacterial toxins (75, 76). Because most bacteria are naturally present in soil, yet only a handful of these bacteria have become successful plant pathogens, it stands to reason that plants, using their staggering array of root-secreted phytochemicals, may have evolved the ability to interfere with bacteria via their QS systems.

Indeed, a fair body of evidence suggests that cross talk between plants and bacteria may occur through QS signal mimics. QS mediates several plant-microbe interactions, both pathogenic and beneficial. The first

Quorum-sensing (QS): the density-dependent mechanism used by many bacteria to regulate gene expression in a coordinated manner

AI: autoinducer molecules

AHL: N-acyl homoserine lactones

described examples of plant-secreted QS mimics were halogenated furanones produced by the marine red algae, *Delisea pulchra* (59). These compounds are structurally similar to bacterial AHLs and are capable of interfering with QS-controlled processes such as swarming and bioluminescence (59), as well as production of virulence factors and biofilm formation in *Pseudomonas aeruginosa* (76). These particular compounds displaced tritiated AHLs from *E. coli* cells engineered to overproduce LuxR receptors (116), leading to reduced LuxR activity by destabilizing this protein, and resulting in accelerated proteolytic degradation (115). Furthermore, halogenated furanone concentrations found on the algal surface were sufficient to prevent gram-negative bacteria from colonizing algal thalli (43, 97).

AHL signal mimics have also been found in secretions of higher plants and in the unicellular green algae, *Chlamydomonas reinhardtii*, but their exact chemical nature has not been identified (55, 168, 169). Limited studies have shown that several higher plants, including *Pisum sativum* (pea), *Coronilla varia* (crown vetch), *Medicago truncatula*, *Oryza sativa* (rice), *Glycine max* (soybean), and *Lycopersicum lycopersicon* (tomato), all contain components in their exudates that are capable of activating bioluminescence in several QS reporter strains (169). These compounds partitioned into polar solvents, suggesting that they are not structurally similar to the AHLs, and probably interact with bacterial QS systems differently than structural analogues such as the halogenated furanones. These signal mimics appear to stimulate QS-controlled processes in most cases. For instance, swarming in *Serratia liquefaciens* appeared to be specifically induced by *P. sativum* exudates as well as several other plant compounds, as indicated by parallel induction of both swarming and *swr*A gene expression and synthesis of serrawettin, a lipopeptide surfactant required for surface swimming (46). In addition, exudates of several other plants activated bioluminescence in LuxRI', AhyRI', and LasRI' plasmid

reporters. On the other hand, pea seedling exudates inhibited AHL-controlled behaviors in *Chromobacterium violaceum* (169), and a purified AHL mimic from *C. reinhardtii* specifically stimulated the LasR receptor in *P. aeruginosa*; however, the effect on *Sinorhizobium meliloti* was ambiguous, with some QS-related proteins being stimulated and others being suppressed (168). These data hint that QS signal mimics may be widespread in the plant kingdom, and suggest that these mimic compounds interact specifically with different QS receptors from bacteria, leading to either the activation of transcription of QS-controlled genes or the destabilization and degradation of the receptor protein (14).

Although QS signal mimics have been found in a range of plant species, they appear to be particularly prevalent among nodulating plants, such as *P. sativum*, *C. varia*, and *M. truncatula*. As previously discussed, an intricate two-way signaling between nitrogen-fixing rhizobia and leguminous host plants is required to form a symbiotic relationship. The nodulating plant *M. truncatula* has the ability to detect and respond to nanomolar concentrations of bacterial AHLs from both *S. meliloti* and *P. aeruginosa* (119). Proteome analysis revealed significant changes in the accumulation of more than 150 proteins in response to these bacterial AHLs, with about one third of those proteins showing distinct differences in terms of direction or magnitude of change in accumulation, or timing of the response to the different AHLs. This suggests that a general set of genes is activated in response to bacterial AHLs, but that the plant can also differentiate between AHLs to activate specific genes. Exposure to C_6-HL, the principal AHL produced by several bacterial species, including some *Rhizobium* strains, also led to increased secretion of AHL mimics in exudates of *M. truncatula* (119). Although direct proof remains elusive, indirect lines of evidence suggest that leguminous plants may have evolved the ability to secrete AHL mimics as a means of increasing the efficiency of their nitrogen-fixing symbionts while possibly confusing would-be pathogens by causing them to activate QS-controlled genes before there is a sufficiently large number of bacteria to overcome host defenses.

Ecological Plant-Microbe Interactions

Plant-microbe interactions in the rhizosphere are responsible for a number of intrinsic processes such as carbon sequestration, ecosystem functioning, and nutrient cycling (159). The composition and quantity of microbes in the soil influence the ability of a plant to obtain nitrogen and other nutrients. Plants can influence these net ecosystem changes through deposition of secondary metabolites into the rhizosphere that attract or inhibit the growth of specific microorganisms. This rhizodeposition, made up of small-molecular weight metabolites, amino acids, secreted enzymes, mucilage, and cell lysates, can range from less than 10% of the net carbon assimilation by a plant to as much as 44% of a nutrient-stressed plant's total carbon (64, 138). Soil microbes utilize this abundant carbon source, thereby implying that selective secretion of specific compounds may encourage beneficial symbiotic and protective relationships whereas secretion of other compounds inhibit pathogenic associations (6, 80, 81).

Fons et al. (51) demonstrated that they could change the microbial population dynamics in the rhizosphere of *Trifolium subterraneum* (clover) by adding 1% saponin from *Gypsophila paniculata. Aquaspirrillum* spp., typically found in *G. paniculata* rhizospheres, became the dominant microbe in the *T. subterraneum* rhizosphere. Furthermore, *Chryseomonas* spp. and *Acinetobacter* spp., the two previously dominant bacteria found in the *T. subterraneum* rhizosphere, were significantly decreased (51). Although there were no apparent negative effects on *T. subterraneum* colonized by *Aquaspirillum* spp., other studies have shown that changes in the microbial populations colonizing a plant's rhizosphere can

have detrimental or beneficial effects. Callaway et al. (28) showed that fungicide treatments affected the interactions between the invasive weed *Centaurea maculosa* and neighboring plant species. For instance, *C. maculosa* biomass was increased in untreated soils when growing with two native grass species, *Festuca idahoensis* and *Koelaria cristata*; however, this effect was not seen when *C. maculosa* was grown alone or with these two grasses in Benomyl-treated soils. This indirectly suggests that mycorrhizal fungi associated with these grasses favor the growth of *C. maculosa*. However, when the same experiment was conducted using *C. maculosa* and the forb, *Gaillardia aristata*, the opposite effect was observed, with *G. aristata*-associated fungi apparently having detrimental effects on *C. maculosa* growth. None of the beneficial or detrimental effects were seen when *C. maculosa* was grown in the presence of different soil microbial communities when competing plants were absent, indicating that these effects are not direct, but part of more complex ecosystem-level interactions.

Plant root exudates also affect the level of contamination found in soil and ground water from various environmental pollutants. This rhizoremediation results from root exudate-mediated stimulation of bacterial growth and survival, resulting in more efficient degradation of environmental pollutants (103). In addition, root colonization of pollutant-degrading bacteria allows penetration and spread of these beneficial bacteria to other areas of the soil. This naturally occurring process is effective for degradation of a variety of environmental pollutants. For example, *Pseudomonas putida* strains associated with root systems of *Zea mays* (corn) and *Triticum aestivum* (wheat) effectively rhizoremediate soils containing 3-methyl benzoate and 2,4-D, respectively (95, 154). To enhance this process, select pairings of specific plant species and bacterial species or communities that would allow even more efficient and targeted degradation of environmental contaminants are being sought (103, 104).

Rhizoremediation: the contribution of rhizosphere microbes to the degradation of environmental pollutants

Direct and Indirect Effects of Root Exudates on Rhizosphere Nematodes

As described above, root exudates provide a source of organic carbon to soil microbes, leading to abundant microbial populations in the rhizosphere (53). Microbial-feeding nematodes take advantage of these dense microbial populations as a food source and increase microbial turnover, and thus nutrient supply, to the plant when digesting microbes (65). Plant species and environmental conditions greatly affect the quality and quantity of carbon and nutrient sources secreted into the rhizosphere and the structure of the microbial community around roots, but the influence of these factors on microbe-nematode interactions is still unknown.

Root-feeding nematodes may participate in complex interactions with roots and soil microbes. Rovira et al. (155) estimated that, despite the large microbial populations in the rhizosphere, bacteria occupy <10% of the root surface and that fungal hyphal densities are only 12–14 mm m^{-2} root. At such densities, mobile nematodes may readily avoid nematode microbial pathogens and select uncolonized sections of root on which to feed. In addition, the accumulation of root-secreted nematicidal compounds may be avoided by parasitic nematodes. Until recently, there was little work on the impact of root exudates on rhizosphere interactions between plant roots, microbes, and nematodes. Using a ^{14}C pulse-labeling technique, Yeates et al. (193) demonstrated that infection of white clover (*Trifolium repens*) roots by *Heterodera trifolii* and various other nematodes leads to a significant increase in photosynthetically fixed ^{14}C in soil microbial biomass. These results indicate that white clover plants infected by plant-parasitic nematodes generally release more organic compounds into the rhizosphere. Thus, increasing carbon translocation to the soil microbial biomass as a consequence of the activity of root-feeding nematodes may be another mechanism by which microfaunal grazing enhances microbial turnover. In addition, the ef-

fects of rhizosphere nematodes on the quality and quantity of root exudates in turn influence the activity of both plant pathogenic and beneficial microorganisms in the rhizosphere (20, 93). Roots infected with *Meloidogyne incognita* act as metabolic sinks, and symplastic transport of nutrients from the phloem to the feeding cell, and ultimately the nematode, results in increased leakage into the rhizosphere compared to healthy plants (42). Exudates from tomato roots infected with *M. incognita* contain more water-soluble ^{14}C and larger concentrations of several metal ions than those from healthy roots (173). Associated changes in the rhizospheric carbon:nitrogen (C:N) ratio alter the trophic state of *Rhizoctonia solani*, making the fungus a pathogen. The importance of nematode-associated increases in root exudate concentrations and altered nutrient ratios to interactions between nematodes and microbial pathogens are not yet known.

Most knowledge of microbe-nematode interactions in the rhizosphere has been derived from research with rhizobia, mycorrhizal fungi, and plant pathogens (93). Such research has clearly demonstrated complex tritrophic webs, in which nematodes and microorganisms act in competitive, additive, or synergistic associations to affect the plant host. In addition, a recent study has redefined the beneficial association of the tritrophic interactions between plant roots, microbes, and nematodes. This new study shows that soil-dwelling nematodes, such as *Caenorhabditis elegans*, may mediate interactions between roots and rhizobia in a positive way, leading to nodulation (82). Horiuchi et al. (82) found that *C. elegans* transfers the rhizobium species *Sinorhizobium meliloti* to the roots of the legume *Medicago truncatula* in response to plant root-released volatiles that attract the nematode. Thus, root-secreted volatiles, in addition to other root-secreted chemicals, may also play an important role in multitrophic interactions. Research on the tritrophic interactions between plants, nematodes, and microbial pathogens will contribute much to our understanding of the signaling systems mediated by root exudates in the rhizosphere.

METHODS TO STUDY INTERACTIONS MEDIATED BY ROOT EXUDATES

The biggest hurdle to the study of plant-plant and plant-microbe interactions mediated by root exudates is the underground nature of the roots. The study of root exudation requires knowledge of both the structure and function of a root system, as well as a meaningful assessment of the rhizospheric community. One must consider the abundance and distribution of plant species and the functional diversity and redundancy present in microbial communities. Some striking studies have used the exudation of fluorescent compounds as a marker for such interactions (10). The majority of conventional methods used in studying plant-plant and plant-microbe interactions involve in vitro tissue culture techniques (7, 10). Briefly, to study plant-plant interactions mediated by root exudates, plants are regrown in vitro in an aerated liquid media, root exudates are harvested, and concentrated exudates are tested for phytotoxicity on seedlings that share the rhizosphere of the tested plant (**Figure 3**). This methodological partitioning of root exudates has led to the isolation of a number of phytotoxins secreted by invasive plants. However, the full complexity of interactions occurring in a natural rhizosphere is eliminated in this system, and thus results should be viewed with caution (12, 16, 164, 176). There are two different ways to extract phytochemicals from root exudates: One involves extraction specifically for polar compounds, usually with methanol, whereas the second method targets nonpolar compounds using nonpolar solvents. This differential partitioning of root exudates results in isolation of various classes of chemical compounds, such as flavonoids, quinalones, carbolines, and terpenes (12, 16, 164, 176).

Identifying plant-produced antimicrobials, profiling rhizosphere microbes, and studying microbial colonization requires several methodologies. The diversity of metabolic functions possessed by microbial communities is often examined using BIOLOG GN substrate utilization assays (41), which assess the ability of the community as a whole to utilize select carbon substrates. A DNA microarray technique for the simultaneous identification of ecological function and phylogenetic affiliation of microbial populations has also been developed (96). This approach permits the assessment of growth rate and substrate utilization of individual microbial populations within a community. Advances in microscopy have also greatly facilitated study of root-microbe interactions. Confocal laser scanning microscopy (CLSM), in combination with various other fluorescent markers and reporter gene systems, is used to observe and monitor rhizosphere bacterial populations on the root surface. Most of these studies have been conducted with biocontrol microbes, specifically gram-negative *Pseudomonas* spp. (112). Using a combination of immunofluorescence and an rRNA-targeting probe that monitors the presence and metabolic activity of *P. fluorecens* DR54, Lubeck et al. (111) showed that bacteria at the root tip are the most metabolically active and that endogenous bacteria enter the rhizosphere two days after inoculation. Visualization of interactions among carrot roots, mycorrhizal mycelium, and *P. fluorescens* CHA0 showed that mucoid mutant strains of CHA0 adhere much better to the root, indicating that acidic extracellular polysaccharides can enhance root colonization (18). Also by using microscopy, it was shown that a gram-positive biocontrol bacteria *B. subtilis* competes for space against a pathogenic gram-negative bacteria *P. syringae* on *Arabidopsis* root surfaces (7).

The screening and functional identification of the diverse array of natural compounds present in root exudates that affect

CLSM: confocal laser scanning microscopy

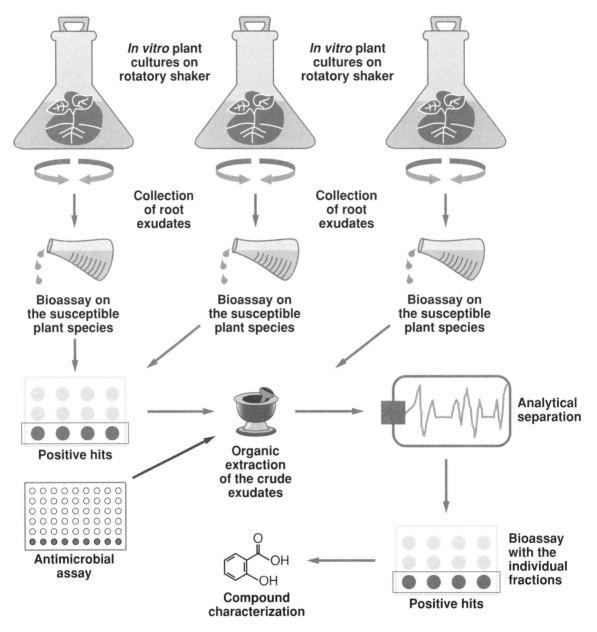

In vitro plant cultures on rotatory shaker

In vitro plant cultures on rotatory shaker

Collection of root exudates

Collection of root exudates

Bioassay on the susceptible plant species

Bioassay on the susceptible plant species

Bioassay on the susceptible plant species

Positive hits

Antimicrobial assay

Organic extraction of the crude exudates

Analytical separation

Bioassay with the individual fractions

Positive hits

Compound characterization

Figure 3

A flow chart representation of methods involved in collection, separation, bioassay, and candid compound characterization from plant root exudates.

rhizospheric microbes is a daunting task. Until recently, only traditional in planta extraction and subsequent testing of crude extracts directly on microbes was available. A caveat of this method is the inability to observe direct interactions between plant roots and microbes. To bypass this shortfall, one could grow plants and microbes together under in vitro conditions and observe the effect either component exerts on the other. This method could also be used to identify antimicrobials or QS mimics from plant root exudates. Studies to observe global gene-expression levels in rhizospheric microbes upon interacting with roots and root exudates are also possible using a number of microbes whose genomes have been sequenced. These studies would highlight the physiological functioning of microbial cells in a specific environment.

CONCLUSION

We presented a partial picture of the interactions that occur in the rhizosphere and the role of root exudates in mediating some of these processes. However, our understanding of these interactions is incomplete due to the difficulty of studying underground processes under controlled yet realistic conditions. Thus, developing novel methodologies to study rhizosphere ecology under natural conditions is needed and will require collaboration between plant biologists, ecologists, and soil scientists to develop rhizotron systems where biochemical and molecular biology studies could be performed on site. It is clear that our understanding of root-mediated processes has moved beyond the classical belief that the sole functions of roots are anchorage and uptake of water and nutrients. It is now understood that roots are rhizosphere ambassadors, facilitating communication between the plant and other organisms in the soil. Ecological knowledge indicates that aboveground interactions could potentially be translated to belowground responses in plants. What does this mean at the rhizosphere level? What is the effect of aboveground herbivory on the ability of roots to initiate microbial symbiosis or to fight microbial attack? A clear understanding of the molecular process involved in the actual secretion of phytochemicals by roots is also needed in order to develop molecular markers for this process. Finally, synthesis of the knowledge of root exudation from the molecular to the ecosystem scale will potentially lead to the development of better plants capable of absorbing more nutrients, detoxifying soils more efficiently, or more effectively warding off invasive weeds and pathogenic microbes.

Rhizotron: a device used to view and manipulate organisms in a natural rhizosphere

ACKNOWLEDGMENTS

This work was supported by grants from the U.S. Department of Defense-SERDP (SI-1388 to J.M.V.) and the National Science Foundation (NSF-IBN 0335203, J.M.V. and S.G.).

LITERATURE CITED

1. Abrahim D, Braguini WL, Kelmer-Bracht AM, Ishii-Iwamoto EL. 2000. Effects of four monoterpenes on germination, primary root growth, and mitochondrial respiration of maize. *J. Chem. Ecol.* 26:611–24
2. **Akiyama K, Matsuzaki K, Hayashi H. 2005. Plant sesquiterpenes induce hyphal branching in arbuscular mycorrhizal fungi. *Nature* 435:824–27**
3. Anaya AL, Pelayo-Benavides HR. 1997. Allelopathic potential of Mirabilis jalapa L., (Nyctaginaceae): effects on germination, growth and cell division of some plants. *Allelopathy* 4:57–68
4. Apel K, Hirt H. 2004. Reactive oxygen species: metabolism, oxidative stress, and signal transduction. *Annu. Rev. Plant Biol.* 55:373–99
5. Bago B, Pfeffer PE, Abubaker J, Jun J, Allen JW, et al. 2003. Carbon export from arbuscular mycorrhizal roots involves the translocation of carbohydrate as well as lipid. *Plant Physiol.* 131:1496–507

The first identification of a compound that induces branching in mycorrhizal fungi.

Evidence that the ability of a bacterial strain to colonize a plant's root system and subsequently to become a pathogen is based on its ability to overcome the plants antimicrobial root exudates.

6. **Bais HP, Prithiviraj B, Jha AK, Ausubel FM, Vivanco JM. 2005. Mediation of pathogen resistance by exudation of antimicrobials from roots. *Nature* 434:217–21**

7. Bais HP, Fall R, Vivanco JM. 2004. Biocontrol of *Bacillus subtilis* against infection of Arabidopsis roots by *Pseudomonas syringae* is facilitated by biofilm formation and surfactin production. *Plant Physiol.* 134:307–19

8. Bais HP, Park SW, Weir TL, Callaway RM, Vivanco JM. 2004. How plants communicate using the underground information superhighway. *Trends Plant Sci.* 9:26–32

9. Bais HP, Vepachedu R, Gilroy S, Callaway RM, Vivanco JM. 2003. Allelopathy and exotic plant invasion: from molecules and genes to species interactions. *Science* 301:1377–80

10. Bais HP, Park SW, Stermitz FR, Halligan KM, Vivanco JM. 2003. Exudation of fluorescent beta-carbolines from *Oxalis tuberosa* L. roots. *Phytochemistry* 61:539–43

11. Bais HP, Walker TS, Schweizer HP, Vivanco JM. 2002. Root specific elicitation and antimicrobial activity of rosmarinic acid in hairy root cultures of sweet basil (*Ocimum basilicum* L.). *Plant Physiol. Biochem.* 40:9837

12. Bais HP, Walker TS, Stermitz FR, Hufbauer RA, Vivanco JM. 2002. Enantiomeric-dependent phytotoxic and antimicrobial activity of ($\pm$)-catechin. A rhizosecreted racemic mixture from spotted knapweed. *Plant Physiol.* 128:1173–79

13. Bais HP, Loyola-Vargas VM, Flores HE, Vivanco JM. 2001. Root-specific metabolism: the biology and biochemistry of underground organs. *In Vitro Plant.* 37:730–41

14. Bauer WD, Mathesius U. 2004. Plant responses to bacterial quorum-sensing signals. *Curr. Opin. Plant Biol.* 7:429–33

15. Bednarek P, Schneider B, Svatos A, Oldham NJ, Hahlbrock K. 2005. Structural complexity, differential response to infection, and tissue specificity of indolic and phenylpropanoid secondary metabolism in Arabidopsis roots. *Plant Physiol.* 138:1058–70

16. Belz RG, Hurle K. 2005. Differential exudation of two benzoxazinoids–one of the determining factors for seedling allelopathy of Triticeae species. *J. Agric. Food Chem.* 53:250–61

17. Bertin C, Yang XH, Weston LA. 2003. The role of root exudates and allelochemicals in the rhizosphere. *Plant Soil* 256:67–83

18. Bianciotto V, Andreotti S, Balestrini R, Bonfante P, Perotto S. 2001. Mucoid mutants of the biocontrol strain *Pseudomonas fluorescens* CHA0 show increased ability in biofilm formation on mycorrhizal and nonmycorrhizal carrot roots. *Mol. Plant- Microbe Interact.* 14:255–60

19. Blilou I, Ocampo JA, Garcia-Garrido JM. 2000. Induction of Ltp (lipid transfer protein) and Pal (phenylalanine ammonia-lyase) gene expression in rice roots colonized by the arbuscular mycorrhizal fungus *Glomus mosseae*. *J. Exp. Bot.* 51:1969–77

20. Bowers JH, Nameth ST, Riedel RM, Rowe RC. 1996. Infection and colonization of potato roots by *Verticillium dahliae* as affected by *Pratylenchus penetrans* and *P. crenatus*. *Phytopathology* 86:614–21

21. Brady NC, Weil RR. 1999. *The Nature and Property of Soils*. Upper Saddle Hall, NJ: Prentice Hall

22. Brigham LA, Michaels PJ, Flores HE. 1999. Cell-specific production and antimicrobial activity of naphthoquinones in roots of *Lithospermum erythrorhizon*. *Plant Physiol.* 119:417–28

23. Brimecombe MJ, De Leij Frans AAM, Lynch JM. 2001. Nematode community structure as a sensitive indicator of microbial perturbations induced by a genetically modified *Pseudomonas fluorescens* strain. *Biol. Fertil. Soils* 34:270–75

24. Bruin J, Sabelis MW. 2001. Meta-analysis of laboratory experiments on plant-plant information transfer. *Biochem. Sys. Ecol.* 29:1089–102

25. Buee M, Rossignol M, Jauneau A, Ranjeva R, Bécard G. 2000. The pre-symbiotic growth of arbuscular mycorrhizal fungi is induced by a branching factor partially purified from plant root exudates. *Mol. Plant-Microbe Interact.* 13:693–98

26. Buer CS, Muday GK. 2004. The transparent testa4 mutation prevents flavonoid synthesis and alters auxin transport and the response of Arabidopsis roots to gravity and light. *Plant Cell* 16:1191–205

27. Burdman S, Dulguerova G, Okon Y, Jurkevitch E. 2001. Purification of the major outer membrane protein of *Azospirillum brasilense*, its affinity to plant roots, and its involvement in cell aggregation. *Mol. Plant- Microbe Interact.* 14:555–58

28. Callaway RM, Thelen GC, Barth S, Ramsey, Gannon JE. 2004. Soil fungi alter interactions between the invader *Centaurea maculosa* and North American natives. *Ecology* 85:1062–71

29. Callaway RM, Aschehoug ET. 2000. Invasive plants versus their new and old neighbors: a mechanism for exotic invasion. *Science* 290:521–23

30. Chamberlain K, Guerrieri E, Pennacchio F, Pettersson J, Pickett JA, et al. 2001. Can aphid-induced plant signals be transmitted aerially and through the rhizosphere? *Biochem. Syst. Ecol.* 29:1063–74

31. Chang M, Netzly DH, Butler LG, Lynn DG. 1986. Chemical-regulation of distance - characterization of the 1st natural host germination stimulant for *Striga asiatica*. *J. Am. Chem. Soc.* 108:7858–60

32. Chen X, Schauder S, Potier N, van Drosselaer A, Pelczer I, et al. 2002. Structural identification of a bacterial quorum-sensing signal containing boron. *Nature* 415:545–49

33. Cooke TJ, Poli D, Sztein AE, Cohen JD. 2002. Evolutionary patterns in auxin action. *Plant Mol. Biol.* 49:319–38

34. Cruz-Ortega R, Ayala-Cordero G, Anaya AL. 2002. Allelochemical stress produced by the aqueous leachate of Callicarpa acuminata: effects on roots of bean, maize, and tomato. *Physiol. Plant.* 116:20–27

35. Czarnota MA, Paul RN, Dayan FE, Nimbal CI, Weston LA. 2001. Mode of action, localization of production, chemical nature, and activity of sorgoleone: a potent PSII inhibitor in *Sorghum* spp. root exudates. *Weed Technol.* 15:813–25

36. Czarnota MA, Rimando AM, Weston LA. 2003. Evaluation of root exudates of seven sorghum accessions. *J. Chem. Ecol.* 29:2073–83

37. Dakora FD, Phillips DA. 2002. Root exudates as mediators of mineral acquisition in low-nutrient environments. *Plant Soil* 245:35–47

38. De Carvalho-Niebel F, Timmers AC, Chabaud M, Defaux-Petras A, Barker DG. 2002. The Nod factor-elicited annexin MtAnn1 is preferentially localized at the nuclear periphery in symbiotically activated root tissues of *Medicago truncatula*. *Plant J.* 32:343–52

39. de Weert S, Vermeiren H, Mulders IH, Kuiper I, Hendrickx N, Bloemberg GV, et al. 2002. Flagella-driven chemotaxis towards exudate components is an important trait for tomato root colonization by *Pseudomonas fluorescens*. *Mol. Plant-Microbe Interact.* 15:1173–80

40. Di Giovanni GD, Watrud LS, Seidler RJ, Widmer F. 1999. Fingerprinting of mixed bacterial strains and BIOLOG gram-negative (GN) substrate communities by enterobacterial repetitive intergenic consensus sequence-PCR (ERIC-PCR). *Curr. Microbiol.* 38:217–23

41. Dorhout RC, Gommers FJ, Kollöffel C. 1993. Phloem transport of carboxyfluorescein through tomato roots infected with *Meloidogyne incognita*. *Physiol. Mol. Plant Pathol.* 43:1–10

42. Dicke M, Dijkman H. 2001. Within-plant circulation of systemic elicitor of induced defence and release from roots of elicitor that affects neighbouring plants. *Biochem. Syst. Ecol.* 29:1075–87

42a. Du YJ, Poppy GM, Powell W, Pickett JA, Wadhams LJ, Woodcock CM. 1998. Identification of semiochemicals released during aphid feeding that attract parasitoid *Aphidius ervi. J. Chem. Ecol.* 24:1355–68

43. Dworjanyn SA, de Nys R, Steinberg PD. 1999. Localization and surface quantification of secondary metabolites in the red algae Delisea pulchra. *Mar. Biol.* 133:727–36

44. Dyer AR. 2004. Maternal and sibling factors induce dormancy in dimorphic seed pairs of *Aegilops triuncialis. Plant Ecol.* 172:211–18

45. Eberhardt A, Burlingame AL, Eberhardt C, Kenyon GL, Nealson KH, Oppenheimer NJ. 1981. Structural identification of autoinducer of Phytobacterium fischeri luciferase. *Biochemistry* 20:2444–49

46. Eberl L, Molin S, Givscov M. 1999. Surface motility of Serratia liquefaciens MG1. *J. Bacteriol.* 181:1703–12

47. Einhellig FA. 1995. Mechanisms of action of allelochemicals in allelopathy. In *Allelopathy: Organisms, Processes, and Applications*, ed. Inderjit, KMM Dakshini, FA Einhellig, pp. 96. Washington, DC: Am. Chem. Soc.

48. Elasri M, Delorme S, Lemanceau P, Stewart G, Laue B, et al. 2001. Acyl-homoserine lactone production is more common among plant-associated *Pseudomonas* spp. than among soilborne *Pseudomonas* spp. *Appl. Environ. Microbiol.* 67:1198–209

49. Fate GD, Lynn DG. 1996. Xenognosin methylation is critical in defining the chemical potential gradient that regulates the spatial distribution in *Striga pathogenesis. J. Am. Chem. Soc.* 118:11369–76

50. Flores HE, Vivanco JM, Loyola-Vargas VM. 1999. "Radicle" biochemistry: the biology of root-specific metabolism. *Trends Plant Sci.* 4:220–26

51. Fons F, Amellal N, Leyval C, Saint-Martin N, Henry M. 2003. Effects of gypsophila saponins on bacterial growth kinetics and on selection of subterranean clover rhizosphere bacteria. *Can. J. Microbiol.* 49:367–73

52. Foreman J, Demidchik V, Bothwell JH, Mylona P, Miedema H, et al. 2003. Reactive oxygen species produced by NADPH oxidase regulate plant cell growth. *Nature* 422:442–46

53. Foster RC. 1986. The ultrastructure of the rhizoplane and rhizosphere. *Annu. Rev. Phytopathol.* 24:211–34

54. Galindo JCG, Hernandez A, Dayan FE, Tellez FA, Macias RN, Paul SO. 1999. Duke, Dehydrozaluzanin C, a natural sesquiterpenolide, causes rapid plasma membrane leakage. *Phytochemistry* 52:805–13

55. Gao M, Teplitski M, Robinson JB, Bauer WD. 2003. Production of substances by Medicago truncatula that affect bacterial quorum sensing. *Mol. Plant-Microbe Interact.* 16:827–34

56. Garcia-Garrido JM, Ocampo JA. 2002. Regulation of the plant defence response in arbuscular mycorrhizal symbiosis. *J. Exp. Bot.* 53:1377–86

57. Gianinazzi-Pearson V. 1996. Plant cell responses to arbuscular mycorrhizal fungi: getting to the roots of the symbiosis. *Plant Cell.* 8:1871–83

58. Giovannetti M, Sbrana C, Silvia A, Avio L. 1996. Analysis of factors involved in fungal recognition response to host-derived signals by arbuscular mycorrhizal fungi. *New Phytol.* 133:65–71

59. **Givskov M, Nys RD, Manefield M, Gram L, Maximilien R, Eberl L, et al. 1996. Eukaryotic interference with homoserine lactone-mediated prokaryotic signaling.** *J. Bacteriol.* **178:6618–22**

60. Gleba D, Borisjuk NV, Borisjuk LG, Kneer R, Poulev A, Skarzhinskaya M, et al. 1999. Use of plant roots for phytoremediation and molecular farming. *Proc. Natl. Acad. Sci. USA* 25:5973–77

61. Glinwood R, Pettersson J, Ahmed E, Ninkovic V, Birkett M, Pickett J. 2003. Change in acceptability of barley plants to aphids after exposure to allelochemicals from couch-grass (*Elytrigia repens*). *J. Chem. Ecol.* 29:261–74

62. Gonzalez VM, Kazimir J, Nimbal C, Weston LA, Cheniae GM. 1997. Inhibition of a photosystem II electron transfer reaction by the natural product sorgoleone. *J. Agric. Food Chem.* 45:1415–21

63. Gray EJ, Smith DL. 2005. Intracellular and extracellular PGPR: commonalities and distinctions in the plant-bacterium signaling processes. *Soil Biol. Biochem.* 37:395–410

64. Grayston SJ, Wang SQ, Campbell CD, Edwards AC. 1998. Selective influence of plant species on microbial diversity in the rhizosphere. *Soil Biol. Biochem.* 30:369–78

65. Griffiths BS. 1989. The role of bacterial feeding nematodes and protozoa in rhizosphere nutrient cycling. *Asp. Appl. Biol.* 22:141–45

66. Guerrieri E, Poppy GM, Powell W, Rao R, Pennacchio F. 2002. Plant-to-plant communication mediating in-flight orientation of *Aphidius ervi*. *J. Chem. Ecol.* 28:1703–15

67. Guyon V, Tang WH, Monti MM, Raiola A, Lorenzo GD, et al. 2004. Antisense phenotypes reveal a role for SHY, a pollen-specific leucine-rich repeat protein, in pollen tube growth. *Plant J.* 39:643–54

68. Harrison MJ. 2005. Signaling in the arbuscular mycorrhizal symbiosis. *Annu. Rev. Microbiol.* 59:19–42

69. Harrison MJ. 1999. Molecular and cellular aspects of the arbuscular mycorrhizal symbiosis. *Annu. Rev. Plant Physiol. Plant Mol. Biol.* 50:361–89

70. Deleted in proof

71. Hawes MC, Gunawardena U, Miyasaka S, Zhao X. 2000. The role of root border cells in plant defense. *Trends Plant Sci.* 5:128–33

72. Hejl AM, Koster KL. 2004. The allelochemical sorgoleone inhibits root H+-ATPase and water uptake. *J. Chem. Ecol.* 30:2181–91

73. Hejl AM, Koster KL. 2004. Juglone disrupts root plasma membrane H+-ATPase activity and impairs water uptake, root respiration, and growth in soybean (*Glycine max*) and corn (*Zea mays*). *J. Chem. Ecol.* 30:453–71

74. Hentzer M, Givskov M. 2003. Pharmacological inhibition of quorum sensing for the treatment of chronic bacterial infections. *J. Clin. Investig.* 112:1300–7

75. Hentzer M, Wu H, Andersen JB, Riedel K, Rasmussen TB, Bagge N, et al. 2003. Attenuation of *Pseudomonas aeruginosa* virulence by quorum-sensing inhibitors. *EMBO J.* 22:3803–15

76. Hentzer M, Riedel K, Rasmussen TB, Heydorn A, Andersen JB, Parsek MR, et al. 2002. Inhibition of quorum sensing in *Pseudomonas aeruginosa* biofilm bacteria by a halogenated furanone compound. *Microbiology* 148:87–102

77. Hierro JL, Callaway RM. 2003. Allelopathy and exotic plant invasion. *Plant Soil* 256:29–39

78. Hiltner L. 1904. Uber neure Erfahrungen und probleme auf dem gebeit der bodenbackteriologie und unter besonderer berucksichtigung der grundungung und brache. *Arb. Deut. Landwirsch Ges.* 98:59–78

The first example of a eukaryotic quorum-sensing signal mimic capable of interfering with bacterial quorum-sensing systems.

79. Hirsch AM, Bauer WD, Bird DM, Cullimore J, Tyler B, Yoder JI. 2003. Molecular signals and receptors: controlling rhizosphere interactions between plants and other organisms. *Ecology* 84:858–68

80. Hoffland E, Findenegg G, Nelemans J, van den Boogaard R. 1992. Biosynthesis and root exudation of citric and malic acids in phosphate-starved rape plants. *New Phytol.* 122:675–80

81. Holden MTG, Chhabra SR, de Nys R, Stead P, Bainton NJ, et al. 1999. Quorum-sensing cross-talk: isolation and chemical characterization of cyclic dipeptides from *Pseudomonas aeruginosa* and other gram-negative bacteria. *Mol. Microbiol.* 33:1254–66

82. Horiuchi JI, Prithiviraj B, Bais HP, Kimball BA, Vivanco JM. 2005. Soil nematodes mediate positive interactions between legume plants and rhizobium bacteria. *Planta* 15:1–10

83. Inderjit, Callaway RM. 2003. Experimental designs for the study of allelopathy. *Plant Soil* 256:1–11

84. Inderjit, Weiner J. 2001. Plant allelochemical interference or soil chemical ecology? *Perspect. Plant Ecol. Evol. Syst.* 4:3–12

85. Jaeger JH, Lindow SE, Miller S, Clark E, Firestone, MK. 1999. Mapping of sugar and amino acid availability in soil around roots with bacterial sensors of sucrose and tryptophan. *Appl. Environ. Microbiol.* 65:2685–90

86. Jha AK, Bais HP, Vivanco JM. 2005. *Enterococcus faecalis* uses mammalian virulence-related factors to exhibit potent pathogenicity in the *Arabidopsis thaliana* plant model. *Infect. Immun.* 73:464–75

87. Johnson JF, Vance CP, Allan DL. 1994. Phosphorus stress-induced proteoid roots show altered metabolism in *Lupinus albus*. *Plant Physiol.* 104:657–65

88. Jones DL, Kuzyakov Y, Hodge A. 2004. Plant and mycorrhizal regulation of rhizodeposition. *New Phytol.* 163:459–80

89. Jose S, Gillespie AR. 1998. Allelopathy in black walnut (*Juglans nigra* L.) alley cropping. I. Spatio-temporal variation in soil juglone in a black walnut-corn (*Zea mays* L.) alley cropping system in the midwestern USA. *Plant Soil* 203:191–97

90. Journet EP, van Tuinen D, Gouzy J, Crespeau H, Carreau V, et al. 2002. Exploring root symbiotic programs in the model legume *Medicago truncatula* using EST analysis. *Nucleic Acids Res.* 30:5579–92

91. Kania A, Neumann G, Martinoia E, Langlade N. 2003. Phosphorus deficiency-induced modifications in citrate catabolism and in cytosolic pH as related to citrate exudation in cluster roots of white lupin. *Plant Soil* 248:117–27

92. Keyes WJ, O'Malley RC, Kim D, Lynn DG. 2000. Signaling organogenesis in parasitic angiosperms: xenognosin generation, perception, and response. *J. Plant Growth Regul.* 19:217–31

93. Khan MW, ed. 1993. *Nematode Interactions*. London: Chapman & Hall. 377 pp.

94. Kim DJ, Kocz R, Boone L, Keyes WJ, Lynn DG. 1998. On becoming a parasite: evaluating the role of wall oxidases in parasitic plant development. *Chem. Biol.* 5:103–17

95. Kingsley MT, Fredrickson JK, Meting FB, Seidler RJ, 1994. Environmental restoration using plant-microbe. In *Bioremediation of Chlorinated and Polyaromatic Hydrocarbon Compounds*, ed. RE Hinchee, A Leeson, L Semprini, S Kong. pp 287–92. Boca Raton, FL: Lewis

96. Kirk JL, Beaudette LA, Hart M, Moutoglis P, Klironomos JN, et al. 2004. Methods of studying soil microbial diversity. *J. Microbiol. Methods* 58:169–88

Evidence suggesting that plant root volatiles may attract soil nematodes, which in turn act as vectors, facilitating the symbiotic relationship between rhizobia and legumes.

97. Kjelleberg S, Steinberg P, Givskov M, Gram L, Manefield M, de Nys R. 1997. Do marine natural products interfere with prokaryotic AHL regulatory systems? *Aquat. Microbial. Ecol.* 13:85–93

98. Kneer R, Poulev AA, Olesinski A, Raskin I. 1999. Characterization of the elicitor-induced biosysnthesis and secretion of genistin from roots of *Lupinus luteus*. *J. Exp. Bot.* 50:1553–59

99. Deleted in proof.

100. Kohler B, Hills A, Blatt MR. 2003. Control of guard cell ion channels by hydrogen peroxide and abscisic acid indicates their action through alternate signaling pathways. *Plant Physiol.* 131:385–88

101. Kong CH, Liang WJ, Xu XH, Hu F, Wang P, Jiang Y. 2004. Release and activity of allelochemicals from allelopathic rice seedlings. *J Agric. Food Chem.* 52:2861–65

102. Kosuta S, Chabaud M, Lougnon G, Gough C, Denarie J, Barker DG, Becard G. 2003. A diffusible factor from arbuscular mycorrhizal fungi induces symbiosis-specific MtENOD11 expression in roots of *Medicago truncatula*. *Plant Physiol.* 131:952–62

103. Kuiper I, Lagendijk EL, Bloemberg GV, Lugtenberg BJJ. 2004. Rhizoremediation: a beneficial plant-microbe interaction. *Mol. Plant-Microbe Interact.* 17:6–15

104. Kuiper I, Bloemberg GV, Lugtenberg BJJ. 2001. Selection of a plant-bacterium pair a novel tool for rhizostimulation of polycyclic aromatic hydrocarbon degrading bacteria. *Mol. Plant-Microbe Interact.* 14:1197–205

105. Kwak JM, Mori IC, Pei ZM, Leonhardt N, Torres MA, et al. 2003. NADPH oxidase AtrbohD and AtrbohF genes function in ROS-dependent ABA signaling in *Arabidopsis*. *EMBO J.* 22:2623–33

106. Lanfranco L, Novero M, Bonfante P. 2005. The mycorrhizal fungus *Gigaspora margarita* possesses a CuZn superoxide dismutase that is up-regulated during symbiosis with legume hosts. *Plant Physiol.* 137:1319–30

107. Levy J, Bres C, Geurts R, Chalhoub B, Kulikova O, Duc G, et al. 2004. A putative Ca^{2+} and calmodulin-dependent protein kinase required for bacterial and fungal symbioses. *Science* 303:1361–64

108. Lipton DS, Blevins DG, Blanchar RW. 1987. Citrate, malate and succinate concentration in exudates from P-sufficient and P-stressed *Medicago sativa* L. seedlings. *Plant Physiol.* 85:315–17

109. Long SR. 2001. Genes and signals in the rhizobium-legume symbiosis. *Plant Physiol.* 125:69–72

110. Deleted in proof

111. Lubeck PS, Hansen M, Sorensen J. 2000. Simultaneous detection of the establishment of seed-inoculated *Pseudomonas fluorescens* strain DR54 and native soil bacteria on sugar beet root surfaces using fluorescence antibody and in situ hybridization techniques. *FEMS Microbiol. Ecol.* 33:11–19

112. Lugtenberg BJ, Dekkers L, Bloemberg GV. 2001. Molecular determinants of rhizosphere colonization by Pseudomonas. *Annu. Rev. Phytopathol.* 39:461–90

113. Lugtenberg BJ, Chin-A-Woeng TF, Bloemberg GV. 2002. Microbe-plant interactions: principles and mechanisms. *Antonie Van Leeuwenhoek.* 81:373–83

114. Macias FA, Simonet AM, Molinillo JMG, Castellano D, Marin D, Oliveros-Bastidas A. 2005. Structure-activity relationships (SAR) studies of benzoxazinones, their degradation products and analogues. Phytotoxicity on standard target species (STS). *J. Agric. Food Chem.* 53:538–48

115. Manefield M, Rasmussen TB, Hentzer M, Andersen JB, Steinberg P, Kjellberg S, et al. 2002. Halogenated furanones inhibit quorum-sensing through accelerated LuxR turnover. *Microbiology* 148:1119–27

116. Manefield M, de Nys R, Kumar N, Read R, Givskov M, et al. 1999. Evidence that halogenated furanones from *Delisea pulchra* inhibit acylated homoserine lactone (AHL)-mediated gene expression by displacing the AHL signal from its receptor protein. *Microbiology* 145:283–91

117. Marschner H. 1995. *Mineral Nutrition of Higher Plants, Second Edition*. London: Academic

118. Masaoka Y, Kojima M, Sugihara S, Yoshihara T, Koshina M, Ichihara A. 1993. Dissolution of ferric phosphate by alfalfa (*Medicago sativa* L.) root exudates. *Plant Soil* 155/156:75–78

119. Mathesius U, Mulders S, Gao M, Teplitski M, Caetano-Anolles G, Rolfe BG, et al. 2003. Extensive and specific responses of a eukaryote to bacterial quorum-sensing signals. *Proc. Natl. Acad. Sci. USA* 100:1444–49

120. McQueen-Mason S, Cosgrove DJ. 1994. Disruption of hydrogen-bonding between plant-cell wall polymers by proteins that induce wall extension. *Proc. Natl. Acad. Sci. USA* 91:6574–78

121. Mo Y, Nagel C, Taylor LP. 1992. Biochemical complementation of chalcone synthase mutants defines a role for flavonols in functional pollen. *Proc. Natl. Acad. Sci. USA* 89:7213–17

122. Morris PF, Bone E, Tyler BM. 1998. Chemotropic and contact responses of *Phytophthora sojae* hyphae to soybean isoflavonoids and artificial substrates. *Plant Physiol.* 117:1171–78

123. Moulin L, Munive A, Dreyfus B, Boivin-Masson C. 2001. Nodulation of legumes by members of the beta-subclass of Proteobacteria. *Nature* 411:948–50

124. Murphy A, Peer WA, Taiz L. 2000. Regulation of auxin transport by aminopeptidases and endogenous flavonoids. *Planta* 211:315–24

125. Nagahashi G, Douds DD Jr. 2003. Action spectrum for the induction of hyphal branches of an arbuscular mycorrhizal fungus: exposure sites versus branching sites. *Mycol. Res.* 107:1075–82

126. Nagahashi G, Douds DD. 1999. A rapid and sensitive bioassay with practical application for studies on interactions between root exudates and arbuscular mycorrhizal fungi. *Biotechnol. Tech.* 13:893–97

127. Nielsen TH, Christophersen C, Anthoni U, Sørensen J. 1999. Viscosinamide, a new cyclic depsipeptide with surfactant and antifungal properties produced by *Pseudomonas fluorescens* DR54. *J. Appl. Microbiol.* 87:80–86

128. Nielsen TH, Thrane C, Christophersen C, Anthoni U, Sorensen J. 2000. Structure, production characteristics and fungal antagonism of tensin - a new antifungal cyclic lipopeptide from *Pseudomonas fluorescens* strain 96.578. *J. Appl. Microbiol.* 89:992–1001

129. Neumann G, Romheld V. 1999. Root excretion of carboxylic acids and protons in phosphorus-deficient plants. *Plant Soil* 211:121–30

130. Newman EI, Reddell P. 1987. The distribution of mycorrhizas among families of vascular plants. *New Phytol.* 106:745–51

131. Nigh EL Jr . 1990. Stress factors influencing *Fusarium* infection in asparagus. *Acta Hort.* 271:315–22

132. Nilsson M-C, Hogberg P, Zackrisson O, Fengyou W. 1993. Allelopathic effects by *Empetrum hermaphroditum* Hagerup on development and nitrogen uptake by roots and mycorrhiza of *Pinus sylvestris* L. *Can. J. Bot.* 71:620–28

133. Nimbal CI, Pedersen JF, Yerkes CN, Weston LA, Weller SC. 1996. Phytotoxicity and distribution of sorgoleone in grain sorghum germplasm. *J. Agric. Food Chem.* 44:1343–47

134. Oger PM, Mansouri H, Nesme X, Dessaux Y. 2004. Engineering root exudation of Lotus toward the production of two novel carbon compounds leads to the selection of distinct microbial populations in the rhizosphere. *Microb. Ecol.* 47:96–103

135. O'Malley RC, Lynn DG. 2000. Expansin message regulation in parasitic angiosperms: marking time in development. *Plant Cell* 12:1455–65

The first evidence that plants can differentially detect and respond to bacterial quorum-sensing signaling molecules.

136. Palma JM, Longa MA, del Rio LA, Arines J. 1993. Superoxide dismutase in vesicular arbuscular mycorrhizal red clover plants. *Physiol Plant* 87:77–83

137. Palmer AG, Gao R, Maresh J, Erbil WK, Lynn DG. 2004. Chemical biology of multi-host/pathogen interactions: chemical perception and metabolic complementation. *Annu. Rev. Phytopath.* 42:439–64

138. Patterson E, Sims A. 2000. Effect of nitrogen supply and defoliation on loss of organic compounds from roots of *Festuca rubra*. *J. Exp. Bot.* 51:1449–57

139. Peer WA, Bandyopadhyay A, Blakeslee JJ, Makam SN, Chen RJ, et al. 2004. Variation in expression and protein localization of the PIN family of auxin efflux facilitator proteins in flavonoid mutants with altered auxin transport in *Arabidopsis thaliana*. *Plant Cell* 16:1898–911

140. Pei ZM, Murata Y, Benning G, Thomine S, Klusener B, et al. 2000. Calcium channels activated by hydrogen peroxide mediate abscisic acid signalling in guard cells. *Nature* 406:731–4

141. Penuelas J, Ribas-Carbo M, Giles L. 1996. Effects of allelochemicals on plant respiration and oxygen isotope fractionation by the alternative oxidase. *J. Chem. Ecol.* 22:801–5

142. Perret X, Staehelin C, Broughton WJ. 2000. Molecular basis of symbiotic promiscuity. *Microbiol. Mol. Biol. Rev.* 64:180–201

143. Perry LG, Johnson C, Alford ER, Vivanco JM, Paschke MW. 2006. Screening of grassland plants for restoration after spotted knapweed invasion. *Rest. Ecol.* In press

144. Perry LG, Thelen GC, Ridenour WM, Weir TL, Callaway RM, et al. 2005. Dual role for an allelochemical: (±)-catechin from *Centaurea maculosa* root exudates regulates conspecific seedling establishment. *J. Ecol.* 93:1125–36

145. Peters NK, Frost JW, Long SR. 1986. A plant flavone, luteolin, induces expression of *Rhizobium meliloti* nodulation genes. *Science* 233:977–80

146. Picman J, Picman AK. 1984. Autotoxicity in *Parthenium hysterophorus* and its possible role in control of germination. *Biochem. Syst. Ecol.* 12:287–92

147. Politycka I. 1996. Peroxidase activity and lipid peroxidation in roots of cucmber seedlings influenced by derivatives of cinnamic and benzoic acids. *Acta Physiol. Plant* 18:365–70

148. Prati D, Bossdorf O. 2004. Allelopathic inhibition of germination by *Alliaria petiolata* (Brassicaceae). *Am. J. Bot.* 91:285–88

149. Pueppke SG, Broughton WJ. 1999. *Rhizobium* sp. strain NGR234 and R. fredii USDA257 share exceptionally broad, nested host ranges. *Mol. Plant-Microbe Interact.* 12:293–318

150. Rahme LG, Stevens EJ, Wolfort SF, Shao J, Tompkins RG, Ausubel FM. 1995. Common virulence factors for bacterial pathogenicity in plants and animals. *Science* 286:1899–902

151. Rahme LG, Tan MW, Le L, Wong SM, Tompkins RG, et al. 1997. Use of model plant hosts to identify *Pseudomonas aeruginosa* virulence factors. *Proc. Natl. Acad. Sci. USA* 94:13245–50

152. Romero-Romero T, Sanchez-Nieto S, San Juan-Badillo A, Anaya AL, Cruz-Ortega R. 2005. Comparative effects of allelochemical and water stress in roots of *Lycopersicum esculentum* Mill. (Solonaceae). *Plant Sci.* 168:1059–66

153. Romheld V, Marschner H. 1985. Evidence for a specific uptake system for iron phytosiderophores in roots of grasses. *Plant Physiol.* 80:175–80

154. Ronchel MC, Ramos JL. 2001. Dual system to reinforce biological containment of recombinant bacteria designed for rhizoremediation. *Appl. Environ. Micro.* 67:2649–56

155. Rovira AD, Newman EI, Bowen HJ, Campbell R. 1974. Quantitative assessment of the rhizosphere microflora by direct microscopy. *Soil Biol. Biochem.* 6:211–16

156. Ryu CM, Farag MA, Hu CH, Reddy MS, Kloepper JW, Pare PW. 2004. Bacterial volatiles induce systemic resistance in Arabidopsis. *Plant Physiol.* 134:1017–26

(±)-catechin may be produced by *C. maculosa* as a means of regulating intraspecific competition by limiting conspecific seedling establishment.

157. Schardl CL, Leuchtmann A, Spiering MJ. 2004. Symbioses of grasses with seed-borne fungal endophyte. *Annu. Rev. Plant Biol.* 55:315–40

158. Sicker D, Schneider B, Hennig L, Knop M, Schulz M. 2001. Glycoside carbamates from benzoxazolin-2(3H)-one detoxification in extracts and exudates of corn roots. *Phytochemistry* 58:819–25

159. Singh BK, Millard P, Whiteley AS, Murrell JC. 2004. Unravelling rhizosphere-microbial interactions: opportunities and limitations. *Trends Microbiol.* 12:386–93

160. Singh HP, Batish DR, Kohli RK. 1999. Autotoxicity: concept, organisms, and ecological significance. *Crit. Rev. Plant Sci.* 18:757–72

161. Smith CE, Ruttledge T, Zeng ZX, Omalley RC, Lynn DG. 1996. A mechanism for inducing plant development: the genesis of a specific inhibitor. *Proc. Natl. Acad. Sci. USA* 93:6986–91

162. Somers E, Vanderleyden J, Srinivasan M. 2004. Rhizosphere bacterial signalling: a love parade beneath our feet. *Crit. Rev. Microbiol.* 30:205–235

163. Steenhoudt O, Vanderleyden J. 2000. Azospirillum, a free-living nitrogen-fixing bacterium closely associated with grasses: genetic, biochemical and ecological aspects. *FEMS Microbiol. Rev.* 24:487–506

164. Stermitz FR, Bais HP, Foderaro TA, Vivanco JM. 2003. 7,8-Benzoflavone: a phytotoxin from root exudates of invasive Russian knapweed. *Phytochemistry* 64:493–97

165. Sugiura Y, Nomoto K. 1984. Phytosiderophores: structures and properties of mugineic acids and their metal complexes. *Struct. Bond.* 58:107–35

166. Tamasloukht M, Sejalon-Delmas N, Kluever A, Jauneau A, Roux C, Becard G, et al. 2003. Root factors induce mitochondrial-related gene expression and fungal respiration during the developmental switch from asymbiosis to pre-symbiosis in the arbuscular mycorrhizal fungus *Gigaspora rosea*. *Plant Physiol.* 131:1468–78

167. Tan J, Bednarek P, Liu J, Schneider B, Svatos A, Hahlbrock K. 2004. Universally occurring phenylpropanoid and species-specific indolic metabolites in infected and uninfected *Arabidopsis thaliana* roots and leaves. *Phytochemistry* 65:691–99

168. Teplitski M, Chen H, Rajamani S, Gao M, Merighi M, Sayre RT, et al. 2004. Chlamydomonas reinhardtii secretes compounds that mimic bacterial signals and interfere with quorum sensing regulation in bacteria. *Plant Physiol.* 134:137–46

169. Teplitski M, Robinson JB, Bauer WD. 2000. Plants secrete substances that mimic bacterial N-acyl homoserine lactone signal activities and affect population density dependent behaviors in associated bacteria. *Mol. Plant-Microbe Interact.* 13:637–648

170. Thrane C, Harder Nielsen T, Neiendam Nielsen M, Sorensen J, Olsson S. 2000. Viscosinamide-producing *Pseudomonas fluorescens* DR54 exerts a biocontrol effect on Pythium ultimum in sugar beet rhizosphere. *FEMS Microbiol. Ecol.* 33:139–46

171. Uhde-Stone C, Temple SJ, Vance CP, Allan DL, Zinn KE, et al. 2003. Acclimation of white lupin to phosphorus deficiency involves enhanced expression of genes related to organic acid metabolism. *Plant Soil* 248:99–116

172. Uren NC. 2000. Types, amounts and possible functions of compounds released into the rhizosphere by soil grown plants. In *The Rhizosphere: Biochemistry and Organic Substances at the Soil Interface*, ed. R Pinton, Z Varanini, P Nannipieri. pp. 19–40. New York: Marcel Dekker

173. Van Gundy SD, Kirkpatrick JD, Golden J. 1977. The nature and role of metabolic leakage from root-knot nematode galls and infection by *Rhizoctonia solani*. *J. Nematol.* 9:113–21

174. van West P, Morris BM, Reid B, Appiah AA, Osborne MC, et al. 2002. Oomycete plant pathogens use electric fields to target roots. *Mol. Plant-Microbe Interact.* 15:790–98

175. Vicre M, Santaella C, Blanchet S, Gateau A, Driouich A. 2005. Root border-like cells of *Arabidopsis*. Microscopical characterization and role in the interaction with rhizobacteria. *Plant Physiol.* 138:998–1008

176. Vivanco JM, Bais HP, Stermitz FR, Thelen GC, Callaway RM. 2004. Biogeographical variation in community response to root allelochemistry: novel weapons and exotic invasion. *Ecol. Lett.* 7:285–92

177. von Bodman SB, Bauer WD, Coplin DL. 2003. Quorum-sensing in plant pathogenic bacteria. *Annu. Rev. Phytopathol.* 41:455–82

178. Von Jagow G, Link TA. 1986. Use of specific inhibitors on the mitochondrial bc1 complex. *Meth. Enzymol.* 126:253–71

179. von Rad U, Huttl R, Lottspeich F, Gierl A, Frey M. 2001. Two glucosyltransferases are involved in detoxification of benzoxazinoids in maize. *Plant J.* 28:633–42

180. Walker TS, Bais HP, Grotewold E, Vivanco JM. 2003. Root exudation and rhizosphere biology. *Plant Physiol.* 132:44–51

181. Wardle DA, Lavelle P. 1997. Linkages between soil biota, plant litter quality, and decomposition. In *Driven by Nature, Plant Litter Quality and Decomposition*, ed. G Cadisch, KE Giller, pp. 107–24. Wallingford: CAB Intl.

182. Wardle DA, Nicholson KS, Ahmed M, Rahman A. 1994. Interference effects of the invasive plant *Carduus nutans* L. against the nitrogen fixation ability of *Trifolium repens* L. *Plant Soil* 163:287–97

183. Wardle DA, Nicholson KS, Rahman A. 1993. Influence of plant age on the allelopathic potential of nodding thistle (*Carduus nutans* L.) against pasture grasses and legumes. *Weed Res.* 33:69–78

184. Wardle DA, Nilsson M-C, Gallet C, Zackrisson O. 1998. An ecosystem-level perspective of allelopathy. *Biol. Rev. Camb Phil. Soc.* 73:305–19

185. Weidenhamer JD, Romeo JT. 2004. Allelochemicals of *Polygonella myriophylla*: chemistry and soil degradation. *J. Chem. Ecol.* 30:1067–82

186. Weir TL, Bais HP, Vivanco JM. 2003. Intraspecific and interspecific interactions mediated by a phytotoxin, (-)-catechin, secreted by the roots of *Centaurea maculosa* (spotted knapweed). *J. Chem. Ecol.* 29:2397–412

187. Weir TL, Park SW, Vivanco JM. 2004. Biochemical and physiological mechanisms mediated by allelochemicals. *Curr. Opin. Plant Biol.* 7:472–79

188. Williams RJ, Spencer JP, Rice-Evans C. 2004. Flavonoids: antioxidants or signalling molecules? *Free Radic. Biol. Med.* 36:838–49

189. Williamson GB. 1990. Allelopathy, Koch's postulates and neck riddles. In *Perspectives in Plant Competition*, ed. JB Grace, D Tilman, pp. 143–62. London: Academic

190. Wu HW, Haig T, Pratley J, Lemerle D, An M. 2000. Allelochemicals in wheat (*Triticum aestivum* L.): variation of phenolic acids in root tissues. *J. Agric. Food Chem.* 48:5321–25

191. Yamada Y, Nihira T. 1998. Microbial hormones and microbial chemical ecology. In *Comprehensive Natural Products Chemistry*. *Vol. 8*, ed. DHR Barton, K Nakanishi, pp. 377–413. Oxford: Elsevier

192. Yang XH, Scheffler BE, Weston LA. 2004. SOR1, a gene associated with bioherbicide production in sorghum root hairs. *J. Exp. Bot.* 55:2251–59

193. Yeates GW. 1999. Effects of plants on nematode community structure. *Annu. Rev. Phytopath.* 37:127–49

194. Yoder JI. 1999. Parasitic plant responses to host plant signals: a model for subterranean plant-plant interactions. *Curr. Opin. Plant Biol.* 2:65–70

195. Yu JQ, Ye SF, Zhang MF, Hu WH. 2003. Effects of root exudates and aqueous root extracts of cucumber (*Cucumis sativus*) and allelochemicals, on photosynthesis and antioxidant enzymes in cucumber. *Biochem. Sys. Ecol.* 31:129–39

196. Zackrisson O, Nilsson M-C. 1992. Allelopathic effects by *Empetrum hermaphroditum* on seed germination of two boreal tree species. *Can. J. Forest Res.* 22:1310–19

Genetics of Meiotic Prophase I in Plants

Olivier Hamant,[1,2] Hong Ma,[3] and W. Zacheus Cande[1]

[1] Department of Molecular and Cell Biology, University of California, Berkeley, California 94720; email: zcande@berkeley.edu

[2] RDP-ENS Lyon, 69364 Lyon cedex 07, France; email: ohamant@ens-lyon.fr

[3] Department of Biology and the Huck Institutes of the Life Sciences, Pennsylvania State University, University Park, Pennsylvania 16802; email: hxm16@psu.edu

Annu. Rev. Plant Biol.
2006. 57:267–302

The *Annual Review of Plant Biology* is online at
plant.annualreviews.org

doi: 10.1146/
annurev.arplant.57.032905.105255

First published online as a
Review in Advance on
January 30, 2006

1543-5008/06/0602-
0267$20.00

Key Words

meiocyte, bouquet, pairing, synapsis, cohesion, recombination

Abstract

During meiotic prophase I, traits are reassorted as a result of a highly organized process involving sister chromatid cohesion, homologous chromosome alignment, pairing, synapsis, and recombination. In the past two years, a number of components involved in this pathway, including Structure Maintenance of Chromosomes (SMC), MRE11, the RAD51 homologs, BRCA2, MSH4, MER3, and ZIP1, have been characterized in plants; in addition, several genes that encode components unique to plants, such as POOR HOMOLOGOUS SYNAPSIS 1 and AMEIOTIC 1, have been cloned. Based on these recent data, essentially from maize and *Arabidopsis*, we discuss the conserved and plant-specific aspects of meiosis commitment and meiotic prophase I features.

Contents

INTRODUCTION

Plants, together with *Drosophila*, historically have served as model systems for the generation of many of the founding concepts of inheritance and meiosis. For instance, observation of chromosome segregation in plants led to the definition of the terms prophase, metaphase, and anaphase by the botanist E. Strasburger in 1875. The laws of heredity were originally discovered by Mendel in 1866; these laws were based on his analysis of pea phenotypes and re-established by three botanists, de Vries, Correns, and Von Tschermak, in 1900. Because of the accessibility of male meiocytes in the anther, plants have been very useful in the study of the conserved mechanism of meiosis at the cytologi-

cal level. Maize (*Zea mays* L.) is one of the first model organisms in which the power of genetics was productively merged with cytology to create the new field of cytogenetics (reviewed in 150). Using maize, the link between recombination and the cytological observation of crossing-over was demonstrated in 1931 by Creighton & McClintock (45). Maize chromosome cytology has remained a fertile field for investigation (e.g., 14, 49, 129, 156) and has been accompanied by the development of sophisticated maize linkage maps (e.g., 47, 165, 205). Furthermore, many meiotic mutants were identified by forward genetics in plants (12, 67, 90, 95). In maize, in particular, a continuously growing collection of over 60 meiotic mutants has been isolated; this collection represents approximately 35 complementation groups (I.N. Golubovskaya, personal communication).

Until the 1990s, it had not been possible to isolate and characterize the genes affected in these plant mutants at a molecular level. However, this has begun to change with the identification of a number of meiotic mutants from *Arabidopsis thaliana*; these mutants have provided the means to clone a range of genes (34, 110). In addition, the use of reverse genetics in this organism has proven to be very powerful, and the functions of homologs of many yeast genes have been characterized in *Arabidopsis*. By comparison, reverse genetics in vertebrates has not been as successful, as homologs of some yeast genes involved in meiosis cannot be studied easily in vertebrates due to their shared mitotic functions and associated mutant lethality (usually not present in plants). Thus reverse genetics in plants can provide unique information on the functions of these genes during meiosis in multicellular organisms. Today, the improved and more accessible molecular tools and mutant banks extend the possibility to clone genes more easily in other plant model systems such as maize or rice.

Although this review is mainly focused on research conducted in *Arabidopsis* and maize, we predict that other plant species, in particular allopolyploid and dioecious species, will be used more often in the future as model organisms for meiosis because of their specific chromosome structure and behavior. Hybridization between two or more species leads to new species called allopolyploids. Important crops such as wheat are allopolyploids. Loci and chromosomes of the genomic sets of different parental origins are defined as homeologous, in contrast to the homologous alleles and chromosomes within the sets of one parent. Studying meiosis in these species will lead to the identification of mechanisms that function to distinguish between homologous and homeologous pairing (See the section Homeologous Pairing below). Furthermore, unlike established wild and cultivated allopolyploids that are genetically stable, allopolyploids of recent origin, such as *Arabidopsis suecica* or synthetic allotetraploids of *Arabidopsis thaliana*, display genomic and phenotypic instability that is in part caused by abnormal meiosis (40, 177). Therefore, allopolyploids are good models for analyzing both the control of meiosis and its evolution. In several dioecious species, heteromorphic chromosomes are associated with chromosomal sex determination (132). The novelty of these plant models is that the origin of sex chromosomes is much more recent in plants than in mammals. In Silene, this origin is estimated at approximately 25 million years, in contrast to 300 million years in mammals. The mechanisms of chromosomal sex determination, including the accumulation of genes determining sexual dimorphism, the controlled arrest of recombination along most regions of X and Y, Y chromosome genetic isolation, and X chromosome dosage compensation, are currently being unraveled and may shed new light on recombination and meiosis in general (35, 57, 108, 132, 133, 192).

MEIOSIS OVERVIEW

Meiosis is a highly conserved process in eukaryotes and occupies a central role in the life cycles of all sexually reproducing organisms, in particular by reassorting traits. Meiosis differs from mitosis in that a single round of DNA replication precedes two sequential cell divisions so that an initially diploid cell generates four haploid cells (**Figure 1**).

Commitment to meiosis is thought to occur at premeiotic S-phase and the first meiotic markers, like the cohesin protein REC8, are loaded onto the chromosomes. Initiation of meiosis can be cytologically recognized at the leptotene stage, as chromosome condensation begins and installation of the axial elements along the chromosomes is completed (204). Double-strand break (DSB) initiation is thought to occur between leptotene and zygotene, as it is accompanied by orchestrated chromatin structural changes. In maize, heterochromatin blocks such as knobs and centromeric heterochromatin elongate, and sister chromatids move slightly apart (31, 49, 50). These transient structural changes may be required to initiate pairing interactions and recombination. Pairing of homologous chromosomes begins at zygotene, when the recruitment of recombination effectors, such as RAD51, on chromosomes reaches a peak. From zygotene to pachytene, homologous chromosomes pair and synapse: A central element is installed between the axial elements, now called lateral elements, to form a tripartite synaptonemal complex (SC) (78, 127, 191, 204). Pachytene is defined as the stage when synapsis and recombination is in its final stages. In diplotene, the SC falls apart and homologous juxtaposition ends. However, the homologues are held together as bivalents until metaphase I by chiasmata, the sites of recombination that lead to crossovers (137, 143). During diakinesis, the chromosomes condense further, thicken, and detach from the nuclear envelope. Homologs separate at anaphase I as cohesins are removed from chromosome arms and chiasmata disassemble. The segregation of homologous pairs of chromosomes at the first division is therefore dependent on their prior pairing, synapsis, and recombination at earlier stages. The second meiotic division is equational and

DSB: double-strand break

SC: synaptonemal complex

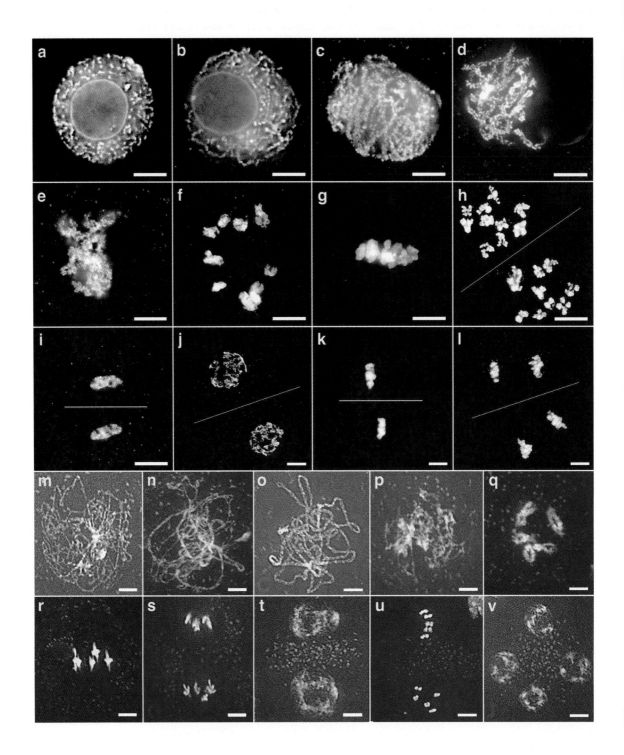

separates the sister chromatids of each chromosome to give rise to the haploid gametes. Subsequent fertilization of female gametes by the male restores the diploid state.

While much has been learned, many questions remain unanswered, and new questions arise: (*a*) the mechanisms underlying homology recognition before and during pairing is mostly unknown; (*b*) despite decades of analysis, the role of the synaptonemal complex (SC) in relationship with pairing and recombination is still under debate; (*c*) how the meiocyte decides between a crossover or a noncrossover event is poorly understood; and (*d*) the centromere, with little sequence data available, remains an obstacle to understanding the biology of the meiotic chromosome. In this review we discuss the recent advances in the genetics of meiosis in angiosperms and focus on early events during prophase I. Other aspects of plant meiosis can be found in several recent reviews (34, 88, 110).

MODEL PLANTS AND APPROACHES

Meiosis in angiosperms is organized rather differently in male and female organs, and the fates of the meiotic products are also divergent. In anthers, sporogenous cells proliferate by asynchronous mitotic divisions until the appropriate number of presumptive meiocytes (also called pollen mother cells) is achieved. In response to a signal, the pollen mother cells enter meiosis in synchrony and proceed through meiosis more or less synchronously to generate microspores (for review see Reference 110). In ovules, archesporial cells give rise to single embryo-sac mother cells, which undergo meiosis to produce four haploid cells (macrospores). In the anther, upon completion of meiosis, all the microspores undergo one round of mitosis and develop into pollen grains, whereas, in the ovule, usually three of the macrospores degenerate to leave one which develops into the embryo sac. The cellular organization of the embryo sac is less stereotyped than pollen and depends on the species as the number of degenerating macrospores and subsequent mitosis varies (e.g., in lily, orchids, and *Plumbagella*). Most of the data on meiosis in plants originate from studies of the pollen mother cell, due to its accessibility.

Forward Genetics

Primary screen: sterility. Both chemical (EMS, nitrosomethyl-urea) and insertional mutagenesis (transposons, T-DNA) have been used to produce populations of mutants in plants, mainly maize and *Arabidopsis* (10, 18, 34, 37, 69, 110, 122, 141, 153, 158, 171, 198). Screening for sterility however depends on the species: In maize, at anthesis, sterile plants exhibit nonprotruding

---

Figure 1

DAPI-stained chromosomes structure and behavior during male meiosis in maize and *Arabidopsis*. (*a–l*) Three-dimensional projections of male meiocyte nuclei in maize. (*a*) Leptotene. The nucleolus is at the center of the nucleus as chromosome threads form. (*b*) Leptotene-zygotene. The nucleolus has moved to the periphery of the nucleus as telomere cluster. (*c*) Late zygotene. Synapsed (middle) and unsynapsed (edges of nucleus) chromosomes can be distinguished. (*d*) Pachytene. Chromosomes are fully synapsed. (*e*) Diplotene. (*f*) Diakinesis. Ten bivalents are individualized. (*g*) Metaphase I. (*h*) Anaphase I. X-shape chromosomes due to the maintenance of centromeric cohesion. (*i*) Telophase I. (*j*) Prophase II. (*k*) Metaphase II. (*l*) Anaphase II. Scale bar = 5 μm. (*m–v*) Male meiosis in *Arabidopsis thaliana*. (*m*) Leptotene. (*n*) Zygotene. Regions of pairing between homologs are indicated (*arrows*). (*o*) Pachytene. (*p*) Diplotene. (*q*) Diakinesis. The positions of the chiasmata (*arrows*) and the centromeric regions (*arrowheads*) are indicated. (*r*) Metaphase I. (*s*) Anaphase I. (*t*) Prophase II. The organelle band between the two groups of chromosomes is indicated (*arrow*). (*u*) Metaphase II. (*v*) Telophase II. The images of male meiosis in Arabidopsis were obtained from DAPI-stained chromosome spreads following the fixation of floral buds and were provided by W. Li. Scale bar = 5 μm.

anthers whereas the wild-type produce big anthers with a high pollen production rate. In *Arabidopsis*, the phenotypic screening for fruit length allows the discrimination between fertile (long silique) and sterile (short silique) plants. In rice, screening for sterility is based on the color of the fruit: Fertile fruits undergo a normal development during which glumes become brown; in contrast, in fruits that contain aborting ovules, glumes remain green (D. Grimanelli, personal communication).

Secondary screen: distinction between developmental and meiotic mutants. Secondary screens, based on cytological approaches, have been used to distinguish sterility due to meiotic defects from sterility due to defects in sporocyte initiation, anther dehiscence, or environmental factors (158, 198). Verification of the phenotype over several generations can also prove to be helpful to confirm that reduced fertility or sterility is caused by a genetic defect in meiosis (153).

At this step, maize presents several advantages that render this secondary screen more effective as cytogenetic approaches are easier in this organism. The meiocytes are embedded in a matrix of callose, and this material allows the dividing cells to be extruded mechanically from the cut end of an anther with minimal damage to the cells. Furthermore, because of their large size, chromosomes can be visualized by light microscopy in acetocarmine-stained, squashed meiocytes. This visualization allows for accurate screening of a great variety of phenotypes as we detail further in this review. In *Arabidopsis*, the smaller size of the chromosomes and the difficulty in obtaining intact meiocytes renders cytological examination of meiotic phenotypes more difficult, although improved cytogenetic techniques has permitted a more complete analysis of meiotic chromosome behavior (7, 9, 154). In addition, the *Arabidopsis* inflorescence produces new floral buds over a periods of weeks, particularly in sterile

mutants; this characteristic allows cytological screens to be performed on the same plants identified as mutant in the primary sterility screen.

A comparison of the power of forward genetics in maize and *Arabidopsis*. Although more meiotic genes have been identified in *Arabidopsis*, there is a larger collection of meiotic mutants in maize than in *Arabidopsis*, more than 60 representing 35 complementation groups. There are several reasons why this has happened.

The initial screen for meiotic mutants in maize is based on the reduction of pollen production, whereas in *Arabidopsis*, fruit size is used as the primary screen. As (*a*) *Arabidopsis* plants produce normal-sized fruits even when the seed number is slightly reduced and (*b*) pollen is normally produced in excess, mutations that result in mild pollen reduction are not easily detected in the screens for reduced fruit size. In contrast, in maize, both the large population of pollen grains in the wild-type and the accessibility of anthers facilitate a relatively easy diagnosis of reduced pollen production. Furthermore, many of the mutants identified to date in *Arabidopsis* have been isolated through T-DNA insertional mutagenesis. Integration of the T-DNA in the genome occurs at a very specific time of plant development, particularly in the female gametophyte, and could bias against those mutations in genes that are important for female gametophyte development. In comparison, EMS and transposon mutagenesis approaches are not dependent on the tissue or the development stage, and have been successful in maize as well as *Arabidopsis* (10, 72, 141, 158, 198).

The future of forward genetics. The quality of the secondary screen is a determinant for the efficient isolation of meiotic mutants by forward genetics. Extended and detailed secondary cytological screens are currently done in maize because of its excellent chromosome morphology and meiocytes accessibility, and we can hope that the use of transposon-tagging strategies will facilitate the cloning of the corresponding genes. Thanks to the still growing number of meiotic genes and phenotypes described in other organisms, yeast especially, candidate approaches will become more efficient towards cloning current maize and *Arabidopsis* mutants without going through map-based cloning protocol (72). With *Arabidopsis*, as cytological techniques improve, performing secondary screens on previously unsuccessful screening pools could provide new kinds of mutants. Furthermore, new forward genetics screens could be performed with *Arabidopsis* such as, for example, a screen based on *Arabidopsis* populations that express meiocyte markers that could be readily visualized or, alternatively, a screen to identify suppressors of known mutants.

Reverse Genetics

Isolation of candidate genes on the basis of sequence identity. Studies in budding and fission yeast over the past decades have identified meiotic genes (reviewed in: 48, 56, 152, 204) that subsequently have been found, based on their sequence homology, in plant genomes (120). A higher level of sequence identity is encountered for genes that encode proteins catalyzing homologous recombination, such as *DISRUPTED MEIOTIC cDNA (DMC)1* (55, 93, 159), *RAD51* (55), and *SPORULATION (SPO) 11* (70, 75). When the level of sequence similarity is too low, the identification of a homolog is more difficult in silico. For instance, the yeast *ZIP1* and rat *Saccharomyces cerevisiae* calponin *(SCP) 1* genes encode proteins that comprise the transverse filaments of the SC. The similarity of these homologs is structural and functional, but cannot be predicted by the level of their sequence similarity (78). Finally, the absence of obvious homologs in plant genomes might suggest either that the nonplant meiotic protein function is dispensable, or that other proteins can perform the needed functions.

Conversely, plant meiotic-specific genes have been identified (see below).

Isolation of candidate genes based on expression patterns. Another way to identify candidate meiotic genes is to focus on meiotically-expressed genes. Although expression of many *Arabidopsis* and maize meiotic genes can be detected in somatic tissues, some, such as *Arabidopsis (At) DMC1*, are upregulated during meiosis (93) or possess meiosis-specific splicing variants such as *SYNAPSIS (SYN)1*, *DETERMINATE INFERTILE (DIF) 1* (11). Approximately 200 genes specific to meiosis and gamete formation had been identified by classical methods by 2000 (146). Probably as many as 1500 genes show altered gene expression as analyzed by microarrays (4, 38, 146); this result leads to an estimate of the total of core genes specific for meiosis at 300 and those specific for sporulation/gametogenesis at 600 (165).

Acquisition of mutants by reverse genetics. Once the candidate gene has been identified, the functional analysis of the protein it encodes can be initiated either through screens of mutant banks or by transgenic approaches. Several mutant banks [e.g., Trait Utility System for Corn (TUSC), Cold Spring Harbor Laboratory (CSHL), Targeting Induced Local Lesions IN Genomes (TILLING)] are available in maize. The availability of the rice genomic sequence is an important resource because (*a*) rice is a diploid rather than an ancient tetraploid like maize, and (*b*) the rice genome is only one-fifth the size of maize (rice is ~480 Mb and maize is 2500 Mb). Furthermore, rice genes average over 85% identity to maize, therefore allowing the use of some of the rice molecular "toolkit" for characterizing maize genes. Finally, microarrays are now available in rice and maize. In *Arabidopsis*, the large number of mutant banks [e.g.,Feldmann, INRA-Versailles, Salk Institute, Syngenta Arabidopsis Insertion Library (SAIL), Institute for Molecular Agrobiology (IMA), Sainsbury Laboratory

Arabidopsis thaliana (SLAT), TILLING] ensures the possibility of getting an allelic series in almost every gene, and several approaches have been used to screen these tagged populations (26). Finally, it is also possible to generate knockdown plants by post-transcriptional gene silencing (73, 80, 170, 193) or by overexpression of a dominant-negative form of the protein.

Limitations of reverse genetics. In addition to imposing a requirement for a priori knowledge, a major limitation in assigning gene function by reverse genetics in plants arises from the finding that many plant genes belong to multigenic families, and there is widespread functional redundancy. For instance, the *Arabidopsis* genome has likely undergone one or more ancient duplication(s) that resulted in approximately 60% of the *Arabidopsis* genome being duplicated, although in some cases, the genes within these duplicated regions have undergone functional divergence (5). Thus, even in cases when putative meiotic genes can be identified on the basis of sequence similarity, there may be several potential candidates whose functions have to be investigated. Furthermore, forward genetics has led to the identification of meiotic genes, such as the maize *POOR HOMOLOGOUS SYNAPSIS (PHS) 1* and *AMEIOTIC 1 (AM1)*, that are not present in nonplant genomes. Although reverse genetics is a powerful tool to study genetics of meiosis in plants, its limitations validate forward genetics as a worthwhile and complementary approach. See **Table 1** for a list of genes included in this review.

MEIOTIC COMMITMENT

Before meiosis commitment, a genetic control determines cell fate, e.g., that the cell will become a meiocyte, and the cell cycle is subsequently switched from mitotic to meiotic. In maize, the *multiple archaesporial cells (mac) 1* mutant produces an increased number of male sporocytes and lacks tapetal cells; this obser-

vation demonstrates a role for *MAC1* in cell fate determination (168, 169). Similar phenotypes have been observed in the *Arabidopsis excess microsporocytes (ems) 1/ extra sporogenous cells (exs) 1* and *tapetum determinant (tpd) 1* mutants as well as the rice *multiple spororcyte (msp) 1* mutant; molecular analyses of these mutants suggest that cell-cell communication between the tapetum and the meiocytes plays a role in cell fate determination (for review see Reference 110).

Little is known regarding the initiation of meiosis in plants. When anther explants are cultured before late S/G2, the pollen mother cell is induced to revert from meiosis to a mitotic division (87). This observation suggests that, as in yeast and animals, entrance into meiosis is probably determined during premeiotic S-phase. The isolation of two mutants, *ameiotic 1* in maize and *switch1* in *Arabidopsis*, has showed that the meiotic switch is genetically determined.

Ameiotic1 and Switch1 Regulate the Initiation of Meiosis

In the *ameiotic1-1 (am1-1)* mutant, meiotic divisions in both male and female meiocytes are replaced by mitotic divisions (65, 149). In addition to a mitotic-like prophase and mitotic chromosome morphology, *am1-1* exhibits mitotic-like spindles and preprophase microtubule bands (179). Furthermore, meiocytes in the *am1-1* mutant do not contain RAD51 foci; this observation indicates that the meiotic recombination machinery is not installed in this mutant.

Six *am1* alleles have been found; for five of these, mutations in the alleles cause male meiocytes to undergo mitosis, and female meiocytes either to undergo mitosis or to arrest at interphase. In the sixth allele, *am1-prophase arrest (pra) 1*, chromosomes display a leptotene morphology but do not form a telomere bouquet (see the section The Bouquet: Facilitating Pairing? below for a discussion of bouquet) and do not exhibit RAD51 foci; this result indicates that,

Table 1 List of genes in the review

Gene	Organism	Mutant	Allele	Homolog
ABSENCE OF FIRST DIVISION 1	Maize	afd1		Rec8
ARABIDOPSIS HOMOLOGUE PAIRING 2	Arabidopsis	ahp2		Hop2
AMEIOTIC 1	Maize	am1	pra1	—
ARABIDOPSIS SKP1-LIKE1	Arabidopsis	ask1-1		—
ASYNAPTIC 1	Maize	asy1		Hop1
BRCA2	Arabidopsis	atbrca2		Brca2
DIF1	Arabidopsis	dif1	syn1	Rec8
DISRUPTED MEIOTIC cDNA 1	Arabidopsis	atdmc1		Dmc1
DESYNAPTIC CS	Maize	dsyCS		—
DYAD	Arabidopsis	dyad	ms4; swi1	—
MALE STERILE 4	Arabidopsis	ms4	dyad; swi1	—
MALE STERILE 5	Arabidopsis	ms5	tdm1; pollenless3	—
MER3	Arabidopsis	atmer3	rck	Mer3
MSH4	Arabidopsis	atmsh4		Msh4
MMS25	Maize	mms25		—
MRE11	Arabidopsis	atmre11		Mre11
PAIR2	Rice	pair2		Hop1
PH1	Wheat	ph1		—
PLURAL ABNORMALITIES OF MEIOSIS 1	Maize	pam1		—
POLLENLESS 3	Arabidopsis	pollenless3	ms5; tdm1	—
POOR HOMOLOGOUS SYNAPSIS	Maize	phs1		—
PROPHASE ARREST	Maize	pra	am1	—
RAD50	Arabidopsis	atrad50		Rad50
RAD51	Arabidopsis	atrad51		Rad51
RAD51-B	Arabidopsis	atrad51B		Rad51B
RAD51-C	Arabidopsis	atrad51C		Rad51C
ROCK N' ROLLER	Arabidopsis	rck	mer3	Mer3
SMC3	Arabidopsis	ttn		Smc3
SOLO DANCERS	Arabidopsis	sds		Cyclin
SPORULATION 11-1	Arabidopsis	atspo11-1		Spo11
SWITCH	Arabidopsis	swi1	dyad; ms4	—
SYN1	Arabidopsis	syn1	dif1	Rec8
TARDY ASYNCHRONOUS MEIOSIS	Arabidopsis	tam		Cyclin A
THREE-DIVISION MUTANT	Arabidopsis	tdm1	pollenless3; ms5	—
X-RAY CROSS COMPLEMENTING 2	Arabidopsis	atxrcc2		Xrcc2
X-RAY CROSS COMPLEMENTING 3	Arabidopsis	atxrcc3		Xrcc3

although meiosis is initiated, this mutant subsequently arrests at the leptotene-zygotene transition in this mutant (66, 140). The *AM1* gene has recently been cloned (W. Pawlowski & W.Z. Cande, unpublished data) by using a Mutator-tagged *am1-489* allele and encodes a protein with unknown biochemical function but partial sequence similarity to the *Arabidopsis* SWITCH1 (SWI1) protein. Four *swi1* alleles have been isolated [*swi1-1*, *swi1-2*, *dyad* and *male sterile 4* (*ms4*)], which show similar defects in female meiosis: Ten univalents are observed at metaphase I, and sister chromatids segregate evenly into two daughter cells (a mitosis-like division) in *swi1-1*, *swi1-2*, *dyad* and *ms4* (122, 128, 171). This result strongly suggests that these two proteins are functional homologs. A role of SWI1 in initiating meiosis is compatible with its expression profile, as the protein is detected during premeiotic S phase but is absent by leptotene, as demonstrated by both GFP fusion and immunocytological analysis (119, 122).

However, male meiosis is initiated in *swi1* mutants. The *swi1-2* mutant exhibits the most extreme phenotype of the four alleles so far described (1, 122, 128). The *swi1-2* mutation results in a lack of bivalent formation, absence of RAD51 foci, and precocious loss of sister chromatid cohesion (SCC) during male meiosis (119, 122). These defects lead to the presence at metaphase I of 20 chromatids rather than five bivalents. At the molecular level, in the *dyad* allele of *swi1*, DMC1 is expressed, as indicated by a line that expresses ß-*glucuronidase (GUS)* under the control of the *DMC1* promoter (*pDMC1::GUS*) (1). The analyses of *am1* mutants suggest that cell division in *am1* meiocytes is more mitosis-like than that of *swi1* in male meiocytes (66). Assuming that *swi1-2* is a null allele, the differences between maize and *Arabidopsis* could be due to a difference in other genetic factors, such as the presence of *SWI1* homologs in the *Arabidopsis* genome, and also possibly in the maize genome. At this point one should stress that male meiosis in maize and *Arabidopsis* are not similar in the wild-type: In particular, maize male meiocytes undergo cytokinesis at the end of both Meiosis I and Meiosis II, whereas, in *Arabidopsis*, cytokinesis occurs only once at the end of Meiosis II. Another way to interpret these phenotypic differences is to propose that downstream components are differently regulated by AM1 and SWI1 in maize and *Arabidopsis*, respectively. In maize, the six *am1* alleles are epistatic to *absence of first division* (*afd*)*1-1*, which is defective in the maize *REC8* homolog (66; I.N. Golubovskaya, O. Hamant & W.Z. Cande,

unpublished data). Similarly, the *swi1-2* mutant is epistatic to *syn1*, which is defective in the *Arabidopsis REC8* homolog (119). This result strongly suggests that the control of the initiation of meiosis occurs before regulation of meiotic SCC. Interestingly, the SWI1 protein contains a domain with weak similarity to Structure Maintenance of Chromosomes (SMC); this observation suggests an involvement of the protein in the SCC complex.

The Commitment Cascade

The control of meiosis progression is not well understood. Sequence analysis suggests that the AM1 protein contains a coiled-coil domain that is likely to be involved in protein-protein interactions; this suggestion is consistent with the idea that commitment to meiosis might involve other regulators of the cell cycle. In addition, other meiotic proteins have been shown to contain either a domain related to or sequence similarity to cell cycle proteins (10, 195).

The *MS5* gene encodes a protein with no clear homology with other known proteins (64). However, stretches of the protein have limited similarity to the SC protein SCP1 from rat and the regulatory subunit of a cyclin-dependent kinase from *Xenopus* (64). There are two other genes in *Arabidopsis* with sequence similarity to *MS5* (*POLLENLESS3-LIKE1* and *POLLENLESS3-LIKE2*) (158). In the *ms5/three-division mutant* (*tdm*)*1/pollenless3* mutant, the pollen mother cells appear to undergo two rounds of normal meiotic division. However, at the end of meiosis II the cell attempts a third division without any further DNA replication (64, 153, 158). The chromosomes recondense, attach to a spindle, and random groups of chromatids eventually form interphase nuclei (153). This phenotype strongly ressembles that of the *polymitotic* mutant in maize (15).

Cyclins seem to play a major role during meiosis progression. The *Arabidopsis* mutant *tardy asynchronous meiosis* (*tam*) is slowed in the progression of male meiosis (111) and has been shown to be defective in the A-type cyclin CYCA1;2 (195). By expressing a CYCA1;2-green fluorescent protein (GFP) fusion protein under the control of the *CYCA1;2 promoter*, Wang et al. (195) showed that CYCA1;2-GFP is only detectable in prophase I. They also demonstrated that the duration of pachytene and meiosis II are longer in *tam* than in wild type. Therefore, CYCA1;2 seems to regulate both meiosis I and meiosis II even though there is little or no CYCA1;2 present after prophase I. Either the CYCA1;2 produced in prophase I indirectly regulates meiosis II progression, or a very low level of CYCA1;2 directly regulates meiosis II progression (195).

The SOLO DANCERS (SDS) protein, which represents a new type of cyclin in *Arabidopsis*, has been found to regulate synapsis and recombination in prophase I (10, 194). The mutant meiocytes fail to form normal pachytene bivalents, consistent with a defect in pairing and/or synapsis. In addition, the mutant meiocytes have greatly reduced levels of meiotic recombination. The sequence similarity of SDS to other proteins suggests that it may regulate several processes during prophase I. However, the SDS protein is distinct from other known or predicted cyclins; this fact suggests that its function may be different from those of other mitotic cyclins. In the rice genomic sequence, there is a putative ortholog of SDS; this observation suggests that SDS is conserved in flowering plants (194). In yeast, the Clb5/Clb6 cyclins are important for both premeiotic S phase and for events during prophase I, including synapsis and recombination (176). In mouse, cyclin A1 is required during spermatogenesis; although mutant meiocytes can undergo chromosome synapsis, they subsequently degenerate (106). It is possible that the *Arabidopsis* SDS, the yeast Clb5/Clb6, and the mouse cyclin A1 may have some conserved functions, although they clearly also have some differences.

CHROMOSOME STRUCTURE AND HOMOLOGY RECOGNITION

Chromosome Structure

As outlined earlier, the commitment proteins are required for meiosis initiation and de facto are required for establishment of the structure of meiotic chromosomes during early prophase I. In *swi1-2*, premature loss of SCC and incomplete chromosome condensation is observed. On the basis of the phenotype of male meiocytes and a very weak sequence similarity of SWI to mammalian SMC proteins, a regulatory role of SWI1 in chromosome structure establishment and SCC was proposed (1, 122).

Sister chromatid cohesion. During premeiotic S-phase, newly replicated sister chromatids are associated via a multiprotein cohesin complex (reviewed in 101, 189). SCC is absolutely required for the control of chromosome structure and many subsequent meiotic events.

Cohesion proteins have been extensively studied in yeast and animals, and some homologs have been characterized in plants. The cohesin complex is ring shaped and comprises a core of three proteins (REC8/RAD21, SMC1 and SMC3) and several associated proteins such as SCC3 and PRECOCIOUS DISSOCIATION OF SISTERS (PDS) 5 (reviewed in 130). The REC8/RAD21 protein is the main regulator of the complex, as, at anaphase, its cleavage by separase releases cohesion and thus allows chromatids to segregate (71). In yeast, RAD21 is present in the mitotic cohesin complex and is mostly replaced at meiosis by REC8. In animal meiotic cells, SMC1ß replaces SMC1, and STROMAL ANTIGEN (STAG) 3 replaces SCC3 (145, 148). In plants, the distinction between the meiotic and mitotic cohesin complex is less clear; plant REC8 homologs like SYN1 or ABSENCE OF FIRST DIVISION (AFD)1 display a stronger sequence similarity with yeast and animal RAD21 than yeast and animal REC8, and the expression of the plant homologs is not meiosis specific (11, 138; I.N. Golubovskaya, O. Hamant & W.Z. Cande, unpublished data). Other meiotic effectors, such as *PHS1*, *ZmSGO1*, or *AM1*, are also expressed in both somatic and meiotic tissues in maize (72, 141; W. Pawlowski & W.Z. Cande, unpublished data). At this point, we can speculate that these differential observations may reflect the fact that in contrast to animals, a true germ line is absent in plants. Furthermore, there is only one SCC3 sequence and no STAG3 sequence in the *Arabidopsis* genome (36). However, at a functional level, analysis of mutants impaired in several cohesins have shown that the cohesion complex is absolutely required for regulation of chromosome structure during meiosis in plants.

Mutations in the *SYN1/DIF1/AtREC8* gene result in a complex meiotic phenotype that affects both male and female fertility (142). A defect can initially be detected as early as leptotene, when chromosome condensation appears irregular (11). Recent analysis supports a function of SYN1/DIF1, in addition to SCC, in chromosome pairing and/or juxtaposition (30). Extensive chromosome fragmentation is clearly observed by anaphase I. Further acentric fragments, together with chromosome bridges, are seen at anaphase II. Subsequent nondisjunction leads to the production of polyads with up to eight spores that contain variable amounts of DNA (18).

Two alternately-spliced *SYN1/DIF1* transcripts have been identified; these transcripts encode proteins that are 627 (expressed at low levels in all tissues) and 617 (expressed in buds only) amino acids long (11). Evidence that SYN1/DIF1 acts as a cohesin is supported by the fact that the protein can partially substitute for the Mcd1 mitotic cohesin protein in yeast complementation tests (54).

Recently, we have cloned *AFD1*, the maize *SYN1* ortholog, and have initiated an analysis of its role in leptotene chromosome structure establishment (I.N. Golubovskaya, O.

Hamant & W.Z. Cande, unpublished data). Using two *afd1* null alleles, we have demonstrated that AFD1/ZmREC8 is absolutely required for the maintenance of SCC, axial element elongation and homologous pairing (see the sections Homologous Chromosome Alignment and Installation of the Synaptonemal Complex). Surprisingly, in weak *afd1* alleles with reduced level of AFD1 expression, we observed leptotene chromosomes as well as bouquet formation (see the section The Bouquet: Facilitating Pairing?") at zygotene. We showed that this new *afd1* phenotype is due to the partial restoration of axial element elongation in the weak alleles, independent of the installation of the recombination machinery. This suggests that the establishment of early prophase I chromosome structure depends on the level of REC8 (I.N. Golubovskaya, O. Hamant & W.Z. Cande, unpublished data). It would be interesting to know if, conversely, the meiocyte has the ability to control the level of AFD1 to regulate the kinetics of early prophase I chromosome structure establishment. Consistent with our data, Chelysheva et al. (36) found that AtREC8 is involved in chromosome axis formation, and that this function is AtSPO11-1 independent in *Arabidopsis*.

In addition to SYN1 and AFD1, three other REC8/RAD21 proteins are present in each of the *Arabidopsis* and maize genomes (54). No mutant alleles of these genes are known. Furthermore, the function of these genes in the cohesin complex can be questioned, as two of the *Arabidopsis* RAD21 homologs cannot complement yeast cells that are deficient in the Mcd1 mitotic cohesin (54). The rice genome also contains four REC8/RAD21 sequences, and *OsRAD21-4* is the closest homolog of *AFD1* (O. Hamant & W.Z. Cande, unpublished data). The expression profile of *OsRAD21-1* is not meiosis specific (200). It remains to be determined whether these putative RAD21 proteins share some of the REC8 functions during meiosis.

Homologs of SMC1, SMC3, and SCC3 have also been identified in *Arabidopsis* (36,

100) and are associated with meiotic chromosomes. Surprisingly, the *Arabidopsis* SMC3 protein is also associated with the meiotic and mitotic spindle from metaphase to telophase, but not with perinuclear microtubules during prophase. Analysis of the *syn1* mutant indicates that the chromosomal localization of SMC3, but not the spindle localization, is dependent on normal SYN1 function (100). These findings suggest that SMC proteins may have both conserved functions similar to those in other organisms, as well as novel functions specific to plants. The characterization of weak *titan7* and *titan8* alleles during meiosis could unravel these functions. AtSCC3 is present on chromosomes from leptotene until metaphase I and is required, together with SYN1, to maintain centromere cohesion and the monopolar orientation of the kinetochores at anaphase I (36; for review on chromosome segregation, see 50, 196). In addition, the *atscc3* mutant shows defective synapsis and abnormal condensation; this observation suggests a role of AtSCC3 in meiotic prophase chromosome structure establishment (36). According to present data, it is still difficult to address the contribution of the different cohesins in establishing prophase I chromosome structure in plants.

Histone modifications. The histone H3 phosphorylation pattern correlates well with the chromosome condensation during meiosis in mammals; however, in plants, the distribution of H3Ser10 phosphorylation correlates better with SCC (61, 89, 112). During the first meiotic division, entire chromosomes are highly phosphorylated, whereas, in the second division, H3 phosphorylation is restricted to the pericentromeric regions (89). During the second meiotic division, single chromatids, which result from equational division of univalents at anaphase I, show low levels of phosphorylation throughout the chromosome (61, 112). Furthermore, in the *afd1/zmrec8* mutant, which is defective in SCC, univalents at metaphase I showed high levels of H3Ser10

phosphorylation only in the pericentromeric regions, and unattached sisters at MII showed no staining at all (89). Therefore, plant H3 phosphorylation at Ser10 correlates better with SCC.

One possibility to explain the differences between plants and animals is that both kingdoms may have evolved different histone codes. Recent observations have shown that H3 phosphorylation on Thr 11 in mammalian cells is restricted to the centromeric region (144). In contrast, in several plants (i.e., *Arabidopsis thaliana*, *Secale cereale*, *Triticum aestivum*, *Hordeum vulgare*, *Vicia faba*, *and Zea mays*), H3Thr11 phosphorylation is distributed along the entire length of condensed chromosomes during meiosis (84; O. Hamant & W.Z. Cande, unpublished data). It is still not known if H3Thr11 phosphorylation in plants is tightly associated with condensation and independent from cohesion.

In addition to cohesins and chromatin modifications, the recruitment of axial elements of the SC is essential for the formation of leptotene chromosomes (see the section Installation of the Synaptonemal Complex below for a discussion of SC installation).

Homologous Chromosome Alignment

The biggest unresolved problem in meiosis is understanding the mechanism that allows homologous chromosomes to find each other and pair. Chromosome morphology, specific sequence distribution, and proteins bound to DNA (perhaps also involved in recombination) all may contribute to chromosome homology recognition, but the molecular mechanism remains to be established (for review, see 50).

Theoretically, the initial establishment of a few paired loci could allow the rest of the chromosome to zip-up mechanically, and therefore would increase the efficiency of homology recognition. The clustering of telomeres into a "bouquet" is one of the mechanisms that is thought to facilitate these initial contacts leading to alignment and subsequent pairing (49, 74).

The bouquet: facilitating pairing? Before chromosomes synapse during zygotene, telomeres attach to the nuclear envelope and cluster to form a structure called the bouquet (74) (**Figure 2b**). The bouquet stage has been observed in every plant species in which three-dimensional reconstructions have been performed (14). As synapsis typically is initiated near the telomeres (29), it has been proposed that the bouquet may help to facilitate pairing and synapsis. In addition to promoting initial contacts before pairing, the cluster may serve to confine homologous sequences to a small volume of the nucleus so as to promote synapsis.

The mechanism by which the bouquet is formed is unknown as very few bouquet mutants have been identified. The ability to culture rye anthers made it possible to obtain intermediates in bouquet formation, to correlate telomere distribution with elapsed time,

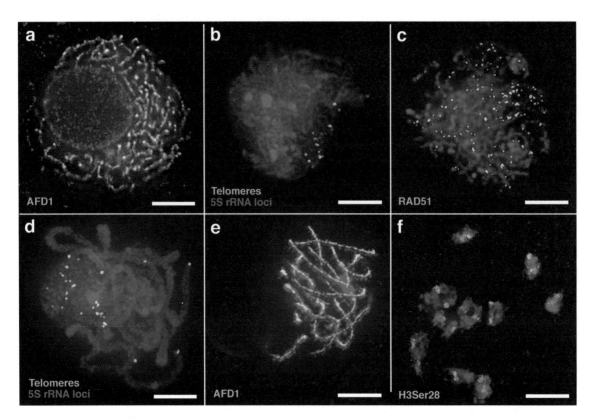

Figure 2

Some prophase I features in maize. DAPI-stained chromatin is shown in red. (*a*) Immunostaining of ABSENCE OF FIRST DIVISION (AFD) 1/ZmREC8, one of the earliest meiotic markers, at the leptotene-zygotene transition. (*b*) The teleomeric "bouquet," indicated by fluorescent in situ hybridization (FISH) at zygotene (see The Bouquet: Facilitating Pairing?); the telomere cluster (*green*) and unpaired 5S rRNA loci (*purple*) are visible. Image provided by I.N. Golubovskaya. (*c*) RAD51 immunostaining at zygotene. Image provided by W. Pawlowski. (*d*) Homologous pairing at pachytene shown by FISH: Paired 5S rRNA loci (*purple*) and spread telomeres (*green*) are visible. Image provided by I.N. Golubovskaya. (*e*) AFD1 immunostaining signal between the synapsed chromosomes at pachytene. (*f*) Histone H3Ser28 phosphorylation occurs at diakinesis; the immunostaining signal localizes to the pericentromeric regions. Scale bar = 5 μm.

and thus to obtain an approximate time course of telomere clustering in rye (32). To determine whether the motion of chromosomes was random or directed, a computer simulation of bouquet formation was compared to empirical observations. Directed motion, as opposed to random diffusion, was required to reproduce the observations; this result implies that an active process moves chromosomes to cause telomere clustering. More generally, data from plants and mouse are consistent with a model in which the telomeres attach to the nuclear envelope at random, and then cluster thanks to an active process (14, 49, 160).

A simple hypothesis proposes that the polarized movement of telomeres is driven by the cytoskeleton. Using a monoclonal antibody to calf centrosomes (6C6), Schmit et al. observed staining at the ends of the zygotene chromosomes (162, 163). As the nuclear envelope functions as a microtubule-organizing center (MTOC) in plants, it is possible that nuclear-envelope-associated microtubules are involved in telomere movement. It was found that, in Lilium and Allium, colchicine reduces pairing when applied during bouquet formation (109, 180). Although bouquet formation in plants is sensitive to colchicine, other microtubule depolymerizing drugs, such as amiprophos methyl and vinblastine, do not inhibit telomere clustering in rye; this result suggests that it is not dependent on cytoplasmic microtubules (44). Whether a novel form of tubulin or some other colchicine-sensitive protein is involved in telomere clustering remains to be determined.

We have identified and characterized a maize meiotic mutant, *plural abnormalities of meiosis 1* (*pam1*), that is deficient in the clustering but not the attachment of telomeres on the nuclear envelope (68). In *pam1*, leptotene chromosomes look completely normal using both deconvolution three-dimensional microscopy and transmission electron microscopy, telomeres attach normally to the nuclear envelope, are normally polarized in the nucleus, and undergo some initial stages

of clustering by forming several small clumps of telomeres; however, telomeres cannot cluster into a normal tight bouquet (68). Interestingly, chromosomes in *pam1* behave similarly to rye chromosomes treated with colchicine.

Beyond bringing chromosomes into close proximity, what is the impact of bouquet formation on subsequent prophase events? The *pam1* meiotic nuclei have aberrant synapsis and a dramatic reduction in homologous pairing. However, RAD51 foci on zygotene chromosomes are normal in number; these observations suggest that (*a*) the early stages of recombination do not require bouquet initiation and (*b*) these two processes can be separated (68). Still, there is no evidence showing that the bouquet is absolutely required for pairing (63, 118). Even though the bouquet was restored in the weakest *afd1* allele, homologous pairing was still impaired, demonstrating a minor contribution of the bouquet in the AFD1-dependent homologous pairing pathway (I.N. Golubovskaya, O. Hamant & W.Z. Cande, unpublished data). Conversely, pairing does not impact bouquet formation as in maize *phs1*, *maize male sterile (mms)25*, and *desynaptic Chris Staiger (dysCS)* mutants, morphologically normal bouquets are observed, but homologous chromosomes do not synapse and RAD51 complexes are not detected cytologically. To conclude, although pairing and bouquet formation are mutually independent, the clustering of telomeres is one of several possible mechanisms that may facilitate the initial homology recognition.

Homeologous pairing. The presence of a polyploid genome creates new problems for the pairing of homologous chromosomes. In polyploids, three or more chromosome sets, either from a given species (autopolyploids) or from related diploid species that sexually hybridized (allopolyploids), coexist. At meiosis, more than two homologous or genetically related (homoeologous) chromosomes can compete for synapsis and recombination. Pairing of homeologous partners would result in multivalent associations and improper segregation of chromosomes at anaphase I to produce unbalanced and unviable gametes. To circumvent this problem, many allopolyploids show a diploid-like meiotic behavior with strict homologous pairing (166).

Little is known about the mechanism that allows the discrimination between homologous and homeologous pairing. In wheat, it has been proposed that the association of homologous chromosomes before meiosis prevents multivalent association and allows a true diploid-type homologous pairing (6, 114). In the wild-type, synapsis with a different partner at each end can occur, and a multivalent configuration results. In the course of prophase I, these multivalent associations are transformed into bivalents. In the *pairing homoeologous (PH)1* mutant, many of the multivalent associations persist until metaphase I (166). However, PH1 cannot prevent nonhomologous/homeologous chromosomes from associating via their centromeres when homologous chromosomes are absent in the hexaploid wheat-rye hybrid (115). This observation suggests that the discrimination between homologous and homeologous does

not occur initially but is performed after chromosome alignment. In this scenario, PH1 would be required to resolve incorrect pairing (126, 151). Isolation of the *PH1* sequence should clarify the mode of action of this gene in wheat and its homologs, if any, in other species.

SYNAPSIS, RECOMBINATION, AND CROSSOVER FORMATION

Installation of the Synaptonemal Complex

Synapsis of homologous chromosomes is observed cytologically during zygotene as the installation of an evolutionarily conserved tripartite structure: the synaptonemal complex (SC) (for reviews see 62, 125, 137, 191, and 204). At leptotene, each chromosome forms chromatin loops that are attached to an axial element. During pairing, these axial elements come together to become the lateral elements of the SC with the central element between them, giving the SC its tripartite structure (**Figure 3**).

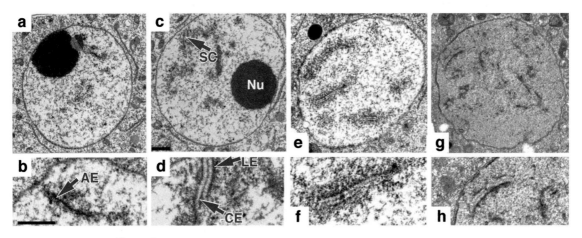

Figure 3

Transmission electron microscopy images of *Arabidopsis* male meiocytes. (*a, b*) Leptotene. Unsynapsed axial elements (AE); early nodules are associated with the axial element in *b*. (*c, d*) Zygotene. There are both unsynapsed and synapsed axial elements, called lateral elements (LE), in the nucleus. An early recombination nodule is present on the central element (CE) of SC in the synaptic fork in *d*. (*e, f*) Early pachytene. All axial elements have become LE of the SC; recombination nodules can be seen regularly on the central element of the SC. (*g, h*) Late pachytene. Only a few recombination nodules can be observed on the central elements of SCs. Images kindly provided by L. Timofejeva.

By far, defects in synapsis are the most frequent phenotype among meiotic mutants in forward genetic screens. This result is mainly due to the fact that defective synapsis can arise as a consequence of several primary defects in SCC, homolog pairing, or recombination (88). In this respect, in both maize *afd1* and *Arabidopsis syn1* mutants, depletion of the key meiotic cohesin REC8 induces defective SC installation and absence of chiasmata; this result shows that SC formation and chiasmata maintenance depends on the presence of cohesion (11; I.N. Golubovskaya, O. Hamant & W.Z. Cande, unpublished data). Several desynaptic mutants have been characterized (for review, see Reference 110) but the corresponding genes have not yet been cloned.

Asynaptic1 (*asy1*) is an *Arabidopsis* mutant that exhibits a failure of homologous chromosome synapsis during prophase I (8, 153). The *ASY1* gene has been cloned and encodes a protein with significant homology to the yeast Hop1 protein over the N-terminal half. The C-terminal half of the ASY1 protein sequence has no obvious similarity to any other protein in the database (33). Yeast *hop1* mutants exhibit reduced levels of meiotic recombination and extremely low levels of spore viability (81). The Hop1 protein is first observed as multiple discrete foci during prophase I and is associated with the axial elements (82, 174). The Hop1 signal disappears at pachytene when full synapsis is completed (174). The phenotypes of the *hop1* mutants in yeast and related proteins in *C. elegans*, *Arabidopsis*, and rice are very similar; this observation suggests that the function of *HOP1* in SC formation is conserved across kingdoms (33, 82, 134, 199). Overall, the ASY1 protein exhibits the same immunostaining pattern in *Arabidopsis*, *Brassica oleracea* and *Zea mays* (8; I.N. Golubovskaya, O. Hamant, R.C.J. Wang & W.Z. Cande, unpublished data) as Hop1 in yeast. However, ASY1 is first detected as early as meiotic interphase as punctate chromatin associated foci and is maintained longer in *Arabidopsis* and *Brassica oleracea* than Hop1, which is lost when the chromosomes desynapse (8). Interestingly, immunogold labeling, which gave a higher resolution than standard immunostaining, revealed a discontinuous pattern along the axial/lateral elements. This observation could suggest a role of ASY1 in recruiting the bases of chromatin loops to the developing axial/lateral elements (8). In maize, the behavior of ASY1 and AFD1 is different during synapsis: ASY1 is released from the chromosomes when chromosomes synapse, whereas AFD1 is maintained (**Figure 2e**). This suggests that AFD1, but not ASY1, has a role in the maturation of axial element into lateral elements during synapsis (I.N. Golubovskaya, O. Hamant, R.C.J. Wang & W.Z. Cande, unpublished data). The rice *pair2* mutant partially phenocopies the *asy1* mutant from *Arabidopsis*, although the *pair2* phenotype is more severe than that of *asy1*, as only univalents are observed at metaphase I. The *PAIR2* gene has been shown to encode a homolog of *ASY1* and *HOP1* (134).

Although central elements have been studied in detail in yeast and later in animals (137), little is known about plant central elements. Recently, the combination of a BLAST search and a prediction of the biochemical properties of the central element proteins led to the identification of two genes called *AtZYP1a* and *AtZYP1b* in the *Arabidopsis* genome (80). The presence of an AtZYP1 immunostaining signal in both *atzyp1a* and *atzyp1b* mutants as well as their identical mutant phenotypes suggest that *AtZYP1a* and *AtZYP1b* are functionally redundant. Both proteins are present in meiocytes during prophase I only. Double immunolocalizations demonstrated a central localization of AtZYP1, bordered by ASY1 on both lateral elements of the SC. Higgins et al. (80) also showed that the initiation of recombination is necessary for AtZYP1 recruitment but is not sufficient for its polymerization in a central element. RNAi lines were generated to deplete both *AtZYP1a* and *AtZYP1b*; knockdown of these genes resulted in delayed meiosis, absence of pairing and synapsis in most meiocytes. However, crossover distribution, as monitored by MutL HOMOLOG

(MLH) 1 immunostaining, was not greatly affected; this result suggests that the loss of AtZYP1 does not prevent progression to the later stages of recombination. Finally, chiasmata observed in the *AtZYP1* RNAi lines were shown to occur between homologs and nonhomologs; this result demonstrates that the absence of AtZYP1 allows nonhomologous recombination to occur. Studies on budding yeast SC proteins have led to the proposal of a surveillance mechanism that monitors progression through prophase I (25). The analysis of AtZYP1 points towards strong similarities between *Arabidopsis* and budding yeast and suggests that the SC might act as a surveillance complex in plants to ensure a correct progression through recombination (80).

The Plant Recombination Pathway

Many genes have been identified that are important for meiotic recombination (for reviews, see 91, 105, 190). Given the high degree of conservation of recombination proteins among species, the reverse genetic approach has proven to be very powerful for the characterization of the functions of plant recombination proteins, in particular in *Arabidopsis* (**Figure 4**) (for reviews, see 3, 17, 110).

The recombination sequence. Meiotic recombination is initiated by DSBs generated by the Spo11 protein (16, 70, 91). The *Arabidopsis* AtSPO11-1 protein (one of three Spo11 homologs of *Arabidopsis*) is the functional homolog of yeast Spo11, as shown by its requirement for initiation of meiotic recombination (70, 75, 76). However, in *atspo11-1* meiocytes, a few bivalents at diakinesis are observed, suggesting that either recombination can still occur, or that bivalents form in a recombination independent way (70).

The initial DSBs are resected from 5′ to 3′ by the MRX complex, which is composed of Mre11, Rad50 and Xrs2/Nbs1. In yeast, the MRX complex is required for the formation of Spo11-induced DSBs and the processing of these DSBs ends (41, 175). *Arabidopsis*

homologs of Rad50 (AtRAD50) and Mre11 (AtMRE11) have been shown to form a complex, and functional analysis of the *atrad50* and *atmre11* mutants strongly suggest that plants have a functional homolog of the MRX complex (22, 46, 60, 147).

Single-stranded DNA ends created by the coordinated action of SPO11 and the MRX complex invade the homologous double-stranded DNA. This step is catalyzed by RAD51 and DMC1, which are homologs of the RecA recombinase that possess single-stranded DNA-binding ability and DNA-dependent ATPase activity (2, 19). In vitro, these two proteins each have the ability to catalyze the strand exchange reaction, which is the motor of homologous recombination (83, 182). RAD51 functions in both the mitotic cell cycle and meiosis, whereas DMC1 is meiosis-specific (97, 117). Homologs of RAD51 and DMC1 have been identified in *Arabidopsis*, maize, lily, and rice (2, 53, 55, 58, 93, 103, 140). In *Arabidopsis*, the *atrad51* mutant is sterile and exhibits meiotic defects in pairing and synapsis as well as severe chromosome fragmentation; this observation suggests that RAD51 in plants is also involved in DSB repair (103). This hypothesis is further supported by the observation that chromosome fragmentation is absent in the *atrad51 atspo11-1* double mutant; this observation indicates that fragmentation is due to failure to repair *SPO11-1*-induced DSBs.

The *Arabidopsis atdmc1* mutant produces meiocytes with mainly univalents instead of bivalents at late prophase I; this observation indicates that *AtDMC1* is crucial for bivalent formation and chromosome segregation during meiosis in *Arabidopsis* (43). However, no chromosome fragmentation was detected in the *atdmc1* mutant; this result suggests that *AtDMC1* is functionally distinct from *AtRAD51*. Unlike yeast DMC1, AtDMC1 is expressed not only in reproductive tissues but also in leaves and cultured cell suspensions (43).

In maize, double mutants of the two RAD51 homologs have recently been obtained and are male sterile. Surviving female

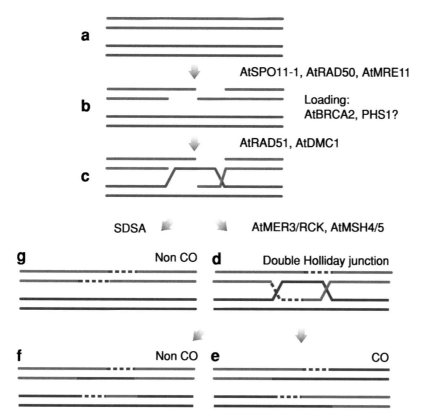

Figure 4

The plant recombination pathway. (*a*) Double-stranded DNA molecules of two nonsister chromatids. (*b*) A DSB is generated by SPO11, and 5′ strands are resected to produce 3′ single-stranded DNAs by the MRE11-RAD50-XRS2 (MRX) complex. (*c*) RAD51/DMC1 driven strand invasion occurs to produce a D-loop. (*d*) DNA synthesis followed by ligation results in a double-Holliday junction, which is stabilized by MutS HOMOLOG (MSH) 4-MSH5 dimers. (*e, f*) Resolution of the double-Holliday junction in the opposite sense (*e*) leads to the formation of an interference sensitive crossover event (*CO*) whereas cleavage in the same sense (*f*) results in a noncrossover event (*Non CO*). (*g*) Alternatively, the Holliday junction progenitors may not be captured by MSH4–MSH5 dimers. At this point, if the invading end is rejected, synthesis-dependent strand annealing (SDSA) may be inititated and a noncrossover arise (*g*); in contrast, capture of the invading end may lead to an interference-insensitive crossover, a pathway in which no plant genes have been described and which is not shown on this figure.

gametes produced by ZmRAD51 double mutants are euploid and exhibit normal rates of crossing-over (P. Schnable, personal communication).

The strand invasion event can proceed down one of two pathways: the classical double-strand break repair (DSBR) pathway or the synthesis-dependent strand-annealing (SDSA) pathway (**Figure 4**) (20). In the DSBR pathway, DNA synthesis from the invading strands and ligation yield the double-Holliday junction. Resolution of the double-Holliday junction following cutting at alternative strands results in products with either crossovers or noncrossovers. X-ray cross complementing (Xrcc) 3, a paralog of Rad51, has been shown to play a role in mitotic recombination, DNA repair, and chromosome stability; it also participates in Holliday junction resolution in vertebrate cells (27, 107, 184, 185). Mutation in *AtXRCC3* induces meiotic chromosome fragmentation, which leads to gametophytic lethality in *Arabidopsis* (24). Although the *atrad51* and *xrcc3* phenotypes are very similar, the phenotypes of the double mutants *atrad51 spo11-1* and *atxrcc3 spo11-1* are different. In *spo11-1* and *atrad51 spo11-1*, no fragmentation is observed during the second meiotic division (70, 103). In contrast, fragmentation is observed during the second meiotic division in *atxrcc3 atspo11-1* plants (23). Therefore, fragmentation during the second division in *atxrcc3 atspo11-1* is specifically caused by the lack of the AtXRCC3 protein. This late fragmentation results from unresolved sister chromatid events, as they are detectable upon the separation of sister chromatids at anaphase II. Based on the post-synapsis meiotic role of AtXRCC3 and the role of the vertebrate Xrcc3 and Rad51C protein in Holliday junction resolution (184), Bleuyard et al. (23) proposed that AtXRCC3 also contributes to Holliday junction resolution.

Four other RAD51 paralogs (XRCC2, RAD51B, RAD51C, and RAD51D) have been identified in mammals and retain distinct functions related to homologous recombination. (59, 98, 99, 123, 161, 172, 183). In vivo, two complexes have been identified, one containing RAD51B, RAD51C, RAD51D, and XRCC2, and the other containing RAD51C and XRCC3 (116, 197). A third one includes RAD51 and XRCC3 (161). *Arabidopsis* homologs of the RAD51B, RAD51C and XRCC2 have been identified in the genomic sequence (21). Two-hybrid analyses have confirmed that AtXRCC3 interacts with AtRAD51 and AtRAD51C (136). Furthermore, gamma-irradiation has shown that transcription of AtXRCC3 and AtRAD51C is induced in response to DNA damage (136). These data strongly suggest that AtXRCC3 and AtRAD51C are the functional homologs of XRCC3 and RAD51C. Recently, analysis of an insertional mutant indicated that *AtRAD51C* is required for the repair of SPO11-1 induced DSBs during meiotic prophase I (21, 104). Similar to the

atrad51 and *atxrcc3* mutants, the *atrad51c* mutant exhibit meiotic chromosome fragmentation in a SPO11-1 dependent fashion and is completely male- and female-sterile. In addition, *AtRAD51C* is important for both (*a*) normal homolog pairing and/or juxtaposition and (*b*) synapsis (104). In contrast, mutants in *AtRAD51B* and *AtXRCC2* are fertile and do not have detectable developmental defects, although they and the *atrad51c* mutant are all hypersensitive to the DNA-crosslinking agent Mitomycin C (21). Therefore, *AtRAD51B*, *AtRAD51C*, and *AtXRCC2* play a role in DNA repair during the mitotic cell cycle. *AtRAD51C* is required for meiotic prophase I and cannot be substituted for *RAD51* or other *RAD51* paralogs. Further analysis is needed to determine the precise roles of these *RAD51* paralogs.

Loading the recombination machinery. BRCA2 facilitates the loading of RAD51 on single-strand DNA (188). *Arabidopsis* possesses two closely related *BRCA2* homologs (170). To date, no *BRCA2* insertional mutant has been characterized in plants; however, an RNAi approach was used to reduce AtBRCA2 expression in *Arabidopsis* (170). In these meiocytes, chromosome fragmentation occurred, and univalents were formed, which led to uneven chromosome segregation; this phenotype is similar to that seen in cells mutant for *atrad51*, *atrad51c*, or *atxrcc3*. The absence of AtSPO11-1 function suppressed chromosome fragmentation in *BRCA2* RNAi plants; this result demonstrates that *AtBRCA2* is required for meiotic recombination and acts downstream of *AtSPO11-1* (170). Interestingly, yeast two-hybrid assays showed that AtBRCA2 interacts with AtRAD51 and AtDMC1; this result strongly suggests that the Brca2 function of loading Rad51 and/or Dmc1 on single-stranded DNA is conserved in plants (170).

In maize, Pawlowski et al. (141) identified a novel gene, *PHS1*, involved in loading the recombination machinery onto chromosomes. Observations by transmission electron microscopy of silver nitrate stained chromosome spreads of male *phs1* meiocytes at different stages of prophase I indicated defects in homologous synapsis. The axial elements of SC are installed properly at pachytene but stretches of the apparently synapsed chromosome segments showed improper chromosome alignment and exchanges of synaptic partners (141). By monitoring homologous pairing using fluorescent in situ hybridization (FISH) to visualize the 5S rRNA locus (**Figure 2d**), it was shown that, although the chromosomes appeared to be synapsed, none of the 5S rRNA loci were paired; this observation indicated that synapsis was completely nonhomologous. The *phs1* mutant meiocytes showed a dramatic decrease in the number of RAD51 foci during zygotene relative to the wild-type, with only three RAD51 foci on average per nucleus. However, the amount of the RAD51 protein in anthers remained the same as in the wild-type meiocytes. Based on the mutant phenotype, Pawlowski et al. (141) proposed that the PHS1 protein is a component of the meiotic recombination pathway and hypothesized that it may be involved in loading RAD51 complexes onto chromosomes. This analysis also showed a link between recombination and homologous pairing (see the section Coordination Between Pairing, Synapsis, and Recombination). The *PHS1* gene was cloned by transposon tagging and encodes a novel protein without significant similarity to any known protein and without any obvious functional features or domains; however, putative homologs are present in *Arabidopsis* and other plants. No homologs have been identified in yeast and animals (141).

Plant recombination proteins: conservation and specificities. Although the recombination pathway seems structurally and functionally conserved among kingdoms, a few phenotypic differences are highlighted among various organisms. Plant genomes contain multigene families of several of the recombination proteins. This is particularly the case for *SPO11* (three homologs in *Arabidopsis*) and *BRCA2* (two homologs in *Arabidopsis*) which, in contrast, are unique in yeast and animal genomes. In the case of *SPO11*, only *SPO11-1* has been shown to be important for meiosis, whereas both copies of *BRCA2* likely have similar meiotic functions. For *RAD51* homologs, functional analysis in fungal, plant, and animal kingdoms suggest that they have evolved distinct functions.

Another main difference is that single mutants in the *RAD51* gene family are embryonic-lethal in mammals but are viable in yeast, *Drosophila*, and plants. The yeast and *Drosophila* mutants are sensitive to radiation and chemicals that induce DNA breaks. In *Arabidopsis*, the mutants are either normal or sensitive to DNA-crosslinking agents. The yeast, *Drosophila*, and plant mutants are similar in that they are defective in meiosis. For instance, the mammalian *rad51* knockout is embryonic-lethal, whereas the *atrad51* mutant seems healthy under normal growth conditions and undergoes mitosis normally (103, 186). Therefore, the meiotic functions of these genes might be conserved between yeast, plants, and animals, but the mitotic DSB repair functions might not be universally critical.

Another way to explain these differences is to assume that members of a multigene family of recombination proteins display redundant functions during mitotic DNA repair, whereas, during meiosis, they have separate functions. The number of DSBs induced during meiosis is very high in comparison with somatic DNA damage, and, although other members of the recombination family could substitute for an absent protein and repair mitotic DSB easily, that might not be the case during meiotic DSB repair. Alternatively, DSBs may be repaired by *RAD51-* and *XRCC3*-independent pathways during mitosis. To investigate this further, it would be helpful to determine whether plant recombination mutants are more sensitive to DSB-inducing agents.

Coordination from Pairing to Chiasmata Resolution

Coordination between pairing, synapsis, and recombination.

Although SC formation appears normal in *phs1* mutants, pairing and recombination are uncoupled from synapsis. Knowing that RAD51 disruption in other organisms does not lead to extensive nonhomologous synapsis, another function of PHS1, in addition to loading RAD51, may be to coordinate pairing, synapsis, and recombination (for review, see 139). This coordination may be temporal: As synapsis is delayed in *phs1*, nonhomologous synapsis in *phs1* might result from delayed homologous pairing that requires a longer synapsis to stabilize chromosome associations. Knockouts of *hop2* in yeast show approximately 60% nonhomologous synapsis (102). This phenotype resembles that of *phs1*. Interestingly, HOP2 interacts with the RAD51/DMC1 complex (139). ARABIDOPSIS HOMOLOGUE PAIRING (AHP) 2, a Hop2 homolog, has been identified in plants. The *ahp2* mutant displays wild-type vegetative development, but is male- and female-sterile. However, contrary to yeast *hop2* and maize *phs1*, the *ahp2* mutant lacks a SC (164).

In addition to its role during recombination, RAD51, which acts in the DNA single-strand invasion process, could facilitate homologous recognition between DNA fragments. In maize, we have analyzed in meiotic nuclei the three-dimensional distribution of RAD51. Distinct RAD51 foci begin to appear at the end of leptotene, and reach a maximum number of approximately 500/nucleus in midzygotene (58). As pairing proceeds, the number of foci decreases until, in midpachytene, only a few (ten to twenty) foci persist. During zygotene, RAD51 foci are preferentially seen on unpaired chromosomes (**Figure 2c**), whereas when chromosomes pair and synapse, foci on adjacent homologs appear to fuse together; by pachytene, only single foci are found (58). We also investigated RAD51 in maize meiotic mutants. Overall, we observed either the same or a reduced number

of RAD51 foci. We found no or very few double RAD51 foci in several desynaptic mutants including *phs1*, *as1*, *dsy9901*, and *mtm99-25* (140). Thus, the behavior of RAD51 is consistent with the idea that it plays a role in homology identification as well as recombination (58, 140). In this respect, the number of RAD51 foci in the wild-type, and even in most of the meiotic mutants, is theoretically much higher than the number needed for crossover and formation of chiasmata. Conversely, in pachytene, the RAD51 foci disappeared more slowly in the meiotic mutants than in wild type; this observation suggests that successful completion of homologous pairing is required for removal of RAD51 from chromosomes (140).

The phenotypes of *atrad51c* and *atxrcc3* mutants (24, 104) suggest that these two *RAD51* paralogs may also be involved in the homology identification that is required for pairing. Furthermore, the *rock-n-roller* (*rck*, also named *atmer3*) mutants also exhibit a reduction in SC formation consistent with the reduced level of chiamata formation (37, 121; also, see below). Therefore, it is likely that, in plant meiosis, pairing, synapsis, and recombination are interdependent and co-regulated. As we mention above, the meiosis-specific cyclin SDS is required for homolog synapsis and recombination (10); it is possible that SDS plays a role in regulating these processes in a coordinated fashion.

Recombination and crossover formation.

Initial experiments in yeast to define the meiotic crossover and noncrossover pathways suggested that these pathways branch during recombination no later than at the single-strand invasion step (20). Findings by Borner et al. (25) suggest that the pathway generating crossovers is more complex than the noncrossover pathway and includes a checkpoint in late leptotene.

If a crossover occurs, the recombination event matures into a chiasma, which is visible at diplotene. During zygotene and pachytene, two types of recombination nodules have been observed by transmission electron microscopy; these are termed early and late nodules, both of which are known to contain recombination enzymes. Early nodules are more numerous, contain Rad51 and Dmc1, and are thought to be the sites of initial single-strand invasion (2). Early nodules are lost by mid-pachytene; the nodules that remain, called late nodules, are thought to be sites of crossovers and are assumed to mature into chiasmata. MLH1, a mismatch repair protein, is a marker of the late nodules (3, 13, 86, 124).

There is almost always one crossover per chromosome arm per meiosis. This crossover guarantees proper alignment of bivalents on the equatorial plate of the first meiotic division and subsequent proper disjunction of homologous chromosomes. Furthermore, the presence of one crossover discourages additional crossovers in its vicinity, a phenomenon known as crossover interference. Several theorical models in yeast based on analyzing the distribution of crossovers in yeasts and animals suggest that crossover interference is tightly coordinated with synapsis (20, 139). Recent analysis in yeast has revealed two genetically separate pathways for crossover formation (51). One of these is dependent on *MER3*, *MSH4*, and *MSH5* genes and is sensitive to interference. The other is independent of these three genes and not sensitive to interference (**Figure 4**) (51). *MSH4* and *MSH5* are two of six homologs of the bacterial *mutS* gene (required for mismatch repair), and they encode subunits of a heterodimer that specializes in meiotic crossover formation (155). MER3 is a DNA helicase and has been shown to unwind double-stranded DNA. In yeast, mutations in *MER3*, *MSH4*, and *MSH5* cause a reduction in crossover formation to approximately 10–15% of the normal levels; the remaining crossovers do not exhibit interference. In mammals, *MSH4* and *MSH5* are required for normal meiosis as shown by mouse knockout mutants (52, 94), although the roles of these genes in the interference-sensitive pathway of crossover formation is not clear.

In maize, interference was detected genetically 50 years ago (150) and supported by cytological studies (178). Genetic analysis in *Arabidopsis* supports the idea that *Arabidopsis* has both interference-sensitive and insensitive pathways for crossover formation (42). In addition, there is evidence that two such pathways operate in humans (85). More recently, reverse genetic analysis has been conducted on the *Arabidopsis* homologs of *MSH4* and *MER3*. The *AtMSH4* gene is required for normal levels of crossover, as mutants or RNAi lines show a reduction of chiasmata (79). In addition, the remaining chiasmata are randomly distributed; this result suggests that the crossovers that lead to these chiasmata are not sensitive to interference. Similarly, the *Arabidopsis MER3* homolog *AtMER3/RCK* is also required for the interference-sensitive pathway of crossover formation (37, 121). This result is the first report of a role for a *MER3* homolog in crossover formation in a multicellular organism. Furthermore, transmission electron microscopy analysis of *rck* alleles indicate that the SC can form at a reduced level in these mutants; this observation suggests that crossover formation is important for SC establishment and/or maintenance (37).

Chiasmata resolution and sister chromatid cohesion. SCC is established during premeiotic S-phase and participates in the control of both chromosome structure and recombination. Release of SCC is also essential to resolve chiasmata. This function is crucial since it subsequently allows the proper segregation of chromosomes to opposite poles of the cell at anaphase I (reviewed in 135, 189). REC8 immunolocalizations simply illustrate this function. For instance, in *C. elegans*, REC8 is partially lost along chiasmata-distal portions of the arms at anaphase I (138). In *Arabidopsis* and maize, the immunolocalization of the REC8 homologs SYN1 and AFD1, respectively, indicates that these proteins are released at the end of prophase I to allow chiasmata resolution (30; I.N Golubovskaya, O. Hamant & W.Z. Cande, unpublished data).

The release of chromosome cohesion is triggered in most organisms by Separase, a cysteine protease that specifically cleaves RAD21/REC8 proteins; this cleavage subsequently leads to the opening of the ring-shape cohesin complex (39, 77, 187). Separase has not been studied in plants. However, some components of the proteolysis cascade have been shown to be involved in the release of SCC in *Arabidopsis*. The *Arabidopsis SKP1-like1* (*ASK1*) gene encodes a homolog of the human and yeast Skp1 proteins (198) and is involved in plant growth and development. In particular, ASK1 has been shown to interact with Unusual Floral Organ (UFO) to regulate flower organ identity (157, 202). The *ask1-1* mutant is also male-sterile, and chromosomes in this mutant fail to segregate at anaphase I; this failure leads to the production of polyads with spores of variable size and chromosome content (198). Interestingly, SYN1 immunostaining is maintained on chromosome arms during diplotene and diakinesis; this observation strongly suggests that ASK1 is required for the removal of SYN1 and SCC during late prophase I (D. Zhao, X. Yang, L. Quan, L. Timofejeva, C. Makaroff & H. Ma, unpublished data). Partners of ASK1 that form the SKP1-Cullin-F-box (SCF) complex, as well as downstream effectors of ASK1 need to be identified to further elucidate the cascade that leads to cohesion release. Data on ASK1 recall results obtained in other organisms: In yeast and *C. elegans*, the anaphase promoting complex (APC) activates Separase and is required for the release of the cohesin complex at the onset of anaphase I (28, 173). However, in addition to the APC-dependent proteolytic pathway that functions at anaphase, a second

pathway, which takes place during prophase, is APC- and separase-independent in vertebrates (77, 181). The *ask1* phenotype might also rely on an alternative early pathway, in particular as SYN1 immunostaining in *ask1-1* is abnormal as early as leptotene (D. Zhao, X. Yang, L. Quan, L. Timofejeva, C. Makaroff & H. Ma, unpublished data).

Other SKP1 homologs may also play a role in meiosis in plants. For instance, the *ask1* chromosome separation defects can be partially rescued by a transgene of the closely related homolog, *ASK2* (201). There are at least 21 SKP1 homologs in *Arabidopsis* (96, 113). In *C. elegans*, a Skp1 homolog has been shown to be involved in pachytene progression; this observation demonstrates that there are SKP1 meiotic functions in animals (131).

OUTLOOK

Very few genes specifically involved in meiosis after prophase I have been identified, as most plant meiotic mutants exhibit defects during prophase I. One exception is maize shugoshin (ZmSGO1), which is specifically required for maintaining centromeric cohesion at metaphase I but has no apparent function during early prophase I (72). The genetic control of meiosis progression is still largely unknown and will need more research efforts in the coming years. Furthermore, after a very successful decade based on a gene-by-gene approach, the use of more global tools in the future, such as microarrays, proteomics, and modeling of genetic and biochemical pathways, should elucidate new genetic interactions and pathways that control the genetics of meiosis in plants.

SUMMARY POINTS

1. Meiosis is mitotic-like in the maize *ameiotic1* mutant and, to a lesser extent, in the *Arabidopsis switch1* mutant; this observation suggests that AM1 and SWI1 are two related proteins required for meiotic commitment.

2. Several meiotic cyclins such as SDS and TAM have been identified in *Arabidopsis*, but the control of meiosis progression remains largely unknown in plants.

3. Changes in chromosome morphology define the different meiotic prophase stages. Chromosome morphology is dependent on cohesion proteins (such as SYN1, AtSCC3 in *Arabidopsis*, and AFD1 in maize), histone modifications, and synaptonemal complex installation.

4. Telomere clustering (the bouquet) precedes homologous chromosome pairing in zygotene and has been proposed to facilitate homologous chromosome alignment by providing the initial paired foci.

5. Defects in synapsis are the most common phenotypes among meiotic mutants; this observation suggests that installation of the synaptonemal complex impacts or is impacted by several pathways, including homologous pairing, recombination, and sister chromatid cohesion establishment.

6. Mutants in genes homologous to *HOP1* have been identified in Arabidopsis (*asy1*) and rice (*pair2*); the relatively similar phenotypes of these mutants suggest that the function of HOP1 in synaptonemal complex formation is conserved.

7. The central element of the synaptonemal complex contains two redundant proteins: AtZYP1a and AtZYP1b. The analysis of the *atzyp1* mutant points towards a role of the SC in verifying the correct progression of recombination.

8. The recombination pathway is highly conserved across kingdoms. Recombination is initiated by SPO11-induced double-strand breaks. Subsequently, the MRX complex generates a single stranded DNA that invades a neighboring double-stranded DNA molecule, a RAD51/DMC1 controlled step. Strand invasion produces a D-loop. DNA synthesis followed by ligation results in a double-Holliday junction which is subsequently resolved by XRCC3. Homologs of all those proteins have been characterized in plants.

9. Crossover versus noncrossover fate depends on the way the double-Holliday junction is resolved. Crossover formation is dependent on MSH4 and MER3/RCK and is cytologically visualized by the presence of MLH1 on pachytene chromosomes and chiasmata at diakinesis. Release of chiasmata requires the dissolution of cohesion, a process that is dependent on ASK1 in Arabidopsis.

10. Several proteins have been shown to be involved in the recruitment of the recombination machinery; these were identified by two-hybrid approaches (e.g., BRCA2) as well as by monitoring the distribution of RAD51 in mutants (e.g., PHS1, AM1, and AFD1).

FUTURE ISSUES TO BE RESOLVED

1. The genetics of meiosis in plants is an immature field that mainly relies on mutant screens for sterility or reverse genetics for identifying meiotic genes. In the future, one challenge will be to elucidate the genetic interactions that exist between these effectors. Identification of suppressors of meiotic mutant phenotypes is a powerful approach, as new genes as well as new interactions will be unraveled.

2. To date, few meiotic proteins have been characterized at the biochemical level. Given the abundance of male meiocytes in many plant model organisms, plants will make a major contribution, as most of the proteins we discuss in this review have unclear biochemical function and unknown partners.

3. Although the cell cycle in plants is relatively well characterized, control of meiosis progression is largely unknown (e.g., the presence of checkpoints is still under debate). A combination of microarrays and proteomics approaches on staged meiotic cells in wild-type and mutants will lead to the identification of proteins that drive meiosis forward, as well as proteins involved in meiosis checkpoints.

4. The involvement of small RNAs in meiosis has not been demonstrated in plants; given the role of nongenic micronuclear transcripts in genome rearrangements and chromosome dynamics, it is likely that small RNAs may have key meiotic functions.

5. The hierarchy of events needed for homologous chromosome pairing has not been elucidated. Future genetic analysis is needed to understand its molecular control.

ACKNOWLEDGMENTS

We thank Ljuda Timofejeva for transmission electron microscopy images of *Arabidopsis* meiosis, Wuxing Li for images of DAPI-stained *Arabidopsis* meiotic chromosome spreads, and Inna Golubovskaya for FISH images in maize. We also thank Inna Golubovskaya, Lisa Harper, and Wojtek Pawlowski for helpful comments on this manuscript. The work in both W.Z. Cande's lab and H. Ma's lab was supported by grants from NIH, NSF, and USDA. H. Ma gratefully acknowledges the support of the John Simon Guggenheim Memorial Foundation.

LITERATURE CITED

1. Agashe B, Prasad CK, Siddiqi I. 2002. Identification and analysis of *DYAD*: a gene required for meiotic chromosome organisation and female meiotic progression in *Arabidopsis*. *Development* 129:3935–43

2. Anderson LK, Offenberg HH, Verkuijlen WM, Heyting C. 1997. RecA-like proteins are components of early meiotic nodules in lily. *Proc. Natl. Acad. Sci. USA* 94:6868–73

3. Anderson LK, Stack SM. 2005. Recombination nodules in plants. *Cytogenet. Genome Res.* 109:198–204

4. Andrews J, Bouffard GG, Cheadle C, Lu J, Becker KG, Oliver B. 2000. Gene discovery using computational and microarray analysis of transcription in the *Drosophila melanogaster* testis. *Genome Res.* 10:2030–43

5. *Arabidopsis* Genome Initiative. 2000. Analysis of the genome sequence of the flowering plant *Arabidopsis thaliana*. *Nature* 408:796–815

6. Aragon-Alcaide L, Reader S, Miller T, Moore G. 1997. Centromeric behaviour in wheat with high and low homoeologous chromosomal pairing. *Chromosoma* 106:327–33

7. Armstrong SJ, Franklin FCH, Jones GH. 2001. Nucleolus-associated telomere clustering and pairing precede meiotic chromosome synapsis in *Arabidopsis thaliana*. *J. Cell Sci.* 114:4207–17

8. Armstrong SJ, Caryl AP, Jones GH, Franklin FC. 2002. Asy1, a protein required for meiotic chromosome synapsis, localizes to axis-associated chromatin in Arabidopsis and Brassica. *J. Cell Sci.* 115:3645–55

9. Armstrong SJ, Jones GH. 2003. Meiotic cytology and chromosome behaviour in wild-type *Arabidopsis thaliana*. *J. Exp. Bot.* 54:1–10

10. Azumi Y, Liu D, Zhao D, Li W, Wang G, et al. 2002. Homolog interaction during meiotic prophase I in *Arabidopsis* requires the *SOLO DANCERS* gene encoding a novel cyclin-like protein. *EMBO J.* 21:3081–95

11. Bai XF, Peirson BN, Dong FG, Xue C, Makaroff CA. 1999. Isolation and characterization of *SYN1*, a *RAD21*-like gene essential for meiosis in Arabidopsis. *Plant Cell* 11:417–30

12. Baker BS, Carpenter AT, Esposito MS, Esposito RE, Sandler L. 1976. The genetic control of meiosis. *Annu. Rev. Genet.* 10:53–134

13. Baker SM, Plug AW, Prolla TA, Bronner CE, Harris AC, et al. 1996. Involvement of mouse Mlh1 in DNA mismatch repair and meiotic crossing over. *Nat. Genet.* 13:336–42

14. Bass HW, Marshall WF, Sedat JW, Agard DA, Cande WZ. 1997. Telomeres cluster de novo before the initiation of synapsis: a three-dimensional spatial analysis of telomere positions before and during meiotic prophase. *J. Cell Biol.* 137:5–18

15. Beadle GW. 1929. A gene for supernumerary mitosis during spore development in Zea mays. *Science* 50:406–7

16. Bergerat A, de Massy B, Gadelle D, Varoutas PC, Nicolas A, Forterre P. 1997. An atypical topoisomerase II from Archaea with implications for meiotic recombination. *Nature* 386:414–17

17. Bhatt AM, Canales C, Dickinson HG. 2001. Plant meiosis: the means to 1N. *Trends Plant Sci.* 6:114–21

18. Bhatt AM, Lister C, Page T, Fransz P, Findlay K, et al. 1999. The *DIF1* gene of *Arabidopsis* is required for meiotic chromosome segregation and belongs to the *REC8/RAD21* cohesin gene family. *Plant J.* 19:463–72

19. Bishop DK, Park D, Xu L, Kleckner N. 1992. DMC1: a meiosis-specific yeast homolog of *Escherichia coli* recA required for recombination, synaptonemal complex formation, and cell cycle progression. *Cell* 69:439–56

20. Bishop DK, Zickler D. 2004. Early decision; meiotic crossover interference prior to stable strand exchange and synapsis. *Cell* 117:9–15

21. Bleuyard JY, Gallego ME, Savigny F, White CI. 2005. Differing requirements for the Arabidopsis Rad51 paralogs in meiosis and DNA repair. *Plant J.* 41:533–45

22. Bleuyard JY, Gallego ME, White CI. 2004. Meiotic defects in the Arabidopsis rad50 mutant point to conservation of the MRX complex function in early stages of meiotic recombination. *Chromosoma* 113:197–203

23. Bleuyard JY, Gallego ME, White CI. 2004. The atspo11-1 mutation rescues atxrcc3 meiotic chromosome fragmentation. *Plant Mol Biol.* 56:217–24

24. Bleuyard JY, White CI. 2004. The Arabidopsis homologue of Xrcc3 plays an essential role in meiosis. *EMBO J.* 23:439–49

25. Borner GV, Kleckner N, Hunter N. 2004. Crossover/noncrossover differentiation, synaptonemal complex formation, and regulatory surveillance at the leptotene/zygotene transition of meiosis. *Cell* 117:29–45

26. Bouche N, Bouchez D. 2001. *Arabidopsis* gene knockout: phenotypes wanted. *Curr. Opin. Plant Biol.* 4:111–17

27. Brenneman MA, Wagener BM, Miller CA, Allen C, Nickoloff JA. 2002. XRCC3 controls the fidelity of homologous recombination: roles for XRCC3 in late stages of recombination. *Mol. Cell* 10:387–95

28. Buonomo SB, Clyne RK, Fuchs J, Loidl J, Uhlmann F, Nasmyth K. 2000. Disjunction of homologous chromosomes in meiosis I depends on proteolytic cleavage of the meiotic cohesin Rec8 by separin. *Cell* 103:387–98

29. Burnham CR, Stout JT, Weinheimer WH, Kowles RV, Phillips RL. 1972. Chromosome pairing in maize. *Genetics* 71:111–26

30. Cai X, Dong FG, Edelmann RE, Makaroff CA. 2003. The *Arabidopsis* SYN1 cohesin protein is required for sister chromatid arm cohesion and homologous chromosome pairing. *J. Cell Sci.* 116:2999–3007

31. Carlton PM, Cande WZ. 2002. Telomeres act autonomously in maize to organize the meiotic bouquet from a semipolarized chromosome orientation. *J. Cell Biol.* 157:231–42

32. Carlton PM, Cowan CR, Cande WZ. 2003. Directed motion of telomeres in the formation of the meiotic bouquet revealed by time course and simulation analysis. *Mol. Biol. Cell* 14:2832–43

33. Caryl AP, Armstrong SJ, Jones GH, Franklin FCH. 2000. A homologue of the yeast *HOP1* gene is inactivated in the *Arabidopsis* meiotic mutant *asy1*. *Chromosoma* 109:62–71

34. Caryl AP, Jones GH, Franklin FCH. 2003. Dissecting plant meiosis using *Arabidopsis thaliana* mutants. *J. Exp. Bot.* 54:25–38

35. Charlesworth D, Charlesworth B. 2005. Sex chromosomes: evolution of the weird and wonderful. *Curr. Biol.* 15:129–31

36. Chelysheva L, Diallo S, Vezon D, Gendrot G, Vrielynck N, et al. 2005. AtREC8 and AtSCC3 are essential to the monopolar orientation of the kinetochores during meiosis. *J. Cell Sci.* 118 (Pt. 20):4621–32

37. Chen CB, Zhang W, Timofejeva L, Gerardin Y, Ma H. 2005. The *Arabidopsis* ROCK-N-ROLLERS gene encodes a homolog of the yeast ATP-dependent DNA helicase MER3 and is required for normal meiotic crossover formation. *Plant J.* 43:321–34

38. Chu S, DeRisi J, Eisen M, Mulholland J, Botstein D, et al. 1998. The transcriptional program of sporulation in budding yeast. *Science* 282:699–705

39. Ciosk R, Zachariae W, Michaelis C, Shevchenko A, Mann M, Nasmyth K. 1998. An ESP1/PDS1 complex regulates loss of sister chromatid cohesion at the metaphase to anaphase transition in yeast. *Cell* 93:1067–76

40. Comai L. 2000. Genetic and epigenetic interactions in allopolyploid plants. *Plant Mol. Biol.* 43:387–99

41. Connelly JC, Leach DR. 2002. Tethering on the brink: the evolutionarily conserved Mre11-Rad50 complex. *Trends Biochem. Sci.* 27:410–18

42. Copenhaver GP, Housworth EA, Stahl FW. 2002. Crossover interference in Arabidopsis. *Genetics* 160:1631–39

43. Couteau F, Belzile F, Horlow C, Grandjean O, Vezon D, Doutriaux MP. 1999. Random chromosome segregation without meiotic arrest in both male and female meiocytes of a *dmc1* mutant of Arabidopsis. *Plant Cell* 11:1623–34

44. Cowan CR, Cande WZ. 2002. Meiotic telomere clustering is inhibited by colchicine but does not require cytoplasmic microtubules. *J. Cell Sci.* 115:3747–56

45. Creighton HB, McClintock B. 1931. A correlation of cytological and genetical crossing-over in Zea mays. *Proc. Natl. Acad. Sci. USA* 17:492–97

46. Daoudal-Cotterell S, Gallego ME, White CI. 2002. The plant Rad50-Mre11 protein complex. *FEBS Lett.* 516:164–66

47. Davis GL, McMullen MD, Baysdorfer C, Musket T, Grant D, et al. 1999. A maize map standard with sequenced core markers, grass genome reference points and 932 expressed sequence tagged sites (ESTs) in a 1736-locus map. *Genetics* 152:1137–72

48. Davis L, Smith GR. 2001. Meiotic recombination and chromosome segregation in Schizosaccharomyces pombe. *Proc. Natl. Acad. Sci. USA* 98:8395–402

49. Dawe RK. 1998. Meiotic chromosome organization and segregation in plants. *Annu. Rev. Plant Physiol. Plant Mol. Biol.* 49:371–95

50. Dawe RK, Sedat JW, Agard DA, Cande WZ. 1994. Meiotic chromosome pairing in maize is associated with a novel chromatin organization. *Cell* 76:901–12

51. de los Santos T, Hunter N, Lee C, Larkin B, Loidl J, Hollingsworth NM. 2003. The Mus81/Mms4 endonuclease acts independently of double-Holliday junction resolution to promote a distinct subset of crossovers during meiosis in budding yeast. *Genetics* 164:81–94

52. de Vries SS, Baart EB, Dekker M, Siezen A, de Rooij DG, et al. 1999. Mouse MutS-like protein Msh5 is required for proper chromosome synapsis in male and female meiosis. *Genes Dev.* 13:523–31

53. Ding ZJ, Wang T, Chong K, Bai SN. 2001. Isolation and characterization of *OsDMC1*, the rice homologue of the yeast *DMC1* gene essential for meiosis. *Sex. Plant Reprod.* 13:285–88

54. Dong F, Cai X, Makaroff CA. 2001. Cloning and characterization of two Arabidopsis genes that belong to the RAD21/REC8 family of chromosome cohesin proteins. *Gene* 271:99–108

55. Doutriaux MP, Couteau F, Bergounioux C, White C. 1998. Isolation and characterisation of the RAD51 and DMC1 homologs from *Arabidopsis thaliana*. *Mol. Gen. Genet.* 257:283–91

56. Dresser ME. 2000. Meiotic chromosome behavior in Saccharomyces cerevisiae and (mostly) mammals. *Mutat. Res.* 451:107–27

57. Ellis NA. 1998. The war of the sex chromosomes. *Nat. Genet.* 20:9–10

58. Franklin AE, McElver J, Sunjevaric I, Rothstein R, Bowen B, Cande WZ. 1999. Three-dimensional microscopy of the Rad51 recombination protein during meiotic prophase. *Plant Cell* 11:809–24

59. French CA, Masson JY, Griffin CS, O'Regan P, West SC, Thacker J. 2002. Role of mammalian RAD51L2 (RAD51C) in recombination and genetic stability. *J. Biol. Chem.* 277:19322–30

60. Gallego ME, Jeanneau M, Granier F, Bouchez D, Bechtold N, White CI. 2001. Disruption of the *Arabidopsis RAD50* gene leads to plant sterility and MMS sensitivity. *Plant J.* 25:31–41

61. Gernand D, Demidov D, Houben A. 2003. The temporal and spatial pattern of histone H3 phosphorylation at serine 28 and serine 10 is similar in plants but differs between mono- and polycentric chromosomes. *Cytogenet. Genome Res.* 101:172–76

62. Gillies CB. 1984. The synaptonemal complex in higher plants. *Crit. Rev. Plant Sci.* 2:81–116

63. Gillies CB, Lukaszewski AJ. 1989. Synaptonemal complex formation in rye (*Secale cereale*) heterozygous for telomeric C-bands. *Genome* 32:901–7

64. Glover J, Grelon M, Craig S, Chaudhury A, Dennis E. 1998. Cloning and characterization of MS5 from Arabidopsis: a gene critical in male meiosis. *Plant J.* 15:345–56

65. Golubovskaya I, Avalkina N, Sheridan WF. 1997. New insights into the role of the maize *ameiotic1* locus. *Genetics* 147:1339–50

66. Golubovskaya I, Grebennikova ZK, Avalkina NA, Sheridan WF. 1993. The role of the ameiotic1 gene in the initiation of meiosis and in subsequent meiotic events in maize. *Genetics* 135:1151–66

67. Golubovskaya IN. 1979. Genetic control of meiosis. *Int. Rev. Cytol.* 58:247–90

68. Golubovskaya IN, Harper LC, Pawlowski WP, Schichnes D, Cande WZ. 2002. The *PAM1* gene is required for meiotic bouquet formation and efficient homologous synapsis in maize (*Zea mays L.*). *Genetics* 162:1979–93

69. Golubovskaya IN, Mashnenkov AS. 1975. Genetic control of meiosis. I. Meiotic mutation in corn (*Zea mays L.*) *afd*, causing the elimination of the first meiotic division. *Sov. Genet.* 11:810–16

70. Grelon M, Vezon D, Gendrot G, Pelletier G. 2001. *AtSPO11-1* is necessary for efficient meiotic recombination in plants. *EMBO J.* 20:589–600

71. Haering CH, Nasmyth K. 2003. Building and breaking bridges between sister chromatids. *BioEssays* 25:1178–91

72. Hamant O, Golubovskaya I, Meeley R, Fiume E, Timofejeva L, et al. 2005. A REC8-dependent plant Shugoshin is required for maintenance of centromeric cohesion during meiosis and has no mitotic functions. *Curr. Biol.* 15:948–54

73. Hannon GJ. 2002. RNA interference. *Nature* 418:244–51

74. Harper L, Golubovskaya I, Cande WZ. 2004. A bouquet of chromosomes. *J. Cell Sci.* 117:4025–32

75. Hartung F, Puchta H. 2000. Molecular characterisation of two paralogous SPO11 homologues in *Arabidopsis thaliana*. *Nucleic Acids Res.* 28:1548–54

76. Hartung F, Puchta H. 2001. Molecular characterization of homologues of both subunits A (SPO11) and B of the archaebacterial topoisomerase 6 in plants. *Gene* 271:81–86

77. Hauf S, Waizenegger IC, Peters JM. 2001. Cohesin cleavage by separase required for anaphase and cytokinesis in human cells. *Science* 293:1320–23

78. Heyting C. 1996. Synaptonemal complexes: structure and function. *Curr. Opin. Cell Biol.* 8:389–96

79. Higgins JD, Armstrong SJ, Franklin FC, Jones GH. 2004. The Arabidopsis MutS homolog AtMSH4 functions at an early step in recombination: evidence for two classes of recombination in Arabidopsis. *Genes Dev.* 18:2557–70

80. Higgins JD, Sanchez-Moran E, Armstrong SJ, Jones GH, Franklin FCH. 2005. The *Arabidopsis* synaptonemal complex protein ZYP1 is required for chromosome synapsis and normal fidelity of crossing-over. *Genes Dev.* 19:2488–500

81. Hollingsworth NM, Byers B. 1989. HOP1: a yeast meiotic pairing gene. *Genetics* 121:445–62

82. Hollingsworth NM, Goetsch L, Byers B. 1990. The *HOP1* gene encodes a meiosis-specific component of yeast chromosomes. *Cell* 61:73–84

83. Hong EL, Shinohara A, Bishop DK. 2001. Saccharomyces cerevisiae Dmc1 protein promotes renaturation of single-strand DNA (ssDNA) and assimilation of ssDNA into homologous super-coiled duplex DNA. *J. Biol. Chem.* 276:41906–12

84. Houben A, Demidov D, Rutten T, Scheidtmann KH. 2005. Novel phosphorylation of histone H3 at threonine 11 that temporally correlates with condensation of mitotic and meiotic chromosomes in plant cells. *Cytogenet. Genome Res.* 109:148–55

85. Housworth EA, Stahl FW. 2003. Crossover interference in humans. *Am. J. Hum. Genet.* 73:188–97

86. Hunter N, Borts RH. 1997. Mlh1 is unique among mismatch repair proteins in its ability to promote crossing-over during meiosis. *Genes Dev.* 11:1573–82

87. Ito M, Takegami MH. 1982. Commitment of mitotic cells to meiosis during the G2 phase of premeiosis. *Plant Cell Physiol.* 23:943–52

88. Jones GH, Armstrong SJ, Caryl AP, Franklin FCH. 2003. Meiotic chromosome synapsis and recombination in *Arabidopsis thaliana*; an integration of cytological and molecular approaches. *Chromosome Res.* 11:205–15

89. Kaszas E, Cande WZ. 2000. Phosphorylation of histone H3 is correlated with changes in the maintenance of sister chromatid cohesion during meiosis in maize, rather than the condensation of the chromatin. *J. Cell Sci.* 113:3217–26

90. Kaul MLH, Murthy TGK. 1985. Mutant genes affecting higher plant meiosis. *Theor. Appl. Genet.* 70:449–66

91. Keeney S. 2001. Mechanism and control of meiotic recombination initiation. *Curr. Top. Dev. Biol.* 52:1–53

92. Deleted in proof

93. Klimyuk VI, Jones JD. 1997. *AtDMC1*, the *Arabidopsis* homologue of the yeast *DMC1* gene characterization, transposon-induced allelic variation and meiosis-associated expression. *Plant J.* 11:1–14

94. Kneitz B, Cohen PE, Avdievich E, Zhu L, Kane MF, et al. 2000. MutS homolog 4 localization to meiotic chromosomes is required for chromosome pairing during meiosis in male and female mice. *Genes Dev.* 14:1085–97

95. Koduru PRK, Rao MK. 1981. Cytogenetics of synaptic mutants in higher plants. *Theor. Appl. Genet.* 59:197–214

96. Kong H, Leebens-Mack J, Ni W, dePamphilis CW, Ma H. 2004. Highly heterogeneous rates of evolution in the SKP1 gene family in plants and animals: functional and evolutionary implications. *Mol. Biol. Evol.* 21:117–28

97. Krogh BO, Symington LS. 2004. Recombination proteins in yeast. *Annu. Rev. Genet.* 38:233–71

98. Kurumizaka H, Ikawa S, Nakada M, Eda K, Kagawa W, et al. 2001. Homologous-pairing activity of the human DNA-repair proteins Xrcc3.Rad51C. *Proc. Natl. Acad. Sci. USA* 98:5538–43

99. Kurumizaka H, Ikawa S, Nakada M, Enomoto R, Kagawa W, et al. 2002. Homologous pairing and ring and filament structure formation activities of the human Xrcc2*Rad51D complex. *J. Biol. Chem.* 277:14315–20

100. Lam WS, Yang X, Makaroff CA. 2005. Characterization of Arabidopsis thaliana SMC1 and SMC3: evidence that AtSMC3 may function beyond chromosome cohesion. *J. Cell Sci.* 118:3037–48

101. Lee JY, Orr-Weaver TL. 2001. The molecular basis of sister-chromatid cohesion. *Annu. Rev. Cell Dev. Biol.* 17:753–77

102. Leu JY, Chua PR, Roeder GS. 1998. The meiosis-specific Hop2 protein of S. cerevisiae ensures synapsis between homologous chromosomes. *Cell* 94:375–86

103. Li WX, Chen CB, Markmann-Mulisch U, Timofejeva L, Schmelzer E, et al. 2004. The *Arabidopsis AtRAD51* gene is dispensable for vegetative development but required for meiosis. *Proc. Natl. Acad. Sci. USA* 101:10596–601

104. Li WX, Yang XH, Lin ZG, Timofejeva L, Xiao R, Makaroff CA, et al. 2005. The AtRAD51C gene is required for normal meiotic chromosome synapsis and double-stranded break repair in Arabidopsis. *Plant Physiol.* 138:965–76

105. Lichten M. 2001. Meiotic recombination: breaking the genome to save it. *Curr. Biol.* 11:R253–56

106. Liu D, Matzuk MM, Sung WK, Guo Q, Wang P, Wolgemuth DJ. 1998. Cyclin A1 is required for meiosis in the male mouse. *Nat. Genet.* 20:377–80

107. Liu N, Lamerdin JE, Tebbs RS, Schild D, Tucker JD, et al. 1998. XRCC2 and XRCC3, new human Rad51-family members, promote chromosome stability and protect against DNA cross-links and other damages. *Mol. Cell* 1:783–93

108. Liu Z, Moore PH, Ma H, Ackerman CM, Ragiba M, et al. 2004. A primitive Y chromosome in papaya marks incipient sex chromosome evolution. *Nature* 427:348–52

109. Loidl J. 1990. The initiation of meiotic chromosome pairing: the cytological view. *Genome* 33:759–78

110. Ma H. 2005. Molecular genetic analyses of microsporogenesis and microgametogenesis in flowering plants. *Annu. Rev. Plant Biol.* 56:393–434

111. Magnard JL, Yang M, Chen YCS, Leary M, McCormick S. 2001. The Arabidopsis gene *Tardy Asynchronous Meiosis* is required for the normal pace and synchrony of cell division during male meiosis. *Plant Physiol.* 127:1157–66

112. Manzanero S, Arana P, Puertas MJ, Houben A. 2000. The chromosomal distribution of phosphorylated histone H3 differs between plants and animals at meiosis. *Chromosoma* 109:308–17

113. Marrocco K, Lecureuil A, Nicolas P, Guerche P. 2003. The Arabidopsis SKP1-like genes present a spectrum of expression profiles. *Plant Mol. Biol.* 52:715–27

114. Martinez-Perez E, Shaw P, Aragon-Alcaide L, Moore G. 2003. Chromosomes form into seven groups in hexaploid and tetraploid wheat as a prelude to meiosis. *Plant J.* 36:21–29

115. Martinez-Perez E, Shaw P, Moore G. 2001. The *Ph1* locus is needed to ensure specific somatic and meiotic centromere association. *Nature* 411:20–47

116. Masson JY, Tarsounas MC, Stasiak AZ, Stasiak A, Shah R, et al. 2001. Identification and purification of two distinct complexes containing the five RAD51 paralogs. *Genes Dev.* 15:3296–307

117. Masson JY, West SC. 2001. The Rad51 and Dmc1 recombinases: a non-identical twin relationship. *Trends Biochem. Sci.* 26:131–36

118. McClintock B. 1951. Chromosome organization and genic expression. *Cold Spring Harbor Symp. Quant. Biol.* 16:13–47

119. Mercier R, Armstrong SJ, Horlow C, Jackson NP, Makaroff CA, et al. 2003. The meiotic protein SWI1 is required for axial element formation and recombination initiation in Arabidopsis. *Development* 130:3309–18

120. Mercier R, Grelon M, Vezon D, Horlow C, Pelletier G. 2001. How to characterize meiotic functions in plants? *Biochimie* 83:1023–28

121. Mercier R, Jolivet S, Vezon D, Huppe E, Chelysheva L, et al. 2005. Two meiotic crossover classes cohabit in Arabidopsis: one is dependent on MER3, whereas the other one is not. *Curr. Biol.* 15:692–701

122. Mercier R, Vezon D, Bullier E, Motamayor JC, Sellier A, et al. 2001. SWITCH1 (SWI1): a novel protein required for the establishment of sister chromatid cohesion and for bivalent formation at meiosis. *Genes Dev.* 15:1859–71

123. Miller KA, Yoshikawa DM, McConnell IR, Clark R, Schild D, Albala JS. 2002. RAD51C interacts with RAD51B and is central to a larger protein complex in vivo exclusive of RAD51. *J. Biol. Chem.* 277:8406–11

124. Moens PB, Kolas NK, Tarsounas M, Marcon E, Cohen PE, Spyropoulos B. 2002. The time course and chromosomal localization of recombination-related proteins at meiosis in the mouse are compatible with models that can resolve the early DNA-DNA interactions without reciprocal recombination. *J. Cell Sci.* 115:1611–22

125. Moens PB, Pearlman RE. 1988. Chromatin organization at meiosis. *BioEssays* 9:151–53

126. Moore G. 2002. Meiosis in allopolyploids – the importance of 'Teflon' chromosomes. *Trends Genet.* 18:456–63

127. Moses MJ. 1969. Structure and function of the synaptonemal complex. *Genetics* 61(Suppl.): 41–51

128. Motamayor JC, Vezon D, Bajon C, Sauvanet A, Grandjean O, et al. 2000. *Switch (swi1)*, an *Arabidopsis thaliana* mutant affected in the female meiotic switch. *Sex. Plant Reprod.* 12:209–18

129. Muehlbauer GJ, Riera-Lizarazu O, Kynast RG, Martin D, Phillips RL, Rines HW. 2000. A maize chromosome 3 addition line of oat exhibits expression of the maize homeobox gene liguleless3 and alteration of cell fates. *Genome* 43:1055–64

130. Nasmyth K. 2002. Segregating sister genomes: the molecular biology of chromosome separation. *Science* 297:559–65

131. Nayak S, Santiago FE, Jin H, Lin D, Schedl T, Kipreos ET. 2002. The Caenorhabditis elegans Skp1-related gene family: diverse functions in cell proliferation, morphogenesis, and meiosis. *Curr. Biol.* 12:277–87

132. Negrutiu I, Vyskot B, Barbacar N, Georgiev S, Moneger F. 2001. Dioecious plants. A key to the early events of sex chromosome evolution. *Plant Physiol.* 127:1418–24

133. Nicolas M, Marais G, Hykelova V, Janousek B, Laporte V, et al. 2005. A gradual process of recombination restriction in the evolutionary history of the sex chromosomes in dioecious plants. *PLoS Biol.* 3:47–56

134. Nonomura KI, Nakano M, Murata K, Miyoshi K, Eiguchi M, et al. 2004. An insertional mutation in the rice *PAIR2* gene, the ortholog of *Arabidopsis ASY1*, results in a defect in homologous chromosome pairing during meiosis. *Mol. Genet. Genomics* 271:121–29

135. Orr-Weaver TL. 1999. The ties that bind: localization of the sister-chromatid cohesin complex on yeast chromosomes. *Cell* 99:1–4

136. Osakabe K, Yoshioka T, Ichikawa H, Toki S. 2002. Molecular cloning and characterization of RAD51-like genes from *Arabidopsis thaliana*. *Plant Mol. Biol.* 50:71–81

137. Page SL, Hawley RS. 2004. The genetics and molecular biology of the synaptonemal complex. *Annu. Rev. Cell Dev. Biol.* 20:525–58

138. Pasierbek P, Jantsch M, Melcher M, Schleiffer A, Schweizer D, Loidl J. 2001. A Caenorhabditis elegans cohesion protein with functions in meiotic chromosome pairing and disjunction. *Genes Dev.* 15:1349–60

139. Pawlowski WP, Cande WZ. 2005. Coordinating the events of the meiotic prophase. *Trends Cell Biol.* 15:674–81.

140. Pawlowski WP, Golubovskaya IN, Cande WZ. 2003. Altered nuclear distribution of recombination protein RAD51 in maize mutants suggests the involvement of RAD51 in meiotic homology recognition. *Plant Cell* 15:1807–16

141. Pawlowski WP, Golubovskaya IN, Timofejeva L, Meeley RB, Sheridan WF, Cande WZ. 2004. Coordination of meiotic recombination, pairing, and synapsis by PHS1. *Science* 303:89–92

142. Peirson BN, Bowling SE, Makaroff CA. 1997. A defect in synapsis causes male sterility in a T-DNA-tagged *Arabidopsis thaliana* mutant. *Plant J.* 11:659–69

143. Petronczki M, Siomos MF, Nasmyth K. 2003. Un menage a quatre: the molecular biology of chromosome segregation in meiosis. *Cell* 112:423–40

144. Preuss U, Landsberg G, Scheidtmann KH. 2003. Novel mitosis-specific phosphorylation of histone H3 at Thr11 mediated by Dlk/ZIP kinase. *Nucleic Acids Res.* 31:878–85

145. Prieto I, Suja JA, Pezzi N, Kremer L, Martinez-A C, et al. 2001. Mammalian STAG3 is a cohesin specific to sister chromatid arms in meiosis I. *Nat. Cell Biol.* 3:761–66

146. Primig M, Williams RM, Winzeler EA, Tevzadze GG, Conway AR, et al. 2000. The core meiotic transcriptome in budding yeasts. *Nat. Genet.* 26:415–23

147. Puizina J, Siroky J, Mokros P, Schweizer D, Riha K. 2004. Mre11 deficiency in Arabidopsis is associated with chromosomal instability in somatic cells and Spo11-dependent genome fragmentation during meiosis. *Plant Cell* 16:1968–78

148. Revenkova E, Eijpe M, Heyting C, Gross B, Jessberger R. 2001. Novel meiosis-specific isoform of mammalian SMC1. *Mol. Cell. Biol.* 21:6984–98

149. Rhoades MM. 1956. Genetic control of chromosome behavior. *Maize Genet. Newsl.* 30:38–42

150. Rhoades MM. 1984. The early years of maize genetics. *Annu. Rev. Genet.* 18:1–29

151. Riley R, Chapman V, Kimber G. 1959. Genetic control of chromosome pairing in intergeneric hybrids with wheat. *Nature* 183:1244–46

152. Roeder GS. 1995. Sex and the single cell: meiosis in yeast. *Proc. Natl. Acad. Sci. USA* 92:10450–56

153. Ross KJ, Fransz P, Armstrong SJ, Vizir I, Mulligan B, et al. 1997. Cytological characterization of four meiotic mutants of *Arabidopsis* isolated from T-DNA-transformed lines. *Chromosome Res.* 5:551–59

154. Ross KJ, Fransz P, Jones GH. 1996. A light microscopic atlas of meiosis in *Arabidopsis thaliana*. *Chromosome Res.* 4:507–16

155. Ross-Macdonald P, Roeder GS. 1994. Mutation of a meiosis-specific MutS homolog decreases crossing over but not mismatch correction. *Cell* 79:1069–80

156. Sadder T, Weber G. 2002. Comparison between genetic and physical maps in Zea mays L. of molecular markers linked to resistance against *Diatraea* spp. *Theor. Appl. Genet.* 104:908–15

157. Samach A, Klenz JE, Kohalmi SE, Risseeuw E, Haughn GW, Crosby WL. 1999. The *UNUSUAL FLORAL ORGANS* gene of *Arabidopsis thaliana* is an F-box protein required for normal patterning and growth in the floral meristem. *Plant J.* 20:433–45

158. Sanders PM, Bui AQ, Weterings K, McIntire KN, Hsu YC, et al. 1999. Anther developmental defects in *Arabidopsis thaliana* male-sterile mutants. *Sex. Plant Reprod.* 11:297–322

159. Sato S, Hotta Y, Tabata S. 1995. Structural analysis of a recA-like gene in the genome of *Arabidopsis thaliana*. *DNA Res.* 2:89–93

160. Scherthan H, Eils R, Trelles-Sticken E, Dietzel S, Cremer T, et al. 1998. Aspects of three-dimensional chromosome reorganization during the onset of human male meiotic prophase. *J. Cell Sci.* 111:2337–51

161. Schild D, Lio YC, Collins DW, Tsomondo T, Chen DJ. 2000. Evidence for simultaneous protein interactions between human Rad51 paralogs. *J. Biol. Chem.* 275:16443–49

162. Schmit AC, Endle MC, Lambert AM. 1996. The perinuclear microtubule-organizing center and the synaptonemal complex of higher plants share a common antigen: its putative transfer and role in meiotic chromosomal ordering. *Chromosoma* 104:405–13

163. Schmit AC, Stoppin V, Chevrier V, Job D, Lambert AM. 1994. Cell cycle dependent distribution of a centrosomal antigen at the perinuclear MTOC or at the kinetochores of higher plant cells. *Chromosoma* 103:343–51

164. Schommer C, Beven A, Lawrenson T, Shaw P, Sablowski R. 2003. *AHP2* is required for bivalent formation and for segregation of homologous chromosomes in *Arabidopsis* meiosis. *Plant J.* 36:1–11

165. Schwarzacher T. 2003. Meiosis, recombination and chromosomes: a review of gene isolation and fluorescent in situ hybridization data in plants. *J. Exp. Bot.* 54:11–23

166. Sears ER. 1976. Genetic control of chromosome pairing in wheat. *Annu. Rev. Genet.* 10:31–51

167. Deleted in proof

168. Sheridan WF, Avalkina NA, Shamrov II, Batygina TB, Golubovskaya IN. 1996. The mac1 gene: Controlling the commitment to the meiotic pathway in maize. *Genetics* 142:1009–20

169. Sheridan WF, Golubeva EA, Abrhamova LI, Golubovskaya IN. 1999. The mac1 mutation alters the developmental fate of the hypodermal cells and their cellular progeny in the maize anther. *Genetics* 153:933–41

170. Siaud N, Dray E, Gy I, Gerard E, Takvorian N, Doutriaux MP. 2004. Brca2 is involved in meiosis in *Arabidopsis thaliana* as suggested by its interaction with Dmc1. *EMBO J.* 23:1392–401

171. Siddiqi I, Ganesh G, Grossniklaus U, Subbiah V. 2000. The dyad gene is required for progression through female meiosis in *Arabidopsis*. *Development* 127:197–207

172. Sigurdsson S, Van Komen S, Bussen W, Schild D, Albala JS, Sung P. 2001. Mediator function of the human Rad51B-Rad51C complex in Rad51/RPA-catalyzed DNA strand exchange. *Genes Dev.* 15:3308–18

173. Siomos MF, Badrinath A, Pasierbek P, Livingstone D, White J, Glotzer M, et al. 2001. Separase is required for chromosome segregation during meiosis I in Caenorhabditis elegans. *Curr. Biol.* 11:1825–35

174. Smith AV, Roeder GS. 1997. The yeast Red1 protein localizes to the cores of meiotic chromosomes. *J. Cell Biol.* 136:957–67

175. Smith KN, Nicolas A. 1998. Recombination at work for meiosis. *Curr. Opin. Genet. Dev.* 8:200–11

176. Smith KN, Penkner A, Ohta K, Klein F, Nicolas A. 2001. B-type cyclins CLB5 and CLB6 control the initiation of recombination and synaptonemal complex formation in yeast meiosis. *Curr. Biol.* 11:88–97

177. Soltis DE, Soltis PS. 1995. The dynamic nature of polyploid genomes. *Proc. Natl. Acad. Sci. USA* 92:8089–91

178. Stack SM, Anderson LK. 2002. Crossing over as assessed by late recombination nodules is related to the pattern of synapsis and the distribution of early recombination nodules in maize. *Chromosome Res.* 10:329–45

179. Staiger CJ, Cande WZ. 1992. Ameiotic, a gene that controls meiotic chromosome and cytoskeletal behavior in maize. *Dev. Biol.* 154:226–30

180. Stern H, Hotta Y. 1973. Biochemical controls of meiosis. *Annu. Rev. Genet.* 7:37–66

181. Sumara I, Vorlaufer E, Gieffers C, Peters BH, Peters JM. 2000. Characterization of vertebrate cohesin complexes and their regulation in prophase. *J. Cell Biol.* 151:749–62

182. Sung P. 1994. Catalysis of ATP-dependent homologous DNA pairing and strand exchange by yeast RAD51 protein. *Science* 265:1241–43

183. Sung P. 1997. Function of yeast Rad52 protein as a mediator between replication protein A and the Rad51 recombinase. *J. Biol. Chem.* 272:28194–97

184. Symington LS, Holloman WK. 2004. Molecular biology. New Year's resolution–resolving resolvases. *Science* 303:184–85

185. Thompson LH, Schild D. 2001. Homologous recombinational repair of DNA ensures mammalian chromosome stability. *Mutat. Res.* 477:131–53

186. Tsuzuki T, Fujii Y, Sakumi K, Tominaga Y, Nakao K, et al. 1996. Targeted disruption of the Rad51 gene leads to lethality in embryonic mice. *Proc. Natl. Acad. Sci. USA* 93:6236–40

187. Uhlmann F. 2004. The mechanism of sister chromatid cohesion. *Exp. Cell. Res.* 296:80–85

188. Valerie K, Povirk LF. 2003. Regulation and mechanisms of mammalian double-strand break repair. *Oncogene* 22:5792–812

189. Van Heemst D, Heyting C. 2000. Sister chromatid cohesion and recombination in meiosis. *Chromosoma* 109:10–26

190. Villeneuve AM, Hillers KJ. 2001. Whence meiosis? *Cell* 106:647–50

191. Von Wettstein D, Rasmussen SW, Holm PB. 1984. The synaptonemal complex in genetic segregation. *Annu. Rev. Genet.* 18:331–413

192. Vyskot B, Hobza R. 2004. Gender in plants: sex chromosomes are emerging from the fog. *Trends Genet.* 20:432–38

193. Wang MB, Waterhouse PM. 2002. Application of gene silencing in plants. *Curr. Opin. Plant Biol.* 5:146–50

194. Wang GF, Kong HZ, Sun YJ, Zhang XH, Zhang W, et al. 2004. Genome-wide analysis of the cyclin family in Arabidopsis and comparative phylogenetic analysis of plant cyclin-like proteins. *Plant Physiol.* 135:1084–1099

195. Wang YX, Magnard JL, McCormick S, Yang M. 2004. Progression through meiosis I and meiosis II in Arabidopsis anthers is regulated by an A-type cyclin predominately expressed in prophase I. *Plant Physiol.* 136:4127–35

196. Watanabe Y. 2005. Sister chromatid cohesion along arms and at centromeres. *Trends Genet.* 21:405–12

197. Wiese C, Collins DW, Albala JS, Thompson LH, Kronenberg A, Schild D. 2002. Interactions involving the Rad51 paralogs Rad51C and XRCC3 in human cells. *Nucleic Acids Res.* 30:1001–8

198. Yang M, Hu Y, Lodhi M, McCombie WR, Ma H. 1999. The *Arabidopsis SKP1-LIKE1* gene is essential for male meiosis and may control homologue separation. *Proc. Natl. Acad. Sci. USA* 96:11416–21

199. Zetka MC, Kawasaki I, Strome S, Muller F. 1999. Synapsis and chiasma formation in Caenorhabditis elegans require HIM-3, a meiotic chromosome core component that functions in chromosome segregation. *Genes Dev.* 13:2258–70

200. Zhang LR, Tao JY, Wang T. 2004. Molecular characterization of OsRAD21-1, a rice homologue of yeast RAD21 essential for mitotic chromosome cohesion. *J. Exp. Bot.* 55:1149–52

201. Zhao D, Han T, Risseeuw E, Crosby WL, Ma H. 2003. Conservation and divergence of ASK1 and ASK2 gene functions during male meiosis in Arabidopsis thaliana. *Plant Mol. Biol.* 53:163–73

202. Zhao D, Yu Q, Chen M, Ma H. 2001. The *ASK1* gene regulates B function gene expression in cooperation with *UFO* and *LEAFY* in *Arabidopsis. Development* 128:2735–46

203. Deleted in proof

204. Zickler D, Kleckner N. 1999. Meiotic chromosomes: integrating structure and function. *Annu. Rev. Genet.* 33:603–754

205. Wang CJ, Harper L, Cande WZ. 2006. High-resolution single-copy gene fluorescence in situ hybridization and its use in the construction of a cytogenetic map of maize chromosome 9. *Plant Cell* 18:529–44

RELATED RESOURCES

Moore G. 2000. Cereal chromosome structure, evolution, and pairing. *Annu. Rev. Plant Physiol. Plant Mol. Biol.* 51:195–222

Nasmyth K. 2001. Disseminating the genome: joining, resolving, and separating sister chromatids during mitosis and meiosis. *Annu. Rev. Genet.* 35:673–745

Zickler D, Kleckner N. 1998. The leptotene-zygotene transition of meiosis. *Annu. Rev. Genet.* 32:619–97

Biology and Biochemistry of Glucosinolates

Barbara Ann Halkier[1] and Jonathan Gershenzon[2]

[1] Plant Biochemistry Laboratory, Department of Plant Biology, Royal Veterinary and Agricultural University, DK-1871 Frederiksberg C, Denmark; email: bah@kvl.dk

[2] Department of Biochemistry, Max Planck Institute for Chemical Ecology, D-07745 Jena, Germany; email: gershenzon@ice.mpg.de

Annu. Rev. Plant Biol.
2006. 57:303–33

The *Annual Review of Plant Biology* is online at
plant.annualreviews.org

doi: 10.1146/
annurev.arplant.57.032905.105228

First published online as a
Review in Advance on
January 30, 2006

1543-5008/06/
0602-0303$20.00

Key Words

metabolic engineering, biosynthesis, degradation, regulation, transport, defense

Abstract

Glucosinolates are sulfur-rich, anionic natural products that upon hydrolysis by endogenous thioglucosidases called myrosinases produce several different products (e.g., isothiocyanates, thiocyanates, and nitriles). The hydrolysis products have many different biological activities, e.g., as defense compounds and attractants. For humans these compounds function as cancer-preventing agents, biopesticides, and flavor compounds. Since the completion of the *Arabidopsis* genome, glucosinolate research has made significant progress, resulting in near-complete elucidation of the core biosynthetic pathway, identification of the first regulators of the pathway, metabolic engineering of specific glucosinolate profiles to study function, as well as identification of evolutionary links to related pathways. Although much has been learned in recent years, much more awaits discovery before we fully understand how and why plants synthesize glucosinolates. This may enable us to more fully exploit the potential of these compounds in agriculture and medicine.

Contents

INTRODUCTION

Glucosinolates, once known as mustard oil glucosides, have been part of human life for thousands of years because of the strong flavors and tastes they elicit in cabbage, broccoli, and other *Brassica* vegetables. In the past few decades, the importance of these nitrogen- and sulfur-containing plant secondary metabolites has increased further following discovery of their potential as cancer-prevention agents, crop-protection compounds, and biofumigants in agriculture. Moreover, the presence of glucosinolates in the model plant, *Arabidopsis thaliana*, has also helped to stimulate a vigorous research effort into these unusual amino acid–derived products. For such a widely studied group of plant compounds, glucosinolates are known from only a few angiosperm families. They have been reported almost exclusively from the order Capparales, which contains 15 families, including the Brassicaceae, Capparaceae, and Caricaceae (144). Curiously, glucosinolates are also known from the genus *Drypetes* of the family Euphorbiaceae, a genus completely unrelated to the other glucosinolate-containing families.

Chemical Structure and Hydrolysis

The approximately 120 described glucosinolates share a chemical structure consisting of a β-D-glucopyranose residue linked via a sulfur atom to a (Z)-N-hydroximinosulfate ester, plus a variable R group (**Figure 1**) derived from one of eight amino acids (49). Glucosinolates can be classified by their precursor amino acid and the types of modification to the R group. Compounds derived from Ala, Leu, Ile, Met, or Val are called aliphatic glucosinolates, those derived from Phe or Tyr are called aromatic glucosinolates, and those derived from Trp are called indole glucosinolates. The R groups of most glucosinolates are extensively modified from these precursor amino acids, with methionine undergoing an especially wide range of transformations (49). Most of the R groups are elongated by one or more methylene moieties. Both elongated and nonelongated R groups are subject to a wide variety of transformations, including hydroxylation, O-methylation, desaturation, glycosylation, and acylation.

Plants accumulating glucosinolates always possess a thioglucoside glucohydrolase

Glucosinolates:
mustard oil
glucosides

activity known as myrosinase, which hydrolyzes the glucose moiety on the main skeleton (140). The products are glucose and an unstable aglycone that can rearrange to form isothiocyanates, nitriles, and other products. Hydrolysis in intact plants appears to be hindered by the spatial separation of glucosinolates and myrosinase or the inactivation of myrosinase, but these components mix together upon tissue damage, leading to the rapid formation of glucosinolate hydrolysis products. Most of the biological activities of glucosinolates are attributed to the actions of their hydrolysis products (170).

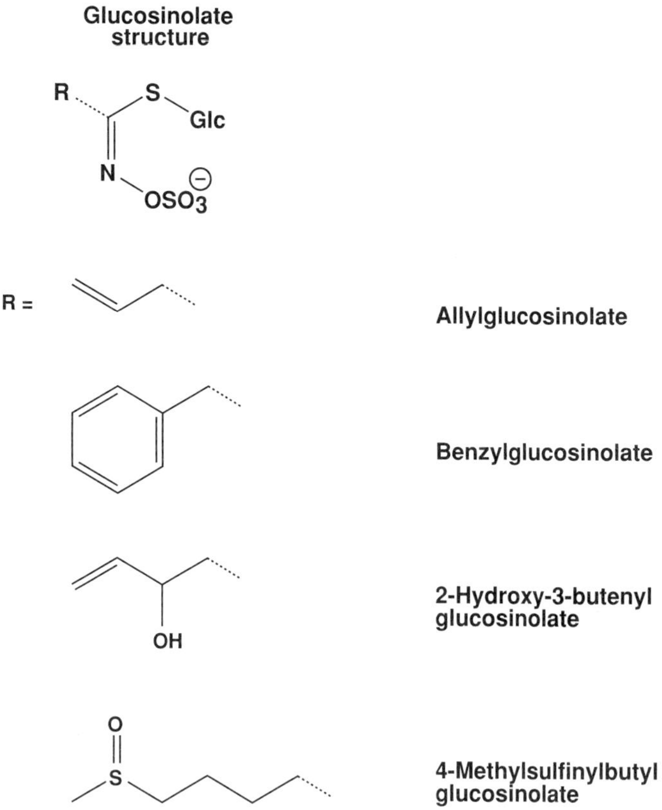

Importance to Humans

Glucosinolates have long been of interest to human society because of their presence in certain Brassicaceae vegetables (cabbage, cauliflower, broccoli) and condiments (mustard, horseradish, wasabi). The distinct taste and flavors of these foods are due primarily to their isothiocyanate hydrolysis products. Indole glucosinolates and those with alkenyl R groups are especially known for causing bitterness (46).

In the past 30 years, glucosinolates have assumed major agricultural significance with the increasing importance of rapeseeds, cultivars of *Brassica napus*, *B. rapa*, and *B. juncea*, as oil crops in temperate and subtropical areas of the world. These species contain glucosinolates in all of their organs. However, plant breeders have drastically reduced the levels of seed glucosinolates to allow the protein-rich seed cake (the residue left after crushing for oil) to be sold as an animal feed supplement. One of the predominant rapeseed glucosinolates, 2-hydroxy-3-butenyl glucosinolate (**Figure 1**), forms a oxazolidine-2-thione upon hydrolysis that causes goiter and has other harmful effects on animal nutrition (63). Breeders have attempted to modify glucosinolate levels in rapeseed foliage to reduce damage from fungal and insect pests (122). In this case, the strategy is not as simple because glucosinolates and their hydrolysis products

Glucosinolate structure

R =

Allylglucosinolate

Benzylglucosinolate

2-Hydroxy-3-butenyl glucosinolate

4-Methylsulfinylbutyl glucosinolate

Figure 1

Chemical structure of glucosinolates. The common structure is shown, as well as examples of some specific glucosinolates cited in the text that show typical variation in the structure of the side chain.

are repellent to some insects, but often serve as attractants for others. *Brassica* cultivars are finding increased use for "biofumigation," in which harvested plant material is incorporated into agricultural soils to suppress pathogens, nematodes, and weeds (22, 164, 174). Here again glucosinolate hydrolysis products are assumed to be the active agents of the treatment.

In the past decade, certain glucosinolates have been identified as potent cancer-prevention agents in a wide range of animal models due to the ability of certain hydrolysis products to induce phase II detoxification enzymes, such as quinone reductase, glutathione-S-transferase, and glucuronosyl transferases (72b, 81). Sulforaphane, the

Myrosinase: β-thioglucosidase

isothiocyanate derivative of 4-methylsulfinyl-butyl glucosinolate (**Figure 1**), found in broccoli, has been the focus of many of these studies (176). Sulforaphane and other isothiocyanates may prevent tumor growth by blocking the cell cycle and promoting apoptosis (81, 107, 155). Moreover, sulforaphane exhibits potential for treating *Helicobacter pylori*-caused gastritis and stomach cancer (48). These results are motivating efforts to increase the sulforaphane content of broccoli and to promote the health benefits of this vegetable.

BIOSYNTHESIS

The formation of glucosinolates can be conveniently divided into three separate phases. First, certain aliphatic and aromatic amino acids are elongated by inserting methylene groups into their side chains. Second, the amino acid moiety itself, whether elongated or not, is metabolically reconfigured to give the core structure of glucosinolates. Third, the initially formed glucosinolates are modified by various secondary transformations.

BIOSYNTHESIS: AMINO ACID CHAIN ELONGATION

The sequence of the chain-elongation pathway for amino acids participating in glucosinolate biosynthesis is based on in vivo feeding studies, the demonstration of enzyme activities in vitro, and the isolation of key intermediates. Initially, the parent amino acid is deaminated to form the corresponding 2-oxo acid (**Figure 2**). Next is a three-step cycle in which (*1*) the 2-oxo acid condenses with acetyl-CoA to form a substituted 2-malate derivative, which then (*2*) isomerizes via a 1,2-hydroxyl shift to a 3-malate derivative that (*3*) undergoes oxidation-decarboxylation to yield a 2-oxo acid with one more methylene group than the starting compound. During each round of the elongation cycle, the two carbons of acetyl-CoA are added to the 2-oxo acid and the COOH group added in the pre-

vious round is lost, for a net gain of one carbon atom. After each turn of the cycle, the extended 2-oxo acid can be transaminated to form the corresponding amino acid and enter the second phase of glucosinolate formation. Or, it can undergo additional cycles of acetyl-CoA condensation, isomerization, and oxidation-carboxylation, resulting in further elongation. Up to nine cycles are known to occur in plants (49). Similar 2-oxo acid–based chain-elongation sequences occur in leucine biosynthesis and in the TCA cycle, as well as elsewhere in plant metabolism (89).

The earliest evidence for the chain-elongation pathway came from feeding studies with radiolabeled precursors beginning in the 1960s (39, 97). More recent in vivo studies with stable isotopes (61, 62) confirmed the outline and major intermediates of the pathway. Most critical was the observation that acetate was readily incorporated into chain-elongated amino acids with the additional methylene group derived exclusively from the C-2 position (acetate methyl group). The acetate carboxyl group is lost during chain elongation or during conversion into the core glucosinolate. Additional support for the chain-elongation pathway was provided by the detection of certain intermediates in the chain elongation of methionine (32) and phenylalanine (43) and by the isolation of the chain-elongated methionine homologs themselves (69). Furthermore, the activity of the aminotransferase producing the initial 2-oxo acid from methionine (33, 60) and the activity of the condensing enzyme of the first round of methionine chain elongation (50) have been demonstrated in cell-free extracts.

The first information about the genetic basis of chain elongation came from the identification of a locus in *Arabidopsis* and *Brassica napus* that controls the chain length of methionine-derived glucosinolates (111). This locus was mapped in *Arabidopsis* using a cross between two ecotypes, Columbia and Landsberg *erecta*, whose major glucosinolates are derived from dihomomethionine and homomethionine, respectively (29). The

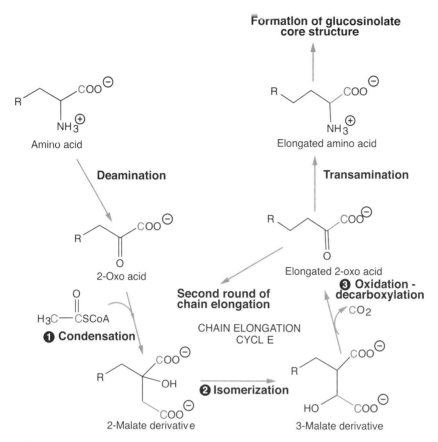

Formation of glucosinolate core structure

Amino acid

Deamination

2-Oxo acid

H_3C—CSCoA

① Condensation

2-Malate derivative

CHAIN ELONGATION CYCLE

② Isomerization

3-Malate derivative

Second round of chain elongation

③ Oxidation - decarboxylation

CO_2

Elongated 2-oxo acid

Transamination

Elongated amino acid

Figure 2

Amino acid chain-elongation cycle for glucosinolate biosynthesis. Illustrated is the first round of elongation. The three principal steps are: (*1*) condensation with acetyl-CoA, (*2*) isomerization, and (*3*) oxidation-decarboxylation. The carbon atoms contributed by acetyl-CoA (retained with each round) are shown in red. The carbon atom from the original COOH function (lost with each round) is shown in blue.

candidate genes were two adjacent sequences with high similarity to genes encoding isopropylmalate synthase, the enzyme catalyzing the condensing reaction of chain elongation in leucine biosynthesis. Further fine-scale mapping identified one of the two genes, *MAM1* (*Methylthioalkylmalate synthase 1*), as responsible for the chain-elongation polymorphism in Columbia and Landsberg *erecta* (91). This finding was confirmed by the isolation of missense mutants for this gene that had altered glucosinolate chain-length profiles and the heterologous expression of *MAM1* in *E. coli*, which gave an extract capable of condensing

ω-methylthio-2-oxoalkanoates with acetyl-CoA to give 2-(ω-methylthioalkyl)malates. The *MAM1* gene product carried out the condensing reaction of only the first two methionine elongation cycles (152), suggesting that the second adjacent sequence (called *MAM-L* for "MAM-like") might encode the protein responsible for the remaining activities. Indeed, a *MAM-L* knockout line was recently reported to lack long-chain methionine-derived glucosinolates, but these were restored after transformation with a functional *MAM-L* gene (51). A survey of *Arabidopsis* ecotypes revealed the presence of a third *MAM*-like gene,

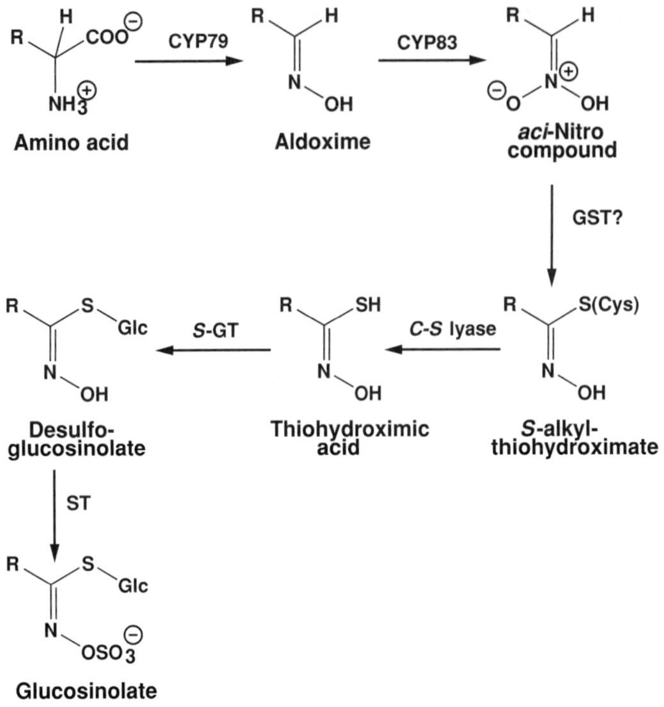

Figure 3

Biosynthesis of the glucosinolate core structure. CYP79 enzymes catalyzing the conversion of amino acids to aldoximes are the only side-chain-specific step in the pathway. The products from the CYP83s are too reactive to be isolated, but are proposed to be either *aci*-nitro compounds or their dehydrated analogs, nitrile oxides. The sulfur-donating enzyme is the only enzyme that remains to be identified, and is proposed to be a glutathione-*S*-transferase-like enzyme that uses cysteine as substrate. Abbreviations: R, variable side chain; GST, glutathione-*S*-transferase; *S*-GT, *S*-glucosyltransferase; ST, sulfotransferase.

sary before we can fully understand how it is regulated and how substrates from primary metabolism are channeled to the core pathway of glucosinolate formation.

BIOSYNTHESIS: CORE STRUCTURE

The biosynthesis of the core glucosinolate structure involves intermediates common to all glucosinolates. Our knowledge on how amino acids are converted into the core glucosinolate structure has increased as research has advanced from traditional in vivo feeding studies and biochemical characterization of the enzymatic activities in plant extracts to identification and characterization of the biosynthetic genes encoding the enzymes. Here the presence of glucosinolates in the model plant *Arabidopsis* has greatly facilitated progress. The intermediates in the pathway from the amino acid to the core structure include *N*-hydroxy amino acids, aldoximes, *aci*-nitro or nitrile oxide compounds (both are too reactive to be isolated), *S*-alkyl thiohydroximates, thiohydroximic acids, and desulfoglucosinolates (**Figure 3**). The genes responsible for all these steps, except the *S*-alkylation, have been identified since 2000.

The Conversion of Amino Acids to Aldoximes

Cytochromes P450 belonging to the CYP79 family are responsible for catalyzing the conversion of amino acids to aldoximes (169). Most of the seven CYP79s in the glucosinolate pathway in *Arabidopsis* were identified using a functional genomics approach (66). This was based on the similarity of the biosynthetic pathways of glucosinolates and cyanogenic glucosides, another group of amino acid–derived natural products with aldoximes as intermediates (78). As CYP79 homologs were identified in the *Arabidopsis* genome project, they were heterologously expressed and characterized with respect to substrate specificity (66).

designated *MAM2* at the same locus (90). The majority of ecotypes examined possessed functional copies of either *MAM1* or *MAM2*, but not both. A functional *MAM1* sequence was correlated with accumulation of glucosinolates having undergone two rounds of chain elongation, whereas a functional *MAM2* sequence was correlated with accumulation of glucosinolates having undergone only one round of elongation. Our knowledge of amino acid chain elongation has advanced rapidly in the past five years, yet much more information about the genes and enzymes of this segment of glucosinolate biosynthesis is neces-

The function of some CYP79 genes was identified using other approaches. A screen in yeast for cDNAs conferring resistance to 5-fluoroindole (the precursor of a toxic tryptophan derivative) led to isolation of CYP79B2 (73), which together with the homolog CYP79B3 catalyze the conversion of tryptophan to indole-3-acetaldoxime (IAOx) (73, 117). A *cyp79B2/cyp79B3* double knockout is completely devoid of indole glucosinolates (178), which shows that no other source of IAOx contributes significantly to biosynthesis of indole glucosinolate. Accordingly, the plasma membrane-bound peroxidase-dependent conversion of tryptophan to IAOx (105, 106), and IAOx produced from the YUCCA pathway (177), are not involved in glucosinolate biosynthesis.

In independent genetic approaches, two mutants, *bushy* (143) and *supershoot* (150), with severe morphological alterations including several hundred axillary shoots were shown to be knockout mutants of *CYP79F1*. These mutants completely lack short-chain aliphatic glucosinolates (143). Based on this finding, it was suggested that CYP79F1 metabolizes the short-chain methionine derivatives (with one to four additional methylene groups), and that the homolog *CYP79F2* that is 88% identical at the amino acid level metabolizes the long-chain-elongated methionine derivatives (143). However, biochemical characterization of CYP79F1 and CYP79F2 showed that CYP79F1 metabolizes mono- to hexahomomethionine, resulting in both short- and long-chain aliphatic glucosinolates, whereas CYP79F2 exclusively metabolizes long-chain penta- and hexahomomethionines (34, 69). The substrate specificities of CYP79F1 and CYP79F2 explain the absence of short-chain aliphatic glucosinolates in a knockout mutant of *CYP79F1*, and why the level of short-chain aliphatic glucosinolates is not affected in a *CYP79F2* knockout mutant, whereas the level of long-chain aliphatic glucosinolates is substantially reduced (34). The results emphasize the importance of biochemical characterization of proteins because assignment of function based solely on genetic data can be misleading.

The five characterized CYP79s in *Arabidopsis* (Col-0) are responsible for aldoxime production in the biosynthesis of the major glucosinolates derived from tryptophan (CYP79B2/CYP79B3) and chain-elongated methionine derivatives (CYP79F1/CYP79F2), as well as from phenylalanine (CYP79A2) (169). However, the role of CYP79C1 and CYP79C2 is unknown. These transcripts are present at very low levels (U. Wittstock and B.A. Halkier, unpublished results), which suggests that the CYP79C homologs may be responsible for aldoxime production of low abundant glucosinolates such as those derived from, e.g., homophenylalanine, methionine (86), and tyrosine (35). It can, however, not be excluded that the in vitro activities of the recombinant CYP79s could differ from their in vivo activities, and that CYP79F1 can metabolize methionine, for example, or that CYP79A2 can convert homophenylalanine and possibly tyrosine, albeit at very low efficiency.

The Conversion of Aldoximes to Thiohydroximic Acids

The aldoxime-metabolizing enzyme CYP83B1 in the glucosinolate pathway of *Arabidopsis* has been identified by several approaches (11, 12, 42, 68, 149). Knockout mutants of *CYP83B1* have a characteristic high-auxin phenotype (see below). Biochemical characterization of CYP83B1 and its homolog CYP83A1 shows that aliphatic aldoximes are primarily metabolized by CYP83A1 (8, 128), whereas aromatic aldoximes derived from tryptophan, phenylalanine, and tyrosine are metabolized by both enzymes. CYP83B1 has higher affinity for these aromatic aldoximes than CYP83A1, particularly for IAOx, where there is a 50-fold difference in K_m value (8), indicating that CYP83A1 and CYP83B1 are not redundant under normal physiological conditions in the plant. Interestingly, a *cyp83A1* knockout

IAOx: indole-3-acetaldoxime

mutant was identified in a screen for plants having altered phenylpropanoids as it contains reduced levels of several phenylpropanoids, such as sinapoylmalate, suggesting a metabolic link between glucosinolate biosynthesis and phenylpropanoid metabolism (71). As expected, *cyp83A1* knockout mutants have reduced levels of aliphatic glucosinolates, but also increased levels of indole glucosinolates. The latter may be due to upregulation of *CYP79B2* and *CYP79B3* in the metabolically stressed plant.

The CYP83 enzymes produce an activated, oxidized form of the aldoxime, e.g., an *aci*-nitro compound or a nitrile oxide (**Figure 3**). Due to its instability, the product has not been isolated, but in vitro it reacts efficiently with nucleophilic S-donors to form *S*-alkyl thiohydroximates (11, 68). This suggests that conjugation with cysteine, the likely S-donor as evidenced by in vivo feeding studies (166), is enzymatically controlled, possibly by a glutathione-*S*-transferase-like enzyme to ensure conjugation of the proper S-donor in vivo.

In vitro, *S*-(hydroximoyl)-L-cysteine conjugates rapidly undergo internal cyclization to produce 2-substituted thiazoline-4-carboxylic acids. This suggests that the next enzyme in the pathway, the *C-S* lyase that cleaves *S*-alkyl thiohydroximate to produce the thiohydroximic acid, is tightly coupled to the *S*-donating enzyme, which in turn is tightly coupled to the CYP83 enzymes, forming a complex to carry out this sulfur chemistry without loss of reactive sulfur intermediates to the surroundings. A *C-S* lyase involved in biosynthesis of glucosinolates in *Arabidopsis* was recently identified using a bioinformatics approach (118). Metabolite profiling of the *C-S* lyase knockout mutant showed the complete absence of both aliphatic and aromatic glucosinolates. This had not previously been reported for any mutants with altered glucosinolate biosynthesis, and suggests that the *C-S* lyase constitutes a single gene family.

The Conversion of Thiohydroximic Acids to Glucosinolates

A UDP-glucose:thiohydroximic acid *S*-glucosyltransferase, UGT74B1 (At1g24100), that glucosylates phenylacetothiohydroximic acid to produce the corresponding desulfoglucosinolate was identified in *Arabidopsis* based on its homology to a patented ortholog from *Brassica napus* (65). Knockout mutants of *UGT74B1* significantly decreased, but did not abolish, glucosinolate accumulation, which suggests that additional UGTs are present in the genome. The PAPS:desulfoglucosinolate sulfotransferase, AtST5a (At1g74100), catalyzing the last step in the synthesis of the core structure was recently identified by differential RNA display of coronatine-regulated genes (136). Biochemical characterization of AtST5a and its close homologs AtST5b (At1g74090) and AtST5c (At1g18590) showed that AtST5a prefers tryptophan- and phenylalanine-derived desulfoglucosinolates, whereas AtST5b and AtST5c prefer long-chain aliphatic desulfoglucosinolates (136).

The Evolutionary Link between Glucosinolates and Cyanogenic Glucosides

Cyanogenic glucosides are widespread in the plant kingdom, being found in ferns and gymnosperms as well as angiosperms. Glucosinolates are evolutionarily younger and found only in the order Capparales and in one outgroup, the genus *Drypetes* of the Euphorbiaceae. Because both groups of natural products are derived from amino acids and have aldoximes as intermediates, it has been hypothesized that glucosinolates developed based on a predisposition for making cyanogenic glucosides. This theory is supported by the demonstration that CYP79 homologs catalyze the conversion of amino acids to aldoximes in both pathways. Consistent with an evolutionary relationship between the cyanogenic glucoside and glucosinolate pathways, the aldoxime-metabolizing enzymes in both pathways belong to the same CYP family, as CYP71E1 metabolizes *p*-hydroxyphenylacetaldoxime in the biosynthesis of the cyanogenic glucoside dhurrin in *Sorghum bicolor* (9), and the CYP83 enzymes, which should be assigned to the CYP71 family based on sequence homology, metabolize aldoximes in the glucosinolate pathway (11, 68, 128). In contrast to the CYP79 family of amino acid *N*-hydroxylases, the CYP71 family represents cytochromes P450 with very diverse enzymatic activities, only some of which are involved in aldoxime metabolism. A possible scenario for the evolution of glucosinolates is that a mutation in the aldoxime-metabolizing enzyme in the cyanogenic pathway resulted in the production not of the expected hydroxynitrile, but rather a toxic compound, which the plant subsequently had to get rid of (68). From this perspective, the postaldoxime enzymes of the glucosinolate pathway can be viewed as enzymes recruited from the detoxification processes to metabolize the *aci*-nitro compound or nitrile oxide. Consistent with this hypothesis, both glucosyltransferases and sulfotransferases represent detoxification mechanisms widely used in nature.

BIOSYNTHESIS: SECONDARY TRANSFORMATIONS

The initially formed parent glucosinolate is subject to a wide range of further modifications of the R group. These reactions are of biological as well as biochemical interest because they influence the direction of glucosinolate hydrolysis and the resulting activity of the hydrolysis products. The R group of glucosinolates derived from methionine and its chain-elongated homologs is especially subject to further modifications, such as the stepwise oxidation of the sulfur atom in the methylthioalkyl side chain leading successively to methylsulfinylalkyl and methylsulfonylalkyl moieties (**Figure 4**). Methylsulfinylalkyl side chains can be further modified by oxidative cleavage to afford alkenyl or hydroxyalkyl chains. Genetic loci controlling each of these conversions have been identified in *Brassica* species and in *Arabidopsis* (56, 67, 123, 132).

In *Arabidopsis*, mapping using recombinant inbred lines derived from interecotype crosses implicated a cluster of three genes in controlling oxidation of the side chain (67, 87). These genes all encode 2-oxoacid-dependent dioxygenases, members of a large family of nonmembranous, nonheme iron-containing enzymes that catalyze many hydroxylation, epoxidation, and desaturation reactions of plant metabolism (139). To date, two genes of the cluster have been functionally characterized (87). The *AOP2* gene product, which is expressed only in ecotypes accumulating alkenyl glucosinolates, converts methylsulfinylalkyl to alkenyl glucosinolates when heterologously expressed in *E. coli* (**Figure 4**). On the other hand, the *AOP3* gene product, which is expressed only in ecotypes accumulating hydroxyalkyl glucosinolates, converts a methylsulfinylalkyl to a hydroxyalkyl glucosinolate. The differences in AOP activity among ecotypes are a result of differences in the promoter regions of *AOP2* and *AOP3* and a deletion in the open reading frame of *AOP2*, which leads to a highly truncated protein (87). Inheritance studies and sequencing of BAC clones indicate that analogous 2-oxoacid-dependent dioxygenase gene clusters are present in *Brassica oleracea*, which also control glucosinolate side-chain oxidation (55, 100). Little is known about the biochemical or molecular basis of other secondary transformations, such as the esterification of free hydroxyl groups by benzoic acid, except that these reactions follow the formation of the core glucosinolate skeleton (61).

REGULATION OF BIOSYNTHESIS

In the economically important family Brassicaceae, individual species typically produce between 30–40 different glucosinolates, with

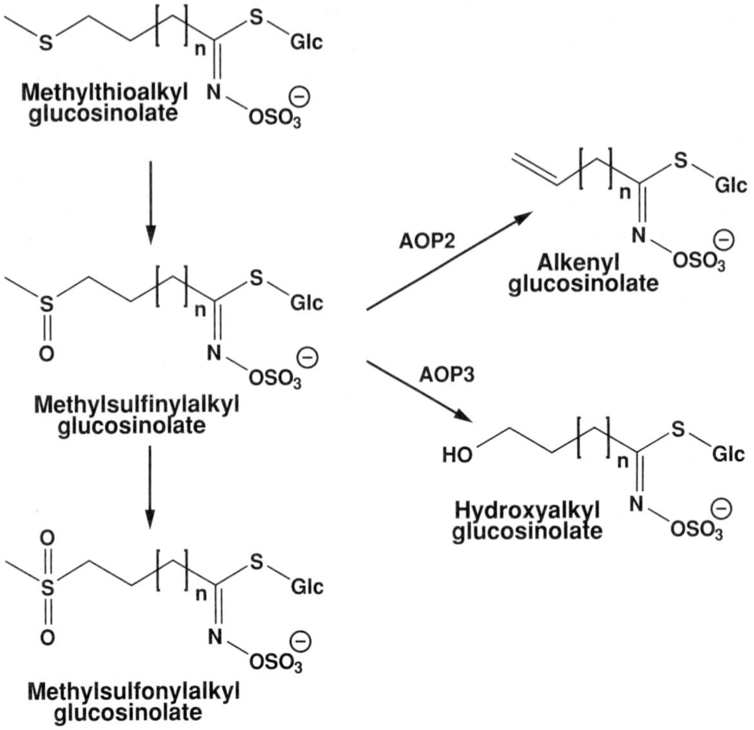

Figure 4

Some common oxidative secondary transformations of methionine-derived glucosinolates. AOP2 and AOP3 indicate the 2-oxoacid-dependent dioxygenases catalyzing these reaction types in *Arabidopsis*. For each category of glucosinolate, a different range of chain lengths is known to occur naturally (49). For methylthioalkyl and methylsulfonylalkyl, n = 1–8; for methylsulfinylalkyl, n = 1–9; for alkenyl, n = 1–5; for hydroxyalkyl, n = 0–2.

the aliphatic, methionine-derived glucosinolates contributing most to the diversity. Quantitative trait locus (QTL) analysis is a powerful method to study the qualitative and quantitative variation in glucosinolate profiles. This approach has identified four to six QTLs that control aliphatic glucosinolate concentration in seeds of *B. napus* (159, 162). In *Arabidopsis*, a QTL mapping experiment using Landsberg *erecta* (Ler) X Cape Verde Islands (Cvi-0) recombinant inbred lines has identified a number of QTLs controlling the accumulation of aliphatic, aromatic, and indole glucosinolates in leaves and seeds (85). Under these conditions, six QTLs determine total aliphatic glucosinolate accumulation, of which two are the biosynthetic loci *GS-Elong* and *GS-AOP*, six QTLs control total indole glucosinolates, and

three loci regulate the less dominant aromatic glucosinolates. Five additional loci were specific to subsets of the indole glucosinolates. Except for the *GS-Elong* locus that controls both total leaf aliphatic and seed aromatic glucosinolates, no correlation was found between the QTLs for the different classes of glucosinolates, which suggests that the classes are independently regulated.

The above QTL analysis demonstrates that a large number of variable loci control glucosinolate accumulation. Apart from *GS-Elong* and *GS-AOP*, none of the loci have been cloned and characterized. However, the indole glucosinolate controlling locus *DF119L* on chromosome V maps in the vicinity of *ATR1*, the *AtMyb34* transcription factor, which has been identified as a regulator of indole glucosinolates (31). It is therefore likely that *DF119L* is *ATR1*, although the authors argue against this proposition based on the assumption that Cvi-0 should then behave as an *ATR1 null* mutant. However, this is not a prerequisite as Cvi-0 has approximately 50% of the indole glucosinolate of L*er* (86). The dominant mutant *atr1D* was isolated in a screen for altered tryptophan regulation (*atr*) and caused elevated expression of the indole glucosinolate biosynthetic genes *CYP79B2*, *CYP79B3*, and *CYP83B1*, and the Trp biosynthetic gene *ASA1* (13). The level of indole glucosinolates is upregulated in the *atr1D* mutant, whereas an *atr1* loss-of-function mutant impairs expression of the genes and confers reduced indole glucosinolate levels. This implies that ATR1 can be manipulated to coordinately control the enzymes that synthesize indole glucosinolates.

The level and composition of glucosinolates in plants reflect both genetic and environmental factors as some glucosinolates are constitutively present and others can be induced. The induction of specific *CYP79* genes correlates with accumulation of the corresponding glucosinolates, indicating that induction is regulated at the transcriptional level (119). Several studies with different plant species have shown that methyl jasmonate and wounding induce specific indole glucosinolates (16, 17, 20, 44, 119). *CYP79B2* and *CYP79B3* appear to have different functions as *CYP79B3* is primarily induced by methyl jasmonate (20, 119), whereas *CYP79B2* is primarily induced during camalexin production (59). The pathogen response signaling molecule, salicylic acid, is a less pronounced inducer of glucosinolates. It induces specifically 4-methoxyindol-3-ylmethyl glucosinolate in several *Arabidopsis* ecotypes (84, 119). In leaves of *B. napus*, salicylic acid increases the overall level of glucosinolates, with 2-phenylethyl glucosinolate showing the highest accumulation (82). With few exceptions, the aliphatic glucosinolates in *Arabidopsis* appear to be primarily developmentally regulated (84, 119). QTL analysis of the genetic variation influencing glucosinolate profiles in *Arabidopsis* under various environmental conditions shows a high level of variation, indicating the involvement of several different signal transduction pathways (84). Cloning and characterization of the genes underlying the QTLs will generate a detailed understanding of the molecular and biochemical basis for regulating glucosinolate profiles. In a recent paper, Saito and coworkers integrated metabolomics and transcriptomics to elucidate gene-to-gene and metabolite-to-gene networks in *Arabidopsis* grown under sulfur deficiency (72). The batch-learning self-organizing mapping approach classified metabolites and transcripts according to their time-dependent pattern of changes in accumulation and expression. This allowed the re-identification of all biosynthetic genes as well as the discovery of new putative transcription factors in the glucosinolate pathway (72). Similar experiments under other abiotic or biotic stresses may identify regulators under these conditions.

Camalexin: cruciferous indole phytoalexin

DEGRADATION

Glucosinolates are degraded upon plant damage to a variety of hydrolysis products that are responsible for virtually all of the biological activities of this compound class. The process begins with myrosinase-catalyzed hydrolysis of the thioglucoside linkage, leading to the formation of glucose and an unstable aglycone (19, 140). Depending on the structure of the side chain and the presence of additional proteins and cofactors, the aglycone then rearranges to form different products, including isothiocyanates, oxazolidine-2-thiones, nitriles, epithionitriles, and thiocyanates (**Figure 5**).

Hydrolysis Products

The most common glucosinolate hydrolysis products in many species are isothiocyanates, which are formed from the aglycone by a Lossen rearrangement involving the

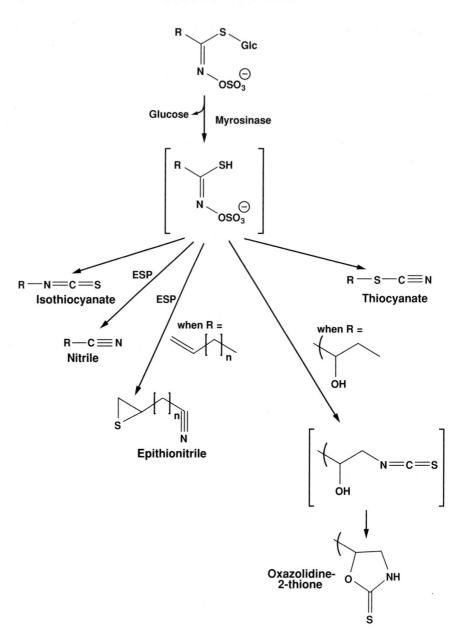

Figure 5

Outline of glucosinolate hydrolysis. Brackets indicate unstable intermediates. Abbreviations: ESP, epithiospecifier protein; R, variable side chain.

migration of the side chain from the oxime carbon to the adjacent nitrogen. When the glucosinolate side chain bears a hydroxyl group at C-2, the isothiocyanates formed are unstable and cyclize to oxazolidine-2-thiones, a class of substances known to cause goiter. In other plants, a major percentage of glucosinolate hydrolysis products are nitriles (40, 94). The formation of nitriles in vitro is favored at a pH of less than three or in the presence of

Fe^{2+} ions (54, 58). However, protein factors may be involved in nitrile formation in vivo, such as the epithiospecifier protein (ESP) (15, 52, 109, 157). When the glucosinolate side chain has a terminal double bond, ESP promotes the reaction of the sulfur atom of the thioglucoside linkage with the double bond to form a thirane ring, giving an epithionitrile (**Figure 5**). The process occurs only in the presence of myrosinase, and ESP is not known to have any catalytic abilities by itself. The recent isolation of an *Arabidopsis* gene encoding an ESP showed that this protein not only promotes the formation of epithionitriles, but also the formation of simple nitriles from a large variety of glucosinolates (94).

Other hydrolysis products include thiocyanates, which are formed from only three glucosinolates: benzyl-, allyl-, and 4-methylsulfinylbutyl-glucosinolate (**Figure 1**), all of which form stable side-chain cations. Like nitrile formation, thiocyanate production is also associated with specific protein factors (70), but these have not yet been identified. The hydrolysis of indole glucosinolates is somewhat different from that of the other glucosinolate types, because the initially formed isothiocyanates are unstable at neutral or slightly acidic pH, and are converted to further metabolites, including indole-methanols, ascorbic acid conjugates, and oligomeric mixtures (1, 27, 95).

Biochemistry and Physiology of Myrosinases

The initial catalysts in glucosinolate degradation have been the subject of many biochemical and molecular investigations (19, 140). As members of Glycoside Hydrolase Family 1 (171), myrosinases have three-dimensional structures and properties like those of certain O-glucosidases (25). The abundance of salt bridges, disulfide bridges, and H bonds apparent in the structure may promote stability in the extracellular environment in which myrosinase must function following tissue damage. Myrosinases are also heavily glycosylated with carbohydrate contributing up to 20% of their molecular masses. Glycosylation may serve to enhance protein stability as well or to protect the enzyme from being inactivated by reactive hydrolysis products. X-ray crystallography of myrosinase revealed a role for ascorbate as an essential cofactor (26). This finding helps account for the long-observed role of ascorbate in stimulating myrosinase activity at low millimolar concentrations. As the only group of β-thioglucosidases known in nature, myrosinases use only glucosinolates as substrates and have no activity toward any O-glycosides or other S-glycosides in vitro. However, among the different types of glucosinolates their substrate range is variable. Whereas most myrosinases hydrolyze multiple glucosinolate substrates, e.g., (36), some are highly specific (14, 110). In all plants investigated to date, myrosinase is encoded by a multigene family. For example, *Arabidopsis* has 4 functional myrosinase genes (171, 173) whereas *B. napus* and *Sinapis alba* each have 20 or more (140), many of which have distinct patterns of organ- and tissue-specific expression (99, 172).

The cellular and subcellular localization of myrosinase has been a question of long-standing interest in glucosinolate research because this is presumed to be part of the strategy to help keep glucosinolates and myrosinase from reacting in the intact plant but bring them together rapidly after damage, the "mustard oil bomb" sensu Lüthy & Mathile (108). For more than 100 years, it has been reported that myrosinase is localized in idioblasts with high vacuolar protein content, called myrosin cells, which are scattered in all organs of Brassicaceae species. This has been confirmed by histological, immunocytochemical and in situ hybridization methods and more recently by the use of *Arabidopsis* lines containing GUS fusion constructs with the promoters of myrosinase genes (74, 154). In these latest studies, myrosinase was found in idioblast cells of the phloem parenchyma occurring in leaves, stems, and inflorescences (6, 74, 154), and

ESP: epithiospecifier protein

Idioblast: cell that differs in form from others in same tissue

also in guard cells (74, 154). When these results are taken together with the recent report that glucosinolates in *Arabidopsis* flower stalks are localized in elongated, sulfur-rich "S cells" situated just distal to the phloem (88), they suggest that myrosinase and glucosinolates are segregated in this species in separate but adjacent cells. However, the arrangement may be different in other species because, in *Brassica* spp., myrosin cells are widespread outside the vascular system (6, 154). For example, in *B. juncea* seeds and seedlings, myrosinase is located in aleurone-type cells that appear to contain glucosinolates (80). The colocalization of both of these components in one cell type means that in some cases the glucosinolate-myrosinase system might be spatially separated at the subcellular rather than the cellular level. Alternatively, myrosinases could be located in the same compartment as glucosinolates but might be inactivated by high amounts of ascorbate (19).

Extracts of myrosinase-containing plants possess a number of other proteins that coprecipitate with antibodies to myrosinase, known as myrosinase-binding proteins, myrosinase-binding protein-related proteins, or myrosinase-associated proteins (140). Many representatives of these classes are induced by wounding or insect feeding (7, 137, 138), but their relation to glucosinolate hydrolysis is still obscure. For example, certain myrosinase-binding proteins in *B. napus* seeds with lectin-like properties form high-molecular weight complexes with myrosinase that might be expected to stabilize their activities (47). However, antisense plants lacking myrosinase-binding proteins in their seeds show no changes in myrosinase activity.

METABOLIC LINKS BETWEEN GLUCOSINOLATE METABOLISM, IAA, AND OTHER INDOLE COMPOUNDS

Several lines of evidence suggest that there is a metabolic link between indole glucosinolates and the plant hormone indole-3-acetic acid (IAA). First, indole glucosinolates can be degraded into indole acetonitrile (IAN), which in turn can be hydrolyzed by nitrilases into IAA. The conversion of indole glucosinolates into IAN may require the presence of both myrosinase and an ESP (94) (see under degradation). However, an ESP is notably not present in the frequently studied *Arabidopsis* Columbia ecotype. Additional evidence for a glucosinolate-IAA link is the role of IAOx as intermediate in the biosynthesis of indole glucosinolate and as precursor of IAA, although the genes involved in conversion of IAOx to IAA remain to be identified. Several high-auxin loss-of-function *Arabidopsis* mutants gain their phenotype by blockage of postaldoxime enzymes in the glucosinolate pathway, which supposedly leads to accumulation of IAOx that is channeled into IAA. These mutants include *superroot1/afl1/rooty/hls3* (18, 30, 83, 98) (hereafter referred to as *sur1*), which is knocked out in the *C-S* lyase, and *cyp83B1/superroot2/runt1/atr4*, (11, 12, 42, 149) (hereafter referred to as *sur2*). The recently discovered *ugt74B1* mutant has a less pronounced high-auxin phenotype, probably due to redundancy (65). The gain-of-function YUCCA mutant, which has a strong high-auxin phenotype, is proposed to overproduce IAOx due to upregulation of a flavin-monooxygenase that can hydroxylate tryptamine to N-hydroxytryptamine (177). This, however, implies that the tryptamine conversion is rate limiting for IAA production, which remains to be shown.

Until recently, it was an open question whether CYP79B2 and CYP79B3, which convert amino acids to aldoximes, contribute to IAA production in wild-type *Arabidopsis* plants. Their role in IAA biosynthesis is evidenced by increased levels of free IAA in six-day-old seedlings of *CYP79B2* overexpression lines and decreased levels of free IAA in *cyp79B2cyp79B3* double mutants (178). Furthermore, decreased IAA synthesis was measured in the apical 0–2 mm of excised roots of seven-day-old seedlings of *cyp79B2cyp79B3* double mutants (103). Their role in root-specific IAA synthesis is supported by studies with *CYP79B2* and *CYP79B3* GUS reporter constructs, which show distinct expression of each gene in the primary root meristem and at the sites of lateral root formation (103).

Another unanswered question is whether or not IAOx plays a role in IAA biosynthesis in plants that do not produce indole glucosinolates. To date, indole glucosinolates have been found in only five families of the order Capparales (64), and no *CYP79B* homologs have been identified in plant species outside these families (9). This suggests that a role of *CYP79B* homologs in IAA biosynthesis is limited to a small group of plants. On the other hand, this does not rule out that IAOx originating from other sources is an intermediate in IAA biosynthesis.

The role of IAN in IAA biosynthesis is uncertain. Attempts to rescue the high-auxin phenotype of *sur2* by crossing *sur2* to the *nit1* null mutant (NIT1 is the nitrilase with highest specificity toward IAN) were unsuccessful, which suggests that IAN is not an intermediate in the biosynthetic pathway from IAOx to IAA (11). However, Kutz et al. (93) provide evidence that, under conditions of sulfur starvation, an increase in glucobrassicin turnover and NIT3 accumulation initiate the production of extra IAA from IAN, leading to increased root growth and branching. This allows the root system to penetrate new soil areas. Interestingly, IAN was recently recognized as a phytoalexin that is induced upon fungus attack in *Brassica juncea* (134).

Based on structure similarity, it has been suggested that the indole alkaloid, brassinin, and possibly other cruciferous phytoalexins are derived from indol-3-ylmethylglucosinolate (glucobrassicin). However, camalexin (the indole alkaloid of *Arabidopsis*) is synthesized directly from IAOx by CYP79B2 and CYP79B3 (59). Furthermore, in vivo feeding studies with roots of turnip (*Brassica rapa*) using deuterated IAOx and glucobrassicin showed that IAOx, and not glucobrassicin, was incorporated into brassinin and

brassinin-derived phytoalexins (133). These data suggest that the characteristic cruciferous sulfur-containing indole alkaloids are synthesized from tryptophan via IAOx by CYP79B homologs.

In *Arabidopsis*, IAOx represents a key metabolic branch point where the flow of IAOx into the biosynthetic pathways of indole glucosinolates, camalexin, and IAA must be tightly regulated (**Figure 6**). Further studies are needed to identify genes in the biosynthesis of camalexin and IAA, which will allow investigations into the organization and regulation of the different metabolons around IAOx. The emerging knowledge of IAOx synthesis and metabolism has opened an exciting area of research at the borderline between primary and secondary metabolism.

TRANSPORT IN PLANTS

Glucosinolate accumulation varies between tissues and developmental stages, both with regard to concentration and composition (23). In *Arabidopsis*, young leaves and reproductive tissues such as siliques and seeds contain the highest concentrations, whereas senescing rosette leaves contain the lowest concentrations of glucosinolates. Intermediate concentrations are found throughout the "large" organs such as the roots, leaves, and stem (23, 135). The high accumulation of glucosinolates in the seeds does not have a correspondingly high level of associated biosynthesis, which suggests the presence of an import system in this tissue (45). Several lines of evidence indicate long-distance transport of glucosinolates from parts other than the siliques to the seeds. First, glucosinolates possess the physicochemical properties required to travel in the phloem (24), fulfilling one prerequisite for long-distance transport. Secondly, examination of phloem exudates following aphid feeding has shown glucosinolate concentrations of up to 10 mM in phloem sap (114). Finally, the strongest indication of long-distance transport of glucosinolates comes from a study by Chen et al. (35). When

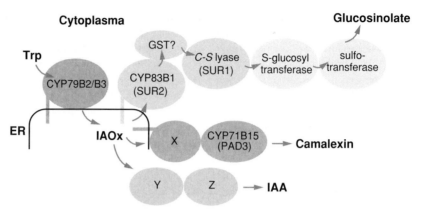

Cytoplasma

Glucosinolate

Trp

GST?

C-S lyase
(SUR1)

S-glucosyl
transferase

sulfo-
transferase

CYP79B2/B3

CYP83B1
(SUR2)

ER

IAOx

X

CYP71B15
(PAD3)

Camalexin

Y

Z

IAA

Figure 6

Visualization of a metabolic grid around indole-3-acetaldoxime (IAOx). IAOx represents a key metabolic branching point between primary and secondary metabolism as IAOx flows into the metabolons of indole glucosinolates, camalexin, and indole-3-acetic acid (IAA). The reactivity of the CYP83 product combined with the ability of the *C-S* lyase substrate to undergo internal cyclization in the absence of the *C-S* lyase suggest a very tight coupling between CYP83B1, the unidentified GST, and the *C-S* lyase. Abbreviations: GST, glutathione-*S*-transferase; SUR2, SUPERROOT2; SUR1, SUPERROOT1; ER, endoplasmic reticulum.

young 35S::CYP79A1 *Arabidopsis* plants were fed [^{14}C]tyrosine to their rosette leaves, radio-labelled exogenous *p*-hydroxybenzyl glucosinolate was formed. Upon bolting, the radio-labeled glucosinolate was exported from the leaves to the seeds, possibly via transport in the phloem.

Several experiments have biochemically characterized the transport system. Excised immature *B. napus* embryos take up glucosinolates from the culture medium in an energy-dependent, carrier-mediated transport system (57). Similarly, leaf protoplasts of *B. napus* take up a variety of glucosinolates (37). Both embryo and protoplasts displayed an ability to take up glucosinolates against a concentration gradient that was dependent on a pH gradient, and was abolished by the uncoupling protonophores 2,4-dinitrophenol and carbonylcyanide *p*-chlorophenyl hydrazone (37, 57). The transport system was specific toward glucosinolates as compared to other glucosides, sugars, and amino acids. This was further supported by the facile absorption of the exogenous alkenyl glucosinolate sinigrin observed in uptake experiments using microspore-derived embryos of *B. na-*

pus (75). The data suggest the presence of a specific H^+/glucosinolate symporter, which is unaffected by the structure of the side chain.

Several questions are unresolved regarding glucosinolate transport. First, the sulfur-rich cells (S-cells) localized in the floral stalk of *Arabidopsis* contain approximately 100 mM glucosinolate (88), and could constitute a sink for glucosinolate transport, in addition to seeds. More experiments are needed to establish whether these cells possess the biosynthetic machinery to account for their high glucosinolate content or whether they rely on import from surrounding tissues. Second, some controversy exists about the form in which glucosinolates are transported. Sulfotransferase activity has been identified in embryos of *B. napus*, which suggests that desulfoglucosinolates may be the transport form (158). Experiments with radiolabeled desulfoglucosinolates fed to silique walls and seedlings showed the glucosinolate precursor to be taken up and converted into glucosinolates (153). On the contrary, Chen et al. (35) isolated intact indole glucosinolates from phloem exudates of leaves of *B. napus*. Whether desulfoglucosinolates or glucosinolates are the long-distance transport form of glucosinolates awaits identification and characterization of a transporter.

BIOLOGICAL FUNCTION

The activation of glucosinolates upon plant damage and the biological properties of their hydrolysis products have long suggested that the major function of these compounds in plants is to defend against herbivores and pathogens. The glucosinolate-myrosinase system has been actively investigated as a feature of plant defense for nearly 100 years, but there are still many gaps in our knowledge. Given the large literature on this subject and the regular appearance of reviews (38, 104, 170), here we emphasize only the major themes and recent contributions.

Numerous studies have demonstrated that glucosinolates exhibit outright toxicity, growth inhibition, or feeding deterrence to a wide range of potential plant enemies, including mammals, birds, insects, mollusks, aquatic invertebrates, nematodes, bacteria, and fungi (e.g., 28, 96, 131, 161). When hydrolysis products have been explicitly tested in such studies, isothiocyanates are frequently responsible for the activity of the parent glucosinolates (3, 28, 101, 156). Unfortunately, little is known about the specific mechanism by which isothiocyanates exert their toxicity aside from their general propensity to react with amino and sulfhydryl groups of proteins in vitro (79). Several recent studies have reported that plants respond to insect damage by systemically accumulating higher levels of glucosinolates, which presumably increases their resistance to subsequent attacks (2, 115, 160, 163).

As with other plant-defense compounds, the same glucosinolates that serve as general poisons and deterrents for many herbivores also attract adapted herbivores. Many insect herbivores have come to specialize on glucosinolate-containing plants and often use these compounds as cues for feeding or oviposition (53, 116, 121, 145). Attraction from

a distance may be mediated by volatile hydrolysis products, whereas the intact glucosinolates can serve as contact cues for feeding or oviposition stimulation. Evidence for specialist insect attraction in such studies comes not only from behavioral experiments, but also from electrophysiological investigations in which receptor organs or cells respond directly to glucosinolates or their hydrolysis products (121, 145). Not all specialist feeders on glucosinolate-containing plants use these compounds in mediating host choice; some employ entirely different plant chemicals in this capacity (41, 112, 142).

Herbivores that specialize on glucosinolate-containing plants must have some mechanism of overcoming the toxicity of their host. In theory, they could rapidly excrete glucosinolates from their bodies, metabolize them to nontoxic derivatives, or be completely insensitive to their toxic action. The larvae of two lepidopteran species were recently shown to employ divergent metabolic strategies to circumvent the toxicity of glucosinolates. *Plutella xylostella*, the diamondback moth, cleaves the sulfate residue from the glucosinolate core structure with its own endogenous sulfatase to give a product that can no longer be hydrolyzed by myrosinase (141). *Pieris rapae*, the cabbage white butterfly, secretes a protein factor into the gut with an action similar to that of the ESP. It redirects myrosinase-catalyzed hydrolysis toward the formation of nitriles instead of isothiocyanates, and the resulting nitriles are excreted with the feces (167). Thus, both species avoid the formation of isothiocyanate hydrolysis products in their digestive tracts, which, at least for *P. rapae*, are deleterious to larval growth and survival (3). Other specialist insects that seem to feed on glucosinolate-containing plant tissue with impunity, such as the flea beetles of the genus *Phyllotreta* (129), may have similar mechanisms.

Once specialist herbivores have overcome the defensive chemistry of their hosts, they may be able to sequester plant-defensive compounds in their own tissues without harm and exploit them in self-protection. Several examples of glucosinolate-sequestering insects were recently described, including the harlequin bug, *Murgantia histrionica* (Hemiptera) (4), the sawfly, *Athalia rosae* (Hymenoptera) (125), and the aphids, *Brevicoryne brassicae* and *Lipophis erysimi* (Homoptera) (21). As a counter example, it was shown that *Pieris* sp., which were once suspected of sequestering dietary glucosinolates, do not actually exhibit this ability (124). In *M. histrionica* and *A. rosae*, sequestration deterred predators such as birds, lizards, and ants (126, 165). The exploitation of glucosinolates by herbivores for their own defensive purposes is complicated by the fact that myrosinase is also needed to catalyze the formation of toxic hydrolysis products. In fact, the aphid *B. brassicae* does have a myrosinase activity of its own that is quite distinct from plant myrosinases (77). This enzyme is apparently stored in the aphid body separately from glucosinolates and forms isothiocyanates from the sequestered glucosinolates when the aphid is damaged or killed, serving to alarm other members of the colony (21). For other glucosinolate-sequestering insects, it is not clear if they possess an endogenous myrosinase or just rely on the myrosinase activity normally present in the guts of their enemies to make the defense effective. Some bacterial species resident in the human and rat intestine have the ability to degrade glucosinolates to isothiocyanates and other metabolites (92, 146), and this may be a widespread phenomenon in the animal kingdom. The use of plant glucosinolates by herbivores in their own defense not only extends the ecological significance of these compounds, but also underscores the intrinsic defensive value of glucosinolates to the plant that produces them.

In light of the many reports demonstrating the toxicity of glucosinolate hydrolysis products to bacteria and fungi in vitro (20, 113, 148), glucosinolates might be expected to defend plants against pathogens. In some cases, resistance to pathogens in vivo is indeed positively associated with glucosinolate content (102). But a defensive role cannot automatically be assumed because many pathogens, especially biotrophic organisms, may not cause enough cell damage to activate the glucosinolate-myrosinase system. The *Arabidopsis MAM1* mutant, which has a lower amount of 4-methylsulfinylbutyl glucosinolate than the wild-type, had increased susceptibility to *Fusarium oxysporum*, but not to other fungal and bacterial species (156). Different glucosinolate hydrolysis products seem to have varying effects on different pathogens (20, 147). Once glucosinolates are released into the soil from root exudates or the decay of plant organs, they may have important effects on the rhizosphere community. The dominant fungal species in soil near glucosinolate-containing Brassicaceae are different than the dominant fungal species found elsewhere and show increased tolerance to isothiocyanates (76). The growth of certain ectomycorrhizal species is even stimulated by the hydrolysis products of indole glucosinolates (175).

METABOLIC ENGINEERING OF GLUCOSINOLATES

There is a strong interest in being able to alter levels of specific glucosinolates in crop plants as certain glucosinolates have desirable properties in flavor, insect protection, biofumigation, and cancer prevention, whereas others have undesirable properties. To date, metabolic engineering of glucosinolate profiles has included altering the expression of one or more CYP79 enzymes. Identification of the CYP79s as the enzymes catalyzing the conversion of amino acids to aldoximes has provided important molecular tools for modulating the profile of glucosinolates (for review see Reference 120). Ectopic expression of the endogenous *CYP79* genes under the control of the strong constitutive 35S promoter has resulted in production of transgenic *Arabidopsis* lines that accumulate increased levels of benzyl (*35S::CYP79A2*) (168), indole (*35S::CYP79B2*) (31, 117), and aliphatic (*35S::CYP79F1*) (69) glucosinolates.

Overexpression of *CYP79F1* resulted in no more than a twofold greater accumulation of the homo- to tetrahomomethionine-derived glucosinolates (69, 143), which is significantly less than that for plants overexpressing *CYP79A2* or *CYP79B2*. This is likely to reflect the fact that the rate-liming step of aliphatic glucosinolate biosynthesis in these lines is the chain-elongation pathway.

Overexpression of exogenous CYP79s from the cyanogenic pathway is a means to generate novel glucosinolates. Introduction of *CYP79A1* from the biosynthetic pathway of the tyrosine-derived cyanogenic glucoside dhurrin in *Sorghum bicolor* resulted in *Arabidopsis* plants that accumulate high levels of *p*-hydroxybenzyl glucosinolate (10). Similarly, introduction of *CYP79D2* from the biosynthetic pathway of the cyanogenic glucosides linamarin and lotaustralin in *Manihot esculenta* Crantz (5) resulted in accumulation of the valine- and isoleucine-derived glucosinolates, isopropyl and 1-methylpropyl glucosinolate (119). 1-methylpropyl glucosinolate had not previously been identified in *Arabidopsis* and only trace amounts of isopropyl glucosinolate have been found in just a few ecotypes (86). The ability to alter the concentrations of not only specific endogenous glucosinolates, but also to introduce novel glucosinolates not normally present in *Arabidopsis*, reflects the fact that the postaldoxime enzymes are not specific for the nature of the side chain. The efficiency of metabolic engineering of glucosinolate profiles using CYP79 enzymes varies for the different enzymes. Several factors, such as enzyme stability, K_m value, amino acid pool size, turnover, and targeting influence the success of a metabolic engineering approach. Accordingly, metabolic engineering of glucosinolates will likely remain a largely unpredictable business, which has to be tested in vivo.

Knockout of *CYP79* genes is a means to eliminate specific glucosinolates. However, whereas knockout mutants of CYP79s metabolizing protein amino acids have mostly wild-type morphology, knockout mutants of, e.g.,

CYP79F1 metabolizing chain-elongated methionine derivatives have a severe morphological phenotype with several hundred axillary shoots, reflecting an altered hormone balance (143, 150). *Arabidopsis* (Col-0) knockout mutants of *MAM1* and *MAML* are deficient in C4 and C6, C7, and C8 aliphatic glucosinolates, respectively (51, 91). One may therefore anticipate that a double knockout of these two genes will be devoid of methionine-derived, aliphatic glucosinolates.

Overexpression of regulators could be another approach to metabolic engineering. The dominant *atr1D* mutant that is up-regulated in the transcripts for *CYP79B2*, *CYP79B3*, and *CYP83B1*, accumulates ten-fold more total indole glucosinolates than wild type. Interestingly, although *35S::ATR1* lines produced several-fold-higher transcript levels than *atr1D*, the level of indole glucosinolates was only twofold above wild-type level (31). In comparison, *35S::CYP79B2* lines produced a fivefold increase in indole glucosinolates (117). This shows that ectopic expression of a regulator may be less optimal for metabolic engineering than a gain-of-function mutant that only overexpresses the regulator in the right cells.

Future metabolic engineering efforts with the genes from the chain-elongating pathway, the aldoxime-forming CYP79s, and the enzymes catalyzing secondary transformations provide the possibility to design crop plants enriched in desirable glucosinolates and free of undesirable glucosinolates. This will allow a detailed analysis of the biological function of the individual glucosinolates. Furthermore, with the nearly complete identification of the genes involved in the biosynthesis of the core structure, it has become a realistic possibility to engineer the glucosinolate pathway into heterologous host plants. The entire biosynthetic pathway of the evolutionarily related cyanogenic glucosides has been successfully transferred into noncyanogenic plants, resulting in plants with increased resistance to specific insects (151). The data showed that the heterologous pathway formed a metabolon in the new host plant, and that this metabolon did not affect the morphological phenotype of the plant (130). The positive experience with engineering the cyanogenic glucoside metabolon leaves hope that the entire glucosinolate pathway may be heterologously expressed in microorganisms and heterologous plants to generate high-value products or crops.

PERSPECTIVE

The unprecedented resources supporting functional genomics research on *Arabidopsis* have led to a remarkable increase in our knowledge of the biology and biochemistry of glucosinolates, which are one of the major classes of secondary metabolites in this model plant species. The availability of genetic sequence information, large mutant collections, and tools for expression profiling, along with abundant natural glucosinolate variation among ecotypes, recombinant inbred lines, and markers for mapping have greatly facilitated the identification of genes encoding enzymes of glucosinolate biosynthesis. However, to date this success has been concentrated on the core pathway, and most of the genes and enzymes participating in the chain-elongation cycle, secondary transformations, and proteins controlling glucosinolate breakdown are still unknown. Additionally, more knowledge about the factors that regulate efflux through the pathways of biosynthesis and breakdown are necessary if we are to fully appreciate how glucosinolate accumulation is controlled.

The continued application of genetic and genomic tools along with the development of systems biology technologies to link genetic, protein, and metabolite data should ensure further progress in gene discovery. In the near future, we can expect to understand the precise biochemical and molecular mechanisms underlying how and where plants synthesize glucosinolates. The isolated genes of glucosinolate metabolism should also facilitate metabolic engineering of plants with altered profiles of glucosinolates and glucosinolate hydrolysis products. These will be invaluable for rigorously testing the physiological and ecological roles of glucosinolates in nature. Manipulation of glucosinolate metabolism will also help in exploiting the applied potential of these compounds to improve the pest resistance and health and nutrition benefits of crop plants or to generate high-value products for industry.

SUMMARY POINTS

1. Genes have now been identified in all three phases of glucosinolate biosynthesis (amino acid elongation, core structure formation, and secondary modifications); identification of the genes involved in forming the core structure is nearly complete.

2. The elongation of amino acid side chains proceeds via a three-step acid cycle involving 2-oxo acids analogous to that occurring in leucine biosynthesis. One molecule of acetyl-CoA is added and one molecule of CO_2 is lost during each turn of the cycle for a net gain of one carbon atom.

3. The cytochromes P450, CYP79B2, and CYP79B3, which convert tryptophan to indole-3-acetaldoxime, a precursor for indole glucosinolates, the indole alkaloid camalexin, and the plant hormone indole-3-acetic acid, play a role in indole-3-acetic acid biosynthesis in *Arabidopsis*.

4. The identification of genes encoding myrosinase and the epithiospecifier protein has led to new insights into what controls the mechanism and direction of glucosinolate hydrolysis and how compartmentation prevents hydrolysis in intact plants.

5. Several lines of evidence support the role of glucosinolates in plant defense, including the toxicity and deterrence of glucosinolate hydrolysis products, the existence of specific metabolic mechanisms by which adapted insects circumvent glucosinolate toxicity, and the use of glucosinolates by herbivores in their own defense.

6. Metabolic engineering of glucosinolate profiles in *Arabidopsis* has been established and provides a tool for investigating the functional role of individual glucosinolates, for example in plant-insect or plant-pathogen interactions.

FUTURE ISSUES TO BE RESOLVED

1. What are the major regulatory factors that control flux through the biosynthetic pathway? Identification of these should allow the metabolic engineering of glucosinolate profiles to advance from the empirical to the predictive stage.

2. Identification of glucosinolate transporters to address longstanding questions about transport, storage, and turnover of glucosinolates in the intact plant.

3. Are glucosinolates broken down in the intact plant through mediation of myrosinase or other factors?

4. What are the mechanisms by which glucosinolate hydrolysis products exert their toxicity on herbivores?

5. Do glucosinolates help defend plants against fungal and bacterial pathogens under natural conditions?

ACKNOWLEDGMENTS

We thank Meike Burow, Jan-Willem de Kraker, Peggy Rice, Susanne Textor, and Ute Wittstock for critical reading of the manuscript, Angela Schneider for helping manage the literature cited, and all other members of our research groups, past and present, for their contributions. The generosity of the National Danish Research Foundation, the German National Science Foundation, and the Max Planck Society in supporting glucosinolate research in our laboratories is also gratefully acknowledged.

LITERATURE CITED

1. Agerbirk N, Olsen CE, Soerensen H. 1998. Initial and final products, nitriles, and ascorbigens produced in myrosinase-catalyzed hydrolysis of indole glucosinolates. *J. Agric. Food Chem.* 46:1563–71

2. Agrawal AA, Conner JK, Johnson MTJ, Wallsgrove R. 2002. Ecological genetics of an induced plant defense against herbivores: additive genetic variance and costs of phenotypic plasticity. *Evolution* 56:2206–13

3. Agrawal AA, Kurashige NS. 2003. A role for isothiocyanates in plant resistance against the specialist herbivore *Pieris rapae*. *J. Chem. Ecol.* 29:1403–15

4. Aliabadi A, Renwick JAA, Whitman DW. 2002. Sequestration of glucosinolates by harlequin bug *Murgantia histrionica*. *J. Chem. Ecol.* 28:1749–62

5. Andersen MD, Busk PK, Svendsen I, Moller BL. 2000. Cytochromes P-450 from cassava (*Manihot esculenta* Crantz) catalyzing the first steps in the biosynthesis of the cyanogenic glucosides linamarin and lotaustralin-cloning, functional expression in *Pichia pastoris*, and substrate specificity of the isolated recombinant enzymes. *J. Biol. Chem.* 275:1966–75

6. **Andreasson E, Jorgensen LB, Hoglund AS, Rask L, Meijer J. 2001. Different myrosinase and idioblast distribution in Arabidopsis and *Brassica napus*. Plant Physiol. 127:1750–63**

7. Andreasson E, Taipalensuu J, Rask L, Meijer J. 1999. Age-dependent wound induction of a myrosinase-associated protein from oilseed rape (*Brassica napus*). *Plant Mol. Biol.* 41:171–80

8. Bak S, Feyereisen R. 2001. The involvement of two P450 enzymes, *CYP83B1* and *CYP83A1*, in auxin homeostasis and glucosinolate biosynthesis. *Plant Physiol.* 127:108–18

9. Bak S, Kahn RA, Nielsen HL, Moller BL, Halkier BA. 1998. Cloning of three A-type cytochromes P450, *CYP71E1*, *CYP98*, and *CYP99* from *Sorghum bicolor* (L.) Moech by a PCR approach and identification by expression in *Escherichia coli* of CYP71E1 as a multifunctional cytochrome P450 in the biosynthesis of the cyanogenic glucoside dhurrin. *Plant Mol. Biol.* 36:393–405

10. Bak S, Olsen CE, Petersen BL, Moller BL, Halkier BA. 1999. Metabolic engineering of *p*-hydroxybenzylglucosinolate in Arabidopsis by expression of the cyanogenic *CYP79A1* from *Sorghum bicolor*. *Plant J.* 20:663–71

11. Bak S, Tax FE, Feldmann KA, Galbraith DW, Feyereisen R. 2001. *CYP83B1*, a cytochrome P450 at the metabolic branch paint in auxin and indole glucosinolate biosynthesis in Arabidopsis. *Plant Cell* 13:101–11

12. Barlier I, Kowalczyk M, Marchant A, Ljung K, Bhalerao R, et al. 2000. The SUR2 gene of *Arabidopsis thaliana* encodes the cytochrome P450 *CYP83B1*, a modulator of auxin homeostasis. *Proc. Natl. Acad. Sci. USA* 97:14819–24

13. Bender J, Fink GR. 1998. A Myb homologue, *ATR1*, activates tryptophan gene expression in Arabidopsis. *Proc. Natl. Acad. Sci. USA* 95:5655–60

14. Bernardi R, Finiguerra MG, Rossi AA, Palmieri S. 2003. Isolation and biochemical characterization of a basic myrosinase from ripe *Crambe abyssinica* seeds, highly specific for epi-progoitrin. *J. Agric. Food Chem.* 51:2737–44

15. Bernardi R, Negri A, Ronchi S, Palmieri S. 2000. Isolation of the epithiospecifier protein from oil-rape (*Brassica napus* ssp *oleifera*) seed and its characterization. *FEBS Lett.* 467:296–98

16. Bodnaryk RP. 1992. Effects of wounding on glucosinolates in the cotyledons of oilseed rape and mustard. *Phytochemistry* 31:2671–77

17. Bodnaryk RP. 1994. Potent effect of jasmonates on indole glucosinolates in oilseed rape and mustard. *Phytochemistry* 35:301–5

18. Boerjan W, Cervera MT, Delarue M, Beeckman T, Dewitte W, et al. 1995. *Superroot*, a recessive mutation in Arabidopsis, confers auxin overproduction. *Plant Cell* 7:1405–19

19. Bones AM, Rossiter JT. 1996. The myrosinase-glucosinolate system, its organisation and biochemistry. *Physiol. Plant.* 97:194–208

20. Brader G, Tas E, Palva ET. 2001. Jasmonate-dependent induction of indole glucosinolates in Arabidopsis by culture filtrates of the nonspecific pathogen *Erwinia carotovora*. *Plant Physiol.* 126:849–60

21. Bridges M, Jones AME, Bones AM, Hodgson C, Cole R, et al. 2002. Spatial organization of the glucosinolate-myrosinase system in *Brassica* specialist aphids is similar to that of the host plant. *Proc. R. Soc. London Sci. Ser. B* 269:187–91

This paper documents the compartmentation of glucosinolates and myrosinase in different but adjacent cell types in *Arabidopsis* stems.

22. Brown PD, Morra MJ. 1995. Glucosinolate-containing plant tissues as bioherbicides. *J. Agric. Food Chem.* 43:3070–74

23. Brown PD, Tokuhisa JG, Reichelt M, Gershenzon J. 2003. Variation of glucosinolate accumulation among different organs and developmental stages of *Arabidopsis thaliana*. *Phytochemistry* 62:471–81

24. Brudenell AJP, Griffiths H, Rossiter JT, Baker DA. 1999. The phloem mobility of glucosinolates. *J. Exp. Bot.* 50:745–56

25. Burmeister WP, Cottaz S, Driguez H, Iori R, Palmieri S, Henrissat B. 1997. The crystal structures of *Sinapis alba* myrosinase and a covalent glycosyl-enzyme intermediate provide insights into the substrate recognition and active-site machinery of an S-glycosidase. *Structure* 5:663–75

26. Burmeister WP, Cottaz S, Rollin P, Vasella A, Henrissat B. 2000. High resolution x-ray crystallography shows that ascorbate is a cofactor for myrosinase and substitutes for the function of the catalytic base. *J. Biol. Chem.* 275:39385–93

27. Buskov S, Olsen CE, Sorensen H, Sorensen S. 2000. Supercritical fluid chromatography as basis for identification and quantitative determination of indol-3-ylmethyl oligomers and ascorbigens. *J. Biochem. Biophys. Methods* 43:175–95

28. Buskov S, Serra B, Rosa E, Soerensen H, Soerensen JC. 2002. Effects of intact glucosinolates and products produced from glucosinolates in myrosinase-catalyzed hydrolysis on the potato cyst nematode (*Globodera rostochiensis* cv. Woll). *J. Agric. Food Chem.* 50:690–95

29. Campos de Quiros HC, Magrath R, McCallum D, Kroymann J, Schnabelrauch D, et al. 2000. Alpha-keto acid elongation and glucosinolate biosynthesis in *Arabidopsis thaliana*. *Theor. Appl. Genet.* 101:429–37

30. Celenza JL, Grisafi PL, Fink GR. 1995. A pathway for lateral root-formation in *Arabidopsis thaliana*. *Genes Dev.* 9:2131–42

31. Celenza JL, Quiel JA, Smolen GA, Merrikh H, Silvestro AR, et al. 2005. The Arabidopsis *ATR1* Myb transcription factor controls indolic glucosinolate homeostasis. *Plant Physiol.* 137:253–62

32. Chapple CCS, Decicco C, Ellis BE. 1988. Biosynthesis of 2-(2′-methylthio)ethylmalate in *Brassica carinata*. *Phytochemistry* 27:3461–63

33. Chapple CCS, Glover JR, Ellis BE. 1990. Purification and characterization of methionine: glyoxylate aminotransferase from *Brassica napus*. *Plant Physiol.* 94:1887–96

34. Chen S, Glaswischnig E, Jorgensen K, Naur P, Jorgensen B, et al. 2003. *CYP79F1* and *CYP79F2* have distinct functions in the biosynthesis of aliphatic glucosinolates in Arabidopsis. *Plant J.* 33:923–37

35. Chen S, Petersen BL, Olsen CE, Schulz A, Halkier BA. 2001. Long-distance phloem transport of glucosinolates in Arabidopsis. *Plant Physiol.* 127:194–201

36. Chen SX, Halkier BA. 1999. Functional expression and characterization of the myrosinase MYR1 from *Brassica napus* in *Saccharomyces cerevisiae*. *Protein Expr. Purif.* 17:414–20

37. Chen SX, Halkier BA. 2000. Characterization of glucosinolate uptake by leaf protoplasts of *Brassica napus*. *J. Biol. Chem.* 275:22955–60

38. Chew FS. 1988. Biological effects of glucosinolates. In *Biologically Active Natural Products*, ed. HG Cutler, pp. 155–81. Washington, DC: ACS

39. Chisholm MD, Wetter LR. 1964. Biosynthesis of mustard oil glucosides. IV. The administration of methionine-C[14] and related compounds to horseradish. *Can. J. Biochem.* 42:1033–40

40. Cole R. 1976. Isothiocyanates, nitriles and thiocyanates as products of autolysis of glucosinolates in Cruciferae. *Phytochemistry* 15:759–62

This paper describes a myb transcription factor, which is the most powerful regulator of glucosinolate accumulation known to date.

The most convincing evidence for long-distance glucosinolate transport in plants is described in this paper.

41. de Jong R, Maher N, Patrian B, Stadler E, Winkler T. 2000. Rutabaga roots, a rich source of oviposition stimulants for the cabbage root fly. *Chemoecology* 10:205–9

42. Delarue M, Prinsen E, Van Onckelen H, Caboche M, Bellini C. 1998. *Sur2* mutations of *Arabidopsis thaliana* define a new locus involved in the control of auxin homeostasis. *Plant J.* 14:603–11

43. Dornemann D, Loffelhardt W, Kindl H. 1974. Chain elongation of aromatic acid: the role of 2-benzylmalic acid in the biosynthesis of a C_6C_4 amino acid and a C_6C_3 mustard oil glucoside. *Can. J. Biochem.* 52:916–21

44. Doughty KJ, Kiddle GA, Pye BJ, Wallsgrove RM, Pickett JA. 1995. Selective induction of glucosinolates in oilseed rape leaves by methyl jasmonate. *Phytochemistry* 38:347–50

45. Du LC, Halkier BA. 1998. Biosynthesis of glucosinolates in the developing silique walls and seeds of *Sinapis alba*. *Phytochemistry* 48:1145–50

46. Engel E, Baty C, le Corre D, Souchon I, Martin N. 2002. Flavor-active compounds potentially implicated in cooked cauliflower acceptance. *J. Agric. Food Chem.* 50:6459–67

47. Eriksson S, Andreasson E, Ekbom B, Graner G, Pontoppidan B, et al. 2002. Complex formation of myrosinase isoenzymes in oilseed rape seeds are dependent on the presence of myrosinase-binding proteins. *Plant Physiol.* 129:1592–99

48. Fahey JW, Haristoy X, Dolan PM, Kensler TW, Scholtus I, et al. 2002. Sulforaphane inhibits extracellular, intracellular, and antibiotic-resistant strains of *Helicobacter pylori* and prevents benzo[*a*]pyrene-induced stomach tumors. *Proc. Natl. Acad. Sci. USA* 99:7610–15

49. Fahey JW, Zalcmann AT, Talalay P. 2001. The chemical diversity and distribution of glucosinolates and isothiocyanates among plants. *Phytochemistry* 56:5–51

50. Falk KL, Vogel C, Textor S, Bartram S, Hick A, et al. 2004. Glucosinolate biosynthesis: demonstration and characterization of the condensing enzyme of the chain elongation cycle in *Eruca sativa*. *Phytochemistry* 65:1073–84

51. Field B, Cardon G, Traka M, Botterman J, Vancanneyt G, Mithen R. 2004. Glucosinolate and amino acid biosynthesis in Arabidopsis. *Plant Physiol.* 135:828–39

52. Foo HL, Gronning LM, Goodenough L, Bones AM, Danielsen BE, et al. 2000. Purification and characterisation of epithiospecifier protein from *Brassica napus*: enzymic intramolecular sulphur addition within alkenyl thiohydroximates derived from alkenyl glucosinolate hydrolysis. *FEBS Lett.* 468:243–46

53. Gabrys B, Tjallingii WF. 2002. The role of sinigrin in host plant recognition by aphids during initial plant penetration. *Entomol. Exp. Appl.* 104:89–93

54. Galletti S, Bernardi R, Leoni O, Rollin P, Palmieri S. 2001. Preparation and biological activity of four epiprogoitrin myrosinase-derived products. *J. Agric. Food Chem.* 49:471–76

55. Gao MQ, Li GY, Yang B, McCombie WR, Quiros CF. 2004. Comparative analysis of a Brassica BAC clone containing several major aliphatic glucosinolate genes with its corresponding Arabidopsis sequence. *Genome* 47:666–79

56. Giamoustaris A, Mithen R. 1996. Genetics of aliphatic glucosinolates. 4. Side-chain modification in *Brassica oleracea*. *Theor. Appl. Genet.* 93:1006–10

57. Gijzen M, McGregor I, Seguinswartz G. 1989. Glucosinolate uptake by developing rapeseed embryos. *Plant Physiol.* 89:260–63

58. Gil V, MacLeod AJ. 1980. The effects of pH on glucosinolate degradation by a thioglucoside glucohydrolase preparation. *Phytochemistry* 19:2547–51

59. **Glawischnig E, Hansen BG, Olsen CE, Halkier BA. 2004. Camalexin is synthesized from indole-3-acetaldoxime, a key branching point between primary and secondary metabolism in Arabidopsis. *Proc. Natl. Acad. Sci. USA* 101:8245–50**

This paper demonstrated that the crucifer indole-sulfur alkaloids, such as the *Arabidopsis* phytoalexin, camalexin, are synthesized from indole acetaldoxime, an intermediate in the indole glucosinolate pathway.

60. Glover JR, Chapple CCS, Rothwell S, Tober I, Ellis BE. 1988. Allylglucosinolate biosynthesis in *Brassica carinata*. *Phytochemistry* 27:1345–48

61. Graser G, Oldham NJ, Brown PD, Temp U, Gershenzon J. 2001. The biosynthesis of benzoic acid glucosinolate esters in *Arabidopsis thaliana*. *Phytochemistry* 57:23–32

62. Graser G, Schneider B, Oldham NJ, Gershenzon J. 2000. The methionine chain elongation pathway in the biosynthesis of glucosinolates in *Eruca sativa* (Brassicaceae). *Arch. Biochem. Biophys.* 378:411–19

63. Griffiths DW, Birch ANE, Hillman JR. 1998. Antinutritional compounds in the Brassicaceae—Analysis, biosynthesis, chemistry and dietary effects. *J. Hort. Sci. Biotech.* 73:1–18

64. Griffiths DW, Deighton N, Birch ANE, Patrian B, Baur R, Stadler E. 2001. Identification of glucosinolates on the leaf surface of plants from the Cruciferae and other closely related species. *Phytochemistry* 57:693–700

65. Grubb CD, Zipp BJ, Ludwig-Muller J, Masuno MN, Molinski TF, Abel S. 2004. Arabidopsis glucosyltransferase *UGT74B1* functions in glucosinolate biosynthesis and auxin homeostasis. *Plant J.* 40:893–908

66. Halkier BA, Hansen CH, Mikkelsen MD, Naur P, Wittstock U. 2002. The role of cytochromes P450 in biosynthesis and evolution of glucosinolates. In *Phytochemistry in the Genomics and Post-genomics Eras*, ed. JT Romeo, RA Dixon, pp. 223–48. Amsterdam: Elsevier

67. Hall C, McCallum D, Prescott A, Mithen R. 2001. Biochemical genetics of glucosinolate modification in Arabidopsis and Brassica. *Theor. Appl. Genet.* 102:369–74

68. **Hansen CH, Du LC, Naur P, Olsen CE, Axelsen KB, et al. 2001. CYP83B1 is the oxime-metabolizing enzyme in the glucosinolate pathway in Arabidopsis. *J. Biol. Chem.* 276:24790–96**

69. Hansen CH, Wittstock U, Olsen CE, Hick AJ, Pickett JA, Halkier BA. 2001. Cytochrome P450 *CYP79F1* from Arabidopsis catalyzes the conversion of dihomomethionine and trihomomethionine to the corresponding aldoximes in the biosynthesis of aliphatic glucosinolates. *J. Biol. Chem.* 276:11078–85

70. Hasapis X, MacLeod AJ. 1982. Benzylglucosinolate degradation in heat-treated *Lepidium sativum* seeds and detection of a thiocyanate-forming factor. *Phytochemistry* 21:1009–13

71. Hemm MR, Ruegger MO, Chapple C. 2003. The Arabidopsis *ref2* mutant is defective in the gene encoding *CYP83A1* and shows both phenylpropanoid and glucosinolate phenotypes. *Plant Cell* 15:179–94

72. Hirai MY, Klein M, Fujikawa Y, Yano M, Goodenowe DB, et al. 2005. Elucidation of gene-to-gene and metabolite-to-gene networks in Arabidopsis by integration of metabolomics and transcriptomics. *J. Biol. Chem.* 280:25590–95

72b. Holst B, Williamson G. 2004. A critical review of the bioavailability of glucosinolates and related compounds. *Nat. Prod. Rep.* 21:425–47

73. Hull AK, Vij R, Celenza JL. 2000. Arabidopsis cytochrome P450s that catalyze the first step of tryptophan-dependent indole-3-acetic acid biosynthesis. *Proc. Natl. Acad. Sci. USA* 97:2379–84

74. Husebye H, Chadchawan S, Winge P, Thangstad OP, Bones AM. 2002. Guard cell- and phloem idioblast-specific expression of thioglucoside glucohydrolase 1 (myrosinase) in Arabidopsis. *Plant Physiol.* 128:1180–88

75. Iqbal MCM, Moellers C. 2003. Uptake and distribution of sinigrin in microspore derived embryos of *Brassica napus* L. *J. Plant Physiol.* 160:961–66

The discovery of the role of the CYP83 family in glucosinolate biosynthesis (see also References 8 and 11) revealed a strong link to IAA formation.

76. Ishimoto H, Fukushi Y, Yoshida T, Tahara S. 2000. *Rhizopus* and *Fusarium* are selected as dominant fungal genera in rhizospheres of Brassicaceae. *J. Chem. Ecol.* 26:2387–99

77. Jones AME, Winge P, Bones AM, Cole R, Rossiter JT. 2002. Characterization and evolution of a myrosinase from the cabbage aphid *Brevicoryne brassicae. Insect Biochem. Mol. Biol.* 32:275–84

78. Jones PR, Andersen MD, Nielsen JS, Hoj PB, Moller BL. 2000. The biosynthesis, degradation, transport and possible function of cyanogenic glucosides. In *Evolution of Metabolic Pathways*, ed. JT Romeo, R Ibrahim, L Varin, pp. 191–247. Amsterdam: Elsevier

79. Kawakishi S, Kaneko T. 1987. Interaction of proteins with allyl isothiocyanate. *J. Agric. Food Chem.* 35:85–88

80. Kelly PJ, Bones A, Rossiter JT. 1998. Sub-cellular immunolocalization of the glucosinolate sinigrin in seedlings of *Brassica juncea. Planta* 206:370–77

81. Keum YS, Jeong WS, Kong ANT. 2004. Chemoprevention by isothiocyanates and their underlying molecular signaling mechanisms. *Mutat. Res. Fundam. Mol. Mech. Mutagen.* 555:191–202

82. Kiddle GA, Doughty KJ, Wallsgrove RM. 1994. Salicylic acid-induced accumulation of glucosinolates in oilseed rape (*Brassica napus* L) leaves. *J. Exp. Bot.* 45:1343–46

83. King JJ, Stimart DP, Fisher RH, Bleecker AB. 1995. A mutation altering auxin homeostasis and plant morphology in Arabidopsis. *Plant Cell* 7:2023–37

84. Kliebenstein DJ, Figuth A, Mitchell-Olds T. 2002. Genetic architecture of plastic methyl jasmonate responses in *Arabidopsis thaliana. Genetics* 161:1685–96

85. Kliebenstein DJ, Gershenzon J, Mitchell-Olds T. 2001. Comparative quantitative trait loci mapping of aliphatic, indolic and benzylic glucosinolate production in *Arabidopsis thaliana* leaves and seeds. *Genetics* 159:359–70

86. Kliebenstein DJ, Kroymann J, Brown P, Figuth A, Pedersen D, et al. 2001. Genetic control of natural variation in Arabidopsis glucosinolate accumulation. *Plant Physiol.* 126:811–25

87. Kliebenstein DJ, Lambrix VM, Reichelt M, Gershenzon J, Mitchell-Olds T. 2001. Gene duplication in the diversification of secondary metabolism: tandem 2-oxoglutarate-dependent dioxygenases control glucosinolate biosynthesis in Arabidopsis. *Plant Cell* 13:681–93

88. Koroleva OA, Davies A, Deeken R, Thorpe MR, Tomos AD, Hedrich R. 2000. Identification of a new glucosinolate-rich cell type in Arabidopsis flower stalk. *Plant Physiol.* 124:599–608

89. Kroumova AB, Wagner GJ. 2003. Different elongation pathways in the biosynthesis of acyl groups of trichome exudate sugar esters from various solanaceous plants. *Planta* 216:1013–21

90. Kroymann J, Donnerhacke S, Schnabelrauch D, Mitchell-Olds T. 2003. Evolutionary dynamics of an Arabidopsis insect resistance quantitative trait locus. *Proc. Natl. Acad. Sci. USA* 100:14587–92

91. Kroymann J, Textor S, Tokuhisa JG, Falk KL, Bartram S, et al. 2001. A gene controlling variation in Arabidopsis glucosinolate composition is part of the methionine chain elongation pathway. *Plant Physiol.* 127:1077–88

92. Krul C, Humblot C, Philippe C, Vermeulen M, van Nuenen M, et al. 2002. Metabolism of sinigrin (2-propenyl glucosinolate) by the human colonic microflora in a dynamic in vitro large-intestinal model. *Carcinogenesis* 23:1009–16

For the first time, glucosinolate accumulation was localized to a specific cell type found just outside the phloem.

93. Kutz A, Muller A, Hennig P, Kaiser WM, Piotrowski M, Weiler EW. 2002. A role for nitrilase 3 in the regulation of root morphology in sulphur-starving *Arabidopsis thaliana*. *Plant J.* 30:95–106

94. Lambrix V, Reichelt M, Mitchell-Olds T, Kliebenstein DJ, Gershenzon J. 2001. The Arabidopsis epithiospecifier protein promotes the hydrolysis of glucosinolates to nitriles and influences *Trichoplusia ni* herbivory. *Plant Cell* 13:2793–807

95. Latxague L, Gardrat C, Coustille JL, Viaud MC, Rollin P. 1991. Identification of enzymatic degradation products from synthesized glucobrassicin by gas chromatography-mass spectrometry. *J. Chromatogr.* 586:166–70

96. Lazzeri L, Curto G, Leoni O, Dallavalle E. 2004. Effects of glucosinolates and their enzymatic hydrolysis products via myrosinase on the root-knot nematode *Meloidogyne incognita* (Kofoid et White) Chitw. *J. Agric. Food Chem.* 52:6703–7

97. Lee C-J, Serif GS. 1970. Precursor role of [^{14}C, ^{15}N]-2-amino-6-(methylthio)caproic acid in progoitrin biosynthesis. *Biochemistry* 9:2068–71

98. Lehman A, Black R, Ecker JR. 1996. *HOOKLESS1*, an ethylene response gene, is required for differential cell elongation in the *Arabidopsis* hypocotyl. *Cell* 85:183–94

99. Lenman M, Falk A, Roedin J, Hoeglund A-S, Ek B, Rask L. 1993. Differential expression of myrosinase gene families. *Plant Physiol.* 103:703–11

100. Li G, Riaz A, Goyal S, Abel S, Quiros CF. 2001. Inheritance of three major genes involved in the synthesis of aliphatic glucosinolates in *Brassica oleracea*. *J. Am. Soc. Hortic. Sci.* 126:427–31

101. Li Q, Eigenbrode SD, Stringam GR, Thiagarajah MR. 2000. Feeding and growth of *Plutella xylostella* and *Spodoptera eridania* on *Brassica juncea* with varying glucosinolate concentrations and myrosinase activities. *J. Chem. Ecol.* 26:2401–19

102. Li Y, Kiddle GA, Bennett RN, Wallsgrove RM. 1999. Local and systemic changes in glucosinolates in Chinese and European cultivars of oilseed rape (*Brassica napus*) after inoculation with *Sclerotinia sclerotiorum* (stem rot). *Ann. Appl. Biol.* 134:45–58

103. Ljung K, Hull AK, Celenza JL, Yamada M, Estelle M, et al. 2005. Sites and regulation of auxin biosynthesis in Arabidopsis roots. *Plant Cell* 17:1090–104

104. Louda S, Mole S. 1991. Glucosinolates: chemistry and ecology. In *Herbivores, Their Interactions with Secondary Plant Metabolites*, ed. GA Rosenthal, MR Berenbaum, pp. 123–64. San Diego: Academic

105. Ludwig-Muller J, Hilgenberg W. 1988. A plasma membrane-bound enzyme oxidizes L-tryptophan to indole-3-acetaldoxime. *Physiol. Plant.* 74:240–50

106. Ludwig-Muller J, Rausch T, Langa S, Hilgenberg W. 1990. Plasma membrane bound high pI peroxidase isoenzymes convert tryptophan to indole-3-acetaldoxime. *Phytochemistry* 29:1397–400

107. Lund E. 2003. Non-nutritive bioactive constituents of plants: dietary sources and health benefits of glucosinolates. *Int. J. Vitam. Nutr. Res.* 73:135–43

108. Luthy B, Matile P. 1984. The mustard oil bomb: rectified analysis of the subcellular organization of the myrosinase system. *Biochem. Physiol. Pflanz.* 179:5–12

109. MacLeod AJ, Rossiter JT. 1985. The occurence and activity of epithiospecifier protein in some Cruciferae seeds. *Phytochemistry* 24:1895–98

110. MacLeod AJ, Rossiter JT. 1986. Isolation and examination of thioglucoside glucohydrolase from seeds of *Brassica napus*. *Phytochemistry* 25:1047–52

111. Magrath R, Bano F, Parkin I, Sharpe A, Lister C, et al. 1994. Genetics of aliphatic glucosinolates. I. Side chain elongation in *Brassica napus* and *Arabidopsis thaliana*. *Heredity* 72:290–99

The first nonmyrosinase gene encoding a protein involved in glucosinolate hydrolysis is reported in this paper.

112. Marazzi C, Stadler E. 2004. *Arabidopsis thaliana* leaf-surface extracts are detected by the cabbage root fly (*Delia radicum*) and stimulate oviposition. *Physiol. Entomol.* 29:192–98

113. Mari M, Leoni O, Iori R, Cembali T. 2002. Antifungal vapour-phase activity of allyl-isothiocyanate against *Penicillium expansum* on pears. *Plant Pathol.* 51:231–36

114. Merritt SZ. 1996. Within-plant variation in concentrations of amino acids, sugar, and sinigrin in phloem sap of black mustard, *Brassica nigra* (L) Koch (Cruciferae). *J. Chem. Ecol.* 22:1133–45

115. Mewis I, Apple HM, Hom A, Raina R, Schultz JC. 2005. Major signaling pathways modulate Arabidopsis glucosinolate accumulation and response to both phloem-feeding and chewing insects. *Plant Physiol.* 138:1149–62

116. Mewis IZ, Ulrich C, Schnitzler WH. 2002. The role of glucosinolates and their hydrolysis products in oviposition and host-plant finding by cabbage webworm, *Hellula undalis*. *Entomol. Exp. Appl.* 105:129–39

117. Mikkelsen MD, Hansen CH, Wittstock U, Halkier BA. 2000. Cytochrome P450 *CYP79B2* from Arabidopsis catalyzes the conversion of tryptophan to indole-3-acetaldoxime, a precursor of indole glucosinolates and indole-3-acetic acid. *J. Biol. Chem.* 275:33712–17

118. Mikkelsen MD, Naur P, Halkier BA. 2004. Arabidopsis mutants in the C-S lyase of glucosinolate biosynthesis establish a critical role for indole-3-acetaldoxime in auxin homeostasis. *Plant J.* 37:770–77

119. Mikkelsen MD, Petersen BL, Glawischnig E, Jensen AB, Andreasson E, Halkier BA. 2003. Modulation of *CYP79* genes and glucosinolate profiles in Arabidopsis by defense signaling pathways. *Plant Physiol.* 131:298–308

120. Mikkelsen MD, Petersen BL, Olsen CE, Halkier BA. 2002. Biosynthesis and metabolic engineering of glucosinolates. *Amino Acids* 22:279–95

121. Miles CI, del Campo M, Renwick JAA. 2005. Behavioral and chemosensory responses to a host recognition cue by larvae of *Pieris rapae*. *J. Comp. Phys. A* 191:147–55

122. Mithen R, Campos H. 1996. Genetic variation of aliphatic glucosinolates in *Arabidopsis thaliana* and prospects for map based gene cloning. *Entomol. Exp. Appl.* 80:202–5

123. Mithen R, Clarke J, Lister C, Dean C. 1995. Genetics of aliphatic glucosinolates. 3. Side chain structure of aliphatic glucosinolates in *Arabidopsis thaliana*. 74:210–15

124. Mueller C, Agerbirk N, Olsen CE. 2003. Lack of sequestration of host plant glucosinolates in *Pieris rapae* and *P. brassicae*. *Chemoecology* 13:47–54

125. Mueller C, Agerbirk N, Olsen CE, Boeve JL, Schaffner U, Brakefield PM. 2001. Sequestration of host plant glucosinolates in the defensive hemolymph of the sawfly *Athalia rosae*. *J. Chem. Ecol.* 27:2505–16

126. Mueller C, Boeve JL, Brakefield P. 2002. Host plant derived feeding deterrence towards ants in the turnip sawfly *Athalia rosae*. *Entomol. Exp. Appl.* 104:153–57

127. Deleted in proof

128. Naur P, Petersen BL, Mikkelsen MD, Bak S, Rasmussen H, et al. 2003. *CYP83A1* and *CYP83B1*, two nonredundant cytochrome P450 enzymes metabolizing oximes in the biosynthesis of glucosinolates in Arabidopsis. *Plant Physiol.* 133:67–72

129. Nielsen JK, Hansen ML, Agerbirk N, Petersen BL, Halkier BA. 2001. Responses of the flea beetles *Phyllotreta nemorum* and *P. cruciferae* to metabolically engineered *Arabidopsis thaliana* with an altered glucosinolate profile. *Chemoecology* 11:75–83

130. Nielsen KA, Møller BL. 2005. Cytochrome P450s in plants. In *Cytochrome P450: Structure, Mechanism, and Biochemistry*, ed. P Ortiz de Montellano, pp. 553–83. Kluwer Academic/Plenum

For the first time, the sequestration of glucosinolates by a herbivore for its own defense was reported.

131. Noret N, Mccrts P, Poschenrieder C, Barcelo J, Escarre J. 2005. Palatability of *Thlaspi caerulescens* for snails: influence of zinc and glucosinolates. *New Phytol.* 165:763–72

132. Parkin I, Magrath R, Keith D, Sharpe A, Mithen R, Lydiate D. 1994. Genetics of aliphatic glucosinolates. II. Hydroxylation of alkenyl glucosinolates in *Brassica napus. Heredity* 72:594–98

133. Pedras MSC, Montaut S, Xu Y, Khan AQ, Loukaci A. 2001. Assembling the biosynthetic puzzle of crucifer metabolites: Indole-3-acetaldoxime is incorporated efficiently into phytoalexins but glucobrassicin is not. *Chem. Comm.* 17:1572–73

134. Pedras MSC, Nycholat CM, Montaut S, Xu YM, Khan AQ. 2002. Chemical defenses of crucifers: elicitation and metabolism of phytoalexins and indole-3-acetonitrile in brown mustard and turnip. *Phytochemistry* 59:611–25

135. Petersen BL, Chen SX, Hansen CH, Olsen CE, Halkier BA. 2002. Composition and content of glucosinolates in developing *Arabidopsis thaliana. Planta* 214:562–71

136. Piotrowski M, Schemenewitz A, Lopukhinat A, Mueller A, Janowitz T, et al. 2004. Desulfoglucosinolate sulfotransferases from *Arabidopsis thaliana* catalyze the final step in the biosynthesis of the glucosinolate core structure. *J. Biol. Chem.* 279:50717–25

137. Pontoppidan B, Hopkins R, Rask L, Meijer J. 2003. Infestation by cabbage aphid (*Brevicoryne brassicae*) on oilseed rape (*Brassica napus*) causes a long lasting induction of the myrosinase system. *Entomol. Exp. Appl.* 109:55–62

138. Pontoppidan B, Hopkins R, Rask L, Meijer J. 2005. Differential wound induction of the myrosinase system in oilseed rape (*Brassica napus*): contrasting insect damage with mechanical damage. *Plant Sci.* 168:715–22

139. Prescott AG, John P. 1996. Dioxygenases-molecular structure and role in plant metabolism. *Annu. Rev. Plant Physiol. Plant Mol. Biol.* 47:245–71

140. Rask L, Andreasson E, Ekbom B, Eriksson S, Pontoppidan B, Meijer J. 2000. Myrosinase: gene family evolution and herbivore defense in Brassicaceae. *Plant Mol. Biol.* 42:93–113

141. Ratzka A, Vogel H, Kliebenstein DJ, Mitchell-Olds T, Kroymann J. 2002. Disarming the mustard oil bomb. *Proc. Natl. Acad. Sci. USA* 99:11223–28

142. Reddy GVP, Guerrero A. 2000. Behavioral responses of the diamondback moth, *Plutella xylostella*, to green leaf volatiles of *Brassica oleracea* subsp. *capitata. J. Agric. Food Chem.* 48:6025–29

143. Reintanz B, Lehnen M, Reichelt M, Gershenzon J, Kowalczyk M, et al. 2001. *Bus*, a bushy Arabidopsis *CYP79F1* knockout mutant with abolished synthesis of short-chain aliphatic glucosinolates. *Plant Cell* 13:351–67

144. Rodman JE, Karol KG, Price RA, Sytsma KJ. 1996. Molecules, morphology, and Dahlgrens expanded order Capparales. *Syst. Bot.* 21:289–307

145. Rojas JC. 1999. Electrophysiological and behavioral responses of the cabbage moth to plant volatiles. *J. Chem. Ecol.* 25:1867–83

146. Rouzaud G, Young SA, Duncan AJ. 2004. Hydrolysis of glucosinolates to isothiocyanates after ingestion of raw or microwaved cabbage by human volunteers. *Cancer Epidemiol. Biomarkers Prev.* 13:125–31

147. Sarwar M, Kirkegaard JA, Wong PTW, Desmarchelier JM. 1998. Biofumigation potential of Brassicas - III. In vitro toxicity of isothiocyanates to soil-borne fungal pathogens. *Plant Soil* 201:103–12

148. Smith BJ, Kirkegaard JA. 2002. In vitro inhibition of soil microorganisms by 2-phenylethyl isothiocyanate. *Plant Pathol.* 51:585–93

149. Smolen G, Bender J. 2002. Arabidopsis cytochrome p450 *cyp83B1* mutations activate the tryptophan biosynthetic pathway. *Genetics* 160:323–32

150. Tantikanjana T, Yong JWH, Letham DS, Griffith M, Hussain M, et al. 2001. Control of axillary bud initiation and shoot architecture in Arabidopsis through the *SUPERSHOOT* gene. *Genes Dev.* 15:1577–88

151. Tattersall DB, Bak S, Jones PR, Olsen CE, Nielsen JK, et al. 2001. Resistance to an herbivore through engineered cyanogenic glucoside synthesis. *Science* 293:1826–28

152. Textor S, Bartram S, Kroymann J, Falk KL, Hick A, et al. 2004. Biosynthesis of methionine-derived glucosinolates in *Arabidopsis thaliana*: recombinant expression and characterization of methylthioalkylmalate synthase, the condensing enzyme of the chain-elongation cycle. *Planta* 218:1026–35

153. Thangstad OP, Bones AM. 2001. Microautoradiographic localisation of a glucosinolate precursor to specific cells in *Brassica napus* L. embryos indicates a separate transport pathway into myrosin cells. *Planta* 213:207–13

154. Thangstad OP, Gilde B, Chadchawan S, Seem M, Husebye H, et al. 2004. Cell specific, cross-species expression of myrosinases in *Brassica napus*, *Arabidopsis thaliana* and *Nicotiana tabacum*. *Plant Mol. Biol.* 54:597–611

155. Thornalley PJ. 2002. Isothiocyanates: mechanism of cancer chemopreventive action. *Anti-Cancer Drugs* 13:331–38

156. **Tierens K, Thomma BPH, Brouwer M, Schmidt J, Kistner K, et al. 2001. Study of the role of antimicrobial glucosinolate-derived isothiocyanates in resistance of Arabidopsis to microbial pathogens. *Plant Physiol.* 125:1688–99**

157. Tookey HL. 1973. Crambe thioglucoside glucohydrolase (EC 3.2.3.1): separation of a protein required for epithiobutane formation. *Can. J. Biochem.* 51:1654–60

158. Toroser D, Griffiths H, Wood C, Thomas DR. 1995. Biosynthesis and partitioning of individual glucosinolates between pod walls and seeds and evidence for the occurrence of PAPS:desulphoglucosinolate sulphotransferase in seeds of oilseed rape (*Brassica napus* L.). *J. Exp. Bot.* 46:1753–60

159. Toroser D, Thormann CE, Osborn TC, Mithen R. 1995. RFLP mapping of quantitative trait loci controlling seed aliphatic-glucosinolate content in oilseed rape (*Brassica napus* L.). *Theor. Appl. Genet.* 91:802–8

160. Traw MB. 2002. Is induction response negatively correlated with constitutive resistance in black mustard? *Evolution* 56:2196–205

161. Ulmer B, Gillott C, Erlandson M. 2001. Feeding preferences, growth, and development of *Mamestra configurata* (Lepidoptera: Noctuidae) on Brassicaceae. *Can. Entomol.* 133:509–19

162. Uzunova M, Ecke W, Weissleder K, Robbelen G. 1995. Mapping the genome of rapeseed (*Brassica napus* L).1. Construction of an RFLP linkage map and localization of QTLS for seed glucosinolate content. *Theor. Appl. Genet.* 90:194–204

163. van Dam NM, Raaijmakers CE, van der Putten WH. 2005. Root herbivory reduces growth and survival of the shoot feeding specialist *Pieris rapae* on *Brassica nigra*. *Entomol. Exp. Appl.* 115:161–70

164. Vaughn SF, Isbell TA, Weisleder D, Berhow MA. 2005. Biofumigant compounds released by field pennycress (*Thlaspi arvense*) seedmeal. *J. Chem. Ecol.* 31:167–77

165. Vlieger L, Brakefield PM, Muller C. 2004. Effectiveness of the defence mechanism of the turnip sawfly, *Athalia rosae* (Hymenoptera : Tenthredinidae), against predation by lizards. *Bull. Entomol. Res.* 94:283–89

166. Wetter LR, Chisholm MD. 1968. Sources of sulfur in thioglucosides of various higher plants. *Can. J. Biochem.* 46:931–35

Using a mutant with a modified glucosinolate profile, this paper presents the best evidence to date that glucosinolates have a role in defense against some pathogens.

167. Wittstock U, Agerbirk N, Stauber EJ, Olsen CE, Hippler M, et al. 2004. Successful herbivore attack due to metabolic diversion of a plant chemical defense. *Proc. Natl. Acad. Sci. USA* 101:4859–64

168. Wittstock U, Halkier BA. 2000. Cytochrome P450 *CYP79A2* from *Arabidopsis thaliana* L. catalyzes the conversion of L-phenylalanine to phenylacetaldoxime in the biosynthesis of benzylglucosinolate. *J. Biol. Chem.* 275:14659–66

169. Wittstock U, Halkier BA. 2002. Glucosinolate research in the Arabidopsis era. *Trends Plant Sci.* 7:263–70

170. Wittstock U, Kliebenstein DJ, Lambrix VM, Reichelt M, Gershenzon J. 2003. Glucosinolate hydrolysis and its impact on generalist and specialist insect herbivores. In *Integrative Phytochemistry: from Ethnobotany to Molecular Ecology*, ed. JT Romeo, pp. 101–25. Amsterdam: Elsevier

171. Xu Z, Escamilla-Trevino LL, Zeng L, Lalgondar M, Bevan DR, et al. 2004. Functional genomic analysis of *Arabidopsis thaliana* glycoside hydrolase family 1. *Plant Mol. Biol.* 55:343–67

172. Xue J, Pihlgren U, Rask L. 1993. Temporal, cell-specific, and tissue-preferential expression of myrosinase genes during embryo and seedling development in *Sinapis alba*. *Planta* 191:95–101

173. Xue JP, Jorgensen M, Pihlgren U, Rask L. 1995. The myrosinase gene family in *Arabidopsis thaliana* - gene organization, expression and evolution. *Plant Mol. Biol.* 27:911–22

174. Zasada IA, Ferris H. 2004. Nematode suppression with Brassicaceous amendments: application based upon glucosinolate profiles. *Soil Biol. Biochem.* 36:1017–24

175. Zeng RS, Mallik AU, Setliff E. 2003. Growth stimulation of ectomycorrhizal fungi by root exudates of Brassicaceae plants: Role of degraded compounds of indole glucosinolates. *J. Chem. Ecol* 29:1337–55

176. Zhang Y, Talalay P, Cho C-G, Posner GH. 1992. A major inducer of anticarcinogenic protective enzymes from broccoli: isolation and elucidation of structure. *Proc. Natl. Acad. Sci. USA* 89:2399–403

177. Zhao Y, Christensen SK, Fankhauser C, Cashman JR, Cohen JD, et al. 2001. A role for flavin monooxygenase-like enzymes in auxin biosynthesis. *Science* 291:306–9

178. Zhao Y, Hull AK, Gupta NR, Goss KA, Alonso J, et al. 2002. Trp-dependent auxin biosynthesis in Arabidopsis: involvement of cytochrome P450s *CYP79B2* and *CYP79B3*. *Genes Dev.* 16:3100–12

This was the first characterization of a member of the *Arabidopsis* CYP79 family, the cytochromes P450 catalyzing the oxidation of amino acids to aldoximes.

RELATED RESOURCES

Benveniste P. 2004. Biosynthesis and accumulation of sterols. *Annu. Rev. Plant Biol.* 55:429–57

Dixon RA. 2004. Phytoestrogens. *Annu. Rev. Plant Biol.* 55:225–61

Glazebrook J. 2005. Contrasting mechanisms of defense against biotrophic and necrotrophic pathogens. *Annu. Rev. Phytopathol.* 43:205–27

Schuler MA, Werck-Reichart D. 2003. Functional genomics of P450s. *Annu. Rev. Plant Biol.* 54:629–67

Winkel BSJ. 2004. Metabolic channeling in plants. *Annu. Rev. Plant Biol.* 55:85–107

Bioinformatics and Its Applications in Plant Biology

Seung Yon Rhee,[1] Julie Dickerson,[2] and Dong Xu[3]

[1] Department of Plant Biology, Carnegie Institution, Stanford, California 94305; email: rhee@acoma.stanford.edu

[2] Baker Center for Computational Biology, Electrical and Computer Engineering, Iowa State University, Ames, Iowa 50011-3060; email: julied@iastate.edu

[3] Digital Biology Laboratory, Computer Science Department and Life Sciences Center, University of Missouri-Columbia, Columbia, Missouri 65211-2060; email: xudong@missouri.edu

Annu. Rev. Plant Biol.
2006. 57:335–60

The *Annual Review of Plant Biology* is online at
plant.annualreviews.org

doi: 10.1146/
annurev.arplant.56.032604.144103

First published online as a
Review in Advance on
February 28, 2006

1543-5008/06/0602-
0335$20.00

Key Words

sequence analysis, computational proteomics, microarray data analysis, bio-ontology, biological database

Abstract

Bioinformatics plays an essential role in today's plant science. As the amount of data grows exponentially, there is a parallel growth in the demand for tools and methods in data management, visualization, integration, analysis, modeling, and prediction. At the same time, many researchers in biology are unfamiliar with available bioinformatics methods, tools, and databases, which could lead to missed opportunities or misinterpretation of the information. In this review, we describe some of the key concepts, methods, software packages, and databases used in bioinformatics, with an emphasis on those relevant to plant science. We also cover some fundamental issues related to biological sequence analyses, transcriptome analyses, computational proteomics, computational metabolomics, bio-ontologies, and biological databases. Finally, we explore a few emerging research topics in bioinformatics.

Contents

INTRODUCTION

Recent developments in technologies and instrumentation, which allow large-scale as well as nano-scale probing of biological samples, are generating an unprecedented amount of digital data. This sea of data is too much for the human brain to process and thus there is an increasing need to use computational methods to process and contextualize these data.

Bioinformatics refers to the study of biological information using concepts and methods in computer science, statistics, and engineering. It can be divided into two categories: biological information management and computational biology. The National Institutes of Health (NIH) (**http://www.bisti.nih.gov/**) defines the former category as "research, development, or application of computational tools and approaches for expanding the use of biological, medical, behavioral or health data, including those to acquire, represent, describe, store, analyze, or visualize such data." The latter category is defined as "the development and application of data-analytical and theoretical methods, mathematical modeling, and computational simulation techniques to the study of biological, behavioral, and social systems." The boundaries of these categories are becoming more diffuse and other categories will no doubt surface in the future as this field matures.

The intention of this article is not to provide an exhaustive summary of all the advances made in bioinformatics. Rather, we describe some of the key concepts, methods, and tools used in this field, particularly those relevant to plant science, and their current limitations and opportunities for new development and improvement. The first section introduces sequence-based analyses, including gene finding, gene family and phylogenetic analyses, and comparative genomics approaches. The second section presents computational transcriptome analysis, ranging from analyses of various array technologies to regulatory sequence prediction. In section three, we focus on computational proteomics, including gel analysis and protein identification from mass-spectrometry data. Section four describes computational metabolomics. Section five introduces biological ontologies and their applications. Section six addresses various issues related to biological databases ranging from database development to curation. In section seven, we discuss a few emerging research topics in bioinformatics.

SEQUENCE ANALYSIS

Biological sequence such as DNA, RNA, and protein sequence is the most fundamental object for a biological system at the molecular level. Several genomes have been sequenced to a high quality in plants, including *Arabidopsis thaliana* (130) and rice (52, 147, 148). Draft genome sequences are available for poplar (**http://genome.jgi-psf.org/Poptr1/**) and lotus (**http://www.kazusa.or.jp/lotus/**), and sequencing efforts are in progress for several others including tomato, maize, *Medicago truncatula*, sorghum (11) and close relatives of *Arabidopsis thaliana*. Researchers also generated expressed sequence tags (ESTs) from many plants including lotus, beet, soybean, cotton, wheat, and sorghum (see **http://www.ncbi.nlm.nih.gov/dbEST/**).

Genome Sequencing

Advances in sequencing technologies provide opportunities in bioinformatics for managing, processing, and analyzing the sequences. Shotgun sequencing is currently the most common method in genome sequencing: pieces of DNA are sheared randomly, cloned, and sequenced in parallel. Software has been developed to piece together the random, overlapping segments that are sequenced separately into a coherent and accurate contiguous sequence (93). Numerous software packages exist for sequence assembly (51), including Phred/Phrap/Consed (**http://www.phrap.org**), Arachne (**http://www.broad.mit.edu/wga/**), and GAP4 (**http://staden.sourceforge.net/overview.html**). TIGR developed a modular, open-source package called AMOS (**http://www.tigr.org/software/AMOS/**), which can be used for comparative genome assembly (102). Current limitations in shotgun sequencing and assembly software remain largely in the assembly of highly repetitive sequences, although the cost of sequencing is another limitation. Recently developed methods continue to reduce the cost of sequencing, including sequencing by using differential hybridization of oligonucleotide probes (48, 62, 101), polymorphism ratio sequencing (16), four-color DNA sequencing by synthesis on a chip (114), and the "454 method" based on microfabricated high-density picoliter reactors (87). Each of these sequencing technologies has significant analytical challenges for bioinformatics in terms of experimental design, data interpretation, and analysis of the data in conjunction with other data (33).

Gene Finding and Genome Annotation

Gene finding refers to prediction of introns and exons in a segment of DNA sequence. Dozens of computer programs for identifying protein-coding genes are available (150). Some of the well-known ones include Genscan (**http://genes.mit.edu/GENSCAN.html**), GeneMarkHMM (**http://opal.biology.gatech.edu/GeneMark/**), GRAIL (**http://compbio.ornl.gov/Grail-1.3/**), Genie (**http://www.fruitfly.org/seq_tools/genie.html**), and Glimmer (**http://www.tigr.org/softlab/glimmer**). Several new gene-finding tools are tailored for applications to plant genomic sequences (112).

Ab initio gene prediction remains a challenging problem, especially for large-sized eukaryotic genomes. For a typical *Arabidopsis thaliana* gene with five exons, at least one exon is expected to have at least one of its borders predicted incorrectly by the ab initio approach (19). Transcript evidence from full-length cDNA or EST sequences or similarity to potential protein homologs can significantly reduce uncertainty of gene identification (154). Such methods are widely used in "structural annotation" of genomes, which refers to the identification of features such as genes and transposons in a genomic sequence using ab initio algorithms and other information. Several software packages have been developed for structural annotation (3, 45, 57, 66). In addition, one can use genome comparison tools such as SynBrowse (**http://www.synbrowser.org/**) and VISTA (**http://genome.lbl.gov/vista/index.shtml**) to enhance the accuracy of gene identification. Current limitations of structural annotation include accurate prediction of transcript start sites and identification of small genes encoding less than 100 amino acids, noncoding genes (such as microRNA precursors), and alternative splicing sites.

An important aspect of genome annotation is the analysis of repetitive DNAs, which are copies of identical or nearly identical sequences present in the genome (78). Repetitive sequences exist in almost any genome, and are abundant in most plant genomes (69). The identification and characterization of repeats is crucial to shed light on the evolution, function and organization of genomes and to enable filtering for many types of homology searches. A small library of plant-specific repeats can be found at **ftp://ftp.tigr.org/pub/data/TIGR_Plant_Repeats/**; this is likely to grow substantially as more genomes are sequenced. One can use Repeat-Masker (**http://www.repeatmasker.org/**) to search repetitive sequences in a genome. Working from a library of known repeats, RepeatMasker is built upon BLAST and can screen DNA sequences for interspersed repeats and low complexity regions. Repeats with poorly conserved patterns or short sequences are hard to identify using Repeat-Masker due to the limitations of BLAST. To identify novel repeats, various algorithms were developed. Some widely used tools include RepeatFinder (**http://ser-loopp.tc.cornell.edu/cbsu/repeatfinder.htm**) and RECON (**http://www.genetics.wustl.edu/eddy/recon/**). However, due to the high computational complexity of the problem, none of the programs can guarantee finding all possible repeats as all the programs use some approximations in computation, which will miss some repeats with less distinctive patterns. Inevitably, a combination of repeat finding tools is required to obtain a satisfactory overview of repeats found in an organism.

Sequence Comparison

Comparing sequences provides a foundation for many bioinformatics tools and may allow inference of the function, structure, and evolution of genes and genomes. For example, sequence comparison provides a basis for building a consensus gene model like UniGene (18). Also, many computational methods have been developed for homology identification (136). Although sequence comparison is highly useful, it should be noted that it is based on sequence similarity between two strings of text, which may not correspond to homology (relatedness to a common ancestor in evolution), especially when the confidence level of a comparison result is low. Also, homology may not mean conservation in function.

Methods in sequence comparison can be largely grouped into pair-wise, sequence-profile, and profile-profile comparison. For pair-wise sequence comparison, FASTA (**http://fasta.bioch.virginia.edu/**) and BLAST (**http://www.ncbi.nlm.nih.gov/blast/**) are popular. To assess the confidence level for an alignment to represent homologous relationship, a statistical measure (Expectation Value) was integrated into pair-wise sequence alignments (71). Remote homologous relationships are often missed by pair-wise sequence alignment due to its insensitivity. Sequence-profile alignment is more sensitive for detecting remote homologs. A protein sequence profile is generated by multiple sequence alignment of a group of closely related proteins. A multiple sequence alignment builds correspondence among residues across all of the sequences simultaneously, where aligned positions in different sequences probably show functional and/or structural relationship. A sequence profile is calculated using the probability of occurrence for each amino acid at each alignment position. PSI-BLAST (**http://www. ncbi.nlm.nih.gov/BLAST/**) is a popular example of a sequence-profile alignment tool. Some other sequence-profile comparison methods are slower but even more accurate than PSI-BLAST, including HMMER (**http://hmmer.wustl.edu/**), SAM (**http:// www.cse.ucsc.edu/research/compbio/sam. html**), and META-MEME (**http://met ameme.sdsc.edu/**). A profile-profile alignment is more sensitive than the sequence-profile-based search programs in detecting remote homologs (146). However, due to its high false positive rate, profile-profile comparison is not widely used. Given potential false positive predictions, it is helpful to correlate the sequence comparison results with the relationship observed in functional genomic data, especially the widely available microarray data as discussed in the section Transcriptome Analysis below. For example, when a gene is predicted to have a particular function through sequence comparison, one can gain confidence in the prediction if the gene has strong correlation in gene expression profile with other genes known to have the same function.

Proteins can be generally classified based on sequence, structure, or function. Several sequence-based methods were developed based on sizable protein sequence (typically longer than 100 amino acids), including Pfam (**http://pfam.wustl.edu/**), ProDom (**http:// protein.toulouse.inra.fr/prodom/current/ html/home.php**), and Clusters of Orthologous Group (COG) (**http://www.ncbi. nlm.nih.gov/COG/new/**). Other methods are based on "fingerprints" of small conserved motifs in sequences, as with PROSITE (**http://au.expasy.org/prosite/**), PRINTS (**http://umber.sbs.man.ac.uk/dbbrowser/ PRINTS/**), and BLOCKS (**http://www.psc. edu/general/software/packages/blocks/blo cks.html**). The false positive rate of motif assignment is high due to high probability of matching short motifs in unrelated proteins by chance. Other sequence-based protein family databases are built from multiple sources. InterPro (**http://www.ebi.ac.uk/ interpro/**) is a database that integrates domain information from multiple protein domain databases. Using protein family information to predict gene function is more reliable than using sequence comparison alone. On the other hand, very closely related proteins may not guarantee a functional relationship (97). One can use structure- or function-based protein families (when available) to complement sequence-based family for additional function information. SCOP (**http://scop.mrc-lmb.cam.ac.uk/ scop/**) and CATH (**http://cathwww.bio chem.ucl.ac.uk/**) are the two well-known structure-based family resources. ENZYME (**http://us.expasy.org/enzyme/**) is a typical example of a function family.

A protein family can be represented in a phylogenetic tree that shows the evolutionary relationships among proteins. Phylogenetic analysis can be used in comparative genomics, gene function prediction, and inference of lateral gene transfer among other things (36). The analysis typically starts from aligning the related proteins using tools like ClustalW (**http://bips.u-strasbg.fr/fr/ Documentation/ClustalX/**). Among the popular methods to build phylogenetic trees are minimum distance (also called neighbor joining), maximum parsimony, and maximum likelihood trees (reviewed in 31). Some programs provide options to use any of the three methods, e.g., the two widely used packages PAUP (**http://paup.csit.fsu.edu**), and PHYLIP (**http://evolution.genetics. washington.edu/phylip.html**). Although phylogenetic analysis is a research topic with a long history and many methods have been developed, various heuristics and approximations are used in constructing a phylogenetic tree, as the exact methods are too computationally intense. Hence, different methods sometimes produce significantly different phylogenetic trees. Manual assessment of different results is generally required.

TRANSCRIPTOME ANALYSIS

The primary goal of transcriptome analysis is to learn about how changes in transcript abundance control growth and development of an organism and its response to the environment. DNA microarrays proved a powerful technology for observing the transcriptional profile of genes at a genome-wide level (22, 111). Microarray data are also being combined with other information such as regulatory sequence analysis, gene ontology, and pathway information to infer coregulated processes. Whole-genome tiled arrays are used to detect transcription without bias toward known or predicted gene structures and alternative splice variants. Other types of analysis include ChIP-chip [chromatin immunoprecipitation (ChIP) and microarray analysis (chip)] analysis, which combines microarrays with methods for detecting the chromosomal locations at which protein-DNA interactions occur across the genome (23). A related technique uses DNA immunoprecipitation (DIP-chip) to predict DNA-binding sites (80). This review does not cover all available technologies for measuring expression data such as tag-based transcriptional profiling technologies like massively parallel signature sequencing (MPSS) and SAGE (20, 28).

Microarray Analysis

Microarray analysis allows the simultaneous measurement of transcript abundance for thousands of genes (153). Two general types of microarrays are high-density oligonucleotide arrays that contain a large number (thousands or often millions) of relatively short (25–100-mer) probes synthesized directly on the surface of the arrays, or arrays with amplified polymerase chain reaction products or cloned DNA fragments mechanically spotted directly on the array surface. Many different technologies are being developed, which have been recently surveyed by Meyers and colleagues (89). Competition among microarray platforms has led to lower costs and increased numbers of genes per array. Unfortunately, the diversity of array platforms makes it difficult to compare results between microarray formats that use different probe sequences, RNA sample labeling, and data collection methods (142).

Other important issues in microarray analysis are in processing and normalizing data. Some journals require multiple biological replicates (typically at least three) and statistically valid results before publishing microarray results. Replication of the microarray experiment and appropriate statistical design are needed to minimize the false discovery rate. The microarray data must also be deposited into a permanent public repository with open access. A good overview of microarray data analysis can be found in References 37 and 118. The main difficulty of dealing with microarray data is the sheer amount of data resulting from a single experiment. This makes it very difficult to decide which transcripts to focus on for interpreting the results. Even for standardized arrays such as those from Affymetrix, there are still arguments on the optimal statistical treatment for the sets of probes designed for each gene. For example, the *Affycomp* software compares Affymetrix results using two spike-in experiments and a dilution experiment for different methods of normalization under different assessment criteria (27). This information can be used to select the appropriate normalization methods.

Many tools are available that perform a variety of analysis on large microarray data sets. Examples include commercial software such as Gene Traffic, GeneSpring (**http://www.agilent.com/chem/genespring**), Affymetrix's GeneChip Operating Software (GCOS), and public software such as Cluster (41), CaARRAY (**http://caarray.nci.nih.gov/**), and BASE (109). A notable example is Bioconductor (**http://www.bioconductor.org**), which is an open-source and open-development set of routines written for the open-source R statistical analysis package (**http://www.r-project.org**).

Observing the patterns of transcriptional activity that occur under different conditions such as genotypes or time courses reveals genes that have highly correlated patterns of expression. However, correlation cannot distinguish between genes that are under common regulatory control and those whose expression patterns just happen to correlate. Recent efforts in microarray analysis have focused on analysis of microarray data across experiments (91). A study by the Toxicogenomics research consortium indicates that "microarray results can be comparable across multiple laboratories, especially when a common platform and set of procedures are used" (7). Meta-analysis can investigate the effect of the same treatment across different studies to arrive at a single estimate of the true effect of the treatment (106, 123).

Tiling Arrays

Typical microarray sample known and predicted genes. Tiling arrays cover the genome at regular intervals to measure transcription without bias toward known or predicted gene structures, discovery of polymorphisms, analysis of alternative splicing, and identification of transcription factor-binding sites (90). Whole-genome arrays (WGAs) cover the entire genome with overlapping probes or probes with regular gaps. The WGA ensures that the experimental results are not dependent on the level of current genome annotation as well as discovering new transcripts and unusual forms of transcription. In plants, similar studies have been performed for the entire *Arabidopsis* genome (127, 143) and parts of the rice genome (70, 79). These studies identified thousands of novel transcription units including genes within the centromeres, substantial antisense gene transcription, and transcription activity in intergenic regions. Tiling array data may also be used to validate predicted intron/exon boundaries (132).

Further work is needed to establish the best practices for determining when transcription has occurred and how to normalize array data across the different chips. Visualization of the output from tiling arrays requires viewing the probe sequences on the array together with the sequence assembly and the probe expression data. The *Arabidopsis* Tiling Array Transcriptome Express Tool (also known as ChipViewer) (**http://signal.salk.edu/cgi-bin/atta**) displays information about what type of transcription occurred along the *Arabidopsis* genome (143). Another tool is the Integrated Genome Browser (IGB) from Affymetrix, a Java program for exploring genomes and combining annotations from multiple data sources. Another option for visualizing such data are collaborations such as those between Gramene (137) and PLEXdb (116), which allow users to overlay probe array information onto a comparative sequence viewer.

The major limitations of WGAs include the requirement of a sequenced genome, the large number of chips required for complete genome coverage, and analysis of recently duplicated (and thus highly homologous) genes.

Regulatory Sequence Analysis

Interpreting the results of microarray experiments involves discovering why genes with similar expression profiles behave in a coordinated fashion. Regulatory sequence analysis approaches this question by extracting motifs that are shared between the upstream sequences of these genes (134). Comparative genomics studies of conserved noncoding sequences (CNSs) may also help to find key motifs (56, 67). There are several methods to search over-represented motifs at the upstream of coregulated genes. Roughly they can be categorized into two classes: oligonucleotide frequency-based (68, 134) and probabilistic sequence-based models (76, 85, 108).

The oligonucleotide frequency-based method calculates the statistical significance of a site based on oligonucleotide frequency tables observed in all noncoding regions of the specific organism's genome. Usually, the length of the oligonucleotide varies from 4 to 9 bases. Hexanucleotide (oligonucleotide length of 6) analysis is most widely used. The significant oligonucleotides can then be grouped as longer consensus motifs. Frequency-based methods tend to be simple, efficient, and exhaustive (all over-represented patterns of chosen length are detected). The main limitation is the difficulty of identifying complex motif patterns. The public Web resource, Regulatory Sequence Analysis Tools (RSAT), performs sequence similarity searches and analyzes the noncoding sequences in the genomes (134).

For the probabilistic-based methods, the motif is represented as a position probability matrix, where the motifs are assumed to be hidden in the noisy background sequences. One of the strengths of probabilistic-based methods is the ability to identify motifs with complex patterns. Many potential motifs can be identified; however, it can be difficult to separate unique motifs from this large pool of potential solutions. Probabilistic-based methods also tend to be computationally intense as they must be run multiple times to get an optimal solution. AlignACE, Aligns Nucleic Acid Conserved Elements (**http://atlas.med.harvard.edu/**), is a popular motif finding tool that was first developed for yeast but has been expanded to other species (107).

COMPUTATIONAL PROTEOMICS

Proteomics is a leading technology for the qualitative and quantitative characterization of proteins and their interactions on a genome scale. The objectives of proteomics include large-scale identification and quantification of all protein types in a cell or tissue, analysis of post-translational modification and association with other proteins, and characterization of protein activities and structures. Application of proteomics in plants is still in its initial phase, mostly in protein identification (24, 96). Other aspects of proteomics (reviewed in 152), such as identification and prediction

of protein-protein interactions, protein activity profiling, protein subcellular localization, and protein structure, have not been widely used in plant science. However, recent efforts such as the structural genomic initiative that includes *Arabidopsis* (**http://www.uwstructuralgenomics.org/**) are encouraging.

Electrophoresis Analysis

Electrophoresis analysis can qualitatively and quantitatively investigate expression of proteins under different conditions (54). Several bioinformatics tools have been developed for two-dimensional (2D) electrophoresis analysis (86). SWISS-2DPAGE can locate the proteins on the 2D PAGE maps from Swiss-Prot (**http://au.expasy.org/ch2d/**). Melanie (**http://au.expasy.org/melanie/**) can analyze, annotate, and query complex 2D gel samples. Flicker (**http://open2dprot.sourceforge.net/Flicker/**) is an open-source stand-alone program for visually comparing 2D gel images. PDQuest (**http://www.proteomeworks.bio-rad.com**) is a popular commercial software package for comparing 2D gel images. Some software platforms handle related data storage and management, including PEDRo (**http://pedro.man.ac.uk/**), a software package for modeling, capturing, and disseminating 2D gel data and other proteomics experimental data. Main limitations of electrophoresis analysis include limited ability to identify proteins and low accuracy in detecting protein abundance.

Protein Identification Through Mass Spectrometry

After protein separation using 2D electrophoresis or liquid chromatography and protein digestion using an enzyme (trypsin, pepsin, glu-C, etc.), proteins are identified by typically using mass spectrometry (MS) (1). In contrast to other protein identification techniques, such as Edman degradation microsequencing, MS provides a high-throughput approach for large-scale protein identification. The data generated from mass spectrometers are often complicated and computational analyses are critical in interpreting the data for protein identification (17, 55). A major limitation in MS protein identification is the lack of open-source software. Most widely used tools are expensive commercial packages. In addition, current statistical models for matches between MS spectra and protein sequences are generally oversimplified. Hence, the confidence assessments for computational protein identification results are often unreliable. There are two types of MS-based protein identification methods: peptide mass fingerprinting (PMF) and tandem mass spectrometry (MS/MS).

Peptide mass fingerprinting. PMF peptide/protein identification compares the masses of peptides derived from the experimental spectral peaks with each of the possible peptides computationally digested from proteins in the sequence database. The proteins in the sequence database with a significant number of peptide matches are considered candidates for the proteins in the experimental sample. MOWSE (99) was an earlier software package for PMF protein identification, and Emowse (**http://emboss.sourceforge.net/**) is the latest implementation of the MOWSE algorithm. Several other computational tools have also been developed for PMF protein identification. MS-Fit in the Protein Prospector (**http://prospector.ucsf.edu/**) uses a variant of MOWSE scoring scheme incorporating new features, including constraints on the minimum number of peptides to be matched for a possible hit, the number of missed cleavages, and the target protein's molecular weight range. Mascot (**http://www.matrixscience.com/**) is an extension of the MOWSE algorithm. It incorporates the same scoring scheme with the addition of a probability-based score. A limitation of PMF protein identification is that it sometimes cannot identify proteins because multiple proteins in the database can fit the PMF spectra.

In this case, additional MS/MS experiments are needed to identify the proteins.

Tandem mass spectrometry. MS/MS further breaks each digested peptide into smaller fragments, whose spectra provide effective signatures of individual amino acids in the peptide for protein identification. Many tools have been developed for MS/MS-based peptide/protein identification, the most popular ones being SEQUEST (**http://fields.scripps.edu/sequest/**) and Mascot (**http://www.matrixscience.com/**). Both rely on the comparison between theoretical peptides derived from the database and experimental mass spectrometric tandem spectra. SEQUEST, one of the earliest tools developed for this, produces a list of possible peptide/protein assignments in a protein mixture based on a correlation scoring scheme (145). Mascot, together with its PMF protein identification capacity, uses a similar algorithm as SEQUEST for MS/MS peptide/protein identification. The limitations of these programs are that a significant portion of MS/MS spectra cannot be assigned due to various factors, including sequencing and annotation errors in the search database. In addition, post-translational modifications are currently not handled well using computational approaches.

The de novo sequencing approach based on MS/MS spectra is an active research area (30). Typically the algorithms match the separations of peaks by the mass of one or several amino acids and infer the probable peptide sequences that are consistent with the matched amino acids (25). There are a few popular software packages for peptide de novo sequencing using MS/MS data, including Lutefisk (**http://www.hairyfatguy.com/lutefisk/**) and PEAKS (**http://www.bioinformaticssolutions.com/products/peaks**). One limitation of current de novo methods is that they often cannot provide the exact sequence of a peptide. Instead, several top candidate sequences are suggested.

METABOLOMICS AND METABOLIC FLUX

Metabolomics is the analysis of the complete pool of small metabolites in a cell at any given time. Metabolomics may prove to be particularly important in plants due to the proliferation of secondary metabolites. As of 2004, more than 100,000 metabolites have been identified in plants, with estimates that this may be less that 10% of the total (133). In a metabolite profiling experiment, metabolites are extracted from tissues, separated, and analyzed in a high-throughput manner (44). Metabolic fingerprinting looks at a few metabolites to help differentiate samples according to their phenotype or biological relevance (58, 115). Technology has now advanced to semiautomatically quantify >1000 compounds from a single leaf extract (138).

The key challenge in metabolite profiling is the rapid, consistent, and unambiguous identification of metabolites from complex plant samples (110). Identification is routinely performed by time-consuming standard addition experiments using commercially available or purified metabolite preparations. A publicly accessible database that contains the evidence and underlying metabolite identification for gas chromatography-mass spectrometry (GC–MS) profiles from diverse biological sources is needed. Standards for experimental metadata and data quality in metabolomics experiments are still in a very early stage and a large-scale public repository is not yet available. The ArMet (architecture for metabolomics) proposal (61) gives a description of plant metabolomics experiments and their results along with a database schema. MIAMET (Minimum Information About a Metabolomics Experiment) (13) gives reporting requirements with the aim of standardizing experiment descriptions, particularly within publications. The Standard Metabolic Reporting Structures (SMRS) working group (119) has developed standards for describing the biological sample origin, analytical technologies, and methods used in a metabolite profiling experiment.

Metabolite data have been used to construct metabolic correlation networks (121). Such correlations may reflect the net partitioning of carbon and nitrogen resulting from direct enzymatic conversions and indirect cellular regulation by transcriptional or biochemical processes. However, metabolic correlation matrices cannot infer that a change in one metabolite led to a change in another metabolite in a metabolic reaction network (122).

Metabolic flux analysis measures the steady-state flow between metabolites. Fluxes, however, are even more difficult to measure than metabolite levels due to complications in modeling intracellular transport of metabolites and the incomplete knowledge about the topology and location of the pathways in vivo (115). The most basic approach to metabolic flux analysis is stoichiometric analysis that calculates the quantities of reactants and products of a chemical reaction to determine the flux of each metabolite (39). However, this method is numerically difficult to solve for large networks and it has problems if parallel metabolic pathways, metabolic cycles, and reversible reactions are present (140). Flux-Analyzer is a package for MATLAB that integrates pathway and flux analysis for metabolic networks (75).

Flux analysis using ^{13}C carbon labeling data seeks to overcome some of the disadvantages of stoichiometric flux analysis described above (120). More rigorous analysis is needed for full determination of fluxes from all of the experimental data in ^{13}C constrained flux analysis (stoichiometric model with a few flux ratios as constraints) and the stoichiometric and isotopomer balances. Iterative methods have been used to solve the resulting matrix of isotopomer balances, with the nuclear magnetic resonance or gas chromatography measurements used to provide consistency. As more reliable data are collected, one can use ordinary differential equations for dynamic simulations of metabolic networks and combine information about connectivity, concentration balances, flux balances, metabolic control, and pathway optimization. Ultimately, one may integrate all of the information and perform analysis and simulation in a cellular modeling environment like E-Cell (**http://www.e-cell.org/**) or CellDesigner (**http://www.systems-biology.org**).

ONTOLOGIES

The data that are generated and analyzed as described in the previous sections need to be compared with the existing knowledge in the field in order to place the data in a biologically meaningful context and derive hypotheses. To do this efficiently, data and knowledge need to be described in explicit and unambiguous ways that must be comprehensible to both humans and computer programs. An ontology is a set of vocabulary terms whose meanings and relations with other terms are explicitly stated and which are used to annotate data (5, 10, 14, 124). This section introduces the types of ontologies in development and use today and some applications and caveats of using the ontologies in biology.

Types of Bio-Ontologies

A growing number of shared ontologies are being built and used in biology. Examples include ontologies for describing gene and protein function (59), cell types (9), anatomies and developmental stages of organisms (50, 135, 144), microarray experiments (126), and metabolic pathways (84, 151). A list of open-source ontologies used in biology can be found on the Open Biological Ontologies Web site (**http://obo.sourceforge.net/**). Many ontologies on this site are under development and are subject to frequent change. The Gene Ontology (GO) (**www.geneontology.org**) is an example of bio-ontologies that has garnered community acceptance. It is a set of more than 16,000 controlled vocabulary terms for the biological domains of "molecular function," "sub-

cellular compartment," and "biological process." GO is organized as a directed acyclic graph, which is a type of hierarchy tree that allows a term to exist as a specific concept belonging to more than one general term. Other examples of ontologies currently in development are the Sequence Ontology (SO) project (40) and the Plant Ontology (PO) project (**www.plantontology.org**). The SO project aims to explicitly define all the terms needed to describe features on a nucleotide sequence, which can be used for genome sequence annotation for any organism. The PO project aims to develop shared vocabularies to describe anatomical structures for flowering plants to depict gene expression patterns and plant phenotypes.

A few challenges in the development and use of ontologies remain to be addressed, including redundancies in the ontologies, minimal or lack of formal, computer-comprehensive definitions of the terms in the ontologies, and general acceptance by the research and publishing community (10, 14). There is an opportunity for an international repository of ontology standards that could oversee the development and maintenance of the ontologies.

Applications of Ontologies

Ontologies are used mainly to annotate data such as sequences, gene expression clusters, experiments, and strains. Ontologies that have such annotations to data in databases can be used in numerous ways, including connecting different databases, refining searching, providing a framework for interpreting the results of functional genomics experiments, and inferring knowledge (8, 10, 47). For example, one can ask which functions and processes are statistically significantly over-represented in an expression cluster of interest compared to the functions and processes carried out by all of the genes from a gene expression array. Because GO is one of the more well-established ontologies, this section focuses on GO to illustrate applications of ontologies in biology. Ontologies have been used by many model organism databases to annotate genes and gene products (**http://www.geneontology.org/GO.current.annotations.shtml, http://www.geneontology.org/GO.biblio.shtml#annots**). Function annotations of genes using GO have been used mainly in two ways: predicting protein functions, processes, and localization patterns from various data sources (**http://www.geneontology.org/GO.biblio.shtml#predictions**) and providing a biological framework or benchmark set for interpreting results of large-scale probing of samples such as gene expression profiles and protein-protein interactions (**http://www.geneontology.org/GO.biblio.shtml#gene_exp**). In addition, GO annotations have been used to test the robustness of semantic similarity searching methods (83) and to study adaptive evolution (4).

There are several issues in using GO annotations to predict function and to use as a benchmark for large-scale data. One is the misuse or lack of use of evidence codes, which provide the type of evidence that was used to make the annotation (**http://www.geneontology.org/GO.evidence.shtml**). Only about half of the evidence codes refer to direct experimental evidence. Also, several evidence codes are used for indirect evidence, which indicate less certainty in the assertion of the annotation than those made with direct experimental evidence. Other codes are used for computationally derived annotations and have no experimental support and have a higher probability of being incorrect. Researchers and computer programs that use the annotations for inferring knowledge or analyzing functional genomics data should be familiar with these evidence codes in order to minimize misinterpretation of the data. For example, methods to assess relationship between sequence conservation and coexpression of genes and using GO annotations to validate their results should ensure that no annotations using the ISS and IEA evidence codes are used to avoid circular arguments. Similarly, stud-

ies that attempt to define biological processes and functions from gene expression data using the GO annotations should ensure that no annotation with inferred from expression pattern (IEP) evidence code is used. The other caveat is that annotations to GO are not equivalently represented throughout GO. When looking for statistical over-representation of GO terms in genes of an expression cluster, there is low statistical power for detecting deviations from expectation for terms that are annotated with a small number of genes (74).

Software for Accessing and Analyzing Ontologies and Annotations

There are a number of software tools for visualizing, editing, and analyzing ontologies and their annotations. The GO Web site maintains a comprehensive list of these tools (**http://www.geneontology.org/GO.tools.shtml**). Some of them are accessible via Web browsers and others have to be installed locally. Tools are also needed to facilitate data integrity checks and more flexible and customizable searching and browsing capabilities to explore these complex networks of concepts. Most of the tools that facilitate analysis of the GO annotations are developed to help interpret gene expression studies. These applications allow researchers to compare a list of genes (for example, from an expression cluster) and identify over-represented GO terms in this list as compared to the whole genome or whole list of genes under study. Most of these software programs use statistical models to provide significance in the over-representation. Recently, Khatri and colleagues reported comparisons of 14 of these tools on their functionalities, advantages, and limitations (74). Finally, most of the bio-ontologies are informal in their semantic representation. Definitions of the terms are provided in natural language, which is fine for human comprehension but does not easily allow computers and software to be developed that can help check for ontology integrity and provide more semantically powerful search functions. More tools are needed that can facilitate the conversion of bio-ontologies to be more formal and computer comprehensive.

DATABASES

Traditionally, biologists relied on textbooks and research articles published in scientific journals as the main source of information. This has changed dramatically in the past decade as the Internet and Web browsers became commonplace. Today, the Internet is the first place researchers go to find information. Databases that are available via the Web also became an indispensable tool for biological research. In this section, we describe types and examples of biological databases, how these databases are built and accessed, how data among databases are exchanged, and current challenges and opportunities in biological database development and maintenance.

Types of Biological Databases

Three types of biological databases have been established and are developed: large-scale public repositories, community-specific databases, and project-specific databases. *Nucleic Acids Research* (**http://nar.oxford journals.org/**) publishes a database issue in January of every year. Recently, *Plant Physiology* started publishing articles describing databases (105). Large-scale public repositories are usually developed and maintained by government agencies or international consortia and are places for long-term data storage. Examples include GenBank for sequences (139), UniProt (113) for protein information, Protein Data Bank (32) for protein structure information, and ArrayExpress (100) and Gene Expression Omnibus (GEO) (38) for microarray data. There are a number of community-specific databases, which typically contain information curated with high standards and address the needs of a particular community of researchers. A

prominent example of community-specific databases are those that cater to researchers focused on studying model organisms (77, 104, 144) or clade-oriented comparative databases (53, 88, 92, 137). Other examples of community-specific databases include databases focused on specific types of data such as metabolism (151) and protein modification (129). The concept of community-specific databases is subject to change as researchers are widening their scope of research. For example, databases focused on comparing genome sequences recently emerged (e.g., **http://www.phytome.org** and Reference 64). The third category of databases includes smaller-scale, and often short-lived, databases that are developed for project data management during the funding period. Often these databases and Web resources are not maintained beyond the funding period of the project and currently there is no standard way of depositing or archiving these databases after the funding period.

There are some issues in database management. First, there is a general lack of good documentation on the rationale of the design and implementation. More effort is needed to share the experiences via conferences and publications. Also, there are no accepted standards in making databases, schema, software, and standard operating procedures available. In response to this, the National Human Genome Research Institute (NHGRI) has funded a collaborative project called the Generic Model Organism Database (**http://www.gmod.org**) to promote the development and sharing of software, schemas, and standard operation procedures. The project's major aim is to build a generic organism database toolkit to allow researchers to set up a genome database "off the shelf." Another major issue is that there is a general lack of infrastructure of supporting, managing, and using digital data archived in databases and Web sites in the long term (82). One possibility to alleviate this problem is to create a public archive of biological databases and Web sites to which finished projects could deposit the database, software, and Web sites. There are several projects that are building digital repository systems that can be models for such a repository such as D-Space (**http://dspace.org/**) and the CalTech Collection of Open Digital Archives (CODA; **http://library.caltech.edu/digital/**). Some additional challenges in long-term archiving of data were articulated in a recent National Science Board report (**http://www.nsf.gov/nsb/documents/2005/LLDDC_report.pdf**).

Data Representation and Storage

Databases can be developed using a number of different methods including simple file directories, object-oriented database software, and relational database software. Due to the increasing quantity of data that need to be stored and made accessible using the Internet, relational database management software has become popular and has become the de facto standard in biology. Relational databases provide effective means of storing and retrieving large quantities of data via indexes, normalization, referential integrity, triggers, and transactions. Notable relational database software that is freely available and quite popular in bioinformatics is MySQL (**http://www.mysql.com/**) and PostgreSQL (**http://www.postgresql.org/**). In relational databases, data are represented as entities, attributes (properties of the entities), and relationships between the entities. This type of representation is called Entity-Relationship (ER) and database schemas are described using ER diagrams (e.g., TAIR schema at **http://arabidopsis.org/search/schemas.html**). Entities and attributes become tables and columns in the physical implementation of the database, respectively. Data are the values that are stored in the fields of the tables.

Although relational databases are powerful ways of storing large quantities of data, they have limitations. For example, it is not trivial to represent complex relationships between data such as signal transduction path-ways. Also, it is difficult to create rich semantic relationships in relational databases to ask the database "what if" types of queries without having extensive software built on top of the database. Another limitation of relational databases is that it is very difficult, if not impossible, to preserve all of the changes that occur to attributes of entities.

Data Access and Exchange

The most direct, powerful, and flexible way of accessing data in a database is using structured query language (SQL) (**http://databases.about.com/od/sql/**). SQL has a reasonably intuitive and simple syntax that requires no programming knowledge and is suited for biologists to learn without a steep learning curve. However, to use SQL, users need to know the database schema. In addition, some queries that are based on less optimized database structure could result in slow performance and can even sometimes lock the database system. In most databases, access to the data is provided via database access software and graphical user interface (GUI) that allow searching and browsing of the data. In addition to text-based search user interfaces, more sophisticated ways of accessing data such as graphical displays and tree-based browsers are also common.

Although accessing information from a database is fairly easy if one knows which database to go to, it is not as easy to find information if one does not know which database to search. There are several ways to solve this problem such as indexing the content of database-driven pages, developing software that will connect to individual databases directly, or developing a data warehouse of many different data types or database in one site. A relatively new method that is gaining some attention is to use a registry system where different databases that specialize on particular information can declare what data are available in their system and register methods to access their data. Users can send requests to the registry system, which then contact the appropriate databases to retrieve the requested data. Conceptually, this is an elegant way of integrating different databases without depending on the individual databases' schema. However, this relies on the willingness of individual databases to participate in the registry system. This method is called Web services and has been accepted widely by the Internet industry but has not yet been commonly implemented. Projects like BioMOBY (141) and myGRID (125) are implementing this idea for biological databases, but they have not yet been widely used.

Semantics (meaning) and syntax (format) of data need to be made explicit in order to exchange data for analysis and mining. A simple way of formatting data is using a tag and value system (called markup language). An emerging standard for exchanging data and information via the Web is Extensible Markup Language (XML), which allows information providers to define new tag and attribute names at will and to nest document structures to any level of complexity, among other features. The document that defines the meaning of the tags for an XML document is called Document Type Definition (DTD). The use of a common DTD allows different users and applications to exchange data in XML. Although many databases and bioinformatics projects present their data in XML, currently almost every group has their own DTD. Standardization and common use of DTDs for exchanging common data types will be pivotal. There are notable exceptions to this rule including the specification of microarray data, MAGEML (Microarray Gene Expression Markup Language), provided by the Microarray Gene Expression Database Society (MGED) (**http://www.mged.org/**). To a lesser extent, the BIOPAX (**http://www.biopax.org/**) is also becoming a community-accepted standard to describe pathways and reactions. Other than DTDs, biological database communities do not yet have a standard system in software engineering to communicate with each other.

Data Curation

Data curation is defined as any activity devoted to selecting, organizing, assessing quality, describing, and updating data that result in enhanced quality, trustworthiness, interpretability, and longevity of the data. It is a crucial task in today's research environment where data are being generated at an ever-increasing rate and an increasing amount of research is based on re-use of data. In general, some level of curation is done by data generators, but most curation activities are carried out in data repositories. A number of different strategies to curation are used, including computational, manual, in-house, and those that involve external expertise. Assessing data quality involves both determining the criteria for measuring quality and performing the measurements. Data quality criteria for raw data are tied with methods of data acquisition. In many databases, these criteria are not made explicit and the information on the metrics of data-quality assessment is rare.

Curation of data into public repositories should be a parallel and integrated process with publication in peer-reviewed journals. Although much progress has been made in electronic publication and open-access publishing, there is still a gap between connecting the major conclusions in papers and the data that were used to draw the conclusions. In a few cases, data are required to be submitted to public repositories (e.g., sequence data to GenBank, microarray data to ArrayExpress/GEO, and *Arabidopsis* stock data to ABRC). However, there are no such standards established for other data types (e.g., proteomics data, metabolomics data, protein localization, in situ hybridization, phenotype description, protein function information). Standards, specifications, and requirements for publication of data into repositories should be made more accessible to researchers early on in their data-generation and research-activity processes.

One of the most important aspects of today's changing research landscape is the culture of data and expertise sharing. The now famous Bermuda principle (**http://www.gene.ucl.ac.uk/hugo/bermuda.htm**) was extended to large-scale data at a recent meeting (131). In this meeting, the policy for publicly releasing large-scale data pre-publication and appropriate conduct and acknowledgment of the uses of these data by the scientific community were discussed. Clearly articulated and community-accepted policies are needed on how data from data repositories should be cited and referenced and how the generators of the data should be acknowledged. Establishing this standard should include journal publishers, database scientists, data generators, funding bodies, and representatives of the user community. Additional challenges and opportunities in database curation were recently articulated (82, 103).

EMERGING AREAS IN BIOINFORMATICS

In addition to some of the challenges and opportunities mentioned in this review, there are many exciting areas of research in bioinformatics that are emerging. In this section, we focus on a few of these areas such as text mining, systems biology, and the semantic web. Some additional emerging areas such as image analysis (117), grid computing (46, 49), directed evolution (29), rational protein design (81), microRNA-related bioinformatics (21), and modeling in epigenomics (43) are not covered due to the limitation of space.

Text Mining

The size of the biological literature is expanding at an increasing rate. The Medline 2004 database had 12.5 million entries and is expanding at a rate of 500,000 new citations each year (26). The goal of text mining is to allow researchers to identify needed information and shift the burden of searching from researchers to the computer. Without automated text mining, much of biomolecular in-

teractions and biological research archived in the literature will remain accessible in principle but underutilized in practice. One key area of text mining is relationship extraction that finds relationships between entities such as genes and proteins. Examples include Med-Miner at the National Library of Medicine (128), PreBIND (35), the curated BIND system (2, 6), PathBinderH (155), and iHOP (63). (See Reference 26 for a complete survey of text mining applications.) Results on real-world tasks such as the automatic extraction and assignment of GO annotations are promising, but they are still far from reaching the required performance demanded by real-world applications (15). One key difficulty that needs to be addressed in this field is the complex nature of the names and terminology such as the large range of variants for protein names and GO terms in free text. The current generation of systems is beginning to combine statistical methods with machine learning to capture expert knowledge on how genes and proteins are referred to in scientific papers to create usable systems with high precision and recall for specialized tasks in the near future.

Computational Systems Biology

Classical systems analysis in engineering treats a system as a black box whose inner structure and behavior can be analyzed and modeled by varying internal or external conditions, and studying the effect of the variation on the external observables. The result is an understanding of the inner makeup and working mechanisms of the system (72). Systems biology is the application of this theory to biology. The observables are measurements of what the organism is doing, ranging from phenotypic descriptions to detailed metabolic profiling. A critical issue is how to effectively integrate various types of data, such as sequence, gene expression, protein interactions, and phenotypes to infer biological knowledge. Some areas that require more work include creating coherent validated data sets, developing common formats for pathway data [SBML (65) and BioPAX (**http://www.biopax.org**)], and creating ontologies to define complex interactions, curation, and linkages with text-mining tools. The Systems Biology Workbench project (**http://sbw.kgi.edu/**) aims to develop an open-source software framework for sharing information between different types of pathway models. Other issues are that biological systems are underdefined (not enough measurements are available to characterize the system) and samples are not taken often enough to capture time changes in a system that may occur at vastly different time scales in different networks such as signaling and regulatory networks (98). The long-term goal to create a complete in silico model of a cell is still distant; however the tools that are being developed to integrate information from a wide variety of sources will be valuable in the short term.

Semantic Web

Semantic web is a model to "create a universal mechanism for information exchange by giving meaning, in a machine-interpretable way, to the content of documents and data on the Web" (95). This model will enable the development of searching tools that know what type of information can be obtained from which documents and understand how the information in each document relates to another, which will allow software agents that can use reasoning and logic to make decisions automatically based on the constraints provided in the query (e.g., automatic travel agents, phenotype prediction) (12). Bioinformatics could benefit enormously from successful implementation of this model and should play a leading role in realizing it (95). Current efforts to realize the concepts of the semantic web have been focused on developing standards and specifications of identifying and describing data such as Universal Resource Identifier (URI) and Resource Definition Framework (RDF), respectively (**http://www.w3c.org/2001/sw**). Although

implementation of applications using the semantic web is scarce at this point, there are some useful examples being developed such as Haystack (a browser that retrieves data from multiple databases and allows users to annotate and manage the information to reflect their understanding) (**http://www-db. cs.wisc.edu/cidr/cidr2005/papers/P02.pdf**) and BioDash (a drug development user interface that associates diseases, drug progression stages, molecular biology, and pathway knowledge for users) (**http://www.w3.org/ 2005/04/swls/BioDash/Demo/**).

Cellular Localization and Spatially Resolved Data

Research in nanotechnology and electron microscopy is allowing researchers to select specific areas of cells and tissues and to image spatiotemporal distributions of signaling receptors, gene expression, and proteins. Laser capture microdissection allows the selection of specific tissue types for detailed analysis (42). This technique has been applied to specific plant tissues in maize and *Arabidopsis* (73, 94). Confocal imaging is being used to model auxin transport and gene expression patterns in *Arabidopsis* (60). Methods in electron microscopy are being applied to image the spatiotemporal distribution of signaling receptors (149). Improved methods in laser scanning microscopes may allow measurements of fast diffusion and dynamic processes in the microsecond-to-millisecond time range in live cells (34). These emerging capabilities will lead to new understanding of cell dynamics.

CONCLUSION

In this review, we attempt to highlight some of the recent advances made in bioinformatics in the basic areas of sequence, gene expression, protein, and metabolite analyses, databases, and ontologies, current limitations in these areas, and some emerging areas. A number of unsolved problems exist in bioinformatics today, including data and database integration, automated knowledge extraction, robust inference of phenotype from genotype, and training and retraining of students and established researchers in bioinformatics. Bioinformatics is an approach that will be an essential part of plant research and we hope that every plant researcher will incorporate more bioinformatics tools and approaches in their research projects.

If the next 50 years of plant biology can be summed into one word, it would be "integration." We will see integration of basic research with applied research in which plant biotechnology will play an essential role in solving urgent problems in our society such as developing renewable energy, reducing world hunger and poverty, and preserving the environment. We will see integration of disparate, specialized areas of plant research into more comparative, connected, holistic views and approaches in plant biology. We will also see more integration of plant research and other biological research, from microbes to human, from a large-scale comparative genomics perspective. Bioinformatics will provide the glue with which all of these types of integration will occur. However, it will be people, not tools, who will enable the gluing. Ways in which biological research will be conducted in 2050 will be much different from the way in which it was done in 2000. Each researcher will spend more time on the computer and the Internet to generate and describe data and experiments, to analyze the data and find other people's data relevant for comparison, to find existing knowledge in the field and to relate it to his or her results into the current body of knowledge, and to publish his or her results to the world.

ACKNOWLEDGMENTS

We are grateful to Blake Meyers, Dan MacLean, Shijun Li, Scott Peck, Mark Lange, Bill Beavis, Todd Vision, Stefanie Hartmann, Gary Stacey, Chris Town, Volker Brendel, and Nevin Young for their critical comments on the manuscript. This work has been supported in part by NSF grants DBI-99,78564, DBI-04,17062, DBI-03,21666 (SYR); ITR-IIS-04,07204 (DX); DBI-02,09809 (JD); USDA grants NRI-2002-35,300-12,619 (JD) and CSREES 2004-25,604-14,708 (DX); NIH grants NHGRI-HG002273, R01-GM65466 (SYR); National Center for Soybean Biotechnology (DX); Pioneer-Hi-Bred (SYR); and Carnegie Canada (SYR).

LITERATURE CITED

1. Aebersold R, Mann M. 2003. Mass spectrometry-based proteomics. *Nature* 422:198–207
2. Alfarano C, Andrade CE, Anthony K, Bahroos N, Bajec M, et al. 2005. The Biomolecular Interaction Network Database and related tools 2005 update. *Nucleic Acids Res.* 33:D418–24
3. Allen JE, Pertea M, Salzberg SL. 2004. Computational gene prediction using multiple sources of evidence. *Genome Res.* 14:142–48
4. Aris-Brosou S. 2005. Determinants of adaptive evolution at the molecular level: the extended complexity hypothesis. *Mol. Biol. Evol.* 22:200–9
5. Ashburner M, Ball C, Blake J, Botstein D, Butler H, et al. 2000. Gene ontology: tool for the unification of biology. The Gene Ontology Consortium. *Nat. Genet.* 25:25–29
6. Bader G, Betel D, Hogue C. 2002. BIND: the Biomolecular Interaction Network Database. *Nucleic Acids Res.* 31:248–50
7. Bammler T, Beyer RP, Bhattacharya S, Boorman GA, Boyles A, et al. 2005. Standardizing global gene expression analysis between laboratories and across platforms. *Nat. Methods* 2:351–56

8. Bard J. 2003. Ontologies: formalising biological knowledge for bioinformatics. *Bioessays* 25:501–6

9. Bard J, Rhee SY, Ashburner M. 2005. An ontology for cell types. *Genome Biol.* 6:R21

10. Bard JB, Rhee SY. 2004. Ontologies in biology: design, applications and future challenges. *Nat. Rev. Genet.* 5:213–22

11. Bedell JA, Budiman MA, Nunberg A, Citek RW, Robbins D, et al. 2005. Sorghum genome sequencing by methylation filtration. *PLoS Biol.* 3:e13

12. Berners-Lee T, Hendler J, Lassila O. 2001. The Semantic Web. *Sci. Am.* 284:34–43

13. Bino R, Hall R, Fiehn O, Kopka J, Saito K, et al. 2004. Potential of metabolomics as a functional genomics tool. *Trends Plant Sci.* 9:418–25

14. Blake J. 2004. Bio-ontologies-fast and furious. *Nat. Biotechnol.* 22:773–74

15. Blaschke C, Krallinger M, Leon E, Valencia A. 2005. Evaluation of BioCreAtIvE assessment of task 2. *BMC Bioinformatics* 6:S16

16. Blazej RG, Paegel BM, Mathies RA. 2003. Polymorphism ratio sequencing: a new approach for single nucleotide polymorphism discovery and genotyping. *Genome Res.* 13:287–93

17. Blueggel M, Chamrad D, Meyer HE. 2004. Bioinformatics in proteomics. *Curr. Pharm. Biotechnol.* 5:79–88

18. Boguski MS, Schuler GD. 1995. ESTablishing a human transcript map. *Nat. Genet.* 10:369–71

19. Brendel V, Zhu W. 2002. Computational modeling of gene structure in Arabidopsis thaliana. *Plant Mol. Biol.* 48:49–58

20. Brenner S, Johnson M, Bridgham J, Golda G, Lloyd DH, et al. 2000. Gene expression analysis by massively parallel signature sequencing (MPSS) on microbead arrays. *Nat. Biotechnol.* 18:630–34

21. Brown JR, Sanseau P. 2005. A computational view of microRNAs and their targets. *Drug Discov. Today* 10:595–601

22. Brown P, Botstein D. 1999. Exploring the new world of the genome with DNA microarrays. *Nat. Genet.* 21:33–37

23. Buck MJ, Lieb JD. 2004. ChIP-chip: considerations for the design, analysis, and application of genome-wide chromatin immunoprecipitation experiments. *Genomics* 83:349–60

24. Canovas FM, Dumas-Gaudot E, Recorbet G, Jorrin J, Mock HP, Rossignol M. 2004. Plant proteome analysis. *Proteomics* 4:285–98

25. Chen T, Kao MY, Tepel M, Rush J, Church GM. 2001. A dynamic programming approach to de novo peptide sequencing via tandem mass spectrometry. *J. Comput. Biol.* 8:325–37

26. Cohen AM, Hersh WR. 2005. A survey of current work in biomedical text mining. *Brief Bioinform.* 6:57–71

27. Cope LM, Irizarry RA, Jaffee HA, Wu Z, Speed TP. 2004. A benchmark for Affymetrix GeneChip expression measures. *Bioinformatics* 20:323–31

28. Coughlan SJ, Agrawal V, Meyers B. 2004. A comparison of global gene expression measurement technologies in Arabidopsis thaliana. *Comp. Funct. Genomics* 5:245–52

29. Dalby PA. 2003. Optimising enzyme function by directed evolution. *Curr. Opin. Struct. Biol.* 13:500–5

30. Dancik V, Addona TA, Clauser KR, Vath JE, Pevzner PA. 1999. De novo peptide sequencing via tandem mass spectrometry. *J. Comput. Biol.* 6:327–42

31. Densmore LD 3rd. 2001. Phylogenetic inference and parsimony analysis. *Methods Mol. Biol.* 176:23–36

32. Deshpande N, Addess KJ, Bluhm WF, Merino-Ott JC, Townsend-Merino W, et al. 2005. The RCSB Protein Data Bank: a redesigned query system and relational database based on the mmCIF schema. *Nucleic Acids Res.* 33:D233–37

33. Di X, Matsuzaki H, Webster TA, Hubbell E, Liu G, et al. 2005. Dynamic model based algorithms for screening and genotyping over 100 K SNPs on oligonucleotide microarrays. *Bioinformatics* 21:1958–63

34. Digman MA, Brown CM, Sengupta P, Wiseman PW, Horwitz AR, Gratton E. 2005. Measuring fast dynamics in solutions and cells with a laser scanning microscope. *Biophys. J.* 89:1317–27

35. Donaldson I, Martin J, de Bruijn B, Wolting C, Lay V, et al. 2003. PreBIND and Textomy—mining the biomedical literature for protein-protein interactions using a support vector machine. *BMC Bioinformatics* 4:11

36. Doolittle WF. 1999. Phylogenetic classification and the universal tree. *Science* 284:2124–29

37. Draghici S. 2003. *Data Analysis Tools for DNA Microarrays.* London: Chapman and Hall

38. Edgar R, Domrachev M, Lash AE. 2002. Gene Expression Omnibus: NCBI gene expression and hybridization array data repository. *Nucleic Acids. Res.* 30:207–10

39. Edwards JS, Palsson BO. 2000. The Escherichia coli MG1655 in silico metabolic genotype: its definition, characteristics, and capabilities. *Proc. Natl. Acad. Sci. USA* 97:5528–33

40. Eilbeck K, Lewis SE, Mungall CJ, Yandell M, Stein L, et al. 2005. The Sequence Ontology: a tool for the unification of genome annotations. *Genome Biol.* 6:R44

41. Eisen MB, Spellman PT, Brown PO, Botstein D. 1998. Cluster analysis and display of genome-wide expression patterns. *Proc. Natl. Acad. Sci. USA* 95:14863–68

42. Emmert-Buck MR, Bonner RF, Smith PD, Chuaqui RF, Zhuang Z, et al. 1996. Laser capture microdissection. *Science* 274:998–1001

43. Fazzari MJ, Greally JM. 2004. Epigenomics: beyond CpG islands. *Nat. Rev. Genet.* 5:446–55

44. Fiehn O. 2002. Metabolomics—the link between genotypes and phenotypes. *Plant Mol. Biol.* 48:155–71

45. Foissac S, Bardou P, Moisan A, Cros MJ, Schiex T. 2003. EUGENE'HOM: a generic similarity-based gene finder using multiple homologous sequences. *Nucleic Acids Res.* 31:3742–45

46. Foster I. 2002. What is the Grid? A three point checklist. In *GRIDToday*, pp. 4. Chicago: Argonne National Lab & University of Chicago

47. Fraser AG, Marcotte EM. 2004. A probabilistic view of gene function. *Nat. Genet.* 36:559–64

48. Frazer KA, Chen X, Hinds DA, Pant PV, Patil N, Cox DR. 2003. Genomic DNA insertions and deletions occur frequently between humans and nonhuman primates. *Genome Res.* 13:341–46

49. Gannon D, Alameda J, Chipara O, Christie M, Duke V, et al. 2005. Building grid portal applications from a Web service component architecture. *Proc. IEEE* 93:551–63

50. Garcia-Hernandez M, Berardini TZ, Chen G, Crist D, Doyle A, et al. 2002. TAIR: a resource for integrated Arabidopsis data. *Funct. Integr. Genomics* 2:239–53

51. Gibbs RA, Weinstock GM. 2003. Evolving methods for the assembly of large genomes. *Cold Spring Harb. Symp. Quant. Biol.* 68:189–94

52. Goff SA, Ricke D, Lan TH, Presting G, Wang R, et al. 2002. A draft sequence of the rice genome (Oryza sativa L. ssp. japonica). *Science* 296:92–100

53. Gonzales MD, Archuleta E, Farmer A, Gajendran K, Grant D, et al. 2005. The Legume Information System (LIS): an integrated information resource for comparative legume biology. *Nucleic Acids Res.* 33:D660–65

54. Gorg A, Obermaier C, Boguth G, Harder A, Scheibe B, et al. 2000. The current state of two-dimensional electrophoresis with immobilized pH gradients. *Electrophoresis* 21:1037–53

55. Gras R, Muller M. 2001. Computational aspects of protein identification by mass spectrometry. *Curr. Opin. Mol. Ther.* 3:526–32

56. Guo H, Moose SP. 2003. Conserved noncoding sequences among cultivated cereal genomes identify candidate regulatory sequence elements and patterns of promoter evolution. *Plant Cell* 15:1143–58

57. Haas BJ, Delcher AL, Mount SM, Wortman JR, Smith RK Jr, et al. 2003. Improving the Arabidopsis genome annotation using maximal transcript alignment assemblies. *Nucleic Acids Res.* 31:5654–66

58. Harrigan GG, Goodacre R, eds. 2003. *Metabolic Profiling: Its Role in Biomarker Discovery and Gene Function Analysis*. Boston: Plenum

59. Harris MA, Clark J, Ireland A, Lomax J, Ashburner M, et al. 2004. The Gene Ontology (GO) database and informatics resource. *Nucleic Acids Res.* 32:D258–61

60. Heisler MG, Ohno C, Das P, Sieber P, Reddy GV, et al. 2005. Patterns of auxin transport and gene expression during primordium development revealed by live imaging of the Arabidopsis inflorescence meristem. *Curr. Biol.* 15:1899–911

61. Jenkins H, Hardy N, Beckmann D, Draper J, Smith AR, et al. 2004. A proposed framework for the description of plant metabolomics experiments and their results. *Nat. Biotechnol.* 22:1601–6

62. Hinds DA, Stuve LL, Nilsen GB, Halperin E, Eskin E, et al. 2005. Whole-genome patterns of common DNA variation in three human populations. *Science* 307:1072–79

63. Hoffmann R, Valencia A. 2004. A gene network for navigating the literature. *Nat. Genet.* 36:664

64. Horan K, Lauricha J, Bailey-Serres J, Raikhel N, Girke T. 2005. Genome cluster database. A sequence family analysis platform for Arabidopsis and rice. *Plant Physiol.* 138:47–54

65. Hucka M, Finney A, Bornstein BJ, Keating SM, Shapiro BE, et al. 2004. Evolving a lingua franca and associated software infrastructure for computational systems biology: the Systems Biology Markup Language (SBML) Project. *Syst. Biol.* 1:41–53

66. Hudek AK, Cheung J, Boright AP, Scherer SW. 2003. Genescript: DNA sequence annotation pipeline. *Bioinformatics* 19:1177–78

67. Inada DC, Bashir A, Lee C, Thomas BC, Ko C, et al. 2003. Conserved noncoding sequences in the grasses. *Genome Res.* 13:2030–41

68. Jensen LJ, Knudsen S. 2000. Automatic discovery of regulatory patterns in promoter regions based on whole cell expression data and functional annotation. *Bioinformatics* 16:326–33

69. Jiang N, Bao Z, Zhang X, Eddy SR, Wessler SR. 2004. Pack-MULE transposable elements mediate gene evolution in plants. *Nature* 431:569–73

70. Jiao Y, Jia P, Wang X, Su N, Yu S, et al. 2005. A tiling microarray expression analysis of rice chromosome 4 suggests a chromosome-level regulation of transcription. *Plant Cell* 17:1641–57

71. Karlin S, Altschul SF. 1990. Methods for assessing the statistical significance of molecular sequence features by using general scoring schemes. *Proc. Natl. Acad. Sci. USA* 87:2264–68

72. Kell DB, Brown M, Davey HM, Dunn WB, Spasic I, Oliver SG. 2005. Metabolic footprinting and systems biology: the medium is the message. *Nat. Rev. Microbiol.* 3:557–65

73. Kerk NM, Ceserani T, Tausta SL, Sussex IM, Nelson TM. 2003. Laser capture microdissection of cells from plant tissues. *Plant Physiol.* 132:27–35

74. Khatri P, Draghici S. 2005. Ontological analysis of gene expression data: current tools, limitations, and open problems. *Bioinformatics* 21:3587–95

75. Klamt S, Stelling J, Ginkel M, Gilles ED. 2003. FluxAnalyzer: exploring structure, pathways, and flux distributions in metabolic networks on interactive flux maps. *Bioinformatics* 19:261–69

76. Lawrence CE, Altschul SF, Boguski MS, Liu JS, Neuwald AF, Wootton JC. 1993. Detecting subtle sequence signals: a Gibbs sampling strategy for multiple alignment. *Science* 262:208–14

77. Lawrence CJ, Seigfried TE, Brendel V. 2005. The maize genetics and genomics database. The community resource for access to diverse maize data. *Plant Physiol.* 138:55–58

78. Lewin B. 2003. *Genes VIII*. Upper Saddle River, NJ: Prentice Hall

79. Li L, Wang X, Xia M, Stolc V, Su N, et al. 2005. Tiling microarray analysis of rice chromosome 10 to identify the transcriptome and relate its expression to chromosomal architecture. *Genome Biol.* 6:R52

80. Liu X, Noll DM, Lieb JD, Clarke ND. 2005. DIP-chip: rapid and accurate determination of DNA-binding specificity. *Genome Res.* 15:421–27

81. Looger LL, Dwyer MA, Smith JJ, Hellinga HW. 2003. Computational design of receptor and sensor proteins with novel functions. *Nature* 423:185–90

82. Lord P, Macdonald A. 2003. *e-Science Curation Report–Data Curation for e-Science in the UK: An Audit to Establish Requirements for Future Curation and Provision*. Twickenham, UK: Digital Archiving Consultancy Ltd.

83. Lord PW, Stevens RD, Brass A, Goble CA. 2003. Investigating semantic similarity measures across the Gene Ontology: the relationship between sequence and annotation. *Bioinformatics* 19:1275–83

84. Mao X, Cai T, Olyarchuk JG, Wei L. 2005. Automated genome annotation and pathway identification using the KEGG Orthology (KO) as a controlled vocabulary. *Bioinformatics* 21:3787–93

85. Marchal K, Thijs G, De Keersmaecker S, Monsieurs P, De Moor B, Vanderleyden J. 2003. Genome-specific higher-order background models to improve motif detection. *Trends Microbiol.* 11:61–66

86. Marengo E, Robotti E, Antonucci F, Cecconi D, Campostrini N, Righetti PG. 2005. Numerical approaches for quantitative analysis of two-dimensional maps: a review of commercial software and home-made systems. *Proteomics* 5:654–66

87. Margulies M, Egholm M, Altman WE, Attiya S, Bader JS, et al. 2005. Genome sequencing in microfabricated high-density picolitre reactors. *Nature* 437:376–80

88. Matthews DE, Carollo VL, Lazo GR, Anderson OD. 2003. GrainGenes, the genome database for small-grain crops. *Nucleic Acids Res.* 31:183–86

89. Meyers BC, Galbraith DW, Nelson T, Agrawal V. 2004. Methods for transcriptional profiling in plants. Be fruitful and replicate. *Plant Physiol.* 135:637–52

90. Mockler TC, Ecker JR. 2005. Applications of DNA tiling arrays for whole-genome analysis. *Genomics* 85:1–15

91. Moreau Y, Aerts S, Moor B, Strooper B, Dabrowski M. 2003. Comparison and meta-analysis of microarray data: from the bench to the computer desk. *Trends Genet.* 19:570–77

92. Mueller LA, Solow TH, Taylor N, Skwarecki B, Buels R, et al. 2005. The SOL Genomics Network. A comparative resource for solanaceae biology and beyond. *Plant Physiol.* 138:1310–17

93. Myers EW. 1995. Toward simplifying and accurately formulating fragment assembly. *J. Comput. Biol.* 2:275–90

94. Nakazono M, Qiu F, Borsuk LA, Schnable PS. 2003. Laser-capture microdissection, a tool for the global analysis of gene expression in specific plant cell types: identification of genes expressed differentially in epidermal cells or vascular tissues of maize. *Plant Cell.* 15:583–96

95. Neumann E. 2005. A life science Semantic Web: Are we there yet? *Sci. STKE* 283:pe22

96. Newton RP, Brenton AG, Smith CJ, Dudley E. 2004. Plant proteome analysis by mass spectrometry: principles, problems, pitfalls and recent developments. *Phytochemistry* 65:1449–85

97. Noel JP, Austin MB, Bomati EK. 2005. Structure-function relationships in plant phenylpropanoid biosynthesis. *Curr. Opin. Plant Biol.* 8:249–53

98. Papin JA, Reed JL, Palsson BO. 2004. Hierarchical thinking in network biology: the unbiased modularization of biochemical networks. *Trends Biochem. Sci.* 29:641–47

99. Pappin DJ, Hojrup P, Bleasby AJ. 1993. Rapid identification of proteins by peptide-mass fingerprinting. *Curr. Biol.* 3:327–32

100. Parkinson H, Sarkans U, Shojatalab M, Abeygunawardena N, Contrino S, et al. 2005. ArrayExpress—a public repository for microarray gene expression data at the EBI. *Nucleic Acids Res.* 33:D553–55

101. Patil N, Berno AJ, Hinds DA, Barrett WA, Doshi JM, et al. 2001. Blocks of limited haplotype diversity revealed by high-resolution scanning of human chromosome 21. *Science* 294:1719–23

102. Pop M, Phillippy A, Delcher AL, Salzberg SL. 2004. Comparative genome assembly. *Brief Bioinform.* 5:237–48

103. Rhee SY. 2004. Carpe diem. Retooling the publish or perish model into the share and survive model. *Plant Physiol.* 134:543–47

104. Rhee SY, Beavis W, Berardini TZ, Chen G, Dixon D, et al. 2003. The Arabidopsis Information Resource (TAIR): a model organism database providing a centralized, curated gateway to Arabidopsis biology, research materials and community. *Nucleic Acids Res.* 31:224–28

105. Rhee SY, Crosby B. 2005. Biological databases for plant research. *Plant Physiol.* 138:1–3

106. Rhodes D, Yu J, Shanker K, Deshpande N, Varambally R, et al. 2004. Large-scale meta-analysis of cancer microarray data identifies common transcriptional profiles of neoplastic transformation and progression. *Proc. Natl. Acad. Sci. USA* 101:9309–14

107. Roberts C, Nelson B, Marton M, Stoughton R, Meyer M, et al. 2000. Signaling and circuitry of multiple MAPK pathways revealed by a matrix of global gene expression profiles. *Science* 287:873–80

108. Roth FP, Hughes JD, Estep PW, Church GM. 1998. Finding DNA regulatory motifs within unaligned noncoding sequences clustered by whole-genome mRNA quantitation. *Nat. Biotechnol.* 16:939–45

109. Saal LH, Troein C, Vallon-Christersson J, Gruvberger S, Borg Å, Peterson C. 2002. BioArray Software Environment: a platform for comprehensive management and analysis of microarray data. *Genome Biol.* 3:software0003.1–.6

110. Schauer N, Steinhauser D, Strelkov S, Schomburg D, Allison G, et al. 2005. GC-MS libraries for the rapid identification of metabolites in complex biological samples. *FEBS Lett.* 579:1332–37

111. Schena M, Shalon D, Davis RW, Brown PO. 1995. Quantitative monitoring of gene expression patterns with a complementary DNA microarray. *Science* 270:467–70

112. Schlueter SD, Dong Q, Brendel V. 2003. GeneSeqer@PlantGDB: gene structure prediction in plant genomes. *Nucleic Acids Res.* 31:3597–600

113. Schneider M, Bairoch A, Wu CH, Apweiler R. 2005. Plant protein annotation in the UniProt Knowledgebase. *Plant Physiol.* 138:59–66

114. Seo TS, Bai X, Kim DH, Meng Q, Shi S, et al. 2005. Four-color DNA sequencing by synthesis on a chip using photocleavable fluorescent nucleotides. *Proc. Natl. Acad. Sci. USA* 102:5926–31

115. Shanks JV. 2005. Phytochemical engineering: combining chemical reaction engineering with plant science. *AIChE J.* 51:2–7

116. Shen L, Gong J, Caldo RA, Nettleton D, Cook D, et al. 2005. BarleyBase—an expression profiling database for plant genomics. *Nuceic Acids Res.* 33:D614–18

117. Sinha U, Bui A, Taira R, Dionisio J, Morioka C, et al. 2002. A review of medical imaging informatics. *Ann. NY Acad. Sci.* 980:168–97

118. Slonim DK. 2002. From patterns to pathways: gene expression data analysis comes of age. *Nat. Genet.* 32:502–8

119. SMRS Working Group. 2005. Summary recommendations for standardization and reporting of metabolic analyses. *Nat. Biotechnol.* 23:833–38

120. Sriram G, Fulton DB, Iyer VV, Peterson JM, Zhou R, et al. 2004. Quantification of compartmented metabolic fluxes in developing soybean embryos by employing biosynthetically directed fractional ^{13}C labeling, two-dimensional [^{13}C, ^{1}H] nuclear magnetic resonance, and comprehensive isotopomer balancing. *Plant Physiol.* 136:3043–57

121. Steuer R, Kurths J, Fiehn O, Weckwerth W. 2003. Interpreting correlations in metabolomic networks. *Biochem. Soc. Trans.* 31:1476–78

122. Steuer R, Kurths J, Fiehn O, Weckwerth W. 2003. Observing and interpreting correlations in metabolomic networks. *Bioinformatics* 19:1019–26

123. Stevens J, Doerge R. 2005. Combining Affymetrix microarray results. *BMC Bioinformatics* 6:57

124. Stevens R, Goble CA, Bechhofer S. 2000. Ontology-based knowledge representation for bioinformatics. *Brief Bioinform.* 1:398–414

125. Stevens RD, Robinson AJ, Goble CA. 2003. myGrid: personalised bioinformatics on the information grid. *Bioinformatics* 19(Suppl.)1:i302–4

126. Stoeckert CJ Jr, Causton HC, Ball CA. 2002. Microarray databases: standards and ontologies. *Nat. Genet.* 32(Suppl.):469–73

127. Stolc V, Samanta MP, Tongprasit W, Sethi H, Liang S, et al. 2005. Identification of transcribed sequences in Arabidopsis thaliana by using high-resolution genome tiling arrays. *Proc. Natl. Acad. Sci. USA* 102:4453–58

128. Tanabe L, Scherf U, Smith LH, Lee JK, Hunter L, Weinstein JN. 1999. MedMiner: an internet text-mining tool for biomedical information, with application to gene expression profiling. *BioTechniques* 27:1210–17

129. Tchieu JH, Fana F, Fink JL, Harper J, Nair TM, et al. 2003. The PlantsP and PlantsT Functional Genomics Databases. *Nucleic Acids Res.* 31:342–44

130. The_Arabidopsis_Genome_Initiative. 2000. Analysis of the genome sequence of the flowering plant Arabidopsis thaliana. *Nature* 408:796–815

131. The_Wellcome_Trust. 2003. *Sharing Data from Large-Scale Biological Research Projects: A System of Tripartite Responsibility*. Fort Lauderdale, FL: Wellcome Trust

132. Toyoda T, Shinozaki K. 2005. Tiling array-driven elucidation of transcriptional structures based on maximum-likelihood and Markov models. *Plant J.* 43:611–21

133. Trethewey R. 2004. Metabolite profiling as an aid to metabolic engineering in plants. *Curr. Opin. Plant Biol.* 7:196–201

134. van Helden J. 2003. Regulatory sequence analysis tools. *Nucleic Acids Res.* 31:3593–96

135. Vincent PL, Coe EH, Polacco ML. 2003. Zea mays ontology—a database of international terms. *Trends Plant Sci.* 8:517–20

136. Wan X, Xu D. 2005. Computational methods for remote homolog identification. *Curr. Protein Peptide Sci.* 6:527–46

137. Ware DH, Jaiswal P, Ni J, Yap IV, Pan X, et al. 2002. Gramene, a tool for grass genomics. *Plant Physiol.* 130:1606–13

138. Weckwerth W, Loureiro M, Wenzel K, Fiehn O. 2004. Differential metabolic networks unravel the effects of silent plant phenotypes. *Proc. Natl. Acad. Sci. USA* 101:7809–14

139. Wheeler DL, Smith-White B, Chetvernin V, Resenchuk S, Dombrowski SM, et al. 2005. Plant genome resources at the national center for biotechnology information. *Plant Physiol.* 138:1280–88

140. Wiechert W, Mollney M, Petersen S, de Graaf AA. 2001. A universal framework for 13C metabolic flux analysis. *Metab. Eng.* 3:265–83

141. Wilkinson M, Schoof H, Ernst R, Haase D. 2005. BioMOBY successfully integrates distributed heterogeneous bioinformatics Web Services. The PlaNet exemplar case. *Plant Physiol.* 138:5–17

142. Woo Y, Affourtit J, Daigle S, Viale A, Johnson K, et al. 2004. A comparison of cDNA, oligonucleotide, and affymetrix GeneChip gene expression microarray platforms. *J. Biomol. Tech.* 15:276–84

143. Yamada K, Lim J, Dale JM, Chen H, Shinn P, et al. 2003. Empirical analysis of transcriptional activity in the Arabidopsis genome. *Science* 302:842–46

144. Yamazaki Y, Jaiswal P. 2005. Biological ontologies in rice databases. An introduction to the activities in Gramene and Oryzabase. *Plant Cell Physiol.* 46:63–68

145. Yates JR 3rd, Eng JK, McCormack AL, Schieltz D. 1995. Method to correlate tandem mass spectra of modified peptides to amino acid sequences in the protein database. *Anal. Chem.* 67:1426–36

146. Yona G, Levitt M. 2002. Within the twilight zone: a sensitive profile-profile comparison tool based on information theory. *J. Mol. Biol.* 315:1257–75

147. Yu J, Hu S, Wang J, Wong GK, Li S, et al. 2002. A draft sequence of the rice genome (Oryza sativa L. ssp. indica). *Science* 296:79–92

148. Yuan Q, Ouyang S, Wang A, Zhu W, Maiti R, et al. 2005. The institute for genomic research Osa1 rice genome annotation database. *Plant Physiol.* 138:18–26

149. Zhang J, Leiderman K, Pfeiffer JR, Wilson BS, Oliver JM, Steinberg SL. 2006. Characterizing the topography of membrane receptors and signaling molecules from spatial patterns obtained using nanometer-scale electron-dense probes and electron microscopy. *Micron* 37:14–34

150. Zhang MQ. 2002. Computational prediction of eukaryotic protein-coding genes. *Nat. Rev. Genet.* 3:698–709

151. Zhang P, Foerster H, Tissier CP, Mueller L, Paley S, et al. 2005. MetaCyc and AraCyc. Metabolic pathway databases for plant research. *Plant Physiol.* 138:27–37

152. Zhu H, Bilgin M, Snyder M. 2003. Proteomics. *Annu. Rev. Biochem.* 72:783–812

153. Zhu T, Wang X. 2000. Large-scale profiling of the Arabidopsis transcriptome. *Plant Physiol.* 124:1472–76

154. Zhu W, Schlueter SD, Brendel V. 2003. Refined annotation of the Arabidopsis genome by complete expressed sequence tag mapping. *Plant Physiol.* 132:469–84

155. Ding J, Viswanathan K, Berleant D, Hughes L, Wurtele ES, et al. 2005. Using the biological taxonomy to access biological literature with PathBinderH. *Bioinformatics* 21:2560–62

DISCLOSURE STATEMENT

J.D. is a PI of the PLEXdb database that focuses on using Affymetrix GeneChips for cross-species comparison.

Leaf Hydraulics

Lawren Sack[1] and N. Michele Holbrook[2]

[1] Department of Botany, University of Hawai'i at Mānoa, Honolulu, Hawaii 96822;
email: LSack@hawaii.edu

[2] Department of Organismic and Evolutionary Biology, Harvard University,
Cambridge, Massachusetts 02138

Annu. Rev. Plant Biol.
2006. 57:361–81

The *Annual Review of
Plant Biology* is online at
plant.annualreviews.org

doi: 10.1146/
annurev.arplant.56.032604.144141

First published online as a
Review in Advance on
January 30, 2006

1543-5008/06/0602-
0361$20.00

Key Words

aquaporins, cavitation, embolism, stomata, xylem

Abstract

Leaves are extraordinarily variable in form, longevity, venation architecture, and capacity for photosynthetic gas exchange. Much of this diversity is linked with water transport capacity. The pathways through the leaf constitute a substantial ($\geq 30\%$) part of the resistance to water flow through plants, and thus influence rates of transpiration and photosynthesis. Leaf hydraulic conductance (K_{leaf}) varies more than 65-fold across species, reflecting differences in the anatomy of the petiole and the venation architecture, as well as pathways beyond the xylem through living tissues to sites of evaporation. K_{leaf} is highly dynamic over a range of time scales, showing circadian and developmental trajectories, and responds rapidly, often reversibly, to changes in temperature, irradiance, and water supply. This review addresses how leaf structure and physiology influence K_{leaf}, and the mechanisms by which K_{leaf} contributes to dynamic functional responses at the level of both individual leaves and the whole plant.

Contents

INTRODUCTION

K_{leaf}: leaf hydraulic conductance (units mmol m^{-2} s^{-1} MPa^{-1})

The role of the hydraulic system in constraining plant function has long been recognized (15, 37, 135), but until recently the hydraulic properties of leaves had received little sustained attention. This is somewhat surprising given that the leaf constitutes an important hydraulic bottleneck. Research in previous decades focused on the question of the major pathways for water movement across leaves (14, 38). Current research on leaf hydraulics continues to elucidate these pathways, as well as seeks to understand the influence of the water transport pathways on gas exchange rates, the coordination of hydraulic design with leaf structural diversity, and the dynamics of leaf hydraulic conductance, diurnally, over the leaf lifetime, and in response to multiple environmental factors (**Figure 1**).

LEAF HYDRAULIC CONDUCTANCE

K_{leaf} is a measure of how efficiently water is transported through the leaf, determined as the ratio of water flow rate (F_{leaf}) through the leaf (through the petiole and veins, and across the living tissues in the leaf to the sites where water evaporates into the airspaces) to the driving force for flow, the water potential difference across the leaf ($\Delta\Psi_{leaf}$). K_{leaf} is typically normalized by leaf area (i.e., $F_{leaf}/\Delta\Psi_{leaf}$ is further divided by lamina area; units of mmol water m^{-2} s^{-1} MPa^{-1}). Hydraulic conductance is the inverse of resistance, R_{leaf}. K_{leaf} is the more commonly used metric. However, because resistances are additive in series, R_{leaf} is used in discussion of the leaf as a component of whole-plant resistance, or when partitioning the resistances within the leaf.

Why does K_{leaf} have such a strong influence on water movement through the whole plant? The resistance of open stomata to vapor diffusion out of the leaf is typically hundreds of times greater than the hydraulic resistance to bulk flow of the liquid moving through the plant (37). Transpiration rates are thus dictated by this diffusion process, which in turn depends on the stomatal and boundary-layer conductances and the difference in vapor pressure between the intercellular air spaces of the leaf and the atmosphere (**Figure 1**). However, the maintenance of open stomata depends on having a well-hydrated leaf interior, i.e., a high leaf water potential (Ψ_{leaf}). From the Ohm's law analogy for the soil-plant-atmosphere continuum (52, 135),

$$\Psi_{leaf} = \Psi_{soil} - \rho g h - E/K_{plant.} \qquad 1.$$

where E, Ψ_{soil}, ρ, g, h, and K_{plant} represent, respectively, transpiration rate, soil water potential, the density of water, acceleration due to gravity, plant height, and the whole-plant hydraulic conductance. Thus, at a given soil water supply, Ψ_{leaf} declines with higher E, with a sensitivity that depends on K_{plant}. For a leaf to sustain Ψ_{leaf} at a level high enough to maintain stomata open (i.e., for the leaf to maintain a high E, or a high g_s), K_{plant} must be sufficiently high. Consequently, K_{plant} strongly constrains plant gas exchange. As shown in the following, K_{leaf} is a major determinant of K_{plant}.

Relation to Whole-Plant Hydraulic Conductance

Leaves contribute a majority of the hydraulic resistance to water flow in shoots, and form a substantial part of the hydraulic resistance in whole plants (80, 132, 146). For 34 species of a range of life forms, the leaf, including petiole, contributed on average $\approx 30\%$ of R_{plant} ($R_{plant} = 1/K_{plant}$) (99). However, there are cases in which the leaf is reported to contribute up to 80% to 98% of R_{plant} (23, 80). Notably, the contribution of R_{leaf} will vary with time of day; early in the day, when there is net water movement from stem storage (48,

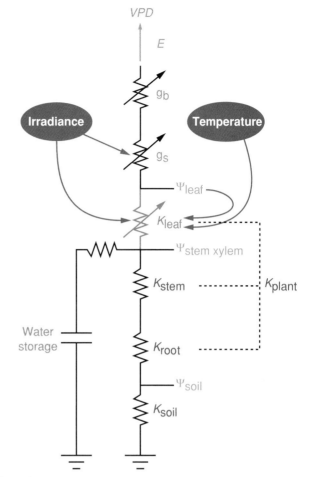

Figure 1

Leaf hydraulic conductance (K_{leaf}) as a component in a simplified electronic circuit analog of the whole-plant system (modified after 52). K_{soil}, K_{root}, K_{stem}, and K_{plant} represent, respectively, the hydraulic conductance (inverse of resistance) of soil, root, stem, and plant; Ψ_{soil}, $\Psi_{stem\ xylem}$, and Ψ_{leaf} represent the water potentials of soil, stem xylem, and leaf; g_s, g_b, E, and VPD represent the stomatal and boundary-layer conductances, transpiration rate, and leaf to air vapor pressure difference. This schema is much simplified, as Ψ_{leaf} will vary across a crown because of height differences as well as differences in transpiration and hydraulic supply to different leaves (88, 130). Impacts of microclimate on g_s and K_{leaf} are shown with red arrows; thus, K_{leaf}, like g_s and g_b, is represented as a variable conductance; decreases in Ψ_{leaf}, an internal variable, "drive" declines in K_{leaf} via its linkage with increasing xylem tensions.

123), leaves are likely to constitute a higher proportion of resistance than when water is obtained directly from the soil (**Figure 1**). Additionally, R_{leaf} changes with temperature, water supply, and irradiance, and as leaves age

E: transpiration rate
(units mmol m^{-2}
s^{-1})

Ψ_{soil}: soil water
potential (units MPa)

Ψ_{leaf}: leaf water
potential (units MPa)

K_{plant}: whole-plant
hydraulic
conductance (units
mmol m^{-2} s^{-1}
MPa^{-1})

K_{leaf}^{max}: maximum
leaf hydraulic
conductance (i.e., for
hydrated leaf; units
mmol m^{-2} s^{-1}
MPa^{-1})

(see section on Dynamics of Leaf Hydraulics Over Short and Long Time Scales), and can thus increase as a proportion of R_{plant} to become the dominant factor in defining whole-plant water transport capacity.

Maximum Leaf Hydraulic Conductance Across Species and Life Forms

Measurements of leaf hydraulic conductance for hydrated leaves (K_{leaf}^{max}), made with several methods (103), indicate a dramatic variability across the 107 species so far examined (**Figure 2**). K_{leaf}^{max} ranges 65-fold from the lowest value (for the fern *Adiantum lunulatum*; 0.76 mmol m^{-2} s^{-1} MPa^{-1}) to the highest (for the tropical tree *Macaranga triloba*; 49 mmol m^{-2} s^{-1} MPa^{-1}). K_{leaf}^{max} is highly variable within a life form, varying by tenfold among coexisting tree species (104), and on average tends to be lowest for conifers and pteridophytes, higher for temperate and tropical woody angiosperms, and highest for crop plants (**Figure 2**). The model species *Arabidopsis thaliana* and *Nicotiana tabacum* have moderate

values of 12 and 26 mmol m^{-2} s^{-1} MPa^{-1}, respectively (68, 115). Interspecific variation in K_{leaf}^{max} reflects differences in the anatomy of the petiole and venation, as well as pathways beyond the xylem through living tissues to sites of evaporation.

PATHWAYS OF WATER MOVEMENT IN THE LEAF

Water Movement Through Leaf Xylem: Petiole and Venation

On entering the petiole of a dicotyledonous leaf, the vascular bundles in the leaf traces reorganize, differentially supplying midrib bundles, which branch into the second- and third-order veins (42, 58). Water exits the major veins into the surrounding tissue, or into the minor veins, the tracheid-containing fine veins embedded in the mesophyll (5, 27). In dicotyledons the minor veins account for the preponderance of the total vein length (e.g., 86%–97% in temperate and tropical trees) (91, 100). Thus, the bulk of transpired water will be drawn out of minor veins, resulting in the major and minor veins acting approximately in series (99, 146).

Leaf vein systems are enormously variable in many aspects: in vein arrangement and density; and in the number, size, and geometry of the vascular bundles in the veins; and of the xylem conduits within the bundles (97). These structural characteristics play a critical role in how water is distributed across the leaf, and thus an increasing number of studies focus on the relationship of K_{leaf}^{max} to venation architecture. K_{leaf}^{max} correlates with the dimensions of conduits in the midrib (1, 3, 79, 100), and for ten species of tropical trees, correlated strongly with the midrib conductivity calculated from the Poiseuille equation for the xylem conduits (100). This correlation does not imply that the midrib is a substantial constraint on the conductance of the venation, or on K_{leaf}^{max}, but rather implies a scaling of hydraulic resistances throughout the leaf (see below) (100). Higher minor vein density in

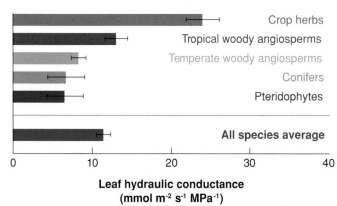

Figure 2

Leaf hydraulic conductance averaged for contrasting life forms (for hydrated whole leaves, including petiole, and when possible for fully illuminated sun leaves; data pooled across plant age and habitat; pteridophytes, 4 species, 19, 24; conifers, 6 species, 7, 24, 133; temperate woody angiosperms, 38 species; 1, 24, 34, 47, 63, 64, 81, 83, 92, 99, 102, 106, 130–133, 146; tropical woody angiosperms, 49 species, 7, 16–20, 24, 41, 104, 118, 131, 133; crop herbs, 7 species, 65, 82, 115, 117, 124–126; all species average for 107 species also includes 2 grass species, 19, 66; and *Arabidopsis*, 68) Error bars = 1 SE.

general corresponds to a higher supply capacity (or $K_{\text{leaf}}^{\text{max}}$), not by increasing the conductance through the vein xylem system per se (34), but rather primarily by increasing the surface area for exchange of xylem water with surrounding mesophyll, and reducing the distance through which water travels outside the xylem (97, 100). By contrast, the arrangement and density of *major veins* is not related to $K_{\text{leaf}}^{\text{max}}$ (100). However, major vein arrangement plays an essential role in distributing water equitably across the lamina (97, 150), and redundancy of major veins could buffer the impacts of damage and/or cavitation (discussed below).

Water Movement Outside the Xylem: Bundle Sheath and Mesophyll

Water movement pathways outside the xylem are complex and potentially vary strongly across species that diverge in leaf mesophyll anatomy. Important progress has been made on this critical topic, although a full understanding will likely require new approaches.

Once water leaves the xylem, it enters the bundle sheath, made up of parenchymatous cells wrapped around the veins (42). A number of early studies concluded that water exits the xylem through cell walls, moving around the bundle sheath protoplasts, because membranes were thought to be too resistive to occur in the transpirational pathways (e.g., 12, 13). However, the presence of aquaporins and the high surface area for water transport across the membranes of bundle sheath cells means that intercellular water movement is, in fact, plausible (53, 68, 102, 112). Indeed, in some species, water seems constrained to enter bundle sheath cells by suberized perpendicular walls, a barrier analogous to the root Casparian strip (60, 136). Dye experiments suggest movement into the bundle sheath cells; in leaves transpiring a solution of apoplastic dye, crystals form in the minor veins (27). Other evidence comes from the temperature response of measured K_{leaf} (69, 102) and the recently demonstrated role of aquaporins (82, but see 68), both consistent with crossing membranes (see below). The bundle sheath cells may be a "control center" in leaf water transport, the locus for the striking temperature and light responses of K_{leaf}.

What happens to water once it passes out of the xylem into the bundle sheath and beyond? Although this is clearly a question of great importance, current evidence remains indirect. A large portion of the mesophyll volume is airspace, with limited cell-to-cell contact, but spongy mesophyll cells are in contact to a far greater degree than palisade cells, and thus would seem better suited to conduct water (142, 143). The epidermis has substantial cell-to-cell contact, and water could move directly there from the minor veins, in species with bundle sheath extensions—tightly packed, chloroplast-free cells that connect the bundle sheath that surrounds the minor veins to the epidermides in many species (70, 145). In those species, the epidermis can remain hydrated despite having little vertical contact with the photosynthetic mesophyll (59, 138). In species lacking bundle sheath extensions, water must move across the mesophyll. Whether water moves principally apoplastically (i.e., in the cell walls), transcellularly (i.e., crossing membranes), or symplastically (i.e., cell-to-cell via plasmodesmata) is not yet known, and probably differs among species and conditions. The first experimental studies on sunflower suggested that apoplastic movement dominates during transpiration, and that water crosses mesophyll membranes only during rehydration or growth (13, 139). However, other experiments showed that movement through symplastic routes was plausible (129, 134); the cell pressure probe has indicated significant symplastic water transport among mesophyll cells in succulent *Kalanchoë* leaves (77).

Finally, there is the question of where in the leaf water evaporates, important because the resistances in the pathways to those sites will determine overall R_{leaf}. Mathematical and physical models predict that evaporation inside the leaf will occur principally near the stomata—from surrounding epidermal cells, and/or from the mesophyll directly above the stomata, and/or from the guard cells themselves (71, 134). However, such models do not account for the fact that in at least several species, the cuticle extends into the substomatal cavity, potentially reducing evaporation (90 and references therein). An alternative scenario is that most water evaporates deep within the mesophyll, close to the veins (13, 14). Circumstantial support for this idea comes from the fact that the measurement of resistance to helium diffusion across an amphistomatous leaf equaled about twice that of water vapor out of the leaf—which travels half the distance (43), suggesting that water begins its diffusion deep within the leaf (14). A third scenario is that water evaporates relatively evenly throughout the mesophyll (87). This scenario predicts a vapor diffusion pathway similar to that of CO_2 assimilated during photosynthesis (though opposite in direction). Indeed, the computation of intercellular CO_2 concentration using typical photosynthesis systems relies on this assumption (44), as does the use of the pressure bomb to estimate the driving force for transpiration (103, 146). Where water principally evaporates within the leaf is not clear; the data from modeling, dye studies, biophysics, and gas exchange measurements do not provide a coherent story. A definitive answer is likely to require new approaches, such as the use of in vivo imaging to track changes in cell dimensions within transpiring leaves (e.g., 111).

A complete understanding of water flow pathways will illuminate several important aspects of leaf function, including the enrichment of oxygen isotopes (6), and the response of stomata to leaf water status. Guard cells can respond within seconds (93, 95, 98, 114); their movement depends on cell water potential and turgor pressure, which in turn depends on where precisely the bulk of water evaporates in the leaf, and on the hydraulic conductances from the veins to epidermis and guard cells (e.g., 26, 45). Quantifying these

parameters should help explain the onset of patchy behavior of stomata at small scales (76).

Partitioning the Leaf Hydraulic Resistance

How is K_{leaf} determined from these complex pathways of water movement? This question is especially important because the way in which the leaf hydraulic resistance ($= 1/K_{leaf}$) is partitioned between the xylem and across the extraxylem pathways will strongly influence the responsiveness of R_{leaf} to changing conditions. If the resistance of the leaf xylem (R_{xylem}) is a major component of R_{leaf}, then the enormous variation in venation architecture across species could reflect strong differences in R_{leaf}. That would be very unlikely, however, if R_{xylem} were negligible relative to the extraxylem resistance ($R_{outside xylem}$); in that case, even large relative differences in R_{xylem} among species would have little impact on overall R_{leaf}. Additionally, the larger R_{xylem} is, relative to $R_{outside xylem}$, the greater the effect on R_{leaf} of changes in R_{xylem} due to environment (e.g., drought-induced cavitation; see 72). Thus, substantial discussion surrounds the issue of where the major resistances to water flow occur within leaves (e.g., 34, 47, 82, 102, 104). Some of this controversy resulted from methodological differences, including the failure to take into account the effect of irradiance on R_{leaf} (see below) and the use of treatments to determine R_{xylem} that opened up pathways for water to move out of low-order veins, bypassing conduit endings and higher-order veins that contain higher resistance; using those methods resulted in estimates of R_{xylem} as 27% of R_{leaf}, averaged for the ten species tested (12, 34, 109, 125, 128–130, 146). Recent studies conducted under high irradiance, in which only minor veins were severed, found R_{xylem} to be 59% of R_{leaf}, averaged for 14 species (47, 82, 102, 104).

The current consensus is that the hydraulic resistance of the leaf's xylem is about the same order as in the extraxylem pathways (47, 79,

82, 102, 104; but see 34), and that species vary in their partitioning. Indeed, among tropical trees, the % of R_{leaf} in the xylem differed significantly between species (ranging from 26% to 89%); species that establish in high-light environments had 70% of R_{leaf} in the xylem on average, whereas those from low irradiance had 52% (104). Despite this variation, across the range of species' values, R_{xylem}, $R_{outside\ xylem}$ and R_{leaf} were linearly correlated across species (104). The implications of this finding are that differences in venation architecture reflect strong differences in R_{leaf}, and also that R_{leaf} will be sensitive to changes in the conductance of both the xylem and extraxylem pathways. Indeed, the ratio of R_{xylem} to $R_{outside\ xylem}$ is dynamic. For example, R_{xylem} will increase if vein xylem embolizes during drought, whereas $R_{outside\ xylem}$ changes according to an endogenous circadian rhythm, and also increases under low irradiance (82, 101, 131); both resistances increase at lower temperatures, with $R_{outside\ xylem}$ increasing more strongly (69, 102; see below).

Because leaf vein systems consist of water movement through a well-defined arrangement of fixed tubes, they should be amenable to quantitative methods used in the study of biological (and other) networks (e.g., 8, 34, 66, 102, 140, 147). In the most anatomically explicit model to date, R_{xylem} is estimated for dicotyledonous leaves by assuming Poiseuille flow through a network parameterized with measured venation densities and conduit numbers and dimensions (34). However, contrary to empirical data, which showed that R_{xylem} constitutes on average over 50% of R_{leaf} (see above), the model suggested from the xylem conduit measurements that R_{xylem} was only ≈2% of R_{leaf}. Thus, anatomical features not included in the model, for example, the resistance to water movement between xylem conduits, must play an important role (34, 121). Next generation studies will improve our ability to scale up from anatomical measurements to accurate prediction of venation network R_{xylem}.

COORDINATION OF MAXIMUM LEAF HYDRAULIC CONDUCTANCE WITH LEAF STRUCTURE AND FUNCTION

The coordination of hydraulics with leaf structure and gas exchange is likely to have played a critical role in the early evolution of the laminate leaf. Lower CO_2 levels and cooler temperatures during the Devonian would have allowed large leaves to avoid overheating, but the higher stomatal densities, which evolved to maintain CO_2 assimilation, would have led to more rapid transpiration (89) and thus required concomitant increases in leaf hydraulic capacity (9–11). The coordination among leaf hydraulic supply and demand and leaf form remains a key design element among modern plants.

Coordination with Gas Exchange

Recent work demonstrates correlations across species between liquid phase (hydraulic) conductances of stems, shoots, or whole plants and vapor phase (stomatal) conductance (g_s) and maximum rates of gas exchange (e.g., 3, 54, 57, 73, 74, 80, 110). Consistent with this matching of hydraulic supply and demand is the strong coordination across species between K_{leaf}^{max} and stomatal pore area per leaf area, maximum g_s, and photosynthetic capacity (3, 19, 24, 99, 104).

What is the basis for the interspecific coordination of leaf hydraulic properties and gas exchange? The coordination of K_{plant} (and K_{leaf}) and maximum g_s and E would arise from convergence among species in Ψ_{leaf}, Ψ_{soil}, boundary-layer conductance and leaf-to-air vapor pressure difference (see Equation 1 and **Figure 1**) (104). Given that hydraulic conductances scale through the plant (99), species would converge also in the water potential of the stem xylem proximal to the leaf ($\Psi_{stem\ xylem}$), the water potential drop across the leaf ($\Delta\Psi_{leaf} = \Psi_{leaf} - \Psi_{stem\ xylem}$), and that across the whole plant ($\Delta\Psi_{plant} = \Psi_{leaf} - \Psi_{soil}$; 74). The linkage indicates a "standardization" of water relations among plants of

g_s: stomatal conductance to water vapor (units mmol m^{-2} s^{-1})

a given life form and vegetation type during peak transpiration, when soil is moist. There is evidence of strong convergence in water relations parameters Ψ_{leaf}, $\Psi_{stem\ xylem}$, $\Delta\Psi_{leaf}$, and Ψ_{soil} during peak transpiration for plants of a given system in moist soil during the growing season (23, 24, 55, 80, 123). The typically modest range in these parameters (typically $\pm <0.5$ MPa) occurs despite variation within a vegetation type in plant size and age, rooting depth and vulnerability to cavitation, as well as divergence among species in the season during which they manifest peak activity, which would further destabilize the coordination (104). The convergence in $\Delta\Psi$ is

analogous to the range of household appliances in a given country being designed to run at a given voltage—from lamps to ovens—with the current through the appliance dependent on the electric conductance, or resistance.

The finding of narrowly constrained water relations in a given vegetation type provides a potentially powerful basis for a general relationship between K_{leaf} and maximum rates of gas exchange. In addition, increased understanding of how the coordination of K_{leaf}^{max} and gas exchange shifts across life forms and habitats will allow prediction of performance differences for plants adapted to different zones around the world. One study so far has demonstrated that the coordination between hydraulics and gas exchange varies among vegetation types: Tropical rainforest trees as a group have higher potential gas exchange relative to K_{leaf} than temperate deciduous trees, consistent with their adaptation to higher Ψ_{leaf} and Ψ_{soil}, and/or lower VPD during peak activity (104).

Coordination with Leaf Flux-Related Structural Traits

Leaves vary tremendously in area, thickness, shape, nutrient concentrations, and capacity for gas exchange. The intercorrelation of many traits places some bound on this diversity, for instance among those related to carbon economy, including leaf mass per area (LMA; leaf dry mass/area), leaf lifespan (e.g., 96, 141), and nitrogen concentration per mass and net maximum photosynthetic rate per mass (A_{mass}; 141), and provides a framework for understanding the integrated function of clusters of traits. Similarly, coordination among traits related to water flux through leaves exists for plants of a particular life form and habitat (99) (**Table 1**). In addition to their higher total maximum stomatal pore area and gas exchange per area (see above; 3, 19, 99), leaves with high K_{leaf}^{max} tend to have wider xylem conduits in the midrib and higher venation densities (3, 102). K_{leaf}^{max} correlated

Table 1 Leaf structural and functional traits, sorted by putative association with maximum water flux per area (and K_{leaf}), leaf mass per area, or drought tolerance[a] across species

Maximum flux-related traits
  Leaf hydraulic conductance
  Stomatal pore area
  Stomatal conductance
  Net maximum photosynthesis per area
  Leaf midrib xylem conduit diameters
  Mesophyll area/leaf area
  Thickness of leaf and palisade mesophyll
  Leaf chlorophyll concentration per area
  Leaf nitrogen concentration per area
  Leaf shape (margin dissection)
  Leaf water storage capacitance per area

Leaf mass per area-related traits
  Leaf density
  Leaf thickness
  Leaf lifespan
  Leaf chlorophyll concentration per mass (negatively related)
  Leaf nitrogen concentration per mass (negatively related)
  Leaf water content per mass (negatively related)

Leaf drought tolerance traits
  Cuticular conductance (negatively related)
  Modulus of elasticity (variably related)
  Leaf density (variably related)
  Leaf water storage capacitance per area
  Osmotic potentials at full and at zero turgor
  Resistance to leaf xylem cavitation

[a]Associations are positive except when noted.

with palisade thickness, and palisade/spongy mesophyll ratio for tropical rainforest tree species (100), and with total leaf thickness and water storage capacitance per area for temperate woody species (99). These correlations arose due to structural coordination— the sharing of an anatomical or developmental basis—and/or due to functional coordination—the coselection of characters for benefit in a particular environment (99, 116).

Independence of Maximum K_{leaf} and Traits Related to Leaf Mass Per Area, or to Leaf Drought Tolerance

Certain leaf traits show a disproportionate number of linkages with other traits (86). *LMA* is one such "hub" trait (**Table 1**). However, K_{leaf}^{max}, a hub trait in its own right (being linked with many water-flux traits), is unrelated to *LMA* (**Table 1**) (20, 78, 99, 104, 133). Because this complex of water flux–related traits is coordinated with net maximum photosynthesis per leaf area, which is equal to *LMA* in its driving differences in A_{mass} across species globally (data in 141), and because A_{mass} generally scales up to whole-plant relative growth rate, water flux–related traits including K_{leaf} are a potentially fundamental determinant of species performance differences. However, K_{leaf}^{max} is apparently independent of a partially interrelated complex of traits associated with leaf drought tolerance, i.e., the ability to maintain positive turgor and gas exchange at low Ψ_{leaf} (**Table 1**). These traits are evidently coselected by desiccating conditions (85, 107), and include low osmotic potentials at full and at zero turgor, and low cuticular conductance (99, 100).

DYNAMICS OF LEAF HYDRAULICS OVER SHORT AND LONG TIME SCALES

K_{leaf} is highly dynamic, varying over a wide range of time scales, from minutes to months, and according to microclimate and growing conditions. The dynamics of K_{leaf} are typically closely correlated with those of gas exchange (Equation 1 and **Figure 1**) (32, 35, 36, 69, 72). As K_{leaf} declines (e.g., owing to dehydration), Ψ_{leaf} will similarly decline, and stomata will close as, or before, Ψ_{leaf} becomes damaging, leading to reduction of g_s and E (32, 108). In droughted plants such a mechanism operates in tandem with chemical signals from the roots to close the stomata (36, 39). Associated declines in intercellular CO_2 concentration (c_i) drive a reduction in photosynthetic rate (46, 69). Declines in Ψ_{leaf} can also directly reduce photosynthetic rate metabolically (40). Why is K_{leaf} dynamic, given that its decline drives such loss of function? K_{leaf} reduction during water stress would protect the xylem by driving stomatal closure, thus alleviating the tensions in the transpiration stream. Also, membrane channels important in maintaining a high K_{leaf} require metabolic energy for expression and potentially for activation.

Responses of Leaf Hydraulic Conductance to Dehydration and Damage

The hydraulic conductance of the petiole ($K_{petiole}$) and of the whole leaf declines during drought, correlating in vivo with declines in gas exchange (**Figure 3a**) (17–19, 25, 30, 32, 33, 49, 50, 62, 63, 81, 83, 105, 108, 109, 117, 124, 125, 149). An important factor contributing to the decline of K_{leaf} at low Ψ_{leaf} is xylem cavitation (55, 83, 149). Petioles with lower conductance take up dye into fewer vessels (25, 149), and dehydrated leaves take up dye into fewer minor veins in the network (83, 105, 124, 125). The xylem can become increasingly vulnerable with increasing drying iterations—i.e., "cavitation fatigue," as shown in petioles of *Aesculus hippocastanum* (50). However, cavitation is not the only potential source of K_{leaf} decline during dehydration. Dehydrating conifer leaves decline in K_{leaf} owing to collapse of xylem conduits, which precedes cavitation (21, 33). The potential collapse of xylem conduits in dicotyledonous

LMA: leaf mass per area (leaf dry mass/area; units g m^{-2})

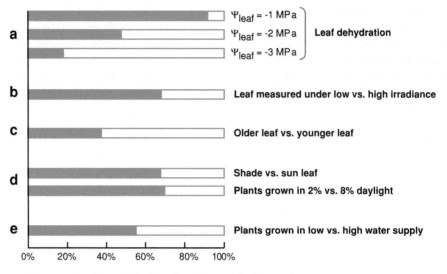

Mean reduction of leaf hydraulic conductance in given conditions

Figure 3

Leaf hydraulic conductance is highly dynamic, as shown by the responses depicted here with respect to controls (color as a proportion of white bars). Note that the averaged responses shown are only indicative—the responses vary strongly in magnitude according to the particular species and ranges of conditions observed. (*a*) Response to branch dehydration (13 species; 17, 19, 63, 83, 124, 125); (*b*) response to incident irradiance, during measurement over minutes to hours (14 species; 34, 47, 82, 101, 131); (*c*) response related to leaf aging (9 tree species; 16, 18, 20, 64, 106); (*d*) response to growth irradiance, including shade vs sun leaves (4 tree species; 99), and leaves of plants grown in 2% versus 8% daylight (2 species, 41); (*e*) response to water supply during growth (3 species; 1, 41).

leaves remains to be investigated, as does the additional possibility of decline in conductance of the extra-xylem paths. A strikingly rapid and complete recovery of K_{leaf} during rehydration has been documented after rewatering droughted plants or rehydrating partially dehydrated leaves (62, 63, 75, 124). Such short-term increases in K_{leaf} result from a diversity of mechanisms. For example, conifers elastically recover their xylem geometry on rewatering (21, 33), whereas rice leaves reverse embolism through root pressure (122). Where root pressure is not operating, an active mechanism may exist for embolism refilling even when xylem tensions exist, involving ion pumping or transient pressures, associated with increasing starch degradation (25, 124, 149).

Because the linkage of K_{leaf} and gas exchange is mediated by Ψ_{leaf} and species diverge in their Ψ_{leaf} responses, the extent to which K_{leaf} and g_s remain coordinated during dehydration varies among species. The distance between Ψ_{leaf} at stomatal closure ($\Psi_{stomatal\ closure}$) and the Ψ_{leaf} at which the xylem is irreversibly embolized is termed the safety margin (19, 119, 120). In species with a wide safety margin, the risk is minimal, as stomata close before K_{leaf} declines substantially (19, 30, 32, 83). However, in other species, with a narrow safety margin, g_s declines by half only after K_{leaf} or $K_{petiole}$ decline by 20% or more (17–19, 25, 62, 63, 80, 105, 108, 125). High safety margins protect the xylem, but lower safety margins allow plants to maintain gas exchange closer to the level of irreversible K_{leaf} decline (19, 120). The decline in K_{leaf} would confer safety to the whole-plant hydraulic system by augmenting the decline in Ψ_{leaf}, accelerating stomatal closure, which would protect portions of the plant that are less easily replaced (18). The protection conferred will vary according to species, because species differ in whether whole leaves, petioles, and midribs are more (17, 22, 28, 49, 84, 105, 108, 125), equally (33), or less (32, 49, 83, 122) vulnerable to loss of conductance compared with the stem as Ψ_{leaf} declines (and xylem tensions increase).

One of the most commonly investigated patterns in stem hydraulics is a trade-off between hydraulic efficiency (i.e., maximum hydraulic conductance) and resistance to drought-induced cavitation (135). This pattern is not found in leaves: The vulnerability of K_{leaf} to drought is not higher for leaves with high K_{leaf}^{max}. In our analysis of the available data for 13 species of ferns, trees, and herbs varying 42-fold in K_{leaf}^{max}, Ψ_{leaf} at 50% loss of conductivity ranged from –1.3 MPa to –3 MPa, and was uncorrelated with K_{leaf}^{max} ($r^2 = 0.07$; $P = 0.4$; data of 17, 19, 63, 83, 124, 125).

K_{leaf} is also reduced by herbivory and other forms of mechanical vein damage. The interruption of major veins was classically held to have no effect on leaf function, as leaves often survive with a perfectly healthy appearance (29, 91). However, damage that interrupts primary veins in dicotyledonous leaves immediately produces massive declines in K_{leaf}, and in g_s and photosynthetic rates, which persist weeks later, after the wounded tissue has scarred over; in some species, the leaves desiccate (4, 51, 81, 98). Whether major vein disruption leads to tissue death or not would depend at least as much on evaporative demand and on the leaf's ability to reduce water loss (i.e., with an impermeable cuticle) as on the leaf's vascular architecture. However, redundancy in the venation—such as conduits in parallel within each vein, and multiple veins of each order—would buffer K_{leaf} against both cavitation and damage, by providing pathways around damaged or blocked veins (29, 51, 84, 97, 137).

Responses of Leaf Hydraulic Conductance to Changes in Temperature and Irradiance

K_{leaf}^{max} increases at higher temperatures, as shown in experiments conducted in vivo, determining gas exchange while manipulating temperature and controlling other microclimatic variables (46). This increase is only partially accounted for by the direct effects of temperature on the viscosity of water. Investigation of the temperature response of water flow through shoots and leaves showed an activation energy of 26–27 kJ mol^{-1}, but when minor veins were severed, so that water was forced through only xylem, the activation energy dropped to $\approx$17 kJ mol^{-1}, which corresponds to changes in the viscosity of water (12, 102, 127, 128). Thus, the viscosity response applies to the xylem pathways, whereas an extraviscosity response applies to the pathways outside the xylem (102), consistent with the flow path crossing membranes (68). The temperature induced changes in K_{leaf}^{max} can allow Ψ_{leaf} and g_s to remain stable even as E increases due to higher VPD (46, 69).

K_{leaf}^{max} responds strongly to irradiance; for many species K_{leaf} is much lower when measured at low irradiance than at high irradiance (i.e., at <10 μmol photons m^{-2} s^{-1} versus at >1000 μmol photons m^{-2} s^{-1}) (**Figure 3b**) (82, 101, 131). The responses vary across species, and can range up to a several-fold increase from low to high irradiance. The kinetics of the K_{leaf}^{max} response to irradiance differs sufficiently from that of stomatal aperture to suggest that the light response arises in the hydraulic pathways through the mesophyll (131), and involves activation of aquaporins (53, 82, 131). These same channels apparently follow an endogenous circadian rhythm: In sunflower, K_{leaf}^{max} increases up to 60% from night to day, and the rhythm can be reversed if photoperiod is switched, and the rhythm continues for days even when plants are kept in constant darkness (82). The response can be removed by treatment with HgCl$_2$, and recovered by using mercaptoethanol,

VPD: mole fraction vapor pressure difference between leaf and outside air (units mol mol^{-1})

implying the agency of aquaporins (82). In sunflower, dark-acclimated leaves show a strong light response, but light-acclimated leaves do not, suggesting that their water channels are already activated (82). The deactivation of aquaporins in the dark would be adaptive, assuming the maintenance of activity requires energy expenditure. For plants kept in the dark for 1 h, or for 4–6 days, K_{leaf}^{max} and shoot hydraulic conductances (measured under high irradiance) were reduced by 20%–75% on average (2, 117). The response of K_{leaf}^{max} to irradiance implies the existence of a previously unknown level of control of a plant's response to environment; this response would facilitate the increases of stomatal aperture and leaf gas exchange with increasing irradiance by improving water supply to the mesophyll.

Diurnal Rhythms in Leaf Hydraulic Conductance

K_{leaf} is dynamic diurnally, and its changes reflect simultaneous responses to multiple factors. As discussed above, K_{leaf} follows an endogenous circadian rhythm; K_{leaf} also increases with incident light over the scale of minutes and hours (64, 101, 131). Additionally, K_{leaf} increases with temperature. By contrast, K_{leaf} declines as leaves dehydrate under high midday temperatures and VPD. Thus, contrasting trends have been observed for the diurnal response of K_{leaf}. For sunflower, and for four tree species, K_{leaf} increased by up to two- to threefold over a few hours from morning to midday, as irradiance and temperature increased, and then declined by evening, in a similar pattern as g and E (64, 126). On the other hand, a midday decline in K_{leaf} by 30% to 50% has been observed for tree species as transpiration increased to high rates by midday (18, 83), apparently as a response to leaf dehydration. Similar diurnal declines in conductance were found for tree petioles and for flow axially across rice leaves (25, 122, 149). In other species no diurnal patterns were observed (31, 149). Such variable patterns in di-

urnal responses of K_{leaf} are likely to reflect the particular combinations of irradiance, leaf and air temperature, soil moisture, and VPD, as well as endogenous rhythms. Thus, one would expect K_{leaf} to increase each morning in response to internal cues, as well as increasing irradiance and temperature; but if E is driven high enough by a high VPD (and/or if soil is dry), low Ψ_{leaf} would result in significant declines in K_{leaf} and in g_s, recovering by the end of the day.

Trajectories of Leaf Hydraulic Conductance During Development and Leaf Aging

K_{leaf} is also dynamic over the lifetime of the leaf. K_{leaf} increases in developing leaves as the vasculature matures (1, 20, 67). Weeks or months after K_{leaf} reaches its maximum, it begins to decline, with reductions of up to 80–90% at abscission (**Figure 3c**) (1, 16, 18, 64, 100, 106). One factor contributing to this decline of K_{leaf} is the accumulation of emboli in the vein xylem, and eventual blockage by tyloses (106, 135). K_{leaf} would decline also owing to reduction of the permeability of cell walls or membranes (see 136). Decreases in K_{leaf} would cause progressive dehydration, potentially contributing to the observed decline in midday Ψ_{leaf} as leaves age (16, 65, 106). Reductions in K_{leaf} are coordinated with age-related declines in other functional traits, including leaf nitrogen concentration, stomatal sensitivity to VPD, leaf osmotic potential, and gas exchange (e.g., 56, 94). Some have hypothesized that the seasonal decline of K_{leaf} is a trigger for leaf senescence (16, 106).

Plasticity of Leaf Hydraulic Conductance Across Growing Conditions

Although most studies of leaf hydraulics have been performed on plants in high-resource conditions, K_{leaf}^{max} is highly plastic across growing conditions, owing to developmental changes in vein density, conduit sizes or numbers (e.g., 3), and/or in the structure and conductivity of extraxylem pathways. Leaves expanded in shade—or in crown positions liable to shade—have low $K_{\text{leaf}}^{\text{max}}$ relative to sun leaves (**Figure 3d**) (99, 113), part of the complex of shade leaf characters including lower vein densities, smaller stomata, thinner leaves, less dissected leaf shape, and lower rates of gas exchange (e.g., 61, 144, 148). In mature sunflower plants, $K_{\text{leaf}}^{\text{max}}$ was linearly related to irradiance from basal to apical leaves (65); in this case an irradiance effect combines with an age effect. $K_{\text{leaf}}^{\text{max}}$ is also plastic across plant growing conditions. $K_{\text{leaf}}^{\text{max}}$ and shoot hydraulic conductance were lower for plants grown several months in lower irradiance (**Figure 3d**) (41), or in lower water or nitrogen supplies (**Figure 3e**) (1–3, 41). Such plasticity in $K_{\text{leaf}}^{\text{max}}$ runs in parallel with adaptive differences, as sun-adapted species tend to have several-fold higher $K_{\text{leaf}}^{\text{max}}$ than shade-adapted species on average, for temperate and tropical species sets (79, 104). These findings suggest that $K_{\text{leaf}}^{\text{max}}$ plays a potentially important role in determining plant resource responses and also in determining ecological preferences among species.

SUMMARY POINTS

1. $K_{\text{leaf}}^{\text{max}}$ varies at least 65-fold across species, and scales with K_{plant}; the leaf is a substantial resistance in the plant pathway, 30% and upward of whole-plant resistance.

2. The partitioning of resistances within the leaf among petiole, major veins, minor veins, and pathways outside the xylem is variable across species. Substantial hydraulic resistances occur both in the leaf xylem as well as in the flow paths across the mesophyll to evaporation sites. These components respond differently to ambient conditions, including irradiance and temperature, indicating an involvement of aquaporins.

3. $K_{\text{leaf}}^{\text{max}}$ is coordinated with maximum gas exchange rates for species of a particular life form and habitat. This coordination arises from convergence in water relations parameters, especially Ψ_{leaf} at peak transpiration. $K_{\text{leaf}}^{\text{max}}$ is also coordinated with a framework of other traits related to leaf water flux, including stomatal pore area, midrib xylem conduit diameters, and palisade richness. However, $K_{\text{leaf}}^{\text{max}}$ is independent of the complex of traits linked with leaf mass per area, and traits relating to leaf drought tolerance.

4. K_{leaf} is highly dynamic—varying diurnally, as leaves age, and in response to changes in leaf hydration, irradiance, temperature, and nutrient supply. The decline in K_{leaf} in response to lower Ψ_{leaf} arises from reductions in xylem conductivity due to cavitation or collapse, and/or from changes in the conductivity of the pathways outside the xylem. Some short-term declines in K_{leaf} can be rapidly reversed. Dynamic changes in K_{leaf} impact gas exchange via stomatal regulation of Ψ_{leaf} and could play a role in leaf senescence.

FUTURE ISSUES

1. Still needed is a fully quantitative understanding of how $K_{\text{leaf}}^{\text{max}}$ is determined by the venation architecture and the extraxylem pathways, including the identity and behavior of aquaporins in these pathways.

2. The precise correlations that link K_{leaf} with gas exchange and leaf structure among species of particular life forms and habitats need to be determined, as well as the shifts of this coordination across life forms and habitats. The patterns of general coordination will enable predictions of water relations behavior for whole sets of species from simply measured hydraulic parameters.

3. The mechanisms for the diurnal and developmental dynamics of K_{leaf}, and for the reversible K_{leaf} responses to irradiance and to dehydration need to be elucidated in detail. Understanding the mechanisms behind these changes will enhance the ability to model the influence of these dynamics on gas exchange over short and long time scales.

ACKNOWLEDGMENTS

We thank Kristen Frole for valuable assistance with the data compilation.

LITERATURE CITED

1. Aasamaa K, Niinemets Ü, Sober A. 2005. Leaf hydraulic conductance in relation to anatomical and functional traits during *Populus tremula* leaf ontogeny. *Tree Physiol.* 25:1409–18

2. Aasamaa K, Sober A. 2001. Hydraulic conductance and stomatal sensitivity to changes of leaf water status in six deciduous tree species. *Biol. Plant.* 44:65–73

3. Aasamaa K, Sober A, Rahi M. 2001. Leaf anatomical characteristics associated with shoot hydraulic conductance, stomatal conductance and stomatal sensitivity to changes of leaf water status in temperate deciduous trees. *Aust. J. Plant Physiol.* 28:765–74

4. Aldea M, Hamilton JG, Resti JP, Zangerl AR, Berenbaum MR, DeLucia EH. 2005. Indirect effects of insect herbivory on leaf gas exchange in soybean. *Plant Cell Environ.* 28:402–11

5. Altus DP, Canny MJ, Blackman DR. 1985. Water pathways in wheat leaves. 2. Water-conducting capacities and vessel diameters of different vein types, and the behavior of the integrated vein network. *Aust. J. Plant Physiol.* 12:183–99

6. Barbour MM, Farquhar GD. 2004. Do pathways of water movement and leaf anatomical dimensions allow development of gradients in $H_2{}^{18}O$ between veins and the sites of evaporation within leaves? *Plant Cell Environ.* 27:107–21

7. Becker P, Tyree MT, Tsuda M. 1999. Hydraulic conductances of angiosperms versus conifers: similar transport sufficiency at the whole-plant level. *Tree Physiol.* 19:445–52

8. Bohn S, Andreotti B, Douady S, Munzinger J, Couder Y. 2002. Constitutive property of the local organization of leaf venation networks. *Phys. Rev. E* 65

9. Boyce CK. 2005. Patterns of segregation and convergence in the evolution of fern and seed plant leaf morphologies. *Paleobiology* 31:117–40

10. Boyce CK. 2005. The evolutionary history of roots and leaves. In *Vascular Transport in Plants*, ed. NM Holbrook and MA Zwieniecki, pp. 479–99. Oxford: Elsevier/Academic

11. Boyce CK, Knoll AH. 2002. Evolution of developmental potential and the multiple independent origins of leaves in Paleozoic vascular plants. *Paleobiology* 28:70–100

12. Boyer JS. 1974. Water transport in plants: mechanism of apparent changes in resistance during absorption. *Planta* 117:187–207

13. Boyer JS. 1977. Regulation of water movement in whole plants. *Symp. Soc. Exp. Biol.* 31:455–70
14. Boyer JS. 1985. Water transport. *Annu. Rev. Plant Physiol.* 36:473–516
15. Boyer JS, Silk WK. 2004. Hydraulics of plant growth. *Funct. Plant Biol.* 31:761–73
16. Brodribb TJ, Holbrook NM. 2003. Changes in leaf hydraulic conductance during leaf shedding in seasonally dry tropical forest. *New Phytol.* 158:295–303
17. Brodribb TJ, Holbrook NM. 2003. Stomatal closure during leaf dehydration, correlation with other leaf physiological traits. *Plant Physiol.* 132:2166–73
18. Brodribb TJ, Holbrook NM. 2004. Diurnal depression of leaf hydraulic conductance in a tropical tree species. *Plant Cell Environ.* 27:820–27
19. Brodribb TJ, Holbrook NM. 2004. Stomatal protection against hydraulic failure: a comparison of coexisting ferns and angiosperms. *New Phytol.* 162:663–70
20. Brodribb TJ, Holbrook NM. 2005. Leaf physiology does not predict leaf habit; examples from tropical dry forest. *Trees Struct. Funct.* 19:290–95
21. Brodribb TJ, Holbrook NM. 2005. Water stress deforms tracheids peripheral to the leaf vein of a tropical conifer. *Plant Physiol.* 137:1139–46
22. Brodribb TJ, Holbrook NM, Edwards EJ, Gutierrez MV. 2003. Relations between stomatal closure, leaf turgor and xylem vulnerability in eight tropical dry forest trees. *Plant Cell Environ.* 26:443–50
23. Brodribb TJ, Holbrook NM, Gutierrez MV. 2002. Hydraulic and photosynthetic coordination in seasonally dry tropical forest trees. *Plant Cell Environ.* 25:1435–44
24. Brodribb TJ, Holbrook NM, Zwieniecki MA, Palma B. 2005. Leaf hydraulic capacity in ferns, conifers and angiosperms: impacts on photosynthetic maxima. *New Phytol.* 165:839–46
25. Bucci SJ, Scholz FG, Goldstein G, Meinzer FC, Sternberg LDL. 2003. Dynamic changes in hydraulic conductivity in petioles of two savanna tree species: factors and mechanisms contributing to the refilling of embolized vessels. *Plant Cell Environ.* 26:1633–45
26. Buckley TN, Mott KA, Farquhar GD. 2003. A hydromechanical and biochemical model of stomatal conductance. *Plant Cell Environ.* 26:1767–85
27. Canny MJ. 1990. What becomes of the transpiration stream? *New Phytol.* 114:341–68
28. Choat B, Lahr EC, Melcher PJ, Zweiniecki MA, Holbrook NM. 2005. The spatial pattern of air seeding thresholds in mature sugar maple trees. *Plant Cell Environ.* 28(9):1082
29. Cholewa E, Vonhof MJ, Bouchard S, Peterson CA, Fenton B. 2001. The pathways of water movement in leaves modified into tents by bats. *Biol. J. Linn. Soc.* 72:179–91
30. Cochard H. 2002. Xylem embolism and drought-induced stomatal closure in maize. *Planta* 215:466–71
31. Cochard H, Bodet C, Ameglio T, Cruiziat P. 2000. Cryo-scanning electron microscopy observations of vessel content during transpiration in walnut petioles. Facts or artifacts? *Plant Physiol.* 124:1191–202
32. Cochard H, Coll L, Le Roux X, Ameglio T. 2002. Unraveling the effects of plant hydraulics on stomatal closure during water stress in walnut. *Plant Physiol.* 128:282–90
33. Cochard H, Froux F, Mayr FFS, Coutand C. 2004. Xylem wall collapse in water-stressed pine needles. *Plant Physiol.* 134:401–8
34. Cochard H, Nardini A, Coll L. 2004. Hydraulic architecture of leaf blades: Where is the main resistance? *Plant Cell Environ.* 27:1257–67
35. Comstock J, Mencuccini M. 1998. Control of stomatal conductance by leaf water potential in *Hymenoclea salsola* (T & G), a desert subshrub. *Plant Cell Environ.* 21:1029–38
36. Comstock JP. 2002. Hydraulic and chemical signalling in the control of stomatal conductance and transpiration. *J. Exp. Bot.* 53:195–200

37. Cowan IR. 1972. Electrical analog of evaporation from, and flow of water in plants. *Planta* 106:221–26
38. Davies WJ. 1986. Transpiration and the water balance of plants. In *Plant Physiology*, ed. FC Steward, pp. 49–154. Orlando, FL: Academic
39. Davies WJ, Wilkinson S, Loveys B. 2002. Stomatal control by chemical signalling and the exploitation of this mechanism to increase water use efficiency in agriculture. *New Phytol.* 153:449–60
40. Ehleringer JR, Cook CS. 1984. Photosynthesis in *Encelia farinosa* Gray in response to decreasing leaf water potential. *Plant Physiol.* 75:688–93
41. Engelbrecht BMJ, Velez V, Tyree MT. 2000. Hydraulic conductance of two co-occuring neotropical understory shrubs with different habitat preferences. *Ann. For. Sci.* 57:201–8
42. Esau K. 1965. *Plant Anatomy*. New York: Wiley. 2nd ed.
43. Farquhar GD, Raschke K. 1978. Resistance to transpiration of sites of evaporation within the leaf. *Plant Physiol.* 61:1000–5
44. Field CB, Ball JT, Berry JA. 2000. Photosynthesis: principles and field techniques. In *Plant Physiological Ecology: Field Methods and Instrumentation*, ed. RW Pearcy, JR Ehleringer, HA Mooney, PW Rundel, pp. 209–53. Dordrecht: Kluwer
45. Franks PJ, Brodribb T. 2005. Stomatal control and water transport in the xylem. In *Vascular Transport in Plants*, ed. NM Holbrook and MA Zwieniecki, pp. 69–89. Oxford: Elsevier/Academic
46. Fredeen AL, Sage RF. 1999. Temperature and humidity effects on branchlet gas-exchange in white spruce: an explanation for the increase in transpiration with branchlet temperature. *Trees Struct. Funct.* 14:161–68
47. Gascó A, Nardini A, Salleo S. 2004. Resistance to water flow through leaves of *Coffea arabica* is dominated by extravascular tissues. *Funct. Plant Biol.* 31:1161–68
48. Goldstein G, Andrade JL, Meinzer FC, Holbrook NM, Cavelier J, et al. 1998. Stem water storage and diurnal patterns of water use in tropical forest canopy trees. *Plant Cell Environ.* 21:397–406
49. Hacke U, Sauter JJ. 1996. Drought-induced xylem dysfunction in petioles, branches, and roots of *Populus balsamifera* L. and *Alnus glutinosa* (L.) Gaertn. *Plant Physiol.* 111:413–17
50. Hacke UG, Stiller V, Sperry JS, Pittermann J, McCulloh KA. 2001. Cavitation fatigue. Embolism and refilling cycles can weaken the cavitation resistance of xylem. *Plant Physiol.* 125:779–86
50a. Holbrook NM, Zwieniecki MA, eds. 2005. *Vascular Transport in Plants*. Oxford: Elsevier/Academic. 564 pp.
51. Hüve K, Remus R, Lüttschwager D, Merbach W. 2002. Water transport in impaired leaf vein systems. *Plant Biol.* 4:603–11
52. Jones HG. 1992. *Plants and Microclimate*. Cambridge: Cambridge Univ. Press. 428 pp. 2nd ed.
53. Kaldenhoff R, Eckert M. 1999. Features and function of plant aquaporins. *J. Photochem. Photobiol. B: Biol.* 52:1–6
54. Katul G, Leuning R, Oren R. 2003. Relationship between plant hydraulic and biochemical properties derived from a steady-state coupled water and carbon transport model. *Plant Cell Environ.* 26:339–50
55. Kikuta SB, LoGullo MA, Nardini A, Richter H, Salleo S. 1997. Ultrasound acoustic emissions from dehydrating leaves of deciduous and evergreen trees. *Plant Cell Environ.* 20:1381–90
56. Kitajima K, Mulkey SS, Samaniego M, Wright SJ. 2002. Decline of photosynthetic capacity with leaf age and position in two tropical pioneer tree species. *Am. J. Bot.* 89:1925–32

57. Kuppers M. 1984. Carbon relations and competition between woody species in a central European hedgerow. 2. Stomatal responses, water-use, and hydraulic conductivity in the root-leaf pathway. *Oecologia* 64:344–54

58. Larson PR. 1984. The role of subsidiary trace bundles in stem and leaf development of the Dicotyledoneae. In *Contemporary Problems in Plant Anatomy*, ed. RA White, WC Dickison, pp. 109–43. London: Academic

59. LaRue CD. 1931. The water supply of the epidermis of leaves. *Mich. Acad. Sci. Arts Lett.* 12:131–39

60. Lersten NR. 1997. Occurrence of endodermis with a casparian strip in stem and leaf. *Bot. Rev.* 63:265–72

61. Lichtenthaler HK. 1985. Differences in morphology and chemical composition of leaves grown at different light intensities and qualities. In *Control of Leaf Growth*, ed. NR Baker, WJ Davies, CK Ong, pp. 201–21. Cambridge: Cambridge Univ. Press

62. Linton MJ, Nobel PS. 2001. Hydraulic conductivity, xylem cavitation, and water potential for succulent leaves of *Agave deserti* and *Agave tequilana*. *Int. J. Plant Sci.* 162:747–54

63. Lo Gullo MA, Nardini A, Trifilo P, Salleo S. 2003. Changes in leaf hydraulics and stomatal conductance following drought stress and irrigation in *Ceratonia siliqua* (carob tree). *Physiol. Plant.* 117:186–94

64. Lo Gullo MA, Nardini A, Trifilo P, Salleo S. 2005. Diurnal and seasonal variations in leaf hydraulic conductance in evergreen and deciduous trees. *Tree Physiol.* 25:505–12

65. Lo Gullo MA, Noval LC, Salleo S, Nardini A. 2004. Hydraulic architecture of plants of *Helianthus annuus* L. cv. Margot: evidence for plant segmentation in herbs. *J. Exp. Bot.* 55:1549–56

66. Martre P, Cochard H, Durand JL. 2001. Hydraulic architecture and water flow in growing grass tillers (*Festuca arundinacea* Schreb.). *Plant Cell Environ.* 24:65–76

67. Martre P, Durand JL, Cochard H. 2000. Changes in axial hydraulic conductivity along elongating leaf blades in relation to xylem maturation in tall fescue. *New Phytol.* 146:235–47

68. Martre P, Morillon R, Barrieu F, North GB, Nobel PS, Chrispeels MJ. 2002. Plasma membrane aquaporins play a significant role during recovery from water deficit. *Plant Physiol.* 130:2101–10

69. Matzner S, Comstock J. 2001. The temperature dependence of shoot hydraulic resistance: implications for stomatal behaviour and hydraulic limitation. *Plant Cell Environ.* 24:1299–307

70. McClendon JH. 1992. Photographic survey of the occurrence of bundle sheath extensions in deciduous dicots. *Plant Physiol.* 99:1677–79

71. Meidner H. 1976. Water vapor loss from a physical model of a substomatal cavity. *J. Exp. Bot.* 27:691–94

72. Meinzer FC. 2002. Co-ordination of vapour and liquid phase water transport properties in plants. *Plant Cell Environ.* 25:265–74

73. Meinzer FC, Grantz DA. 1990. Stomatal and hydraulic conductance in growing sugarcane: stomatal adjustment to water transport capacity. *Plant Cell Environ.* 13:383–88

74. Mencuccini M. 2003. The ecological significance of long-distance water transport: short-term regulation, long-term acclimation and the hydraulic costs of stature across plant life forms. *Plant Cell Environ.* 26:163–82

75. Milburn JA. 1973. Cavitation in *Ricinus* by acoustic detection: induction in excised leaves by various factors. *Planta* 110:253–65

76. Mott KA, Buckley TN. 1998. Stomatal heterogeneity. *J. Exp. Bot.* 49:407–17

77. Murphy R, Smith JAC. 1998. Determination of cell water-relation parameters using the pressure probe: extended theory and practice of the pressure-clamp technique. *Plant Cell Environ.* 21:637–57

78. Nardini A. 2001. Are sclerophylls and malacophylls hydraulically different? *Biol. Plant.* 44:239–45

79. Nardini A, Gortan E, Salleo S. 2005. Hydraulic efficiency of the leaf venation system in sun- and shade-adapted species. *Funct. Plant Biol.* 32:953–61

80. Nardini A, Salleo S. 2000. Limitation of stomatal conductance by hydraulic traits: sensing or preventing xylem cavitation? *Trees Struct. Funct.* 15:14–24

81. Nardini A, Salleo S. 2003. Effects of the experimental blockage of the major veins on hydraulics and gas exchange of *Prunus laurocerasus* L. leaves. *J. Exp. Bot.* 54:1213–19

82. Nardini A, Salleo S, Andri S. 2005. Circadian regulation of leaf hydraulic conductance in sunflower (*Helianthus annuus* L. cv Margot). *Plant Cell Environ.* 6:750–59

83. Nardini A, Salleo S, Raimondo F. 2003. Changes in leaf hydraulic conductance correlate with leaf vein embolism in *Cercis siliquastrum* L. *Trees Struct. Funct.* 17:529–34

84. Nardini A, Tyree MT, Salleo S. 2001. Xylem cavitation in the leaf of *Prunus laurocerasus* and its impact on leaf hydraulics. *Plant Physiol.* 125:1700–9

85. Niinemets Ü. 2001. Global-scale climatic controls of leaf dry mass per area, density, and thickness in trees and shrubs. *Ecology* 82:453–69

86. Niinemets Ü, Sack L. 2006. *Structural Determinants of Leaf Light Harvesting Capacity and Photosynthetic Potentials*. Berlin: Springer Verlag. Progr. Bot. 67. p. 385–418

87. Nonami H, Schulze ED. 1989. Cell water potential, osmotic potential, and turgor in the epidermis and mesophyll of transpiring leaves: combined measurements with the cell pressure probe and nanoliter osmometer. *Planta* 177:35–46

88. Orians CM, Smith SDP, Sack L. 2005. How are leaves plumbed inside a branch? Differences in leaf-to-leaf hydraulic sectoriality among six temperate deciduous tree species. *J. Exp. Bot.* 56:2267–73

89. Osborne CP, Beerling DJ, Lomax BH, Chaloner WG. 2004. Biophysical constraints on the origin of leaves inferred from the fossil record. *Proc. Natl. Acad. Sci. USA* 101:10360–62

90. Pesacreta TC, Hasenstein KH. 1999. The internal cuticle of *Cirsium horridulum* (Asteraceae) leaves. *Am. J. Bot.* 86:923–28

91. Plymale EL, Wylie RB. 1944. The major veins of mesomorphic leaves. *Am. J. Bot.* 31:99–106

92. Raimondo F, Ghirardelli LA, Nardini A, Salleo S. 2003. Impact of the leaf miner *Cameraria ohridella* on photosynthesis, water relations and hydraulics of *Aesculus hippocastanum* leaves. *Trees Struct. Funct.* 17:376–82

93. Raschke K. 1970. Leaf hydraulic system: rapid epidermal and stomatal responses to changes in water supply. *Science* 167:189–9

94. Reich PB. 1984. Loss of stomatal function in aging hybrid poplar leaves. *Ann. Bot.* 53:691–98

95. Reich PB. 1984. Oscillations in stomatal conductance of hybrid poplar leaves in the light and dark. *Physiol. Plant.* 61:541–48

96. Reich PB, Walters MB, Ellsworth DS. 1997. From tropics to tundra: global convergence in plant functioning. *Proc. Natl. Acad. Sci. USA* 94:13730–34

97. Roth-Nebelsick A, Uhl D, Mosbrugger V, Kerp H. 2001. Evolution and function of leaf venation architecture: a review. *Ann. Bot.* 87:553–66

98. Sack L, Cowan PD, Holbrook NM. 2003. The major veins of mesomorphic leaves revisited: tests for conductive overload in *Acer saccharum* (Aceraceae) and *Quercus rubra* (Fagaceae). *Am. J. Bot.* 90:32–39

99. Sack L, Cowan PD, Jaikumar N, Holbrook NM. 2003. The 'hydrology' of leaves: coordination of structure and function in temperate woody species. *Plant Cell Environ.* 26:1343–56

100. Sack L, Frole K. 2006. Leaf structural diversity is related to hydraulic capacity in tropical rainforest trees. *Ecology* 87:483–91

101. Sack L, Melcher PJ, Zwieniecki MA, Holbrook NM. 2002. The hydraulic conductance of the angiosperm leaf lamina: a comparison of three measurement methods. *J. Exp. Bot.* 53:2177–84

102. Sack L, Streeter CM, Holbrook NM. 2004. Hydraulic analysis of water flow through leaves of sugar maple and red oak. *Plant Physiol.* 134:1824–33

103. Sack L, Tyree MT. 2005. Leaf hydraulics and its implications in plant structure and function. In *Vascular Transport in Plants*, ed. NM Holbrook and MA Zwieniecki, pp. 93–114. Oxford: Elsevier/Academic Press

104. Sack L, Tyree MT, Holbrook NM. 2005. Leaf hydraulic architecture correlates with regeneration irradiance in tropical rainforest trees. *New Phytol.* 167:403–13

105. Salleo S, Lo Gullo MA, Raimondo F, Nardini A. 2001. Vulnerability to cavitation of leaf minor veins: any impact on leaf gas exchange? *Plant Cell Environ.* 24:851–59

106. Salleo S, Nardini A, Lo Gullo MA, Ghirardelli LA. 2002. Changes in stem and leaf hydraulics preceding leaf shedding in *Castanea sativa* L. *Biol. Plant.* 45:227–34

107. Salleo S, Nardini A, LoGullo MA. 1997. Is sclerophylly of Mediterranean evergreens an adaptation to drought? *New Phytol.* 135:603–12

108. Salleo S, Nardini A, Pitt F, Lo Gullo MA. 2000. Xylem cavitation and hydraulic control of stomatal conductance in laurel (*Laurus nobilis* L.). *Plant Cell Environ.* 23:71–79

109. Salleo S, Raimondo F, Trifilo P, Nardini A. 2003. Axial-to-radial water permeability of leaf major veins: a possible determinant of the impact of vein embolism on leaf hydraulics? *Plant Cell Environ.* 26:1749–58

110. Santiago LS, Goldstein G, Meinzer FC, Fisher JB, Machado K, et al. 2004. Leaf photosynthetic traits scale with hydraulic conductivity and wood density in Panamanian forest canopy trees. *Oecologia* 140:543–50

111. Sapozhnikova VV, Kamensky VA, Kuranov RV, Kutis I, Snopova LD, Myakov AV. 2004. In vivo visualization of *Tradescantia* leaf tissue and monitoring the physiological and morphological states under different water supply conditions using optical coherence tomography. *Planta* 219:601–9

112. Schaffner AR. 1998. Aquaporin function, structure, and expression: are there more surprises to surface in water relations? *Planta* 204:131–39

113. Schultz HR, Matthews MA. 1993. Xylem development and hydraulic conductance in sun and shade shoots of grapevine (*Vitis vinifera* L.): evidence that low light uncouples water transport capacity from leaf area. *Planta* 190:393–406

114. Sheriff DW, Meidner H. 1974. Water pathways in leaves of *Hedera helix* L. and *Tradescantia virginiana* L. *J. Exp. Bot.* 25:1147–56

115. Siefritz F, Tyree MT, Lovisolo C, Schubert A, Kaldenhoff R. 2002. PIP1 plasma membrane aquaporins in tobacco: from cellular effects to function in plants. *Plant Cell* 14:869–76

116. Sisó S, Camarero JJ, Gil-Pelegrín E. 2001. Relationship between hydraulic resistance and leaf morphology in broadleaf *Quercus* species: a new interpretation of leaf lobation. *Trees Struct. Funct.* 15:341–45

117. Sober A. 1997. Hydraulic conductance, stomatal conductance, and maximal photosynthetic rate in bean leaves. *Photosynthetica* 34:599–603
118. Sobrado MA. 1998. Hydraulic conductance and water potential differences inside leaves of tropical evergreen and deciduous species. *Biol. Plant.* 40:633–37
119. Sperry JS. 2004. Coordinating stomatal and xylem functioning—an evolutionary perspective. *New Phytol.* 162:568–70
120. Sperry JS, Hacke UG, Oren R, Comstock JP. 2002. Water deficits and hydraulic limits to leaf water supply. *Plant Cell Environ.* 25:251–63
121. Sperry JS, Hacke UG, Wheeler JK. 2005. Comparative analysis of end wall resistivity in xylem conduits. *Plant Cell Environ.* 28:456–65
122. Stiller V, Lafitte HR, Sperry JS. 2003. Hydraulic properties of rice and the response of gas exchange to water stress. *Plant Physiol.* 132:1698–706
123. Stratton L, Goldstein G, Meinzer FC. 2000. Stem water storage capacity and efficiency of water transport: their functional significance in a Hawaiian dry forest. *Plant Cell Environ.* 23:99–106
124. Trifilo P, Gasco A, Raimondo F, Nardini A, Salleo S. 2003. Kinetics of recovery of leaf hydraulic conductance and vein functionality from cavitation-induced embolism in sunflower. *J. Exp. Bot.* 54:2323–30
125. Trifilo P, Nardini A, Lo Gullo MA, Salleo S. 2003. Vein cavitation and stomatal behaviour of sunflower (*Helianthus annuus*) leaves under water limitation. *Physiol. Plant.* 119:409–17
126. Tsuda M, Tyree MT. 2000. Plant hydraulic conductance measured by the high pressure flow meter in crop plants. *J. Exp. Bot.* 51:823–28
127. Tyree MT, Benis M, Dainty J. 1973. Water relations of hemlock (*Tsuga canadensis*). 3. Temperature dependence of water exchange in a pressure bomb. *Can. J. Bot.* 51:1537–43
128. Tyree MT, Cheung YNS. 1977. Resistance to water flow in *Fagus grandifolia* leaves. *Can. J. Bot.* 55:2591–99
129. Tyree MT, Cruiziat P, Benis M, Lo Gullo MA, Salleo S. 1981. The kinetics of rehydration of detached sunflower leaves from different initial water deficits. *Plant Cell Environ.* 4:309–17
130. Tyree MT, Nardini A, Salleo S. 2001. Hydraulic architecture of whole plants and single leaves. In *L'Arbre 2000 the Tree*, ed. M Labrecque, pp. 215–21. Montreal: Isabelle Quentin Publ.
131. Tyree MT, Nardini A, Salleo S, Sack L, El Omari B. 2005. The dependence of leaf hydraulic conductance on irradiance during HPFM measurements: any role for stomatal response? *J. Exp. Bot.* 56:737–44
132. Tyree MT, Sinclair B, Lu P, Granier A. 1993. Whole shoot hydraulic resistance in *Quercus* species measured with a new high-pressure flowmeter. *Ann. Sci. For.* 50:417–23
133. Tyree MT, Sobrado MA, Stratton LJ, Becker P. 1999. Diversity of hydraulic conductance in leaves of temperate and tropical species: possible causes and consequences. *J. Trop. For. Sci.* 11:47–60
134. Tyree MT, Yianoulis P. 1980. The site of water evaporation from sub-stomatal cavities, liquid path resistances and hydroactive stomatal closure. *Ann. Bot.* 46:175–93
135. Tyree MT, Zimmermann MH. 2002. *Xylem Structure and the Ascent of Sap*. Berlin: Springer
136. Van Fleet DS. 1950. The cell forms, and their common substance reactions, in the parenchyma-vascular boundary. *Bull. Torrey Bot. Club* 77:340–53
137. Wagner WH. 1979. Reticulate veins in the systematics of modern ferns. *Taxon* 28:87–95
138. Warrit B, Landsberg JJ, Thorpe MR. 1980. Responses of apple leaf stomata to environmental factors. *Plant Cell Environ.* 3:13–22

139. Weatherley PE. 1963. The pathway of water movement across the root cortex and leaf mesophyll of transpiring plants. In *The Water Relations of Plants*, ed. AJ Rutter, FH Whitehead, pp. 85–100. New York: Wiley

140. Wei CF, Tyree MT, Steudle E. 1999. Direct measurement of xylem pressure in leaves of intact maize plants. A test of the cohesion-tension theory taking hydraulic architecture into consideration. *Plant Physiol.* 121:1191–205

141. Wright IJ, Reich PB, Westoby M, Ackerly DD, Baruch Z, et al. 2004. The worldwide leaf economics spectrum. *Nature* 428:821–27

142. Wylie RB. 1943. The role of the epidermis in foliar organization and its relations to the minor venation. *Am. J. Bot.* 30:273–80

143. Wylie RB. 1946. Relations between tissue organization and vascularization in leaves of certain tropical and subtropical dicotyledons. *Am. J. Bot.* 33:721–26

144. Wylie RB. 1951. Principles of foliar organization shown by sun-shade leaves from ten species of deciduous dicotyledonous trees. *Am. J. Bot* 38:355–61

145. Wylie RB. 1952. The bundle sheath extension in leaves of dicotyledons. *Am. J. Bot.* 39:645–51

146. Yang SD, Tyree MT. 1994. Hydraulic architecture of *Acer saccharum* and *A. rubrum*: comparison of branches to whole trees and the contribution of leaves to hydraulic resistance. *J. Exp. Bot.* 45:179–86

147. Zwieniecki MA, Boyce CK, Holbrook NM. 2004. Functional design space of single-veined leaves: role of tissue hydraulic properties in constraining leaf size and shape. *Ann. Bot.* 94:507–13

148. Zwieniecki MA, Boyce CK, Holbrook NM. 2004. Hydraulic limitations imposed by crown placement determine final size and shape of *Quercus rubra* L. leaves. *Plant Cell Environ.* 27:357–65

149. Zwieniecki MA, Hutyra L, Thompson MV, Holbrook NM. 2000. Dynamic changes in petiole specific conductivity in red maple (*Acer rubrum* L.), tulip tree (*Liriodendron tulipifera* L.) and northern fox grape (*Vitis labrusca* L.). *Plant Cell Environ.* 23:407–14

150. Zwieniecki MA, Melcher PJ, Boyce CK, Sack L, Holbrook NM. 2002. Hydraulic architecture of leaf venation in *Laurus nobilis* L. *Plant Cell Environ.* 25:1445–50

Plant Uncoupling Mitochondrial Proteins

Aníbal Eugênio Vercesi,[1] Jiri Borecký,[1]
Ivan de Godoy Maia,[3] Paulo Arruda,[2]
Iolanda Midea Cuccovia,[4]
and Hernan Chaimovich[4]

[1]Laboratório de Bioenergética, Faculdade de Ciências Médicas, [2]Centro de Biologia Molecular e Engenharia Genética, Universidade Estadual de Campinas (UNICAMP), 13083-970, Campinas, SP, Brazil; email: anibal@unicamp.br, jiri@unicamp.br, parruda@unicamp.br

[3]Departamento de Genética, Instituto de Biociências, UNESP, 18618-000, Botucatu, SP, Brazil; email: igmaia@ibb.unesp.br

[4]Departamento de Bioquímica, Instituto de Química, Universidade de São Paulo, São Paulo, SP, 05599-970, Brazil; email: imcuccov@quim.iq.usp.br, hchaimo@iq.usp.br

Annu. Rev. Plant Biol.
2006. 57:383–404

The *Annual Review of Plant Biology* is online at
plant.annualreviews.org

doi: 10.1146/
annurev.arplant.57.032905.105335

First published online as a
Review in Advance on
February 1, 2006

1543-5008/06/0602-
0383$20.00

Key Words

uncoupling proteins, plant mitochondria, oxidative
phosphorylation, reactive oxygen species, energy metabolism

Abstract

Uncoupling proteins (UCPs) are membrane proteins that mediate purine nucleotide-sensitive free fatty acid-activated H^+ flux through the inner mitochondrial membrane. After the discovery of UCP in higher plants in 1995, it was acknowledged that these proteins are widely distributed in eukaryotic organisms. The widespread presence of UCPs in eukaryotes implies that these proteins may have functions other than thermogenesis. In this review, we describe the current knowledge of plant UCPs, including their discovery, biochemical properties, distribution, gene family, gene expression profiles, regulation of gene expression, and evolutionary aspects. Expression analyses and functional studies on the plant UCPs under normal and stressful conditions suggest that UCPs regulate energy metabolism in the cellular responses to stress through regulation of the electrochemical proton potential ($\Delta\mu_H+$) and production of reactive oxygen species.

Contents

Electrochemical proton potential $(\Delta\mu_H+)$: a proton gradient across the inner mitochondrial membrane, also termed the protonmotive force (Δp), generated by proton pumps of the respiratory chain

FA: fatty acid

Respiratory chain: a set of four protein-complexes in the inner mitochondrial membrane that transfer electrons from NADH and $FADH_2$ to oxygen

INTRODUCTION

Uncoupling proteins (UCPs) dissipate the electrochemical proton gradient generated by respiration as heat (78). In the presence of fatty acids (FAs), UCPs facilitate the reentry of protons, extruded by the respiratory chain, into the matrix bypassing the ATP-synthetase (77).

The mammalian UCP, thermogenin, or UCP, now UCP1, was believed to exist only in the brown adipose tissue (BAT) of mammals, as a late evolutionary acquisition (86). For decades, the only physiological role attributed to UCP was its involvement in the transient thermogenesis in newborn, cold-acclimated, and hibernating mammals (59, 78). The discovery of the plant

counterpart of UCP in 1995 (112) initiated a search for UCP homologs. Between 1997 and 2000, several homologs of UCP1 were identified in mammals [UCP2 in several tissues (102), UCP3 in BAT and skeletal muscle, UCP4 and UCP5 in brain], birds (83, 104, 114), ectothermic vertebrates, such as frog (58) and fish (102), insects (30), primitive eukaryotic organisms *Caenorhabditis elegans* (CeUCP, Accession number AAB54239), amoeba (45), *Dictyostelium discoideum* (42), fungi (17, 43), and trophozoites of the malaria parasite *Plasmodium berghei* (108). It is now evident that the UCPs are widespread in eukaryotes, and they may have various physiological roles (13, 29, 68, 88, 115).

THE DISCOVERY OF UNCOUPLING PROTEINS IN PLANTS

The observation (112) that the rate of non-phosphorylating respiration of potato tuber mitochondria incubated in the absence of bovine serum albumin (BSA) is much slower after a period of ADP phosphorylation or after the addition of ATP (**Figure 1a**) suggested that these mitochondria could possess an inner membrane anion channel (IMAC), an UCP, or both.

In collaboration with Beavis, we demonstrated that potato mitochondria contain an anion channel, PIMAC (8). PIMAC is sensitive to propranolol, tributyltin, and the nucleotide analogs Erythrosin B and Cibacron Blue 3GA. PIMAC, however, is unaffected by matrix Mg^{2+}, mercurials, or N,N'-dicyclohexylcarbodiimide. The properties of PIMAC led to the proposal that this anion channel could have a role in volume homeostasis (8). Study of nigericin-induced swelling showed that, besides the electrophoretic Cl^- influx, mitochondria were also permeable to H^+, permitting the reentry of H^+ that had been extruded by nigericin for external K^+. While studying the properties of PIMAC, it was observed that BSA inhibits nigericin-induced swelling of potato tuber mitochondria suspended in a KCl-containing medium. It is well known that BSA efficiently complexes FA (101). Thus, the BSA-sensitive nigericin-induced swelling supported the hypothesis that potato mitochondria might have a FA-activated endogenous protonophore, with properties similar to UCP1. Subsequent work demonstrated that a fully coupled state could be reached in potato mitochondria only by the simultaneous presence of purine nucleotides such as ATP or guanosine diphosphate (GDP) and absence of free FAs (112). The sequential addition of BSA and ATP produced an increase in the transmembrane electrical potential ($\Delta\Psi$) (**Figure 1b**). The

Protonophores: organic compounds that facilitate the transport of H+ across biological membranes

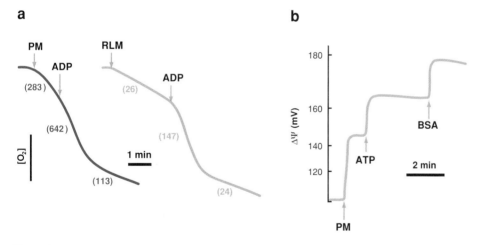

a

b

Figure 1

(*a*) Comparison of resting and phosphorylating respiration in isolated rat liver (RLM) and potato mitochondria (PM). The assay medium contained 0.25 mM sucrose, 10 mM HEPES buffer, pH 7.2, 5 mM P_i, 1.0 mM $MgCl_2$, and 0.5 mM EGTA. PM (0.25 mg/ml), RLM (1 mg/ml), and ADP (400 nmol) were added where indicated. Rates of respiration (nmol O/min/mg) are shown in parentheses. (*b*) Effects of ATP and bovine serum albumin (BSA) on transmembrane electrical potential of isolated PM. Mitochondria (1 mg protein/ml) were added to a reaction medium containing 300 mM mannitol, 20 mM KCl, 10 mM HEPES buffer, pH 7.2, and 3 μM tetraphenylphosphonium (TPP^+). ATP (1 mM) and 0.1% BSA were added where indicated. The concentration of TPP^+ in the extramitochondrial medium was continuously monitored with a TPP^+-selective electrode.

purine nucleotide-induced changes in $\Delta\Psi$, compatible with increased mitochondrial coupling, were unaffected by the inhibitors of the ATP-synthase (oligomycin), ADP/ATP carrier (carboxyatractyloside), and PIMAC (propranolol). The data obtained from plant mitochondria were consistent with the existence of a UCP-like activity in plants. This hypothesis was confirmed upon isolation of a 32-kDa hydrophobic protein (named plant uncoupling mitochondrial protein, PUMP) from potato tuber mitochondria, which, when incorporated into proteoliposomes, exhibited properties similar to UCP1 (112). FA-mediated uncoupling of potato mitochondria was found to be ATP sensitive and induced H^+-dependent mitochondrial swelling in a medium with K^+-acetate (48). Further studies with proteoliposomes demonstrated that the catalytic properties of PUMP were similar to UCP1 except for the Cl^- or pyruvate translocation (48, 50, 51).

The final proof that PUMP is an UCP was obtained after the identification of the genes encoding potato and *Arabidopsis* PUMPs (65, 67). Then, MALDI-mass spectroscopy analysis of peptides resulting from trypsin cleavage of PUMP protein purified from potato tubers (48, 112) yielded 35% coverage of the amino acid sequence deduced from potato PUMP gene (47), suggesting that this gene encodes the isolated potato PUMP. Furthermore, a full-length cDNA-encoding *Arabidopsis* PUMP1 was expressed in the *Escherichia coli* system and the recombinant protein was isolated under conditions that prevent contamination by any other mitochondrial protein (10). When reconstituted into proteoliposomes, this recombinant *Arabidopsis* PUMP1 both cross-reacted with antibodies raised against PUMP isolated from potato tuber mitochondria and displayed properties similar to reconstituted potato PUMP (50) and recombinant UCP2 or UCP3 (41). Thus the existence of a mitochondrial UCP in plants was unequivocally demonstrated.

STRUCTURE AND BIOCHEMISTRY OF PLANT UNCOUPLING MITOCHONDRIAL PROTEINS

PUMPs are integral membrane proteins with apparent molecular masses ranging from 30 to 33 kDa. A charge profile analysis of the deduced amino acid sequences of potato, *Arabidopsis*, and sugarcane PUMPs (GeneRunner program, v. 3.0; **http://www.generunner. com**) estimates their isoelectric points clustered in the pH range from 8.8 to 10.5. At physiological pH (7–7.5), the calculated charge of the PUMP polypeptide is ca. +14. The functional PUMP unit is a homodimer (47). Unlike many nuclear-encoded mitochondrial proteins, PUMPs lack a cleavable targeting presequence within the amino acid sequence. By analogy with UCP1, which contains an internal targeting signal for the inner membrane within the central repeat unit of the protein (90), the existence of one or more internal targeting signals in PUMPs could be postulated.

Using antibodies raised against potato PUMP, we detected PUMP in many climacteric fruits (4), indicating the possible participation of this uncoupler in the climacteric rise of respiration (47, 49). The ubiquitous distribution of PUMP in plants suggests that it could be the counterpart of the animal UCP2. This idea is supported by the fact that there is a higher amino acid sequence homology between PUMP and UCP2 when compared to other UCPs (9).

Plant Uncoupling Mitochondrial Proteins and Uncoupling Protein Polypeptides Have Conserved Structures

PUMP and UCP monomers consist of 295–320 amino acids arranged in a structure containing three homologous domains. Each one of the three ca 100-amino-acid-long domains comprises two transmembrane α-helices linked by a hydrophilic loop located at the

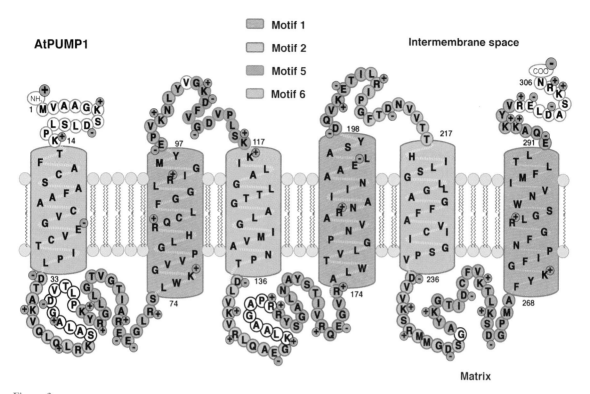

AtPUMP1

Motif 1
Motif 2
Motif 5
Motif 6

Intermembrane space

Matrix

Figure 2

Scheme representation of AtPUMP1 molecule containing conserved motifs. Protein Motif 1 and 2 are common for all members of the subfamily and involve first transmembrane protein domain (Motif 2) or the second domain (Motif 1) of each protein repeat. Motif 5 and 6 are specific for PUMPs and both are exposed to intermembrane space.

matrix side containing the Energy Transfer Protein Signature (ETPS) P-x-[DE]-x-[LIVAT]-[RK]-x-[LRH]-[LIVMFY] typical of all mitochondrial anion carriers. Specific variants of this signature have been identified in both animal and plant UCPs (9).

Sequence motifs specific for mammal and plant UCPs were analyzed using the pattern prediction program package MEME-MAST (**http://www.sdsc.edu/MEME**) (6, 7). In MEME, the motifs are represented by letter-probability matrices that specify the probability of each letter of single-letter amino acid code to appear at each possible position in the motif. Eight predicted motifs have been associated with some complete and specific groups of UCPs/PUMPs (9). Motif 1 and 2 are long (50 and 30 amino acids, respectively) and occur in all UCPs. These

motifs form a tandem within each domain of the polypeptide and the three tandems cover about 80% of the PUMP (**Figure 2**). It is tempting to hypothesize that these tandem motifs are conserved in evolution to maintain the conformation of UCPs. The Motif 5 and 6 are specific for PUMPs and are located within the two external loops. In addition, a specific insertion of an alanine-rich region close to the first ETPS was found in PUMPs from sugarcane, maize, wheat, and rice. This latter motif is absent in the predicted amino acid sequences of PUMP obtained from dicotyledonous plants. Hence, this insertion could be considered as monocotyledonous specific.

Other studies have described the so-called UCP-specific motifs present in the first, second, and fourth α-helix and in the second matrix loop (56). Interestingly, a truncated form, lacking the fifth transmembrane domain, was identified in the skunk cabbage (SfUCPb), suggesting a different physiological regulation of uncoupling by this isoform (40).

Plant Uncoupling Mitochondrial Protein is Activated by Free Fatty Acids

The most distinctive feature of PUMPs, as well as UCPs, is their activation by free FAs. A screening of PUMP activity induced by various FAs in proteoliposomes containing recombinant *Arabidopsis* PUMP1 (10) revealed that AtPUMP1 does not discriminate significantly among FAs, because lauric, myristic, palmitic, oleic, linoleic, and linolenic acids interacted with AtPUMP1 to a similar extent, i.e., they exhibited K_m in the range between 40 and 130 µM and V_{max} between 0.2 and 0.84 µmol H^+ s^{-1} (mg lipid)$^{-1}$. AtPUMP1 affinity was highest to myristic and linoleic acid and lowest to palmitic and linolenic acids (**Figure 3**).

The (two) proposed models describing the mechanism of FA-induced H^+ reuptake by UCPs or PUMPs are still under debate (**Figure 4**). In the FA-buffering model, UCP is considered a true H^+ carrier and FAs are not translocated across the membrane (59). FAs bind to the UCP and their carboxyl groups serve as H^+ donors/acceptors to resident carboxyl groups (asparagine or glutamine). His145 and His147 residues in UCP1 are proposed to be the final relay that liberates the proton into the mitochondrial matrix (59, 118). Alternatively, the FA protonophore model, introduced by Garlid et al. (31, 53–55), considers Skulachev's hypothesis that several integral membrane proteins, namely anion carriers, can mediate uniport of anionic FAs (94). In this latter model, UCP catalyzes the export of FA anions from the matrix side of the inner mitochondrial membrane to the intermembrane-space side, driven by the high inside-negative membrane potential. Subsequently, protonated FAs can return to the matrix side by a spontaneous flip-flop mechanism. Therefore, for each cycle of FA transport, one H^+ remains in the matrix, thereby decreasing $\Delta\mu_{H}+$ and energy availability for energy-consuming processes (31, 94).

Plant Uncoupling Mitochondrial Protein Activation by Reactive Oxygen Species and Their Reaction Products

Superoxide activates UCP1-3 (28) and potato PUMP (20). The proposed mechanism

---

Figure 3

Kinetics of fatty acid-induced H^+ fluxes and dose-response curves for the H^+ flux inhibition in liposomes and proteoliposomes with the reconstituted recombinant *At*PUMP1. Panels a and b show comparison of H^+ flux densities in protein-free liposomes (x and *open symbols*) and proteoliposomes (*solid symbols*). The apparent H^+ flux density of protein-free vesicles in the presence of palmitic (x), linoleic (□), and lauric (△) acid in Panel a, and myristic (◇), oleic (□), and linolenic acid (▽) in Panel b, is compared with densities of AtPUMP1-mediated H^+ fluxes induced by linoleic (■), palmitic (●), and lauric (▲) acid in Panel a, and myristic (◆), oleic (■), and linolenic acid (▼) in Panel b. Panel a also shows basal H^+ flux densities (no FAs) in protein-free liposomes (○) and proteoliposomes (●). Measurements were conducted in the presence of 1.3-µM valinomycin. The fluxes were calculated per µm² of the vesicle membrane. Dose-response curves for the inhibition of fatty acid-induced AtPUMP1-mediated H^+ fluxes by GDP (▲) and GTP (□) at pH 7.1 in Panel c, or ATP at pH 6.3 (○), 7.1 (●), and 7.8–8 (■) in Panel d. The dose-response curves (*solid lines*) represented inhibition of the outwardly oriented PN-binding sites (~50%). The derived K_i were 0.8 mM (GDP), 0.98 mM (GTP), 0.85 mM (ATP at pH 7.1), and 0.54 (ATP at pH 6.3), with Hill coefficients of 1, except for GTP (n = 1.7) and ATP at pH 6.3 (n = 1.4). TEA-TES in EM of pH 8 (7.8 at high-ATP concentrations) was replaced by Tris-TES and EM of pH 6.3 contained 14.4 mM TES and 14.4 mM MES (9.2 mM TEA$^+$).

involves the activation of UCPs by superoxide at the matrix side of the inner mitochondrial membrane (27), where superoxide releases iron from proteins containing iron-sulfur centers such as aconitase. Ferrous ions react with superoxide forming hydroxyl radical that, in turn, promotes generation of carbon-centered radicals that initiate lipid peroxidation,

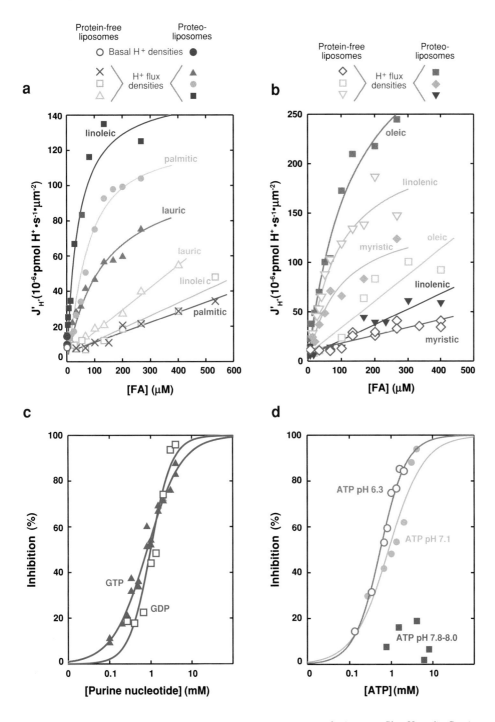

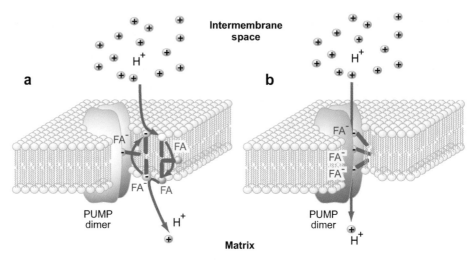

Figure 4

Two supposed mechanisms for H$^+$ reuptake by PUMPs: (*a*) fatty acid (FA) protonophoric model and (*b*) FA-buffering model. FA is represented as a neutral (protonated) molecule with the hydrophilic head in green, or as anion (deprotonated) with the head in blue; the hydrophobic tails are in red. The FA protonophoric model supposes transport of FA anion by PUMP, whereas the FA-buffering model is based on proton transport by PUMP with FA anions "docked" inside the protein as prosthetic groups.

UQ: ubiquinone

yielding breakdown products such as 4-hydroxy-2-*trans*-nonenal. These breakdown products can activate both the rat UCP1-3 (74) and the potato PUMP (99). Activation by similar products across such an evolutionary distance suggests conservation of basic mechanisms of UCP and PUMP.

Plant Uncoupling Mitochondrial Protein Inhibition by Purine Nucleotides: Effect of pH

Similarly to UCP1, FA-mediated proton flux by potato PUMP is sensitive to inhibition by purine di- and trinucleotides (112). The inhibition constant for PUMP by ATP is 778 μM (linoleic acid-mediated activation at pH 7.5) or 910 μM (hexanesulfonate-mediated activation at pH 7.5) in isolated potato mitochondria (48). The K_i values for GDP and GTP are similar (~1 mM). Comparable values are found for recombinant AtPUMP1 (**Figure 3**), with GDP being the strongest inhibitor at pH 7.1 ($K_{i,GDP}$ = 0.80 mM), followed by ATP ($K_{i,ATP}$ = 0.85 mM) and GTP ($K_{i,ATP}$ = 0.98 mM). The inhibition of

AtPUMP1 by ADP was the weakest ($K_{i,ADP}$ = 1.41 mM).

Inhibition of PUMP by purine nucleotides is further regulated by medium composition. The presence of MgCl$_2$ abolishes potato PUMP inhibition by ATP (89), as already observed in mammalian UCP1 (52). Mg^{2+} forms a complex with ATP that cannot block the PUMP. Thus, the actual concentration of free cytosolic Mg^{2+} could regulate the efficiency of PUMP inhibition by purine nucleotides. Furthermore, inhibition appears to be pH dependent. Recombinant AtPUMP1 reconstituted in proteoliposomes (10) is inhibited by ATP in a pH-dependent manner. The $K_{i,ATP}$ is 0.54 mM at pH 6.3, whereas it reaches 0.85 mM at pH 7.1. No inhibition is observed at pH 7.8–8.0. A similar pH dependence was also described for UCP1 (79). The third regulatory factor is the redox state of ubiquinone (UQ). No inhibition of UCP3 (44) or PUMP (76) by purine nucleotides was found when UQ was predominantly in the reduced state. However, the progressive inhibition of succinate uptake by n-butyl malonate that decreases the reduced fraction of the UQ pool leads to a full inhibitory effect of GTP on UCP and PUMP in isolated skeletal muscle and potato mitochondria, respectively. The transition from insensitivity to full inhibition by GTP occurs when the reduced form of UQ varies from 57% to 64% of the total UQ pool for UCP3 (44), and from 32% to 39% for PUMP (76).

PLANT UNCOUPLING MITOCHONDRIAL PROTEIN GENETICS

Cloning and Identification of Plant Uncoupling Mitochondrial Protein Genes

Two years after the discovery of PUMP, the first cDNA encoding a plant UCP homolog was cloned in potato (named StUCP, Accession BAA92172) using a two-hybrid protein-interaction trap (65). Soon thereafter, our group identified an *Arabidopsis* gene (AtPUMP, Accession CAA11757) encoding a polypeptide exhibiting high sequence similarity to StUCP (67). The corresponding gene products displayed uncoupling activities when expressed in yeast (38) or reconstituted in liposomes (10). Genes encoding the PUMPs were subsequently identified in several monocot and dicot species (**Table 1**).

Recently, our group identified six genes coding for PUMPs (*AtPUMP1-6*) in the whole *Arabidopsis* genome (TIGR; **http://www.tigr.org/**). Five homologs (*SsPUMP1-5*) were also found in the Brazilian sugarcane EST collection (SUCEST) (113).

Phylogeny of Plant Uncoupling Mitochondrial Proteins

UCPs are important ensembles within the mitochondrial anion carrier protein superfamily (MACF) (**Figure 5**). Several molecular-based phylogenetic analyses of UCP gene products from different species have been published (9, 12, 35, 37). A conserved feature revealed by these analyses is the presence of a cluster to which type-1 and type-2 PUMPs are assigned (**Figure 5**). This plant-specific subfamily is subdivided into two closely related subgroups corresponding to monocot and dicot PUMPs, with the monocot subgroup being more ancient. Three additional clusters comprise PUMP3 and UCP4, PUMP4-6, and UCP5 (9, 12) (**Figure 5**).

Although it is widely accepted that UCPs diverged early during the phylogenesis, there are contradictory data concerning the evolutionary history of UCP/PUMP genes. Evidence for the ancestral origin of UCP4 was provided by phylogenetic analyses based on UCP-specific signatures (35). In broad agreement with this observation, Borecký et al. (11) identified a subgroup containing mammalian UCP4, PUMP3 from dicot and monocot, as well as an UCP homolog from *C. elegans* as the ancestral cluster from which other UCPs/PUMPs might have evolved. On the other hand, Sokolova & Sokolov (100) recently obtained phylogenetic support for the hypothesis that UCP6, newly identified in invertebrates, may be the ancestor of vertebrate UCP1-3. Although the function of UCP6 is unknown at present, it was proposed that this observation perfectly matches the evolution of UCP functionality, because UCP6 seems to be a functional generalist when compared to UCP4. Unfortunately, no PUMP sequences were included in this study (100).

UCPs are closer to malate/2-oxoglutarate carriers and the existence of an anion/anion antiporter ancestor has been proposed based on the fact that UCPs mediate a transport of FA anions (9). We also suggest that UCPs evolved from a nucleotide/proton symporter that aborted nucleotide transport during functional specialization (85) or from an anion/nucleotide antiporter consistent with the first possibility (9).

The completion of the genome sequences of *Arabidopsis* and rice allowed drawing up the genomic structure and chromosome localization of PUMP genes in these species. The six *Arabidopsis* PUMP genes are dispersed throughout the five chromosomes (*AtPUMP1*

Table 1 Members of the plant uncoupling mitochondrial protein family identified so far and corresponding tissue and/or stress-related expression

Name	Species	Tissue	Stress/Condition	Reference(s)
*St*UCP	*Solanum tuberosum*	Ubiquitous (flowers)	Cold	(65)
*At*PUMP1	*Arabidopsis*	Ubiquitous (flowers, roots)	Cold, salt, osmotic, pathogen attack, induced programmed cell death (PCD)	(62, 67, 103, 109, 117)
*At*PUMP2	*Arabidopsis*	Green siliques	PCD	(11, 103, 116)
*At*PUMP3	*Arabidopsis*	Roots	—	(11)
*At*PUMP4	*Arabidopsis*	Ubiquitous	Cold, drought, oxidative stress, abscisic acid (ABA)	(11, 26, 92, 93)
*At*PUMP5	*Arabidopsis*	Ubiquitous	Cold, drought, ABA, osmotic, wounding, pathogen attack	(11, 26, 62, 92, 93, 109, 117)
*Sf*UCPa and b	*Symplocarpus fetidus*	Spadix	Cold	(40)
*Hm*UCPa	*Helicodiceros muscivorus*	Ubiquitous	n.d.	(39)
*Wh*UCP1a and 1b	*Triticum aestivum*	Ubiquitous	—	(73)
*Mn*UCP	*Mangifera indica*	n.d. (fruit)	Fruit ripening	(19)
*Le*UCP	*Lycopersicum esculetum*	n.d. (fruit)	Cold, fruit ripening	(36)
*Zm*PUMP	*Zea mays*	Ubiquitous	Oxidative stress	(15)
*Os*UCP1 and 2	*Oriza sativa*	n.d. (leaves)	—	(116)
*Ss*PUMP1	*Saccharum* sp.	Flowers (d.d.)	n.d.	
*Ss*PUMP2	*Saccharum* sp.	Ubiquitous (roots)	—	
*Ss*PUMP3	*Saccharum* sp.	Stems (d.d.)	—	(11)
*Ss*PUMP4	*Saccharum* sp.	Ubiquitous (leaves and roots)	Cold	
*Ss*PUMP5	*Saccharum* sp.	Ubiquitous (leaves and roots)	Cold	

d.d., determined digitally; n.d., not determined.

on chromosome 3, *AtPUMP2* and *AtPUMP6* on chromosome 5, *AtPUMP3* on chromosome 1, *AtPUMP4* on chromosome 4, and *AtPUMP5* on chromosome 2). In rice, the four predicted PUMP genes (*OsPUMP1-4*) are dispersed on 4 of the 12 chromosomes (*OsPUMP1* on chromosome 1, *OsPUMP2* on chromosome 11, *OsPUMP3* on chromosome 4, and *OsPUMP4* on chromosome 8) (81).

The analysis of the *Arabidopsis* genome revealed no conservation of a major exon/intron pattern in the genomic structures of the PUMP genes (81). The coding sequences of *AtPUMP1* and *2* are distributed over nine exons, whereas the corresponding regions in *AtPUMP3* and *-6* (and also in *OsPUMP3*) are concentrated in only two exons. The position and size of introns are also variable among PUMP genes (9), and intronless genes have been identified in *Arabidopsis* (*AtPUMP4-5*) and rice (*OsPUMP4*) (12).

Gene duplication is a frequent mechanism for the appearance of new genes with similar functions. Different lines of evidence suggest that PUMP genes evolved through gene duplication events, the most evident being the location of different *AtPUMP* genes within or close to duplicated regions of the *Arabidopsis* genome (11). The similar intron/exon structure of *AtPUMP1* and *-2* genes may be a

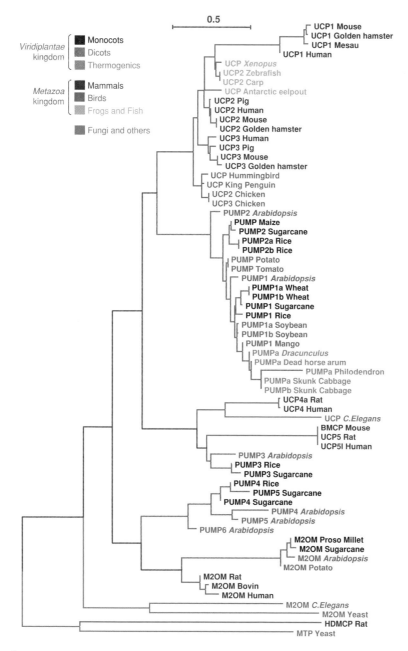

Scale bar: 0.5

UCP1 Mouse
UCP1 Golden hamster
UCP1 Mesau
UCP1 Human
UCP *Xenopus*
UCP2 Zebrafish
UCP2 Carp
UCP Antarctic eelpout
UCP2 Pig
UCP2 Human
UCP2 Mouse
UCP2 Golden hamster
UCP3 Human
UCP3 Pig
UCP3 Mouse
UCP3 Golden hamster
UCP Hummingbird
UCP King Penguin
UCP2 Chicken
UCP3 Chicken
PUMP2 *Arabidopsis*
PUMP Maize
PUMP2 Sugarcane
PUMP2a Rice
PUMP2b Rice
PUMP Potato
PUMP Tomato
PUMP1 *Arabidopsis*
PUMP1a Wheat
PUMP1b Wheat
PUMP1 Sugarcane
PUMP1 Rice
PUMP1a Soybean
PUMP1b Soybean
PUMP1 Mango
PUMPa *Dracunculus*
PUMPa Dead horse arum
PUMPa Philodendron
PUMPa Skunk Cabbage
PUMPb Skunk Cabbage
UCP4a Rat
UCP4 Human
UCP *C.Elegans*
BMCP Mouse
UCP5 Rat
UCP5I Human
PUMP3 *Arabidopsis*
PUMP3 Rice
PUMP3 Sugarcane
PUMP4 Rice
PUMP5 Sugarcane
PUMP4 Sugarcane
PUMP4 *Arabidopsis*
PUMP5 *Arabidopsis*
PUMP6 *Arabidopsis*
M2OM Proso Millet
M2OM Sugarcane
M2OM *Arabidopsis*
M2OM Potato
M2OM Rat
M2OM Bovin
M2OM Human
M2OM *C.Elegans*
M2OM Yeast
HDMCP Rat
MTP Yeast

Figure 5

Phylogenetic tree of uncoupling protein (UCP)/PUMP subfamily. Consensus phylogram (1000 bootstraps) of all known UCPs/PUMPs was constructed using the MEGA3 program and rooted with yeast mitochondrial transport protein. Malate/oxoglutarate carrier (M2OM) sequences were included to distinguish genes encoding these closest neighbors of MACF. The green branches represent the *Viridiplantae* kingdom, with names of monocot species in dark green, dicot species in grass green, and thermogenic plant species in olive green. The red branches represent *Metazoa* kingdom (animals), with names of mammalian species in dark red, avian species in bright red, and frog and fish species in orange. The blue branches represent species from fungi and other organisms.

Oxidative stress: an imbalance between cellular production and elimination of reactive oxygen species toward their overproduction and/or reduced elimination

Metabolic thermogenesis: metabolic heat produced in some plants and in hibernating or newborn mammals (nonshivering thermogenesis)

Reactive oxygen species (ROS): a group of molecules or ions mostly formed by the incomplete one-electron reduction of oxygen that includes singlet oxygen, superoxide anion radical, peroxides, hydroxyl radical, and hypochlorous acid

reflection of such duplications. Moreover, the placement of an UCP gene from *C. elegans* within a group of mammalian and plant genes suggests that gene duplication events in this family occurred prior to the divergence of vertebrates and invertebrates from a common ancestor.

Plant Uncoupling Mitochondrial Protein Gene Expression

The spatiotemporal patterns of expression of several PUMP genes so far investigated are summarized in **Table 1**. Three (*AtPUMP1, AtPUMP4,* and *AtPUMP5*) of the six *Arabidopsis* PUMP genes are expressed ubiquitously; one (*AtPUMP2*) is expressed exclusively in green siliques whereas *AtPUMP3* is root specific (11). Although the transcripts of *AtPUMP4* and *AtPUMP5* are the most abundant, those of *AtPUMP6* are not detected. In sugarcane, a high abundance of ESTs representing certain *SsPUMPs* is found in cDNA libraries generated from proliferating or highly synthesizing tissues (lateral buds or immature flowers), suggesting their functional importance (11). In rice, defective processing of premRNA of the OsPUMP1-2 resulting in multiple abnormal transcripts and the absence of any functional PUMP have been described (the rice PUMPs are referred to as OsUCPs) (116). PUMP expression is strongly enhanced at the senescence stages of mango fruit ripening (19) and at the later stages of on-vine tomato fruit ripening (36). These latter results are in good agreement with the fact that a higher state of coupling is observed in respiring mitochondria isolated from green tomatoes when compared with those obtained from red tomatoes (22). In contrast, decreased amount and activity of PUMP protein are found during the later stages of postharvest fruit ripening (2).

PUMP expression can also be modulated by several environmental stimuli. In *Arabidopsis*, circumstantial evidence from large-scale expression profiling experiments reveal a stress-dependent regulation of PUMP transcripts (26, 62, 92, 93). PUMP genes are upregulated by low temperature (75, 80), drought, wound (18), and abscisic acid (ABA). Enhanced expression patterns were also observed during heat-induced programmed cell death (103) and in response to pathogenic attack (109, 111, 117). A downregulated expression pattern promoted by high-salinity stress was observed for AtPUMP4 and 5 (93).

The response of PUMP genes to low temperature is puzzling. Cold treatment leads to the selective upregulation of PUMP transcripts in both nonthermogenic plants such as *Arabidopsis* (AtPUMP1, AtPUMP4, and AtPUMP5) (11), sugarcane (SsPUMP4 and SsPUMP5) (11), and potato (65), and thermogenic skunk cabbage (40). Cold induction is not observed in wheat (73), *Arabidopsis* (AtPUMP2), and sugarcane (SsPUMP1, SsPUMP2, and SsPUMP3) (11). In maize, expression of *Zm*PUMP remains unaltered under cold exposure but is increased in response to oxidative stress (15).

POSSIBLE PHYSIOLOGICAL ROLES OF PLANT UNCOUPLING MITOCHONDRIAL PROTEINS

The physiological roles of UCPs fall in different categories: generation of metabolic (nonshivering) thermogenesis (78), control of reactive oxygen species (ROS) production by mitochondria (95), response to stress situations (71), and regulation of energy metabolism (98). In each case the role of UCP is related to both the capacity of uncoupling and the tissue-specific metabolic status.

Plant mitochondria exhibit two energy-dissipating systems: a proton electrochemical potential-dissipating system represented by PUMPs and a redox potential-dissipating system represented by alternative oxidases (AOxs) (for review, see 21, 57, 72, 97). AOx, a cyanide-resistant quinol oxidase, is a nonprotonmotive terminal oxidase that can significantly decrease proton pumping. Together with succinate dehydrogenase (respiratory complex II) or the alternative external and internal NAD(P)H dehydrogenases (for review, see 84), AOx can promote substrate oxidation without any oxidative phosphorylation. In principle, the activity of both AOx and PUMP leads to a decrease in ATP synthesis. Despite this similarity in final effect, these proteins may have different functions. In fact, AOx and PUMP are regulated in opposite directions by free FAs (96). Although PUMP is activated by an increase in FA concentration, the activity of AOx is progressively switched off, suggesting that AOx and PUMP cannot express their maximal activities simultaneously. PUMP and AOx have some common regulators, i.e., FAs that function as the activity switch (96) and ROS that upregulate expression of PUMP and AOx genes (20, 82). However, the activities of both systems are regulated by quite different mechanisms. For example, the driving force for PUMPs is $\Delta\mu_H+$ and their substrates/activators are FAs. PUMP activity is enhanced by ROS or hydroxynonenal and inhibited by purine nucleotides (99). AOx, in contrast, is driven by high concentration of O_2 and its substrate is ubiquinol (1). AOx activity depends on the reducing power and the presence of pyruvate, the Krebs cycle input substrate (110). The expression of AOx is induced by silicic acid (82) and organic acids of the Krebs cycle—citrate, malate, and 2-oxoglutarate (33).

The existence of multiple members of the PUMP and AOx protein families suggests that the members of each mitochondrial energy-dissipating system are subject to different transcriptional regulation, and may be expressed in a cell-, tissue-, or organ-specific manner. *PUMP* genes are generally expressed at higher levels in monocotyledonous sugarcane as well as dicotyledonous *Arabidopsis* when compared with *AOx* genes (11). *PUMP* and *AOx* genes display different tissue-enriched expression patterns and parallel expression has been observed only in sugarcane meristem, leaves, and roots, or in *Arabidopsis* aboveground organs except for flowers and green siliques. These observations strengthen the hypothesis that PUMP and AOx do not work simultaneously at their maximal activities and have different physiological functions.

Thermogenesis

Uncoupling between respiration and phosphorylation leads to direct dissipation of the electrochemical energy as heat, suggesting a possible involvement of the UCPs in nonshivering thermogenesis. Until now, this function is clear only for the mammalian UCP1, abundant in BAT, where it may constitute up to 5% of total mitochondrial proteins in acclimated mammals. PUMPs are present in plant mitochondria in much lower amounts and probably are not able to promote thermogenesis (16, 37). Other data provide evidence that UCP2-5 are also not thermogenic (5, 32).

Expression profile analysis of a PUMP gene from *Helicodiceros muscivorus* (HmUCPa) (39), a highly thermogenic arum lily, reveals that this gene is ubiquitously expressed both in thermogenic and in nonthermogenic flower organs, suggesting that the gene product is not involved in organ-specific heat production. Thermogenesis in thermogenic plants seems to be related mainly to the activity of AOx (66). AOx activity leads to temperature rises involved in reproductive processes (25, 70) and possibly in the ripening of some climacteric fruits (24, 63, 64).

Control of Reactive Oxygen Species Production

Skulachev (94) demonstrated that ROS production by mitochondria is low and constant up to a certain level of $\Delta\Psi_m$; however, above this threshold, ROS production increases almost linearly with $\Delta\Psi_m$. The threshold is at the transition from state 3 (phosphorylating respiration) to state 4 (nonphosphorylating, resting respiration). It is enticing to postulate that a possible physiological role of PUMP is fine tuning of $\Delta\Psi_m$ to a level optimal for

Oxidative phosphorylation: the process in which the electrochemical proton potential generated by respiration is utilized by the ATP-synthase to phosphorylate ADP to ATP

oxidative phosphorylation and minimal ROS production. A mild uncoupling increases the rate of respiration and lowers superoxide generation because it decreases both the tissue O_2 tension and the steady-state concentration of respiratory components in the reduced state. This condition decreases the amounts of components of respiratory Complex I and III in the form of one-electron donor (23, 107) thus protecting mitochondria from oxidative damage (61).

Stress Response

The induction of PUMP can be a consequence of increased cellular ROS production under biotic and abiotic stressful conditions, such as pathogenic attack (69), high light, drought, low or high temperature, and mechanical stress (3). However, note that high-salinity stress downregulates PUMP gene expression (93), in contrast with other stresses. Mitochondria represent one of the major sources of ROS during stress in plant cells (71). Several lines of evidence suggest that the contribution of PUMP may be important for antioxidant response. Some PUMP genes are upregulated when plants are exposed to oxidative stress-generating agents, such as H_2O_2 or menadione (15, 26). Transgenic plants with high levels of AtPUMP1 show increased tolerance to oxidative stress (14). In addition, ROS and superoxide stimulate proton leak in mitochondria through the uncoupling activity (20, 60).

Induction of PUMP gene expression by cold stress was observed in potato (65) and *Arabidopsis* (67). More recently, microarray data revealed that *AtPUMP1* and *AtPUMP5* genes are induced by drought (62, 93), and by infection with *Alternaria brassicicola* and RNA viruses (109, 117). *AtPUMP5* is also upregulated by wounds caused by abiotic stress factors such as wind, rain, and hail, and by biotic factors, particularly insect feeding (18), indicating a possible physiological role of At-PUMP5 in plant response to stress. Expression of *AtPUMP1* and -2 increases in heat-induced programmed cell death but not in senescence, implying that some of the At-PUMP gene products may play a role in limiting ROS formation following exposure to heat (103).

Directing Energy Flow

Mild uncoupling of mitochondria, as a consequence of PUMP activity, may not only reduce the rate of mitochondrial ROS production but also increase TCA cycle flux (99). Reoxidation of NADH by respiratory chain couples TCA cycle flux to electron transport and, consequently, to ATP synthesis. This tight coupling between TCA cycle flux and ATP synthesis is metabolically useful when the sole function of the TCA cycle is to provide reducing power to respiration. However, the TCA cycle also has an anabolic role, for instance, providing intermediates for biosynthesis of a number of molecules including amino acids and terpenoids (106). Under anabolic-demand conditions, the flux of the TCA cycle needs to be greater than that required for respiration alone, and dissipation of the proton gradient by PUMP could modulate coupling between the TCA cycle and ATP synthesis. Smith et al. (99) demonstrated that under bioenergetic conditions in which the TCA cycle flux is limited by the extent of mitochondrial coupling, increased PUMP protein content leads to a significant increase in TCA cycle flux. This latter putative role of PUMP may be particularly important in autotrophic organisms such as plants, where the biosynthetic demands on the TCA cycle are large (91). This role of PUMP is also suggested by the observation that the abundance of *PUMP* transcript is significantly increased during metabolic changes that occur in plant tissues subjected to carbohydrate deprivation (105).

An increase in respiration can also occur by "alternative" respiration involving rotenone-insensitive NAD(P) dehydrogenases and AOx that do not build $\Delta\mu_H+$ and therefore are not coupled to ATP-synthase activity (84,

110). Given the differences of expression and regulation of PUMP- and AOx-mediated mitochondrial uncoupling, it is unlikely that these energy-dissipating pathways are simply redundant; rather, they may perform specific roles in specific cell types and under specific conditions.

Participation in Tissue/Organ Development

The expression of PUMP genes is strongly enhanced at the senescence stages during fruit ripening, suggesting a developmental stage-specific regulation of PUMP (19). The increase in mRNA levels after the climacteric ripening phase directly correlates with the increase of mango PUMP content. In tomato, the studies on fruit ripening show that *PUMP* expression adapts to physiological conditions. For example, Holtzapffel et al. (36) reported an increase in transcript and protein levels in the later stages of on-vine fruit ripening, and Almeida et al. (2) found that the amount and activity of PUMP decreases during the later stages of postharvest fruit ripening (2).

Almeida et al. (2) also reported a higher amount of AOx in tomato fruit in postharvest ripening. However, FA concentrations also increase during the postgrowing stage (34, 87). The PUMP and AOx pathways could therefore operate with different efficiencies under distinct physiological conditions, i.e., AOx would be active mainly during high biosynthetic activities in early stages of tomato fruit ripening whereas PUMP would be functionally silent. With increasing FFA concentration in postgrowth stages—as in fruit ripening but perhaps also in senescence and flowering—PUMP activity could reach maximum velocity while AOx activity is switched off (46). In this context, it should be noted that immunoblotting of tomato fruit AOx and PUMP indicates that the level of AOx protein abruptly decreases with ripening after the mature green stage whereas that of PUMP decreases steadily from the mature green to red stage (46).

CONCLUSIONS

Plants have a family of uncoupling mitochondrial proteins, PUMPs, consisting of up to six members. The tissue- and temporal-specific expression profile is distinct for each member of PUMP family, suggesting that PUMP isoforms play different physiological roles during the development of plant tissues and/or organs. Plant UCPs are present in mitochondria in much lower amounts than mammalian UCP1, hence their role in thermogenesis is unimportant. The physiological roles of the stress-inducible isoforms are most likely related to the control of ROS overproduction. On the other hand, constitutively expressed PUMPs may regulate mitochondrial energy flow and some stages of plant tissue/organ development.

SUMMARY POINTS

1. Uncoupling proteins are widespread in eukaryotes such as mammals, monocotyledonous and dicotyledonous plants, birds, frogs, fishes, insects, and primitive eukaryotic organisms.

2. Uncoupling proteins are integral membrane proteins with apparent molecular masses ranging from 30 to 33 kDa. These nuclear-coded proteins are localized in the inner mitochondrial membrane.

3. Plants have a family of uncoupling proteins consisting of up to six members.

4. The ancestor of plant uncoupling protein is probably an anion/anion antiporter or an anion/nucleotide antiporter.

5. The amount of uncoupling proteins in plant mitochondria is not high enough to promote thermogenesis.

6. Plant uncoupling protein isoforms 1, 4, and 5 are stress inducible and their physiological role seems to be related to the control of reactive oxygen species overproduction.

7. Plant uncoupling protein isoforms 2 and 3 are constitutive and are presumably involved in mitochondrial energy flow regulation.

8. The tissue- and temporal-specific expression profile is distinct for each member of the plant uncoupling protein family, suggesting that the isoforms play different physiological roles during the development of plant tissues and/or organs.

LITERATURE CITED

1. Affourtit C, Albury MS, Crichton PG, Moore AL. 2002. Exploring the molecular nature of alternative oxidase regulation and catalysis. *FEBS Lett.* 510:121–26

2. Almeida AM, Jarmuszkiewicz W, Khomsi H, Arruda P, Vercesi AE, et al. 1999. Cyanide-resistant, ATP-synthesis-sustained, and uncoupling-protein-sustained respiration during postharvest ripening of tomato fruit. *Plant Physiol.* 119:1323–29

3. Apel K, Hirt H. 2004. Reactive oxygen species: metabolism, oxidative stress, and signal transduction. *Annu. Rev. Plant Biol.* 55:373–99

4. Apostol I, Heinstein PF, Low PS. 1989. Rapid stimulation of an oxidative burst during elicitation of cultured plant cells. Role in defense and signal transduction. *Plant Physiol.* 90:106–16

5. Argyropoulos G, Harper M-E. 2002. Invited review: uncoupling proteins and thermoregulation. *J. Appl. Physiol.* 92:2187–98

6. Bailey TL, Elkan C. 1994. Fitting a mixture model by expectation maximization to discover motifs in biopolymers. *Proc. Second Intl. Conf. Intell. Syst. Mol. Biol.*, pp. 28–36. Menlo Park, Calif.: AAAI Press

7. Bailey TL, Gribskov M. 1998. Combining evidence using p-values: application to sequence homology searches. *Bioinformatics* 14:48–54

8. Beavis AD, Vercesi AE. 1992. Anion uniport in plant mitochondria is mediated by a Mg^{2+}-insensitive inner membrane anion channel. *J. Biol. Chem.* 267:3079–87

9. Borecký J, Maia IG, Arruda P. 2001. Mitochondrial uncoupling proteins in mammals and plants. *Biosci. Rep.* 21:201–11

10. Borecký J, Maia IG, Costa AD, Ježek P, Chaimovich H, et al. 2001. Functional reconstitution of *Arabidopsis thaliana* plant uncoupling mitochondrial protein (AtPUMP1) expressed in *Escherichia coli*. *FEBS Lett.* 505:240–44

11. Borecký J, Nogueira FTS, de Oliveira KAP, Maia IG, Arruda P, Vercesi AE. 2006. The plant energy-dissipating mitochondrial systems: depicting the genomic structure and the expression profiles of the gene families of uncoupling protein and alternative oxidase in monocots and dicots. *J. Exp. Bot.* In press

12. Borecký J, Vercesi AE. 2005. Plant uncoupling mitochondrial protein and alternative oxidase: energy metabolism and stress. *Biosci. Rep.* 25:271–86

13. Boss O, Samec S, Paolonigiacobino A, Rossier C, Dulloo A, et al. 1997. Uncoupling protein-3: a new member of the mitochondrial carrier family with tissue-specific expression. *FEBS Lett.* 408:39–42

14. Brandalise M, Maia IG, Borecký J, Vercesi AE, Arruda P. 2003. Overexpression of plant uncoupling mitochondrial protein in transgenic tobacco increases tolerance to oxidative stress. *J. Bioenerg. Biomembr.* 35:203–9

15. Brandalise M, Maia IG, Borecký J, Vercesi AE, Arruda P. 2003. ZmPUMP encodes a maize mitochondrial uncoupling protein that is induced by oxidative stress. *Plant Sci.* 165:329–35

16. Calegario FF, Cosso RG, Fagian MM, Almeida FV, Jardim WF, et al. 2003. Stimulation of potato tuber respiration by cold stress is associated with an increased capacity of both plant uncoupling mitochondrial protein (PUMP) and alternative oxidase. *J. Bioenerg. Biomembr.* 35:211–20

17. Cavalheiro RA, Fortes F, Borecký J, Faustinoni VC, Schreiber AZ, et al. 2004. Respiration, oxidative phosphorylation, and uncoupling protein in *Candida albicans*. *Br. J. Med. Biol. Res.* 37:1455–61

18. Cheong YH, Chang HS, Gupta R, Wang X, Zhu T, et al. 2002. Transcriptional profiling reveals novel interactions between wounding, pathogen, abiotic stress, and hormonal responses in *Arabidopsis*. *Plant Physiol.* 129:661–77

19. Considine MJ, Daley DO, Whelan J. 2001. The expression of alternative oxidase and uncoupling protein during fruit ripening in mango. *Plant Physiol.* 126:1619–29

20. Considine MJ, Goodman M, Echtay KS, Laloi M, Whelan J, et al. 2003. Superoxide stimulates a proton leak in potato mitochondria that is related to the activity of uncoupling protein. *J. Biol. Chem.* 278:22298–302

21. Considine MJ, Holtzapffel RC, Day DA, Whelan J, Millar AH. 2002. Molecular distinction between alternative oxidase from monocots and dicots. *Plant Physiol.* 129:949–53

22. Costa ADT, Nantes IL, Ježek P, Leite A, Arruda P, et al. 1999. Plant uncoupling mitochondrial protein activity in mitochondria isolated from tomatoes at different stages of ripening. *J. Bioenerg. Biomembr.* 31:527–33

23. Crofts AR. 2004. The cytochrome bc1 complex: function in the context of structure. *Annu. Rev. Physiol.* 66:689–733

24. Cruz-Hernandez A, Gomez-Lim MA. 1995. Alternative oxidase from mango (*Mangifera indica*, L) is differentially regulated during fruit ripening. *Planta* 197:569–76

25. Day DA, Arron GP, Laties GG. 1980. Nature and control of respiratory pathways in plants: the interaction of cyanide resistant respiration with cyanide-sensitive pathway. In *Biochemistry of Plants*, ed. DD Davies, 4:197–241. New York: Academic.

26. Desikan R, A-H-Mackerness S, Hancock JT, Neill SJ. 2001. Regulation of the *Arabidopsis* transcriptome by oxidative stress. *Plant Physiol.* 127:159–172

27. Echtay KS, Murphy MP, Smith RA, Talbot DA, Brand MD. 2002. Superoxide activates mitochondrial uncoupling protein 2 from the matrix side. Studies using targeted antioxidants. *J. Biol. Chem.* 277:47129–35

28. Echtay KS, Roussel D, St-Pierre J, Jekabsons MB, Cadenas S, et al. 2002. Superoxide activates mitochondrial uncoupling proteins. *Nature* 415:96–99

29. Fleury C, Neverova M, Collins S, Raimbault S, Champigny O, et al. 1997. Uncoupling protein-2: a novel gene linked to obesity and hyperinsulinemia. *Nat. Genet.* 15:269–72

30. Fridell Y-WC, Sánchez-Blanco A, Silvia BA, Helfand SL. 2004. Functional characterization of a *Drosophila* mitochondrial uncoupling protein. *J. Bioenerg. Biomembr.* 36:219–28

31. Garlid KD, Orosz DE, Modriansky M, Vassanelli S, Ježek P. 1996. On the mechanism of fatty acid-induced proton transport by mitochondrial uncoupling protein. *J. Biol. Chem.* 270:2615–20

32. Goglia F, Skulachev VP. 2003. A function for novel uncoupling proteins: antioxidant defense of mitochondrial matrix by translocating fatty acid peroxides from the inner to the outer membrane leaflet. *FASEB J.* 17:1585–91

33. Gray GR, Maxwell DP, Villarimo AR, McIntosh L. 2004. Mitochondria/nuclear signaling of alternative oxidase gene expression occurs through distinct pathways involving organic acids and reactive oxygen species. *Plant Cell Rep.* 23:497–503

34. Güçlü J, Paulin A, Soudain P. 1989. Changes in polar lipids during ripening and senescence of cherry tomato (*Lycopersicon esculentum*): relation to climacteric and ethylene increases. *Plant Physiol.* 77:413–19

35. Hanák P, Ježek P. 2001. Mitochondrial uncoupling proteins and phylogenesis - UCP4 as the ancestral uncoupling protein. *FEBS Lett.* 495:137–41

36. Holtzapffel RC, Finnegan PM, Millar AH, Badger MR, Day DA. 2002. Mitochondrial protein expression in tomato fruit during on-vine ripening and cold storage. *Funct. Plant Biol.* 29:827–834

37. Hourton-Cabassa C, Matos AR, Zachowski A, Moreau F. 2004. The plant uncoupling protein homologues: a new family of energy-dissipating proteins in plant mitochondria. *Plant Physiol. Biochem.* 42:283–90

38. Hourton-Cabassa C, Mesneau A, Miroux B, Roussaux J, Ricquier D, et al. 2002. Alteration of plant mitochondrial proton conductance by free fatty acids. Uncoupling protein involvement. *J. Biol. Chem.* 277:41533–38

39. Ito K, Abe Y, Johnston SD, Seymour RS. 2003. Ubiquitous expression of a gene encoding for uncoupling protein isolated from the thermogenic inflorescence of the dead horse arum *Helicodiceros muscivorus*. *J. Exp. Bot.* 54:1113–14

40. Ito K. 1999. Isolation of two distinct cold-inducible cDNAs encoding plant uncoupling proteins from the spadix of skunk cabbage (*Symplocarpus foetidus*). *Plant Sci.* 149:167–73

41. Jabůrek M, Vařecha M, Gimeno RE, Dembski M, Ježek P, et al. 1999. Transport function and regulation of mitochondrial uncoupling proteins 2 and 3. *J. Biol. Chem.* 274:26003–7

42. Jarmuszkiewicz W, Behrendt M, Navet R, Sluse FE. 2002. Uncoupling protein and alternative oxidase of *Dictyostelium discoideum*: occurrence, properties and protein expression during vegetative life and starvation-induced early development. *FEBS Lett.* 532:459–64

43. Jarmuszkiewicz W, Milani G, Fortes F, Schreiber AZ, Sluse FE, et al. 2000. First evidence and characterization of an uncoupling protein in fungi kingdom: CpUCP of *Candida parapsilosis*. *FEBS Lett.* 467:145–49

44. Jarmuszkiewicz W, Navet R, Alberici LC, Douette P, Sluse-Goffart CM, et al. 2004. Redox state of endogenous Coenzyme Q modulates the inhibition of linoleic acid-induced uncoupling by guanosine triphosphate in isolated skeletal muscle mitochondria. *J. Bioenerg. Biomembr.* 36:493–502

45. Jarmuszkiewicz W, Sluse-Goffart CM, Hryniewiecka L, Sluse FE. 1999. Identification and characterization of a protozoan uncoupling protein in *Acanthamoeba castellanii*. *J. Biol. Chem.* 274:23198–220

46. Jarmuszkiewicz W, Sluse-Goffart CM, Vercesi AE, Sluse FE. 2001. Alternative oxidase and uncoupling protein: thermogenesis versus cell energy balance. *Biosci. Rep.* 21:213–22

47. Ježek P, Borecký J, Záčková M, Costa ADT, Arruda P. 2001. Possible basic and specific functions of plant uncoupling proteins (pUCP). *Biosci. Rep.* 21:237–45

48. Ježek P, Costa AD, Vercesi AE. 1996. Evidence for anion-translocating plant uncoupling mitochondrial protein in potato mitochondria. *J. Biol. Chem.* 271:32743–48

49. Ježek P, Costa AD, Vercesi AE. 2000. Important amino acid residues of potato plant uncoupling protein (StUCP) *Braz. J. Med. Biol. Res.* 33:1413–20

50. Ježek P, Costa ADT, Vercesi AE. 1997. Reconstituted plant uncoupling mitochondrial protein allows for proton translocation via fatty acid cycling mechanism. *J. Biol. Chem.* 272:24272–78

51. Ježek P, Garlid KD. 1990. New substrates and competitive inhibitors of the Cl⁻ translocating pathway of the uncoupling protein of brown adipose tissue mitochondria. *J. Biol. Chem.* 265:19303–11

52. Ježek P, Houšt'ek J, Drahota Z. 1988. Alkaline pH, membrane potential, and magnesium cations are negative modulators of purine nucleotide inhibition of H^+ and Cl^- transport through the uncoupling protein of brown adipose tissue mitochondria. *J. Bioenerg. Biomembr.* 20:603–22

53. Ježek P, Modrianský M, Garlid KD. 1997. Inactive fatty acids are unable to flip-flop across the lipid bilayer. *FEBS Lett.* 408:161–65

54. Ježek P, Modrianský M, Garlid KD. 1997. A structure-activity study of fatty acid interaction with mitochondrial uncoupling protein. *FEBS Lett.* 408:166–70

55. Ježek P, Orosz DE, Modrianský M, Garlid KD. 1994. Transport of anions and protons by the mitochondrial uncoupling protein and its regulation by nucleotides and fatty acids. A new look at old hypotheses. *J. Biol. Chem.* 269:26184–90

56. Ježek P, Urbánková E. 2000 Specific sequence motifs of mitochondrial uncoupling proteins. *IUBMB Life* 49:63–70

57. Juszczuk IM, Rychter AM. 2003. Alternative oxidase in higher plants. *Acta Biochim. Pol.* 50:1257–71

58. Klein SL, Strausberg RL, Wagner L, Pontius J, Clifton SW, Richardson P. 2002. Genetic and genomic tools for *Xenopus* research: the NIH *Xenopus* initiative. *Dev. Dyn.* 225:384–91

59. Klingenberg M. 1990. Mechanism and evolution of the uncoupling protein of brown adipose tissue. *Trends Biochem. Sci.* 15:108–12

60. Kowaltowski AJ, Costa ADT, Vercesi AE. 1998. Activation of the potato plant uncoupling mitochondrial protein inhibits reactive oxygen species generation by the respiratory chain. *FEBS Lett.* 425:213–16

61. Kowaltowski AJ, Vercesi AE. 1999. Mitochondrial damage induced by conditions of oxidative stress. *Free Rad. Biol. Med.* 26:463–71

62. Kreps JA, Wu Y, Chang HS, Zhu T, Wang X, et al. 2002. Transcriptome changes for Arabidopsis in response to salt, osmotic, and cold stress. *Plant Physiol.* 130:2129–41

63. Kumar S, Patil BC, Sinhá SK. 1990. Cyanide-resistant respiration is involved in temperature rise in ripening mangoes. *Biochem. Biophys. Res. Commun.* 168:818–22

64. Kumar S, Sinha SK. 1992. Alternative respiration and heat production in ripening banana fruits (*Musa paradisica* var. *Mysore Kadali*). *J. Exp. Bot.* 43:1639–42

65. Laloi M, Klein M, Riesmeier JW, Muller-Rober B, Fleury C, et al. 1997. A plant cold-induced uncoupling protein. *Nature* 389:135–36

66. Leach GR, Krab K, Whitehouse DG, Moore AL. 1996. Kinetic analysis of the mitochondrial quinol-oxidizing enzymes during development of thermogenesis in Arum maculatum L. *Biochem. J.* 317:313–19

67. Maia IG, Benedetti CE, Leite A, Turcinelli SR, Vercesi AE, et al. 1998. AtPUMP: an *Arabidopsis* gene encoding a plant uncoupling mitochondrial protein. *FEBS Lett.* 429:403–6

68. Mao WG, Yu XX, Zhong A, Li WL, Brush J, et al. 1999. UCP4, a novel brain-specific mitochondrial protein that reduces membrane potential in mammalian cells. *FEBS Lett.* 443:326–30

69. Maxwell DP, Nickels R, McIntosh L. 2002. Evidence of mitochondrial involvement in the transduction of signals required for the induction of genes associated with pathogen attack and senescence. *Plant J.* 29:269–79

70. Meeuse BJD. 1975. Thermogenic respiration in Aroids. *Annu. Rev. Plant Physiol.* 26:117–26

71. Møller IM 2001. Plant mitochondria and oxidative stress: electron transport, NADPH turnover, and metabolism of reactive oxygen species. *Annu. Rev. Plant Physiol. Plant Mol. Biol.* 52:561–91

72. Moore AL, Umbach AL, Siedow JN. 1995. Structure-function relationships of the alternative oxidase of plant mitochondria: a model of the active site. *J. Bioenerg. Biomembr.* 27:367–77

73. Murayama S, Handa H. 2000. Isolation and characterization of cDNAs encoding mitochondrial uncoupling proteins in wheat: wheat UCP genes are not regulated by low temperature. *Mol. Gen. Genet.* 264:112–18

74. Murphy MP, Echtay KS, Blaikie FH, Asin-Cayuela J, Cocheme HM, et al. 2003. Superoxide activates uncoupling proteins by generating carbon-centered radicals and initiating lipid peroxidation: studies using a mitochondria-targeted spin trap derived from alpha-phenyl-N-tert-butylnitrone. *J. Biol. Chem.* 278:48534–45

75. Nantes IL, Fagian MM, Catisti R, Arruda P, Maia IG, et al. 1999. Low temperature and aging-promoted expression of PUMP in potato tuber mitochondria *FEBS Lett.* 457:103–6

76. Navet R, Douette P, Puttine-Marique F, Sluse-Goffart CM, Sluse FE. 2005. Activation and regulation of plant uncoupling protein in potato tuber mitochondria. *FEBS Lett.* 579:4437–42

77. Nicholls DG, Locke RM. 1984. Thermogenic mechanisms in brown fat. *Physiol Rev.* 64:1–64

78. Nicholls DG, Rial E. 1999. A history of the first uncoupling protein, UCP1. *J. Bioenerg. Biomembr.* 31:399–418

79. Nicholls DG. 1976. Hamster brown-adipose-tissue mitochondria. Purine nucleotide control of the ion conductance of the inner membrane, the nature of the nucleotide binding site. *Eur. J. Biochem.* 62:223–28

80. Nogueira FT, De Rosa VE Jr, Menossi M, Ulian EC, Arruda P. 2003. RNA expression profiles and data mining of sugarcane response to low temperature. *Plant Physiol.* 132:1811–24

81. Nogueira FTS, Borecký J, Vercesi AE, Arruda P. 2005. Genomic structure and regulation of mitochondrial uncoupling protein genes in mammals and plants. *Biosci. Rep.* 25:209–24

82. Norman C, Howell KA, Millar AH, Whelan JM, Day DA. 2004. Salicylic acid is an uncoupler and inhibitor of mitochondrial electron transport. *Plant Physiol.* 134:492–501

83. Raimbauld S, Dridi S, Denjean F, Lachuer J, Couplan E, et al. 2001. An uncouplig protein homologue putatively involved in facultative muscle thermogenesis in birds. *Biochem. J.* 353:441–44

84. Rasmusson AG, Soole Kl, Elthon TE. 2004. Alternative NAD(P)H dehydrogenases of plant mitochondria. *Annu. Rev. Plant Biol.* 55:23–39

85. Ricquier D, Bouillaud F. 2000. The uncoupling protein homologues: UCP1, UCP2, UCP3, StUCP and AtUCP. *Biochem. J.* 345:161–79

86. Ricquier D, Kader JC. 1976. Mitochondrial protein alteration in active brown fat: a sodium dodecyl sulfate-polyacrylamide gel electrophoretic study. *Biochem. Biophys. Res. Commun.* 73:577–83

87. Rouet-Mayer MA, Valentova O, Simond-Côte F, Daussant J, Thévenot C. 1995. Critical analysis of phospholipid hydrolyzing activities in ripening tomato fruits. Study by spectrofluorimetry and high-performance liquid chromatography. *Lipids* 30:739–46

88. Sanchis D, Fleury C, Chomiki N, Goubern M, Huang QL, et al. 1998. BMCP1, a novel mitochondrial carrier with high expression in the central nervous system of humans and rodents, and respiration uncoupling activity in recombinant yeast. *J. Biol. Chem.* 273:34611–15

89. Saviani EE, da Silva A Jr, Martins IS. 1997. Photoaffinity labelling of the uncoupling protein from potato tuber mitochondria. *Plant Physiol. Biochem.* 35:701–6

90. Schleiff E, McBride H. 2000. The central matrix loop drives import of uncoupling protein 1 into mitochondria. *J. Cell Sci.* 113:2267–72

91. Schwender J, Ohlrogge JB, Shachar-Hill Y. 2003. A flux model of glycolysis and the oxidative pentosephosphate pathway in developing *Brassica napus* embryos. *J. Biol. Chem.* 278:29442–53

92. Seki M, Ishida J, Narusaka M, Fujita M, Nanjo T, et al. 2002. Monitoring the expression pattern of around 7,000 Arabidopsis genes under ABA treatments using a full-length cDNA microarray. *Funct. Integr. Genomics* 2:282–91

93. Seki M, Narusaka M, Ishida J, Nanjo T, Fujita M, et al. 2002. Monitoring the expression profiles of 7000 Arabidopsis genes under drought, cold and high-salinity stresses using a full-length cDNA microarray. *Plant J.* 31:279–92

94. Skulachev VP. 1991. Fatty acid circuit as a physiological mechanism of uncoupling of oxidative phosphorylation. *FEBS Lett.* 294:158–62

95. Skulachev VP. 1996. Role of uncoupled and non-coupled oxidations in maintenance of safely levels of oxygen and its one-electron reductants. *Quart. Rev. Biophys.* 29:169–202

96. Sluse FE, Almeida AM, Jarmuszkiewicz W, Vercesi AE. 1998. Free fatty acids regulate the uncoupling protein and alternative oxidase activities in plant mitochondria. *FEBS Lett.* 433:237–40

97. Sluse FE, Jarmuszkiewicz W. 1998. Alternative oxidase in the branched mitochondrial respiratory network: an overview on structure, function, regulation, and role. *Braz. J. Med. Biol. Res.* 31:733–47

98. Sluse FE, Jarmuszkiewicz W. 2000. Activity and functional interaction of alternative oxidase and uncoupling protein in mitochondria from tomato fruit. *Braz. J. Med. Biol. Res.* 33:259–68

99. Smith AM, Ratcliffe RG, Sweetlove LJ. 2004. Activation and function of mitochondrial uncoupling protein in plants. *J. Biol. Chem.* 279:51944–52

100. Sokolova IM, Sokolov EP. 2005. Evolution of mitochondrial uncoupling proteins: novel invertebrate UCP homologues suggest early evolutionary divergence of the UCP family. *FEBS Lett.* 579:313–17

101. Spector AA, John K, Fletcher JE. 1969. Binding of long-chain fatty acids to bovine serum albumin. *J. Lipid Res.* 10:56

102. Stuart JA, Harper JA, Brindle KM, Brand MD. 1999. Uncoupling protein 2 from carp and zebrafish, ectothermic vertebrates. *Biochim. Biophys. Acta* 1413:50–54

103. Swidzinski JA, Sweetlove LJ, Leaver CJ. 2002. A custom microarray analysis of gene expression during programmed cell death in *Arabidopsis thaliana*. *Plant J.* 30:431–46

104. Talbot DA, Hanuise N, Rey B, Rouanet J-L, Duchamp C, et al. 2003. Superoxide activates a GDP-sensitive proton conductance in skeletal muscle mitochondria from king penguin (*Aptenodytes patagonicus*). *Biochem. Biophys. Res. Commun.* 312:983–88

105. Thimm O, Blasing O, Gibon Y, Nagel A, Meyer S, et al. 2004. MAPMAN: a user-driven tool to display genomics data sets onto diagrams of metabolic pathways and other biological processes. *Plant J.* 37:914–39

106. Tielens AG, Van Hellemond JJ. 1998. The electron transport chain in anaerobically functioning eukaryotes. *Biochim. Biophys. Acta* 1365:71–78

107. Turrens JF, Boveris A. 1980. Generation of superoxide anion by the NADH dehydrogenase of bovine heart mitochondria. *Biochem J.* 191:421–27

108. Uemura SA, Luo S, Moreno SNJ, Docampo R. 2000. Oxidative phosphorylation, Ca^{2+} transport, and fatty acid-induced uncoupling in malaria parasites mitochondria. *J. Biol. Chem.* 275:9709–15

109. van Wees SC, Chang HS, Zhu T, Glazebrook J. 2003. Characterization of the early response of Arabidopsis to *Alternaria brassicicola* infection using expression profiling. *Plant Physiol.* 132:606–17

110. Vanlerberghe GC, McIntosh L. 1997. Alternative oxidase: from gene to function. *Annu. Rev. Plant Physiol. Plant Mol. Biol.* 48:703–34

111. Vercauteren I, Van Der Schueren E, Van Montagu M, Gheysen G. 2001. *Arabidopsis thaliana* genes expressed in the early compatible interaction with root-knot nematodes. *Mol. Plant Microbe Interact.* 14:288–99

112. Vercesi AE, Martins IS, Silva MAP, Leite HMF, Cuccovia IM, et al. 1995. PUMPing plants. *Nature* 375:24

113. Vettore AL, da Silva FR, Kemper EL, Souza GM, da Silva AM, et al. 2003. Analysis and functional annotation of an expressed sequence tag collection for tropical crop sugarcane. *Genome Res.* 13:2725–35

114. Vianna CR, Hagen T, Zhang C-Y, Bachman E, Boss O, et al. 2001.Cloning and functional characterization of an uncoupling protein homolog in hummingbirds. *Physiol. Genomics* 5:137–45

115. Vidal-Puig A, Solanes G, Grujic D, Flier JS, Lowell BB. 1997. UCP3: an uncoupling protein homologue expressed preferentially and abundantly in skeletal muscle and brown adipose tissue. *Biochem. Biophys. Res. Commun.* 235:79–82

116. Watanabe A, Hirai A. 2002. Two uncoupling protein genes of rice (*Oryza sativa* L.): molecular study reveals the defects in the pre-mRNA processing for the heat-generating proteins of the subtropical cereal. *Planta* 215:90–100

117. Whitham SA, Quan S, Chang HS, Cooper B, Estes B. 2003. Diverse RNA viruses elicit the expression of common sets of genes in susceptible *Arabidopsis thaliana* plants. *Plant J.* 33:271–283

118. Winkler E, Klingenberg M. 1994. Effect of fatty acids on H^+ transport activity of the reconstituted uncoupling protein. *J. Biol. Chem.* 269:2508–15

Genetics and Biochemistry of Seed Flavonoids

Loïc Lepiniec, Isabelle Debeaujon,
Jean-Marc Routaboul, Antoine Baudry,
Lucille Pourcel, Nathalie Nesi,
and Michel Caboche

Seed Biology, Institut Jean-Pierre Bourgin (IJPB), INRA, 78026 Versailles,
France; email: lepiniec@versailles.inra.fr

Annu. Rev. Plant Biol.
2006. 57:405–30

The *Annual Review of
Plant Biology* is online at
plant.annualreviews.org

doi: 10.1146/
annurev.arplant.57.032905.105252

Key Words

bHLH, condensed tannins, flavonols, MYB, proanthocyanidins,
WDR

Abstract

Flavonoids are secondary metabolites that accumulate in most plant
seeds and are involved in physiological functions such as dormancy
or viability. This review presents a current view of the genetic and
biochemical control of flavonoid metabolism during seed development. It focuses mainly on proanthocyanidin accumulation in Arabidopsis, with comparisons to other related metabolic and regulatory
pathways. These intricate networks and their fine-tuned regulation,
once they are determined, should contribute to a better understanding of seed coat development and the control of PA and flavonol
metabolism. In addition, flavonoids provide an interesting model
to study various biological processes and metabolic and regulatory
networks.

Contents

INTRODUCTION

Like many other secondary metabolites, flavonoids play important roles in the interactions of plants with their environments (20, 45, 153): in protection against diverse biotic and abiotic stresses; in various physiological or developmental functions including seed physiology (22, 127, 141); and in the agronomic and industrial qualities of plant products. There is growing evidence for their positive effects on human health (110, 116, 119). Many flavonoids are readily detectable pigments that are not essential for basic cellular functions. Thus, they have long been used as tractable markers for genetic analysis of a wide variety of biological processes and their evolution, including biochemical pathways, metabolic channeling, intracellular transport, cell differentiation, (epigenetic) regulation of gene expression, and the activity of transposable elements (64, 90, 152). These positive attributes explain why the study of flavonoid metabolism has gained interest in recent years, especially in the seed of the model plant *Arabidopsis thaliana*. Here we summarize the most recent advances in our understanding of this metabolism and its regulation, and detail some important and specific questions still outstanding.

NATURE AND TISSUE SPECIFICITY OF SEED FLAVONOIDS

Seed Flavonoids

Over 6000 different flavonoids have been reported (45) and subdivided into different classes that include flavonols, flavones, flavanols, and anthocyanins, according to the oxidation level of the C-ring (**Figure 1**). Additionally, the stereochemistry, position,

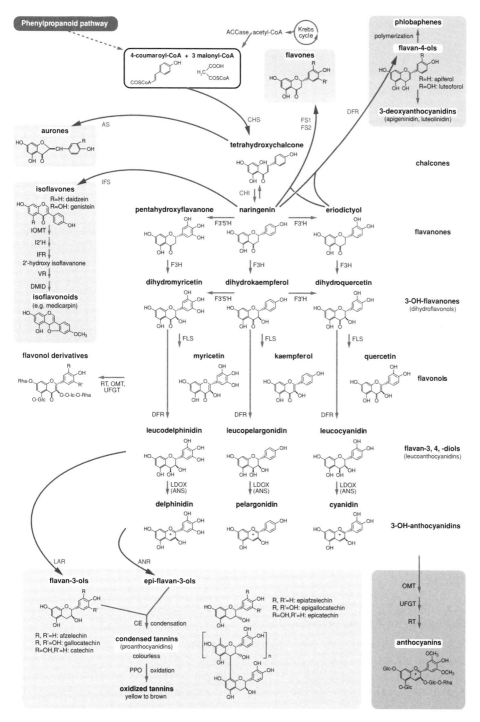

Figure 1

Flavonoid
biosynthetic
pathway. Adapted
from (27, 152).
ACCase, acetyl CoA
carboxylase; ANS,
anthocyanidin
synthase; AS,
aureusidin synthase;
DFR,
dihydroflavonol
4-reductase; DMID,
7,2′-dihydroxy, 4′-
methoxyisoflavanol
dehydratase; F3H,
flavanone
3-hydroxylase; F3′H,
flavonoid
3′-hydroxylase;
F3′5′H, flavonoid
3′5′ hydroxylase;
FLS, flavonol
synthase; FSI/FS2,
flavone synthase;
I2′H, isoflavone
2′-hydroxylase; IFR,
isoflavone reductase;
IFS, isoflavone
synthase; IOMT,
isoflavone
O-methyltransferase;
LAR,
leucoanthocyanidin
reductase; LDOX,
leucoanthocyanidin
dioxygenase; OMT,
O-methyltransferase;
RT, rhamnosyl
transferase; UFGT,
UDP flavonoid
glucosyl transferase;
VR, vestitone
reductase.

and nature of the substitutions (hydroxyl, methyl, galloyl, glycosyl), combination, degree of polymerization, and linkages between the basic units allow for the multitude of compounds characterized in plants. Flavonoids are found in most seeds and grains (127). The type, amount, and localization of these flavonoids vary according to plant species and developmental stage of the tissues and may be modulated by environmental signals. The major types of flavonoids in seeds are flavonols, anthocyanins, phlobaphenes, isoflavones, and proanthocyanidins (PAs, also called condensed tannins). (See Table in supplemental material. Follow the Supplemental Material link from the Annual Reviews home page at **http://www.annualreviews.org**.) Anthocyanins are found in the seed of both monocots and dicots, such as barley grains, which accumulate delphinidin derivatives (70), the seed coat of bean (8), and the pericarp, and the underlying aleurone layer in maize (107). Phlobaphenes (also known as deoxyflavonoids) are red polymers of flavan-4-ol precursors found in maize and other monocots in the fused pericarp and seed coat (44, 127). Flavonols contribute to seed pigmentation mainly as copigments with anthocyanins, as in maize (135). The most frequent flavonol forms are glycoside derivatives. The usual glycosylation sites are the positions C-3 and C-7, and the preferred sugar substitutions are glucose and rhamnose. Finally, isoflavones are colorless compounds that occur in the Papilionoideae subfamily of the Leguminosae, to which soybean belongs (158). They are major metabolites in the embryo and in the seed coat (26, 41).

Flavonols and PAs in Arabidopsis

Arabidopsis seeds accumulate only flavonols and proanthocyanidins (**Figures 2** and **3**), each representing approximately half of the measurable flavonoids. Flavonols are present in both the testa and the embryo (110a). In mature seeds, quercetin-3-O-rhamnoside (also called quercitrin) is the major flavonol,

although other aglycones (kaempferol and isorhamnetin) or glycosides (combinations of one or two rhamnoside and/or glucoside residues esterified in positions 3 and/or 7) have also been detected. In addition, a specific group of biflavonols is assembled from the main quercetin-rhamnoside. Arabidopsis leaves, stems, flowers, and seedlings mainly accumulate kaempferol glycosides (16, 99, 100, 145).

PAs accumulate in the seed coat and protect the embryo and endosperm (23). Their oxidation during the course of seed desiccation leads to the formation of brown pigments that confer color to the mature seed. The seed coat results from differentiation of the integuments and chalazal tissue of the ovule after fertilization. Arabidopsis seeds have two integuments: the outer integument with two cell layers, and the inner integument with three cell layers (**Figure 4**). PAs are synthesized in the endothelium, the innermost cell layer of the inner integument. They are also present in the chalazal area (pigment strand) and in a few cells of the outer integument at the micropyle. Biosynthesis of PAs starts early, around 1 to 2 days after fertilization (daf) at the micropylar level, and deposition progresses in the endothelium toward the chalaza until around 5 to 6 daf. Other seeds such as barley and sorghum also accumulate PAs in the testa of the grain (127).

The acid hydrolysis of PAs into colored anthocyanidins provides a classical assay for quantification and underlies the naming of these compounds. More recently, LC-MS has allowed the fractionation, quantification, and biochemical identification of PAs. Most PAs found in seeds are polymers of two stereoisomers: epicatechin (EC, 2-3–*cis*) and catechin (C, 2-3–*trans*) (45). However, Arabidopsis seeds accumulate only EC with a mean degree of polymerization between 5 and 8, depending on the accessions (2, 110a). There is also natural variation in the quantity of PA accumulated in these accessions (**Figure 2**). Although the linkage of successive monomeric units has not yet been determined in

Procyanidins

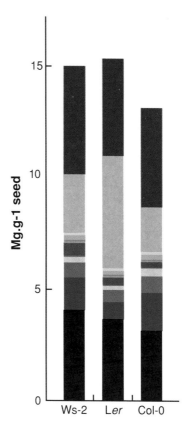

- ■ Insoluble procyanidins
- ▨ Soluble procyanidins
- ▨ Isorhamnetin-hexoside-rhamnoside
- ▨ Isorhamnetin-di-rhamnoside
- ▨ Isorhamnetin-rhamnoside
- ▨ Kaempferol-3-O-glucoside-7-O-rhamnoside
- ■ Kaempferol-3,7-O-di-rhamnoside
- ■ Kaempferol-rhamnoside
- ▨ Biflavonols
- ■ Quercetin-3-O-glucoside-7-O-rhamnoside
- ■ Quercetin-3,7-O-di-rhamnoside
- ■ Quercetin-3-O-rhamnoside

Flavonols

R=H: kaempferol

R=OH: quercitin

R=OCH$_3$: isorhamnetin

Figure 2

Flavonoids in Arabidopsis seed. The contents are presented for three accessions: Wassilewskija-2 (ws-2), Landsberg (Ler), and Columbia-0 (Col-0). Data are adapted from Reference 110a and L. Kerhoas, D. Aouak, A. Cingöz, N. Birlirakis, J-M. Routaboul, and J. Einhorn, unpublished data.

Arabidopsis, in most species it is between the 4-position of the "extension" unit and the 8-position of the "starter" units on the C-ring. An alternative linkage can occur between the C_4 and the C_6 in grape, or between both C_2 and C_4 of the "upper" unit and the oxygen at C_7 and position 6 or 8, respectively, for the "lower" unit, notably for peanuts. (See the Table in the supplemental materials. Follow the Supplemental Material link from the Annual Reviews home page at **http://www.annualreviews.org**.) During

Vanillin assay

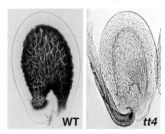

DPBA assay

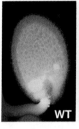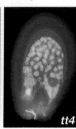

Figure 3

Histochemical detection of seed flavonoids in Arabidopsis. Immature seeds at the late globular-heart stage of embryo development stained as whole mounts. The vanillin assay is used to detect flavan-3-ols and their proanthocyanidin polymers. The DPBA assay is used to detect flavonols. In wild-type Arabidopsis seeds, quercetin is stained orange. Both tests are specific for flavonoids, as no staining is detected in the *tt4* mutant seeds deprived of flavonoids.

seed maturation, PA may interact with other phenolics, proteins, or cell wall polysaccharides to limit the efficiency of their extraction. They also undergo secondary changes to produce oxidized compounds that may not be measurable (83). Thus, current estimates of the amount of PAs in seeds are probably too low.

INSIGHTS FROM GENETICS: IDENTIFICATION OF THE PROTEINS INVOLVED

Genetic Analyses

The isolation and characterization of mutants affected in seed coat, pericarp, or aleurone layer pigmentation has bolstered genetic and molecular studies in a variety of plant species including Arabidopsis, maize, barley, Brassica, bean, and soybean (90, 127). For example, because PAs have a significant effect in determining the quality of beer, over 600 barley mutants that are deficient in PA accumulation have been characterized (52). These mutants belong to 10 independent *ant* loci. Almost no PAs have been detected in the *ant26* mutant, although catechin is synthesized, which suggests the existence of a condensing enzyme catalyzing the polymerization

of flavan-3-ols and leucoanthocyanidins into PAs (52).

In Arabidopsis, most of the mutants impaired in flavonoid accumulation have been identified through screenings for altered seed pigmentation that result in the *transparent testa* (*tt*) mutants (66) (**Figure 5**).

All known *tt* mutations are recessive and show maternal inheritance of the seed phenotype (11, 22, 63, 92, 129). Over 20 complementation groups have been characterized (**Table 1**). Six new groups of mutants defective in PA biosynthesis have recently been reported (3), although it is unclear whether these represent additional loci, with the exception of *TDS4* (2), which is allelic to *TT18*. Seventeen genes have been identified to date at the molecular level (**Table 1**) encoding structural proteins (DFR, CHS, CHI, F3H, F3′H, LDOX, FLS1, and ANR), regulatory proteins (TT1, TT2, TT8, TT16, TTG1, and TTG2), and proteins that are probably involved in flavonoid compartmentation (TT12, TT19, and AHA10). Except for flavonol synthases (FLS), there is no functional redundancy for the structural genes (101, 129, 154).

Recent Advances in PA Metabolism

Substantial progress has been made in our understanding of PA biosynthesis through the isolation and characterization of the genes encoding leucoanthocyanidin reductase (LAR) and anthocyanidin reductase (ANR) (27, 140, 156). These genes act at the entrances to the two major stereospecific pathways of PA biosynthesis. The corresponding recombinant proteins catalyze the formation of *trans* flavan-3-ols and *cis* flavan-3-ols, respectively (140, 155). In Arabidopsis, the ANR is encoded by the *BANYULS* (*BAN*) gene (25), but no LAR has been characterized. This is consistent with the fact that only *cis* flavan-3-ol (epicatechin) is synthesized in this species (3, 110a). The recently cloned *TT10* gene of *Arabidopsis* encodes a polyphenol oxidase of the laccase type that is involved in oxidative

a

Arabidopsis seed   **Maize caryopsis**

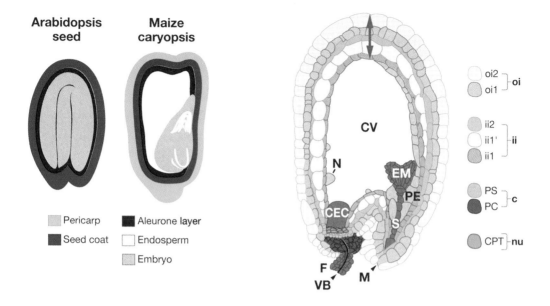

Pericarp
Seed coat
Embryo
Aleurone layer
Endosperm

b

CV
N
EM
PE
CEC
S
F
VB
M

oi2 ⎫
oi1 ⎬ oi
ii2 ⎫
ii1' ⎬ ii
ii1 ⎭
PS ⎫
PC ⎬ c
CPT ⎤ nu

c

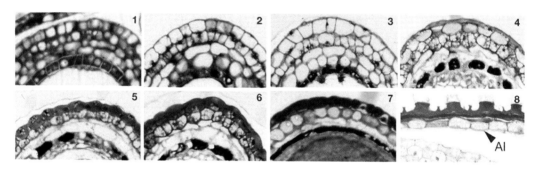

Figure 4

Seed anatomy, with emphasis on Arabidopsis testa structure. (*a*) Schematic organization of an
Arabidopsis seed and a maize caryopsis. (*b*) Arabidopsis seed anatomy adapted from (23). (*c*) Seed coat
development in Arabidopsis. Sections in the curving zone (*red arrow* in *B*), showing in blue
proanthocyanidins in the endothelium. Developmental stages are: (*i*) mature ovule, (*ii*) 2-cell embryo
stage, (*iii*) early heart, (*iv*) early torpedo, (*v*) mid-torpedo, (*vi*) walking stick, (*vii*) cotyledon, and (*viii*)
mature seed. Al, aleurone layer; C, chalaza; CEC, chalazal endosperm cyst; CPT, chalazal proliferating
tissue; CV, central vacuole. Bar = 135 mm for Arabidopsis and 2 mm for maize.

polymerization of flavonoids (106a). TT10,
which is involved in the formation of brown
polymeric pigments from epicatechin, may
catalyze the oxidative browning of colorless
PAs.

Several important questions remain, especially regarding PA metabolism (27). What,
for example, is the precise enzymatic function of TT10, and is the condensation of epicatechin into PAs enzymatic or spontaneous

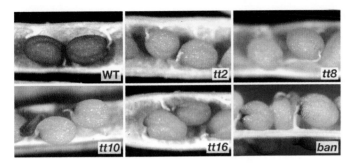

Figure 5

Arabidopsis seed
phenotypes in
wild-type and some
transparent testa
mutants.

in the acidic environment of the vacuole? The degree and function of glycosylations and other substitutions (51) of flavonoids in seeds have not yet been characterized. With the characterization of some glycosyltransferases, genetic analyses and careful examination of their localization and spatial and temporal regulation may help to address this question (56). The systematic use of new sophisticated metabolomic characterization of mutants, reverse genetics approaches, and transcriptome analyses should help in characterizing new proteins involved in the flavonoid pathway (143).

SUBCELLULAR ORGANIZATION OF THE METABOLIC PATHWAY

Biosynthesis and Metabolons

The enzymes of phenylpropanoid and flavonoid pathways appear to be organized as multiprotein enzyme complexes (metabolons) that channel the flux of substrate through specific subpathways (57, 151). For instance, CHS, CHI, F3H, and DFR colocalize on the endoplasmic reticulum (ER) in Arabidopsis. Membrane-bound cytochrome P450 proteins such as F3′H (113), C4H (4), and IFS (78) would anchor multienzyme complexes to the ER. For PA biosynthesis, a new model can be proposed in which all of the enzymes up to those involved in the formation of both types of flavan-3-ol isomer are localized on the cytoplasmic face of the ER or vacuolar membrane (57, 83). Whether LAR and ANR colocalize with these enzymes has not been

determined. Recently, the polymerization of PAs was shown to be dependent on intact membranes (83). In Arabidopsis, at least two enzymes have been found in the nucleus, pointing to the possible existence of a differential targeting of the biosynthetic machinery (114).

Transport and Compartmentation

Flavonoids may accumulate in cellular compartments that differ from those in which they are synthesized (**Figure 6**). The most common sites for sequestration are the vacuoles for anthocyanins, glycosylated flavonols, and proanthocyanidins, and the cell wall for the polymeric phlobaphenes and methylated flavonols (42, 157). In maize, the vacuolar accumulation of anthocyanins involves a transporter on the tonoplast (MRP-type) and a glutathione S-transferase (GST)-like protein (39, 84). Functionally homologous GST-like genes have been found in *Petunia* and carnation (64 and references therein). MRPs transport various glutathione conjugates and are thus often referred to as glutathione (GS-X) pumps. However, no anthocyanin-glutathione conjugate(s) has been detected, suggesting that the GSTs may provide flavonoids directly to the transporter (39, 64).

In Arabidopsis, three genes are thought to be involved in vacuolar transport of flavan-3-ols. The *TT12* gene encodes a transporter exhibiting strong homology with putative Multidrug and Toxic Compound Extrusion (MATE) secondary transporters (24). Its mutation affects PA accumulation in the testa. *AHA10* encodes a H$^+$-ATPase that is also involved in PA metabolism (7). Both *tt12* and *aha10* mutants, as well as *tt19*, exhibit an aberrant vacuolar structure in endothelial cells. *TT19* encodes a GST whose mutation affects both PA and anthocyanin biosynthesis (63). GST may participate in the cytoplasmic transport of PAs before they are transported into the vacuole via a tonoplast protein that

Table 1 *Loci* involved in PA biosynthesis in *Arabidopsis* seed

Locus	Seed coat color[a]	Gene product	Branch[b]	References
Structural genes				
tt3	Yellow	Dihydroflavonol reductase (DFR)	P, A	(66, 128, 129)
tt4	Yellow	Chalcone synthase (CHS)	P, F, A	(33, 66, 129)
tt5	Yellow	Chalcone isomerase (CHI)	P, F, A	(66, 128, 129)
tt6	Pale brown spotted	Flavanone-3-hydroxylase (F3H)	P, F, A	(66, 102, 129, 154)
tt7	Pale brown spotted	Flavanone-3'-hydroxylase (F3'H)	P, F, A	(66, 67, 121, 129)
tt10	Dark yellow/brown C[c]	Polyphenol oxidase (PPO)	P, F	(66, 129; e)
tt12	Pale brown	MATE secondary transporter	P	(24)
tt15	Pale brown/brown CM	Glycosyltransferase (GT)	P	(34; f)
tt18/ tds4/ tt11	Yellow	Leucocyanidin dioxygenase (LDOX)[d]	P, A	(2, 93, 126; g)
tt19/tt14	Dark yellow[3]	Glutathione S-transferase (GST)	P, A	(24, 63; g)
ban	Pale gray/gray CM	Anthocyanidin reductase (ANR)	P	(25, 139, 156)
aha10	Pale brown	Autoinhibited H$^+$-ATPase isoform 10	P	(7)
Regulatory genes				
tt1	Yellow/brown CM	Transcription factor WIP-type Zn-Finger	P	(66, 111, 129)
tt2	Yellow	Transcription factor AtMYB123	P	(66, 93, 129)
tt8	Yellow	Transcription factor AtbHLH042	P, A	(66, 91, 129)
tt16 /abs	Yellow/brown CM	Transcription factor MADS AtAGL32	P	(59, 92)
ttg1	Yellow	Regulatory protein ("WD40" or "WDR")	P, A	(65, 129, 149)
ttg2	Yellow	Transcription factor AtWRKY44	P	(55)
Other loci				
tt9	Pale gray/dark CM	Unknown	?	(66, 129)
tt13	Pale brown	Unknown	?	(24)
tt17	Pale brown	Unknown	?	(11)
tds1,3, 5, 6	Pale brown	Unknown	P	(3)
tds2	Pale brown	Unknown	P, A	(3)

[a]Wild-type seed coat color is brown. [b]Affected metabolic branch: P, proanthocyanidins (only in seed coat); F, flavonols; A, anthocyanins (only in vegetative parts). [c]Seeds brownish with storage time. [d]Also called anthocyanidin synthase (ANS). C, Chalaze; M, Micropyle. Unpublished work from (e) L. Pourcel, J.-M. Routaboul, L. Kerhoas, M. Caboche, L. Lepiniec & I. Debeaujon; (f) I. Debeaujon, N. Nesi & L. Lepiniec; and (g) I. Debeaujon & M. Koornneef.

requires H$^+$-ATPase activity. To date, GST activity has been linked only with transport by MRPs, which suggests that both MATE and MRP transport systems may occur in Arabidopsis (39). In tomato, a similar MATE transporter and GST genes, which are coregulated with other anthocyanin genes, have been identified (86). Thus, although vesicular transport, GST, MATE, and MRP transporters and H$^+$-ATPase may all be involved in flavonoid transport of and sequestration in vacuoles, the molecular mechanisms involved have not been identified. Furthermore, the mechanisms may well differ, depending on the nature of the flavonoid and the species under consideration.

CHARACTERIZATION OF THE REGULATORY LOCI

Regulation of Flavonoid Biosynthesis

Regulatory proteins controlling anthocyanin accumulation have been well characterized in various species such as maize, *Petunia*, *Antirrhinum*, and Arabidopsis (90, 107a, and references therein). Most of these belong to one of the two largest families of regulatory proteins in plants: the MYB and bHLH families (47, 69, 137). The first proteins were identified in maize, C1/Pl1 (R2R3-type MYB proteins) and R/B/Lc/Sn-family (bHLH) (38, 81, 97). R/C1 is required in kernels (aleurone, scutellum, and embryo) and B/Pl in pericarp,

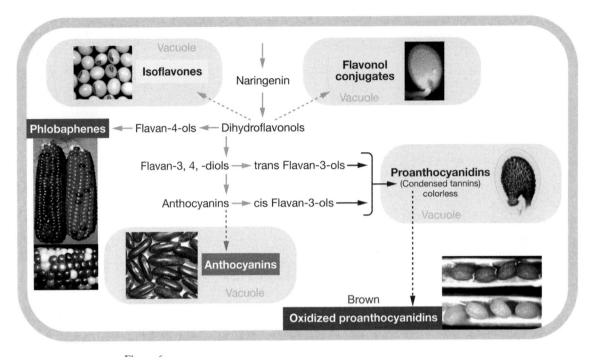

Figure 6

Intracellular distribution of seed flavonoids.

seed integument, as well as in plant body (19, 81, 106, 107). Some genes encoding structurally related proteins have been cloned from *Antirrhinum*, e.g., *DELILA*, which encodes a bHLH protein (40), and *Petunia*, e.g., *AN1* and *JAF13*, which encode two bHLH proteins, and *AN2*, which encodes a MYB protein (108, 132). Some proteins with "WD40" repeats (WDR) are also involved in anthocyanin biosynthesis such as AN11 in *Petunia* (21), PFWD in *Perilla* (131), and PAC1, which is required for strong pigmentation in the aleurone and scutellum of the maize seed (18, 122).

P, a MYB protein involved in phlobaphene biosynthesis, can activate target genes alone (44, 75). Negative regulators have been also identified (107a); examples include the FaMYB1 protein (5), AtMYB4 (54), different *C1* alleles (112, 130), or the truncated bHLH *IN1* (17). Finally, the *Arabidopsis ICX1*, as yet unidentified, acts as a negative regulator of different pathways that induce flavonoid biosynthetic genes (148).

Regulatory Loci in Arabidopsis

Six loci, *TT1*, *TT2*, *TT8*, *TT16*, *TTG1*, and *TTG2*, have a regulatory function in PA biosynthesis (**Table 1**). Two of these genes may control cellular/tissue differentiation rather than PA biosynthesis directly. *TT1* codes a zinc-finger protein expressed mainly in the endothelium cell layer of the developing seed (111). *TT16/ABS* encodes a MADS box, protein of the "B-sister" group, in which expression is restricted to early flower and seed development, and that interacts with floral homeotic proteins (59, 92). Both TT1 and TT16 are necessary for PA accumulation in the core region of the endothelium (i.e., region 2 in **Figure 7**) but not in the micropyle and chalazal areas. Still undetermined is whether cell differentiation and PA accumulation are the default pathways or if redundant functions occur specifically in these areas.

TT2, *TT8*, and *TTG1* encode a R2R3-MYB protein (93), a bHLH protein (91), and a WDR protein (149), respectively. The three

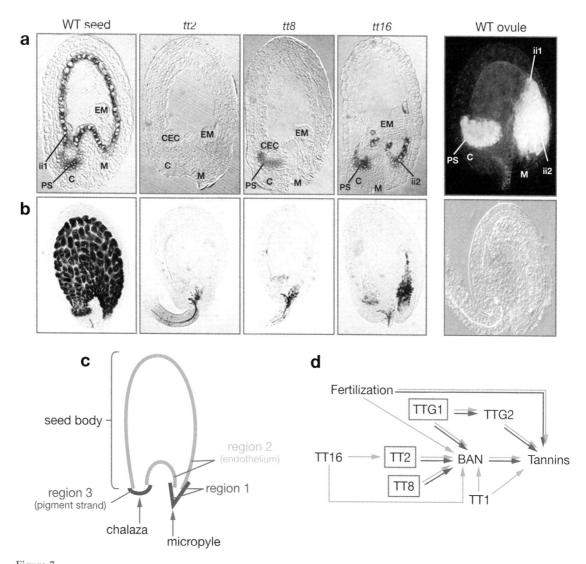

WT seed — *tt2* — *tt8* — *tt16* — **WT ovule**

a

EM, ii1, PS, C, M (WT seed)
CEC, EM, C, M (*tt2*)
CEC, EM, PS, C, M (*tt8*)
EM, PS, C, M, ii2 (*tt16*)
PS, C, M, ii1, ii2 (WT ovule)

b

c

seed body
region 2 (endothelium)
region 3 (pigment strand)
region 1
chalaza
micropyle

d

Fertilization
TTG1 ⟹ TTG2
TT16 ⟶ TT2 ⟹ BAN ⟹ Tannins
TT8
TT1

Figure 7

Regulation of *ANR* expression and PA accumulation in Arabidopsis seed. (*a*) Activity of the *BANYULS* promoter, at the globular/heart stage of embryo development of wild-type and mutant seeds, and in wild-type ovule. (*b*) PA accumulation. (*c*) Schematic of PA-accumulating cells. (*d*) Genetic regulatory pathway (*red* for regions 1 and 3, *blue* for region 2). Adapted from Reference 23.

corresponding mutants produce seeds lacking PAs. The mutations in *TTG1* and *TT8* also affect anthocyanin production in the vegetative parts (65, 129). This is consistent with the specific expression of *TT2* in the endothelium (23, 93), whereas *TT8* and *TTG1* are expressed in both seed and vegetative parts (6, 93, 149). *TTG1* has additional roles in the development of trichomes and root hairs and in seed mucilage accumulation (65, 149). *TTG2* encodes a WRKY transcription factor. The mutation of this gene leads to the formation of yellow seeds and affects mucilage production and trichome development but not anthocyanin metabolism in vegetative parts nor root hair formation (55). Epistatic relationships suggest that *TTG2* acts downstream of *TTG1* in regulating PA accumulation.

GL3 and EGL3 are two bHLH proteins (96, 159), and ANL2 is a homeodomain protein belonging to the GLABRA2 group (72), which is required for the accumulation of anthocyanins in vegetative tissues. These proteins are also involved in other functions described below. Ectopic expression of two homologous MYB proteins, PAP1 and PAP2, leads to anthocyanin, flavonol, and hydroxycinnamic acid accumulations (12). It would be interesting to test whether the redundancy of PAP1 and PAP2 can explain the lack of visible phenotype of antisense transgenic lines (12) and to further investigate the phenotype of single and/or double *pap1pap2* loss-of-function alleles. Two other closely related proteins, AtMYB113 and AtMYB114 (137), need to be investigated. AtMYB12 is a flavonol-specific activator in young seedlings (89). Two closely related proteins have been found, AtMYB11 and MYB111 (137), the latter being expressed in siliques (69), but their function is not known.

REGULATION OF THE EXPRESSION OF STRUCTURAL GENES

Coregulation of Different Genes of the Pathway

In maize, the structural genes encoding the biosynthetic enzymes are coordinately activated (90). In *Arabidopsis*, two types of coregulated structural genes can be distinguished: Early Biosynthetic Genes (EBGs), i.e., *CHS*, *CHI*, *F3H*, and *FLS*, which are induced prior to the Late Biosynthetic Genes (LBGs), i.e., *DFR*, *LDOX* during seedling development (71, 152). *BAN* and *TT12* are regulated in the same way as the LBGs (91, 93). The patterns in other dicots such as *Antirrhinum* and *Petunia* are similar, although in *Antirrhinum*, the *F3H* belongs to the LBGs (85, 152). In Arabidopsis, TT2 and TTG1 control the expression of several LBGs including *TT12*, *DFR*,

and *LDOX* (91, 93, 101). Similarly, TT8 is also important for the expression of the *DFR* in seed (91, 93), but not in seedling (101). Ectopic expression of *PAP* genes can induce the expression of several *EBGs* (12, 142), and a dominant negative, PAP1, suppresses the expression of different *EBGs* (88). In addition, there is evidence that TT2 can also activate the expression of different *EBGs* when ectopically expressed (A. Baudry & L. Lepiniec, unpublished data). Although these results may potentially have biotechnological application, additional genetic analyses (multiple loss-of-function mutants) are needed to confirm the significance of these regulations in wild-type plants. Indeed, of the regulatory loss-of-function alleles so far characterized in Arabidopsis none clearly affects the expression of any *EBG*. Thus, the expression of the *EBGs* may be coregulated by distinct but functionally redundant regulatory proteins. These regulations raise questions about the molecular mechanisms involved, including the structure/function relationships of the target promoters.

Analyses of the *cis*-Regulatory Sequences of the Promoters

In maize, either C1 and R/B or P alone direct high levels of expression from different promoters containing the haPBS box (high-affinity P1-binding sites), although this sequence is not functional alone (44, 48). In Arabidopsis, an 86-bp DNA fragment of the *BAN* promoter functions as a PA-accumulating cell-specific enhancer (23). This PA-box contains two putative MYB and bHLH binding sites linked to a *cis*-sequence resembling the haPBS (23). Similar structures have also been found in *DFR* but not in *TT12*, both of which are also LBGs. Functional analysis of the promoters of four *EBGs* (i.e., *CHS*, *CHI*, *F3H*, and *FLS*) suggests that a MYB binding site is likely to be involved, with a *cis*-element recognized by a bZIP protein in light regulation and a bHLH binding site for tissue specificity (46). However, there is limited understanding of what sites the regulators prefer to bind in planta. Functional results cannot yet be used in a predictive manner and further analyses of target promoters are required (1). Elucidation of the molecular mechanisms that determine the specificity of the regulators in planta is a prerequisite for genetic engineering of the metabolic pathways. In addition, this information should also help in identifying new putative targets for genes involved in the flavonoid pathway that cannot be detected easily or directly by genetic approaches (86).

Regulation of *BANYULS* Gene Expression and PA Accumulation

In Arabidopsis, the expression of *BAN* is detected in cells accumulating PAs (23, 25). Fertilization is necessary for both endothelium differentiation and expression of *BAN* in the seed body (**Figure 7**). This relationship needs to be examined to determine whether there is cross-talk in the signals regulating endosperm and seed coat development (36). In addition, a mechanism occurring downstream from *BAN* transcription may delay tannin accumulation in the chalazal area. Because the micropyle and chalaza are not adjacent, a signal diffusing from the micropyle to the chalaza may be required for PA accumulation. TT2, TT8, and TTG1 are necessary for *BAN* expression (23). Although no PAs are detected in *tt8*, faint promoter activity is still detected in the chalazal area (region 3 in **Figure 7c**). Mutations in *TT16* restrict the expression of *BAN* to the chalaza and micropyle, according to the restricted accumulation of PAs in *tt16*. Conversely, the pattern of *BAN* expression seems to be only slightly affected in a *tt1* background. A decrease and delay in *BAN* expression may be consistent with a decrease in mRNA accumulation (111) but insufficient to explain the lack of PA. Mutation of TTG2 has no influence on the activity of the *BAN* promoter. Both TT1 and TTG2 may be involved in either posttranscriptional regulation of *BAN* expression or regulation of downstream differentiation processes leading to the formation of PA-accumulating cells. Thus, the direct targets of TT1, TT16, and TTG2 remain to be identified.

A Set of Homologous Proteins Controls Different Aspects of Epidermal Cell Differentiation

In Arabidopsis, the bHLH proteins involved in regulating the flavonoid pathways (i.e., GL3, EGL3, and TT8) have other partially redundant functions that are TTG1 dependent and related to the differentiation of epidermal cells such as the development of trichomes, root-hair organogenesis, or mucilage biosynthesis in seed (13, 109) (**Figure 8**). Two homologous R2R3-MYB proteins, GL1 and WER, control trichome development and the formation of nonhair cells in root, respectively (76, 95). These proteins belong to the same group as AtMYB23 (137). But ectopic expression of AtMYB23 can only partially complement *wer* and *gl1* mutations (60), and a dominant negative mutant is also deficient for seed coat mucilage (87). These results, taken together, show that the specific function of the homologous R2R3-MYB regulators is determined by both their expression profiles and protein structures. Some regulators (e.g., WER, GL3, EGL3, and TTG1) are also involved in the patterning of stomata in the embryonic stem (10, 125).

In *Petunia*, the mutation of AN1 (bHLH) or AN11 (WDR) affects not only the development of seed coat epidermis but also the acidification of the vacuole in petals (64, 107a, 132). However, no defects in trichome formation have been described to date for these flavonoid mutants of *Petunia* (21, 64) or of maize (18, 122). The fact that the expression of several WDR proteins from different species can complement the *ttg1* mutant (18, 64, 109) may indicate only a structural conservation of these regulators. Thus, the functions of TTG1 and associated regulators may be species specific and depend on the pathway under consideration. Other R2R3-MYB proteins are involved in epidermal cell

WDR	TTG1				
bHLH	TT8				
		EGL3			
		GL3			
MYB	TT2	MYB61	PAP1/PAP2	WER	GL1 / MYB23
S-MYB	?	?	?	CPC-ETC1-TRY	ETC2

| PA Biosynthesis | Mucilage Biosynthesis | Anthocyanin Biosynthesis | Root-Hair Patterning | Trichome Initiation |

Figure 8

MYB-bHLH-WDR complexes and redundant functions in Arabidopsis. The pictures of trichomes and root hairs were kindly provided by Jaap Nijsse and Tita Ritsema, and John Schiefelbein, respectively.

differentiation processes, although none has been demonstrated to act with a WDR protein. AtMYB61 is required for mucilage deposition and extrusion (103), and At-MYB103 may be involved in trichome development (49). In *Antirrhinum*, AmMYBML1 and MIXTA, two similar R2R3-MYB proteins, direct epidermal cell differentiation processes in petals, including multicellular trichome and/or conical cell formation, respectively (94, 104).

STRUCTURE AND REGULATION OF THE MYB-bHLH-WDR (MBW) COMPLEX

Posttranslational Regulation of the MBW Complex

Several R2R3-MYB proteins can bind directly to DNA either on their own or in the presence of bHLH proteins, although direct binding of the bHLH alone to DNA has not been demonstrated (6, 48, 107a, 160). However, bHLH activity may require a specific *cis*-regulatory element, and some MYB proteins cannot bind DNA without a bHLH partner.

Therefore, the bHLH may be recruited to DNA by other regulators and/or modify the binding specificity of the MYB. Part of the function of the bHLH may also be to relieve the R2R3-MYB from a specific inhibitor (48). Several bHLH and MYB proteins interact together in yeast or in vitro (6, 9, 76, 96, 115, 147, 159, 160). For instance, the homologous bHLH proteins from Arabidopsis subgroup IIIf (i.e., TT8, GL3, EGL3, and AtMYC1) interact with R2R3 MYBs from various subgroups such as TT2 (subgroup 5), PAP1, PAP2, AtMYB113, and AtMYB114 (subgroup 6), with WER, GL1, and AtMYB23 (subgroup 15, but excluding TT8), with AtMYB5, and also with C1 of maize. The N-terminal region of the bHLH factor interacts with the R3 repeat of the MYB domain. A few amino acid changes in the MYB domain are sufficient to confer similar functionality to P, a maize R2R3-MYB acting usually without a bHLH (48). The exhaustive functional and structural analyses of the Arabidopsis R2R3-MYB and bHLH interactions have also revealed a conserved amino acid signature in the MYB R3 domain, including some important residues also found in the maize C1 protein (160).

418   *Lepiniec et al.*

The WDR proteins involved in flavonoid biosynthesis interact with some of the bHLH and R2R3-MYB proteins (6, 9, 64, 96, 131, 159). A three-hybrid experiment suggests that TTG1 participates directly in the activation complex (6). Consistent with this hypothesis, PFWD is transferred from the cytoplasm into the nucleus when coexpressed with a bHLH protein (131). In addition, ectopic expression of different bHLHs (e.g., R, Lc, AN1, GL3, and EGL3) can partially complement the WDR mutants (21, 35, 79, 80, 96, 159, 107a). Therefore, the "flavonoid" WDR may be involved in a posttranslational regulation of the complex and act on the bHLH. Another possibility is that the WDR protein is necessary to prevent the effect of a negative regulator. Unfortunately, the function of the most closely related proteins in plants (i.e., AtAN11a and AtAN11b in Arabidopsis, and MP1 in maize) and in nonplant species are not known (18, 21). However, their structures are well conserved, inasmuch as a homologous gene from human can, at least in part, replace *AN11* in functional assays (64). In Arabidopsis, some distantly related proteins such as COP1 and SPA1, which also interact with different transcription factors, are involved in protein degradation (74, 123, 124). UPL3/KAKTUS is a putative E3 ubiquitin ligase that represses branching and endoreplication of Arabidopsis trichomes, and a putative target is GL3 (29, 30). Lastly, other WDR proteins are involved in regulating gene expression at the chromatin level (13).

Small MYB proteins (S-MYB) that possess a single R3 domain and lack a putative activation domain, such as CPC, TRY, ETC1, ETC2, AtMYBL2, and perhaps At4g01060, act as inhibitors of the initiation of trichome or nonhair cells in roots (32, 61, 62, 105, 109, 115, 117, 120, 146, 147). These proteins can interact with different bHLHs of the MBW complex, as demonstrated for MYC1 (with AtMYBL2, CPC, ETC1, and ETC2), EGL3 or GL3 (with AtMYBL2, CPC, ETC1, and TRY), TT8 (with CPC and AtMYBL2), and R with CPC (9, 105, 115, 147, 159, 160).

These interactions can disrupt the interaction with the R2R3-MYB and/or the binding of the complex to DNA (31, 68). Similarly, a small MYB homolog from *Petunia* (MYBx) can interact with AN1 (bHLH), and its constitutive expression downregulates anthocyanin synthesis (64, 107a).

However, the significance of these interactions has not been fully confirmed in planta. Indeed, several interactions have been demonstrated to be less efficient in vivo, depending on both the proteins and the target promoters studied. For instance, AtMYC1 can interact with TT2 in vitro, but only weakly induces the DFR promoter in transient expression experiments (160), is unable to activate *BAN* (6), and does not suppress any *ttg1* phenotypes when ectopically expressed (96). In addition, ectopic expression of the regulatory proteins can lead to misinterpretation of the real network. Functional analyses of (multiple) loss-of-function alleles are needed. Chimeric proteins with a glucocorticoid receptor (GR) hormone-binding domain (79) were used to show that AN1 directly (i.e., without protein synthesis) activates the expression of target genes in planta (133). Similarly, TT2, TT8, and TTG1 can activate different LBGs (6). The next important steps will be to demonstrate the physical interactions "protein-protein" or "protein-DNA" in planta, ideally in the correct cellular contexts within the normal range of expression levels.

Transcriptional Regulation of the MBW Complex

In maize, both developmental and environmental factors (light) control the expression of the regulatory genes in seed (28, 90, 106, 107). *C1* expression is also modulated by abscisic acid and VP1 (58, 138). In Arabidopsis, homologous transcription factors with a B3 domain (e.g., FUS3) appear to regulate flavonoid biosynthesis negatively (37). Consistent with this finding, FUS3 prevents *TTG1* expression in different cellular domains of the embryo (144).

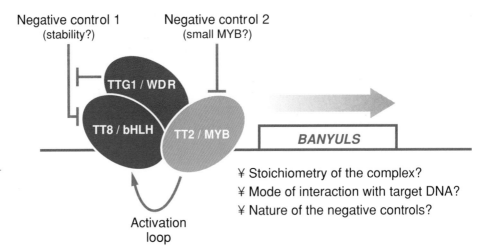

Figure 9

Schematic
regulation of the
MBW complex
involved in PA
biosynthesis in
Arabidopsis seed.

In an earlier model for trichome or nonhair-cell development in roots, patterning results from a regulatory feedback loop and lateral inhibition mechanism mediated by the small MYB inhibitors (31, 50, 73, 77, 82, 105, 118, 120). This model implied that (*a*) the activators activate both the activators and the inhibitors (e.g., S-MYB), (*b*) the inhibitors inhibit the activators, and (*c*) the inhibitors can move between cells and faster than the other regulators. Consistent with this model, TTG1, WER, R, GL3, and EGL3 positively regulate *CPC* expression (9, 68, 77, 105, 146, 159), and GL1 acts cell autonomously (105), in marked contrast to CPC and thus perhaps to other small MYB proteins (61, 62, 77, 117, 146). In *Petunia*, the activations of *AN1* (bHLH) by AN2 and AN4 (two MYB proteins) and of the inhibitor (*MYBx*) by AN1 and AN11 fit part of the model (64). A similar positive feedback loop is also involved in regulating PA metabolism (6), although negative feedback involving small MYB proteins has not been studied.

Developmental control of PA accumulation in Arabidopsis seed is also tightly controlled at the cellular level (**Figure 4**), mainly by the expression of *TT2* (6, 23, 93). Ectopic expression of *TT2* induces the transcription of both *TT8* and *BAN*, but not in a *tt8* background (23, 93; A. Baudry & L. Lepiniec, unpublished data). This suggests that *TT8* is under the control of the MBW complex in a positive regulatory loop (**Figure 9**). Control of *TTG1* and *TT2* expression remains to be investigated.

However, an even more complex regulatory network was recently determined. Contrary to expectation, the small MYB proteins activate the expression of the bHLH-encoding genes (*EGL3/GL3*) in the developing hair cells and these bHLH proteins inhibit their own expression in developing nonhair cells (10). In addition, the bHLH proteins can also move from cell to cell, suggesting a new model that would help to establish and to re-enforce cell-fate patterning (10).

Evolutionary Considerations

The involvement of homologous MBW protein complexes in different plant epidermal cell fates appears limited to a few species (e.g., Arabidopsis and *Petunia*). Therefore, some of these functions might have been acquired only recently. The ancestral function of the MBW complex may be related to the regulation of flavonoid metabolism. Indeed, some flavonoids are found in mosses, liverworts, and algae (43, 134, 136). They may have evolved to protect new land plants against UV radiation or to regulate hormonal signaling (14, 64, 98). However, because the regulators—particularly the WDR—are well conserved among the eukaryotes (53, 64, 137), they probably have functions older than the regulation of flavonoid metabolism. The ancestral eukaryotic factors might have been involved in regulating the cell cycle and/or in differentiation, as suggested by the current functions of other MYB and bHLH proteins conserved between animals and plants (15, 47, 137, 150). Examination of the regulators in various species and exhaustive and comprehensive phylogenetic analyses should provide new insight into their evolution and will perhaps enable us to understand how they are recruited to regulate different epidermal cell fates in plants.

UNRESOLVED ISSUES AND FUTURE DIRECTIONS

1. What are the mechanisms involved in the condensation of EC/C into PAs and their transport? Still needed are improved techniques for extraction, quantification, and characterization of seed PAs.

2. What are the mechanisms involved, in planta, in the regulation of flavonoid genes, including the precise function of TT1, TT16, TTG2, TTG1, and the other regulatory proteins and their own regulation?

3. What are the mechanisms involved in signaling between the seed coat, endosperm, fertilization, and embryo development?

ACKNOWLEDGMENTS

The authors thank Cathie Martin for helpful corrections and comments on this review and the editor for correcting the manuscript. They acknowledge the INRA, Genoplante, Limagrain, the CETIOM, and EC (Project FOOD-CT-2004–51,3960, **http://www.flavo.info**) for support on the research related to seed flavonoids.

LITERATURE CITED

1. Abe H, Urao T, Ito T, Seki M, Shinozaki K, Yamaguchi-Shinozaki K. 2003. Arabidopsis AtMYC2 (bHLH) and AtMYB2 (MYB) function as transcriptional activators in abscisic acid signaling. *Plant Cell* 15:63–78

2. Abrahams S, Lee E, Walker AR, Tanner GJ, Larkin PJ, Ashton AR. 2003. The Arabidopsis TDS4 gene encodes leucoanthocyanidin dioxygenase (LDOX) and is essential for proanthocyanidin synthesis and vacuole development. *Plant J.* 35:624–36

3. Abrahams S, Tanner GJ, Larkin PJ, Ashton AR. 2002. Identification and biochemical characterization of mutants in the proanthocyanidin pathway in Arabidopsis. *Plant Physiol.* 130:561–76

4. Achnine L, Blancaflor EB, Rasmussen S, Dixon RA. 2004. Colocalization of L-phenylalanine ammonia-lyase and cinnamate 4-hydroxylase for metabolic channeling in phenylpropanoid biosynthesis. *Plant Cell* 16:3098–109

5. Aharoni A, De Vos CH, Wein M, Sun Z, Greco R, et al. 2001. The strawberry FaMYB1 transcription factor suppresses anthocyanin and flavonol accumulation in transgenic tobacco. *Plant J.* 28:319–32

6. Baudry A, Heim MA, Dubreucq B, Caboche M, Weisshaar B, Lepiniec L. 2004. TT2, TT8, and TTG1 synergistically specify the expression of *BANYULS* and proanthocyanidin biosynthesis in *Arabidopsis thaliana*. *Plant J.* 39:366–80

7. Baxter IR, Young JC, Armstrong G, Foster N, Bogenschutz N, et al. 2005. A plasma membrane H$^+$-ATPase is required for the formation of proanthocyanidins in the seed coat endothelium of *Arabidopsis thaliana*. *Proc. Natl. Acad. Sci. USA* 102:2649–54

8. Beninger CW, Hosfield GL. 2003. Antioxidant activity of extracts, condensed tannin fractions, and pure flavonoids from *Phaseolus vulgaris* L. seed coat color genotypes. *J. Agric. Food Chem.* 51:7879–83

9. Bernhardt C, Lee MM, Gonzalez A, Zhang F, Lloyd A, Schiefelbein J. 2003. The bHLH genes *GLABRA3* (*GL3*) and *ENHANCER OF GLABRA3* (*EGL3*) specify epidermal cell fate in the Arabidopsis root. *Development* 130:6431–39

10. Bernhardt C, Zhao M, Gonzalez A, Lloyd A, Schiefelbein J. 2005. The bHLH genes *GL3* and *EGL3* participate in an intercellular regulatory circuit that controls cell patterning in the Arabidopsis root epidermis. *Development* 132:291–98

11. Bharti AK, Khurana JP. 2003. Molecular characterization of *transparent testa* (*tt*) mutants of *Arabidopsis thaliana* (ecotype Estland) impaired in flavonoid biosynthetic pathway. *Plant Sci.* 165:1321–32

12. Borevitz JO, Xia Y, Blount J, Dixon RA, Lamb C. 2000. Activation tagging identifies a conserved MYB regulator of phenylpropanoid biosynthesis. *Plant Cell* 12:2383–94

13. Broun P. 2005. Transcriptional control of flavonoid biosynthesis: a complex network of conserved regulators involved in multiple aspects of differentiation in Arabidopsis. *Curr. Opin. Plant Biol.* 8:272–79

14. Brown DE, Rashotte AM, Murphy AS, Normanly J, Tague BW, et al. 2001. Flavonoids act as negative regulators of auxin transport in vivo in Arabidopsis. *Plant Physiol.* 126:524–35

15. Buck M, Atchley W. 2003. Phylogenetic analysis of plant basic helix-loop-helix proteins. *J. Mol. Evol.* 56:742–50

16. Burbulis IE, Winkel-Shirley B. 1999. Interactions among enzymes of the Arabidopsis flavonoid biosynthetic pathway. *Proc. Natl. Acad. Sci. USA* 96:12929–34

17. Burr FA, Burr B, Scheffler BE, Blewitt M, Wienand U, Matz EC. 1996. The maize repressor-like gene *intensifier1* shares homology with the *r1/b1* multigene family of transcription factors and exhibits missplicing. *Plant Cell* 8:1249–59

18. Carey CC, Strahle JT, Selinger DA, Chandler VL. 2004. Mutations in the pale aleurone *color1* regulatory gene of the *Zea mays* anthocyanin pathway have distinct phenotypes relative to the functionally similar *TRANSPARENT TESTA GLABRA1* gene in *Arabidopsis thaliana*. *Plant Cell* 16:450–64

19. Cone KC, Burr FA, Burr B. 1986. Molecular analysis of the maize anthocyanin regulatory locus *C1*. *Proc. Natl. Acad. Sci. USA* 83:9631–35

20. D'Auria JC, Gershenzon J. 2005. The secondary metabolism of *Arabidopsis thaliana*: growing like a weed. *Curr. Opin. Plant Biol.* 8:308–16

21. de Vetten N, Quattrocchio F, Mol J, Koes R. 1997. The an11 locus controlling flower pigmentation in petunia encodes a novel WD-repeat protein conserved in yeast, plants, and animals. *Genes Dev.* 11:1422–34

22. Debeaujon I, Leon-Kloosterziel KM, Koornneef M. 2000. Influence of the testa on seed dormancy, germination, and longevity in Arabidopsis. *Plant Physiol.* 122:403–14

23. Debeaujon I, Nesi N, Perez P, Devic M, Grandjean O, et al. 2003. Proanthocyanidin-accumulating cells in Arabidopsis testa: regulation of differentiation and role in seed development. *Plant Cell* 15:2514–31

24. Debeaujon I, Peeters AJ, Leon-Kloosterziel KM, Koornneef M. 2001. The *TRANSPARENT TESTA12* gene of Arabidopsis encodes a multidrug secondary transporter-like

protein required for flavonoid sequestration in vacuoles of the seed coat endothelium. *Plant Cell* 13:853–71

25. Devic M, Guilleminot J, Debeaujon I, Bechtold N, Bensaude E, et al. 1999. The *BANYULS* gene encodes a DFR-like protein and is a marker of early seed coat development. *Plant J.* 19:387–98

26. Dhaubhadel S, McGarvey BD, Williams R, Gijzen M. 2003. Isoflavonoid biosynthesis and accumulation in developing soybean seeds. *Plant Mol. Biol.* 53:733–43

27. Dixon RA, Xie DY, Sharma SB. 2005. Proanthocyanidins—a final frontier in flavonoid research? *New Phytol.* 165:9–28

28. Dooner HK, Robbins TP, Jorgensen RA. 1991. Genetic and developmental control of anthocyanin biosynthesis. *Annu. Rev. Genet.* 25:173–99

29. Downes BP, Stupar RM, Gingerich DJ, Vierstra RD. 2003. The HECT ubiquitin-protein ligase (UPL) family in Arabidopsis: UPL3 has a specific role in trichome development. *Plant J.* 35:729–42

30. El Refy A, Perazza D, Zekraoui L, Valay JG, Bechtold N, et al. 2003. The Arabidopsis *KAKTUS* gene encodes a HECT protein and controls the number of endoreduplication cycles. *Mol. Genet. Genomics* 270:403–14

31. Esch JJ, Chen M, Sanders M, Hillestad M, Ndkium S, et al. 2003. A contradictory *GLABRA3* allele helps define gene interactions controlling trichome development in Arabidopsis. *Development* 130:5885–94

32. Esch JJ, Chen MA, Hillestad M, David Marks M. 2004. Comparison of *TRY* and the closely related *At1g01380* gene in controlling Arabidopsis trichome patterning. *Plant J.* 40:860–69

33. Feinbaum RL, Ausubel FM. 1988. Transcriptional regulation of the *Arabidopsis thaliana* chalcone synthase gene. *Mol. Cell. Biol.* 8:1985–92

34. Focks N, Sagasser M, Weisshaar B, Benning C. 1999. Characterization of *tt15*, a novel transparent testa mutant of *Arabidopsis thaliana* (L.) Heynh. *Planta* 208:352–57

35. Galway ME, Masucci JD, Lloyd AM, Walbot V, Davis RW, Schiefelbein JW. 1994. The TTG gene is required to specify epidermal cell fate and cell patterning in the Arabidopsis root. *Dev. Biol.* 166:740–54

36. Garcia D, Fitz Gerald JN, Berger F. 2005. Maternal control of integument cell elongation and zygotic control of endosperm growth are coordinated to determine seed size in Arabidopsis. *Plant Cell* 17:52–60

37. Gazzarrini S, Tsuchiya Y, Lumba S, Okamoto M, McCourt P. 2004. The transcription factor FUSCA3 controls developmental timing in Arabidopsis through the hormones gibberellin and abscisic acid. *Dev. Cell* 7:373–85

38. Goff SA, Cone KC, Chandler VL. 1992. Functional analysis of the transcriptional activator encoded by the maize B gene: evidence for a direct functional interaction between two classes of regulatory proteins. *Genes Dev.* 6:864–75

39. Goodman CD, Casati P, Walbot V. 2004. A multidrug resistance-associated protein involved in anthocyanin transport in *Zea mays*. *Plant Cell* 16:1812–26

40. Goodrich J, Carpenter R, Coen ES. 1992. A common gene regulates pigmentation pattern in diverse plant species. *Cell* 68:955–64

41. Graham TL. 1991. Flavonoid and isoflavonoid distribution in developing soybean seedling tissues and in seed and root exudates. *Plant Physiol.* 95:594–603

42. Grotewold E. 2004. The challenges of moving chemicals within and out of cells: insights into the transport of plant natural products. *Planta* 219:906–9

43. Grotewold E. 2005. Plant metabolic diversity: a regulatory perspective. *Trends Plant Sci.* 10:57–62

44. Grotewold E, Drummond BJ, Bowen B, Peterson T. 1994. The *myb*-homologous P gene controls phlobaphene pigmentation in maize floral organs by directly activating a flavonoid biosynthetic gene subset. *Cell* 76:543–53

45. Harborne JB, Williams CA. 2000. Advances in flavonoid research since 1992. *Phytochemistry* 55:481–504

46. Hartmann U, Sagasser M, Mehrtens F, Stracke R, Weisshaar B. 2005. Differential combinatorial interactions of *cis*-acting elements recognized by R2R3-MYB, BZIP, and BHLH factors control light-responsive and tissue-specific activation of phenylpropanoid biosynthesis genes. *Plant Mol. Biol.* 57:155–71

47. Heim MA, Jakoby M, Werber M, Martin C, Weisshaar B, Bailey PC. 2003. The basic helix-loop-helix transcription factor family in plants: a genome-wide study of protein structure and functional diversity. *Mol. Biol. Evol.* 20:735–47

48. Hernandez JM, Heine GF, Irani NG, Feller A, Kim M-G, et al. 2004. Different mechanisms participate in the R-dependent activity of the R2R3 MYB transcription factor C1. *J. Biol. Chem.* 279:48205–13

49. Higginson T, Li SF, Parish RW. 2003. AtMYB103 regulates tapetum and trichome development in *Arabidopsis thaliana*. *Plant J.* 35:177–92

50. Hulskamp M. 2004. Plant trichomes: a model for cell differentiation. *Nat. Rev. Mol. Cell. Biol.* 5:471–80

51. Ibrahim RK. 2005. A forty-year journey in plant research: original contributions to flavonoid biochemistry. *Can. J. Bot.* 83:433–50

52. Jende-Strid B. 1993. Genetic control of flavonoid biosynthesis in barley. *Hereditas* 119:187–204

53. Jiang C, Gu J, Chopra S, Gu X, Peterson T. 2004. Ordered origin of the typical two- and three-repeat *Myb* genes. *Gene* 326:13–22

54. Jin H, Cominelli E, Bailey P, Parr A, Mehrtens F, et al. 2000. Transcriptional repression by AtMYB4 controls production of UV-protecting sunscreens in Arabidopsis. *EMBO J.* 19:6150–61

55. Johnson CS, Kolevski B, Smyth DR. 2002. *TRANSPARENT TESTA GLABRA2*, a trichome and seed coat development gene of Arabidopsis, encodes a WRKY transcription factor. *Plant Cell* 14:1359–75

56. Jones P, Messner B, Nakajima J, Schaffner AR, Sait K. 2003. UGT73C6 and UGT78D1, glycosyltransferases involved in flavonol glycoside biosynthesis in *Arabidopsis thaliana*. *J. Biol. Chem.* 278:43910–18

57. Jorgensen K, Rasmussen AV, Morant M, Nielsen AH, Bjarnholt N, et al. 2005. Metabolon formation and metabolic channeling in the biosynthesis of plant natural products. *Curr. Opin. Plant Biol.* 8:280–91

58. Kao CY, Cocciolone SM, Vasil IK, McCarty DR. 1996. Localization and interaction of the *cis*-acting elements for abscisic acid, VIVIPAROUS1, and light activation of the *C1* gene of maize. *Plant Cell* 8:1171–79

59. Kaufmann K, Anfang N, Saedler H, Theissen G. 2005. Mutant analysis, protein-protein interactions and subcellular localization of the Arabidopsis B(sister) (ABS) protein. *Mol. Genet. Genomics* 274:103–18

60. Kirik V, Lee MM, Wester K, Herrmann U, Zheng Z, et al. 2005. Functional diversification of MYB23 and GL1 genes in trichome morphogenesis and initiation. *Development* 132:1477–85

61. Kirik V, Simon M, Huelskamp M, Schiefelbein J. 2004. The *ENHANCER OF TRY AND CPC1* gene acts redundantly with TRIPTYCHON and CAPRICE in trichome and root hair cell patterning in Arabidopsis. *Dev. Biol.* 268:506–13

62. Kirik V, Simon M, Wester K, Schiefelbein J, Hulskamp M. 2004. *ENHANCER of TRY AND CPC2 (ETC2)* reveals redundancy in the region-specific control of trichome development of Arabidopsis. *Plant Mol. Biol.* 55:389–98

63. Kitamura S, Shikazono N, Tanaka A. 2004. *TRANSPARENT TESTA 19* is involved in the accumulation of both anthocyanins and proanthocyanidins in Arabidopsis. *Plant J.* 37:104–14

64. Koes R, Verweij W, Quattrocchio F. 2005. Flavonoids: a colorful model for the regulation and evolution of biochemical pathways. *Trends Plant Sci.* 10:236–42

65. Koornneef M. 1981. The complex syndrom of *ttg* mutant in Arabidopsis. *Arabidopsis Inf. Serv.* 18:45–51

66. Koornneef M. 1990. Mutations affecting the testa colour in Arabidopsis. *Arabidopsis Inf. Serv.* 27:1–4

67. Koornneef M, Luiten W, De Vlaming P, Schram AW. 1982. A gene controlling flavonoid-3′-hydroxylation in Arabidopsis. *Arabidopsis Inf. Serv.* 19:113–15

68. Koshino-Kimura Y, Wada T, Tachibana T, Tsugeki R, Ishiguro S, Okada K. 2005. Regulation of *CAPRICE* transcription by MYB proteins for root epidermis differentiation in Arabidopsis. *Plant Cell Physiol.* 46:817–26

69. Kranz HD, Denekamp M, Greco R, Jin H, Leyva A, et al. 1998. Towards functional characterisation of the members of the *R2R3-MYB* gene family from *Arabidopsis thaliana*. *Plant J.* 16:263–76

70. Kristiansen K. 1984. Biosynthesis of procyanidins in barley, genetic control of the conversion of dihydroquercetin to catechin and procyanidins. *Carlsberg Res. Commun.* 49:503–4

71. Kubasek WL, Shirley BW, McKillop A, Goodman HM, Briggs W, Ausubel FM. 1992. Regulation of flavonoid biosynthetic genes in germinating Arabidopsis seedlings. *Plant Cell* 4:1229–36

72. Kubo H, Peeters AJ, Aarts MG, Pereira A, Koornneef M. 1999. *ANTHOCYANINLESS2*, a homeobox gene affecting anthocyanin distribution and root development in Arabidopsis. *Plant Cell* 11:1217–26

73. Larkin JC, Brown ML, Schiefelbein J. 2003. How do cells know what they want to be when they grow up? Lessons from epidermal patterning in Arabidopsis. *Annu. Rev. Plant Biol.* 54:403–30

74. Laubinger S, Fittinghoff K, Hoecker U. 2004. The SPA quartet: a family of WD-repeat proteins with a central role in suppression of photomorphogenesis in Arabidopsis. *Plant Cell* 16:2293–306

75. Lechelt C, Peterson T, Laird A, Chen J, Dellaporta SL, et al. 1989. Isolation and molecular analysis of the maize P locus. *Mol. Gen. Genet.* 219:225–34

76. Lee MM, Schiefelbein J. 1999. WEREWOLF, a MYB-related protein in Arabidopsis, is a position-dependent regulator of epidermal cell patterning. *Cell* 99:473–83

77. Lee MM, Schiefelbein J. 2002. Cell pattern in the Arabidopsis root epidermis determined by lateral inhibition with feedback. *Plant Cell* 14:611–18

78. Liu CJ, Dixon RA. 2001. Elicitor-induced association of isoflavone O-methyltransferase with endomembranes prevents the formation and 7-O-methylation of daidzein during isoflavonoid phytoalexin biosynthesis. *Plant Cell* 13:2643–58

79. Lloyd AM, Schena M, Walbot V, Davis RW. 1994. Epidermal cell fate determination in Arabidopsis: patterns defined by a steroid-inducible regulator. *Science* 266:436–39

80. Lloyd AM, Walbot V, Davis RW. 1992. *Arabidopsis* and *Nicotiana* anthocyanin production activated by maize regulators *R* and *C1*. *Science* 258:1773–75

81. Ludwig SR, Habera LF, Dellaporta SL, Wessler SR. 1989. Lc, a member of the maize R gene family responsible for tissue-specific anthocyanin production, encodes a protein similar to transcriptional activators and contains the *myc*-homology region. *Proc. Natl. Acad. Sci. USA* 86:7092–96

82. Marks MD, Esch J. 2003. Initiating inhibition, control of epidermal cell patterning in plants. *EMBO Rep.* 4:24–25

83. Marles MA, Ray H, Gruber MY. 2003. New perspectives on proanthocyanidin biochemistry and molecular regulation. *Phytochemistry* 64:367–83

84. Marrs KA, Alfenito MR, Lloyd AM, Walbot V. 1995. A glutathione S-transferase involved in vacuolar transfer encoded by the maize gene *Bronze-2*. *Nature* 375:397–400

85. Martin C, Prescott A, Mackay S, Bartlett J, Vrijlandt E. 1991. Control of anthocyanin biosynthesis in flowers of *Antirrhinum majus*. *Plant J.* 1:37–49

86. Mathews H, Clendennen SK, Caldwell CG, Liu XL, Connors K, et al. 2003. Activation tagging in tomato identifies a transcriptional regulator of anthocyanin biosynthesis, modification, and transport. *Plant Cell* 15:1689–703

87. Matsui K, Hiratsu K, Koyama T, Tanaka H, Ohme-Takagi M. 2005. A chimeric At-MYB23 repressor induces hairy roots, elongation of leaves and stems, and inhibition of the deposition of mucilage on seed coats in Arabidopsis. *Plant Cell Physiol.* 46:147–55

88. Matsui K, Tanaka H, Ohme-Takagi M. 2004. Suppression of the biosynthesis of proanthocyanidin in Arabidopsis by a chimeric PAP1 repressor. *Plant Biotechnol. J.* 2:487–93

89. Mehrtens F, Kranz H, Bednarek P, Weisshaar B. 2005. The Arabidopsis transcription factor MYB12 is a flavonol-specific regulator of phenylpropanoid biosynthesis. *Plant Physiol.* 138:1083–96

90. Mol J, Grotewold E, Koes R. 1998. How genes paint flowers and seeds. *Trends Plant Sci.* 3:212–17

91. Nesi N, Debeaujon I, Jond C, Pelletier G, Caboche M, Lepiniec L. 2000. The *TT8* gene encodes a basic helix-loop-helix domain protein required for expression of *DFR* and *BAN* genes in Arabidopsis siliques. *Plant Cell* 12:1863–78

92. Nesi N, Debeaujon I, Jond C, Stewart AJ, Jenkins GI, et al. 2002. The *TRANSPARENT TESTA16* locus encodes the ARABIDOPSIS BSISTER MADS domain protein and is required for proper development and pigmentation of the seed coat. *Plant Cell* 14:2463–79

93. Nesi N, Jond C, Debeaujon I, Caboche M, Lepiniec L. 2001. The Arabidopsis *TT2* gene encodes an R2R3 MYB domain protein that acts as a key determinant for proanthocyanidin accumulation in developing seed. *Plant Cell* 13:2099–114

94. Noda K, Glover BJ, Linstead P, Martin C. 1994. Flower colour intensity depends on specialized cell shape controlled by a Myb-related transcription factor. *Nature* 369:661–64

95. Oppenheimer DG, Herman PL, Sivakumaran S, Esch J, Marks MD. 1991. A *myb* gene required for leaf trichome differentiation in Arabidopsis is expressed in stipules. *Cell* 67:483–93

96. Payne CT, Zhang F, Lloyd AM. 2000. GL3 encodes a bHLH protein that regulates trichome development in Arabidopsis through interaction with GL1 and TTG1. *Genetics* 156:1349–62

97. Paz-Ares J, Ghosal D, Wienand U, Peterson P, Saedler H. 1987. The regulatory *c1* locus of *Zea mays* encodes a protein with homology to *myb* proto-oncogene products and with structural similarities to transcriptional activators. *EMBO J.* 6:3553–58

98. Peer WA, Bandyopadhyay A, Blakeslee JJ, Makam SN, Chen RJ, et al. 2004. Variation in expression and protein localization of the PIN family of auxin efflux facilitator proteins in flavonoid mutants with altered auxin transport in *Arabidopsis thaliana*. *Plant Cell* 16:1898–911

99. Peer WA, Brown DE, Tague BW, Muday GK, Taiz L, Murphy AS. 2001. Flavonoid accumulation patterns of *transparent testa* mutants of Arabidopsis. *Plant Physiol.* 126:536–48

100. Pelletier MK, Burbulis IE, Winkel-Shirley B. 1999. Disruption of specific flavonoid genes enhances the accumulation of flavonoid enzymes and end-products in Arabidopsis seedlings. *Plant Mol. Biol.* 40:45–54

101. Pelletier MK, Murrell JR, Shirley BW. 1997. Characterization of flavonol synthase and leucoanthocyanidin dioxygenase genes in Arabidopsis. Further evidence for differential regulation of "early" and "late" genes. *Plant Physiol.* 113:1437–45

102. Pelletier MK, Shirley BW. 1996. Analysis of flavanone 3-hydroxylase in Arabidopsis seedlings. Coordinate regulation with chalcone synthase and chalcone isomerase. *Plant Physiol.* 111:339–45

103. Penfield S, Meissner RC, Shoue DA, Carpita NC, Bevan MW. 2001. MYB61 is required for mucilage deposition and extrusion in the Arabidopsis seed coat. *Plant Cell* 13:2777–91

104. Perez-Rodriguez M, Jaffe FW, Butelli E, Glover BJ, Martin C. 2005. Development of three different cell types is associated with the activity of a specific MYB transcription factor in the ventral petal of *Antirrhinum majus* flowers. *Development* 132:359–70

105. Pesch M, Hulskamp M. 2004. Creating a two-dimensional pattern de novo during Arabidopsis trichome and root hair initiation. *Curr. Opin. Genet. Dev.* 14:422–27

106. Piazza P, Procissi A, Jenkins GI, Tonelli C. 2002. Members of the *c1/pl1* regulatory gene family mediate the response of maize aleurone and mesocotyl to different light qualities and cytokinins. *Plant Physiol.* 128:1077–86

106a. Pourcel L, Routaboul JM, Kerhoas L, Caboche M, Lepiniec L, Debeaujon I. 2005. *TRANSPARENT TESTA10* encodes a laccase-like enzyme involved in oxidative polymerization of flavonoids in Arabidopsis seed coat. *Plant Cell* 17:2966–80

107. Procissi A, Dolfini S, Ronchi A, Tonelli C. 1997. Light-dependent spatial and temporal expression of pigment regulatory genes in developing maize seeds. *Plant Cell* 9:1547–57

107a. Quattrocchio F, Baudry A, Lepiniec L, Grotewold E. 2006. The regulation of flavonoid biosynthesis. In *The Science of Flavonoids*, ed. E Grotewold, pp. 97–122. New York: Springer Sci. Business Media

108. Quattrocchio F, Wing JF, van der Woude K, Mol JN, Koes R. 1998. Analysis of bHLH and MYB domain proteins: species-specific regulatory differences are caused by divergent evolution of target anthocyanin genes. *Plant J.* 13:475–88

109. Ramsay NA, Glover BJ. 2005. MYB-bHLH-WD40 protein complex and the evolution of cellular diversity. *Trends Plant Sci.* 10:63–70

110. Ross JA, Kasum CM. 2002. Dietary flavonoids: bioavailability, metabolic effects, and safety. *Annu. Rev. Nutr.* 22:19–34

110a. Routaboul JM, Kerhoas L, Debeaujon I, Pourcel L, Caboche M, et al. 2006. Flavonoid diversity and biosynthesis in seed of *Arabidopsis thaliana*. *Planta*. In press

111. Sagasser M, Lu GH, Hahlbrock K, Weisshaar B. 2002. *A. thaliana TRANSPARENT TESTA 1* is involved in seed coat development and defines the WIP subfamily of plant zinc finger proteins. *Genes Dev.* 16:138–49

112. Sainz MB, Grotewold E, Chandler VL. 1997. Evidence for direct activation of an anthocyanin promoter by the maize C1 protein and comparison of DNA binding by related Myb domain proteins. *Plant Cell* 9:611–25

113. Saslowsky D, Winkel-Shirley B. 2001. Localization of flavonoid enzymes in Arabidopsis roots. *Plant J.* 27:37–48

114. Saslowsky DE, Warek U, Winkel BSJ. 2005. Nuclear localization of flavonoid enzymes in Arabidopsis. *J. Biol. Chem.* 280:23735–40

115. Sawa S. 2002. Overexpression of the *AtmybL2* gene represses trichome development in Arabidopsis. *DNA Res.* 9:31–34

116. Scalbert A, Johnson IT, Saltmarsh M. 2005. Polyphenols: antioxidants and beyond. *Am. J. Clin. Nutr.* 81:215S–17

117. Schellmann S, Schnittger A, Kirik V, Wada T, Okada K, et al. 2002. *TRIPTYCHON* and *CAPRICE* mediate lateral inhibition during trichome and root hair patterning in Arabidopsis. *EMBO J.* 21:5036–46

118. Schiefelbein J. 2003. Cell-fate specification in the epidermis: a common patterning mechanism in the root and shoot. *Curr. Opin. Plant Biol.* 6:74–78

119. Schijlen EGWM, Ric de Vos CH, van Tunen AJ, Bovy AG. 2004. Modification of flavonoid biosynthesis in crop plants. *Phytochemistry* 65:2631–48

120. Schnittger A, Folkers U, Schwab B, Jurgens G, Hulskamp M. 1999. Generation of a spacing pattern: the role of triptychon in trichome patterning in Arabidopsis. *Plant Cell* 11:1105–16

121. Schoenbohm C, Martens S, Eder C, Forkmann G, Weisshaar B. 2000. Identification of the *Arabidopsis thaliana* flavonoid 3'-hydroxylase gene and functional expression of the encoded P450 enzyme. *Biol. Chem.* 381:749–53

122. Selinger DA, Chandler VL. 1999. A mutation in the pale aleurone *color1* gene identifies a novel regulator of the maize anthocyanin pathway. *Plant Cell* 11:5–14

123. Seo HS, Yang JY, Ishikawa M, Bolle C, Ballesteros ML, Chua NH. 2003. LAF1 ubiquitination by COP1 controls photomorphogenesis and is stimulated by SPA1. *Nature* 423:995–99

124. Serino G, Deng X-W. 2003. The COP9 signalosome: regulating plant development through the control of proteolysis. *Annu. Rev. Plant Biol.* 54:165–82

125. Serna L. 2005. Epidermal cell patterning and differentiation throughout the apical-basal axis of the seedling. *J. Exp. Bot.* 56:1983–89

126. Shikazono N, Yokota Y, Kitamura S, Suzuki C, Watanabe H, et al. 2003. Mutation rate and novel *tt* mutants of *Arabidopsis thaliana* induced by carbon. *Genetics* 163:1449–55

127. Shirley BW. 1998. Flavonoids in seeds and grains: physiological function, agronomic importance and the genetics of biosynthesis. *Seed Sci. Res.* 8:415–22

128. Shirley BW, Hanley S, Goodman HM. 1992. Effects of ionizing radiation on a plant genome: analysis of two Arabidopsis *transparent testa* mutations. *Plant Cell* 4:333–47

129. Shirley BW, Kubasek WL, Storz G, Bruggemann E, Koornneef M, et al. 1995. Analysis of Arabidopsis mutants deficient in flavonoid biosynthesis. *Plant J.* 8:659–71

130. Singer T, Gierl A, Peterson PA. 1998. Three new dominant *C1* suppressor alleles in *Zea mays*. *Genet. Res.* 71:127–32

131. Sompornpailin K, Makita Y, Yamazaki M, Saito K. 2002. A WD-repeat-containing putative regulatory protein in anthocyanin biosynthesis in *Perilla frutescens*. *Plant Mol. Biol.* 50:485–95

132. Spelt C, Quattrocchio F, Mol J, Koes R. 2002. *Anthocyanin1* of petunia controls pigment synthesis, vacuolar pH, and seed coat development by genetically distinct mechanisms. *Plant Cell* 14:2121–35

133. Spelt C, Quattrocchio F, Mol JN, Koes R. 2000. *Anthocyanin1* of petunia encodes a basic helix-loop-helix protein that directly activates transcription of structural anthocyanin genes. *Plant Cell* 12:1619–32

134. Stafford HA. 1991. Flavonoid evolution—an enzymatic approach. *Plant Physiol.* 96:680–85

135. Stafford HA. 1998. Teosinte to maize—some aspects of missing biochemical and physiological data concerning regulation of flavonoid pathways. *Phytochemistry* 49:285–93

136. Stafford HA. 2000. The evolution of phenolics in plants. In *Evolution of Metabolic Pathways*, ed. JT Romeo, R Ibrahim, L Varin, V De Luca, pp. 25–54. Amsterdam: Pergamon

137. Stracke R, Werber M, Weisshaar B. 2001. The *R2R3-MYB* gene family in *Arabidopsis thaliana. Curr. Opin. Plant Biol.* 4:447–56

138. Suzuki M, Kao CY, McCarty DR. 1997. The conserved B3 domain of VIVIPAROUS1 has a cooperative DNA binding activity. *Plant Cell* 9:799–807

139. Tanaka A, Tano S, Chantes T, Yokota Y, Shikazono N, Watanabe H. 1997. A new Arabidopsis mutant induced by ion beams affects flavonoid synthesis with spotted pigmentation in testa. *Genes Genet. Syst.* 72:141–48

140. Tanner GJ, Francki KT, Abrahams S, Watson JM, Larkin PJ, Ashton AR. 2003. Proanthocyanidin biosynthesis in plants: purification of legume leucoanthocyanidin reductase and molecular cloning of its cDNA. *J. Biol. Chem.* 278:31647–56

141. Taylor LP, Grotewold E. 2005. Flavonoids as developmental regulators. *Curr. Opin. Plant Biol.* 8:317–23

142. Tohge T, Matsui K, Ohme-Takagi M, Yamazaki M, Saito K. 2005. Enhanced radical scavenging activity of genetically modified Arabidopsis seeds. *Biotechnol. Lett.* 27:297–303

143. Tohge T, Nishiyama Y, Hirai MY, Yano M, Nakajima J-I, et al. 2005. Functional genomics by integrated analysis of metabolome and transcriptome of Arabidopsis plants over-expressing an MYB transcription factor. *Plant J.* 42:218–35

144. Tsuchiya Y, Nambara E, Naito S, McCourt P. 2004. The FUS3 transcription factor functions through the epidermal regulator TTG1 during embryogenesis in Arabidopsis. *Plant J.* 37:73–81

145. Veit M, Pauli GF. 1999. Major flavonoids from *Arabidopsis thaliana* leaves. *J. Nat. Prod.* 62:1301–3

146. Wada T, Kurata T, Tominaga R, Koshino-Kimura Y, Tachibana T, et al. 2002. Role of a positive regulator of root hair development, *CAPRICE*, in Arabidopsis root epidermal cell differentiation. *Development* 129:5409–19

147. Wada T, Tachibana T, Shimura Y, Okada K. 1997. Epidermal cell differentiation in Arabidopsis determined by a *Myb* homolog, CPC. *Science* 277:1113–16

148. Wade HK, Sohal AK, Jenkins GI. 2003. Arabidopsis ICX1 is a negative regulator of several pathways regulating flavonoid biosynthesis genes. *Plant Physiol.* 131:707–15

149. Walker AR, Davison PA, Bolognesi-Winfield AC, James CM, Srinivasan N, et al. 1999. The *TRANSPARENT TESTA GLABRA1* locus, which regulates trichome differentiation and anthocyanin biosynthesis in Arabidopsis, encodes a WD40 repeat protein. *Plant Cell* 11:1337–50

150. Weston K. 1998. Myb proteins in life, death and differentiation. *Curr. Opin. Genet. Dev.* 8:76–81

151. Winkel BS. 2004. Metabolic channeling in plants. *Annu. Rev. Plant Biol.* 55:85–107

152. Winkel-Shirley B. 2001. Flavonoid biosynthesis. A colorful model for genetics, biochemistry, cell biology, and biotechnology. *Plant Physiol.* 126:485–93

153. Winkel-Shirley B. 2002. Biosynthesis of flavonoids and effects of stress. *Curr. Opin. Plant Biol.* 5:218–23

154. Wisman E, Hartmann U, Sagasser M, Baumann E, Palme K, et al. 1998. Knock-out mutants from an En-1 mutagenized *Arabidopsis thaliana* population generate phenylpropanoid biosynthesis phenotypes. *Proc. Natl. Acad. Sci. USA* 95:12432–37

155. Xie DY, Sharma SB, Dixon RA. 2004. Anthocyanidin reductases from *Medicago truncatula* and *Arabidopsis thaliana*. *Arch. Biochem. Biophys.* 422:91–102

156. Xie DY, Sharma SB, Paiva NL, Ferreira D, Dixon RA. 2003. Role of anthocyanidin reductase, encoded by *BANYULS* in plant flavonoid biosynthesis. *Science* 299:396–99

157. Yazaki K. 2005. Transporters of secondary metabolites. *Curr. Opin. Plant Biol.* 8:301–7

158. Yu O, McGonigle B. 2005. Metabolic engineering of isoflavone biosynthesis. *Adv. Agron.* 86:147–90

159. Zhang F, Gonzalez A, Zhao M, Payne CT, Lloyd A. 2003. A network of redundant bHLH proteins functions in all TTG1-dependent pathways of Arabidopsis. *Development* 130:4859–69

160. Zimmermann IM, Heim MA, Weisshaar B, Uhrig JF. 2004. Comprehensive identification of *Arabidopsis thaliana* MYB transcription factors interacting with R/B-like BHLH proteins. *Plant J.* 40:22–34

RELATED RESOURCES

Grotewold E. 2006. Genetics and biochemistry of floral pigments. *Annu. Rev. Plant Biol.* 57:761–80

Larkin JC, Brown ML, Schiefelbein J. 2003. How do cells know what they want to be when they grow up? Lessons from epidermal patterning in Arabidopsis. *Annu. Rev. Plant Biol.* 54:403–30

Winkel BSJ. 2004. Metabolic channeling. *Annu. Rev. Plant Biol.* 55:85–107

Cytokinins: Activity, Biosynthesis, and Translocation

Hitoshi Sakakibara

RIKEN Plant Science Center, Tsurumi, Yokohama 230-0045, Japan;
email: sakaki@riken.jp

Annu. Rev. Plant Biol.
2006. 57:431–49

The *Annual Review of
Plant Biology* is online at
plant.annualreviews.org

doi: 10.1146/
annurev.arplant.57.032905.105231

First published online as a
Review in Advance on
February 1, 2006

1543-5008/06/0602-
0431$20.00

Key Words

adenosine phosphate-isopentenyltransferase, *Agrobacterium
tumefaciens*, cytochrome P450 monooxygenase, plant hormones,
plastid, root/shoot signaling, *trans*-zeatin

Abstract

Cytokinins (CKs) play a crucial role in various phases of plant
growth and development, but the basic molecular mechanisms of
their biosynthesis and signal transduction only recently became clear.
The progress was achieved by identifying a series of key genes encoding enzymes and proteins controlling critical steps in biosynthesis, translocation, and signaling. Basic schemes for CK homeostasis
and root/shoot communication at the whole-plant level can now be
devised. This review summarizes recent findings on the relationship between CK structural variation and activity, distinct features
in CK biosynthesis between higher plants and *Agrobacterium* infected
plants, CK translocation at whole-plant and cellular levels, and CKs
as signaling molecules for nutrient status via root-shoot communication.

Contents

INTRODUCTION

Half a century has passed since the discovery of cytokinin (CK). Triggered by the isolation of kinetin in autoclaved products of herring sperm DNA as a cell division promoting factor in 1955 (4, 62, 63), a number of compounds with CK activity have been identified, including *trans*-zeatin (tZ) as a naturally occurring CK (54), diphenylurea as a synthetic compound (66, 84), and several natural CKs with aromatic side chains (36, 93). Subsequent studies have clarified structural requirements for CK activity. Our current understanding is that naturally occurring CKs are adenine derivatives carrying either an isoprene-derived or an aromatic side chain at the N^6 terminus (66, 93); conventionally, these families are called isoprenoid CKs and aromatic CKs, respectively. In both groups, there are small variations in side-chain structure such as the absence or presence of hydroxyl groups and their stereoisomeric position; the physiological significance of these variations has not yet been fully elucidated.

CK: cytokinin

tZ: *trans*-zeatin

CK plays a crucial role in regulating the proliferation and differentiation of plant cells, and also controls various processes in plant growth and development, such as delay of senescence (30, 67), control of shoot/root balance (112, 113), transduction of nutritional signals (77, 80, 100), and increased crop productivity (6). In spite of its biological and agricultural importance, only in the past few years have the basic molecular mechanisms of biosynthesis and signal transduction been elucidated. This progress was facilitated by the identification of genes encoding enzymes and proteins controlling key steps in CK biosynthesis and signaling, by in-depth analysis of the biochemical properties of the enzymes and proteins, and by thorough determination of the whole-plant and subcellular compartmentation of CKs. Generally, CK biosynthesis and homeostasis are finely controlled by internal and external factors such as other phytohormones and inorganic nitrogen sources (77). Recent findings demonstrated that the CK biosynthesis pathway in *Agrobacterium* infected plants is distinct from that in higher plants in terms of substrate choice, and that this difference is part of the surviving strategy of *Agrobacterium* in the host plant cells (78).

The previously widely accepted idea that CK and auxin are synthesized only in root tips and shoot apices, respectively, is now overturned. Both hormones have coordinated functions as long-distance messengers as well as local paracrine signals; they are synthesized and act at various sites in a plant body, although the physiological differentiation and the mechanisms of the dual signaling system have not been fully elucidated. In basipetal polar auxin transport, the AUX1/PIN-PGP system takes a major role, and the molecular basis of auxin translocation has been characterized (16, 70). The nature of CK translocation systems is less clear, but several lines of evidence point to a common translocation mechanism for purines, nucleosides, and CKs.

In this review, I focus on activity, biosynthesis, translocation, and root-shoot communication, which complements recent excellent reviews on CK signaling (44) and metabolism (66).

STRUCTURAL VARIATION AND BIOLOGICAL ACTIVITY

Structural Diversity of Natural Cytokinins

Both isoprenoid and aromatic CKs are naturally occurring, with the former more frequently found in plants and in greater abundance than the latter. Common natural isoprenoid CKs are N^6-(Δ^2-isopentenyl)-adenine (iP), tZ, *cis*-zeatin (cZ), and dihydrozeatin (DZ) (**Figure 1**). Among them, the major derivatives generally are tZ and iP as well as their sugar conjugates, but there is a lot of variation depending on plant species, tissue, and developmental stage. For instance, tZ- and iP-type CKs are the major forms in *Arabidopsis*, whereas substantial amounts of cZ-type CKs are found in maize (109), rice (41), and chickpea (24). As for aromatic CKs, *ortho*-topolin (oT), *meta*-topolin (mT), their methoxy-derivatives (meoT and memT, respectively), and benzyladenine (BA) are only found in some plant species (93) (**Figure 1**). Several synthetic derivatives possess CK activity (40, 69, 86, 89) but have not been found in nature so far. Human urine contains kinetin (8), but there is no evidence for its occurrence in plants. Usually, all natural CK nucleobases have the corresponding nucleosides, nucleotides, and glycosides (**Figure 2**).

Biological Activity

Results from classical bioassays such as those using tobacco pith (81) and moss (*Funaria hygrometrica*) (92) suggested that CK nucleobases are the active forms. In these assays, tZ and iP generally exhibited higher activities than cZ. tZ and iP generally exhibited higher activity, but cZ had lower or no activity. However, the results between different bioassays were not always consistent (55). It is likely that exogenous-applied CKs could be further

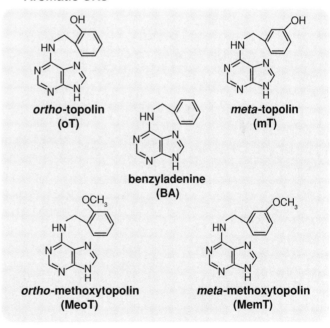

Isoprenoid CKs

N^6-(Δ^2-isopentenyl)adenine (iP)

trans-zeatin (tZ)

cis-zeatin (cZ)

dihydrozeatin (DZ)

Aromatic CKs

ortho-topolin (oT)

meta-topolin (mT)

benzyladenine (BA)

ortho-methoxytopolin (MeoT)

meta-methoxytopolin (MemT)

Figure 1

Structures of representative active cytokinin (CK) species occurring naturally. Only trivial names are given, with commonly used abbreviations in parentheses.

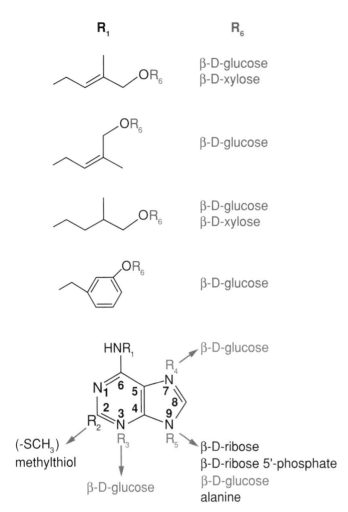

R_1	R_6
	β-D-glucose β-D-xylose
	β-D-glucose
	β-D-glucose β-D-xylose
	β-D-glucose

Figure 2

Cytokinin (CK) conjugates with sugars, sugar phosphates, and others. *O*-Glycosylation of side chain (colored in *blue*) is catalyzed by zeatin *O*-glucosyltransferase or *O*-xylosyltransferase. *N*-glucosylation of adenine moiety (colored in *red*) is catalyzed by cytokinin *N*-glucosyltransferase.

iP: N6-(Δ2-isopentenyl)adenine

cZ: *cis*-zeatin

the receptors whereas the sugar conjugates are less active or inactive. In a heterologous assay system, a CK receptor from maize (ZmHK1) responded to cZ with a similar sensitivity to tZ, and another one (ZmHK2) responded to tZ riboside (tZR) as well as to tZ (115). The *Arabidopsis* CK receptor, AHK3, was as sensitive to tZR and tZR 5′-monophosphate (tZRMP) as to tZ (91), suggesting that each receptor has a specific spectrum of ligand preference (91, 114, 115). Thus, structural variations of CK side chains and modifications of the adenine moiety confer specificity of the CK-receptor interaction.

CYTOKININ BIOSYNTHESIS AND METABOLISM

Basic Schemes of Cytokinin Metabolism

Cytokinin metabolism and homeostasis. CK metabolic pathways can be broadly classified into two types: the modification of the adenine moiety and that of the side chain. The concomitant occurrence of CK nucleobases with the corresponding nucleosides and nucleotides in plant tissues suggests that important metabolic steps are shared with the purine metabolic pathway [i.e., salvage pathway (22, 66, 76)]. Thus, the metabolic flow from CK nucleotides to the active nucleobases is probably not unidirectional but circular (**Figure 3**). In fact, exogenously applied CK nucleobases are rapidly metabolized into the corresponding nucleotides and nucleosides in plant tissues (56, 65, 88, 115). Enzymes of the purine salvage pathway in plants are encoded by small multigene families. It is now supposed that some of the isoenzymes have broad substrate specificities, enabling them to act on CKs as well as on authentic adenine. In this regard, two isoenzymes of adenine phosphoribosyltransferase from *Arabidopsis*, APT2 and APT3, have a particularly strong preference for CK nucleobases as compared with other isoenzymes (3, 83). Such preference is also

converted into other metabolites during the experiments. The identification of CK receptors and the detailed analysis of their ligand specificity helped us to better understand the relative activity of various CKs. CK receptors in higher plants are encoded by a small gene family (39, 97, 108, 115). Bioassays based on heterologous expression of CK receptors in budding or fission yeast (39, 97) and in *Escherichia coli* (91, 97, 114, 115) confirmed that CK nucleobases are the primary ligands for

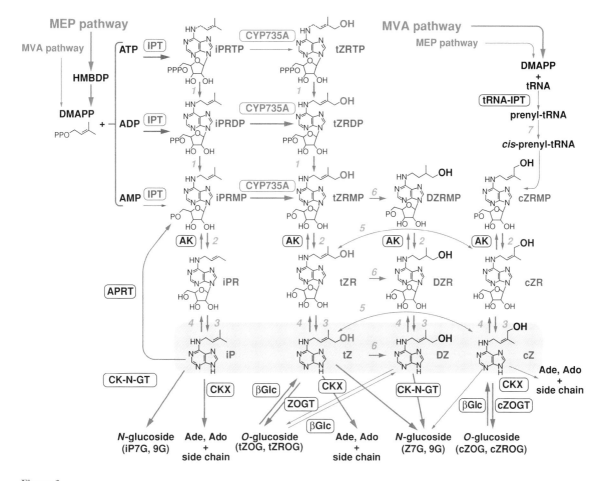

Figure 3

Current model of isoprenoid cytokinin (CK) biosynthesis pathways in *Arabidopsis*. Isoprenoid side chains of N^6-(Δ^2-isopentenyl)adenine (iP) and *trans*-zeatin (tZ) predominantly originate from the methylerythritol phosphate (MEP) pathway, whereas a large fraction of the *cis*-zeatin (cZ) side chain is derived from the mevalonate (MVA) pathway (*green arrows*) (46). Plant adenosine phosphate-isopentenyltransferases (IPTs) preferably utilize ATP or ADP as isoprenoid acceptors to form iPRTP and iPRDP, respectively (*blue arrows*) (43, 76). Dephosphorylation of iPRTP and iPRDP by phosphatase (*1*), phosphorylation of iPR by adenosine kinase (AK), and conjugation of phosphoribosyl moieties to iP by adenine phosphoribosyltransferase (APRT) create the metabolic pool of iPRMP and iPRDP. APRT utilizes not only iP but also other CK nucleobases. The CK nucleotides are converted into the corresponding tZ-nucleotides by CYP735A (*red arrows*). iP, tZ, and the nucleosides can be catabolized by CKX to adenine (Ade) or adenosine (Ado). cZ and tZ can be enzymatically interconverted by zeatin *cis-trans* isomerase (*5*). tZ can be reversibly converted to the *O*-glucoside by zeatin *O*-glucosyltransferase (ZOGT) and β-glucosidase (βGlc). CK nucleobases also can be converted to the *N*-glucoside by CK *N*-glucosyltransferase (CK-N-GT). The width of the arrowheads and lines in the green, blue, and red arrows indicates the strength of metabolic flow. Flows indicated by black arrows are not well characterized to date. tZRDP, tZR 5′-diphosphate; tZRTP, tZR 5′-triphosphate; *2*, 5′-ribonucleotide phosphohydrolase; *3*, adenosine nucleosidase; *4*, purine nucleoside phosphorylase; *6*, zeatin reductase; *7*, CK *cis*-hydroxylase. Modified from Reference 104.

CKX: cytokinin oxidase/dehydrogenase

DMAPP: dimethylallyl diphosphate

HMBDP: hydroxymethylbutenyl diphosphate

IPT: adenosine phosphate-isopentenyltransferase

reported from an isoform of tobacco adenosine kinase, ADK2S (50).

On the other hand, the enzymes for the N-glucosylation of the adenine moiety (37) and those for the hydroxylation (104), O-glucosylation, and O-xylosylation of the side chain (59–61) are specific for particular CK substrates.

Glycosylation of Cytokinins. Glucosylation of CK has been observed at the N3, N7, and N9 position of the purine moiety as N-glucosides, and at the hydroxyl group of the side chains of tZ, DZ, and cZ as O-glucosides or O-xylosides (**Figure 2**). O-glucosylation is reversible; the deglycosylation is catalyzed by β-glucosidase (18). On the other hand, N-glucoconjugates are not efficiently cleaved by β-glucosidase (18); as a result, N-glucosylation is practically irreversible. The physiological consequences of the differences in stability of N-glucosides and O-glucosides are not fully understood to date. However, it has been suggested that the readily cleaved O-glucosides represent inactive, stable storage forms of CKs.

Although genes involved in the O-glycosylation of CKs have been well characterized (59–61, 68, 109), information on the molecular biology of N-glucosylation is scarce. In *Arabidopsis*, two enzymes (UGT76C1 and UGT76C2) glucosylate a series of CK nucleobases at the N7- or N9-positions, and also tZ-O-glucoside (tZOG) at N7 (37). Both enzymes prefer glucosylation at N7 to that at N9, which corresponds well with the concentrations of various CK N-glucosylates in *Arabidopsis* tissues (78).

Determinants of the levels of active Cytokinins. Steady-state levels of active CK in planta are determined by the rate of release of CK nucleobase from the conjugates and that of CK degradation and inactivating conjugation. CK oxidase/dehydrogenase (CKX) catalyzes the irreversible degradation by cleavage of the side chain (5, 28, 82), and glycosyltransferases, described above, inactivate

CKs by glycosylation (**Figure 3**). Phosphoribosylation of CK nucleobase by adenine phosphoribosyltransferase also reduces the biological activity (**Figure 3**). The deribosylation of CK nucleoside to release the nucleobase might be an important step to regulate the level of active CKs, but the enzymes catalyzing it and their genes have not been identified yet.

Stability among CKs also has an effect on biological activity and is determined by its affinity to metabolic enzymes. For instance, tZ and iP are readily catalyzed by CKXs from various plant species (13, 29), whereas cZ is generally less amenable (13). Because CKXs recognize the double bond of the isoprenoid side chain, DZ and aromatic CKs are resistant to CKX (5).

Cytokinin Biosynthesis

Primary reaction of de novo cytokinin biosynthesis. The first step in the isoprenoid CK biosynthesis is N-prenylation of adenosine 5'-phosphates (AMP, ADP, or ATP) at the N^6-terminus with dimethylallyl diphosphate (DMAPP) or hydroxymethylbutenyl diphosphate (HMBDP); this reaction is catalyzed by adenosine phosphate-isopentenyltransferase (IPT; EC 2.5.1.27) (**Figure 3**). It had long been thought that DMAPP and AMP were the only substrates for CK biosynthesis, but now it seems clear that substrate specificities of IPTs vary depending on the origin and the species.

The first identification of substrates for the isoprenoid CK biosynthesis was achieved in the slime mold, *Dictyostelium discoideum*, which produces discadenine [3-(3-amino-3-carboxypropyl)-N^6-(Δ²-isopentenyl)adenine], an inhibitor of spore germination (1). The first step of discadenine biosynthesis is the IPT-catalyzed prenylation of AMP. *D. discoideum* IPT utilizes AMP or ADP as a prenyl side-chain acceptor, but not ATP or cyclic AMP (38, 107). The K_m value for AMP is 100 nM and for DMAPP it is 2.2 μM (38).

The first characterization of an *IPT* gene was carried out in *Agrobacterium tumefaciens*, a crown gall-forming bacterium (2, 9). *A. tumefaciens* has two IPT genes, *Tmr* and *Tzs*. *Tmr* is encoded on the T-DNA region of the Ti-plasmid and *Tzs* is located on the virulence region of nopaline-type Ti-plasmids, whose role is to promote T-DNA transfer efficiency (42, 73). After infection, *Tmr* is integrated into the host nuclear genome and functions in the host cell, whereas *Tzs* acts within the bacterial cells. Both recombinant enzymes have been purified and their kinetic parameters characterized: The K_m value of Tmr for AMP is 85 nM (14) and those for DMAPP and HMBDP are 10.1 μM and 13.6 μM, respectively (78). Tzs also utilizes HMBDP as an isoprene donor (48), and the affinities for HMBDP and DMAPP are similar (H. Sakakibara, unpublished results). Both Tmr and Tzs do not utilize adenosine phosphates other than AMP.

The reaction pathway of iP riboside 5′-moophosphate (iPRMP) synthesis in higher plants has been assumed to resemble that found in *D. discoideum* and *A. tumefaciens*. Although many attempts have been made to purify and characterize plant IPT, only a few biochemical properties have been reported (15, 21), probably due to low contents or enzyme instability. Higher plant *IPT* genes have been identified in *Arabidopsis* (43, 99), petunia (116), and hop (79). In *Arabidopsis*, seven *IPT* genes (*AtIPT1* and *AtIPT3* to *AtIPT8*) are involved in CK biosynthesis (43, 95, 99). Biochemical studies strongly suggest that plant IPTs predominantly use ADP or ATP rather than AMP as prenyl acceptors, resulting in the production of iP riboside 5′-diphosphate (iPRDP) or iP riboside 5′-triphosphate (iPRTP) (43, 76, 79, 103). The K_m values of AtIPT1 for AMP, ADP, and ATP were 185 μM, 14.6 μM, and 11.4 μM, respectively, and for DMAPP it was 8.3 μM (99, 103). AtIPT4 had K_m values of 9.1 μM for ADP, 3.4 μM for ATP, and 11.6 μM for DMAPP (43, 76). The predominant accumulation of iP-type CKs in transgenic lines of *Arabidopsis* that overexpress any

of the AtIPTs suggested that all AtIPTs have similar substrate preferences in terms of the isoprenoid donor (78).

Although some *Arabidopsis* IPTs could utilize HMBDP as a prenyl donor in vitro, the affinities were low and there is little evidence that tZ-type species are formed via this reaction in vivo (78, 98).

Metabolic origin of the isoprenoid side chain. HMBDP is a metabolic intermediate of the methylerythritol phosphate (MEP) pathway, which occurs in bacteria and plastids (33). Thus, in higher plants, it is believed that HMBDP is formed only in plastids. DMAPP is synthesized via the MEP pathway and the mevalonate (MVA) pathway, which is commonly found in the cytosol of eukaryotes (57, 75). When DMAPP is used as a substrate for CK biosynthesis, the primary product is iP nucleotide (**Figure 3**). tZ nucleotide can be formed directly when IPT acts on HMBDP. Before the characterization of the MEP pathway (57, 75), the MVA pathway was the only reaction sequence known to produce the isoprenoid precursors DMAPP and isopentenyl diphosphate in higher plants. In cultured tobacco BY-2 cells, lovastatin, an inhibitor of the MVA pathway, significantly decreases CK accumulation (51, 52), corroborating the idea that the MVA pathway is the metabolic origin of isoprenoid CK side chains. However, in *Arabidopsis*, a large number of the AtIPTs (AtIPT1, AtIPT3, AtIPT5, and AtIPT8) are located in the plastids (46), and AtIPT3 and AtIPT5 are the dominant isoforms in young and mature plants under normal conditions (64, 102). Thus, it seems that plastids are the major subcellular compartment for iP-type CK biosynthesis in higher plants. Selective labeling experiments using ^{13}C-labeled precursors specific for either the MEP or MVA pathway demonstrate that the isoprenoid side chain of iP- and tZ-type CKs predominantly originates from the MEP pathway (46), which is consistent with the IPT subcellular location. On the other hand, AtIPT4 and AtIPT7 are localized in the cytosol and mitochondria,

MEP: pathway: methylerythritol phosphate pathway

MVA: pathway: mevalonate pathway

P450: Cytochrome P450 monooxygenase is a heme-containing enzyme that catalyzes the oxidative reaction of a wide variety of organic compounds by utilizing atmospheric O_2

respectively (46). Therefore, a major role of the MEP pathway in the biosynthesis of tZ- and iP-type CK does not rule out a greater contribution of the MVA pathway to the synthesis of these CKs under different growth or environmental conditions, if the relative abundance of IPT isoenzymes is modulated.

The hydroxylation step in tZ biosynthesis. In higher plants, there are two possible pathways for tZ biosynthesis, the iP nucleotide-dependent and the iP nucleotide-independent one (7, 72, 104) (**Figure 3**). In the iP nucleotide-dependent pathway, tZ synthesis is catalyzed by a cytochrome P450 monooxygenase (P450); two such enzymes, CYP735A1 and CYP735A2, were recently identified in *Arabidopsis* (104). Although previous studies on microsomal fractions isolated from cauliflower showed *trans*-hydroxylation of iP and iPR only (20), CYP735A1 and CYP735A2, which lack *cis*-hydroxylation activity (104), utilize iP nucleotides but not the nucleoside and free-base forms (104). Comparison of the specificity constants (k_{cat}/K_m) for iP-nucleotides suggests that CYP735As predominantly acts on iPRMP or iPRDP rather than on iPRTP (104). Although the physiological role of the CK nucleotides has not been fully clarified, the nucleotide-specific hydroxylation indicates that they form a metabolic pool for side-chain modifications. If the CK nucleobases iP and tZ serve distinct physiological functions that are determined by side-chain structure, the metabolic compartmentalization of the corresponding nucleotides would be important to maintain the physiological division of tasks at the nucleobase level.

In the iP nucleotide-independent pathway, tZ nucleotides are assumed to be produced directly by IPT using an unknown hydroxylated side-chain precursor (7). This precursor probably is derived from the MVA pathway, because mevastatin, an inhibitor of that pathway, reduces the rate of tZ biosynthesis (7). Although the biochemical nature of the iP nucleotide-independent pathway remains obscure, one possible explanation is that tZ biosynthesis via the iP nucleotide-independent pathway might be mediated by *cis-trans* isomerization of cZ derivatives, in which the prenyl side chain is primarily derived from the MVA pathway (46) (**Figure 3**). It will be necessary to identify the postulated isomerase (10) to understand the fabric of the pathway.

The strategy of Agrobacterium to modify cytokinin biosynthesis. In vitro studies on the substrate preference of Tmr (78) and measurements of CK contents in *Tmr*-overexpressing transgenic plants (7, 25, 78) and crown galls (71, 94) suggested that Tmr utilizes HMBDP as the primary substrate and produces tZRMP. However, because Tmr lacks any apparent sequences for subcellular localization, it was believed that Tmr functions in the cytosol. However, recent work demonstrated that Tmr is targeted to and functions in the plastids of infected host plant cells (78) (**Figure 4**). In the stroma of the

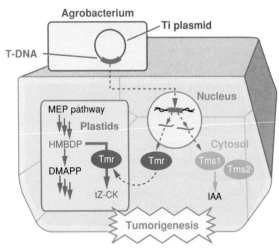

Figure 4

Proposed mechanism for the modification of cytokinin (CK) biosynthesis by Tmr upon *Agrobacterium* infection. On infection, the T-DNA region is transferred to the host plant cells and integrated into the nuclear genome. A series of genes including biosynthesis of CK (Tmr) and auxin (Tms1 and Tms2) are expressed in the host plants. Among them, Tmr is targeted into the plastids and directly produces *trans*-zeatin (tZ)-type CK by using 1-hydroxy-2-methyl-2(E)-butenyl 4-diphosphate (HMBDP).

plastids, Tmr creates a CK biosynthesis by-pass using HMBDP, an intermediate of the MEP pathway, without the requirement for CYP735A-mediated hydroxylation (78). This bypass enables *A. tumefaciens* to produce high amounts of tZ in order to induce tumorigenesis while the host's CYP735A-mediated CK hydroxylation activity could be repressed by auxin (104). Moreover, HMBDP reductase produces isopentenyl diphosphate and DMAPP at a ratio of 5:1 (74), and these compounds are used as common building blocks for all isoprenoids. Therefore, the pool size of HMBDP available for Tmr may be larger than that of DMAPP in the plastids.

Aromatic cytokinins. Aromatic CKs, BA, and topolins (**Figure 1**) were identified in several plant species including poplar (93) and *Arabidopsis* (106), but it is not yet clear whether they are ubiquitous in plants. Although they exhibit strong CK activity, their biosynthesis and degradation pathways remain to be elucidated. The mechanisms of glycosylation of aromatic CKs and of their interaction with the cellular signaling system appear to be shared with isoprenoid CKs because the enzymes and receptors involved recognize members of both groups (39, 66, 68, 114). In tomato pericarp tissue, the modification of BA is greatly inhibited by metyrapone, a potent inhibitor of P450 enzymes (58). Although details are unknown, CYP735A or some other P450s may be involved in the biosynthesis of topolins.

A neglected pathway: cytokinins derived from tRNA degradation. Shortly after the discovery of CKs, it was assumed that tRNA is a major source of CKs because isoprenoid CKs were identified in the hydrolysates of tRNAs (45, 90, 110, 111). Several of the tRNA species with anticodons complementary to codons beginning with uridine, such as tRNA[Leu] and tRNA[Ser], carry a prenylated adenosine adjacent to the anticodon. Thus, tRNA prenylation could contribute, at least to some extent, to CK production. The first step of the pathway leading to CKs is catalyzed by tRNA-isopentenyltransferase (tRNA-IPT; EC 2.5.1.8) (32) (**Figure 3**). Because the prenyl-moiety of the tRNA contains a *cis*-hydroxylated group (111), tRNA-degradation is a source of cZ-type CKs; the biochemical nature of the *cis*-hydroxylating enzyme has not been characterized yet. A large fraction of the cZ side chain in *Arabidopsis* is derived from the MVA pathway, suggesting that plants are able to independently modulate the levels of tZ and cZ (46). Early calculations of turnover rates of tRNA led to the conclusion that tRNA degradation was not a major pathway of CK synthesis (47). However, tRNA-derived CKs should not be neglected as some plant species such as maize and rice contain substantial amounts of cZ-type CKs.

Regulation of Cytokinin Biosynthesis

Spatial expression of AtIPTs. Analyses of spatial expression patterns of *AtIPTs* using their promoter::reporter genes revealed tissue- and organ-specific patterns of CK synthesis by IPT (64, 102). *AtIPT1* is expressed in xylem precursor cell files in root tips, leaf axils, ovules, and immature seeds; *AtIPT3* is expressed in phloem companion cells; *AtIPT4* and *AtIPT8* are expressed in immature seeds with highest expression in the chalazal endosperm; *AtIPT5* is expressed in lateral root primordia, columella root caps, upper parts of young inflorescences, and fruit abscission zones; *AtIPT6* is expressed in siliques; *AtIPT7* is expressed in phloem companion cells, the endodermis of the root elongation zones, trichomes on young leaves, and occasionally in pollen tubes. CK biosynthesis in aerial organs was also confirmed by in vivo deuterium labeling methods (72).

Regulation by plant hormones. The expression of key genes for CK biosynthesis and homeostasis such as *IPT*, *CKX*, and *CYP735A* is regulated by phytohormones including CKs, auxin, and abscisic acid (ABA). In *Arabidopsis*, the accumulation of the transcripts of *AtIPT5* and *AtIPT7* is promoted by auxin in roots, whereas the transcript levels of *AtIPT1*, *AtIPT3*, *AtIPT5*, and *AtIPT7* are negatively regulated by CK (64). On the other hand, the expression of both *CYP735A1* and *CYP735A2* is upregulated by CKs in roots but downregulated by auxin or ABA (104). Genes for CKX in maize are upregulated by CK and ABA (17). These regulation patterns suggest that the enzymes antagonistically regulate cellular CK levels and the balance between iP and tZ, which interact with auxin and/or ABA. The interdependent regulation of phytohormones might provide a basis for the variable morphogenetic responses of plants to environmental factors.

Cytokinins as a local signal. In the control of outgrowth and dormancy of axillary buds, the mutual regulation of auxin, ABA, and CKs has been proposed to play a central role (85). In pea, the expression of two IPT genes, *PsIPT1* and *PsIPT2*, which are expressed in nodes, is negatively regulated by auxin (105). Although an antagonistic role of auxin and CKs in the regulation of axillary bud outgrowth has been postulated for a considerable time, little is known about the underlying molecular mechanisms. Recent studies revealed that one role of apex-derived auxin in apical dominance is to repress CK biosynthesis in the nodes and that after decapitation CKs are locally synthesized in the stem rather than being transported to the stem from the roots (105).

Regulation by nitrogen supply. Inorganic nitrogen strongly affects plant growth and development. Plants constantly sense the nutrient status and modulate their metabolic activities and developmental program to adapt efficiently to the nutritional environment. CK is a pivotal signaling substance communicating the nitrogen nutrient status from root to shoot via the xylem vessels (87, 100, 101). Recent studies reveal a molecular mechanism of nitrogen-dependent CK biosynthesis and regulation (**Figure 5**); *AtIPT3* and *AtIPT5* are regulated differentially depend-

ing on the nitrogen sources available (64, 102). *AtIPT3* rapidly and specifically responds to NO_3^- under nitrogen-limited conditions whereas *AtIPT5* responds to both NO_3^- and NH_4^+ under long-term treatment (102). This dual-response system might be important for plants coping with unpredictably changing nitrogen availability. AtIPT3 and AtIPT5 are the dominant IPTs in *Arabidopsis* under normal conditions (64, 102); they are localized in plastids (46), strongly suggesting that CK biosynthesis is affected by nitrogen sources. In a *Ds* transposon-insertion mutant of *AtIPT3*, NO_3^--dependent CK accumulation was greatly reduced (102), indicating that *AtIPT3* is a key determinant of CK biosynthesis in response to rapid changes in NO_3^- in the soil.

Cytokinins as a long-range signal. Expression of *CYP735A2* in roots is strongly upregulated by CK application (104). In this context the fact that *AtIPT3* is upregulated by NO_3^- seems to explain the observation that applying NO_3^- induces tZ-nucleotide accumulation in roots (100) (**Figure 5**). tZR is the major species of CKs in the xylem (53, 80, 100). Interestingly, its translocation rate in xylem vessels is controlled by NO_3^- in the root medium (100). Thus, xylem-mediated signaling by tZ-type CKs in the transpiration stream appears important for the communication of nutrient signals on the whole-plant level. However, leaf exudates contain mainly iP-type CKs (23). Note that NO_3^--dependent expression of *AtIPT3* occurs in phloem tissue (64, 102). One possible explanation is that *trans*-hydroxylation controls the differential compartmentalization of CK species and thus also controls the direction of CK translocation, although the detailed mechanisms remain to be elucidated.

TRANSLOCATION

Cytokinin Nucleobase Transport

Because de novo CK biosynthesis catalyzed by IPTs is tissue- and cell-specific, the CKs must

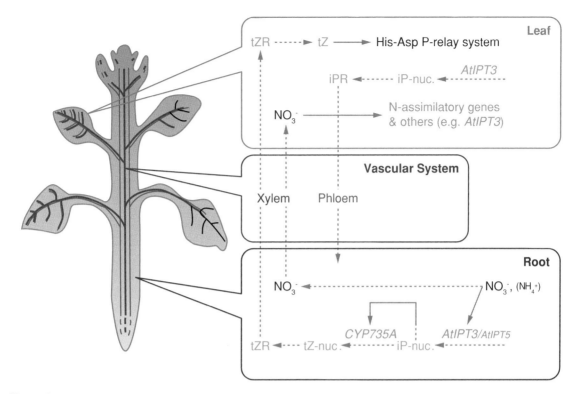

Figure 5

Nitrogen-dependent regulation of cytokinin (CK) biosynthesis and root/shoot communication via xylem and phloem. Solid arrows indicate positive regulation of gene expression. Broken lines with arrowheads show metabolic flow or translocation of CKs. Xylem stream and phloem stream are indicated in violet and red lines, respectively. Although CK functions as both a local signal and a long-range signal, only the long-range signal is illustrated in this figure. iP-nuc., iP nucleotides; tZ-nuc., tZ nucleotides. Other abbreviations as defined in the text. Modified from Reference 77.

be moved to target cells by diffusion and/or by selective transport systems. The idea of selective transport is supported by reports that plant cells are capable of absorbing CK nucleobases (19, 27) and nucleosides (88), and that tZ-type and iP-type CKs accumulate in xylem and phloem, respectively (23, 53, 100).

In cultured *Arabidopsis* cells, adenine and CK nucleobase cross membranes using the same proton-coupled high-affinity transport system (19). Two genes for *Arabidopsis* purine permeases, *AtPUP1* and *AtPUP2*, encode transporters that mediate CK nucleobase uptake (19, 31). When expressed in budding yeast cells, AtPUP1 and AtPUP2 mediate tZ uptake, and the affinity of AtPUP1 for tZ (K_i = 20–35 μM) is comparable to that of other CK

metabolizing enzymes for their substrates (19, 31). PUPs have a broad substrate specificity and mediate uptake of several adenine derivatives, such as adenine itself and caffeine. The expression of *AtPUP1* observed in the epithem of hydathodes and the stigma surface suggests a role for this transporter in the retrieval of CK from xylem sap to prevent loss during guttation; similarly, *AtPUP2* expression in the phloem implies a function in the long-distance transport of CKs (19).

PUP: purine permease

Cytokinin Nucleoside Transport

Although CK nucleobases are present in xylem as well as phloem, the major CK forms in the xylem are nucleosides such as tZR (11,

12, 100). In addition, the mobility of kinetin riboside in the xylem exceeds that of BA and kinetin (34). Therefore, nucleosides are considered the major translocation form of CKs. In higher plants, some members of the equilibrative nucleoside transporter (ENT) family appear to mediate the selective translocation of CK nucleosides. The rice genome contains four *ENT* genes (*OsENT1 - OsENT4*); one of the gene products, OsENT2, mediates the uptake of CK nucleosides as well as that of adenosine (35). OsENT2 prefers iPR (K_m = 32 μM) over tZR (K_m = 660 μM), suggesting that it may be responsible in part for the selective transport of CK nucleosides in the vascular tissues (35). *OsENT2* expression was detected in the scutellum during germination and in the vascular tissues in germinated seedlings, suggesting that OsENT2 participates in the retrieval of endosperm-derived nucleosides in the germinating embryo and in the long-distance transport of nucleosides in growing plants (35). In *Arabidopsis*, an ENT gene, *SOI33/AtENT8*, was also suggested to function in CK nucleoside transport (96). In summary, our current understanding of CK translocation in planta is that CK transport is achieved by the translocation systems that also mediate the transport of purine derivatives and nucleosides.

Compared with the highly elaborated polar transportation system for auxin, CK transport appears somewhat unspecific. However, differential loading into xylem or phloem might be sufficient for acropetal and systemic transport of CKs, respectively. It is interesting, though, that CK transport seems to occur in parallel with that of fundamentally important building blocks of the genetic apparatus and the energy transduction machinery, such as purine and nucleosides, which may be related to the CKs' function as a signal in the coordination of growth and development.

Intracellular Traffic of Cytokinin

Plastids are the major subcellular compartments of de novo CK biosynthesis through IPT (46, 102). This leads us to speculate on a transport system of CKs from plastids to the cytosol. At present, we have no evidence as to which form of CKs is transported across the plastid membranes. There is a report that AtIPT7 is localized in mitochondria (46). CK glycosides accumulate in the vacuole (26), and the deglucosylating enzyme, β-glucosidase, is localized in the plastids (49). Such complexity in the subcellular location of CK biosynthesis and metabolism points to an intricate intracellular CK transport network. It is still unknown whether the intracellular traffic of CK is also based on a transporting system for structurally related compounds.

SUMMARY POINTS

1. Structural variations at the side chain of isoprenoid and aromatic CKs affect the interaction with CK receptors, perhaps signifying functional specificity.

2. The initial step of CK biosynthesis (iP nucleotide synthesis) is catalyzed by adenosine phosphate-isopentenyltransferase; plastids are the major subcellular compartment for this initial step.

3. *trans*-Hydroxylation in tZ biosynthesis is catalyzed by a P450 enzyme, CYP735A. The hydroxylation predominantly occurs at the nucleotide step.

4. Tmr of *Agrobacterium* is targeted to the plastids of infected cells despite lacking a typical plastid-targeting sequence, and creates a CK biosynthesis bypass using an intermediate in the plastid-specific MEP pathway to synthesize tZ.

5. CK translocation shares the same transport systems moving purines and nucleosides at the whole-plant and perhaps at the cellular level.

6. Root/shoot signaling may be related to movement of tZ and iP derivatives, respectively, in the xylem and phloem streams.

7. CK biosynthesis and homeostasis are fine-tuned by internal and external factors such as phytohormones and inorganic nitrogen sources, which appears important in linking nutrient signals and morphogenetic responses.

FUTURE ISSUES TO BE RESOLVED

1. Identification of genes involved in cZ biosynthesis and cZ-tZ isomerization: It is essential to understand the physiological function of cZ and the physiological significance of tRNA-derived CK production.

2. Identification and characterization of genes encoding CK nucleosidases: Because CK nucleobase is the active form, their release from the nucleobases is one of the critical steps to control active CK level.

3. Analysis of knockout mutants of genes involved in side-chain modification: It is important to understand the possible unique properties and physiological roles of different isoprenoid and aromatic CKs.

4. Determine the molecular mechanism of Tmr import into the plastid: It would be of interest to know if the Toc-Tic system is involved in the translocation.

ACKNOWLEDGMENTS

The author acknowledges Dr. David W. S. Mok for his critical reading of the manuscript and for giving helpful comments. The writing of this review and research conducted in the author's laboratory are supported by the Ministry of Education, Culture, Sports, Science, and Technology and the Ministry of Agriculture, Forestry, and Fisheries, Japan.

LITERATURE CITED

1. Abe H, Uchiyama M, Tanaka Y, Saito H. 1976. Structure of discadenine, a spore germination inhibitor from cellular slime-mold, *Dictyostelium discoideum. Tetrahedron Lett.* 42:3807–10

2. Akiyoshi DE, Klee H, Amasino RM, Nester EW, Gordon MP. 1984. T-DNA of *Agrobacterium tumefaciens* encodes an enzyme of cytokinin biosynthesis. *Proc. Natl. Acad. Sci. USA* 81:5994–98

3. Allen M, Qin W, Moreau F, Moffatt B. 2002. Adenine phosphoribosyltransferase isoforms of *Arabidopsis* and their potential contributions to adenine and cytokinin metabolism. *Physiol. Plant.* 115:56–68

4. Amasino R. 2005. 1955: kinetin arrives. The 50th anniversary of a new plant hormone. *Plant Physiol.* 138:1177–84

5. Armstrong DJ. 1994. Cytokinin oxidase and the regulation of cytokinin degradation. In *Cytokinins: Chemistry, Activity, and Function*, ed. DWS Mok, MC Mok, pp. 139–54. Boca Raton, Florida: CRC Press

6. Ashikari M, Sakakibara H, Lin S, Yamamoto T, Takashi T, et al. 2005. Cytokinin oxidase regulates rice grain production. *Science* 309:741–45

7. Åstot C, Dolezal K, Nordström A, Wang Q, Kunkel T, et al. 2000. An alternative cytokinin biosynthesis pathway. *Proc. Natl. Acad. Sci. USA* 97:14778–83

8. Barciszewski J, Mielcarek M, Stobiecki M, Siboska G, Clark BF. 2000. Identification of 6-furfuryladenine (kinetin) in human urine. *Biochem. Biophys. Res. Commun.* 279:69–73

9. Barry GF, Rogers SG, Fraley RT, Brand L. 1984. Identification of a cloned cytokinin biosynthetic gene. *Proc. Natl. Acad. Sci. USA* 81:4776–80

10. Bassil NV, Mok D, Mok MC. 1993. Partial purification of a *cis-trans*-isomerase of zeatin from immature seed of *Phaseolus vulgaris* L. *Plant Physiol.* 102:867–72

11. Beck E, Wagner BM. 1994. Quantification of the daily cytokinin transport from the root to the shoot of *Urtica dioica* L. *Bot. Acta* 107:342–48

12. Beveridge CA, Murfet IC, Kerhoas L, Sotta B, Miginiac E, Rameau C. 1997. The shoot controls zeatin riboside export from pea roots. Evidence from the branching mutant *rms4*. *Plant J.* 11:339–45

13. Bilyeu KD, Cole JL, Laskey JG, Riekhof WR, Esparza TJ, et al. 2001. Molecular and biochemical characterization of a cytokinin oxidase from maize. *Plant Physiol.* 125:378–86

14. Blackwell JR, Horgan R. 1993. Cloned *Agrobacterium tumefaciens ipt1* gene product, DMAPP:AMP isopentenyl transferase. *Phytochemistry* 34:1477–81

15. Blackwell JR, Horgan R. 1994. Cytokinin biosynthesis by extracts of *Zea mays*. *Phytochemistry* 35:339–42

16. Blakeslee JJ, Peer WA, Murphy AS. 2005. Auxin transport. *Curr. Opin. Plant Biol.* 8:494–500

17. Brugiere N, Jiao S, Hantke S, Zinselmeier C, Roessler JA, et al. 2003. Cytokinin oxidase gene expression in maize is localized to the vasculature, and is induced by cytokinins, abscisic acid, and abiotic stress. *Plant Physiol.* 132:1228–40

18. Brzobohaty B, Moore I, Kristoffersen P, Bako L, Campos N, et al. 1993. Release of active cytokinin by a beta-glucosidase localized to the maize root meristem. *Science* 262:1051–54

19. **Burkle L, Cedzich A, Dopke C, Stransky H, Okumoto S, et al. 2003. Transport of cytokinins mediated by purine transporters of the PUP family expressed in phloem, hydathodes, and pollen of *Arabidopsis*. *Plant J.* 34:13–26**

20. Chen C-M, Leisner SM. 1984. Modification of cytokinins by cauliflower microsomal enzymes. *Plant Physiol.* 75:442–46

21. Chen C-M, Melitz DK. 1979. Cytokinin biosynthesis in a cell-free system from cytokinin-autotrophic tobacco tissue cultures. *FEBS Lett.* 107:15–20

22. Chen CM. 1997. Cytokinin biosynthesis and interconversion. *Physiol. Plant.* 101:665–73

23. Corbesier L, Prinsen E, Jacqmard A, Lejeune P, Van Onckelen H, et al. 2003. Cytokinin levels in leaves, leaf exudate and shoot apical meristem of *Arabidopsis thaliana* during floral transition. *J. Exp. Bot.* 54:2511–17

24. Emery RJN, Leport L, Barton JE, Turner NC, Atkins A. 1998. *cis*-Isomers of cytokinins predominate in chickpea seeds throughout their development. *Plant Physiol.* 117:1515–23

25. Faiss M, Zalubilová J, Strnad M, Schmülling T. 1997. Conditional transgenic expression of the *ipt* gene indicates a function for cytokinins in paracrine signaling in whole tobacco plants. *Plant J.* 12:401–15

This article reported the first characterization of purine permeases involved in transport of CK nucleobases.

26. Fusseder A, Ziegler P. 1988. Metabolism and compartmentation of dihydrozeatin exogenously supplied to photoautotrophic suspension-cultures of *Chenopodium rubrum. Planta* 173:104–9

27. Fusseder A, Ziegler P, Peters W, Beck E. 1989. Turnover of *O*-glucosides of dihydrozeatin and dihydrozeatin-9-riboside during the cell-growth cycle of photoautotrophic cell-suspension cultures of *Chenopodium rubrum. Bot. Acta* 102:335–40

28. Galuszka P, Frebort I, Sebela M, Sauer P, Jacobsen S, Pec P. 2001. Cytokinin oxidase or dehydrogenase? Mechanism of cytokinin degradation in cereals. *Eur. J. Biochem.* 268:450–61

29. Galuszka P, Frebortova J, Werner T, Yamada M, Strnad M, et al. 2004. Cytokinin oxidase/dehydrogenase genes in barley and wheat. *Eur. J. Biochem.* 271:3990–4002

30. Gan S, Amasino RM. 1995. Inhibition of leaf senescence by autoregulated production of cytokinin. *Science* 270:1986–88

31. Gillissen B, Burkle L, Andre B, Kuhn C, Rentsch D, et al. 2000. A new family of high-affinity transporters for adenine, cytosine, and purine derivatives in *Arabidopsis. Plant Cell* 12:291–300

32. Golovko A, Sitbon F, Tillberg E, Nicander B. 2002. Identification of a tRNA isopentenyltransferase gene from *Arabidopsis thaliana. Plant Mol. Biol.* 49:161–69

33. Hecht S, Eisenreich W, Adam P, Amslinger S, Kis K, et al. 2001. Studies on the non-mevalonate pathway to terpenes: the role of the GcpE (IspG) protein. *Proc. Natl. Acad. Sci. USA* 98:14837–42

34. Hill-Cottingham DG, Lloyd-Jones CP. 1968. Relative mobility of some organic nitrogenous compounds in the xylem of apple shoots. *Nature* 220:389–90

35. **Hirose N, Makita N, Yamaya T, Sakakibara H. 2005. Functional characterization and expression analysis of a gene, *OsENT2*, encoding an equilibrative nucleoside transporter in rice suggest a function in cytokinin transport. *Plant Physiol.* 138:196–206**

36. Horgan R, Hewett EW, Purse JG, Wareing PF. 1973. A new cytokinin from *Populus robusta. Tetrahedron Lett.* 14:2827–28

37. Hou B, Lim EK, Higgins GS, Bowles DJ. 2004. *N*-Glucosylation of cytokinins by glycosyltransferases of *Arabidopsis thaliana. J. Biol. Chem.* 279:47822–32

38. Ihara M, Taya Y, Nishimura S, Tanaka Y. 1984. Purification and some properties of delta 2-isopentenylpyrophosphate:5′AMP delta 2-isopentenyltransferase from the cellular slime mold *Dictyostelium discoideum. Arch. Biochem. Biophys.* 230:652–60

39. Inoue T, Higuchi M, Hashimoto Y, Seki M, Kobayashi M, et al. 2001. Identification of CRE1 as a cytokinin receptor from *Arabidopsis. Nature* 409:1060–63

40. Iwamura H. 1994. Cytokinin antagonists: synthesis and biological activity. In *Cytokinins: Chemistry, Activity, and Function*, ed. DWS Mok, MC Mok, pp. 43–55. Boca Raton, Florida: CRC Press

41. Izumi K, Nakagawa S, Kobayashi M, Oshio H, Sakurai A, Takahashi N. 1988. Levels of IAA, cytokinins, ABA and ethylene in rice plants as affected by a gibberellin biosynthesis inhibitor, uniconazole-P. *Plant Cell Physiol.* 29:97–104

42. John MC, Amasino RM. 1988. Expression of an *Agrobacterium* Ti plasmid gene involved in cytokinin biosynthesis is regulated by virulence loci and induced by plant phenolic compounds. *J. Bacteriol.* 170:790–95

43. **Kakimoto T. 2001. Identification of plant cytokinin biosynthetic enzymes as dimethylallyl diphosphate:ATP/ADP isopentenyltransferases. *Plant Cell Physiol.* 42:677–85**

This article reported the first identification and characterization of rice ENT genes involved in transport of CK nucleosides.

This article reported the first identification and characterization of *Arabidopsis* IPT genes.

44. Kakimoto T. 2003. Perception and signal transduction of cytokinins. *Annu. Rev. Plant Biol.* 54:605–27

45. Kaminek M. 1982. Mechanisms preventing the interference of tRNA cytokinins in hormonal regulation. In *Plant Growth Substances 1982*, ed. PF Wareing, pp. 215–23. New York: Academic

46. Kasahara H, Takei K, Ueda N, Hishiyama S, Yamaya T, et al. 2004. Distinct isoprenoid origins of *cis*- and *trans*-zeatin biosyntheses in *Arabidopsis*. *J. Biol. Chem.* 279:14049–54

47. Klämbt D. 1992. The biogenesis of cytokinins in higher plants: our present knowledge. In *Physiology and Biochemistry of Cytokinins in Plants*, ed. M Kaminek, DWS Mok, E Zazímalová, pp. 25–27. The Hague: SPB Academic

48. Krall L, Raschke M, Zenk MH, Baron C. 2002. The Tzs protein from *Agrobacterium tumefaciens* C58 produces zeatin riboside 5′-phosphate from 4-hydroxy-3-methyl-2-(*E*)-butenyl diphosphate and AMP. *FEBS Lett.* 527:315–18

49. Kristoffersen P, Brzobohaty B, Hohfeld I, Bako L, Melkonian M, Palme K. 2000. Developmental regulation of the maize *Zm-p60.1* gene encoding a beta-glucosidase located to plastids. *Planta* 210:407–15

50. Kwade Z, Swiatek A, Azmi A, Goossens A, Inzé D, et al. 2005. Identification of four adenosine kinase isoforms in tobacco BY-2 cells and their putative role in the cell cycle-regulated cytokinin metabolism. *J. Biol. Chem.* 280:17512–19

51. Laureys F, Dewitte W, Witters E, Van Montagu M, Inzé D, Van Onckelen H. 1998. Zeatin is indispensable for the G_2-M transition in tobacco BY-2 cells. *FEBS Lett.* 426:29–32

52. Laureys F, Smets R, Lenjou M, Van Bockstaele D, Inzé D, Van Onckelen H. 1999. A low content in zeatin type cytokinins is not restrictive for the occurrence of G_1/S transition in tobacco BY-2 cells. *FEBS Lett.* 460:123–28

53. Lejeune P, Bernier G, Requier M-C, Kinet J-M. 1994. Cytokinins in phloem and xylem saps of *Sinapis alba* during floral induction. *Physiol. Plant.* 90:522–28

54. Letham DS. 1963. Zeatin, a factor inducing cell division from *Zea mays*. *Life Sci* 8:569–73

55. Letham DS, Palni LMS, Tao G-Q, Gollnow BI, Bates CM. 1983. Regulators of cell division in plant tissues XXIX. The activities of cytokinin glucosides and alanine conjugates in cytokinin bioassays. *J. Plant Growth Regul.* 2:103–15

56. Letham DS, Zhang R. 1989. Cytokinin translocation and metabolism in lupin species. II. New nucleotide metabolites of cytokinins. *Plant Sci.* 64:161–65

57. Lichtenthaler HK. 1999. The 1-deoxy-D-xylulose-5-phosphate pathway of isoprenoid biosynthesis in plants. *Annu. Rev. Plant Physiol. Plant Mol. Biol.* 50:47–65

58. Long AR, Chism GW 3rd. 1987. The effect of metyrapone on cytokinin ([8-^{14}C]benzylaminopurine) metabolism in mature green tomato pericarp. *Biochem. Biophys. Res. Commun.* 144:109–14

59. Martin RC, Mok MC, Habben JE, Mok DW. 2001. A maize cytokinin gene encoding an *O*-glucosyltransferase specific to *cis*-zeatin. *Proc. Natl. Acad. Sci. USA* 98:5922–26

60. Martin RC, Mok MC, Mok DW. 1999. A gene encoding the cytokinin enzyme zeatin *O*-xylosyltransferase of *Phaseolus vulgaris*. *Plant Physiol.* 120:553–58

61. Martin RC, Mok MC, Mok DW. 1999. Isolation of a cytokinin gene, *ZOG1*, encoding zeatin *O*-glucosyltransferase from *Phaseolus lunatus*. *Proc. Natl. Acad. Sci. USA* 96:284–89

62. Miller CO, Skoog F, Okumura FS, von Saltza MH, Strong FM. 1955. Structure and synthesis of kinetin. *J. Am. Chem. Soc.* 78:2662–63

63. Miller CO, Skoog F, Saltza vNH, Strong M. 1955. Kinetin, a cell division factor from deoxyribonucleic acid. *J. Am. Chem. Soc.* 77:1329–34

This article first reported that the side chain of iP- and tZ-type CKs is derived from the MEP pathway.

64. **Miyawaki K, Matsumoto-Kitano M, Kakimoto T. 2004. Expression of cytokinin biosynthetic isopentenyltransferase genes in *Arabidopsis*: tissue specificity and regulation by auxin, cytokinin, and nitrate. *Plant J.* 37:128–38**

65. Moffatt B, Pethe C, Laloue M. 1991. Metabolism of benzyladenine is impaired in a mutant of *Arabidopsis thaliana* lacking adenine phosphoribosyltransferase activity. *Plant Physiol.* 95:900–8

66. Mok DW, Mok MC. 2001. Cytokinin metabolism and action. *Annu. Rev. Plant Physiol. Plant Mol. Biol.* 52:89–118

67. Mok MC. 1994. Cytokinins and plant development–An overview. In *Cytokinins: Chemistry, Activity, and Function*, ed. DWS Mok, MC Mok, pp. 155–66. Boca Raton, Florida: CRC Press

68. Mok MC, Martin RC, Dobrev PI, Vankova R, Ho PS, et al. 2005. Topolins and hydroxylated thidiazuron derivatives are substrates of cytokinin *O*-glucosyltransferase with position specificity related to receptor recognition. *Plant Physiol.* 137:1057–66

69. Mok MC, Mok DWS, Armstrong DJ, Shudo K, Isogai Y, Okamoto T. 1982. Cytokinin activity of *N*-phenyl-*N'*-1,2,3-thiadiazol-5-ylurea (Thidiazuron). *Phytochemistry* 21:1509–11

70. Morris DA, Friml J, Zazimalova E. 2005. The transport of auxin. In *Plant Hormones: Biosynthesis, Signal Transduction, Action!*, ed. PJ Davies, pp. 437–70. Dordrecht: Kluwer Academic

71. Morris RO. 1986. Genes specifying auxin and cytokinin biosynthesis in phytopathogens. *Annu. Rev. Plant Physiol. Plant Mol. Biol.* 37:509–38

72. Nordström A, Tarkowski P, Tarkowska D, Norbaek R, Åstot C, et al. 2004. Auxin regulation of cytokinin biosynthesis in *Arabidopsis thaliana*: A factor of potential importance for auxin-cytokinin-regulated development. *Proc. Natl. Acad. Sci. USA* 101:8039–44

73. Powell GK, Hommes NG, Kuo J, Castle LA, Morris RO. 1988. Inducible expression of cytokinin biosynthesis in *Agrobacterium tumefaciens* by plant phenolics. *Mol. Plant Microbe Interact.* 1:235–42

74. Rohdich F, Hecht S, Gartner K, Adam P, Krieger C, et al. 2002. Studies on the nonmevalonate terpene biosynthetic pathway: metabolic role of IspH (LytB) protein. *Proc. Natl. Acad. Sci. USA* 99:1158–63

75. Rohmer M. 1999. The discovery of a mevalonate-independent pathway for isoprenoid biosynthesis in bacteria, algae and higher plants. *Nat. Prod. Rep.* 16:565–74

76. Sakakibara H. 2004. Cytokinin biosynthesis and metabolism. In *Plant Hormones: Biosynthesis, Signal Transduction, Action!*, ed. PJ Davies, pp. 95–114. Dordrecht: Kluwer Academic

77. Sakakibara H. 2005. Cytokinin biosynthesis and regulation. *Vit. Hor.* 72:271–87

78. **Sakakibara H, Kasahara H, Ueda N, Kojima M, Takei K, et al. 2005. *Agrobacterium tumefaciens* increases cytokinin production in plastids by modifying the biosynthetic pathway in the host plant. *Proc. Natl. Acad. Sci. USA* 102:9972–77**

79. Sakano Y, Okada Y, Matsunaga A, Suwama T, Kaneko T, et al. 2004. Molecular cloning, expression, and characterization of adenylate isopentenyltransferase from hop (*Humulus lupulus* L.). *Phytochemistry* 65:2439–46

80. Samuelson ME, Larsson C-M. 1993. Nitrate regulation of zeatin riboside levels in barley roots: effects of inhibitors of N assimilation and comparison with ammonium. *Plant Sci.* 93:77–84

81. Schmitz RY, Skoog F. 1972. Cytokinins: synthesis and biological activity of geometric and position isomers of zeatin. *Plant Physiol.* 50:702–5

This article reported the first characterization of expression patterns of *AtIPT* genes.

This article reported the first identification of plastid-location of Tmr in the host plant cell.

82. Schmülling T, Werner T, Riefler M, Krupkova E, Bartrina y Manns I. 2003. Structure and function of cytokinin oxidase/dehydrogenase genes of maize, rice, *Arabidopsis* and other species. *J. Plant Res.* 116:241–52

83. Schnorr KM, Gaillard C, Biget E, Nygaard P, Laloue M. 1996. A second form of adenine phosphoribosyltransferase in *Arabidopsis thaliana* with relative specificity towards cytokinins. *Plant J.* 9:891–98

84. Shantz EM, Steward FC. 1955. The identification of compound A from coconut milk as 1,3-diphenylurea. *J. Am. Chem. Soc.* 77:6351–53

85. Shimizu-Sato S, Mori H. 2001. Control of outgrowth and dormancy in axillary buds. *Plant Physiol.* 127:1405–13

86. Shudo K. 1994. Chemistry of phenylurea cytokinins. In *Cytokinins: Chemistry, Activity, and Function*, ed. DWS Mok, MC Mok, pp. 35–42. Boca Raton, Florida: CRC Press

87. Simpson RJ, Lambers H, Dalling MJ. 1982. Kinetin application to roots and its effect on uptake, translocation and distribution of nitrogen in wheat (*Triticum aestivum*) grown with a split root system. *Physiol. Plant.* 56:430–35

88. Singh S, Letham DS, Jameson PE, Zhang R, Parker CW, et al. 1988. Cytokinin biochemistry in relation to leaf senescence. IV. Cytokinin metabolism in soybean explants. *Plant Physiol.* 88:788–94

89. Skoog F, Armstrong DJ. 1970. Cytokinins. *Annu. Rev. Plant Physiol.* 21:359–84

90. Skoog F, Armstrong DJ, Cherayil JD, Hampel AE, Bock RM. 1966. Cytokinin activity: localization in transfer RNA preparations. *Science* 154:1354–56

91. Spichal L, Rakova NY, Riefler M, Mizuno T, Romanov GA, et al. 2004. Two cytokinin receptors of *Arabidopsis thaliana*, CRE1/AHK4 and AHK3, differ in their ligand specificity in a bacterial assay. *Plant Cell Physiol.* 45:1299–305

92. Spiess LD. 1975. Comparative activity of isomers of zeatin and ribosyl-zeatin on *Funaria hygrometrica*. *Plant Physiol.* 55:583–85

93. Strnad M. 1997. The aromatic cytokinins. *Physiol. Plant.* 101:674–88

94. Stuchbury T, Palni LMS, Horgan R, Wareing PF. 1979. The biosynthesis of cytokinins in crown-gall tissue of *Vinca rosea*. *Planta* 147:97–102

95. Sun J, Niu QW, Tarkowski P, Zheng B, Tarkowska D, et al. 2003. The *Arabidopsis* *AtIPT8/PGA22* gene encodes an isopentenyl transferase that is involved in *de novo* cytokinin biosynthesis. *Plant Physiol.* 131:167–76

96. Sun JP, Hirose N, Wang XC, Wen P, Xue L, et al. 2005. *Arabidopsis SOI33/AtENT8* gene encodes a putative equilibrative nucleoside transporter that is involved in cytokinin transport *in planta*. *J. Integr. Plant Biol.* 47:588–603

97. Suzuki T, Miwa K, Ishikawa K, Yamada H, Aiba H, Mizuno T. 2001. The *Arabidopsis* sensor His-kinase, AHK4, can respond to cytokinins. *Plant Cell Physiol.* 42:107–13

98. Takei K, Dekishima Y, Eguchi T, Yamaya T, Sakakibara H. 2003. A new method for enzymatic preparation of isopentenyladenine-type and *trans*-zeatin-type cytokinins with radioisotope-labeling. *J. Plant Res.* 116:259–63

99. **Takei K, Sakakibara H, Sugiyama T. 2001. Identification of genes encoding adenylate isopentenyltransferase, a cytokinin biosynthesis enzyme, in *Arabidopsis thaliana*. *J. Biol. Chem.* 276:26405–10**

100. Takei K, Sakakibara H, Taniguchi M, Sugiyama T. 2001. Nitrogen-dependent accumulation of cytokinins in root and the translocation to leaf: implication of cytokinin species that induces gene expression of maize response regulator. *Plant Cell Physiol.* 42:85–93

101. Takei K, Takahashi T, Sugiyama T, Yamaya T, Sakakibara H. 2002. Multiple routes communicating nitrogen availability from roots to shoots: a signal transduction pathway mediated by cytokinin. *J. Exp. Bot.* 53:971–77

This article reported the first identification and characterization of *Arabidopsis* IPT genes.

102. Takei K, Ueda N, Aoki K, Kuromori T, Hirayama T, et al. 2004. *AtIPT3*, an *Arabidopsis* isopentenyltransferase gene, is a key determinant of macronutrient-responsive cytokinin biosynthesis. *Plant Cell Physiol.* 45:1053–62

103. Takei K, Yamaya T, Sakakibara H. 2003. A method for separation and determination of cytokinin nucleotides from plant tissues. *J. Plant Res.* 116:265–69

104. Takei K, Yamaya T, Sakakibara H. 2004. *Arabidopsis CYP735A1* and *CYP735A2* encode cytokinin hydroxylases that catalyze the biosynthesis of *trans*-zeatin. *J. Biol. Chem.* 279:41866–72

105. Tanaka M, Takei K, Kojima M, Sakakibara H, Mori H. 2006. Auxin controls local cytokinin biosynthesis in the nodal stem in apical dominance. *Plant J.* doi: 10.1111/j.1365-313x.2006.02656.x

106. Tarkowska D, Dolezal K, Tarkowski P, Åstot C, Holub J, et al. 2003. Identification of new aromatic cytokinins in *Arabidopsis thaliana* and *Populus* x canadensis leaves by LC-(+)ESI-MS and capillary liquid chromatography/frit-fast atom bombardment mass spectrometry. *Physiol. Plant.* 117:579–90

107. Taya Y, Tanaka Y, Nishimura S. 1978. 5′-AMP is a direct precursor of cytokinin in *Dictyostelium discoideum*. *Nature* 271:545–47

108. Ueguchi C, Koizumi H, Suzuki T, Mizuno T. 2001. Novel family of sensor histidine kinase genes in *Arabidopsis thaliana*. *Plant Cell Physiol.* 42:231–35

109. Veach YK, Martin RC, Mok DW, Malbeck J, Vankova R, Mok MC. 2003. *O*-Glucosylation of *cis*-zeatin in maize. Characterization of genes, enzymes, and endogenous cytokinins. *Plant Physiol.* 131:1374–80

110. Vreman HJ, Skoog F. 1972. Cytokinins in *Pisum* transfer ribonucleic acid. *Plant Physiol.* 49:848–51

111. Vreman HJ, Thomas R, Corse J. 1978. Cytokinins in tRNA obtained from *Spinacia oleracea* L. leaves and isolated chloroplasts. *Plant Physiol.* 61:296–306

112. Werner T, Motyka V, Laucou V, Smets R, Van Onckelen H, Schmülling T. 2003. Cytokinin-deficient transgenic *Arabidopsis* plants show multiple developmental alterations indicating opposite functions of cytokinins in the regulation of shoot and root meristem activity. *Plant Cell* 15:2532–50

113. Werner T, Motyka V, Strnad M, Schmülling T. 2001. Regulation of plant growth by cytokinin. *Proc. Natl. Acad. Sci. USA* 98:10487–92

114. Yamada H, Suzuki T, Terada K, Takei K, Ishikawa K, et al. 2001. The *Arabidopsis* AHK4 histidine kinase is a cytokinin-binding receptor that transduces cytokinin signals across the membrane. *Plant Cell Physiol.* 42:1017–23

115. Yonekura-Sakakibara K, Kojima M, Yamaya T, Sakakibara H. 2004. Molecular characterization of cytokinin-responsive histidine kinases in maize: differential ligand preferences and response to *cis*-zeatin. *Plant Physiol.* 134:1654–61

116. Zubko E, Adams CJ, Machaekova I, Malbeck J, Scollan C, Meyer P. 2002. Activation tagging identifies a gene from *Petunia hybrida* responsible for the production of active cytokinins in plants. *Plant J.* 29:797–808

This article reported the identification of *AtIPT3* as a key determinant for nitrogen-dependent CK biosynthesis.

This article reported the first identification and characterization of CYP735A as CK *trans*-hydroxylase.

This article reported the first evidence for direct binding of CK to the receptor in vitro.

RELATED RESOURCE

Forde BG. 2002. Local and long-range signaling pathways regulating plant responses to nitrate. *Annu. Rev. Plant Physiol. Plant Mol. Biol.* 53:203–24

Global Studies of Cell Type-Specific Gene Expression in Plants

David W. Galbraith[1] and Kenneth Birnbaum[2]

[1] Department of Plant Sciences and Bio5 Institute, University of Arizona, Tucson, Arizona 85721; email: galbraith@arizona.edu

[2] Center for Comparative Functional Genomics, Department of Biology, New York University, New York, New York 10003; email: ken.birnbaum@nyu.edu

Annu. Rev. Plant Biol.
2006. 57:451–75

The *Annual Review of Plant Biology* is online at
plant.annualreviews.org

doi: 10.1146/
annurev.arplant.57.032905.105302

Key Words

cell-specific expression analysis, cell identity, differentiation, microdissection

Abstract

Technological advances in expression profiling and in the ability to collect minute quantities of tissues have come together to allow a growing number of global transcriptional studies at the cell level in plants. Microarray technology, with a choice of cDNA or oligo-based slides, is now well established, with commercial full-genome platforms for rice and *Arabidopsis* and extensive expressed sequence tag (EST)-based designs for many other species. Microdissection and cell sorting are two established methodologies that have been used in conjunction with microarrays to provide an early glimpse of the transcriptional landscape at the level of individual cell types. The results indicate that much of the transcriptome is compartmentalized. A minor but consistent percentage of transcripts appear to be unique to specific cell types. Functional analyses of cell-specific patterns of gene expression are providing important clues to cell-specific functions. The spatial dissection of the transcriptome has also yielded insights into the localized mediators of hormone inputs and promises to provide detail on cell-specific effects of microRNAs.

Contents

INTRODUCTION

Why Study Global Gene Expression in Specific Cell Types?

With the completion of genome sequencing for a number of different organisms, methods are emerging for charting changes in gene expression that are global in scope, i.e., can address most if not all genes within the genome simultaneously and in parallel, rather than the traditional method of studying genes individually and serially. Our understanding of gene expression, broadly comprising the series of processes that link genotype to phenotype, is evidently defined by the technologies employed in these studies. For the purposes of this review, we have restricted our discussion to the results of expression profiling, which in the most part measure global intracellular transcript abundances. Other levels of gene expression, for example, studied by measurement of changes in protein or metabolite abundances, are not considered here, and the reader is referred to recent reviews (58, 59, 112). Within our chosen context, it is reasonable to accept that changes in global gene expression reflect changes in cellular state, as proposed by Hughes et al. (48). If enough genes are studied, and such combined changes map to cell state in a one-to-one manner, it follows that measuring global gene expression can precisely define the cellular state and unambiguously identify the cell being analyzed. This is particularly important in the study of complex eukaryotic organisms, for which the organs and tissues comprise mixtures of different cell types. For measurement of global gene expression to provide meaningful information concerning cell state, it is either required that the organs and tissues be separated into their constituent cell types prior to such analysis, or that alternative methods be designed that can deconvolute the contributions of specific cell types from the overall mixture of cell types.

Separation of specific cell types implies physical manipulations, which are constrained by the manner in which multicellular plants adapt cell division and cell structure to adopt their three-dimensional form. Cytokinesis in plants involves separation of daughter cells by a phragmoplast, which partitions and subdivides the daughter cells within a shared parental cell wall. Cell wall expansion then distances the daughter cells from the site of division (the meristem). This process is accompanied by cellular differentiation, mediated by factors known and unknown that are recognized within cells and exchanged between them, and that act either in a cell autonomous or nonautonomous fashion. Physical separation of different cell types then either requires prior production of wall-less cells (protoplasts) through enzymatic digestion of the cell wall, or is achieved through specialized micromanipulation or manual microdissection techniques using fixed tissue sections. In all cases, means are required to recognize specific cell types, which are compatible with the means of separation and purification of the specific cell types. As a general rule, the amounts of the individual cell types that can be purified using these techniques are not unlimited, and thus many scientists are becoming interested in cell types that are present in very few numbers within source tissues or organs. This raises questions of stochastic variability, an area of increasing importance both in terms of technical aspects as well as biological relevance to control networks, as discussed below. An increasing level of interest is accompanying developments in this area, and the reader is referred to the following particularly relevant recent reviews (15, 69, 71).

THE TECHNOLOGIES

What Methods are Available for Global Studies of Gene Expression and What are Their Specific Advantages and Disadvantages?

Microarrays. For the purposes of this review, microarrays are defined as encompassing all forms of transcript analysis involving hybridization of targets to immobilized DNA probes. A number of platforms are in widespread use.

Microarrays having spotted array elements (classically "microarrays"). First described by Schena et al. (100), these microarrays comprise DNA elements that are robotically printed onto solid surfaces, typically glass microscope slides coated with derivatized silane. Although originally formed from polymerase chain reaction (PCR) amplicons, the DNA elements are increasingly produced by synthesis as single-stranded molecules 30–70 bases in length, depend-

ing on the platform. Printing is most commonly achieved using split-ended printing pins, which move across the surface of the glass slides guided by servo motors and arms. One manufacturer (Agilent) employs ink-jet technologies to deposit preformed oligonucleotides for some microarray applications. Spotted microarrays are interrogated using fluorescent targets derived from RNA extracted from the cells or tissues of interest. Targets are hybridized to the microarrays in a pair-wise manner, using fluorochromes that are spectrally distinct, most frequently the Cy3 and Cy5 dye combinations originally synthesized by Waggoner's group (125). Using oligonucleotides as probes, rather than amplicons, avoids problems of cross-hybridization associated with shared sequence motifs. It also results in improved hybridization behavior because probe sets can be designed with uniform melting temperature values.

Microarrays with elements synthesized in situ. Three companies produce microarrays whose elements are synthesized by progressive base extension from the microarray surface. Most widespread are the GeneChips™ produced by Affymetrix, for which the array elements comprise sets (10–25 per gene) of 25-mer pairs of elements. The sequences are chosen to span the transcript of interest, and are provided in pairs comprising perfect match (PM) and mismatch (MM) sequences. The latter sequences replace the central position of the 25-mer with a single mismatched base, and are intended to provide a basis to determine specificity of hybridization. Synthesis involves progressive photodeprotection of sites of oligonucleotide extension upon the array surface via a predefined series of masks, followed by coupling of blocked nucleotides to these sites using conventional DNA synthesis chemistries. The requirement for design and production of these masks limits the flexibility of GeneChips, although they remain the preeminent method for producing large numbers of identical microarrays. Flexibility, in contrast, is a key feature of

Targets: the fluorescent DNA or RNA molecules that are employed for microarray hybridization

Probes: the DNA elements that are immobilized on the surface of microarrays

NimbleGen, the second company producing microarrays having elements synthesized in situ. In this case, photodeprotection is achieved by steering the light onto the microarray using an integrated microchip, developed for the computer display and projection industry and comprising arrays of micromirrors. Array elements are generally longer than those of GeneChips. The final company, Agilent, produces microarrays through ink-jet-based deposition of nucleotide precursors at the locations of synthesis of the array elements. This approach has been made possible as a consequence of advances in the dpi resolution of ink-jet technologies, driven by the computer printing industry, and provides similar flexibility to NimbleGen. Affymetrix GeneChips differ from NimbleGen and Agilent microarrays in that they employ single-dye labeling, rather than mixtures of dyes, during the hybridization step.

For most of the microarrays described above, selection of sequence information optimal for the design of array elements relies on the availability, preferably, of whole-genome sequence information. Recent studies have raised fundamental questions concerning our overall understanding of transcription within the context of gene expression (10, 21, 107, 108, 122). These arise from the results of experiments using Affymetrix GeneChips and NimbleGen microarrays designed to "tile" the entire genome. At its most complete, tiling arrays sequentially represent the entire genome of interest, in progressive tiles encompassing positions $1 \rightarrow m$, $2 \rightarrow m + 1$, $3 \rightarrow m + 2, \ldots, n \rightarrow m + n - 1$, and so on, where m is the oligo length (25 for GeneChips, 36 for NimbleGen Arrays), starting with chromosome 1 and extending over the complete genome. This requires a large number of GeneChips or microarrays and incurs significant costs. Therefore, tiling arrays with less resolution have also been described and employed (10, 107, 108, 122), in which the loss of resolution is balanced by the cost advantage derived from the requirement for fewer GeneChips for complete genome coverage. Transcript mapping is done by hybridization of fluorescent targets produced in the usual way. For targets derived from well-understood transcripts, such as those of polyadenylated RNAs from annotated genes, hybridization identifies the transcriptional start and stop sites, the locations of introns, and the occurrence of alternative splicing. Tiling arrays therefore provide a valuable resource for confirming gene annotations. However, they also reveal a large number of transcripts for which no conventional explanations and/or mechanisms are yet available. Termed transcripts of unidentified function (TUFs), these include antisense transcripts, transcripts that are not polyadenylated, transcripts that do not exit from the nucleus, and transcripts that preferentially associate with polyribosomes. All the various combinations of these classes appear present within eukaryotic tissues, cells, and cell lines, and many appear developmentally relevant (for a recent review, see 53a). Sorting out these transcripts, and in particular defining genes with which they are associated (if such a concept is even epistemologically meaningful), will be one of the most important challenges of the next few years (29). The use of cell-specific expression profiling in combination with tiling arrays may be especially informative in finding the spatial distribution of alternative splice forms and possibly microRNA precursors (54a).

Microarray hybridization and analyses. Microarrays have become the method of choice for high-throughput analysis of global gene expression, and are most commonly employed for analyzing mRNA transcript accumulation within the tissues of interest. This is done following hybridization of fluorescently labeled representations of these transcripts, in the form either of cDNA or cRNA, with or without intervening amplification steps. The microarrays are then scanned and the intensity values of the pixels corresponding to the sites of hybridization are determined. Slightly different strategies are then followed, depending on the platform. For Affymetrix Genechips, single-color measurements are done, and the values from the adjacent PM and MM sites are processed to provide composite signal intensity values representing the amounts of hybridization for the individual genes. The different algorithms available for processing GeneChips have surprisingly large effects on the reproducibility of the platform (51), and on the detection of individual genes (compare references 24 and 101, for example). The other microarray platforms accommodate two-color fluorescence hybridization and scanning, with the individual signal intensity values generated from the scanned image files using spot-finding programs that permit considerable user intervention. For all of the platforms, the processed signal values scale linearly over several logarithmic decades, but between element values cannot be directly compared in terms of numbers of transcript molecules detected, because the individual hybridization characteristics are array element dependent. Total signal output from an individual array is generally considered proportional to total RNA input, and is routinely employed for data normalization (99), although this may not always be appropriate (128).

As for all high-throughput methods, considerable importance should be attached to characterization of the statistical significance of the results that are generated. Not least is the concern that with the very large number of comparisons that are being done on any single microarray, the number of false positives, even under stringent conditions of significance, can be considerable. A number of statistical designs have been developed for handling microarray experiments, as well as corresponding methods for dealing with the resultant data (see for example, 98 and 124), and the reader is recommended to consult sources such as these prior to starting their experiments.

In terms of the technical properties of the platforms, it is clear that microarrays produced from cDNA amplicons produce data that are both less reproducible and less specific than GeneChips and microarrays produced from long oligomers. Competition between target and the complementary ds-DNA probe molecules during hybridization of amplicon-based microarrays might result in variable hybridization behavior for the different probe-target pairs. This cannot occur for oligonucleotide-based arrays. In terms of specificity, Xu et al. (121) systematically examined the degree of cross-hybridization between closely related gene sequences within the Arabidopsis cytochrome P450 superfamily. Cross-hybridization is essentially eliminated when sequences diverge by more than about 30%, with the caveat that patches of identity be less than ~20 bases. These results provide empirical criteria to include during the design of long oligonucleotide array elements that are specific for individual transcripts.

A number of cross-platform comparisons are beginning to appear for microarrays (70, 117), which highlight multiple issues, including that the results of different laboratories exhibit different degrees of reproducibility and fidelity to known expression profiles, that different sequence designs for array elements can report different levels of hybridization for the same transcripts, that alternative splicing can complicate matters, that the use of different methods for target preparation introduces additional levels of variation into the data, and that under optimal conditions, biological variation appears to greatly exceed technical variation. These studies also highlight the problems associated with false positives, and the danger of squandering resources during downstream follow-up.

Northerns. Northern analysis represents one of the most venerable methods for qualitatively estimating RNA transcript abundances. Northern analysis is not readily adapted to a high-throughput format and has not been employed in such a manner for analysis of plants, although it has been used in this way for analyzing yeast (18). Comparisons were made between the results obtained with

Northerns and those from cDNA/amplicon microarrays. It is encouraging that broad concordance was found, with the caveat that the work was done relatively early on following the development of microarrays and therefore did not employ optimal conditions or appropriate statistical procedures.

High-throughput RT-PCR. PCR following reverse transcription provides a sensitive means to detect RNA, and can be adapted for high-throughput analysis. For example, Czechowski et al. (24) described its use in Arabidopsis for profiling the abundances of more than 1,400 transcription factors. High costs and lack of convenience likely restrict the general application of this method for global transcript profiling of multiple samples.

Sampling sequence information in RNA populations. A number of methods have emerged that examine gene expression through quantifying the numbers of different RNA transcripts within RNA populations, using cDNA libraries as the first step. This general approach started with the observation that RNA abundances could be measured, in the form of "electronic Northerns," by simply counting the number of occurrences of different DNA sequences in cDNA libraries produced from different cells, tissues, or organs. To provide meaningful data sets, it is essential that the sequencing procedure adequately sample the available cDNA pools, and that the production of cDNAs not bias the representation. Conventional DNA sequencing did not satisfy these two criteria, and additional technologies [serial analysis of gene expression (SAGE), and massively parallel signature sequencing (MPSS)] were developed that considerably increase the depth of sequence sampling [for a recent SAGE review see (39); for examples of applications of these methods to plants, see (35, 81, 84–86, 97)]. However, both methods have the major drawback that they are costly, which limits the number of different samples that can be processed. Two recent technological develop-

ments promise greatly decreased sequencing costs (80, 106). Even if further improvements in read lengths are not achieved, the availability of extremely low-cost sequencing will increase the number of different conditions and genes that can be sampled, and might make these methods of choice for future expression profiling work.

What Methods are Available for Determining the Contributions of Specific Cell Types?

Methods requiring prior physical separation and purification of specific cell types or their organelles. The most obvious means to define the contributions of different cell types is to physically separate them prior to global analysis of gene expression. This requires a means to identify the specific cell type and a means for their separation and purification in quantities sufficient for downstream analysis. Evidently, the means for identification and separation of the cell types must not affect the observed patterns of gene expression. For cell types that exist as natural single-cell suspensions or low-complexity aggregations of cells, such as pollen, means for identification and separation are straightforward (6, 96). In this case, flow cytometric analysis identified differences in light scattering and autofluorescence that was then used for sorting viable hydrated pollen. Purification of sperm cells from osmotically lysed maize pollen has also been reported, using a combination of Percoll gradient centrifugation and fluorescence-activated sorting based on Hoechst 33342 staining (28). In specialized circumstances, other cell types, for example xylem elements, can be generated through manipulation of in vitro culture conditions (25, 30). Conversely, others have employed in vitro cell suspension cultures as a defined "cell type" for exploring gene expression in undifferentiated cells.

For cell types embedded within, or attached to, tissues organized in three dimensions, additional techniques for identification and purification are required. Cell types on surfaces, for example trichomes and root hairs, can be directly collected by clipping (120). Some, such as guard cells, are differentially resistant to tissue disruption and digestion, in comparison to mesophyll, and can be therefore isolated in pure form using mechanical and enzymatic procedures (52, 72). For purifying other cell types, three general methods have emerged, involving fluorescence-activated sorting, laser-capture manipulation, and microsampling, respectively, which roughly speaking are ordered in decreasing rank according to the amounts of purified tissues and cells that they can reasonably provide.

Fluorescence-activated sorting. Separation of individual cell types from organized plant tissues requires the production of suspensions of wall-less plant cells (protoplasts). It has long been established that protoplasts can be subjected to fluorescence-activated sorting (FAS) and recovered in viable form (1, 40). Some protoplasts can be identified and sorted based simply on endogenous properties, such as size, viability, and chlorophyll content, and these properties can be employed to examine gene regulation as a function of cell type in leaves (41). The development of the Green Fluorescent Protein (GFP) of *Aequorea victoria* (20), the prototypical Fluorescent Protein (FP), provides a more-general means to specifically identify many individual cell types using FAS, by placing transgenic FP expression under the control of appropriate regulatory sequences (11, 32, 33, 92, 105). Another advantage of FAS is that the sorting process can be rapid, providing as many as 1,000 purified protoplasts per second or more. Details of this approach are given below.

The method of protoplast sorting can equally be applied to subcellular organelles and, for nuclei, this can also be employed for characterization of global patterns of gene expression. The Galbraith group demonstrated the isolation and characterization of RNA

transcripts from sorted nuclei (78), and nuclear polyA$^+$ RNA was also successfully employed for microarray hybridization following linear amplification (C.Q. Zhang, G. M. Lambert & D. W. Galbraith, unpublished data). Because nuclei can be rapidly isolated through tissue homogenization from most organs and from many species (32, 34), this approach avoids problems associated with changes in gene expression that accompany protoplast production and the recalcitrance of certain tissues or species to protoplast production (31).

Laser capture microdissection. Two major laser-based methods have been developed for separating individual cells or groups of cells from intact tissues (27). The original process involves overlaying thin sections of tissues with a transfer film. The desired cells are physically attached to this film using a pulsed infrared laser, which is manipulated such that it melts and fuses the film at the locations of these cells. The film and the attached cells are then transferred into microchambers for further manipulation. The second method employs an UV laser to physically dissect the cells within the regions of interest, which then can be captured either passively or actively by laser pressure catapulting using a single high-power pulse of laser irradiance (103). In certain cases, living animal cells can be captured (82). However, for plant tissues and organs, laser capture microdissection (LCM) usually requires use of sectioned tissues, which therefore must be fixed or frozen. Reports of the application of LCM to plants include production of cDNA libraries from RNA of captured rice phloem cells (3), array-based analysis of gene expression in maize seedling epidermal and vascular tissues (91), evaluation of technical improvements for RNA isolation from miscellaneous plant tissues (60), and characterization of expression of individual genes within Arabidopsis phloem (52). Inada & Wildermuth (50) recently described the use of rapid microwave paraffin embedding without prior fixation as a means to improve the laser microdissection properties of *Arabidopsis* leaves.

Microsampling. One of the most direct methods for characterizing the molecular properties of single-cell types involves minimal invasive sampling (15) using glass microcapillaries to collect the cellular contents. This approach has been employed for root hairs (54), mesophyll cells (76), and the phloem (16). Repetitive sampling of individual cell types, followed by amplification, can provide sufficient RNA for array hybridization (17). Glass microcapillaries have also been used to collect phloem-derived protoplasts via micromanipulation (52), using GFP expression to selectively mark the phloem companion cells. One recent study employed hand dissection of xylem and phloem from tissues derived from the lateral meristem of Arabidopsis (127). Although they can be extremely accurate in terms of access to specific cell types, and have the advantage of minimal perturbation of the host tissue, the primary drawback of microsampling methods is that they result in very small amounts of materials for downstream analysis. In terms of global gene expression, the development of more sensitive methods of detection and of transcript amplification, with retention of accuracy and reproducibility, would no doubt lead to greater adoption of microsampling methods.

Methods involving downstream separation of the contributions of specific cell types. This approach is exemplified by the work of Zanetti et al. (126), which in this case involves identification of ribosomal proteins suitable for incorporating epitope tags, then placing these tagged proteins under the control of promoters whose expression is cell type-specific. Total polyribosomes are then prepared from transgenic plants expressing these constructs, and immunoprecipitation is used to isolate the polyribosomes that are epitope tagged. Amplification of the associated mRNA can then be used for preparing the tar-

get for microarray expression analysis. Other platforms for downstream analysis can be employed for expression profiling. One advantage of this general approach is that it can be extended to any other class of protein implicated in the general process of gene expression (for example, RNA-binding proteins), and that it can be extended to other eukaryotic organisms. The separation of contributions from specific cells has also been done by profiling whole plants in which comparative techniques separate out the contributions of specific cells. Typically, a cell type is ablated or over-represented by using mutants or misexpression of cell identity genes. The profiles of wild-type plants are then compared to plants with the cell-specific manipulation (9, 114).

Identification of specific cell types. The methods that have been described above require the identification of specific cell types that then can be manipulated for analysis. Conventional anatomical descriptions are often sufficient (c.f. experiments involving laser capture, microsampling, purification of known cell types), or can be supplemented through the use of antibodies that mark specific cells. At the molecular level, increased specificity in defining cell types can also be achieved through transgenic expression of FP constructs under the control of known or unknown regulatory sequences. In the first category are the vast numbers of transgenic plants in which FP expression is regulated by defined promoters of genes of known or unknown function. In the second category are the increasing numbers of transgenic plants expressing FPs in tissue- and cell type-specific manners as a consequence of promoter or enhancer trapping screens (for a recent example, see 53, and for background see 42). FP expression is not compatible with some types of fixation (113). FPs can be targeted to most if not all compartments of the plant cell (see, for example, 22, 23, 36, 37, 65, 111). An interesting recent development is the ability to mark specific cell lineages in complex organs via spatially controlled transgenic FP expression

Cell identity regulator: a gene that acts as a genetic switch that controls the specification of a cell fate with a unique differentiation program

(67). In this case, laser heating was employed to activate transposon excision, thereby tagging specific cells and their progeny. Further means to define cell types include in situ hybridization (95), and it is possible that technologies such as color bar coding (73) may find applicability in plant systems.

Amplification methods. Implicit in many of the above procedures is the production of limiting amounts of RNA, which leads to the requirement for amplification of the RNA populations prior to further analysis. The ability of amplification methods to multiply the amounts of input RNA by factors of as much as 10^6-fold raises a number of concerns, both methodological and biological. Obvious methodological concerns are that different transcripts will be amplified to different degrees due to differences in the primary and secondary structure of the RNA or the cognate cDNA. Associated with this concern is the phenomenon of transcript truncation, which can particularly affect results from microarray platforms in which individual genes are represented by one oligonucleotide sequence. If this sequence is located far from the 3'-end of the gene, 5'-truncation during amplification will reduce and can even eliminate the signal from these transcripts. A number of different types of amplification methods are available, many in commercial kit form. Appropriate experimental design can measure and, to varying degrees of satisfaction, accommodate biases inherent to amplification. Generally, procedures that provide linear amplification, many based on the pioneering work of Eberwine (115), are more satisfactory than those based on PCR (for a thorough discussion, see 15).

The second general area of concern relates to an emerging appreciation of the importance of stochasticity of gene expression as a biological phenomenon (56). Stochasticity in this context is defined as variation in gene expression of genetically identical cells in the same environmental and developmental context, and an important driver of this phenomenon is system size relative to the numbers of molecules within the system. As system size decreases, the molecular-level noise increases due to the "finite-number" effect (56). Reciprocally, as we sample fewer and fewer cells of specific types, the potential for discovering stochastic representations of global gene expression is inevitably enhanced (c.f. 15, 57). The population characteristics of these representations can be determined by recording the responses of multiple individual samples, although this is not cost effective unless one uses single-cell populations and methods such as flow cytometry (56). Stochastic mechanisms will also affect the molecular markers that are employed to recognize specific cell types, whether they be anatomical descriptions (xylem, phloem, guard cells, etc.) or FP-based expression patterns, and by choosing cells based on these markers we are inevitably restricting ourselves to specific classes of cells within which to study the patterns of gene regulation.

LESSONS FROM CELLULAR GENOMICS

The Private Transcriptome: What is Unique to a Specialized Cell?

Specialized cells can differ dramatically in their morphology and function and discovering the function of genes that contribute to cell specialization is one goal of transcriptional profiling at the cell level (**Table 1**). But what is the scope of the specificity; that is, how many genes appear to be cell specific? A few global cell-profiling studies that offer a comparative perspective show that something on the order of several hundred transcripts are unique to specialized cells, or at least highly localized to a few widely dispersed cell types (11, 45, 46). For example, a developmental profile of maturing *Arabidopsis* pollen showed that about 650 to 850 transcripts are specifically expressed at each one of four stages of pollen development compared to expression profiles in six other organs

Table 1 List of available data on cell-type or tissue-specific expression profiling

Target tissue/cell type	Species	Platform	Data availability	Ref.
Pollen stages	*Arabidopsis thaliana*	Affymetrix ATH1	http://affymetrix.arabidopsis.info/narrays/experimentbrowse.pl	(46)
Xylem	*Zinnia elegans*	Spotted cDNA arrays	http://www.pnas.org/content/vol0/issue2002/images/data/232590499/DC1/5904Table1.xls	(25)
Embryo poles	*Arabidopsis thaliana*	Affymetrix ATH1	http://affymetrix.arabidopsis.info/narrays/experimentbrowse.pl	(19)
Vascular cambium region	*Populus tremula*	Spotted cDNA arrays	http://www.plantcell.org/content/vol0/issue2004/images/data/tpc.104.024190/DC1/024190SupplTable1.xls	(102)
Maturing xylem	*Populus tremula* x *Populus tremuloides*	Spotted cDNA arrays	http://genomebiology.com/2005/6/4/R34#IDAVXRIK	(89)
Root cells	*Arabidopsis thaliana*	Affymetrix ATH1	http://www.arexdb.org/index.jsp	(11)
Root quiescent center	*Arabidopsis thaliana*	Affymetrix ATH1	http://www.plantcell.org/cgi/content/full/tpc.105.031724/DC1	(92)
Pericycle/initiating lateral root	*Arabidopsis thaliana*	Spotted cDNA arrays	http://www.psb.ugent.be/papers/lateralroot/	(44)
Guard cells	*Arabidopsis thaliana*	Affymetrix Genome Array	http://www.plantcell.org/cgi/content/full/tpc.019000/DC1	(72)
Epidermal/vascular tissue	*Zea mays*	Spotted cDNA arrays	http://www.plantgenomics.iastate.edu/microarray/data/	(91)
Secondary xylem, phloem, and other vascular cells	*Arabidopsis thaliana*	Affymetrix ATH1	http://www.plantphysiol.org/cgi/content/full/pp.105.060202/DC1	(127)

of the sporophyte phase, including leaf, cotyledons, petiole, roots, stems, and root hair zone (46) (see **Figure 1**). In this case, the authors defined cell specificity as genes consistently present in a male gametophyte stage and absent in any sporophyte stage. These specifically expressed genes represent an impressive 7–8.5% of the transcripts detected in pollen.

The male gametophyte may represent an extreme case in having a high proportion of unique transcripts, possibly due to its complex, specialized role. A reanalysis of cell-sorting data in the *Arabidopsis* root shows that about 200–400 transcripts are uniquely expressed in only one of the five tissues or cell types profiled in the root (11). In this case, cell-specific expression was defined as an average hybridization signal above detection levels (defined in the study as a signal above 75) in only one cell type. Again, these

unique transcripts represent a minor but consistent proportion of transcripts detected in the root, about 2–4%. On a broader spatial scale, Schmid et al. (101) found a smaller number of genes unique to the eight major organ systems examined in *Arabidopsis*. Thus, cell specificity may be more common than organ specificity, but many more samples were analyzed in the organ-level assessment. This underscores the likelihood that cell-specific estimates will likely be revised downward as more cell types are profiled. However, at minimum, these cell-specific genes represent a class of highly localized transcripts.

A higher proportion of the genome is enriched in specific cells rather unique to them, where enrichment is typically defined as a two- or fourfold higher expression level in a particular cell type compared to any other cell type. For example, in the root data, 52% of all transcripts detected had a fourfold

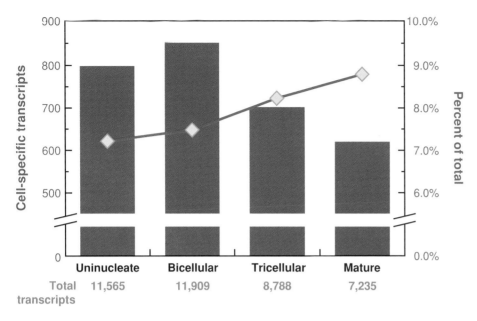

Figure 1

Global patterns in cell-specific transcripts within *Arabidopsis* pollen. The vertical axis (*left*) and bars show the absolute number of cell-specific transcripts in each stage of pollen development determined by their absence from profiles of six sporophytic tissues. The vertical axis (*right*) and line show the percentage of cell-specific transcripts at each pollen stage, showing an increase in the percentage of cell-specific transcripts but an absolute decrease in the number of specific transcripts detected in later stages of pollen maturity. The total number of transcripts detected at each stage is shown in green below the label. Data are from Reference 46.

difference in hybridization between the highest and lowest zones of expression. Many of these transcripts were enriched in more than one cell type. Cell-specific enrichment (as opposed to uniqueness) generally increased the number of cell-specific transcripts by a factor of two when using a twofold enrichment criterion. Thus, there are dramatic differences in the number of cell-specific genes depending on how they are defined. Whether any functional significance underlies these different patterns of specificity will require further phenotypic analysis of mutant forms of these genes or other types of functional analysis. In this review, we use specificity to mean either uniqueness or enrichment within a single cell type, using the widest possible definition for now.

Another global property of cellular transcriptomes is that gene expression appears to change dramatically during development. In

the four stages of pollen development examined, the first two early stages and the last two late stages were highly correlated (R = 0.96 and 0.86, respectively) (46). However, the earliest and latest stages were poorly correlated (R = 0.194). Remarkably, this made the transcriptional profile of early-stage pollen more similar to that of cell suspensions than to that of late-stage pollen. In the root, a K means analysis of expression profiles among genes with a fourfold range in expression values showed that the most abundant patterns were comprised of genes upregulated either early or late in development (11). During seed development, a large number of genes were upregulated early and another large set was upregulated later in development (101). What are the regulatory cues that coordinate gene expression among cell types during organogenesis? To effectively answer these questions, more cell-profiling studies that separate cells by small increments in a given development stage are critical.

Cell-Specific Phenotypes

The effort put into isolating specific cells for transcriptional profiling comes with a logical but narrowly tested assumption: Genes that are uniquely (or preferentially) expressed in certain cells have a role in conferring the identity, differentiation, or patterning of those cells. From a developmental perspective, cell-specific genes ought to confer or reflect cell-specific phenotypes.

Large-scale reverse genetics using insertional mutants has generally yielded low phenotype discovery rates on the order of 2% or so (14). One promise is that reverse genetics on genes enriched in specific cells will improve phenotype hit rates by focusing screens on defects at the cell level. Some studies suggest that key regulators of cell fate or differentiation are lurking in the lists of cell-specific transcripts. For example, Bergmann et al. (9) used a null mutation and a constitutive expresser of *YODA*, a putative MAPKKK that regulates guard-cell fate, to generate plants with either an overabundance or deficiency of stomata. These genetic manipulations, coupled with microarray analysis, were used to identify a set of transcripts that were presumably enriched in guard cells and potentially controlled their development. Of 82 candidate genes examined with insertional mutations, 10 showed stomatal or epidermal phenotypes. Mutations in one transcription factor, called *FAMA*, showed severe defects in guard-cell development. The other nine mutants had subtle stomatal or epidermal defects but no gross morphological phenotypes (D. Bergmann, personal communication). Thus, the vast majority of mutants showing phenotypes in epidermal cells would have been missed in a reverse genetic approach screening at the whole-plant or organ level.

Global assays of the transcriptional or proteomic contents of specific cells have also led to the identification of numerous other critical developmental regulators. Aida et al. (2) used a genome-wide enhancer trap screen in a global search for transcripts specifically expressed in the quiescent center (QC) of the root, which maintains the stem cell niche. The screen led to *PLETHORA1* (*PLT1*), which together with *PLETHORA2* (*PLT2*), both of which are AP2-like transcription factors, are essential for QC specification and stem cell activity. More than 25 years ago, Fukuda & Komamine (30) developed a powerful in vitro xylem differentiation system in Zinnia that was subsequently used to screen for xylem-specific transcripts and compounds using both biochemical and genomic analyses (25, 30, 87, 90, 93). A compound called xylogen was isolated from cell-specific extracts that promoted xylem differentiation and the genetic loci encoding xylogen in *Arabidopsis* were eventually identified as *A. thaliana xylogen protein 1* (*AtXYP1*) and *AtXYP2*, which together are essential for continuous xylem development (90). Another follow-up to the in vitro xylem cell analysis implicated new HD-Zip transcription factors in xylem development (93). In a study employing isolated guard cells, mutational analysis showed the guard-cell-specific phosphatase 2C (*AtP2C-HA*) to be hypersensitive to abscisic acid regulation in stomatal closing and seed germination (72). A LCM study of embryos found many genes enriched in the poles of the embryo. At least one insertional mutation in a transcription factor (At5g16780) segregated with a dominant phenotype for embryonic patterning defects specific to the basal pole (19). Although more large-scale reverse genetics on cell-specific genes needs to be done, these studies suggest that cell-specific genomic profiling can be a powerful tool for exploring the function of "unknown" genes by focusing reverse genetic analysis at the cellular level.

Expression of Gene Duplicates at the Cellular Level

The cases of *PLT1* and *PLT2* and *AtXYP1* and *AtXYP2* mentioned above underscore an important consequence of plant genome organization. In both cases, double mutants were required to observe strong phenotypes (2, 90). Plant genomes appear to retain many gene duplicates (77), suggesting that genetic redundancy may be common, including genes that act in a cell-specific fashion. Other reverse genetic analyses based on cell-specific expression provide strong indications that redundancy is common. For example, Nawy et al. (92) used the cell-sorting method to obtain a global expression profile of the four to seven cells that comprise the *Arabidopsis* QC and a few surrounding cells, the veritable epicenter of root development. The function of 11 transcription factors with QC-specific expression were examined using insertional mutants and detailed analysis of growth parameters and cellular morphology. However, no phenotypes were discovered. Although other factors may account for a lack of phenotypes, genetic redundancy seems to be one likely cause.

Several studies have examined one potential phenomenon that sheds light on the scope of genetic redundancy in *Arabidopsis*. Global analysis of duplicate genes in plants, like those of many species, shows that expression correlation between duplicate gene pairs diverges rapidly (12). For example, ribosomal proteins and cell wall components have quite distinct expression profiles at the cell level within their respective families (47, 116). However, other studies have shown that, despite a rapid departure in expression correlation, many duplicate gene pairs remain coexpressed within cell types. One study used principal components analysis on global profiles of root cells to simplify expression into two major patterns of gene expression. The study found that duplicate gene pairs tended to have similar trends of expression with respect to major patterns (47) due to their retained coexpression within specific cells. On the organ level, other studies showed that members of gene families retain much higher expression correlation than would be expected among random pairs (101). Thus, duplicate gene coexpression appears to

be common at the finest spatial scales. These coexpressed duplicate genes may or may not be genetically redundant. Global cell profiling should greatly assist in parsing out candidates for redundancy by providing a stringent criterion for expression overlap.

Functional Patterns at the Cell Level

Global analyses of the cellular transcriptome have revealed new spatial details about the compartmentalization of genetic pathways. One emergent theme is that plants appear to follow a manufacturing principle of local biosynthesis for local consumption rather than distant biosynthesis and transport, at least for some well-characterized pathways. For example, LCM of maize leaf cells followed by microarray analysis revealed many flavonoid biosynthetic enzymes enriched in epidermal cells, consistent with findings that detected flavonoids in epidermal cells (91). The well-characterized lignin biosynthetic pathway was enriched in the vascular tissue in both maize and *Arabidopsis* (11, 91).

The vasculature is perhaps the most widely characterized tissue among the cell-specific studies with profiling by microarrays or expressed sequence tag (EST) libraries in pine (123), poplar (43, 89, 102), and *Arabidopsis* (11). Many of these studies found genes known to be involved in developmentally regulated cell death and other aspects of specialized cell wall synthesis, and many new candidates involved in these processes have also been identified (43, 89, 123). In general, these studies support the notion that even common properties of plant cells are customized to the cell type, as has been suggested for the cell wall machinery (49, 116). For example, a reanalysis of cell-specific data in three studies shows that different genes encoding expansins, which loosen the cell wall during cell elongation, can be highly specific to cell types or tissues (**Figure 2**).

To uncover genes with highly specialized roles in plant reproduction, global cell profiling has been used in combination with

Genetic redundancy: a phenomenon in which two or more genes perform the same function

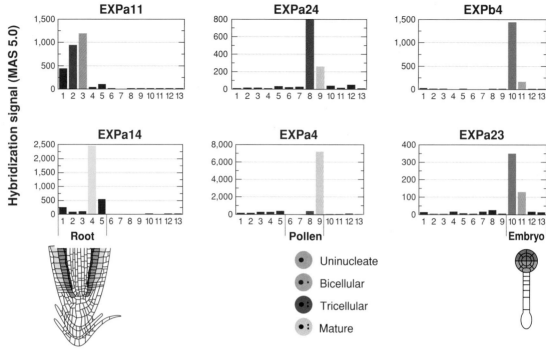

Figure 2

Cell-specific expression patterns of members of the expansin family showing a high level of diversity in the family for cell-specific expression. The vertical axis represents expression signal from the Affymetrix ATH1 microarray. The horizontal axis represents the cell or tissue profiled: root, 1 = stele, 2 = endodermis, 3 = endodermis/cortex, 4 = epidermis, 5 = lateral root cap; pollen, 6 = uninucleate microspores, 7 = bicellular pollen, 8 = tricellular pollen, 9 = mature pollen grain; embryo, 10 = globular stage basal axis cells, 11 = globular stage apical axis cells, 12 = heart stage cotyledon, 14 heart stage root. Gene identifiers are as follows: EXPa24 (AT5G39310), EXPa4 (AT2G39700), EXPa9 (AT5G02260), EXPa14 (AT5G56320), EXPb4 (AT2G45110), EXPa23 (AT5G39280), EXPA11 (AT1G20190). All cell files were reanalyzed in Affymetrix MAS 5.0 with a common target intensity of 200. Data are from References 11, 19, and 46.

bioinformatics or biochemical analysis. Global profiles of genes enriched in the stigmatal epidermis and transmitting tract in *Arabidopsis* were obtained by genetically ablating those cells and identifying underrepresented genes compared to normal tissue using microarrays (114). The study identified about 50 proteins predicted to be secreted that appeared to be enriched in transmitting tract cells, isolating an intriguing set of genes potentially involved in pollen interactions. On the other side of the interaction, a set of genes with potential roles on the surface of the male gametophyte were identified using transcriptional profiles of pollen coupled with

bioinformatic identification of glycosylphosphatidylinositol (GPI) anchored proteins. GPI anchoring tethers proteins to the plasma membrane for protrusion into the cell wall or for cleavage and subsequent release (68). A proteomics approach confirmed that at least 11 of 41 predicted GPI proteins were present in pollen membranes, including three β-1,3 glucanases, three phytocyanins, two fasciclin-like arabinogalactans, and one potential lipid-transfer-like protein. This work provided an intriguing set of candidate genes involved in cell wall or cell-cell contact in pollen. Analysis of the pollen transcriptome also revealed that 18 of the 28 members of a novel cation/H^+ exchanger gene (*CHX*) family were highly enriched in pollen, leading to speculation that these genes may have a role in maintaining K^+ homeostasis during pollen desiccation and rehydration (109).

Localized Hormone Responses

Another aspect of plant development that global cell profiling promises to inform is how the plant mediates broad hormone fluxes to elicit local responses that trigger cell fate, patterning, differentiation, and tropisms. Recent work has revealed an intricate relay of redundant PIN efflux carriers, named for the *pin-formed* phenotype, that precisely shuttle auxin around the plant to initiate organ formation (8). In the root, these efflux carriers create an auxin maxima that patterns the expression of *PLT* genes, which feed back to maintain PIN gene expression and the auxin maxima (13). Although an auxin flux from the shoot affects root development, recent work that analyzed auxin synthesis with tissue-specific resolution determined that the meristematic region of the root near the QC is also an auxin source (75). This study reanalyzed the root cell profiling data to confirm the presence of several genes known to be involved in auxin biosynthesis, including *CYP79B2*, *CYP79B3*, *ASA1*, and *ASA2*. Meanwhile, the global profile of the root QC, which is patterned by the auxin maxima, revealed QC enrichment of both *SUPER-ROOT1 (SUR1)* and *SUR2*, which negatively regulate auxin biosynthesis (92). Thus, global cell-specific analysis provides evidence for both positive and negative regulation of auxin in the root tip, where it is known to pattern the stem cell niche, on an extremely fine scale.

Downstream of auxin gradients, auxin responses appear to be mediated by the pairing of specific Auxin Response Factors (ARFs), which are transcription factors that induce auxin-responsive genes, and AUX/IAA proteins, which inhibit ARF activity and are degraded by auxin (64, 118, 119). One recent study using stabilized AUX/IAA proteins showed that *BDL/IAA12* and *IAA13*, two closely related AUX/IAA proteins, inhibit *MP/ARF5* activity to mediate embryonic root initiation. However, different AUX/IAA paralogs showed weaker inhibition of *MP*. This led to a model in which specific pairs of AUX/IAA proteins and ARFs distinctly mediated embryonic root initiation, hypocotyl cell elongation, and root growth and gravitropism (118).

Weijers & Jurgens (119) reanalyzed global transcriptional profiles of root cell types to show that AUX/IAA and ARFs had diverse enrichment patterns in specific tissues or developmental stages. In addition, global profiles have provided evidence for specific pairing of ARFs and AUX/IAAs in other organs and in different species. In the zinnia in vitro xylem system, a *MP* homolog together with a homolog closely related to IAA8 and IAA9 were induced together during xylem differentiation (25). In the LCM study of the major poles of the embryo, *ARF1* and the IAA/AUX family member *BDL* were enriched in basal regions whereas *ARF3/ETTIN* was enriched in the apical region of globular and heart-staged embryos (19). Together, these studies provide further evidence for widespread pairing of ARFs and AUX/IAAs in localized domains in order to trigger local responses to auxin.

MicroRNAs and Cell Specificity

Like hormones, microRNAs (miRNAs) can provide regulatory cues that influence the expression of many genes during development in plants (38, 61–63, 79, 88). miRNAs are small noncoding transcripts that form hairpin structures that are processed by *DICER* (5), yielding ~21–24-nt double-stranded RNAs that direct the cleavage of complementary transcripts (54a). Global studies of miRNA activity at the cell level are at preliminary stages, in part because specialized microarrays are needed to measure them. One prerequisite that could motivate cell-specific miRNA studies is a strong indication that many miRNAs exert cell-specific effects. On one hand,

Paralogs: genes that have arisen by duplication within a genome

knockouts in the miRNA machinery generally exhibit broad developmental defects, and this is true of some miRNA targets with mutated miRNA target sites. For example, plants transformed with an ARF17 gene bearing a mutated miRNA recognition site had overlapping phenotypes with *DCL1, AGO1, HYL1,* and *HEN1,* which are critical components of the miRNA processing machinery (79). Thus, misregulation of some miRNA target transcripts exhibit broad developmental defects, providing one possible explanation for the pleiotropic phenotypes of mutations in the miRNA processing machinery but not precluding the possibility of more refined regulation on smaller spatial scales. For miRNAs, the telltale signs of a cell-specific effect may include widespread distribution within a tissue but conspicuous absence from one or more cell types.

A series of recent publications has helped refine the role of microRNAs in development. For example, miRNAs were shown to regulate MYB33 and MYB65, which have a redundant role in anther formation (88, 94) and leaf development (94). In lateral organ initiation, mutations in mir164a and mir164b had increased levels of *NAC1* transcript and produced more lateral roots (38). A few studies provided compelling evidence that certain miRNAs are enriched or specifically expressed in small numbers of cell types, apparently leading to cell-specific effects on their targets. For example, two miRNAs, miR165 and miR166, direct the cleavage of the class III homeodomain/leucine zipper genes *PHABULOSA (PHB), PHAVOLUTA (PHV),* and *REVOLUTA (REV)* (26, 110). Gain-of-function mutations in *PHB* and *PHV* that destroy miRNA recognition sites for the two transcripts result in ectopic expression of *PHB* and *PHV* in the abaxial (bottom) domain of leaves where the transcripts are excluded in wild-type plants (83). Thus, loss of miRNA recognition sites in *PHB* and *PHV* led to leaves with only adaxial (top) cell fates. It was recently shown that miR165 is specifically localized to the abaxial domain of

leaves, exactly where it can repress *PHB* and *PHV* activity and thus influence tissue polarity and cell fate (61). In maize, the class III homeodomain/leucine zipper gene homolog, *rolled leaf1,* also appears to be regulated by a spatially restricted miRNA homolog (55), indicating that cell-specific miRNA activity appears to be a conserved developmental mechanism. Bao et al. (4) showed that the miR165 and miR166 sites are required for methylation of *PHB* and *PHV,* but the authors cite evidence that miRNAs may not be the main regulators of cell-specific transcript enrichment in the leaf.

Thus, there is growing evidence in plants that miRNAs exert cell-specific effects as a common mode of regulation. An intriguing result suggests that miRNAs may act in a combinatorial fashion in translational repression, a mechanism that may also be present in plants (66). Combinatorial control by miRNAs would enable further refinement in the spatial domains by restricted overlap between miRNA combinatorial partners. The small size of miRNAs means that many are not represented in the available T-DNA insertion lines commonly used for reverse genetic approaches (but see 38). Thus, the role of miRNAs in plants has largely been assessed by the construction of "resistant" targets (79, 88). This methodology may obscure more localized roles in development in the endogenous environment. Assuming miRNAs that regulate in a cell-specific manner should be characteristically absent from those cell types, but in contrast would be found within all others, global cell-specific profiling for miRNAs could help delineate the spatial domains of miRNA activity and focus the analysis on specific cells or tissues.

Marching to the Beat of a Different Cell Cycle

Global analysis of the cell cycle in *Arabidopsis* and *Physcomitrella* has led to an intriguing connection between cell cycle and the developmental competence of plant cells. In *Arabidopsis,* an interesting study on lateral root primordia used cell cycle markers to track the cell cycle state of so-called founder cells, which are pericycle cells that will redifferentiate and ultimately form lateral roots (7). In particular, CycB1;1-gus promoter fusions were used in conjunction with hydroxyurea, which inhibits progression from G1 to S phase, to show that founder cells were arrested in G2, unlike other differentiated pericycle cells, which remained in G1. Interestingly, researchers working on the basal land plant *Physcomitrella* examined the global cell cycle properties of germinating spores using flow cytometry. In *Physcomitrella*, the dominant haploid phase gives rise to spores, which germinate to form a chloronema cell. Under the right conditions, chloronema cells can differentiate into caulonema cells, which are distinct in having fewer chloroplasts and different cell wall orientation. Cell-specific flow cytometry analysis showed that the multipotent chloronema cells appear to be arrested in G2 whereas caulonema cells are arrested in G1 (104). These two cases point to an intriguing possibility that competence to regain stem cell-like activity in plants may be tied to a prior competence to re-enter the cell cycle, which is marked by a G2 resting state. In another cell-specific profiling study, Himanen et al. (44) used hormone treatments to essentially convert all pericycle cells to founder cells and then applied the treated and untreated roots to microarrays to obtain an expression profile of lateral root initiating pericycle cells. These global profiles showed no enrichment of G2 transcript markers but the artificial hormone applications might have obscured or bypassed the G2 resting phase. Further global studies of cells that undergo redifferentiation will be needed to clarify this issue and determine whether a G2 resting state is common among regenerative or stem cells in plants.

PROSPECTS

The vast majority of global expression studies have involved mixtures of many different cell types, leaving a critical blind spot in our expanding view of gene expression. The current state of cell-specific transcript profiling provides a first glimpse of global patterns in cell specificity, showing that much of the genome, if not the vast majority of it, is regulated on a fine spatial scale. Although technical improvements need to be made, particularly in the fidelity of amplification of RNA from small numbers of cells, a much more intricate and precise view of the transcriptional landscape is emerging. Many cell-specific transcripts have critical roles in cell identity, local patterning, and specialized cell differentiation. In addition to cell-specific transcripts, many genes are sharply upregulated in a subset of cells or distinct tissues. We expect that many of these genes will mediate common properties of the few cells in which they are expressed, but the underlying cause of this phenomenon is not yet clear. Overall, no clear "rules" have emerged in how spatial distribution predicts function. We expect that the next phase of cell-specific profiling in plants will yield not only interesting developmental genes but new patterns in genetic networks, genome organization, and evolution that tell us why so many genes are intricately regulated on a spatial scale. Technical improvements in our abilities to characterize the process of gene expression within specific cell types will include subdividing and analyzing the various subcomponents of this process. This will lead inevitably to consideration of global changes of other macromolecules and metabolites. Increases in sensitivity of our analyses will focus increasing attention on the role of stochastic processes in defining specific cell types. Furthermore, given that it has been suggested that most mRNAs are present at less than 10 copies per cell (74), that the nuclei of specific cell types appear probabilistic in terms of the repertoire of genes that are expressed following specific treatments (73), and that there exists a large number of transcripts for which functions are not yet assigned (29), it is clear that a good deal of work needs to be done before we can attain a clear consensus as to how specific cell types achieve and maintain their specificity.

AUTHORS' NOTE

A recent report published while this manuscript was being edited used an in vitro xylem cell culture system in *Arabidopsis* to identify two transcription factors that appear to direct cell fate (66a). One gene, *VASCULAR-RELATED NAC-DOMAIN6* (*VND6*), conferred metaxylem fate and *VND7* conferred protoxylem fate. This represents another case where cell-specific expression profiling led to the discovery of two critical developmental regulators.

SUMMARY POINTS

1. The majority of the genes in the transcriptome have restricted domains of enrichment.
2. Cell-specific transcripts have yielded critical cell fate, differentiation, and patterning regulators.
3. Gene duplicates often retain overlapping expression at the cell level.
4. Cell-specific readouts provide a blueprint for how localized auxin responses are mediated.

ACKNOWLEDGMENTS

Support for work in the authors' laboratories is from the National Science Foundation (D.G., grants DBI 0211857, DBI 0321663, and DBI 0501914) and (K.B., grant DBI 0519984). Support for K.B.'s lab is also provided by the U.S. Department of the Army award W81XWH-04-01-0307, concerning which the content of this material does not necessarily reflect the position or policy of the U.S. government.

LITERATURE CITED

1. Afonso CL, Harkins KR, Thomas-Compton M, Krejci A, Galbraith DW. 1985. Production of somatic hybrid plants through fluorescence activated sorting of protoplasts. *Nat. Biotechnol.* 3:811–16

2. **Aida M, Beis D, Heidstra R, Willemsen V, Blilou I, et al. 2004. The PLETHORA genes mediate patterning of the Arabidopsis root stem cell niche. *Cell* 119:109–20**

3. Asano T, Masumura T, Kusano H, Kikuchi S, Kurita A, et al. 2002. Construction of a specialized cDNA library from plant cells isolated by laser capture microdissection: toward comprehensive analysis of the genes expressed in the rice phloem. *Plant J.* 32:401–8

4. Bao N, Lye KW, Barton MK. 2004. MicroRNA binding sites in Arabidopsis class III HD-ZIP mRNAs are required for methylation of the template chromosome. *Dev. Cell* 7:653–62

5. Bartel DP. 2004. MicroRNAs: genomics, biogenesis, mechanism, and function. *Cell* 116:281–97

6. Becker JD, Boavida LC, Carneiro J, Haury M, Feijó JA. 2003. Transcriptional profiling of Arabidopsis tissues reveals the unique characteristics of the pollen transcriptome. *Plant Physiol.* 133:713–25

7. Beeckman T, Burssens S, Inze D. 2001. The peri-cell-cycle in Arabidopsis. *J. Exp. Bot.* 52:403–11

This research put faith in the notion that localization was an important clue to developmental function, resulting in *PLT* genes that pattern the stem cell niche and lie downstream of auxin signaling.

8. Benkova E, Michniewicz M, Sauer M, Teichmann T, Seifertova D, et al. 2003. Local, efflux-dependent auxin gradients as a common module for plant organ formation. *Cell* 115:591–602

9. **Bergmann DC, Lukowitz W, Somerville CR. 2004. Stomatal development and pattern controlled by a MAPKK kinase. *Science* 304:1494–97**

10. Bertone P, Stolc V, Royce TE, Rozowsky JS, Urban AE, et al. 2004. Global identification of human transcribed sequences with genome tiling arrays. *Science* 306:2242–46

11. **Birnbaum K, Shasha DE, Wang JY, Jung JW, Lambert GM, et al. 2003. A gene expression map of the Arabidopsis root. *Science* 302:1956–60**

12. Blanc G, Wolfe KH. 2004. Functional divergence of duplicated genes formed by polyploidy during Arabidopsis evolution. *Plant Cell* 16:1679–91

13. Blilou I, Xu J, Wildwater M, Willemsen V, Paponov I, et al. 2005. The PIN auxin efflux facilitator network controls growth and patterning in Arabidopsis roots. *Nature* 433:39–44

14. Bouche N, Bouchez D. 2001. Arabidopsis gene knockout: phenotypes wanted. *Curr. Opin. Plant Biol.* 4:111–17

15. Brandt SP. 2005. Microgenomics: gene expression analysis at the tissue-specific and single-cell levels. *J. Exp. Bot.* 56:495–505

16. Brandt S, Kehr J, Walz C, Impau A, Willmitzer L, Fisahn J. 1999. A rapid method for detection of plant gene transcripts from epidermal, mesophyll and companion cells of intact leaves. *Plant J.* 20:245–50

17. Brandt S, Kloska S, Altman T, Kehr J. 2002. Using array hybridization to monitor gene expression at the single cell level. *J. Exp. Bot.* 53:2315–23

18. Brown AJP, Planta RJ, Restuhadi F, Bailey DA, Butler PR, et al. 2001. Transcript analysis of 1003 novel yeast genes using high-throughput Northern hybridizations. *EMBO J.* 20:3177–86

19. Casson S, Spencer M, Walker K, Lindsey K. 2005. Laser capture microdissection for the analysis of gene expression during embryogenesis of Arabidopsis. *Plant J.* 42:111–23

20. Chalfie M, Tu Y, Euskirchen G, Ward WW, Prasher DC. 1994. Green Fluorescent Protein as a marker for gene-expression. *Science* 263:802–5

21. Cheng J, Kapranov P, Drenkow J, Dike S, Brubaker S, et al. 2005. Transcriptional maps of 10 human chromosomes at 5-nucleotide resolution. *Science* 308:1149–54

22. Chytilova E, Macas J, Galbraith DW. 1999. Green Fluorescent Protein targeted to the nucleus, a transgenic phenotype useful for studies in plant biology. *Ann. Bot.* 83:645–54

23. Cutler SR, Ehrhardt DW, Griffitts JS, Somerville CR. 2000. Random GFP::cDNA fusions enable visualization of subcellular structures in cells of *Arabidopsis* at a high frequency. *Proc. Natl. Acad. Sci. USA* 97:3718–23

24. Czechowski T, Bari RP, Stitt M, Scheible WR, Udvardi MK. 2004. Real-time RT-PCR profiling of over 1400 *Arabidopsis* transcription factors: unprecedented sensitivity reveals novel root- and shoot-specific genes. *Plant J.* 38:366–79

25. Demura T, Tashiro G, Horiguchi G, Kishimoto N, Kubo M, et al. 2002. Visualization by comprehensive microarray analysis of gene expression program during transdifferentiation of mesophyll cells into xylem cells *Proc. Natl. Acad. Sci. USA* 99:15794–99

26. Emery JF, Floyd SK, Alvarez J, Eshed Y, Hawker NP, et al. 2003. Radial patterning of Arabidopsis shoots by class III HD-ZIP and KANADI genes. *Curr. Biol.* 13:1768–74

27. Emmert-Buck MR, Bonner RF, Smith PD, Chuaqui RF, Zhuang Z, et al. 1996. Laser capture microdissection. *Science* 274:998–1001

A thorough genetic analysis provided one of the most comprehensive reverse genetic analyses of cell-specific candidates to date.

An excellent resource for reverse genetics and cell-specific pattern finding.

28. Engel ML, Chaboud A, Dumas C, McCormick S. 2003. Sperm cells of *Zea mays* have a complex complement of mRNAs. *Plant J.* 34:697–707

29. Frith MC, Pheasant M, Mattick JS. 2005. The amazing complexity of the human transcriptome. *Eur. J. Hum. Genet.* 13:894–97

30. Fukuda H, Komamine, A. 1980. Establishment of an experimental system for the study of tracheary element differentiation from single cells isolated from the mesophyll of *Zinnia elegans*. *Plant Physiol.* 65:57–65

31. Galbraith DW, Elumalai R, Gong F-C. 2004. Integrative flow cytometric and microarray approaches for use in transcriptional profiling. *Methods Mol. Biol.* 263:259–79

32. Galbraith DW, Bartos J, Dolezel J. 2005. Flow cytometry and cell sorting in plant biotechnology. In *Flow Cytometry in Biotechnology*, ed. LA Sklar, pp. 291–322. New York: Oxford Univ. Press

33. Galbraith DW, Grebenok RJ, Lambert GM, Sheen J. 1995. Flow cytometric analysis of transgene expression in higher plants: Green Fluorescent Protein. *Methods Cell Biol.* 50:3–12

34. Galbraith DW, Harkins KR, Maddox JR, Ayres NM, Sharma DP, et al. 1983. Rapid flow cytometric analysis of the cell cycle in intact plant tissues. *Science* 220:1049–51

35. Gowda M, Jantasuriyarat C, Dean RA, Wang GL. 2004. Robust-LongSAGE (RL-SAGE): a substantially improved LongSAGE method for gene discovery and transcriptome analysis. *Plant Physiol.* 134:890–97

36. Grebenok RJ, Pierson EA, Lambert GM, Gong F-C, Afonso CL, et al. 1997. Green-Fluorescent Protein fusions for efficient characterization of nuclear localization signals. *Plant J.* 11:573–86

37. Grebenok RJ, Lambert GM, Galbraith DW. 1997. Characterization of the targeted nuclear accumulation of GFP within the cells of transgenic plants. *Plant J.* 12:685–96

38. Guo HS, Xie Q, Fei JF, Chua NH. 2005. MicroRNA directs mRNA cleavage of the transcription factor NAC1 to downregulate auxin signals for Arabidopsis lateral root development. *Plant Cell* 17:1376–86

39. Harbers M, Carninci P. 2005. Tag-based approaches for transcriptome research and genome annotation. *Nat. Methods* 2:495–502

40. Harkins KR, Galbraith DW. 1984. Flow sorting and culture of plant protoplasts. *Physiol. Plant.* 60:43–52

41. Harkins KR, Jefferson RA, Kavanagh TA, Bevan MW, Galbraith DW. 1990. Expression of photosynthesis-related gene fusions is restricted by cell-type in transgenic plants and in transfected protoplasts. *Proc. Natl. Acad. Sci. USA* 87:816–20

42. **Haseloff J. 2001–present. http://www.arabidopsis.org/abrc/haseloff.jsp; http://www.plantsci.cam.ac.uk/Haseloff/IndexCatalogue.html**

43. Hertzberg M, Aspeborg H, Schrader J, Andersson A, Erlandsson R, et al. 2001. A transcriptional roadmap to wood formation. *Proc. Natl. Acad. Sci. USA* 98:14732–37

44. Himanen K, Vuylsteke M, Vanneste S, Vercruysse S, Boucheron E, et al. 2004. Transcript profiling of early lateral root initiation. *Proc. Natl. Acad. Sci. USA* 101:5146–51

45. Honys D, Twell D. 2003. Comparative analysis of the Arabidopsis pollen transcriptome. *Plant Physiol.* 132:640–52

46. **Honys D, Twell D. 2004. Transcriptome analysis of haploid male gametophyte development in Arabidopsis. *Genome Biol.* 5:R85**

47. Hughes AL, Friedman R. 2005. Expression patterns of duplicate genes in the developing root in *Arabidopsis thaliana*. *J. Mol. Evol.* 60:247–56

An invaluable resource of information about GFP, transgenic Arabidopsis lines, and microscopy.

A dynamic view of the transcriptome during pollen development.

48. Hughes TR, Marton MJ, Jones AR, Roberts CJ, Stoughton R, et al. 2000. Functional discovery via a compendium of expression profiles. *Cell* 102:109–26

49. Imoto K, Yokoyama R, Nishitani K. 2005. Comprehensive approach to genes involved in cell wall modifications in Arabidopsis thaliana. *Plant Mol. Biol.* 58:177–92

50. Inada N, Wildermuth MC. 2005. Novel tissue preparation method and cell-specific marker for laser microdissection of *Arabidopsis* mature leaf. *Planta* 221:9–16

51. Irizarry RA, Hobbs B, Collin F, Beazer-Barclay YD, Antonellis KJ, et al. 2003. Exploration, normalization, and summaries of high density oligonucleotide array probe level data. *Biostatistics* 4:249–64

52. Ivashikina N, Deeken R, Ache P, Kranz E, Pommerrenig B, et al. 2003. Isolation of AtSUC2 promoter-GFP-marked companion cells for patch-clamp studies and expression profiling. *Plant J.* 36:931–45

53. Johnson AAT, Hibberd JM, Gay C, Essah PA, Haseloff J, et al. 2005. Spatial control of transgene expression in rice (*Oryza sativa* L.) using the GAL4 enhancer trapping system. *Plant J.* 41:779–89

53a. Johnson JM, Edwards S, Shoemaker D, Schadt EE. 2005. Dark matter in the genome: evidence of widespread transcription detected by microarray tiling experiments. *Trends Genet.* 21:93–102

54. Jones MA, Grierson CS. 2003. A simple method for obtaining cell-specific cDNA from small numbers of growing root-hair cells in *Arabidopsis thaliana*. *J. Exp. Bot.* 54:1373–78

54a. Jones-Rhoades M, Bartel DP, Bartel B. 2006. MicroRNAs and their regulatory roles in plants. *Annu. Rev. Plant Biol.* 57:

55. Juarez MT, Kui JS, Thomas J, Heller BA, Timmermans MC. 2004. microRNA-mediated repression of rolled leaf1 specifies maize leaf polarity. *Nature* 428:84–88

56. Kærn M, Elston TC, Blake WJ, Collins JJ. 2005. Stochasticity in gene expression: from theories to phenotypes. *Nat. Rev. Genet.* 6:451–64

57. Karrer EE, Lincoln JE, Hogenhout S, Bennett AB, Bostock RM, et al. 1995. In situ isolation of mRNA from individual plant cells: creation of cell-specific cDNA libraries. *Proc. Natl. Acad. Sci. USA* 92:3814–18

58. Kehr J. 2001. High resolution spatial analysis of plant systems. *Curr. Opin. Plant Biol.* 4:197–210

59. Kehr J. 2003. Single cell technology. *Curr. Opin. Plant Biol.* 6:1–5

60. Kerk NM, Ceserani T, Tausta SL, Sussex IM, Nelson TM 2003. Laser capture microdissection of cells from plant tissues. *Plant Physiol.* 132:27–35

61. Kidner CA, Martienssen RA. 2004. Spatially restricted microRNA directs leaf polarity through ARGONAUTE1. *Nature* 428:81–84

62. Kidner CA, Martienssen RA. 2005. The developmental role of microRNA in plants. *Curr. Opin. Plant Biol.* 8:38–44

63. Kidner CA, Martienssen RA. 2005. The role of ARGONAUTE1 (AGO1) in meristem formation and identity. *Dev. Biol.* 280:504–17

64. Knox K, Grierson CS, Leyser O. 2003. AXR3 and SHY2 interact to regulate root hair development. *Development* 130:5769–77

65. Koroleva OA, Tomlinson ML, Leader D, Shaw P, Doonan JH. 2005. High-throughput protein localization in *Arabidopsis* using *Agrobacterium*-mediated transient expression of GFP-ORF fusions. *Plant J.* 41:162–74

66. Krek A, Grun D, Poy MN, Wolf R, Rosenberg L, et al. 2005. Combinatorial microRNA target predictions. *Nat. Genet.* 37:495–500

66a. Kubo M, Udagawa M, Nishikubo N, Horiguchi G, Yamaguchi M, et al. 2005. Transcription switches for protoxylem and metaxylem vessel formation. *Genes Dev.* 19:1855–60

67. Kurup S, Runions J, Köhler U, Laplaze L, Hodge S, et al. 2005. Marking cell lineages in living tissues. *Plant J.* 42:444–53

68. Lalanne E, Honys D, Johnson A, Borner GH, Lilley KS, et al. 2004. SETH1 and SETH2, two components of the glycosylphosphatidylinositol anchor biosynthetic pathway, are required for pollen germination and tube growth in Arabidopsis. *Plant Cell* 16:229–40

69. Lange BM 2005. Single-cell genomics. *Curr. Opin. Plant Biol.* 8:236–41

70. Larkin JE, Frank BC, Gavras H, Sultana R, Quackenbush J. 2005. Independence and reproducibility across microarray platforms. *Nat. Methods* 2:337–43

71. Lee J-Y, Levesque M, Benfey PN. 2005. High-throughput RNA isolation technologies. New tools for high-resolution gene expression profiling in plant systems. *Plant Physiol.* 138:585–90

72. Leonhardt N, Kwak JM, Robert N, Waner D, Leonhardt G, Schroeder JI. 2004. Microarray expression analysis of Arabidopsis guard cells and isolation of a recessive abscisic acid hypersensitive protein phosphatase 2c mutant. *Plant Cell* 16:596–615

73. Levsky JM, Shenoy SM, Pezo RC, Singer RH. 2002. Single cell gene expression profiling. *Science* 297:836–40

74. Levsky JM, Singer RH. 2003. Gene expression and the myth of the average cell. *Trends Cell Biol.* 13:4–6

75. Ljung K, Hull AK, Celenza J, Yamada M, Estelle M, et al. 2005. Sites and regulation of auxin biosynthesis in Arabidopsis roots. *Plant Cell* 17:1090–104

76. Lu CG, Koroleva OA, Farrar JF, Gallagher JA, Pollock CJ, Tomos AD. 2002. Rubisco small subunit, chlorophyll *a/b*-binding protein and sucrose: fructan-6-fructosyl transferase gene expression and sugar status in single barley leaf cells in situ. Cell type specificity and induction by light. *Plant Physiol.* 130:1335–48

77. Lynch M, Conery JS. 2000. The evolutionary fate and consequences of duplicate genes. *Science* 290:1151–55

78. Macas J, Lambert GM, Dolezel D, Galbraith DW. 1998. NEST (Nuclear Expressed Sequence Tag) analysis: a novel means to study transcription through amplification of nuclear RNA. *Cytometry* 33:460–68

79. Mallory AC, Bartel DP, Bartel B. 2005. MicroRNA-directed regulation of Arabidopsis AUXIN RESPONSE FACTOR17 is essential for proper development and modulates expression of early auxin response genes. *Plant Cell* 17:1360–75

80. Margulies M, Egholm M, Altman WE, Attiya S, Bader JS, et al. 2005. Genome sequencing in microfabricated high-density picolitre reactors. *Nature* 437:376–80

81. Matsumura H, Nirasawa S, Terauchi R. 1999. Transcript profiling in rice (*Oryza sativa* L.) seedlings using serial analysis of gene expression (SAGE). *Plant J.* 20:719–26

82. Mayer A, Stich M, Brocksch D, Schütze K, Lahr G. 2002. Going in vivo with laser microdissection. *Methods Enzymol.* 356:25–33

83. McConnell JR, Emery J, Eshed Y, Bao N, Bowman J, Barton MK. 2001. Role of PHABULOSA and PHAVOLUTA in determining radial patterning in shoots. *Nature* 411:709–13

84. Meyers BC. 2005. *Arabidopsis thaliana* MPSS site. **http://mpss.udel.edu/at/**

85. Meyers BC, Vu TH, Singh Tej S, Ghazal H, Matvienko M el al. 2004. Analysis of the transcriptional complexity of *Arabidopsis thaliana* by massively parallel signature sequencing. *Nat. Biotechnol.* 22:1006–11

This paper describes the thorough and comprehensive approach to characterization of transcription in Arabidopsis using MPSS.

86. Meyers BC, Tcj SS, Vu TH, Haudenschild CD, Agrawal V el al. 2004. The use of MPSS for whole-genome transcriptional analysis in *Arabidopsis*. *Genome Res.* 14:1641–53

87. Milioni D, Sado P-E, Stacey NJ, Roberts K, McCann MC. 2002. Early gene expression associated with the commitment and differentiation of a plant tracheary element is revealed by cDNA-amplified fragment length polymorphism analysis. *Plant Cell* 14:2813–24

88. Millar AA, Gubler F. 2005. The Arabidopsis GAMYB-like genes, MYB33 and MYB65, are microRNA-regulated genes that redundantly facilitate anther development. *Plant Cell* 17:705–21

89. Moreau C, Aksenov N, Lorenzo MG, Segerman B, Funk C, et al. 2005. A genomic approach to investigate developmental cell death in woody tissues of Populus trees. *Genome Biol.* 6: R34

90. Motose H, Sugiyama M, Fukuda H. 2004. A proteoglycan mediates inductive interaction during plant vascular development. *Nature* 429:873–78

91. Nakazono M, Qiu F, Borsuk LA, Schnable PS. 2003. Laser-capture microdissection, a tool for the global analysis of gene expression in specific plant cell types: identification of genes expressed differentially in epidermal cells or vascular tissues of maize. *Plant Cell* 15:583–96

92. Nawy T, Lee JY, Colinas J, Wang JY, Thongrod SC, et al. 2005. Transcriptional profile of the Arabidopsis root quiescent center. *Plant Cell* 17:1908–25

93. Ohashi-Ito K, Fukuda H. 2003. HD-zip III homeobox genes that include a novel member, ZeHB-13 (Zinnia)/ATHB-15 (Arabidopsis), are involved in procambium and xylem cell differentiation. *Plant Cell Physiol.* 44:1350–58

94. Palatnik JF, Allen E, Wu X, Schommer C, Schwab R, et al. 2003. Control of leaf morphogenesis by microRNAs. *Nature* 425:257–63

95. Pesquet E, Barbier O, Ranocha P, Jauneau A, Goffner D. 2004. Multiple gene detection by in situ RT-PCR in isolated plant cells and tissues. *Plant J.* 39:947–59

96. Pina C, Pinto F, Feijó JA, Becker JD 2005. Gene family analysis of the arabidopsis pollen transcriptome reveals biological implications for cell growth, division control, and gene expression regulation. *Plant Physiol.* 138:744–56

97. Poroyko V, Hejlek LG, Spollen WG, Springer GK, Nguyen HT, et al. 2005. The maize root transcriptome by serial analysis of gene expression. *Plant Physiol.* 138:1700–10

98. Qin LX, Kerr KF, Toxicogenomics Res. Consort. 2004. Empirical evaluation of data transformations and ranking statistics for microarray analysis. *Nucleic Acids Res.* 32:5471–79

99. Quackenbush J. 2002. Microarray data normalization and transformation. *Nat. Genet.* (Suppl.) 32:496–501

100. Schena M, Shalon D, Brown PO, Davis RW. 1995. Quantitative monitoring of gene-expression patterns with a complementary-DNA microarray. *Science* 270:467–70

101. Schmid M, Davison TS, Henz SR, Pape UJ, Demar M, et al. 2005. A gene expression map of *Arabidopsis thaliana* development. *Nat. Genet.* 37:501–6

102. Schrader J, Nilsson J, Mellerowicz E, Berglund A, Nilsson P, et al. 2004. A high-resolution transcript profile across the wood-forming meristem of poplar identifies potential regulators of cambial stem cell identity. *Plant Cell* 16:2278–92

103. Schütze K, Lahr G 1998. Identification of expressed genes by laser-mediated manipulation of single cells. *Nat. Biotechnol.* 16:737–42

104. Schween G, Gorr G, Hohe A, Reski R. 2003. Unique tissue-specific cell cycle in Physcomitrella. *Plant Biol.* 5:50–8

One of the early cell-specific developmental systems bears another fruit in this thorough and elegant work.

105. Sheen J, Hwang S, Niwa Y, Kobayashi H, Galbraith DW. 1995. Green Fluorescent Protein as a new vital marker in plant cells. *Plant J.* 8:777–84

106. Shendure J, Porreca GJ, Reppas NB, Lin X, McCutcheon JP, et al. 2005. Accurate multiplex polony sequencing of an evolved bacterial genome. *Science* 309:1728–32

107. Stolc V, Gauhar Z, Mason C, Halasz G, van Batenburg MF, et al. 2004. A gene expression map for the euchromatic genome of *Drosophila melanogaster*. *Science* 306:655–60

108. Stolc V, Samanta MP, Tongprasit W, Sethi H, Liang SD, et al. 2005. Identification of transcribed sequences in *Arabidopsis thaliana* by using high-resolution genome tiling arrays. *Proc. Natl. Acad. Sci. USA* 102:4453–58

109. Sze H, Padmanaban S, Cellier F, Honys D, Cheng NH, et al. 2004. Expression patterns of a novel AtCHX gene family highlight potential roles in osmotic adjustment and K+ homeostasis in pollen development. *Plant Physiol.* 136:2532–47

110. Tang G, Reinhart BJ, Bartel DP, Zamore PD. 2003. A biochemical framework for RNA silencing in plants. *Genes Dev.* 17:49–63

111. Tian GW, Mohanty A, Chary SN, Li SJ, Paap B, et al. 2004. High-throughput fluorescent tagging of full-length arabidopsis gene products in planta. *Plant Physiol.* 135:25–38

112. Tomos AD, Sharrock RA. 2001. Cell sampling and analysis (SiCSA): metabolites measured at single cell resolution. *J. Exp. Bot.* 52:623–30

113. Tsien RY. 1998. The green fluorescent protein. *Annu. Rev. Biochem.* 67:509–44

114. Tung CW, Dwyer KG, Nasrallah ME, Nasrallah JB. 2005. Genome-wide identification of genes expressed in Arabidopsis pistils specifically along the path of pollen tube growth. *Plant Physiol.* 138:977–89

115. Van Gelder RN, von Zastrow ME, Yool A, Dement WC, Barchas JD, Eberwine JH. 1990. Amplified RNA synthesized from limited quantities of heterogeneous cDNA. *Proc. Natl. Acad. Sci. USA* 87:1663–67

116. Vissenberg K, Oyama M, Osato Y, Yokoyama R, Verbelen JP, et al. 2005. Differential expression of AtXTH17, AtXTH18, AtXTH19 and AtXTH20 genes in Arabidopsis roots. Physiological roles in specification in cell wall construction. *Plant Cell Physiol.* 46:192–200

117. Wang HX, He XM, Band M, Wilson C, Liu L. 2005. A study of inter-lab and inter-platform agreement of DNA microarray data. *BMC Genomics* 6: Art. No. 71

118. Weijers D, Benkova E, Jager KE, Schlereth A, Hamann T, et al. 2005. Developmental specificity of auxin response by pairs of ARF and Aux/IAA transcriptional regulators. *EMBO J.* 24:1874–85

119. Weijers D, Jurgens G. 2004. Funneling auxin action: specificity in signal transduction. *Curr. Opin. Plant Biol.* 7:687–93

120. Wienkoop S, Zoeller D, Ebert B, Simon-Rosin U, Fisahn J, et al. 2004. Cell-specific protein profiling in *Arabidopsis thaliana* trichomes: identification of trichome-located proteins involved in sulfur metabolism and detoxification. *Phytochemistry* 65:1641–49

121. Xu W, Bak S, Decker A, Paquette SM, Feyereisen R, et al. 2001. Microarray-based analysis of gene expression in very large gene families: the cytochrome P450 gene superfamily of *Arabidopsis thaliana*. *Gene* 272:61–74

122. Yamada K, Lim J, Dale JM, Chen HM, Shinn P, et al. 2003. Empirical analysis of transcriptional activity in the *Arabidopsis* genome. *Science* 302:842–46

123. Yang SH, van Zyl L, No EG, Loopstra CA. 2003. Microarray analysis of genes preferentially expressed in differentiating xylem of loblolly pine (*Pinus taeda*). *Plant Sci.* 166:1185–95

124. Yang YH, Speed T. 2002. Design issues for cDNA microarray experiments. *Nat. Rev. Genet.* 3:579–88

This work provides important evidence that the specificity of pairing between antagonistic ARF and AUX/IAA interactions occurs at both the level of both localization and protein interaction.

A comprehensive analysis of transcriptional activity in the Arabidopsis genome, using a combination of tiling microarrays and cDNA analysis.

125. Yu H, Chao J, Patek D, Mujumdar R, Mujumdar S, et al. 1994. Cyanine dye dUTP analogs for enzymatic labeling of DNA probes. *Nucleic Acids Res.* 22:3226–32

126. Zanetti ME, Chang I-F, Gong FC, Galbraith DW, Bailey-Serres J. 2005. Immunopurification of polyribosomal complexes of Arabidopsis for global analysis of gene expression. *Plant Physiol.* 138:624–35

127. Zhao CS, Craig JC, Petzold HE, Dickerman AW, Beers EP. 2005. The xylem and phloem transcriptomes from secondary tissues of the Arabidopsis root-hypocotyl. *Plant Physiol.* 138:803–18

128. Zhao YD, Li MC, Simon R. 2005. An adaptive method for cDNA microarray normalization. *BMC Bioinform.* 6: Art. No. 28

Mechanism of Leaf-Shape Determination

Hirokazu Tsukaya

Graduate School of Science, University of Tokyo, 7-3-1 Hongo, Bunkyo-ku, Tokyo 113-0033, Japan; National Institute for Basic Biology, Myodaiji-cho, Okazaki 444-8585, Japan; email: tsukaya@biol.s.u-tokyo.ac.jp

Annu. Rev. Plant Biol. 2006. 57:477–96

The *Annual Review of Plant Biology* is online at plant.annualreviews.org

doi: 10.1146/ annurev.arplant.57.032905.105320

First published online as a Review in Advance on February 22, 2006

1543-5008/06/ 0602-0477$20.00

Key Words

compensation, flatness, leaf index, leaf margin, leaf size

Abstract

Biodiversity of plant shape is mainly attributable to biodiversity of leaf shape and the shape of floral organs, the modified leaves. However, the exact mechanisms of leaf-shape determination remain unclear due to the complexity of flat-structure organogenesis that includes the simultaneous cell cycling and cell enlargement in primordia. Recent studies in developmental and molecular genetics have revealed several important aspects of leaf-shape control mechanisms. For example, understanding of polar control in leaf-blade expansion has advanced greatly. A curious phenomenon called "compensated cell enlargement" found in leaf organogenesis studies should also provide interesting clues regarding the mechanisms of multicellular organ development. This paper reviews recent research findings with a focus on leaf development in *Arabidopsis thaliana*.

Contents

THE LEAF AS A MAJOR PART OF THE PLANT-BODY PLAN

A seed-plant body is composed of two distinct systems: the shoot system and the root system. The shoot system is unique to plants and is composed of a stack of units called phytomers (25). By stacking these units, plants acquire indeterminate growth. Each phytomer consists of a leaf, an internode, and a lateral bud that differentiates into a lateral shoot. A leaf is the basic form of almost all lateral plant organs; scales, bracts, and certain kinds of needles are also derived from leaves. Even the most specialized organs in plants, floral organs, such as the sepal, petal, stamen, and perhaps also the carpel, are also believed to be modified leaves. Thus, leaf morphogenesis is key to understanding shoot morphogenesis. Moreover, because leaves, with their ability to photosynthesize, play an important role in natural and agricultural productivity, the details

of leaf morphogenesis should be useful not only for understanding plant morphogenesis but also for plant improvement via so-called biodesign.

However, the complexity of leaf morphogenesis particularly in dicotyledonous plants has hindered our understanding of leaf-shape control mechanisms until recently. The process of leaf development, with division and elongation of cells occurring throughout leaf expansion in various areas of the leaf (24, 57, 74), has posed an especially difficult research question. However, applications of developmental molecular genetics to studies of leaf morphogenesis in a model plant, *Arabidopsis thaliana*, have helped clarify mechanisms of leaf-shape control. Moreover, analyzing mechanisms of leaf-shape control has revealed another interesting phenomenon, "compensation," which suggests integrated mechanisms of cell proliferation and cell enlargement related to harmonious organogenesis of multicellular organs. The following section reviews recent findings on leaf-shape control mechanisms, focusing on Arabidopsis genes determined from a major genetic research project. All mutants or transgenics discussed in this paper were derived from Arabidopsis.

BIOLOGICAL IMPORTANCE OF LEAF SHAPE

Before examining leaf-shape controls, it is necessary to define the term "leaf." The ancestral form of a plant shoot was a branch system like that of today's *Psilotum nudum* L. At least two types of leaves are thought to have evolved from the branch system: microphyll and megaphyll, which protrude from branches and are fused to branches, respectively (the telome theory) (108). Seed-plant leaves are megaphylls. According to recent molecular phylogenetic studies (77), evolution of megaphylls appears to have occurred at least twice, in a clade of Moniliformopses (ferns) and in a clade of Spermatophyta in which gymnosperms and angiosperms (both seed plants) are included. Thus, "leaves" may have heterogenic origins, although interestingly, regulation systems of leaf organogenesis (at least in part) seem to be conserved among all land plants, i.e., angiosperms, gymnosperms, ferns, lycopods, and mosses (27, 37). This review focuses on megaphylls of dicotyledonous angiosperms. In this sense, the leaf (megaphyll) can be defined as a lateral organ that develops on a shoot and has dorsoventrality; there is no accompanying organ on the abaxial side of the leaf base, with the exception of adventitious roots, and there is usually a lateral bud on the adaxial side of the base (89).

From a functional viewpoint, leaves are photosynthetic organs; thus, the shapes and sizes of leaves are critical factors influencing plant success. To absorb sufficient light energy, leaves must be as wide as possible. At the same time, to facilitate gas exchange (CO_2, O_2, and H_2O), leaves must be as flat and thin as possible. Thus, megaphylls, which are characterized by their branched venations and planate form and characteristic of today's ferns and seed plants, appear to be adapted for active photosynthesis.

However, curiously, megaphylls were relatively uncommon in land plants until the close of the Devonian Period ca. 360 million years (Myr) ago, although the first megaphylls likely appeared in the Early Devonian. Evidence indicates that 40 Myr after their appearance, flat, planate megaphylls had not spread widely. Recent research has solved this enigma. Plants had required a high density of stomata on the flat structure to avoid lethal overheating in the Late Paleozoic when atmospheric pCO_2 dropped by 90% (5). Thus, adaptation to overheating is also an important factor for determining leaf structure. In fact, ancient plant forms such as the leafless shoots of *P. nudum* and the shoots with microphylls of lycophytes are found in shaded environments even now. The flat structure of megaphylls also has another restrictive factor: Structures that are too wide and too thin can become rapidly desiccated. Thus, flat and thin leaf structures with

a high density of stomata would have become optimized to various environmental factors.

Such adaptive leaf shape against environmental factors can be seen in rheophytes that are adapted to frequent flooding in riparian habitats. Rheophyte leaves are narrower than those of closely related species and can thus resist strong water flows (101). However, leaf shape is not always genetically fixed. Many species show leaf-shape plasticity in response to environmental conditions. For example, in light-deficient situations plants may show shade-avoidance responses. In Arabidopsis, for example, leaf-blade expansion is inhibited and petiole elongation is enhanced (54, 60, 79, 96). Additionally, the anatomical structure of leaves can change in accordance with light intensity, i.e., sun-type leaves for high-intensity light and shade-type leaves for low-intensity light (reviewed in 50). Similar plasticity in leaf shape, size, and structure has been found for various environmental factors, reinforcing the importance of leaf shape as an environmental adaptation in plants (reviewed in 50, 94).

As noted above, leaf shape impacts plant success and has been refined through evolution. This section briefly reviews genetic systems of leaf-shape control in Arabidopsis. Due to space limitations, see other recent reviews of leaf morphogenesis for additional details: e.g., leaf initiation related to expression regulation of the homeobox *KNOX* gene (reviewed in 12, 34), auxin distribution in the shoot apical meristem (reviewed in 26), and establishment of dorsoventrality via miRNA-mediated gene regulation (reviewed in 10, 15). Additional reviews have examined the basic repetition of blades (i.e., as complex or simple leaves) (8, 30, 52). Donnelly et al. (24) described detailed processes of leaf morphogenesis in Arabidopsis from cell-cycling and cell-enlargement viewpoints. For an additional overview of leaf morphogenesis mechanisms in Arabidopsis, please see the author's previous review (90), which also describes the history of leaf-morphogenesis studies on Arabidopsis.

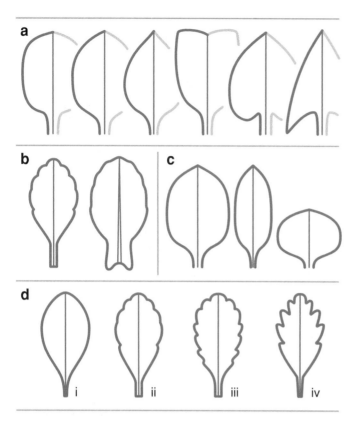

Figure 1

Leaf-shape variation and traditional parameters used to describe the biodiversity of leaf shape in plant taxonomy. (*a*) Even under the same length and width of leaf blades, leaf shape can vary significantly. (*b*) Presence/absence of leaf petiole. The right type of leaves leaf blades are decurrent along the petiole. (*c*) Variation in leaf index (a ratio of leaf length to leaf width). (*d*) Margin type. See text for details.

PARAMETERS OF LEAF SHAPE

How is leaf shape controlled? This review focuses on the following traditional parameters used to describe the biodiversity of leaf shape in plant taxonomy: presence/absence of leaf petiole, flatness, leaf index (a ratio of leaf length to leaf width), margin type, and overall size (**Figure 1**). The shapes of leaf apices, bases, and outlines are also important characteristics of leaf shape (**Figure 1a**) and are described by terms such as oblongus, ovatus, spatulatus, sagittatus, and cuneiform by Lindley in 1832 (cited in 84). However, to date, we have no knowledge of the genetic controls of such parameters except for whether leaf blades are decurrent along the petiole (discussed below), although numerous mutants and natural variations in leaf shape have been isolated from Arabidopsis (6, 72, 80, 82). Thus, these features are reserved for future reviews.

PRESENCE/ABSENCE OF PETIOLE

Arabidopsis leaves are clearly divided into two morphological parts: the petiole and leaf blades. Although this is a basic form in dicots, many plants have only leaf blades and no petioles. In some species, leaf blades are decurrent along the petiole (**Figure 1b**), forming along the dorsoventral (adaxial/abaxial) boundary of a leaf. How does this kind of leaf develop? The Arabidopsis *JAGGED* (*JAG*) gene encodes a protein with a single C_2H_2-type zinc finger; ectopic overexpression of *JAG* promotes leaf lamina-like growth in the area with potential for the organogenesis of lamina and cryptic bracts evident (23, 68). Interestingly, overexpressors of the *JAG* gene develop a winged-leaf petiole (23, 68). Similar phenotypes are also known for overexpressing the *LEAFY PETIOLE* (*LEP*) (100) and for the *blade-on-petiole1-1* (*bop1-1*) mutation (33). The *LEP* encodes a transcription factor with a DNA-binding domain for members of the AP2/EREBP family (100). Unfortunately, loss of function of the mutant of the *LEP* gene has no visible phenotype, and the native function of *LEP* is still unknown. The *BOP1* gene encodes a NONEXPRESSOR OF PR GENES1 (NPR1)-like protein with four ankyrin repeats and negatively regulates expression of class I *KNOX* genes in leaf primordia (32, 33, 38). The Arabidopsis genome has a closely related homolog of *BOP1* called *BOP2*; a loss-of-function mutant of *BOP2* showed no obvious phenotypes in the leaf (38). Null alleles of the *BOP1* mutation have shown no winged-leaf petiole (32), but the double-mutant *bop1 bop2* developed ectopic outgrowths on the leaf petioles known for *bop1-1*. Because *bop1-1* was somewhat semidominant, the winged-leaf-petiole phenotype in *bop1-1* may be due to a dominant negative effect of the truncated form of the product of the *bop1-1* allele on *BOP1* and *BOP2* (38). Interestingly, the *JAG* mRNA expression is upregulated in leaves of the *bop1 bop2* double mutant (38), suggesting that these genes may also funda-mentally regulate the extent of leaf lamina-like growth. Thus, suppression of cell cycling in the leaf-petiole region might be overcome by these mutations/ectopic expressions based on the potential along the adaxial/abaxial identities.

Although mechanisms of dorsoventrality establishment in leaf primordia are beyond the focus of this article (see 10, 15), brief mention of the tight linkage between dorsoventrality and the flat structure of leaf lamina is relevant. Marginal growth may be triggered by a junction established between cells of abaxial fate and adaxial fate (102), as in animal organs. For example, several mutants of the *YABBY* gene family that is involved in identifying the abaxial fate of leaf primordia (83) show an expanded-growth defect in leaf lamina. Kim et al. (52) found correlations among the extent of adaxialization of leaf petioles, the expression pattern of the MYB *ASYMMETRIC LEAVES1-ROUGH SHEATH2-PHANTASTICA* (*ARP*) gene, and the positioning pattern of leaflets in compound leaves of various species. Given that leaflet formation in compound leaf-type primordia is tightly linked with the establishment of expanded growth in flat leaf blades, this finding again suggests that establishment of the dorsoventral boundary is essential for determining marginal growth in leaf blades. However, the role of these genes in the lateral development of lamina varies greatly among plant species. For example, the morphological phenotypes of mutants of the *ARP* gene family differ within Arabidopsis, as well as within snapdragon, tobacco, and maize. The *as1* mutant of Arabidopsis shows an irregularly rough surface in the blade and an extremely short petiole, while the *phan* of snapdragon and *rs2* of maize show "petiolization," i.e., reduced leaf lamina and an increased petiole. These mutations suggest that some unknown, overlooked function(s) may be behind the argued roles of these genes.

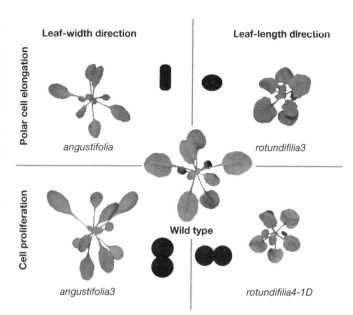

Leaf-width direction

Leaf-length direction

Polar cell elongation

angustifolia

rotundifilia3

Cell proliferation

Wild type

angustifolia3

rotundifilia4-1D

LENGTH AND WIDTH AND THEIR RATIO: THE LEAF INDEX

A leaf or leaflet blade has a two-dimensional flat shape that expands from the border of adaxial/abaxial polarities, as mentioned above. Lateral cell proliferation in a leaf primordial sustains the two-dimensional leaf expansion. Although long misunderstood, this process largely depends on the plate meristem; the role of the so-called marginal meristem is rather limited in transforming rod-shaped early leaf primordia into flat forms (24). Variations in the leaf index value are frequently observed in wild species, suggesting that leaf expansion is controlled along two main axes: longitudinal (proximodistal or leaf length) and lateral (mediolateral, left–right, or leaf width). These polarity-dependent controls are further divided into two different mechanisms, i.e., polar cell cycling and polar cell expansion, as evidenced from analyses of Arabidopsis leaves discussed below (88, 94) (**Figures 1c, 2**). Here, an overview of leaf-size regulation via two simple dimensions, length and width, is provided. Although many factors can influence the polarized dimensions of leaves, e.g., cell-wall composition (e.g., 69),

Figure 2

Mutants of the regulators of the two-dimensional control of polar cell expansion and cell proliferation in leaves. Black dots schematically represent shape and arrangement of palisade cells. See text for details. Modified from Tsukaya (94) with permission.

microtubule control (e.g., 9, 11), and phytohormones, these factors affect not only leaf size but also overall plant size. Genes that specifically influence leaf width or length are examined here.

As noted, two polarities (longitudinal and lateral axes) appear to control both cell expansion and proliferation in the leaf primordia. Longitudinal leaf growth is governed both by *ROTUNDIFOLIA3* (*ROT3*), which regulates the polarized growth of leaf cells in the leaf-length (longitudinal) direction (88), and *ROTUNDIFOLIA4* (*ROT4*), which specifically regulates the number of leaf cells in the leaf-length direction (63). Polarized growth of leaf blades in the leaf-width direction is also divided into polar elongation of leaf cells and polar cell proliferation. Thus, the leaf index is controlled by four regulating systems (**Figure 2**).

The *rot3* mutant was first isolated as a specific defect in leaf-cell expansion in the leaf-length direction (88). *ROT3* encodes a plant-type cytochrome P450, *CYP90C1*, and sequence analysis suggests that *ROT3* is involved in the biosynthesis of steroids (49). The null allele of the *rot3* mutation, *rot3-1*, caused only stunted leaves and flowers, and the overexpression of *ROT3* triggered the specific longitudinal elongation of leaves (48). A homology search revealed a closely related P450, *CYP90D1*, in the Arabidopsis genome. Although the loss of function of *CYP90D1* did not possess any morphological phenotype, *cyp90d1/rot3-1* double mutants had a severe dwarf phenotype (46) like that observed for mutants defective in the biosynthesis of brassinosteroids (BRs). Biochemical analyses have strongly suggested that ROT3 catalyzes the conversion of typhasterol to castasterone, which has been deemed the activation step of BRs (46). Gene mutations related to the biosynthesis and/or sensing of BRs can cause severe dwarfism and a characteristic defect in skotomorphogenesis. Defects in cell expansion and decreased cell numbers create severely decreased leaf sizes in such mutants (61). Thus, the spe-

cific defects of the *rot3-1* null mutation in leaf length are surprising. Why does *rot3-1* have only mild phenotypes? Because some alleles of mutants of BR receptors and signaling molecules have mild leaf-growth defects, as seen in *rot3-1* (e.g., 55), signaling from BRs may play a major role in longitudinal growth in leaves. Interestingly, the darkness-induced petiole elongation governed by phytochromes and cryptochromes (54) has been lost in the *rot3-1* mutant (46). Thus, *ROT3* may be a leaf-specific factor of BR biosynthesis that is involved in leaf photomorphogenesis. Mechanisms of leaf photomorphogenesis, particularly the shade-avoidance syndrome (54), may be revealed in future studies of the photoregulation of *ROT3* and *CYP90D1* gene functions.

On the other hand, leaf length can also be specifically controlled via the regulation of the number of leaf cells by the ROTUNDIFOLIA4 (ROT4) peptide (63) (**Figure 2**). The *ROT4* gene was overlooked by the Arabidopsis genome project and had been unannotated because of its small size (*ROT4* encodes 53 amino acids and has no intron); analysis revealed that *ROT4* was part of the enhancer-trap line of Arabidopsis, *rot4-1D*, which has stunted leaves (63). *Rot4-1D* leaves have fewer leaf cells predominantly in the leaf-length direction and show no defects in the size of leaf cells (63). The Arabidopsis genome has 22 homologs of *ROT4* (*RTFL* = *ROT FOUR-LIKE*) (63), which include 21 members of the DEVIL family (105). The *RTFL* gene family has thus far been found only in plant genomes (63); the rice genome also has 23 *RTFL* members (107). All members of the RTFL family contain a conserved 29-amino acid domain called the RTF domain; the overexpression of the ROT4 RTF domain can decrease leaf length. Because the overexpression of *DEVIL1* (= *RTFL18*) and an *RTFL* member from rice in Arabidopsis also cause a phenotype very similar to *ROT4* overexpression (105, 107), the fundamental function of the *RTFL* members should be the same. No visible phenotype has been shown for loss of function of an *RTFL* member, which might be explained by the high redundancy of the *RTFL* gene family (63).

For leaf width, specific control of leaf expansion in the leaf-width direction was first revealed from analysis of an *angustifolia* (*an*) mutant with narrow, thick leaves of normal length (88, 98) (**Figure 2**). *AN* encodes a homolog of the animal carboxyl-terminal-binding protein (CtBP) and may be related to the control of the cortical microtubule arrangement in leaf cells (47). AN can associate with a kinesin-like protein ZWICHEL (28) and is homodimerized (47) in yeast cells. *AN* homologs from plants are very similar to each other and have specific motifs not found in animal CtBPs (18, 28, 47). CtBPs function in the nucleus as corepressors and regulate the developmental processes in *Drosophila melanogaster*, *Xenopus laevis*, and other animals, whereas a closely related homolog of CtBPs, brefeldin A-ADP ribosylated substrate protein (BARS), functions in cytoplasm and is involved in the formation and maintenance of the Golgi apparatus (16, 62). The amino acid sequence cannot distinguish the CtBPs and BARS functions. Thus, AN appears to be the third member of the enigmatic CtBP/BARS family, called CBA (CtBP-BARS-AN) (95). Comparative and functional analyses of AN and CtBP/BARS should supply some important clues on the role and evolution of the CBA family.

The *spike1* (*spk1*) mutant also has narrow and irregularly distorted leaves (78). A mutation in a *spk1* adaptor protein gene, which may play a role in cytoskeletal reorganization, causes defects, specifically protrusions in the leaf-width direction in epidermal cells (78). Similarly, overexpression of a homeodomain leucine zipper protein AtHB13 causes specific inhibition of leaf-width expansion in epidermal cells without affecting the number of cells in cotyledons when transgenic seedlings were germinated on medium containing a high concentration of sucrose (36). Although the observed system for the AtHB13 transgenics was artificial, the phenotype had a cell shape highly similar to that in the epidermis of

an cotyledons (98). The phenotypic similarity among *an*, *spk1*, and *AtHB13* overexpressors suggests the importance of an appropriate arrangement of cortical MTs to leaf growth in the leaf-width direction.

However, the specific control of cell proliferation in the leaf-width direction remains unclear, although comparative, anatomical studies of narrow-leaved rheophytes in angiosperms strongly suggest the presence of such a control (reviewed in 92). We found that loss of function in the *ANGUSTIFOLIA3* (*AN3*) gene resulted in a narrow leaf shape (**Figure 2**) with a decreased number of leaf cells. *AN3* encodes a homolog of the human transcription coactivator SYT (40) and is identical to *GRF-INTERACTING FACTOR1* (*AtGIF1*) (51). The defect in a number of cells in the *an3/atgif1* mutant was not specific to the leaf-width direction (40). Interestingly, no defect was found in *an3/atgif1* in the initial cell proliferation of early leaf primordia that predominantly supplies cells in the longitudinal direction; however, the activity of the plate meristem, which is activated in later stages of leaf primordia and supplies the cells in the lamina with randomized directions of cell division, decreased in *an3/atgif1* (40). Thus, *an3/atgif1* leaves had severer defects in the number of cells in the leaf-width direction than in the longitudinal direction, creating a large leaf index value. Additionally, the final volume of the leaf cells was much larger than that in the wild type, which compensated for the defect in the final size of leaf blades to some extent (40). As a result, the full size *an3/atgif1* leaves seemed to have a leaf width specific defect (**Figure 2**).

This curious "compensation" system will be discussed in a later section. Regarding the molecular function of AN3/AtGIF1, we found that the GROWTH-REGULATING FACTOR5 (AtGRF5), a putative transcription factor, was associated with AN3/ATGIF1 in a yeast two-hybrid system and expressed in leaf primordia in an overlapping manner with *AN3/AtGIF1* (40). Moreover, altered expression of *AtGRF5* caused weaker but similar phenotypes of *AN3* (40). Thus, AN3/ATGIF1 and AtGRF5 appear to be important in the positive control of cell cycling in the leaf primordia plate meristem that sustains two-dimensional growth of leaf blades.

MARGIN TYPE

Leaf margins can be characterized as entire (integrated) (**Figure 1***d, i*), serrated, or lobed in terms of marginal division (**Figure 1***d*). In serrated leaves, hydathodes are usually positioned on the tip of teeth, as in Arabidopsis leaves (14, 99). Although the genetic control of these characteristics remains largely unknown, some genes that influence the margin were recently identified.

First, note that at least two distinctions can be made regarding serrated leaf appearances: an increased number of teeth (**Figure 1***d, ii, iii*) and increased sinus depth or teeth sharpness ("serratus" or "dentatus") (**Figure 1***d, ii–iv*). These two types are often confused, but are important parameters for discussing the mechanisms of leaf-margin control. For example, *asymmetric leaves1* (*as1*) had an increased sinus depth but a lower number of teeth than wild-type leaves (99). Most known Arabidopsis mutants with a serrated leaf shape fall into the latter category and show an increased sinus depth. One exception was a weak allele of the *serrate* (*se*) mutant that had a defect in a gene for a protein with a single C_2H_2-type zinc finger (76). The *se* mutation not only deepened the teeth in the leaf margins, but also accelerated the progression of heteroblasty (70, 76). Because the number of teeth per leaf blade increases in accordance with the progression of heteroblasty (97), the *se* mutation resulted in an increased number of teeth per leaf blade at a particular position compared to wild-type leaves at the same leaf position. In *as1* and *as2* mutants that ectopically express the class I *KNOX* gene in leaves (13, 81), the observed alteration in the sinus depth may have been under a different control than that for depth of teeth. Continuing expression of the class I *KNOX* gene in leaf primordia, which is negatively controlled by *AS1* and *AS2*, is tightly linked with the morphogenesis of compound leaves (8, 30) and may thus correspond to leaflet formation in compound leaves.

In contrast, a decrease of cell cycling in the leaf lamina often deepens the sinus of leaf lamina. Direct and negative controls on cell cycling increase the sinus depth, as known for constitutive expressers of CDK inhibitors such as ICK1, KRP2, and p22^{ACK1} (17, 22, 35, 103) (**Figure 3***a*). In these cases, the number of teeth is unaffected but the sinus depth increases in association with the decreased number of leaf cells. Indirect negative effects on cell cycling can also deepen the sinus. For example, as mentioned previously, the loss-of-function mutation of *JAG* also deepens the sinus of leaves (23, 68). The number of teeth seems to be unaffected by the *jag* mutation. Considering that overexpression of *JAG* causes ectopic leaf lamina-like growth, the serrated leaf shape in the *jag* mutant may be attributable to a shortage of leaf cells in the lamina. Similarly, the *swellmap*^{epi} (*smp*^{epi}) mutant was also found to have deep serration in the leaves (19). The *smp*^{epi} mutation did not affect expression levels of cell-cycle genes such as *CYCD3;1* and *CDCD2A*, but did suppress expression of *STRUWWELPETER* (*SWP*), a subunit of the Mediator complex (2) that regulates the duration of the cell proliferation phase in leaf primordia. Transgenic Arabidopsis constitutively expressing TuMV-encoded RNA-silencing suppressor, P1/HC-Pro, has also shown a deep leaf sinus (45). Moreover, some chloroplast-deficient mutants have had slight deepening of the sinus due to poor expansion of leaf lamina relative to the vascular tissue (e.g., 85). These examples suggest that cells around the teeth in the leaf margin may be the most sensitive to decreased cell cycling. Unbalanced growth between vasculature and parenchymatous tissue may determine teeth position.

Interestingly, however, a decreased leaf-cell number does not always increase the

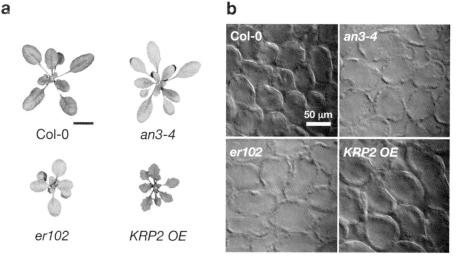

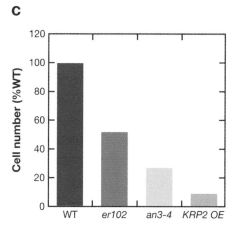

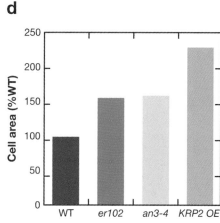

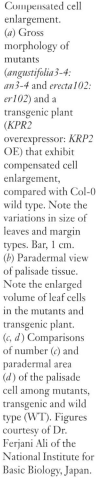

Figure 3

Compensated cell enlargement. (a) Gross morphology of mutants (*angustifolia3-4*: *an3-4* and *erecta102*: *er102*) and a transgenic plant (*KPR2* overexpressor: *KRP2* OE) that exhibit compensated cell enlargement, compared with Col-0 wild type. Note the variations in size of leaves and margin types. Bar, 1 cm. (b) Paradermal view of palisade tissue. Note the enlarged volume of leaf cells in the mutants and transgenic plant. (c, d) Comparisons of number (c) and paradermal area (d) of the palisade cell among mutants, transgenic and wild type (WT). Figures courtesy of Dr. Ferjani Ali of the National Institute for Basic Biology, Japan.

sinus depth. Rather, a decreased number of leaf cells due to defects in genes that are not involved in direct cell-cycle regulation usually cause narrow, small leaves with an integrated leaf margin (i.e., no evident serration). Defects in cytoplasmic ribosomal protein S13 (*pfl2*), the elongator-associating protein DEFORMED ROOTS AND LEAVES1 (DRL1), and *AN3* are such examples (43, 65). Curiously, the *swp* mutant developed leaves with an integrated entire margin (2), whereas mutants of the *SWP*-related *SMP* gene *smp*[epi] had deep serration, as mentioned above (19). Although Clay & Nelson (19) speculated that leaf-shape differences between *swp* and *smp*[epi] might be due to differences in ecotypes or the genetic backgrounds from which the mutants were isolated, these explanations seem implausible. New insight on controls of leaf-margin types will emerge from careful comparison of the roles of cell cycling and its effects on sinus depth. Note that all previously mentioned mutations of cell cycling showed typical compensation, i.e., increased cell volume followed by a decreased cell number (90, 91, 93, 94) (see below for details). Further detailed studies should supply important clues for understanding the mechanisms of overall leaf shape from the viewpoint of cell supply in the lamina.

Taken together, variation of the margin can be attributed to relative differences in leaf-cell proliferation in the mediolateral direction or along the leaf-lamina contour. Pien et al. (73) found that a local supply of EXPANSIN protein, which could increase cell-wall extensibility to flanks of tobacco-leaf primordial, promoted local cell proliferation and local outgrowth in the leaf margin. Wyrzykowska et al. (106) also showed that local and direct acceleration of cell cycling in the flank of tobacco-leaf lamina caused local suppression of lamina growth, creating local indentation in leaf blades. In contrast, local suppression of CDK activity in the flank of tobacco-leaf lamina caused local expansion of the lamina. These results suggest two interesting effects: local alteration of cell cycling affects leaf shape, and transient-accelerated cell cycling results in decreased cell division for leaf-blade formation. Further study may clarify the mechanisms that control marginal shape as well as organ-level control of cell behavior in leaf morphogenesis (discussed later).

FLATNESS

Leaves can also be characterized as concave (wavy: undulatus) or flat. A flat leaf can maximize the efficiency of light capture; such a smooth, flat design requires fine integration of cell expansion and proliferation. Nath et al. (64) and Palatnik et al. (71) showed that certain types of *TEOSINTE BRANCHED1/CYCLOIDEA/PCF* (*TCP*) transcription factors have a role in the cooperated control of cell proliferation that makes leaf lamina flat. When *CINCINNATA* (*CIN*), a *TCP* gene of snapdragon, lost that function, snapdragon leaves developed several concave parts between veins due to excess cell proliferation in the intervein and marginal regions. In the *cin* mutant, Nath et al. (64) found that arrest-front progression of cell cycling that generally proceeds from the tip to the base of the leaf primordia was retarded, particularly in the marginal area

of the leaf primordia. Nath et al. (64) thus speculated that *CIN* may make leaf cells sensitive to the arrest-front signal. However, *CIN* does not appear to be a key gene that specifically determines the type of leaf margin because the *cin* mutant of snapdragon had excess cell proliferation not only in the leaf margin but also in intervein regions. Similar phenotypes can also be induced by upregulation of the class1 *KNOX* gene expression in leaf primordia. For example, Tamaoki et al. (87) found that when a class 1 *KNOX* gene of tobacco, *NTH1*, was expressed ectopically and constitutively in tobacco-leaf primordial, mature leaves became wrinkled and excessive growth occurred in the intervein regions. Further study is needed to determine the precise function of *TCP* in control of cell proliferation in leaf primordia.

The expression level of *TCP* in leaf primordia is controlled by a microRNA locus, *JAW* (71), in Arabidopsis. The mi-*JAW* targets *TCP4* that is normally expressed in parenchymatous cells; the highest expression level is usually seen in the most distal part of the leaf primordia. Overexpression of *JAW* causes downregulation of the *TCP4* mRNA level, epinastic growth of cotyledons, and crinkly, serrated leaves (71). Note that concave growth of the intervein was also recognized in mutants with a defect in the suppression of the class I *KNOX* gene in the leaf primordia, such as the *as1* mutant.

LEAF-SIZE CONTROL: COMPENSATION AND SPECIFIC MECHANISMS IN MULTICELLULAR ORGANS

Overall size is also an important factor for determining leaf morphology. For organ and body size in animals, "total mass control" seems to play a major role; altering the cell number and/or size usually does not affect the overall size or shape of organs (reviewed in 75). In animal organs, cells may be overproduced; apoptosis then appropriately adjusts the cell numbers in the organ (reviewed in

20). Thus, in animal organs, the cell number is not the definitive factor in determining organ size. As noted by Su & O'Farrell (86), "if mass does not increase, [cell cycling] will simply subdivide the same mass into smaller and smaller packets." In other words, total mass control should be a more important factor than control of cell cycling in determining animal organ and body sizes. In plants, the size-control system appears to lack the cell death-dependent adjustment of cell numbers (so-called "cell competition") (e.g., 21, 59) and is largely dependent on both cell size and cell numbers. In particular, leaf size is highly correlated to the number of leaf cells when natural variation and environmental effects on leaf size are considered (31, 53, 91). Moreover, as noted above, leaf-size variants due to altered cell proliferation are often accompanied by leaf-shape defects, especially in terms of the leaf index and/or the leaf-margin type. Leaf-shape control may thus depend on leaf-size control.

Recent research has revealed that controls on cell number and cell size interact during leaf organogenesis, as evidenced by the abnormal enlargement of leaf cells that appears to be triggered by an insufficient supply of cells in the lamina (e.g., 2, 17, 22, 35, 43, 65, 103) (**Figure 3**). This phenomenon causes partial cancellation of the leaf-area decrease and is thus referred to as "compensation" (4, 39, 90, 91, 93) or, more precisely, as "compensated cell enlargement," considering the unidirectional causal relationship between the defect in cell cycling and the accelerated cell enlargement. A similar phenomenon has also been reported for some animal systems (66, 104), suggesting that an organ-level adjustment system related to total cell volume may be universal among multicellular organisms. Additional studies on the compensatory system should provide a better understanding of the mechanisms of multicellular organogenesis.

Is total mass control in animal system, then, directly related to the compensated cell enlargement in plants? Compensated cell enlargement in leaves is often misunderstood to be a result of simple negative correlation between cell number and size within a given total leaf mass. For example, organismal theory is based on the idea that cell division merely follows a developmental plan, and thus a negative correlation could occur between cell number and size (42, 44). Indeed, size and number of cells are negatively correlated in an early embryo in which cell division simply decreases the cell volume. Negative correlation between cell number and cell size has also been reported in the pericarp of tomato fruits, and has been simply explained as being attributable to resource competition among sinks (7).

However, the compensated cell enlargement observed in leaf organogenesis differs from the above systems and is not a mere simple negative correlation between the number and size of cells. Leaf shapes and sizes have not been completely compensated at the wild-type level in all known mutants, and transgenics have exhibited compensation, developing smaller-sized leaves than wild types (**Figure 3**), suggesting a lack of total mass control in leaves. Second, increased cell proliferation simply increases leaf size, whereas decreased cell proliferation triggers compensation, again denying the role of total mass control in compensation. For example, a loss-of-function mutation in *AINTEGUMENTA* (*ANT*) or *ANGUSTIFOLIA3* (*AN3*) caused decreased cell numbers associated with an increased cell volume, whereas increased levels of expression of these genes caused an increased number of leaf cells with normal-sized cells (40, 58). Third, a decreased number of leaf cells does not necessarily trigger compensation, denying the simple negative correlation between cell number and size. For example, overexpression of the *ROT4* gene causes a decrease in cell numbers in the leaf-length direction but does not trigger compensation (63). Further, the authors' data suggest the existence of a decreased cell-number threshold that triggers compensated cell enlargement (39). Taken together, ideas such as total mass control and organismal theory cannot explain compensation in leaf morphogenesis.

Instead, existing data strongly suggest that the development of proper leaf size and shape requires genetic network interactions between processes of cell cycling and cell enlargement in the context of developmental control (neo-cell theory) (see 91, 93 for detailed discussions). Thus, the framework of leaf-shape and leaf-size control cannot be explained by the simple sum of regulators. Although many studies have attempted to reveal the genetic factors behind single cell-level control of the size or shape of multicellular organs such as leaves, organogenesis of multicellular organs must be controlled by a genetic network beyond the level of single-cell behavior. Understanding the detailed interactions of this genetic network for leaf development is indispensable for understanding mechanisms of not only leaf morphogenesis but also morphogenesis in multicellular organs in general.

How, then, is leaf-cell expansion accelerated in compensation? To date, the process is unclear, but some clues exist. First, a threshold level in decreased cell numbers appeared to trigger compensated cell enlargement (39). Interestingly, compensation was not triggered even when the cell number was significantly decreased by shutting down cytokinin signaling by multiple Arabidopsis *Histidine Kinase* (*AHK*) mutations (67), suggesting that cytokinin signaling may bridge genetic networks for cell proliferation and cell enlargement. Second, in plants, the ploidy level sometimes correlates with final cell volume (4a) but not necessarily with compensated cell enlargement. Both the *swp* mutant and overexpressor of *KRP2* have shown strong accelerated cell enlargement; the former had an increased ploidy level (2) and the latter had no enhanced endoreduplication (22). Our preliminary results also suggest that compensated cell enlargement may be governed by several genetic factors for cell expansion that do not affect the ploidy level (U. Fujikura, A. Ferjani, G. Horiguchi & H. Tsukaya, unpublished data). On the other hand, a parenchymatous cell-specific decrease (nearly half) in the number of leaf cells by the *lower cell density1-1*

(*lcd1-1*) mutation did not trigger compensating cell enlargement (3). This fact suggests that a simple decrease in the number of cells does not trigger the compensated cell enlargement. Further detailed analyses may reveal the mechanisms for the compensatory system and, moreover, for the total mass volume of multicellular organs.

OTHER TYPES OF "COMPENSATION" AND INTERACTIONS AMONG CELL TYPES IN A LEAF

The term "compensation" has also been used for other phenomena in leaf morphogenesis. For example, Aluru et al. (1) analyzed the anatomy of a variegated mutant, *immutans* (*im*), and reported that green sectors of the variegated *im* leaves were composed of palisade cells larger than wild-type palisade cells. These cells had higher rates of O_2 evolution and elevated chlorophyll *a/b* ratios. Because white sectors of the *im* leaves had small, photosynthetically inactive palisade cells, Aluru et al. (1) interpreted the accelerated enlargement of palisade cells in the green part as a result of an adaptive mechanism that "attempted to compensate for a lack of photosynthesis in the white sectors." Because Aluru et al. (1) analyzed only fully mature leaves, exactly when and how differential cell growth was triggered between the white and green sectors was unclear. Time-course analysis of the cell growth is required to examine the causal relationship.

Another interesting case of "compensation" was reported for the size of the integument that directly influences seed size (29). When the number of integument cells was decreased by overexpression of *KRP2*, as known for leaf cells, seed size was compensated by an enhanced enlargement of integument cells. Uniquely, this compensation was suppressed by mutation on the *HAIKU* gene that decreased the size of the endosperm enveloped by the integument (29), suggesting that the seed integument could adjust cell elongation to the size defined by the endosperm. This suggests that tension or turgor provided from the endosperm may control the degree of cell elongation in the covering integument. If so, this "compensation" might differ slightly in mechanism from that observed in leaves, because the compensated cell enlargement in leaves appears to be independent of the turgor provided by inner tissue. Further detailed analyses on this phenomenon may help clarify compensated cell enlargement in leaves.

PERSPECTIVE

Leaf morphogenesis apparently depends on coordinated growth of leaf cells, although this mechanism is not fully understood. Marcotrigiano (56) analyzed periclinal chloroplast chimeras of *Abutilon x hybrida*; those consisting of genotype G developed large green leaves, whereas those of genotype W developed small white leaves. Leaves from G-type plants were significantly larger than those from chimeras in which only the L2 layer was composed of W-type cells, suggesting that L1 and L3 are not critical to leaf-size determination. When half of the leaf was the chimera and the other half was the G-type, with the halves meeting at the midrib, the leaf became bent as the G-type half grew larger than the chimeric half. Thus, cells in an organ could pursue their developmental program even if their neighbors were genetically programmed to make a differently shaped organ. Furthermore, Marcotrigiano (56) reported that when a G-type cell clone was surrounded by W-type cells, the tissue consisting of G-type cells developed a leaf coordinated with the surrounding W-type cells. In contrast, if a clone of G-type cells were not completely surrounded by W-type cells, for example when a clone with G-type cells was situated at the margin of a leaf primordium, tissue derived from these G-type cells expanded and became larger than the other parts of the leaf governed by the W-type cells. Thus, positional signal(s) for the coordinated organogenesis of leaf primordia appear to be supplied from all directions to cells in a primordium, but only when cells of one type are in contact with cells of another. One such possible positional signal(s) may partially depend on the physical pressure of tissue from a biophysical viewpoint, as Marcotrigiano (56) suggested. Alternatively, diffusive chemical substances may also create a positional signal(s).

Taken together, leaf-shape determination can sometimes be explained by a simple relationship between cell-level function of a gene with leaf morphology, such as with the *AN* gene (47, 88, 98). However, large parts of leaf-shape determination seem attributable to complex interactions among genetic networks, as exemplified by compensated cell enlargement. Further analyses on the genetic and cell-to-cell interactions in leaf morphogenesis are required to understand the mechanisms of leaf-shape control (95a). Considering the complexity of genetic networks, a combination of mutational analyses and systems biology may provide important findings (4a).

SUMMARY POINTS

1. Development of a flat-shaped leaf blade on a leaf primordia by the plate meristem depends on the establishment of dorsoventrality in the primordia.

2. Plate meristem activity is gradually lost temporally and spatially from distal to proximal parts in leaf primordia of dicots. The presence/absence of a winged petiole seems to depend on the temporal and spatial control of the plate meristem in the leaf primordia.

3. Two-dimensional genetic controls of leaf shape can be divided into two axes: longitudinal and lateral, which help govern polar cell expansion and polar cell proliferation.

4. Margin variation can be at least partially attributed to the relative difference in leaf-cell proliferation in the mediolateral direction or along the contour of the leaf lamina.

5. Although leaf-size control is not yet fully understood, "compensated cell enlargement" seems to be triggered by a shortage in cell numbers in the leaf primordial and appears to be a key to understanding the role of cell-cell communication in determining leaf size and shape.

FUTURE ISSUES TO BE ADDRESSED

1. Further examination of relationships between the establishment of dorsoventrality and leaf-lamina growth is required. Research should particularly focus on the precise role(s) of the *ARP* gene family in leaf development.

2. The specific control on the number of leaf cells aligned along the leaf-width direction is not yet known. Positional information factors that "teach" leaf cells the polarities in the leaf primordia are also unknown.

3. An integrated understanding of the regulation of the leaf-margin type must also be obtained. Specifically, questions as to why some mutants have an integrated leaf margin and why others have serrated margins remain unanswered. Similarly, researchers do not yet know how the supply of cells is controlled in a leaf blade.

4. Mechanisms of "compensated cell enlargement" should be revealed to understand leaf-size control, as well as the control of organ size in multicellular organisms. Current data suggest that organogenesis of multicellular organs is controlled by a genetic network that functions beyond the level of single-cell behavior. Pursuing the knowledge of such organ-level control is the most important issue in this research field.

LITERATURE CITED

1. Aluru MR, Bae H, Wu D, Rodermel SR. 2001. The *Arabidopsis immutans* mutation affects plastid differentiation and the morphogenesis of white and green sectors in variegated plants. *Plant Physiol.* 127:67–77

2. Autran D, Jonak C, Belcram K, Beemster GTS, Kronenberger J, et al. 2002. Cell numbers and leaf development in *Arabidopsis*: a functional analysis of the *STRUWWELPETER* gene. *EMBO J.* 21:6036–49

3. Barth C, Conklin PL. 2003. The lower cell density of leaf parenchyma in the *Arabidopsis thaliana* mutant *lcd1-1* is associated with increased sensitivity to ozone and virulent *Pseudomonas syringae*. *Plant J.* 35:206–18

4. Beemster GTS, Fiorani F, Inzé D. 2003. Cell cycle: the key to plant growth control? *Trends Plant Sci.* 8:154–58

4a. Beemster GTS, Vercruysse S, De Veylder L, Kuiper M, Inzé D. 2006. The Arabidopsis leaf as a model system for investigating the role of cell cycle regulation in organ growth. *J. Plant Res.* 119:DOI 10.1007/s10265-005-0234-2

5. Beerling DJ, Osborne CP, Chaloner WG. 2001. Evolution of leaf-form in land plants linked to atmospheric CO_2 decline in the Late Palaeozoic era. *Nature* 410:352–54

6. Berná G, Robles P, Micol JL. 1999. A mutational analysis of leaf morphogenesis in *Arabidopsis thaliana*. *Genetics* 152:729–42

7. Bertin N. 2005. Analysis of the tomato fruit growth response to temperature and plant fruit load in relation to cell division, cell expansion and DNA endoreduplication. *Ann. Bot.* 95:439–47

8. Bharathan G, Goliber TE, Moore C, Kessler S, Pham T, Sinha NR. 2002. Homologies in leaf form inferred from *KNOX* gene expression during development. *Nature* 296:1858–60

9. Bichet A, Desnos T, Turner S, Grandjean O, Höfte H. 2001. *BOTERO1* is required for normal orientation of cortical microtubules and anisotropic cell expansion in *Arabidopsis*. *Plant J.* 25:137–48

10. Bowman JL. 2004. Class III HD-Zip gene regulation, the golden fleece of ARGONAUTE activity? *BioEssays* 26:938–42

11. Burk DH, Liu B, Zhong R, Morrison WH, Ye Z-H. 2001. A katanin-like protein regulates normal cell wall biosynthesis and cell elongation. *Plant Cell* 13:807–27

12. Byrne ME. 2005. Networks in leaf development. *Curr. Opin. Plant Biol.* 8:59–66

13. Byrne ME, Barley R, Curtis M, Arroyo JM, Dunham M, et al. 2000. Asymmetric leaves mediate leaf patterning and stem cell function in *Arabidopsis*. *Nature* 408:967–71

14. Candela H, Martínez-Laborda A, Micol JL. 1999. Venation pattern formation in *Arabidopsis thaliana* vegetative leaves. *Dev. Biol.* 205:205–16

15. Castellano MM, Sablowski R. 2005. Intercellular signaling in the transition from stem cells to organogenesis in meristems. *Curr. Opin. Plant Biol.* 8:26–31

16. Chinnadurai G. 2002. CtBP, an unconventional transcriptional corepressor in development and oncogenesis. *Mol. Cell* 9:213–24

17. Cho JW, Park SC, Shin EA, Kim CK, Han W, et al. 2004. Cyclin D1 and p22[ACK1] play opposite roles in plant growth and development. *Biochem. Biophys. Res. Commun.* 324:52–57

18. Cho K-H, Shindo T, Kim G-T, Nitasaka E, Tsukaya H. 2005. Characterization of a member of the *AN* subfamily, *IAN*, from *Ipomoea nil*. *Plant Cell Physiol.* 46:250–55

19. Clay NK, Nelson T. 2005. The recessive epigenetic *swellmap* mutation affects the expression of two step II splicing factors required for the transcription of the cell proliferation gene *STRUWWELPETER* and for the timing of cell cycle arrest in the *Arabidopsis* leaf. *Plant Cell* 17:1994–2008

20. Conlon I, Raff M. 1999. Size control in animal development. *Cell* 96:235–44

21. De la Cova C, Abril M, Bellosta P, Gallant P, Johnson LA. 2004. *Drosophila* Myc regulates organ size by inducing cell competition. *Cell* 117:107–16

22. De Veylder L, Beeckman T, Beemster GTS, Krols L, Terras F, et al. 2001. Functional analysis of cyclin-dependent kinase inhibitors of *Arabidopsis*. *Plant Cell* 13:1653–67

23. Dinneny JR, Yadegari R, Fischer RL, Yanofsky MF, Weigel D. 2004. The role of *JAGGED* in shaping lateral organs. *Development* 131:1101–10

24. Donnelly PM, Bonetta D, Tsukaya H, Dengler RE, Dengler N. 1999. Cell cycling and cell enlargement in developing leaves of *Arabidopsis*. *Dev. Biol.* 215:407–19

25. Evans MW, Grover FO. 1940. Developmental morphology of the growing point of the shoot and the inflorescence in grasses. *J. Agric. Res.* 61:481–520

26. Fleming AJ. 2005. Formation of primordia and phyllotaxy. *Curr. Opin. Plant Biol.* 8:53–58

27. Floyd SK, Bowman JL. 2004. Gene regulation: Ancient microRNA target sequences in plants. *Nature* 428:485–86

28. Folkers U, Kirik V, Schobinger U, Falk S, Krishnakumar S, et al. 2002. The cell morphogenesis gene *ANGUSTIFOLIA* encodes a CtBP/BARS-like protein and is involved in the control of the microtubule cytoskeleton. *EMBO J.* 21:1280–88

29. Garcia D, Fitz Gerald JN, Berger F. 2005. Maternal control of integument cell elongation and zygotic control of endosperm growth are coordinated to determine seed size in *Arabidopsis. Plant Cell* 17:52–60

30. Goliber T, Kessler S, Chen J-J, Bharathan G, Sinha N. 1999. Genetic, molecular, and morphological analysis of compound leaf development. *Curr. Topics Dev. Biol.* 43:259–90

31. Granier C, Turc O, Tardieu F. 2000. Co-ordination of cell division and tissue expansion in sunflower, tobacco, and pea leaves: dependence or independence of both processes? *J. Plant Growth Regul.* 19:45–54

32. Ha C-H, Jun J-H, Nam H-G, Fletcher JC. 2004. *BLADE-ON-PETIOLE1* encodes a BTB/POZ domain protein required for leaf morphogenesis in *Arabidopsis thaliana. Plant Cell Physiol.* 45:1361–70

33. Ha C-H, Kim G-T, Kim B-C, Jun J-H, Soh M-S, et al. 2003. The *BLADE-ON-PETIOLE* gene controls leaf pattern formation through regulation of meristematic activity. *Development* 130:161–72

34. Hake S, Smith HMS, Holtan H, Magnani E, Mele G, Ramirez J. 2004. The role of *knox* genes in plant development. *Annu. Rev. Cell Dev. Biol.* 20:125–51

35. Han W, Rhee H-I, Cho JW, Ku MSB, Song PS, Wang M-H. 2005. Overexpression of *Arabidopsis ACK1* alters leaf morphology and retards growth and development. *Biochem. Biophys. Res. Commun.* 330:887–90

36. Hanson J, Johannesson H, Engström, P. 2001. Sugar-dependent alterations in cotyledon and leaf development in transgenic plants expressing the HDZhdip gene *ATHB13. Plant Mol. Biol.* 45:247–62

37. Harrison CJ, Corley SB, Moylan EC, Alexander DL, Scotland RW, Langdale JA. 2005. Independent recruitment of a conserved developmental mechanism during leaf evolution. *Nature* 434:509–14

38. Hepworth SR, Zhang Y, McKim S, Li X, Haughn GW. 2005. BLADE-ON-PETIOLE-dependent signaling controls leaf and floral patterning in *Arabidopsis. Plant Cell* 17:1434–48

39. Horiguchi G, Ferjani A, Fujikura U, Tsukaya H. 2006. Coordination of cell proliferation and cell expansion in the control of leaf size in *Arabidopsis thaliana. J. Plant Res.* 119:DOI 10.1007/s10265-005-0232-4

40. Horiguchi G, Kim G-T, Tsukaya H 2005. The transcription factor AtGRF5 and the transcription coactivator AN3 regulate cell proliferation in leaf primordia of *Arabidopsis thaliana. Plant J.* 43:68–78

41. Deleted in proof

42. Inzé D. 2005. Green light for the cell cycle. *EMBO J.* 24:657–62

43. Ito T, Kim GT, Shinozaki K. 2000. Disruption of an *Arabidopsis* cytoplasmic ribosomal protein S13-homologous gene by transposon-mediated mutagenesis causes aberrant growth and development. *Plant J.* 22:257–64

44. Kaplan DR, Hagemann W. 1991. The relationship of cell and organism in vascular plants. *BioScience* 41:693–703

45. Kasschau KD, Xie Z, Allen E, Llave C, Chapman EJ, et al. 2003. P1/HC-Pro, a viral suppressor of RNA silencing, interferes with *Arabidopsis* development and miRNA function. *Dev. Cell.* 4:205–17

46. Kim G-T, Fujioka S, Kozuka T, Tax FE, Takatsuto S, et al. 2005. CYP90C1 and CYP90D1 are involved in the different steps in the brassinosteroids biosynthesis pathway in *Arabidopsis thaliana. Plant J.* 41:710–21

47. Kim G-T, Shoda K, Tsuge T, Cho K-H, Uchimiya H, et al. 2002. The *ANGUSTIFOLIA* gene of *Arabidopsis*, a plant *CtBP* gene, regulates leaf-cell expansion, the arrangement of cortical microtubules in leaf cells and expression of a gene involved in cell-wall formation. *EMBO J.* 21:1267–79

48. Kim G-T, Tsukaya H, Saito Y, Uchimiya H. 1999. Changes in the shapes of leaves and flowers upon overexpression of the novel cytochrome P450 in *Arabidopsis. Proc. Natl. Acad. Sci. USA* 96:9433–37

49. Kim G-T, Tsukaya H, Uchimiya H. 1998. The *ROTUNDIFOLIA3* gene of *Arabidopsis thaliana* encodes a new member of the cytochrome P450 family that is required for the regulated polar elongation of leaf cells. *Genes Dev.* 12:2381–91

50. Kim G-T, Yano S, Kozuka T, Tsukaya H. 2005. Photomorphogenesis of leaves: shade-avoidance syndrome and differentiation of sun/shade leaves. *Photochem. Photobiol. Sci.* 4:770–74

51. Kim JH, Kende H. 2004. A transcriptional coactivator, AtGIF1, is involved in regulating leaf growth and morphology in *Arabidopsis. Proc. Natl. Acad. Sci. USA* 101:13374–79

52. Kim M, McCormick S, Timmermans M, Sinha N. 2003. The expression domain of *PHANTASTICA* determines leaflet placement in compound leaves. *Nature* 424:438–43

53. Körner C, Menendez-Riedl SP, John PCL. 1989. Why are Bonsai plants small? A consideration of cell size. *Aust. J. Plant Physiol.* 16:443–48

54. Kozuka T, Horiguchi G, Kim G-T, Ohgishi M, Sakai T, Tsukaya H. 2005. The different growth responses of the *Arabidopsis thaliana* leaf blade and the petiole during shade avoidance are regulated by photoreceptors and sugar. *Plant Cell Physiol.* 46:213–23

55. Li J, Nam KH. 2001. Regulation of brassinosteroid signaling by a GSK3/SHAGY-like kinase. *Science* 295:1299–1301

56. Marcotrigiano M. 2001. Genetic mosaics and the analysis of leaf development. *Int. J. Plant Sci.* 162:513–25

57. Maksymowych R. 1963. Cell division and cell elongation in leaf development of *Xanthium pennsylvanicum. Am. J. Bot.* 50:891–901

58. Mizukami Y, Fischer RL. 2000. Plant organ size control: AINTEGUMENTA regulates growth and cell numbers during organogenesis. *Proc. Natl. Acad. Sci. USA* 97:942–47

59. Moreno E, Basler K. 2004. dMyc transforms cells into super-competitors. *Cell* 117:117–29

60. Nagatani A, Chory J, Furuya M. 1991. Phytochrome B is not detectable in the *hy3* mutant of *Arabidopsis*, which is deficient in responding to end-of-day far-red light treatments. *Plant Cell Physiol.* 32:1119–22

61. Nakaya M, Tsukaya H, Murakami N, Kato M. 2002. Brassinosteroids control the proliferation of the leaf cells in *Arabidopsis thaliana. Plant Cell Physiol.* 43:239–44

62. Nardini M, Spano S, Cericola C, Pesce A, Massaro A, et al. 2003. CtBP/BARS: a dual-function protein involved in transcription corepression, and Golgi membrane fission. *EMBO J.* 22:3122–30

63. Narita NN, Moore S, Horiguchi G, Kubo M, Demura T, et al. 2004. Over-expression of a novel small peptide ROTUNDIFOLIA4 decreases of cell proliferation and alters leaf shape in *Arabidopsis. Plant J.* 38:699–713

64. Nath U, Crawford BCW, Carpenter R, Coen E. 2003. Genetic control of surface curvature. *Science* 299:1404–7

65. Nelissen H, Clarke JH, De Block M, De Block S, Vanderhaeghen R, et al. 2003. DRL1, a homolog of the yeast TOK4/KTI12 protein, has a function in meristem activity and organ growth in plants. *Plant Cell* 15:639–54

66. Neufeld TN, de la Cruz AFA, Johnston LA, Edgar BA. 1998. Coordination of growth and cell division in the *Drosophila* wing. *Cell* 93:1183–93

67. Nishimura C, Ohashi Y, Sato S, Kato T, Tabata S, Ueguchi C. 2004. Histidine kinase homologs that act as cytokinin receptors possess overlapping functions in the regulation of shoot and root growth in *Arabidopsis*. *Plant Cell* 16:1365–77

68. Ohno CK, Reddy GV, Heisler MGB, Meyerowitz EM. 2004. The *Arabidopsis JAGGED* gene encodes a zinc finger protein that promotes leaf tissue development. *Development* 131:1111–22

69. O'Neill MA, Eberhard S, Alberstein P, Darvill AG. 2001. Requirement of borate cross-linking of cell wall rhamnogalacturonan II for *Arabidopsis* growth. *Science* 294:846–49

70. Ori N, Eshed Y, Chuck G, Bowman JL, Hake S. 2000. Mechanisms that control *knox* gene expression in the *Arabidopsis* shoot. *Development* 127:5523–32

71. Palatnik JF, Allen E, Wu X, Schommer C, Schwab R, et al. 2003. Control of leaf morphogenesis by microRNAs. *Nature* 425:257–63

72. Péréz-Péréz JM, Serrano-Cartagene JS, Micol JL. 2002. Genetic analysis of natural variations in the architecture of *Arabidopsis thaliana* vegetative leaves. *Genetics* 162:893–915

73. Pien S, Wyrzykowska J, McQueen-Mason S, Smart C, Fleming A. 2001. Local expression of expansion induces the entire process of leaf development and modifies leaf shape. *Proc. Natl. Acad. Sci. USA* 98:11812–17

74. Poethig RS, Sussex IM. 1985. The developmental morphology and growth dynamics of the tobacco leaf. *Planta* 165:158–69

75. Potter CJ, Xu T. 2001. Mechanisms of size control. *Curr. Opin. Genet. Dev.* 11:279–86

76. Prigge MJ, Wagner DR. 2001. The *Arabidopsis SERRATE* gene encodes a Zinc-finger protein required for normal shoot development. *Plant Cell* 13:1263–79

77. Pryer KM, Schneider H, Smith AR, Cranfill R, Wolf PG, et al. 2001. Horsetails and ferns are a monophyletic group and the closest living relatives to seed plants. *Nature* 409:618–22

78. Qiu J-L, Jilk R, Marks MD, Szymanski DB. 2002. The *Arabidopsis SPIKE1* gene is required for normal cell shape control and tissue development. *Plant Cell* 14:101–18

79. Reed JW, Nagpal P, Poole DS, Furuya M, Chory J. 1993. Mutations in the gene for the red/far-red light receptor phytochrome B alter cell elongation and physiological responses throughout *Arabidopsis* development. *Plant Cell* 5:147–57

80. Robles P, Micol JL. 2001. Genome-wide linkage analysis of *Arabidopsis* genes required for leaf development. *Mol. Gen. Genet.* 266:12–19

81. Semiarti E, Ueno Y, Tsukaya H, Iwakawa H, Machida C, Machida Y. 2001. The *ASYMMETRIC LEAVES2* gene of *Arabidopsis thaliana* regulates formation of a symmetric lamina, establishment of venation and repression of meristem-related homeobox genes in leaves. *Development* 128:1771–83

82. Serrano-Cartagene JS, Robles P, Ponce MR, Micol JL. 1999. Genetic analysis of leaf form mutants from the *Arabidopsis* Information Service Collection. *Mol. Gen. Genet.* 261:725–39

83. Siegfried KR, Eshed Y, Baum SF, Otsuga D, Drews GN, Bowman JL. 1999. Members of the *YABBY* gene family specify abaxial cell fate in *Arabidopsis*. *Development* 126:4117–28

84. Stearn WT. 1992. *Botanical Latin*, 4th ed. Devon, UK: David & Charles

85. Streatfield SJ, Weber A, Kinsman EA, Häusler RE, Li J, et al. 1999. The phos-phoenolpyruvate/phosphate translocator is required for phenolic metabolism, palisade cell development, and plastid-dependent nuclear gene expression. *Plant Cell* 11:1609–21

86. Su TT, O'Farrell P. 1998. Size control: Cell proliferation does not equal growth. *Curr. Biol.* 8:R687–R689

87. Tamaoki M, Nishimura A, Aida M, Tasaka M, Matsuoka M. 1999. Transgenic tobacco over-expressing a homeobox gene shows a developmental interaction between leaf mor-phogenesis and phyllotaxy. *Plant Cell Physiol.* 40:657–67

88. Tsuge T, Tsukaya H, Uchimiya H. 1996. Two independent and polarized processes of cell elongation regulate leaf blade expansion in *Arabidopsis thaliana* (L.) Heynh. *Development* 122:1589–600

89. Tsukaya H. 1995. Developmental genetics of leaf morphogenesis in dicotyledonous plants. *J. Plant Res.* 108:407–16

90. Tsukaya H. 2002. Leaf development. In *The Arabidopsis Book*, CR Somerville, EM Meyerowitz, eds. Rockville, MD: Am. Soc. Plant Biol. doi/10.1199/tab.0072, **http://www.aspb.org/downloads/arabidopsis/tsukaya.pdf**

91. Tsukaya H. 2002. Interpretation of mutants in leaf morphology: genetic evidence for a compensatory system in leaf morphogenesis that provides a new link between cell and organismal theory. *Int. Rev. Cytol.* 217:1–39

92. Tsukaya H. 2002. The leaf index: heteroblasty, natural variation, and the genetic control of polar processes of leaf expansion. *Plant Cell Physiol.* 43:372–78

93. Tsukaya H. 2003. Organ shape and size: a lesson from studies of leaf morphogenesis. *Curr. Opin. Plant Biol.* 6:57–62

94. Tsukaya H. 2005. Leaf shape: genetic controls and environmental factors. *Int. J. Dev. Biol.* 49:547–55

95. Tsukaya H. 2006. A new member of the CtBP/BARS family from plants: Angustifo-lia. In *CtBP Family Proteins*, G. Chinnadurai, ed., ch. 12. Georgetown, TX: G. Landes Biosci.

95a. Tsukaya H, Beemster GTS. 2006. Genetics, cell cycle and cell expansion in organogenesis in plants. *J. Plant Res.* 119:DOI 10.1007/s10265-005-0254-y

96. Tsukaya H, Kozuka T, Kim G-T. 2002. Genetic control of petiole length in *Arabidopsis thaliana*. *Plant Cell Physiol.* 43:1221–28

97. Tsukaya H, Shoda K, Kim G-T, Uchimiya H. 2000. Heteroblasty in *Arabidopsis thaliana* (L.) Heynh. *Planta* 210:536–42

98. Tsukaya H, Tsuge T, Uchimiya H. 1994. The cotyledon: a superior system for studies of leaf development. *Planta* 195:309–12

99. Tsukaya H, Uchimiya H. 1997. Genetic analyses of developmental control of serrated margin of leaf blades in *Arabidopsis*—combination of mutational analysis of leaf morpho-genesis with characterization of a specific marker gene, which expresses in hydathodes and stipules in *Arabidopsis*. *Mol. Gen. Genet.* 256:231–38

100. Van der Graaff E, Dulk-Ras AD, Hooykaas PJJ, Keller B. 2000. Activation tagging of the *LEAFY PETIOLE* gene affects leaf petiole development in *Arabidopsis thaliana*. *Development* 127:4971–80

101. Van Steenis CGGJ. 1981. *Rheophytes of the World*. Alpen aan den Rijn, The Netherlands: Sijthoff and Noordhoff

102. Waites R, Hudson A. 1995. *Phantastica*: a gene required for dorsoventrality in leaves of *Antirrhinum majus*. *Development* 121:2143–54

103. Wang H, Zhou Y, Gilmer S, Whitwill S, Fowke LC. 2000. Expression of the plant cyclin-dependent kinase inhibitor ICK1 affects cell division, plant growth and morphology. *Plant J.* 24:613–23

104. Weigmann K, Cohen SM, Lehner CF. 1997. Cell cycle progression, growth and patterning in imaginal discs despite inhibition of cell division after inactivation of *Drosophila* Cdc2 kinase. *Development* 124:3555–63

105. Wen J, Lease KA, Walker JC. 2004. DVL, a novel class of small polypeptides: overexpression alters *Arabidopsis* development. *Plant J.* 37:668–77

106. Wyrzykowska J, Pien S, Shen WH, Fleming AJ. 2002. Manipulation of leaf shape by modulation of cell division. *Development* 129:957–64

107. Yamaguchi T, Tsukaya H. 2006. ROTUNDIFOLIA4, a plant-specific small peptide involved in the polar cell proliferation of leaves in *Arabidopsis thaliana*. In *Handbook of Biologically Active Peptides*, AJ Kastin, ed. San Diego: Elsevier. In press

108. Zimmermann, W. 1953. Main results of the "telome theory." *Paleobotany* 1:456–70

Mosses as Model Systems for the Study of Metabolism and Development

David Cove,[1,2] Magdalena Bezanilla,[3] Phillip Harries,[4] and Ralph Quatrano[2]

[1] Center for Plant Sciences, University of Leeds, Leeds LS2 9JT, United Kingdom; email: d.j.cove@leeds.ac.uk

[2] Department of Biology, Washington University, St. Louis, Missouri 63130-4899

[3] Department of Biology, University of Massachusetts, Amherst, Massachusetts 01002-9297

[4] Plant Biology Division, Samuel Roberts Noble Foundation, Ardmore, Oklahoma 73401

Annu. Rev. Plant Biol.
2006. 57:497–520

The *Annual Review of Plant Biology* is online at
plant.annualreviews.org

doi: 10.1146/
annurev.arplant.57.032905.105338

First published online as a
Review in Advance on
February 1, 2006

1543-5008/06/
0602-0497$20.00

Key Words

auxin, cytokinin, abscisic acid, cell polarity, cytoskeleton

Abstract

The haploid gametophyte stage of the moss life cycle is amenable to genetic and biochemical studies. Many species can be cultured on simple defined media, where growth is rapid, making them ideal material for metabolic studies. Developmental responses to hormones and to environmental inputs can be studied both at the level of individual cells and in multicellular tissues. The protonemal stage of gametophyte development comprises cell filaments that extend by the serial division of their apical cells, allowing the investigation of the generation and modification of cell polarity and the role of the cytoskeleton in these processes. Molecular techniques including gene inactivation by targeted gene replacement or by RNA interference, together with the nearly completed sequencing of the *Physcomitrella patens* genome, open the way for detailed study of the functions of genes involved in both development and metabolism.

Contents

INTRODUCTION

This review, a companion to one published earlier this year (27), which concentrated on the genetics of *Physcomitrella patens*, does not deal with genetic topics in detail, but concentrates on metabolic and developmental studies, many of which have exploited genetic techniques. Most such studies have been carried out on a limited number of species, principally *Funaria hygrometrica*, *P. patens*, and *Ceratodon purpureus*.

The potential utility of mosses for developmental studies was recognized more than 50 years ago (6, 7, 117). In addition to their simplicity for genetic studies, the attractiveness of mosses for studying metabolism lies in their ease of culture under defined and controlled conditions, and the simplicity of their tissues, particularly in the gametophyte stage, makes developmental studies especially attractive.

Mosses, like most plants, show an alternation of generations. The haploid gametophyte stage is dominant, and constitutes most of the familiar moss plant. Gametes are produced on gametophores, shoots bearing leaf-like structures. Different species show a range of sexual morphology, some producing male and female gametes on the same shoot, some on different shoots but on the same plant, and some having distinct and separate male and female plants. This makes mosses attractive for evolutionary studies.

Life Cycle

Cove's work (27) contains details of the life cycle of *P. patens*. **Figure 1** illustrates the life cycle diagrammatically and **Figure 2** shows images of different stages. A detailed description of the moss life cycle is not given here, but reference is made to aspects of the life cycle in the relevant sections of this review. Like many moss species, including *F. hygrometrica* and *C. purpureus*, *P. patens* has a vigorous and persistent filamentous stage, the protonema. In *F. hygrometrica*, two types of protonemal cell are clearly differentiated, chloronema and caulonema, the former having an assimilatory and the latter an adventitious role. This distinction is less marked in *P. patens* and is much less apparent in *C. purpureus*. The protonemal stage in some species (e.g., *Pottia intermedia*) is transitory and is absent in a few (e.g., *Spagnum*). Gemmae, specialized cells with a role in propagation, are produced by protonema of many moss species. Duckett et al. (40) gives a review of protonemal morphogenesis in more than 300 moss species.

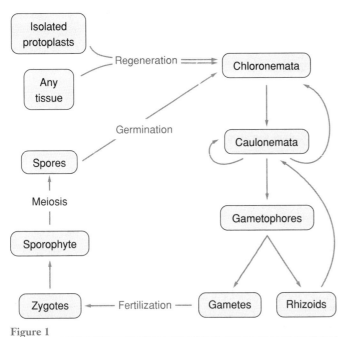

Figure 1

Life cycle of *P. patens*. All stages are haploid except for zygotes and sporophytes.

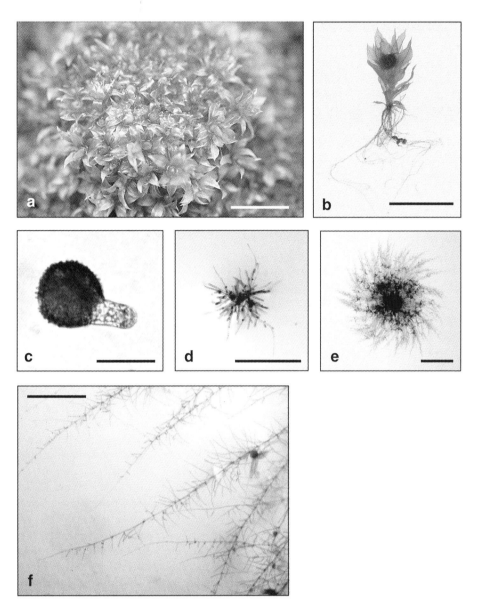

Figure 2

Stages in the life cycle of *P. patens*. (*a*) Gametophyte with abundant sporophytes. Scale bar: 10 mm.
(*b*) Dissected gametophore with a sporophyte in its apex. The spore capsule is borne on a very short seta,
and is therefore loosely surrounded by gametophore tissue. Abundant pigmented rhizoids originate
from the base of the gametophore. Scale bar: 5 mm. (*c*) Germinating spore. Scale bar: 50 μm.
(*d*) Seven-day-old sporeling. The first rapidly growing caulonemal filaments can be seen emerging from
the central chloronemal tissue. Scale bar: 500 μm. (*e*) Twenty-two-day-old culture. Scale bar: 10 mm.
(*f*) Detail of 22-day-old culture. The main axes are caulonemal filaments, extending by the division of
their apical cells. Most subapical cells have divided to produce one or two side branches, the majority of
which have developed into chloronemal filaments, but a few of which are developing into gametophores.
Scale bar: 1 mm. All photographs except (*a*) are of cultures growing on basal medium solidified with agar.
The culture in (*a*) is growing on a commercial compost.

METABOLIC STUDIES

Gametophyte: the haploid stage of the life cycle, comprising protonema and gametophores, upon which gametes are produced

Gametophores: leafy shoots, arising as side branches of caulonemal filaments, upon which archegonia and antheridia develop

Antheridia: male gametangia, in which motile male gametes (spermatozoids) are produced

Archegonia: female gametangia, in which female gametes are produced

Caulonema(ta): rapidly growing filament containing cells with few poorly developed chloroplasts, the adventitious component of protonemal tissue (q.v.)

Chloronema(ta): slow-growing filament containing cells with many large chloroplasts, the assimilatory component of protonemal tissue (q.v.)

Most bryophytes can be cultured on simple defined media (38), and it is possible to grow some species in continuous culture (17, 33, 57). Bryophytes are a rich source of metabolites (8, 58). The availability of both forward and reverse genetic techniques makes bryophytes superb potential material for metabolic studies. This potential is now beginning to be exploited, but metabolic studies are still not extensive.

Engel (41) isolated the first auxotrophic mutants of mosses in *P. patens*. These included mutants requiring vitamins for growth. Subsequent studies using *P. patens* have added further auxotrophs, mutants requiring sucrose, and mutants unable to utilize nitrate as a nitrogen source (73). In no case has the gene associated with the mutant phenotype been isolated.

Studies using reverse genetic approaches are now increasing. This review does not attempt to catalogue such studies but illustrates their potential by focusing on two examples.

The first example is the study of sulfur assimilation. Plants, like fungi and bacteria, acquire sulfur by the reduction of sulfate ions, by way of sulfite, to sulfide and thence to the sulfur-containing amino acids. The reduction of sulfate to sulfite may proceed by two possible routes. The formation of adenosine 5'-phosphosulfate (APS) from ATP and sulfate is catalyzed by the enzyme ATP sulfurylase. APS may then be reduced to sulfite by APS reductase, or alternatively, be phosphorylated by APS kinase to form phosphoadenosine 5'-phosphosulfate (PAPS), which is then reduced to sulfite by PAPS reductase. To investigate the route used by *P. patens*, the APS reductase gene, which is present in the genome in a single copy, was disrupted by targeted gene replacement (77), exploiting the very high rate at which recombination occurs in *P. patens* between transforming DNA and homologous genomic sequences (27). Although this resulted in the complete absence of APS reductase activity, and of the APS reductase gene

transcript, knockout plants were still able to utilize sulfate as their sole source of sulfur (77), and sulfate assimilation was only reduced by about 50%, showing that a second route for sulfate assimilation must exist in *P. patens*. A putative *P. patens* gene for PAPS reductase has been identified and inactivation of this gene by homologous recombination should establish if this gene is required for the alternative route.

The next step in sulfate assimilation is converting sulfite to sulfide by sulfite reductase. This enzyme is also coded for by a single-copy gene in *P. patens*, and has been inactivated by homologous recombination (G. Wiedemann, S. Kopriva & R. Reski, unpublished data). Although knockout plants show some retardation of growth, they can still use sulfate as the sole source of sulfur, and it has been proposed that this may be because nitrite reductase, an enzyme of nitrate assimilation, also has sulfite reductase activity (G. Wiedemann, S. Kopriva & R. Reski, unpublished data). These studies have already advanced knowledge of the pathways of sulfate assimilation in plants and further studies utilizing homologous recombination to inactivate other genes should soon characterize the metabolic network responsible.

The role of sugar metabolism in developmental signaling provides a second example of a metabolic study in *P. patens*. The gene coding for the major hexokinase, Hxk1, has been disrupted (92). Hxk1 knockout mutants have only about 20% of the wild-type glucose phosphorylating activity, indicating that this gene codes for the major *P. patens* hexokinase. Consistent with this, growth in darkness on medium containing glucose is much reduced in the mutant compared to the wild type (92). Another effect of the inactivation of the gene is to eliminate the effect of glucose on the induction of caulonemal filaments.

In *Saccharomyces cerevisiae*, the product of the Hxk2 gene, the major hexokinase, also plays a role in glucose repression. A protein kinase encoded by Snf1 forms part of the chain leading to the transcriptional shut down of carbon catabolism in the presence of glucose. The Hxk2 hexokinase is needed for inhibiting Snf1 by glucose, but details of its involvement are not clear. There is some evidence that similar systems may exist in plants and *P. patens* provides excellent material to advance these studies (113). Two Snf-related genes, Snf1a and Snf1b, have been cloned from *P. patens*, and the genes have been inactivated, both singly and in combination. Strains in which only one of the genes was inactivated have no obvious phenotype, but the double knockout strain, in which no Snf1-like kinase activity can be detected, has a number of developmental abnormalities, including an overproduction of caulonemata, which are opposite to the effects shown by the Hxk1 knockout strain. This is consistent with energy supply being involved in the control of the balance between chloronemata and caulonemata, and with both the Hxk1 gene and the Snf1a and Snf1b genes playing a role in the control and monitoring of energy supply (114). Another unexpected pleiotropic effect of the *snf1a snf1b* double mutant is its inability to grow in a light-dark cycle, conditions under which wild-type strains of *P. patens* thrive (113), suggesting that these gene products are necessary for the metabolic adjustments required for survival in darkness. These studies should go on to elucidate whether or not the link between hexokinase and the snf1 gene products is direct.

DEVELOPMENTAL STUDIES

Hormone Synthesis and Action

Auxin. In mosses, exogenous auxin induces chloronemal to caulonemal differentiation and inhibits chloronemal branching (4, 26, 49, 109, 114). The mosses *F. hygrometrica* and *P. patens* both contain at least one native auxin, indole-3-acetic acid (IAA) in gametophytic tissue (5, 60). The use of a β-glucuronidase (GUS) reporter gene driven by the auxin inducible promoters GH3 and DH5 has been used to determine auxin levels in different *P.*

patens tissues (15). GUS staining reveals that all cell types are capable of responding to auxin, although the strongest GUS expression was found in young, actively growing cells of protonemal and gametophore tissue.

The isolation of *P. patens* mutants resistant to the auxin analog, 1-naphthalene acetic acid (NAR mutants) (4) reveals a connection between auxin sensitivity and cytokinin production. When category 2 NAR mutants are treated with auxin, they show increased chloronemal production in comparison to wild type and produce no gametophores. These mutants are restored to wild-type morphology by cytokinin treatment, indicating that category 2 mutants are defective in cytokinin production. Likewise, mutants resistant to the cytokinin analog, 6-benzyl aminopurine (BAR mutants) can be rescued by exogenous auxin and are thus likely defective in auxin biosynthesis. Dependency of cytokinin-induced bud formation upon auxin concentration was first noted in the moss *Aocectangium thomsonii* (22) and has been interpreted as a necessity for auxin to create target cells competent for cytokinin response (79). Experiments in which the medium supply is continuously replaced confirm that in *P. patens* and *Physcomitium sphaericum* auxin is required for caulonemata production, and that cytokinin does not induce bud formation in the absence of auxin (26). Although more remains to be learned about the connection between these two hormones, these mutants demonstrate that sensitivity of *P. patens* to either auxin or cytokinin requires the presence of both hormones.

Relatively little is known regarding auxin-signaling pathways in moss. Work in *P. patens*, however, has begun to reveal the complex and diverse signaling cascades in which auxin plays a role. The auxin antagonist, naphthylphthalamic acid (NPA), was used to demonstrate that auxin efflux into the media is required for protoplasts to establish cellular polarity necessary for asymmetric division (13). This auxin efflux precedes and seems to be required for a polar redistribution of calcium channels. It

GUS:
β-glucuronidase

was recently shown that chloronemal tip cells of *F. hygrometrica* respond to auxin treatment with a rapid influx of calcium ions (Ca^{2+}) into the cell, followed by establishment of a tip to base Ca^{2+} gradient (14). A similar response was also noted in *F. hygrometrica* treated with cytokinin (53).

Evidence integrating auxin and light-receptor signaling was provided by the disruption of cryptochrome genes (blue-light receptors), which increases sensitivity of *P. patens* to exogenous auxin and suppresses auxin-induced gene expression (59). It is proposed that blue light acts to suppress auxin sensitivity by downregulating the expression of auxin-induced genes. In other experiments, auxin induced the expression of the homeodomain gene *Pphb7*, which had been implicated in rhizoid differentiation (100). The establishment of these links between auxin and major developmental regulators such as light signaling and homeodomain genes emphasizes the critical and complex role that auxin and other hormones play in plant growth and development.

Cytokinin. Treating mosses with cytokinins has long been known to induce bud formation (51). The strength of the cytokinin response in mosses has made them attractive plant models for studying cytokinin perception and signaling. The enhancement of bud production in response to cytokinin has been demonstrated in more than 20 species of moss (28) including *P. patens* (4). Cytokinin treatment of *P. patens* induces a large increase in gametophore production resulting from the formation of buds on caulonemal filaments, and also in some cases chloronemal filaments (4, 97).

The haploidy of moss gametophyte tissue makes mutant isolation relatively straightforward. By screening a mutagenized population of *P. patens*, 25 gametophore over-producing (OVE) mutants have been identified (3), one class of which cross feeds adjacent wild-type cultures, to overproduce gametophores, suggesting that these mutants might be cytokinin overproducers. This was confirmed by demonstrating that these mutants produce greatly elevated levels of the cytokinins isopentenyladenine and zeatin in their growth media (120, 122). Complementation analysis between 15 OVE mutants showed that 14 are recessive, and are thus likely loss-of-function mutants. Seven of these mutants were grouped into three complementation groups (44). The identities of these genes remain to be elucidated. Isolating a temperature-sensitive OVE mutant from *P. patens* that strongly overproduces cytokinin at 25°C (approximately 260 times wild-type levels) represents a valuable tool for further characterizing cytokinin response and synthesis in moss (104).

Biochemical techniques have also been used to identify proteins involved in the moss cytokinin response. Using radio labeling, coupled with sodium dodecyl sulfate-polyacrylamide gel electrophoresis (SDS-PAGE) analysis, cytokinins induce expression of a 14-kDA extracellular protein in *P. patens* (91). Additionally, photo-affinity labeling with a cytokinin agonist identified a protein potentially involved in cytokinin signaling (47). Although the function of these proteins remains unknown in mosses, the identification of proteins involved with cytokinin signaling and response is critical to achieving an understanding of cytokinin- related processes.

A proteomic approach has identified eight cytokinin upregulated proteins that comprise three key energy-conversion enzymes (67). This reflects the strong energy requirement associated with the morphological changes induced by cytokinin. Additionally, recent work with phospholipase C mutants implicated the phosphoinostitide (PI)-signaling pathway in the cytokinin response (96). In *P. patens*, phospholipase C mutants show reduced gametophore formation and a loss of sensitivity to exogenous cytokinin.

The mode of cytokinin synthesis is still unclear. Because tRNA hydrolysis provides a possible source of cytokinins (21), research has attempted to distinguish this possibility from de novo cytokinin synthesis. When *P. patens* OVE mutants are fed radio-labeled adenine, it is rapidly converted to isopentenyladenine, which in turn is excreted into the culture medium (121), providing strong evidence for de novo synthesis of cytokinin in *P. patens* and arguing against tRNA degradation as the route of cytokinin production. Further support for de novo synthesis comes from the finding that tRNA levels in OVE mutants are comparable to wild type (93). Additionally, ribose to base conversion, the last step of isopentenyladenine formation, is upregulated in OVE mutants (104).

To date, relatively little work has focused on cytokinin metabolism in mosses. Following feeding *P. patens* with labeled cytokinins, the major metabolites are adenine and adenine nucleotides (123). The recent cloning of an adenosine kinase from *P. patens* and the demonstration of its ability to phosphorylate cytokinin in vivo provides evidence that moss can indeed metabolize cytokinin to its nucleotide in a single step (116).

Abscisic acid. In angiosperms, abscisic acid (ABA) plays a key role in seed development, including the control of the synthesis of nutrient reserves, desiccation tolerance, the acquisition of dormancy, as well as the inhibition of the developmental transition from embryonic to vegetative growth. ABA also mediates, at least in part, adaptation to stresses during vegetative growth, e.g., temperature extremes, wounding, and drought.

ABA is present in bryophytes and evidence for a signaling pathway has been clearly established (see below), but its role(s) has not been elucidated. Bryophytes represent examples of the first land plants, and as such had to adjust to environmental stresses not found in water. Consequently, mechanisms have evolved to cope with drought and other stresses that may represent the earliest form of a stress-signaling pathway. Most research on ABA in bryophytes has concentrated on the role of ABA in acquiring tolerance to environmental stresses.

Less than 10% of cells of *P. patens* can survive a slow drop in temperature to 4°C, but pretreatment with ABA significantly increases the survival rate (86) and increases the expression of 14 ABA-responsive genes within 24 hours, indicating not only that an ABA response pathway is operative, but that the resulting enhancement of freezing tolerance is associated with an increase in specific gene expression. Treatment with sodium chloride and mannitol also enhances freezing tolerance and increases the expression of 11 of the 14 ABA-responsive genes. These results suggest that at least these 11 genes are likely responsive to multiple stresses. It was recently shown that freezing injury in *P. patens* results in ultrastructural changes that do not occur when ABA is added prior to the cold treatment (90). The ABA treatment also increases the osmotic concentration of the protonemal cells by accumulating free soluble sugars, which may mitigate the freezing-induced structural changes and lead to freezing tolerance. Freezing tolerance of protonemal cells is greatly increased by incubating at 0°C for several days (87). This treatment results in the accumulation of transcripts of Late Embryo Accumulating (LEA) and "boiling soluble" proteins. Both of these classes of proteins play a major role in protecting cells during water stress in desiccating seeds and vegetative tissues of angiosperms.

Protonema of *F. hygrometrica* tolerate slow desiccation but not rapid dehydration. Application of ABA enables protonemal tissue to survive rapid drying and is correlated with increases in endogenous ABA during drying (124). ABA exerts its influence in this system through specific proteins that are synthesized during drying, some of which resemble dehydrins (16, 103). It has also been reported that short, thick-walled desiccation-tolerant protonemal cells form under the influence of desiccation or ABA in *Aloina aloides* (50) and *Diphyscium foliosum* (39).

In *Atrichum androgynum*, ABA treatment or partial dehydration increases resistance to desiccation-induced cation leakage (9). Pretreatment of *Atrichum undulatum* with

ABA: abscisic acid

PSII: photosystem II

ABA also increases desiccation tolerance (11). More specifically, ABA treatment improves the tolerance of photosystem II (PSII) to water stress by allowing PSII to recover faster. Other parameters of photosynthesis that were measured also indicate that ABA allows recovery of photosynthetic damage during desiccation much faster than untreated tissue. This protective effect of ABA on photosynthesis might explain, in part, how ABA has a more general protective effect on many different stresses. It was later shown that pretreatment with ABA induces the synthesis of proteins that enhance desiccation tolerance in *Atrichum* (10). Interestingly, the ABA-induced desiccation tolerance is much less when plants are pretreated with ABA in the dark. Red light could not be substituted for white light, suggesting that ABA action for protection does not require phytochrome. Like the results above in *Atrichum* and *F. hygrometrica*, Machuka et al. (80) showed that treatment of seven-day-old *P. patens* protonemal tissue with ABA led to upregulation of genes that could be identified as responders to oxidative and chemical stresses, as well as those associated with protection of cells during desiccation and extreme temperature changes.

Investigation of the desiccation/ rehydration cycle in *Atrichum* after pretreatment with ABA shows that pretreatment increases the rate of recovery of PSII activity, increases the concentration of soluble sugars, and also doubles the amount of nonphotochemical quenching (84). An increase of nonphotochemical quenching reduces reactive oxygen species and may explain how ABA enhances pathways that protect moss during desiccation. Finally, the effects of ABA pretreatment on changes in lipid composition during desiccation and rehydration have been studied and reveal that ABA pretreatment reduces the overall extent of changes in lipid/membrane components, thereby reducing membrane damage during desiccation (52). The increase in freezing and drought tolerance induced by ABA treatment is likely the result of increased expression of genes that participate in protecting protonemal cells during stress.

Although exogenous ABA clearly enhances tolerance to these stresses, it is not clear whether endogenous ABA or the ABA-signaling pathway is required for such an effect. In fact, ABA has not been detected in one of the most desiccation-tolerant species of moss, *Tortula ruralis*, nor does this moss synthesize detectable proteins when ABA is added exogenously (12, 94). Additionally, transcripts that specifically accumulate during drying in *T. ruralis* (125) are not associated with an increased accumulation of endogenous ABA. The molecular techniques now available for *P. patens* offer unique opportunities to identify genes that participate in the acquisition of stress tolerance.

The involvement of abscisic acid in regulating gene expression and in signaling pathways has also been studied. In *F. hygrometrica*, cytokinin-stimulated bud formation is inhibited by ABA in a concentration-dependent manner (23), providing a potentially specific and quantitative bioassay for ABA. Experiments in which protonema were transferred between cytokinin and cytokinin plus ABA show that ABA does not interfere with the initial perception of cytokinin. Supporting this result, it was shown that ABA is not a competitive inhibitor of cytokinin. Through these studies, a new regulatory step that involves ABA in the developmental process of bud formation in mosses is proposed. Although this study did not identify ABA-induced transcripts, a separate study (32) reported that ABA treatment of protonemal cells results in a rapid increase in the activity of a 38-kDa protein kinase. The transcription of this gene was also enhanced by NaCl, and when added together with ABA, an additive response is observed, suggesting that both ABA and NaCl act via independent and parallel pathways (32).

More recently, it was demonstrated that *P. patens* is tolerant to drought, salt, and osmotic stress and that specific transcripts are induced under these conditions (46). Using a cDNA macro array composed of 45 putative stress-associated cDNAs from *P. patens*, many cDNAs were identified that were induced under the stresses imposed, and by exogenous application of ABA. Both overlapping as well as unique expression patterns were observed, indicating that there are both ABA-dependent and -independent stress-responsive pathways.

The presence of an ABA-responsive pathway in *P. patens* was first demonstrated by transforming moss with a wheat promoter from the ABA-responsive Em gene linked to the GUS reporter gene (76). Following transformation, adding ABA to moss protonema results in GUS expression. Mutational analysis of the promoter indicated that the same nucleotides that are responsible for expression in angiosperms are also responsible for expression in moss. This indicates that at least at the transcription level the controls for expression from the Em promoter appear to be conserved between bryophytes and seed plants. Furthermore, gel retardation and DNAase footprint analyses demonstrate that the transcription factors in moss that react with the Em promoter display the same footprint as proteins from seed plants that interact with the Em promoter. The synthesis of several stress-related polypeptides in response to ABA was also reported in this study. These results clearly point the way toward comparative studies to identify conserved signaling intermediates, promoter elements, and genes that will help to elucidate the evolution of the ABA-signaling pathway.

An example of such an approach comes from results recently obtained (H. Marella, Y. Sakata & R. Quatrano, unpublished data). The transcriptional regulator ABI3 from *Arabidopsis* and VP1 from maize are part of the transcriptional regulatory complex that controls a set of genes required for seeds to survive desiccation (45). An ABI3-like gene from *P. patens* (PpABI3) was recently identified that can function similarly to ABI3 and VP1 in enhancing the ABA responsiveness of reporter genes in both *P. patens* and aleurone cells of barley. Furthermore, PpABI3 can

partially complement the *abi3-6* mutant allele from *Arabidopsis*. By comparing sequences between PpABI3 and ABI3/VP1, it is possible to start to decipher the domains that have been conserved along with specific functions, and understand how regulation of ABA-induced gene expression has evolved from drought/desiccation tolerance in the vegetative tissues of moss to the seeds of angiosperms.

Organelle Structure and Function

Organelle studies in mosses have so far concentrated almost exclusively on chloroplasts, and most have been carried out using *P. patens*. Under normal growth conditions, *P. patens* chloronemal cells contain approximately 50 chloroplasts randomly distributed in the cortex of the cell (68). Sequencing the chloroplast genome revealed some of the evolutionary history of *P. patens* (112). The genome is 122,890 bp and encodes for 83 proteins, 31 tRNAs, 4 rRNAs, and 1 pseudo gene. Although the overall structure of the chloroplast genome resembles the liverwort *M. polymorpha*, some key differences indicate that *P. patens* diverged from hepatic bryophytes and is more closely related to vascular plants. One unique finding from the sequence is that mosses transferred a critical gene from the chloroplast to the nucleus. The alpha subunit of the RNA polymerase (rpoA), used to transcribe genes in the chloroplast, has been lost from the chloroplast genome and is instead encoded in the nucleus. Using green fluorescent protein (GFP) fusions of the nuclear rpoA gene, it was shown that its gene product is imported into the chloroplast (112).

P. patens chloroplasts are particularly amenable for studying photosynthesis. A recent study shows that, like in cyanobacteria, it is possible to measure fluorescent parameters in *P. patens* tissue in vivo (115). This is in contrast to vascular plants, where these measurements have only been performed on isolated thylakoid membranes. In addition, this study showed that *C. purpureus* could be easily

GFP: green
fluorescent protein

mutagenized to produce photosynthetic mutants (115).

Chloroplast import pathways appear to be conserved between *P. patens* and vascular plants. Sequence information from expressed sequence tag (EST) databases shows that *P. patens* contains genes involved in all known chloroplast import pathways, including thylakoid membrane transport (56). By performing protein import assays on isolated chloroplasts, all major protein-targeting pathways in the chloroplasts operated similarly between *P. patens* and vascular plants (56). This conservation of pathways coupled with the near completion of the *P. patens* genome validate the use of *P. patens* as a model system for studying plant gene function, particularly in the chloroplast.

Gene targeting has also been used to disrupt a chloroplast gene that codes for a transfer RNA (trnR-CCG) (111). Lines were generated that contained plastids lacking the trnR-CCG gene, which, when selfed, retained this genotype but were not impaired in growth. This study confirms that this tRNA is not essential for chloroplast function (111) and lays the foundation for a detailed analysis of the function of individual chloroplast genes using gene-disruption techniques in *P. patens*.

Similar to other plant systems, *P. patens* chloroplasts use RNA editing to regulate gene expression in the chloroplast (89). The rps14 transcript is modified by RNA editing in a unique way that is not observed in any other plant system (89). This modification, originally detected at very low efficiency, is a C to U transition that creates a translation initiation codon AUG (89). A recent study demonstrated that the modification is regulated in a tissue- and stage-specific manner, indicating that RNA editing in chloroplasts is a regulated process required to precisely control chloroplast gene expression (88).

Because many plastid and mitochondrial proteins are encoded in the nucleus, N-terminal transit peptides are used to target these proteins into plastids and mitochondria. *P. patens* employs translation initiation as a mechanism to differentially target a single gene to two different subcellular compartments (71, 98). In the cases studied, the initial translation initiation site targets the chloroplast. For an *rpo* gene, the second initiation site targets the mitochondria (98), and for FtsZ1-2 the second site targets the cytoplasm (71).

FtsZ2–1 encodes one of four FtsZ isoforms in *P. patens* (71). FtsZ is the bacterial ancestor of tubulin and is essential for cell division in bacteria (42). It is present in the chloroplasts of plants and by inference was thought to be involved in chloroplast division, which has been shown for vascular plants (42) and for *P. patens* (110). Deletion of FtsZ2-1 blocks chloroplast division, resulting in one macrochloroplast per cell (110).

Localization of the FtsZ isoforms in *P. patens* has revealed novel structures within the chloroplast that resemble cytoskeletal networks. Functional GFP fusions of FtsZ2-1 and FtsZ2-2 localize to the chloroplast, forming filamentous structures (70). In contrast to bacterial FtsZ, that only forms a ring at the time of cell division, the *P. patens* FtsZ isoforms form networks of filaments at all times. Additionally, FtsZ2-2 appears to form a ring during chloroplast division (70). It was also demonstrated that the novel FtsZ1-2 isoform can be targeted to both the chloroplast and the cytoplasm via regulation of translation initiation (see above). This isoform also localizes to rings in the cytoplasm and is hypothesized to link cell division to chloroplast division (71).

In addition to mutations in the FtsZ gene, chloroplast division can also be blocked by treating *P. patens* protonema with antibiotics that inhibit the bacterial peptidoglycan synthesis pathway. The β-lactam antibiotics form covalent complexes with penicillin-binding proteins of bacteria. This is a lethal complex, because it interferes with the bacteria's ability to synthesize a cell wall. After two days of treatment with β-lactam-type antibiotics, chloroplast division is blocked, as evidenced by a decreasing number of chloroplasts per cell (68). However, cell division occurs normally and results in chloroplast separation. The sensitivity of *P. patens* to β-lactam antibiotics indicates that *P. patens* chloroplast division has conserved enzymes derived from the bacterial peptidoglycan synthesis pathway. It is pertinent to note that not all antibiotics result in the same severity of phenotype, possibly indicating that the plant enzymes have diverged sufficiently from their bacterial homologs to confer a certain amount of resistance. Alternatively, it is possible that not all the antibiotics have the same permeability.

P. patens chloroplasts alter their position in the cell in response to the quality and fluency of light. *P. patens* chloroplasts accumulate in low-fluency red and blue light and avoid high-fluency red and blue light (66). This response is nullified for red light by simultaneously illuminating with far-red light, suggesting that both dichroic phytochrome and a dichroic blue-light receptor are involved in chloroplast photorelocation (66). The cytoskeletal networks driving chloroplast movement are discussed below.

Studies of mitochondrion structure and function in mosses are much more limited. Mitochondrial DNA has been isolated from *P. patens* (83), but no complete sequence is yet available. The mitochondrion-encoded cytochrome oxidase III gene (*cox*3) from *P. patens* has been sequenced and contains no introns (82). Its protein-encoding sequence showed a strong similarity (about 72%) to *cox*3 sequences from seed plants (82). RNA editing of the *cox*3 gene is observed in the mosses *Tetraphis pellucida* and *C. purpureus*, indicating that RNA editing in the mitochondria predates the evolution of the tracheophytes (81).

Morphogenesis

Moss development provides outstanding opportunities for studying the control of pattern formation and cell polarity, shape, and division—all fundamental processes in the regulation of morphogenesis.

Polar axis determination. Spore germination and the regeneration of isolated protoplasts involve polar outgrowth from apparently unpolarized structures to generate protonemal filaments. These processes therefore provide material for studying polar axis establishment. Spores of *F. hygrometrica* and *C. purpureus* do not require light for germination, but spores of *P. patens* only germinate in light, with a peak activity at wavelengths around 660 nm (30). The point of outgrowth cannot be aligned by either gravity or light (D. J. Cove, unpublished data).

Protoplasts of *P. patens* undergo cell wall synthesis in darkness and cell division in low-light intensities, but require high intensities of light to form a polar axis (18, 64). Photon fluence rates of about 7 µmol quanta $m^{-2} s^{-1}$ for either red (665 nm) or blue (442 nm) light are required to achieve polar outgrowth from 50% of protoplasts (64). The effects of light direction on polar axis orientation can therefore only be studied in high-light intensities. To regenerate protoplasts in unidirectional light, the light source is usually placed so that light falls on the side of the Petri dish containing the regenerating protoplasts, which are embedded in soft agar (64). Because the Petri dish and agar attenuate the light intensity, it is difficult to standardize light treatments. Burgess & Linstead (18) reported that light intensity fell more than threefold across a 50-mm Petri dish, and thus regeneration occurred in a range of intensities. They provided unidirectional white light by a mirror, and the light was therefore partially polarized. Response to polarized light is generally taken as evidence that the photoreceptors detecting the light direction are held in the cell, at or near the plasma membrane, in a fixed array (62). In their studies, Burgess & Linstead (18) showed that 90% of regeneration axes of protoplasts in the part of the dish nearest to the light source were away from the direction of light. They later showed that regeneration axes can also be aligned by an electrical field (19). In a similar experimental setup, but not using reflected light, regeneration axes in high-intensity (75 µmol quanta m^2 s^{-1}) white light were not strongly aligned but tended to be oriented at right angles to the light direction (D.J. Cove, unpublished data). The problem of standardizing light intensities is much reduced if polarized light is used, as this can be shone directly at the protoplasts. Studies using polarized light are now in hand (54; D.J. Cove, unpublished data).

C. *purpureus* protoplasts regenerate in darkness, making it possible to study the effect of a wider range of light conditions on the formation of a polar axis in this species. Measuring the orientation of the polar regeneration axes of large populations of protoplasts shows that, in darkness, gravity is not an important input, the distribution being only slightly biased upward (31). When regeneration occurs in unidirectional light, the axis distributions vary with different wavelengths (31). In red light, regeneration axes are well aligned to the direction of light, although about 25% of protoplasts orient their outgrowth away from the light source. In blue light, most protoplast regeneration axes are oriented toward the light source, but are much more poorly aligned to it (31). C. *purpureus* protoplasts do not regenerate synchronously and this allows the kinetics of axis determination to be investigated (31). When protoplasts, regenerating in unidirectional light, are reoriented, the cohort of protoplasts regenerating over the next 8 to 9 hours align their regeneration axes to the original light direction, indicating that the alignment of the regeneration axis is fixed well in advance of polar outgrowth. The protoplasts that align their axes to the new light direction are evenly divided between those growing toward and those growing away from the light source, showing that although alignment to the new direction can be established, the correct orientation, i.e., toward or away from the light source, is established much more slowly (31).

Modification of polar axes. Although the direction or plane of polarization of light does not influence the point of outgrowth of ger-

minating P. *patens* spores, the apical cells of the chloronemal filaments they produce respond to either the direction or plane of polarization of light (62). Chloronemal apical cells show alternative responses depending on the wavelength and intensity of light. The low-intensity response is growth toward a light source, or perpendicular to the E-vector of polarized light, whereas the high-level response is perpendicular to the direction of the light source or parallel to the E-vector. The change between the low- and high-intensity responses can only be observed at some wavelengths (480–500 nm and 630–690 nm), and then the switch occurs over a narrow range of fluence rates. At other wavelengths, only either the high-intensity response (<480 nm) or the low-intensity response (500–630 nm and >690 nm) is observed.

In contrast to chloronemal filaments, which do not grow in darkness and show no response to gravity in light, the apical cells of caulonemal filaments (or of older protonemal filaments in species where the morphological distinction between chloronemata and caulonemata is not apparent) of a number of moss species grow well in darkness if supplied with a reduced carbon source, and respond to gravity by growing upward (20, 63, 108, 126). The response to gravity in P. *patens* and C. *purpureus* only occurs in darkness, but the apical cells of protonemal filaments of C. *purpureus* mutants, deficient in the synthesis of the phytochrome chromophore, continue to respond to gravity in light (78). The response to gravity is therefore actively switched off by light, by way of phytochrome.

The kinetics of the gravitropic response was studied in P. *patens* (72, 74) and C. *purpureus* (126), using time-lapse microscopy. In C. *purpureus*, plastids sediment upon reorientation, in a zone within the apical cell, and it is proposed that these plastids have a gravity perception function (126). In P. *patens*, C. *purpureus*, and F. *hygrometrica* (108), the immediate response to 90° reorientation is a brief period of up to 30 minutes of downward growth. Thereafter, filaments begin to respond by growing upward, but this response is interrupted and even reversed each time the apical cell divides. It has been proposed that the correlation of cell division with the reversal of the gravitropic response arises because the reorganization of the microtubule cytoskeleton, required during the division of the nucleus and the formation of a new cell wall, disturbs the mechanisms for the perception of gravity (74). In dark-grown protonemata of *C. purpureus*, microtubules are mostly axially oriented throughout the entire apical cell and are closely associated with plastids. Cells that were gravistimulated for more than 20 minutes show an accumulation of microtubules proximal to the sedimented plastids and near the part of the tip that elongates more to produce curvature. Inhibitors of the microtubule cytoskeleton disrupt the gravitropic response, but do not inhibit plastid sedimentation (107). In fact, plastid sedimentation is increased upon treatment with the inhibitor, suggesting that microtubules restrict the sedimentation of plastids along the length of the cell and are load-bearing for all plastids in the apical cell (106). In dark-grown caulonemata of *P. patens*, microtubules accumulate in the lower flank of the tip cell 30 minutes after reorientation (1). These studies demonstrate that microtubules are involved in sensing and responding to changes in the gravity vector.

Mutants affecting the gravitropic response of apical cells have been isolated in both *P. patens* (63, 75) and *C. purpureus* (118). These include not only mutants that are unable to align to the gravity vector (*P. patens gtr*A), but also mutants that align to gravity as well as the wild type, but orient their response downward rather than upward (*P. patens gtr*C), a further example of the independence of alignment and orientation to a directional input. Complementation analysis of *C. purpureus* mutants indicates that some agravitropic mutants are likely allelic with response-reversed mutants (D.J. Cove, unpublished data). The gametophores of *P. patens gtr* mutants show a wild-type upward-growth phenotype, and so the *gtr*A and C gene products are not required

for the gravitropic response of the multicellular gametophore axis.

Caulonemal apical cells also respond to a directional light input, or to the plane of polarized light. A number of lines of evidence identify phytochrome as the photoreceptor responsible for the photo- and polarotropic response (55, 78). The most direct evidence is provided by the aphototropic phenotype of *ptr* mutants of *C. purpureus* blocked in their synthesis of the phytochrome chromophore (43, 78). These mutants have an extended phenotype, being deficient in other phytochrome-mediated processes including chlorophyll synthesis. A further class of aphototropic mutants of *C. purpureus* is only impaired in the phototropic response, showing none of the pleiotropic traits associated with phytochrome function (78). These mutants are presumably downstream of the action of phytochrome in the perception of light direction. Similar mutants of *P. patens* have been isolated and complementation analysis shows that at least three genes (*ptr*A, B, and C) can mutate to give a similar phenotype (24, 30). These mutants also are impaired in the phototropic response of their gametophores. *P. patens ptr* mutants have a puzzling phenotype with respect to chloronemal phototropism, showing the same low- and high-intensity responses as the wild type, but the intensity at which the change from the low- to high-intensity response occurs is lower (61). The products of the three *ptr* genes must therefore be required for detecting light direction by caulonemal apical cells and gametophores, but not by chloronemal apical cells, where their role instead appears to be to detect light intensity.

The chloronemal filaments produced as side branches from caulonemal filaments (secondary chloronemata) differ from chloronemata arising from spores or regenerating tissue (primary chloronemata) in that their apical cells grow toward the light, even at high intensities (30). In high intensities of polarized white light, caulonemal apical cells show alternative alignments, aligning to the E-vector

± 16°, and often switch between the two alignments after a few cell divisions (29). Secondary chloronemal side branches also show alternative alignments, but these depend on the alignment of the caulonemal filament from which they arise (D.J. Cove, unpublished data). The adoption by caulonemal apical cells of alternative alignments to polarized light is consistent with the relevant photoreceptors being arranged spirally around the cell, with the choice of alignment depending on whether photoreceptors are activated on the upper side or lower side of the cell.

The interaction between light and gravity on the orientation of caulonemal apical cells of *P. patens* has been studied by growing cultures in unidirectional monochromatic red light (660 nm) supplied at right angles to the gravity vector (30, 63). At intensities down to 200 nmol quanta $m^{-2} s^{-1}$, growth is toward the light source. At 60 nmol quanta $m^{-2} s^{-1}$, growth is aligned at 45° to both the light direction and gravity vector, but at intermediate intensities alignment switches between growth toward the light and upward growth (29).

In contrast to gravitropic responses that depend on the microtubule cytoskeleton, the phototropic response in *C. purpureus* depends on the actin cytoskeleton. Actin filaments are localized in the apical cell of dark-grown protonemata such that bundles of filaments run from subapical regions to the apex axially along the cell cortex where they converge toward a central area of the tip (85, 119). This produces a collar-like structure. Dark-grown protonemal tip cells irradiated with unilateral red light form a bulge preceding a light-directed outgrowth. During an irradiation, the actin filaments reorient toward the irradiated apical flank. The collar-like structure is essential for tubular outgrowth. This process can proceed in the absence of microtubules. In fact, unilateral red light suppresses morphological distortion induced by inhibitors of microtubules and restores the actin collar structure. However, without microtubules, the actin reorientation is no longer restricted to the apical region of the tip cell (85). The actin collar-like structure has also been observed in *F. hygrometrica* during side-branch initiation (95).

Protonemal patterning. The protonemal stage of moss development is essentially two dimensional, comprising branching filaments that grow by extension at the tip of their apical cells. New filaments are produced as side branches from filament subapical cells. In *P. patens* and related species, spore germination gives rise to chloronemal filaments, but these also arise from tissue regeneration and as the most common fate of caulonemal side branches. Caulonemal filaments arise as a result of a transition of some chloronemal apical cells, but also occur as side branches from caulonemal filaments and, rarely, as a result of the transition of a rhizoid apical cell. In *P. patens*, the transition of a chloronemal to a caulonemal apical cell can be rapid and completed within a single cell cycle, but usually takes several cell divisions (99). The transition depends on auxin and the supply of exogenous auxin increases the production of caulonemal filaments (4). Some mutants unable to produce caulonemata are likely impaired in auxin synthesis, whereas others are blocked in their response to auxin (4).

The apical cells of the two filament types have contrasting growth patterns. Chloronemal apical cells extend slower and have a longer cell cycle than caulonemal apical cells (27). No studies have been carried out to investigate the basis of these differences.

The pattern of caulonemal development has been studied in *P. patens* using a combination of the analysis of large numbers of caulonemal filaments together with time-lapse video microscopy of living cultures (99). The pattern is affected by both genotype and the environment. For a given environment and genotype, pattern is not rigidly determined, but the probabilities of occurrence of each cell transition vary little, and so patterning is far from random. The alternative fates of caulonemal side-branch initials into chloronema, caulonema, or buds is influenced not only by inputs such as the supply of exogenous hormones but also by the developmental fates of adjacent side branches. Thus, the probability of a side branch developing into a bud is greatly increased by the addition of cytokinins, but also by buds developing on side branches adjacent to it on the same filament. As a result, buds tend to be clustered (99).

The pattern of caulonemal side-branch fate in *P. patens* is strongly dependent on light intensity. In darkness, few side branches are produced. At low-light intensities, caulonemal side-branch development is favored, at intermediate intensities almost all side-branch initials remain undivided, and at high intensities most initials develop into secondary chloronemal filaments, with less than 5% becoming either caulonemal filaments or buds (D.J. Cove, unpublished data). Patterning is also influenced by the source of nitrogen in the medium. The basal medium used in most *P. patens* studies is a modified Knop's, and contains nitrate as the nitrogen source. Adding an ammonium salt leads to the culture producing more chloronemata, largely as a result of secondary chloronemal filaments being more branched and containing more cells. The effect of including a sugar in the medium depends on the concentration used. Using 0.15 M glucose in medium containing an ammonium salt leads to an increase in the production of caulonemal filaments (92), but no detailed analysis of patterning has yet been carried out. Including glucose concentrations higher than 0.2 M leads to a general inhibition of growth, and this is likely an osmotic effect, because the nonmetabolizable sugar, mannitol, has a similar effect at the same concentrations (92).

Gametophore and sporophyte development. The development of caulonemal side-branch initials into gametophores is characterized at its first cell division, which occurs diagonally, producing a more apical cell containing many chloroplasts, and a basal cell containing few chloroplasts (99). The apical cell divides further to produce the gametophore axis, and division of the basal cell produces most of the rhizoids (99). Treatment with auxin or cytokinin affects this pattern of development. Treatment with 1 μM benzylaminopurine greatly increases bud production, but the buds produced have no rhizoids and do not develop into gametophores. Treatment with 1 μM 1-naphthylene acetic acid leads to buds that do not form a gametophore axis, but have abundant rhizoids (4).

A detailed study of the role of auxin in rhizoid production has identified two types of rhizoid, one developing from the base of the gametophore and the other from specific cell lineages in the gametophore epidermis (100). Once an epidermal cell is committed to rhizoid development, expression of a homeodomain-leucine zipper I gene is induced, but knockout of this gene does not affect rhizoid production, suggesting that it functions downstream of the auxin input.

Mutants affected in gametophore development have been isolated following chemical mutagenesis (25) or gene disruption (105). Mutant phenotypes include alterations in leaf shape and leaf number. Gametophore leaves consist of a single cell layer. Although no detailed analysis of their programming has yet been undertaken, they should provide good material for morphogenetic study.

Variations in the distribution of gametangia on gametophores of *P. patens* have been reported, but these studies were carried out on a single strain and so the variations are not genetic (2). Sporophyte production by this line was low, probably as a result of it having been cultured vegitatively for many years (2). No detailed studies have been made of sporophyte development.

Role of the cytoskeleton. Both the microtubule- and actin-based cytoskeletons have been visualized in a number of moss species (34, 36, 48, 69, 85, 95, 119). The extensive gene database now available for *P. patens* contains a relatively large number of genes coding for actin (at least seven) and for beta tubulin (at least six) (65). Both

Sporophyte: the diploid phase of the life cycle, comprising the spore capsule, in which spores are produced by meiosis, borne on a short seta

cytoskeletons appear to be predominately associated with the cortex. Microtubules have been visualized in protonemal tissue by immunofluorescence and microfilaments have been visualized by immunofluorescence or with fluorescent phalloidin (35, 36, 48).

Using immunofluorescence, microtubules have been shown to be oriented along the long axis of the cell with an accumulation at the apex of the tip cell (36, 107). During mitosis, microtubules comprise the spindle that separates the chromosomes, and what appear to be "astral" microtubules may play a role in reorienting the spindle during anaphase. During cytokinesis, microtubules are incorporated into a phragmoplast similar to that observed in other plant cells (35). In the subapical cell, microtubules appear to be preferentially associated with the apical cross wall. It is from this cross wall that the nucleus migrates toward a central position in the subapical cell. When a subapical cell branches, the nucleus migrates toward the site of branch formation. Bundles of microtubules exist between the nucleus and the prospective division site. These become progressively thicker and shorter as the nucleus migrates. Treatment with Cremart, a microtubule destabilizing drug, inhibits nuclear migration and concomitant treatment with taxol, a microtubule stabilizer, relieves this inhibition (37), demonstrating a clear role for microtubules during nuclear migration. Microtubules also appear to play a role in polarizing cells. Treatment with concentrations of Cremart that disorganize the microtubule cytoskeleton can alter the direction of growth away from the apex of the cell. Concentrations of Cremart that completely destroy the microtubule cytoskeleton cause the apical region of the cell to swell, but do not entirely stop tip growth (36).

In contrast, actin filaments, which also appear to be axially oriented along the cortex and concentrated at the apex of the tip cell, are required for tip growth (36). Depolymerization of these apical actin filaments by cytochalasin D inhibits tip growth (36).

A recent study shows the importance of the actin cytoskeleton in tip growth by examining the role of the actin filament-nucleating Arp2/3 complex. This study employed RNA interference (RNAi) to reduce the function of the ARPC1 subunit of the Arp2/3 complex in *P. patens* (54). Deregulation of proper actin dynamics through perturbation of the Arp2/3 complex function has dramatic effects on tip growth, polar outgrowth, and cell differentiation. *P. patens* lines containing an RNAi construct targeting degradation of ARPC1 have multiple defects. During protoplast regeneration, *arpc1-rnai* plants are unable to establish a polar axis, although they eventually begin to grow chloronemal filaments of abnormal size and shape from an unpolarized group of cells. These phenotypes can be mimicked by treatment with the actin depolymerization drug latrunculin B. The protonemal filaments that do grow remain chloronemal in character. There are no apparent caulonemal cells and thus no gametophore formation in *arpc1-rnai* plants, even in response to cytokinin treatment (54).

Both the microtubule and actin cytoskeletons appear to play a role in chloroplast photorelocation (101). *P. patens* chloroplasts accumulate in low-fluence red and blue light, and avoid high-fluence red and blue light (66). Chloroplast photorelocation was studied in the presence/absence of drugs that affect the microtubule and actin cytoskeletons. The red-light response is mediated only by microtubules and not actin. However, the blue-light response is mediated by both microtubules and actin. The rate of microtubule-driven movement (around 2.5 μm/min), measured using the blue-light response and drugs that selectively inhibit one of the cytoskeletal networks, is five times faster than actin-driven movement (101).

In addition to movement in response to light signals, chloroplasts also move in response to mechanical perturbation of the cell, assembling at the pressure point. This movement depends on microtubules and calcium. This is in contrast to chloroplast photorelocation, which does not depend on calcium (102). The mechanism behind chloroplast movement remains unclear, although initial studies indicate that the actin-based movements in photorelocation do not appear to depend on class VIII myosins (M. Bezanilla & Y. Sato, unpublished data). Future studies, taking advantage of the tools available for studies in *P. patens*, should elucidate whether this type of motility is driven by cytoskeletal motors or by the dynamic character of actin and microtubules.

SUMMARY POINTS

1. The ability to grow on simple liquid or solid media allows metabolic studies to be carried out, similar to those used with micro-organisms.

2. Responsiveness to the plant hormones, auxin, cytokinin, and abscisic acid enables investigation of their synthesis and mode of action.

3. The accessibility of living cells to direct observation allows unrivaled opportunities for cell biological research.

4. The simple pattern of development, with few cell types, allows detailed study of morphogenesis.

5. The effects of environmental inputs on polarity can be studied in both single cells and multicellular structures.

6. The involvement of the actin and microtubule cytoskeleton in the programming of cell shape can be studied using gene knockout and RNAi technologies.

UNRESOLVED ISSUES AND FUTURE DIRECTIONS

1. The link between mutant phenotype and genes is still often obscure.

2. A publically available forward genetic resource of tagged lines is required to enable genes associated with specific phenotypes to be isolated.

3. An international stock center is now required.

LITERATURE CITED

1. Allen N, Chattaraj P, Collings D, Johannes E. 2003. Gravisensing: ionic responses, cytoskeleton and amyloplast behavior. *Adv. Space Res.* 32:1631–37
2. Ashton NW, Raju M. 2000. The distribution of gametangia on gametophores of *Physcomitrella (Aphanoregma) patens* in culture. *J. Bryol.* 22:9–12
3. Ashton NW, Cove DJ, Featherstone DR. 1979. The isolation and physiological analysis of mutants of the moss, *Physcomitrella patens*, which over-produce gametophores. *Planta* 144:437–42
4. Ashton NW, Grimsley NH, Cove DJ. 1979. Analysis of gametophytic development in the moss, *Physcomitrella patens*, using auxin and cytokinin resistant mutants. *Planta* 144:427–35

5. Ashton NW, Schulze A, Hall P, Bandurski RS. 1985. Estimation of indole-3-acetic acid in gametophytes of the moss, *Physcomitrella patens*. *Planta* 164:142–44

6. Barthelmess A. 1939. Mutationsversuche mit einem Laubmoos *Physcomitrium piriforme*. I. Phänanalyse der Mutanten. *Z. Vererbungsl.* 78:479–518

7. Barthelmess A. 1940. Mutationsversuche mit einem Laubmoss *Physcomitrium pyriforme*. II. Morphologische und physiologische Analyse der univalenten und bivalenten Protonemen einiger Mutanten. *Z. Vererbungsl.* 79:153–70

8. Becker H. 1989. Bryophytes, a rich source of secondary metabolites. *Bot. Acta* 102:181–82

9. Beckett RP. 1999. Partial dehydration and ABA induce tolerance to desiccation-induced ion leakage in the moss *Atrichum androgynum*. *South African J. Bot.* 65:1–6

10. Beckett RP. 2001. ABA-induced tolerance to ion leakage during rehydration following desiccation in the moss *Atrichum androgynum*. *Plant Growth Reg.* 35:131–35

11. Beckett RP, Csintalan A, Tuba Z. 2000. ABA treatment increases both the desiccation tolerance of photosynthesis, and nonphotochemical quenching in the moss *Atrichum undulatum*. *Plant Ecol.* 151:65–71

12. Bewley JD, Reynolds TL, Oliver MJ. 1993. Evolving strategies in the adaptation to desiccation. Plant responses to cellular dehydration during environmental stress. In *Current Topics in Plant Physiology 10*, ed. TJ Close, EA Bray, pp. 193–201. Rockville, Maryland: Am. Soc. Plant Physiol.

13. Bhatla SC, Kiessling J, Reski R. 2002. Observation of polarity induction by cytochemical localization of phenylalkylamine-binding sites in regenerating protoplasts of the moss *Physcomitrella patens*. *Protoplasma* 219:99–105

14. Bhatla SC, Haschke HP, Hartmann E. 2003. Distribution of activated calmodulin in the chloronema tip cells of the moss *Funaria hygrometrica*. *J. Plant Phys.* 160:469–74

15. Bierfreund NM, Reski R, Decker E. 2003. Use of an inducible reporter gene system for the analysis of auxin distribution in the moss *Physcomitrella patens*. *Plant Cell Rep.* 21:1143–52

16. Bopp M, Werner O. 1993. Abscisic acid and desiccation tolerance in mosses. *Bot. Acta* 106:103–6

17. Boyd PJ, Hall J, Cove DJ. 1988. An airlift fermenter for the culture of the moss *Physcomitrella patens*. In *Methods in Bryology. Proceedings of the Bryological Methods Workshop, Mainz*, ed. J.M. Glime, pp. 41–45. Nichinan: Hattori Bot. Lab.

18. Burgess J, Linstead PJ. 1981. Studies on the growth and development of protoplasts of the moss, Physcomitrella patens, and its control by light. *Planta* 151:331–38

19. Burgess J, Linstead PJ. 1982. Cell-wall differentiation during growth of electrically polarised protoplasts of *Physcomitrella*. *Planta* 156:241–48

20. Chaban C, Kern V, Ripetskyj RT, Demkiv OT, Sack FD. 1998. Gravitropism in caulonemata of the moss *Pottia intermedia*. *J. Bryol.* 20:287–99

21. Chen CM, Hall RH. 1969. Biosynthesis of N 6-(2-isopentenyl) adenosine in transfer ribonucleic acid of cultured tobacco pith tissue. *Phytochem.* 8:1687–96

22. Chopra RN, Rashid A. 1969. Auxin-cytokinin interaction in shoot-bud formation of a moss: *Anoectangium thomsonii mitt. Z. Pflanzenphysiol.* 61:192–98

23. Christianson ML. 2000. ABA prevents the second cytokinin-mediated event during the induction of shoot buds in the moss *Funaria hygrometrica*. *Am. J. Bot.* 87:1540–45

24. Courtice GRM. 1980. *Developmental genetic studies of Physcomitrella patens*. PhD thesis. Univ. Cambridge, Cambridge

25. Courtice GRM, Cove DJ. 1983. Mutants of the moss *Physcomitrella patens* which produce leaves of altered morphology. *J. Bryol.* 12:595–609

26. Cove D. 1984. The role of cytokinin and auxin in protonemal development in *Physcomitrella patens* and *Physcomitrium sphaericum*. *J. Hattori Lab.* 55:79–86

27. Cove D. 2005. The moss Physcomitrella patens. *Annu. Rev. Genet.* 39:339–58

28. Cove D, Ashton NW. 1984. The hormonal regulation of gametophyte development in bryophytes. In *The Experimental Biology of Bryophytes*, ed. AF Dyer, JG Duckett, pp. 177–201. London: Academic

29. Cove D, Knight C. 1987. Gravitropism and phototropism in the moss, *Physcomitrella patens*. In *Developmental Mutants in Higher Plants*, ed. H Thomas, D Grierson, pp. 181–96. London: Cambridge Univ. Press

30. Cove D, Schild A, Ashton N, Hartmann E. 1978. Genetic and physiological studies of the effect of light on the development of the moss, *Physcomitrella patens. Photochem. Photobiol.* 27:249–54

31. Cove D, Quatrano RS, Hartmann E. 1996. The alignment of the axis of asymmetry in regenerating protoplasts of the moss, *Ceratodon purpureus*, is determined independently of axis polarity. *Development* 122:371–79

32. D'Souza JS, Johri MM. 2002. ABA and NaCl activate myelin basic protein kinase in the chloronema cells of the moss *Funaria hygrometrica. Plant Phys. Biochem.* 40:17–24

33. Decker EL, Reski R. 2004. The moss bioreactor. *Curr. Opin. Plant Biol.* 7:166–70

34. Demkiv O, Khorkavtsiv O, Pundiak O. 2003. Changes of protonemal cell growth related to cytoskeleton organization. *Cell Biol. Int.* 27:187–89

35. Doonan JH, Cove DJ, Lloyd CW. 1985. Immunofluorescence microscopy of microtubules in intact cell lineages of the moss, Physcomitrella patens. I. Normal and CIPC-treated tip cells. *J. Cell Sci.* 75:131–47

36. Doonan JH, Cove DJ, Lloyd CW. 1988. Microtubules and microfilaments in tip growth: evidence that microtubules impose polarity on protonemal growth in *Physcomitrella patens. J. Cell Sci.* 89:533–40

37. Doonan JH, Jenkins GI, Cove DJ, Lloyd CW. 1986. Microtubules connect the migrating nucleus to the prospective division site during side branch formation in the moss, *Physcomitrella patens. Eur. J. Cell Biol.* 41:157–64

38. Duckett J, Burch J, Fletcher P, Matcham H, Read D, Russell A, Pressel S. 2004. *In vitro* cultivation of bryophytes: a review of practicalities, problems, progress and promise. *J. Bryol.* 26:3–20

39. Duckett JG. 1994. Studies of protonemal morphogenesis in mosses. 5. *Diphyscum foliosum* (Hedw.) Mohr (Buxbaumiales). *J. Bryol.* 18:223–38

40. Duckett JG, Schmid AM, Ligrone R. 1998. Protonemal morphogenesis. In *Bryology for the Twenty-First Century*, ed. JW Bates, NW Ashton, JG Duckett, pp. 223–46. Leeds: Maney and Br. Bryol. Soc.

41. Engel PP. 1968. The induction of biochemical and morphological mutants in the moss *Physcomitrella patens. Am. J. Bot.* 55:438–46

42. Errington J, Daniel R, Scheffers D. 2003. Cytokinesis in bacteria. *Microbiol. Mol. Biol. Rev.* 67:52–65

43. Esch H, Hartmann E, Cove D, Wada M, Lamparter T. 1999. Phytochrome-controlled phototropism of protonemata of the moss *Ceratodon purpureus*: physiology of the wild type and class 2 *ptr⁻* mutants. *Planta* 209:290–98

44. Featherstone DR, Cove D, Ashton NW. 1990. Genetic anaalysis by somatic hybridization

of cytokinin overproducing developmental mutants of the moss, *Physcomitrella patens*. *Mol. Gen. Genet.* 222:217–24

45. Finkelstein R, Srinivas R, Gampala SL, Rock CD. 2002. Abscisic acid signaling in seeds and seedlings. *Plant Cell* 14:S15–S45

46. Frank W, Ratnadewi D, Reski R. 2005. *Physcomitrella patens* is highly tolerant against drought, salt and osmotic stress. *Planta* 220:384–94

47. Gonneau M, Pagant S, Brun F, Laloue M. 2001. Photoaffinity labeling with the cytokinin agonist azido-CPPU of a 34 kDa peptide of the intracellular pathogenesis-related family in the moss *Physcomitrella patens*. *Plant Mol. Biol.* 46:539–48

48. Goode J, Alfano F, Stead A, Duckett JG. 1993. The formation of aplastidic abscission (tmema) cells and protonemal disruption in the moss, *Bryum tenuisetum* Limpr. is associated with transverse arrays of microtubules and microfilaments. *Protoplasma* 174:158–74

49. Goode JA, Duckett JG, Stead AD. 1992. Protonemal morphogenesis of the moss *Tetraphis pellucida Hedw.* in culture and in the wild. *Ann. Bot.* 70:519–30

50. Goode JA, Stead AD, Ligrone R, Duckett JG. 1994. Studies of protonemal morphogenesis in mosses. 4. *Aloina* (Pottiales). *J. Bryol.* 18:27–41

51. Gorton B, Eakin R. 1957. Development of the gametophyte in the moss, Tortella caespitosa. *Bot. Gaz.* 119:31–38

52. Guschina IA, Harwood JL, Smith M, Beckett RP. 2002. Abscisic acid modifies the changes in lipids brought about by water stress in the moss *Atrichum androgynum*. *New Phytol.* 156:255–64

53. Hahm SH, Saunders MJ. 1991. Cytokinin increases intracellular Ca2+ in *Funaria*: detection with Indo-1. *Cell Calcium* 12:675–81

54. Harries PA, Pan A, Quatrano RS. 2005. Actin related protein2/3 complex component ARPC1 is required for proper cell morphogenesis and polarized cell growth in *Physcomitrella patens*. *Plant Cell* 17:2327–39

55. Hartmann E, Klingenberg B, Bauer L. 1983. Phytochrome-mediated phototropism in protonemata of the moss *Ceratodon purpureus* BRID. *Photochem. Photobiol.* 38:599–603

56. Hofmann NR, Theg SM. 2003. *Physcomitrella patens* as a model for the study of chloroplast protein transport: conserved machineries between vascular and non-vascular plants. *Plant Mol. Biol.* 53:621–32

57. Hohe A, Decker EL, Gorr G, Schween G, Reski R. 2002. Tight control of growth and cell differentiation in photoautotrophic growing moss (*Physcomitrella patens*) bioreactor cultures. *Plant Cell Rep.* 20:1135–40

58. Huneck S. 1983. Chemistry and biochemistry of bryophytes. In *New Manual of Bryology*, ed. RM Schuster. Nichinan, Japan: Hattori Bot. Lab.

59. Imaizumi T, Kadota A, Hasebe M, Wada M. 2002. Cryptochrome light signals control development to suppress auxin sensitivity in the moss *Physcomitrella patens*. *Plant Cell* 14:373–86

60. Jayaswal R, Johri M. 1985. Occurrence and biosynthesis of auxin in protonema of the moss *Funaria hygrometrica*. *Phytochem.* 24:1061–64

61. Jenkins GI, Cove D. 1983. Phototropism and polarotropism of primary chloronemata of the moss *Physcomitrella patens*: responses of mutants strains. *Planta* 159:432–38

62. Jenkins GI, Cove DJ. 1983. Phototropism and polarotropism of primary chloronemata of the moss Physcomitrella patens: responses of the wild-type. *Planta* 158:357–64

63. Jenkins GI, Courtice GRM, Cove DJ. 1986. Gravitropic responses of wild-type and mutant strains of the moss *Physcomitrella patens*. *Plant Cell Environ.* 9:637–44

64. Jenkins GI, Cove DJ. 1983. Light requirements for regeneration of protoplasts of the moss *Physcomitrella patens*. *Planta* 157:39–45

65. Jost W, Baur A, Nick P, Reski R, Gorr G. 2004. A large plant beta-tubulin family with minimal C-terminal variation but differences in expression. *Gene* 340:151–60

66. Kadota A, Sato Y, Wada M. 2000. Intracellular chloroplast photorelocation in the moss Physcomitrella patens is mediated by phytochrome as well as by a blue-light receptor. *Planta* 210:932–37

67. Kasten B, Buck F, Nuske J, Reski R. 1997. Cytokinin affects nuclear- and plastome-encoded energy-converting plastid enzymes. *Planta* 201:261–72

68. Katayama N, Takano H, Sugiyama M, Takio S, Sakai A, et al. 2003. Effects of antibiotics that inhibit the bacterial peptidoglycan synthesis pathway on moss chloroplast division. *Plant Cell Phys.* 44:776–81

69. Khorkavtsiv O, Kardash O. 2001. Gravity-dependent reactions of the moss *Pohlia nutans* protonemata. *Adv. Space Res.* 27:989–93

70. Kiessling J, Kruse S, Rensing SA, Harter K, Decker EL, Reski R. 2000. Visualization of a cytoskeleton-like FtsZ network in chloroplasts. *J. Cell Biol.* 151:945–50

71. Kiessling J, Martin A, Gremillon L, Rensing SA, Nick P, et al. 2004. Dual targeting of plastid division protein FtsZ to chloroplasts and the cytoplasm. *EMBO Rep.* 5:889–94

72. Knight C, Cove D. 1991. The polarity of gravitropism in the moss *Physcomitrella patens* is reversed during mitosis and after growth on a clinostat. *Plant Cell Environ.* 14:995–1001

73. Knight C, Cove D, Boyd PJ, Ashton NW. 1988. The isolation of biochemical and developmental mutants in *Physcomitrella patens*. In *Methods in Bryology. Proceedings of the Bryological Methods Workshop, Mainz.*, ed. JM Glime, pp. 47–58. Nichinan, Japan: Hattori Bot. Lab.

74. Knight C, Cove DJ. 1988. Time-lapse microscopy of gravitropism in the moss *Physcomitrella patens*. In *Methods in Bryology. Proceedings of the Bryological Methods Workshop, Mainz*, ed. JM Glime, pp. 127–29. Nichinan, Japan: Hattori Bot. Lab.

75. Knight C, Futers TS, Cove DJ. 1991. Genetic analysis of a mutant class of *Physcomitrella patens* in which the polarity of gravitropism is reversed. *Mol. Gen. Genet.* 230:12–16

76. Knight CD, Sehgal A, Atwal K, Wallace JC, Cove DJ, et al. 1995. Molecular responses to abscisic acid and stress are conserved between moss and cereals. *Plant Cell* 7:499–506

77. Koprivova A, Meyer AJ, Schween G, Herschbach C, Reski R, Kopriva S. 2002. Functional knockout of the adenosine 5′-phosphosulfate reductase gene in *Physcomitrella patens* revives an old route of sulfate assimilation. *J. Biol. Chem.* 277:32195–201

78. Lamparter T, Esch H, Cove D, Hughes J, Hartmann E. 1996. Aphototropic mutants of the moss *Ceratodon purpureus* with spectrally normal and with spectrally dysfunctional phytochrome. *Plant Cell Environ.* 19:560–68

79. Lehnert B, Bopp M. 1983. The hormonal regulation of protonema development in mosses. I. Auxin-cytokinin interaction. *Zeit. Planzenphysiol.* 110:379–91

80. Machuka J, Bashiardes S, Ruben E, Spooner K, Cuming A, et al. 1999. Sequence analysis of expressed sequence tags from an ABA-treated cDNA library identifies stress response genes in the moss *Physcomitrella patens*. *Plant Cell Phys.* 40:378–87

81. Malek O, Lattig K, Hiesel R, Brennicke A, Knoop V. 1996. RNA editing in bryophytes and a molecular phylogeny of land plants. *EMBO J.* 15:1403–11

82. Marienfeld JR, Reski R, Abel WO. 1991. The first analysed archegoniate mitochondrial gene (COX3) exhibits extraordinary features. *Curr. Genet.* 20:319–29

83. Marienfeld JR, Reski R, Friese C, Abel WO. 1989. Isolation of nuclear, chloroplast and mitochondrial DNA from the moss *Physcomitrella patens*. *Plant Sci.* 61:235–44

84. Mayaba N, Beckett RP, Csintalan Z, Tuba Z. 2001. ABA increases the desiccation tolerance of photosynthesis in the afromontane understorey moss *Atrichum androgynum*. *Ann. Bot.* 88:1093–100

85. Meske V, Hartmann E. 1995. Reorganization of microfilaments in protonemal tip cells of the moss *Ceratadon purpureus* during the phototropic response. *Protoplasma* 188:59–69

86. Minami A, Nagao M, Arakawa K, Fujikawa S, Takezawa D. 2003. Abscisic acid-induced freezing tolerance in the moss *Physcomitrella patens* is accompanied by increased expression of stress-related genes. *J. Plant Phys.* 160:475–83

87. Minami A, Nagao M, Ikigami K, Koshiba T, Arakawa K, et al. 2005. Cold acclimation in bryophytes: low temperature-induced freezing tolerance in *Physcomitrella patens* is associated with increases in expression levels of stress-related genes but not with increase in level of endogenous abscisic acid. *Planta* 220:414–23

88. Miyata Y, Sugita M. 2004. Tissue- and stage-specific RNA editing of rps 14 transcripts in moss (*Physcomitrella patens*) chloroplasts. *J. Plant Phys.* 161:113–15

89. Miyata Y, Sugiura C, Kobayashi Y, Hagiwara M, Sugita M. 2002. Chloroplast ribosomal S14 protein transcript is edited to create a translation initiation codon in the moss Physcomitrella patens. *Biochim. Biophys. Acta.* 1576:346–49

90. Nagao M, Minami A, Arakawa K, Fujikawa S, Takezawa D. 2005. Rapid degradation of starch of chloroplasts and concomitant accumulation of soluble sugars associated with ABA-induced freezing tolerance in the moss *Physcomitrella patens*. *J. Plant Phys.* 162:169–80

91. Neuenschwander U, Fleming AJ, Kuhlemeier C. 1994. Cytokinin induces the developmentally restricted synthesis of an extracellular protein in *Physcomitrella patens*. *Plant J.* 5:21–31

92. Olsson T, Thelander M, Ronne H. 2003. A novel type of chloroplast stromal hexokinase is the major glucose-phosphorylating enzyme in the moss *Physcomitrella patens*. *J. Biol. Chem.* 278:44439–47

93. Perry K, Cove D. 1986. Transfer RNA pool sizes and half lives in wild-type and cytokinin over-producing strains of the moss, *Physcomitrella patens*. *Phys. Plant.* 67:680–84

94. Phillips JR, Oliver MJ, Bartels D. 2002. Molecular genetics of desiccation and drought tolerant systems. In *Desiccation and Survival in Plants: Drying Without Dying*, ed. M Black, HW Pritchard, pp. 319–36. Wallingford, UK: CABI Publ.

95. Quader H, Schnepf E. 1989. Actin filament array during side branch initiation in protonema cells of the moss *Funaria hygrometrica*: an actin organizing center at the plasma membrane. *Protoplasma* 151:161–70

96. Repp A, Mikami K, Mittmann F, Hartmann E. 2004. Phosphoinositide-specific phospholipase C is involved in cytokinin and gravity responses in the moss *Physcomitrella patens*. *Plant J.* 40:250–59

97. Reski R, Abel WO. 1985. Induction of budding on chronemata and caulonemata of the moss, *Physcomitrella patens*, using isopentyladenine. *Planta* 165:354–58

98. Richter U, Kiessling J, Hedtke B, Decker E, Reski R, et al. 2002. Two *RpoT* genes of Physcomitrella patens encode phage-type RNA polymerases with dual targeting to mitochondria and plastids. *Gene* 290:95–105

99. Russell A. 1993. *Morphogenesis in the moss Physcomitrella patens*. PhD thesis. University of Leeds, Leeds. 228 pp.

100. Sakakibara K, Nishiyama T, Sumikawa N, Kofuji R, Murata T, Hasebe M. 2003. Involvement of auxin and a homeodomain-leucine zipper 1 gene in rhizoid development of the moss *Physcomitrella patens*. *Development* 130:4835–46

101. Sato Y, Wada M, Kadota A. 2001. Choice of tracks, microtubules and/or actin filaments for chloroplast photo-movement is differentially controlled by phytochrome and a blue light receptor. *J. Cell Sci.* 114:269–79

102. Sato Y, Wada M, Kadota A. 2003. Accumulation response of chloroplasts induced by mechanical stimulation in bryophyte cells. *Planta* 216:772–77

103. Schnepf E, Reinhard C. 1997. Brachycytes in *Funaria* protonemata, induction by abscisic acid and fine structure. *J. Plant Phys.* 151:166–75

104. Schulz PA, Hofmann AH, Russo V-EA, Hartmann E, Laloue M, von Schwartzenberg K. 2001. Cytokinin overproducing ove mutants of *Physcomitrella patens* show increased riboside to base conversion. *Plant Phys.* 126:1224–31

105. Schween G, Egener T, Fritzowsky D, Granado J, Guitton M-C, et al. 2005. Large-scale analysis of 73,329 *Physcomitrella* plants transformed with different gene disruption libraries: production parameters and mutant phenotypes. *Plant Biol.* 7:228–37

106. Schwuchow J, Sack F. 1994. Microtubules restrict plastid sedimentation in protonemata of the moss *Ceratodon*. *Cell Motil. Cytoskel.* 29:366–74

107. Schwuchow J, Sack F, Hartmann E. 1990. Microtubule distribution in gravitropic protonemata of the moss *Ceratodon purpureus*. *Protoplasma* 159:60–69

108. Schwuchow J, Kim D, Sack FD. 1995. Caulonmeal gravitropism and amyloplast sedimentation in the moss, *Funaria*. *Can. J. Bot.* 73:1029–35

109. Sneh S, Hackenberg D. 1979. Interaction of auxin, antiauxin and cytokinin in relation to the formation of buds in moss protonema. *Ziet. Pflanzenphysiol.* 91

110. Strepp R, Scholz S, Kruse S, Speth V, Reski R. 1998. Plant nuclear gene knockout reveals a role in plastid division for the homolog of the bacterial cell division protein FtsZ, an ancestral tubulin. *Proc. Natl. Acad. Sci. USA* 95:4368–73

111. Sugiura C, Sugita M. 2004. Plastid transformation reveals that moss tRNA(Arg)-CCG is not essential for plastid function. *Plant J.* 40:314–21

112. Sugiura C, Koboyashi Y, Aoki S, Sugita C, Sugita M. 2003. Complete chloroplast DNA sequence of the moss *Physcomitrella patens*: evidence for the loss and relocation of *rpoA* from the chloroplast to the nucleus. *Nucleic Acid Res.* 31:5324–31

113. Thelander M, Olsson T, Ronne H. 2004. Snf1-related protein kinase 1 is needed for growth in a normal day-night cycle. *EMBO J.* 23:1900–10

114. Thelander M, Olsson T, Ronne H. 2005. Effect of the energy supply on filamentous growth and development in *Physcomitrella patens*. *J. Exp. Bot.* 412:653–62

115. Thornton LE, Keren N, Ohad I, Pakrasi HB. 2005. *Physcomitrella patens* and *Ceratadon purpureus*, mosses as model organisms in photosynthesis studies. *Photosynth. Res.* 83:87–96

116. von Schwartzenberg K, Kruse S, Reski R, Moffatt B, Laloue M. 1998. Cloning and characterization of an adenosine kinase from *Physcomitrella* involved in cytokinin metabolism. *Plant J.* 13:249–57

117. von Wettstein F. 1925. Genetische Untersuchungen an Moosen. *Bibl. Genet.* 1:1–38

118. Wagner T, Cove D, Sack F. 1997. A positively gravitropic mutant mirrors the wild-type protonemal response in the moss *Ceratodon purpureus*. *Planta* 202:149–54

119. Walker L, Sack F. 1995. Microfilament distribution in protonemata of the moss *Ceratodon*. *Protoplasma* 189:229–37

120. Wang TL, Horgan R, Cove D. 1981. Cytokinins from the moss, Physcomitrella patens. *Plant Physiol.* 68:735–38

121. Wang TL, Beutelmann P, Cove D. 1981. Cytokinin biosynthesis in mutants of the moss, *Physcomitrella patens*. *Plant Physiol.* 68:739–44

122. Wang TL, Cove DJ, Beutelmann P, Hartmann E. 1980. Isopentenyladenine from mutants of the moss, *Physcomitrella patens*. *Phytochem.* 19:1103–5

123. Wang TL, Futers TS, McGeary F, Cove D. 1984. Moss mutants and the analysis of cytokinin metabolism. In *The Synthesis and Metabolism of Plant Hormones*, ed. A Crozier, JR Hillman, pp. 135–64. London: Cambridge Univ. Press

124. Werner O, Espin RMR, Bopp M, Atzorn R. 1991. Abscisic acid-induced drought tolerance in *Funaria hygrometrica* Hedw. *Planta* 186:99–103

125. Wood AJ, Oliver MJ. 1999. Translational control in plant stress: formation of messenger ribonucleoprotein complexes (mRNPs) in *Tortula ruralis* in response to desiccation. *Plant J.* 18:359–70

126. Young J, Sack FD. 1992. Time-lapse analysis of gravitropism in Ceratodon protonemata. *Am. J. Bot.* 79:1348–58

RELATED RESOURCES

http://biology4.wustl.edu/moss

http://moss.nibb.ac.jp

http://www.biologie.fu-berlin.de/lampart/links.html

http://www.cosmoss.org

http://www.plant-biotech.net

http://www.mossgenome.org

Structure and Function of Photosystems I and II

Nathan Nelson[1] and Charles F. Yocum[2]

[1] Department of Biochemistry, George S. Wise Faculty of Life Sciences, Tel Aviv University, Tel Aviv 69978, Israel; email: nelson@post.tau.ac.il

[2] Department of Molecular, Cellular and Developmental Biology, University of Michigan, Ann Arbor, Michigan 48109-1048; email: cyocum@umich.edu

Annu. Rev. Plant Biol.
2006. 57:521–65

The *Annual Review of Plant Biology* is online at plant.annualreviews.org

doi: 10.1146/
annurev.arplant.57.032905.105350

First published online as a
Review in Advance on
February 7, 2006

1543-5008/06/0602-
0521$20.00

Key Words

chloroplasts, cyanobacteria, electron transfer, O_2 evolution, light harvesting, photosynthesis

Abstract

Oxygenic photosynthesis, the principal converter of sunlight into chemical energy on earth, is catalyzed by four multi-subunit membrane-protein complexes: photosystem I (PSI), photosystem II (PSII), the cytochrome b_6f complex, and F-ATPase. PSI generates the most negative redox potential in nature and largely determines the global amount of enthalpy in living systems. PSII generates an oxidant whose redox potential is high enough to enable it to oxidize H_2O, a substrate so abundant that it assures a practically unlimited electron source for life on earth. During the last century, the sophisticated techniques of spectroscopy, molecular genetics, and biochemistry were used to reveal the structure and function of the two photosystems. The new structures of PSI and PSII from cyanobacteria, algae, and plants has shed light not only on the architecture and mechanism of action of these intricate membrane complexes, but also on the evolutionary forces that shaped oxygenic photosynthesis.

Contents

INTRODUCTION

cyt: cytochrome

Chl: chlorophyll

Photosynthetic O$_2$ production and carbon dioxide assimilation established the composition of the biosphere and provide all life forms with essential food and fuel. Oxygenic photo-synthesis in plants is accomplished by a series of reactions that occur mainly, but not exclusively, in the chloroplast. Early biochemical studies showed that chloroplast thylakoid membranes oxidize H$_2$O, reduce NADP, and synthesize ATP. These reactions are catalyzed by two photosystems [photosystem I (PSI) and photosystem II (PSII)], an ATP synthase (F-ATPase) that produces ATP at the expense of the protonmotive force (pmf) formed by light-driven electron-transfer reactions, and the cytochrome (cyt) b$_6$f complex, which mediates electron transport between PSII and PSI and converts the redox energy into part of the proton gradient used for ATP formation. The knowledge obtained from biophysical, biochemical, and physiological research during the twentieth century set the stage at the beginning of the twenty-first century for the determination at high resolution of the structures of most of the proteins involved in oxygenic photosynthesis (219). This review attempts to capture the excitement generated by the determination of the three-dimensional structures of the chlorophyll (Chl) containing complexes that catalyze oxygenic photosynthesis. Several reviews have been published that contain detailed discussions and list original references to earlier work (18, 44, 60, 62, 110, 121, 125, 137, 238, 246, 273). In this review, we focus on the photosystems of higher plants but also refer to the wealth of structural information that is available on the photosystems of the thermophilic cyanobacteria, especially in the case of PSII, for which a plant crystal structure is currently unavailable.

Molecular Architecture of Thylakoid Membranes

In eukaryotes, most of the reactions of photosynthesis occur in the chloroplast. The four protein complexes required for the light-driven reactions of photosynthesis reside in a membrane continuum of flattened sacs called thylakoids (219). Thylakoids form a physically continuous three-dimensional network enclosing an aqueous space called the lumen and are differentiated into two distinct physical domains: cylindrical stacked structures (called grana) and interconnecting single membrane regions (stroma lamellae). The protein complexes that catalyze electron transfer and energy transduction are unevenly distributed in thylakoids: PSI is located in the stroma lamellae, PSII is found almost exclusively in the grana (**Figure 1**), the F-ATPase is located mainly in the stroma lamellae, and the cyt b_6f complex is found in grana and grana margins (3, 13, 14, 154, 161).

Low-resolution models of thylakoid structure resulted from reconstituting serial thin sections, freeze etching, immuno-gold labeling, and biochemical and spectroscopic analyses (232). For example, fractionation of membrane fragments by aqueous polymer two-phase separation (3–5, 73) revealed five domains: grana surface, core, margins, stroma lamellae, and stroma lamellae Y-100 (**Figure 1**). A calculation of the total number of Chl associated with PSI and PSII suggested that more Chl (approximately 10%) are associated with PSI than with PSII, in agreement with results showing that PSI absorbs approximately 20% more photons than PSII (3, 5, 149, 150). Two distinct photosystem subtypes (PSIα, PSIβ and PSIIα, PSIIβ) were identified by biophysical experiments. Assuming an antenna size for PSIIβ in stroma lamellae of 100 Chl, the other antenna sizes are (*a*) PSIα (grana margins), 300 Chls; (*b*) PSIβ (stroma lamellae), 214 Chl; and (*c*) PSIIα (grana core), 280 Chl (73). These complexes were not characterized by biochemical methods, and the PSI results are inconsistent with those from an analysis of the recent structure of plant PSI (28). Moreover, the cyt b_6f complex and the F-ATPase were not quantified in these domains. Future studies of components of the thylakoid membrane must employ a concerted biochemical and structural approach, using current methods and available high-resolution structures. Used alone, any of the current methods runs the risk of producing artifacts. For example, treatment of thylakoid membranes with 0.5% dodecyl maltoside releases most of the F-ATPase, and surprisingly, PSII with very little contamination by PSI (9, 32). The current model for defined domains in the thylakoid membrane cannot explain this phenomenon.

Thylakoid Membrane-Protein Complexes: Definitions and Limits

Resolution-reconstitution biochemistry and molecular genetics have identified the functions of individual proteins in many membrane complexes, which are defined as the minimal structures that catalyze specific biochemical reactions. Analysis by sodium dodecyl sulfate (SDS) gels of the first isolated thylakoid membrane complexes revealed a shocking number of subunits (12, 26, 27, 84, 165, 193, 214). By biochemical standards, these preparations were reasonably pure, but this criterion alone cannot establish a polypeptide as a genuine subunit (218). An authentic subunit must be present in stoichiometric amounts, be necessary for activity, and also be required for assembly and/or stability of the holoenzyme (305). Even purified preparations may contain irrelevant polypeptides or may lose genuine subunits during isolation without a detectable effect on activity. Because eukaryotic and prokaryotic PSI and PSII reaction centers (RCs) are almost identical in their subunit composition, *Synechocystis* genetics has been invaluable for determination of the subunit structure and function of both photosystems (62, 291) and has also identified special properties of individual subunits.

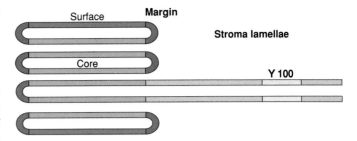

Grana

Surface

Margin

Stroma lamellae

Core

Y 100

Figure 1
A schematic model of domains of the thylakoid membrane. Mechanically disrupted thylakoids were separated into various fractions by differential centrifugation and phase separation (3).

RC: reaction center

Sequencing of the *Synechocystis* genome ended the race for discovery of new genes in this cyanobacterium and opened up the post-genomic era (62, 146, 324).

The PSI subunit composition is now defined by the polypeptides identified in the detergent-isolated, highly active complex and by the subunits detected in the crystal structure of plant PSI (28, 142, 258). Thus, PsaA-PsaL and light-harvesting, Chl-binding protein (LHC) LHCa1, LHCa2, LHCa3, and LHCa4 were proven to be genuine subunits of plant PSI. The PsaN and O proteins that were not detected in the structure are likely to be genuine subunits, but this hypothesis is not certain at the present time (142, 143, 167). Several other proteins may function as assembly factors (211, 212, 278, 316).

The subunit composition of PSII is much more complex than that of PSI. Identification of polypeptides in the highly active detergent-isolated preparations from spinach (33, 179), coupled with stepwise removal of various subunits (48), defined the minimum protein complex capable of O_2 evolution activity. Intrinsic light-harvesting proteins, such as LHCII, LHCb4 [Chl-binding protein (CP) 29], LHCb5 (CP26), and LHCb6 (CP24)] are easily removed with minimal activity loss; the remaining subunits cannot be extracted from the plant enzyme without affecting activity. These biochemical results, combined with mutagenesis experiments carried out in *Synechocystis* 6803 (291), defined the major intrinsic proteins as Psb A (D1), B (CP47), C (CP43), D (D2), and E and F, the polypeptides that donate axial His ligands to the heme iron of cyt b_{559}. Nuclear-encoded extrinsic proteins (PsbO, P, and Q) are required for O_2 evolution activity under physiological conditions. Cyanobacterial PSII contains PsbO (53), but a cyt (c_{550}, PsbV) and a 12 kDa polypeptide (PsbU) replace the PsbP and Q subunits in eukaryotes (269). The other polypeptides found in PSII are authentic subunits that are not directly involved in light harvesting or electron transfer reaction. The PsbS subunit (162, 299) is unique to eukaryotes and is required for nonphotochemical quenching (185). A report that it binds Chl (112) has not been substantiated (91). Of the other polypeptides (Psb H-L, N, R, T, and W-Z) associated with PSII, the functions of PsbN (4.7 kDa) and R (10.2 kDa) are unclear at the present time. The other subunits are discussed below.

Formation of Supercomplexes

Photosystems interact with other membrane complexes such as light-harvesting proteins or soluble proteins that mediate electron transport. Whereas PSI and PSII form supercomplexes with light-harvesting proteins (LHCI, LHCII), PSI also forms complexes with soluble electron donors and acceptors (82). The plant PSI structure (28, 32) revealed two distinct complexes: the RC and LHCI (see below and **Figure 1**). Models of the interactions between PSI and its soluble electron donors and acceptors are discussed in detail below. Because PSII utilizes a bound inorganic ion cluster of four Mn, one Ca^{2+}, and one Cl^- to oxidize H_2O and produce the electrons for reduction of plastoquinone, it has no soluble proteinaceous electron donors or acceptors (48, 89, 90). Nevertheless, PSII exhibits extensive protein-protein interactions in thylakoids. The plant RC is a dimer surrounded by tightly bound trimeric primary LHCII complexes (18); this supercomplex can interact with different numbers of additional LHCII units depending on light intensity and quality (57, 82, 140, 250). Barber & Nield (19) constructed detailed models using data on individual subunits, subcomplexes, two-dimensional projection maps, and electron microscopy (EM) single particle analyses; the high-resolution structure of the cyanobacterial PSII dimer and single particle images of intact PSII were then used to model the interaction between plant PSII and LHCII (18, 36, 82, 126). These models contain useful details, but three-dimensional structures of the plant PSII RC, both alone and with as many attached LHCII units as possible, are still highly desirable goals.

Information about the evolution of PSII-LHCII interactions comes from recent studies on bacteria and algae (20, 59). The Chl d light-harvesting system of *Acaryochloris marina* is composed of Pcb proteins, which associate with the PSII RC to form a giant supercomplex (approximately 2300 kDa) (59) composed of two PSII-RC core dimers arranged end-to-end and flanked by eight symmetrically-related Pcb proteins on each side. The *pcb* genes encoding these antenna proteins are present in multiple copies in low-light strains but as a single copy in high-light strains (35). Therefore, it is possible that adaptation of *Acaryochloris* to low-light environments triggered a multiplication and specialization of Pcb proteins comparable to that found for Chl a- and Chl b-binding antenna proteins in eukaryotes (35). If so, then attempts to regulate light absorption by modulating light-harvesting complexes are ancient and are probably necessary for efficient light harvesting and protecting RCs.

Higher-Order Interactions: Fact and Fiction

The PSI and PSII supercomplexes that form with variable amounts of membrane-bound peripheral antenna complexes also associate into megacomplexes or even semicrystalline domains (82). Whether these associations are physiological or preparative artifacts is debatable. Biochemical methods for detecting complex association use mild detergent solubilization, followed by size analysis using sucrose-density gradient centrifugation or electrophoresis on blue native gels and analysis of the subunit composition or spectroscopic properties of an individual band. For example, biochemical experiments on digitonin-solubilized thylakoids subjected to 2D blue native polyacrylamide gel electrophoresis resolved two high-molecular-weight PSI complexes (approximately 1060 and 1600 kDa), which were assigned to dimers and trimers (130). Whereas the evidence for these supercomplexes is quite convincing,

their origin and nature is unclear. A second method of analysis, using a combination of mild detergents and EM, identified similar aggregates: Dimers and larger aggregates of PSI were observed in spinach PSI preparations (40). However, a closer inspection of these particles revealed that they are composed of dimers and trimers that could not exist in native membranes, so it was concluded that these particles were formed during detergent treatment (173). It was also concluded that high-molecular weight bands detected on blue native gel electrophoresis, like the PSI dimers and trimers, do not constitute proof of the existence of native particles in the membrane.

EM investigations of the PSI–LHCI complex from spinach had already indicated that the LHCI subunits bind in one cluster at the side of the core complex occupied by PSI-F and PSI-J (38) when the plant PSI crystal structure revealed that it is a supercomplex containing an RC and a LHCI complex composed of four LHCa proteins (28). In contrast, *Chlamydomonas* is reported to contain considerably more LHCa polypeptides and is much larger than plant PSI (114, 156). One proteomics approach revealed up to 18 different LHCa proteins (134), but biochemical studies and a more recent proteomic analysis yielded 9 to 10 different subunits (277). Single particle analysis of EM projections revealed two particles (21 and 18 nm), on which 18 and 11 LHCa proteins, respectively, were modeled (114, 156). Modeling of the pea PSI structure into that of *Chlamydomonas* suggested nine bound LHCa proteins, a result consistent with recent biochemical studies (282). Eight or nine LHCa polypeptides would occupy the PsaF side of the complex and one would be found between PsaL, A and K (82). However, recent observations suggest that only one row of four LHCa is bound on the PsaF side, and the extra density is attributed to a detergent layer (J. Neild, personal communication). Also, the number of Chl molecules per *Chlamydomonas* PSI was reduced to approximately 215 to agree with the LHCI structure of plant PSI, with the addition of two or three additional LHCa, bound proximal to PsaK and G. These results emphasize the facts that single particle analysis must be viewed with some caution if x-ray structural data are unavailable.

BIOCHEMISTRY OF PHOTOSYSTEM I AND II

Biochemical Preparations of P700 Containing Complexes

Although Bessel Kok discovered the PSI RC Chl, P700, in the 1950s (169, 170), isolation of a well-defined PSI complex required the advent of SDS-polyacrylamide gel electrophoresis (181, 298). This technique, which is probably as important to membrane bio-

chemistry as the PCR reaction is to molecular biology, gave relatively precise identifications of proteins in membrane complexes. Initial studies with Chl-protein complexes separated from chloroplast thylakoids (26, 27) indicated that the photosystems are much more complex than bacterial RCs, which consist of three polypeptides, four bacteriochlorophylls, two bacteriopheophytins, and a nonheme iron (66, 228). Three well-defined biochemical preparations that catalyze light-induced oxidation of P700 have been isolated. As shown in **Figure 2**, the minimal structure that catalyzes this reaction, the P700 RC, contains two homologous polypeptides (PsaA and B) and approximately 80 Chl molecules (26, 27). The PSI RC, isolated from eukaryotes and cyanobacteria, catalyzes light-induced plastocyanin (PC)-ferredoxin (Fd) oxido-reduction and contains multiple protein subunits, approximately 100 Chl molecules and up to 14 different polypeptides (142, 143, 258). The largest complex, the PSI RC and LHCI, contains approximately 200 Chl molecules (17, 23, 210, 214, 218). The plant PSI structure identified 12 subunits in the RC and four different subunits in LHCI (28). Two subunits (PsaN and O) were not detected in the crystal structure. Future studies should determine whether they are genuine subunits or assembly factors.

Biochemical Preparations of O_2-Evolving PSII

The pioneering efforts to isolate plant PSII used Triton X-100 (292) or digitonin (11); the resulting preparations retained some PSI and had low O_2-evolution activity. A surprising insight into the complexity of the biochemical composition of PSII was provided by Akerlund et al. (2), who showed that "inside-out" thylakoids contained an extrinsic polypeptide that was required for O_2-evolution activity. Lastly, Izawa et al. (254) discovered artificial electron acceptors (i.e., p-phenylenediamines and p-benzoquinones) that provided an unambiguous assay of PSII

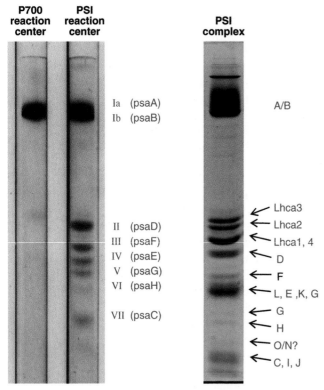

Figure 2

Subunit structure of photosystem I (PSI) preparations capable of light-induced P700 oxidation. Preparations of P700 RC and PSI RC were analyzed on cylinder SDS-gels (26). The PSI complex is the pea preparation used for crystallization. The probable subunit identities are indicated.

activity. These discoveries facilitated the isolation of highly active PSII preparations (33, 179) and demolished the myth that the O_2-evolving reaction was an "Inner Sanctum" (171) that was impervious to biochemical manipulations. Isolation of cyanobacterial PSII from *Synechocystis* 6803 was much more challenging (226), and His tagging has been used to facilitate rapid isolation (49). Like PSI, analysis of the composition of spinach PSII required SDS polyacrylamide slab gels. Unlike PSI, the final subunit count exceeded 20 (125), excluding the major light-harvesting polypeptides mentioned earlier. Cyanobacteria contain a comparable number of subunits, several of which have been resolved in the cyanobacterial crystal structures discussed below. The largest intrinsic membrane proteins of PSII (PsbB, 56.3 kDa) and C (CP 43, 51.8 kDa) bind Chl a and function as antennas. Isolation of PsbA and D in a complex with cyt b_{559} settled the early debates about the identity and composition of the PSII RC (256); PsbA (38.8 kDa) and PsbD (38.4 kDa) provide the ligands for the cofactors [i.e., 6 Chl a, 2 pheophytin a (Pheo a) molecules], 2 plastoquinones, a non-heme iron, the redox active tyrosines (Y_Z, Y_D), and the inorganic ions that catalyze H_2O oxidation] that make up the PSII electron transfer chain. Roles of the small intrinsic subunits of PSII are reviewed in detail by Thornton et al. (284). These subunits of PSII are genuine components of the multisubunit membrane complex, although they do not ligate electron transfer cofactors. Instead, they are required for assembly and stability of the enzyme complex.

The extrinsic proteins of plant PSII are PsbO (the manganese stabilizing protein, 26.5 kDa), PsbP (called the 23 kDa subunit, which is actually 20 kDa) and PsbQ (the 17 kDa subunit) (261). Cyanobacterial PSII contains PsbO; PsbV (cyt c_{550}, 17 kDa) and PsbU (12 kDa) replace PsbP and Q (269). The PsbP and Q subunits, along with PsbO, form a structure that facilitates retention of inorganic cofactors (Ca^{2+}, Cl^-) of the O_2-evolving reaction (115, 187, 205, 261). As PsbP and Q can be removed without significant loss of Ca^{2+} (302), some reevaluation of their functions may be necessary. The plant subunits also protect the manganese atoms from damage from reductants such as plastohydroquinone (116). In cyanobacteria, the small extrinsic subunits also appear to play a role in cofactor retention (268, 270). In addition, Kashino et al. (157) identified a protein in PSII from *Synechocystis* 6803 with some sequence identity to PsbQ. Thornton et al. (283) described site-directed mutations that eliminate the putative PsbQ subunit and a polypeptide that bears a sequence similarity to the PsbP subunit. The phenotypes of both mutants display a defect in O_2-evolution activity when the cells are grown on medium deficient in Ca^{2+} and Cl^-. PsbQ is stoichiometric with other PSII polypeptides but the PsbP homolog is present at much lower levels. The authors conclude that these subunits have a regulatory role in cyanobacteria and are required during the assembly of cyanobacterial PSII to produce a fully active enzyme system.

All oxygenic photosynthetic organisms contain PsbO [the manganese stabilizing protein (MSP)]. Extraction of PsbO from PSII lowers the rate of O_2 evolution and the residual activity requires unphysiologically high concentrations of Cl^- (261); PsbO-depleted PSII slowly loses Mn atoms and activity upon dark incubation, phenomena that are reversed by high Cl^- concentrations (206). Deletion of PsbO by mutagenesis in *Synechocystis* produces a phenotype that assembles PSII and grows photoautotrophically (53). Eukaryotic PSII is quite different: A *Chlamydomonas* mutant lacking PsbO could not assemble PSII (194), and a recent study using RNAi to suppress MSP levels in *Arabidopsis* produced a very similar result (313). There are other differences between eukaryotic and bacterial PsbO. The crystal structures of *Thermosynechococcus elongatus* and *T. vulcanus* contain one copy of PsbO (95, 155, 322). Low resolution EM structures of plant PSII were interpreted to indicate a similar stoichiometry. However, reconstitution studies (184, 306) and the effects of site-directed mutagenesis on the ability of PsbO to bind to PSII (34) support the hypothesis that two copies of PsbO are present, as does the absence from cyanobacterial PsbO of one of two N-terminal amino acid sequences in spinach PsbO that are necessary for binding of two copies of the protein to spinach PSII (239, 240). One PSII-PsbO interaction site is the latter's N terminus (92), which was localized by crosslinking to the large extrinsic domain of PsbB, between E364 and D440 (227). Specific N-terminal PsbO sequences required for binding have been identified (239, 240). In plant PSII, PsbO provides binding sites for attachment of PsbP and PsbQ, probably by electrostatic interactions or salt bridges (47, 285). The results of these experiments provide useful information on protein-protein interactions among the extrinsic and intrinsic subunits of PSII, but a complete understanding of such interactions requires high-resolution structural data that would be provided by crystals of plant PSII.

STRUCTURAL STUDIES ON PHOTOSYSTEM I AND II

The past two years have brought major additions to the steadily growing collection of molecular pictures of the components of the photosynthetic apparatus (**Figure 3**) (201, 218, 221). New structural work on PSII (37, 95, 160) and on LHCII (188, 276) has provided higher resolution structures than were previously available (155, 166, 175, 322). A portrait of the first membrane supercomplex of a plant PSI RC associated with its antenna LHCI also became available (**Figure 4**) (28). The similarity in composition and arrangement of cofactors in complexes that are separated by a billion years of evolution is striking (29, 220, 221), and the differences in protein-protein interactions and new features added during the long-term evolution of eukaryotic complexes emphasize the unique biological adaptations to ecological niches and environmental variation of these complex enzyme systems (220, 221). At the mechanistic level, the

new structures place restrictions on theoretical speculations and suggest experiments to support or reject old and new hypotheses.

The Structure of Plant Photosystem I

PSI is a remarkable nano-photoelectric machine that operates with a quantum yield close to 1.0 (219, 222). Theoretical quantum-mechanics solutions for such a mechanism exist (87, 105, 251, 311, 312), but no synthetic systems have approached this efficiency. This efficiency is why structural biologists who like to solve intricate structures were attracted to RCs (8, 80). The complexity of plant PSI is one of these challenges (262); as it is composed of a RC and LHCI, the resulting supercomplex presents an even bigger challenge than the bacterial RC (139, 219). It is therefore not surprising that the first PSI structure to be solved was that of the thermophilic cyanobacterium *T. elongatus* (111, 152, 260). The 2.5 Å structure (152), which contains a model of 12 protein subunits and 127 cofactors (96 Chl, 22 carotenoids, 2 phylloquinones, 3 Fe_4S_4 clusters, and 4 lipids), is a landmark achievement that provided the first detailed insights into the molecular architecture of PSI. The cofactor orientations and their interactions with protein subunits and other cofactors were determined (152). In crystals and in vivo, *T. elongatus* PSI is a trimer with a diameter of 210 Å and a maximum height of 90 Å. In contrast, plant PSI is a monomer, which, at 4.4 Å resolution, contains the models of 16 protein subunits, 167 Chl, 2 phylloquinones, and 3 Fe_4S_4 clusters (28). The main features of cyanobacterial and plant PSI are summarized in **Table 1**.

A stromal view of plant PSI (**Figure 4**) reveals two distinct, loosely-associated moieties: the RC and LHCI, which are separated by a deep cleft. The four LHCI subunits form two dimers arranged in series to create a half-moon-shaped belt docked on the F subunit side of the RC. This belt is the most prominent addition to the plant PSI structure. The RC retains the same location and

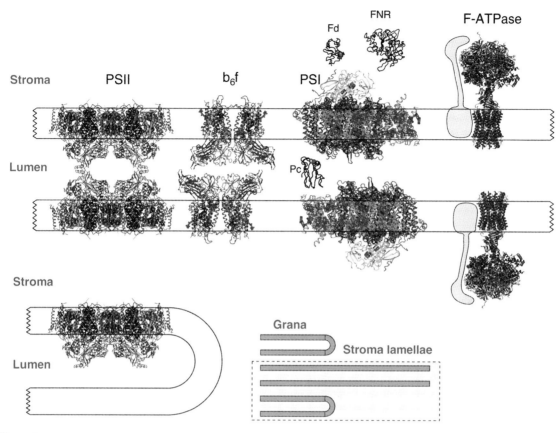

Grana   Stroma lamellae

Figure 3

The architecture of thylakoid membrane complexes and soluble proteins based on high-resolution structures. Available structural data on membrane-protein complexes and soluble proteins have been adjusted to the relative size of plant photosystem I (PSI). The structural data were obtained from Protein Data Bank (PDB): PSI – 1QZV, 1YO9 (theoretical model); Fd – 1A70; PC – 1AG6; ferredoxin-NADP-reductase – 1QG0. The structure of chloroplast F-ATPase was constructed from data on mitochondrial and bacterial F-ATPase-PDB 1H8E (catalytic) and 1YCE (membranal) (O. Drory, unpublished communication). The insert presents a schematic depiction of the segment of the thylakoid that was modeled with the structures.

orientation of electron transfer components and transmembrane helices found in cyanobacterial PSI, except for those of subunits X and M, which were either lost during chloroplast evolution or added to cyanobacterial PSI after it diverged from eukaryotic PSI (29, 220). Two additional subunits (PsaG and H) are present in plant PSI (**Figure 4**). PsaH, located adjacent to PsaL, has a single transmembrane helix followed by a 20 Å

long helix that lies on the stromal side of the membrane and coordinates one Chl molecule. PsaG is homologous to PsaK (230); it is situated on the opposite side of PsaK and contributes most of the contact surface area for association with LHCI (**Figure 4**). The two transmembrane helices of PsaG are connected by a relatively long loop that was assigned to the stromal side of the membrane (28), in agreement with recent biochemical data

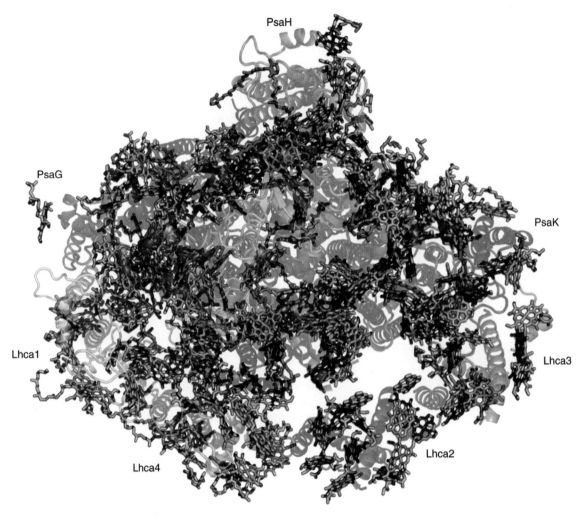

Figure 4

A view of the structure of plant photosystem I from the stromal side. The structural coordinates were taken from the theoretical refinement (PDB) of original structural data (PDB 1QZV) (26, 151). The Chl molecules (*green*) and the calculated positions of carotenoids and lipids (*red*) are shown. The protein backbone of the 16 subunits is in the background. The positions of PsaG, PsaH, PsaK, and LHCa1-4 subunits are shown.

(252). Although PsaK is so flexible in its position near PsaA that its loop was not apparent, even in the high-resolution structure of cyanobacterial PSI (152), PsaG is firmly bound to PsaB and also has helix-helix interactions with LHCa1 (**Figure 4**). Also on the stromal side, the general structure of the peripheral subunits PsaC, D, and E is almost identical to that of cyanobacterial PSI except for an N-terminal extension of PsaD that is unique to the eukaryotic subunit (**Figure 5**). We attribute the greater resistance of this domain of chloroplast PSI to chaotropic agents to this PsaD extension. On the lumenal side, the most noticeable distinction between plant and cyanobacterial RCs is the helix-loop-helix motif contributed by the longer N-terminal domain of plant PsaF (28), which facilitates more efficient PC binding. As a result, electron transfer from this copper protein to P_{700}

Table 1 Chlorophylls and transmembrane helices in PSI of cyanobacteria and higher plants[*]

Subunits	Transmembrane helices		Chlorophylls	
	Cyano	Plant	Cyano	Plant
A	11	11	40	40
B	11	11	39	39
F	1	1	—	—
I	1	1	—	—
J	1	1	3	2
K	2	2	2	2
L	3	3	3	3
M	1	—	1	—
X	1	—	1	—
G	—	2		1
H	—	1		1
Lhca1	—	3	—	13
Lhca2	—	3	—	13
Lhca3	—	3	—	12
Lhca4	—	3	—	13
RC			7	13
Linker (Chl)			—	5
Gap (Chl)			—	10
	32	45	96	167

[*]About eight additional densities in plant PSI are likely to be Chl molecules, giving a total of about 175 Chl molecules in plant PSI. The subunit-specific Chs coordinate the polypeptide chain. RC: Chls present in the reaction center with no apparent contact to specific subunit. Linker: Chls connecting the LHCa units. Gap: Chls situated between the reaction center and LHCI.

is two orders of magnitude faster than in cyanobacteria (135, 231).

In summary, the crystal structure of plant PSI reveals not only its architecture but also the possible mode of interaction with LHCI that causes supercomplex formation. The structure also provides new insights into the nature of the sites of interaction between PSI and PC, Fd, ferredoxin-NADP-reductase (FNR), and LHCII. As such, the structure provides a framework for investigating the mechanism of light harvesting and energy conversion, as well as the evolutionary forces that shaped the photosynthetic apparatus of terrestrial plants.

Electron Donors

PC is the universal PSI electron donor, although a cytochrome can replace it in cyanobacteria and algae; under certain physiological conditions, cyt c_6 can alternate with PC as an electron carrier between cyt f and P700 (159, 245). Reports that plants contain an equivalent of cyt c_6 that can function as electron donor to PSI (123, 296) were called into question by results showing that *Arabidopsis* plants mutated in both PC genes but with a functional cyt c_6 could not grow photoautotrophically (208, 300, 301). The complete block in light-driven electron transport in these mutants, even in the presence of an increased dosage of the gene encoding the cyt c_6-like protein, makes it highly likely that PC is the only mobile electron donor to higher plant PSI.

Information on the PSI-PC interaction came from PsaF-depleted PSI RCs that exhibited impaired $P700^+$ reduction by PC and slowed photo-oxidation of cyt c_{552} (a PC analog from green algae) (27). Although this result suggested that PsaF provided the PC binding site (27, 135, 231), a null mutation in PsaF in *Synechocystis* grew photoautotrophically at nearly wild-type rates (61). This enigma was resolved by the cyanobacterial PSI structure and by studies in *Chlamydomonas* that demonstrated the presence of a hydrophobic binding site shared by PsaA and B that exposes a conserved tryptophan residue to the lumen surface (152, 275). A *Chlamydomonas* PsaA mutation (W651F) abolished formation of a first-order electron transfer complex between PC and PSI (274). Thus, the PC binding site comprises mainly a hydrophobic interaction with PsaA and B and is facilitated and controlled by charge-charge interactions with PsaF. As a result, electron transfer from PC to PSI is two orders of magnitude faster in plants than in cyanobacteria, and the release of

FNR: ferredoxin-NADP-oxidoreductase

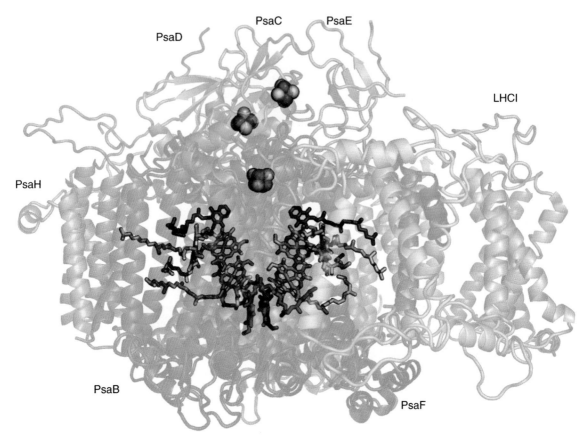

Figure 5

A side view of the structure of plant photosystem I. This figure was constructed as in **Figure 4**. The Chl, carotenoids, and lipids were eliminated. The cofactors involved in light-induced electron transport, i.e., P700, A_0, A_1, F_X, F_A, and F_B, are shown along with the backbones of the 16 subunits. The positions of PsaB, PsaC, PsaD, PsaE, and PsaF are shown. In the electron transport chain, the P700 Chl (*red*) and the other Chl (*green*) are indicated. The quinones (*blue*) and, in the iron-sulfur clusters, the iron (*red*) and the sulfur (*yellow*) are also indicated.

oxidized PC limits the electron-transfer rates (99, 119, 132, 133, 135). This effect was attributed to more efficient PC binding in plants that was mediated by the extra 18 amino acid residues in the plant PsaF N terminus. In the plant PSI structure, this extra N-terminal domain forms an amphipathic helix-loop-helix motif on the lumenal side of the thylakoid membrane (28), which, in comparison to the cyanobacterial structure (152), is the only alteration in the PC binding pocket. A model for the interaction of plant PC and PSI positions PC so that it interacts with the hydrophobic surface on PsaA and B and a positively charged site on PsaF (28). Superfluous degrees of freedom have been resolved by bringing a cluster of negatively charged conserved residues (i.e., Asp42, Glu43, Asp44, and Glu45) of PC into contact with the positively charged N-terminal domain of PsaF, which contains a few lysine residues that are missing in cyanobacteria (61, 135, 231, 246). The model in **Figure 6** suggests that the additional charges are responsible for more efficient PC binding in chloroplasts. One wonders whether this new interaction might generate

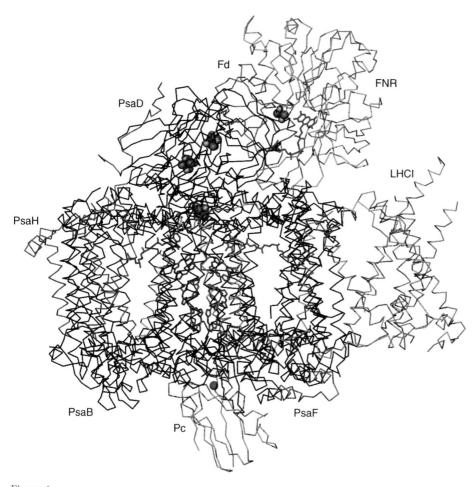

Figure 6

A side view model of putative interactions between plant photosystem I (PSI), plastocyanin, and the ferredoxin-ferredoxin-NADP-reductase complex. The four light-harvesting proteins (LHCa1-4) are shown (*green*). Novel structural elements within the RC (core) absent from cyanobacterial PSI (*red*) and the conserved features of both RC (*black*) are indicated. The Fe (*red balls*) and S (*green balls*) of the Fe-S clusters are shown. PC (*green*), its copper atom (*blue*), Fd (*magenta*), FNR (*orange*), and its FAD (*blue*), as well as the positions of the PsaB, PsaD, PsaF, and PsaH subunits, are also shown. The cofactors involved in light-induced electron transport from P700 to F_X are indicated (*blue*). The crystallographic data were from PDB: PSI – 1QZV, PC – 1AG6, and Fd-FNR complex – 1GAQ.

a constraint that restricts donor flexibility and therefore evolutionary loss of functional cyt c_6 in vascular plants (201).

Electron Transport Chain

The components of the PSI electron transport chain (ETC), P700, A_0, A_1, F_X, F_A, and F_B, were first identified spectroscopically dur-

ing the last half-century (44). Light-induced charge separation oxidizes the primary electron donor P700 (Redox potential E'_m + 430 mV), a Chl a/a' heterodimer, and reduces the primary electron acceptor A_0 ($E'_m \sim$ –1000 mV), a Chl a monomer. The electron is transferred to A_1 ($E'_m \sim$ –800 mV), a phylloquinone in most organisms; to F_X (E'_m –705 mV), an interpolypeptide (4Fe-4S)

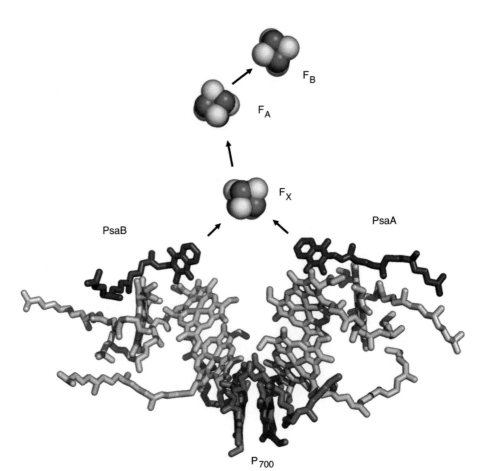

Figure 7
Structural model of
the pathway for
light-induced
electron transport
from P700 to F_B in
photosystem I
(PSI). The
cofactors involved
in light-induced
electron transport
in PSI are
presented using the
same color scheme
as in **Figure 5**.
PsaA and PsaB
indicate the
sidedness of the
model.

cluster; and finally to F_A (E'_m − 520 mV)
and F_B (E'_m − 580 mV), which are 4Fe-
4S clusters bound to the extrinsic subunit
PsaC (**Figures 7** and **8**). The high-resolution
structure of PSI established the spatial arrangement among these cofactors but also
raised questions about their mode of action
and the possible involvement of neighboring molecules in their activity (120, 152,
317). The ETC is arranged in two quasi-
symmetrical branches consisting of six Chl,
two phylloquinones (A_1), and three Fe_4S_4
clusters (F_X, F_A, and F_B). P700 is composed of a Chl pair, Chl a and Chl a',
that are not identical and therefore deviate from perfect symmetry. A pair of Chl a
molecules situated symmetrically approximately 16 Å from P700 were assigned to the
spectroscopically-characterized primary acceptor A_0. To complicate matters, another pair
of Chl a monomers is located approximately
halfway between P700 and A_0 (**Figures 7**
and **8**) that are assigned as accessory Chl
that may participate in excitation and/or electron transfer (see below). From A_0, the electron is transferred to one of two clearly resolved quinones and from there to F_X. The
quinones are placed on a pseudo-twofold-
symmetry axis, but their angles and interactions with the protein are clearly not identical.

The presence of two symmetrical cofactor
branches in PSI (**Figures 7** and **8**) raised the
question of whether one or both are active in
electron transport under physiologically relevant conditions (43, 45, 74). By analogy to the
RC in purple bacteria, it was proposed that
electron transfer in PSI occurs preferentially
along one branch. Alternatively, the fact that

PSI is related to the green bacterial type I RC, which is a homodimer (29, 54, 55, 93, 108, 128, 129, 186, 220), and the nearly perfect symmetry of the PSI ETC suggested that electron transfer should occur along either branch (243). Electron-nuclear double resonance (ENDOR) studies of PSI mutations in the residues binding P700 showed that the Chl on the PsaB side carries most of the electron spin density of $P700^+$ (174, 297); this observation indicates that there are differences in the electronic characteristics of the two branches. Low-temperature Electron Paramagnetic Resonance (EPR) experiments on the accumulation or reoxidation of the quinone acceptor A_1 detected a single quinone, but the identity of the active branch was unclear (213, 247).

In cyanobacterial PSI, site-directed mutations on the PsbA branch markedly alter the kinetics of the first steps of electron transfer and the spectral properties of the primary electron acceptor A_0, whereas mutations on the PsaB-branch yield kinetics and spectral properties that are essentially undistinguishable from the wild-type (68, 308, 309). It was therefore concluded that most of the electron transfer takes place on the PsaA branch in prokaryotes. Studies on eukaryotes, however, find evidence of significant PsaB-branch activity (41, 94, 122, 148, 213, 241, 242). Picosecond optical spectroscopy showed that the replacement of the Met axial ligand to Chl a (either eC-A3 or eC-B3) (152) by His in *C. reinhardtii* PSI partially blocked electron transfer; this observation indicates that both branches are active in electron transfer (243). However, these data were challenged by a low-temperature transient EPR study (197). This result raises the point that, although site-directed mutants are useful tools for mechanistic research, studies of the mutants have to be complemented by high-resolution structures; small changes due to a slight movement in one of the polypeptides that bind cofactors could lead to erroneous conclusions.

At the present time, the most convincing studies on the sidedness of electron trans-

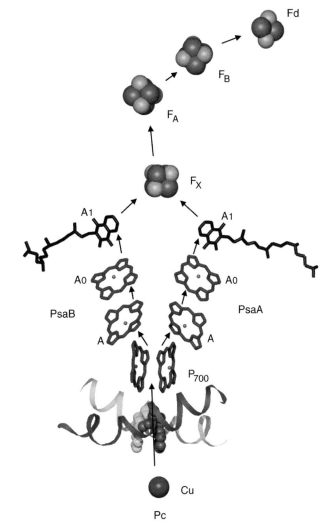

Figure 8

Structural model of the pathway for light-induced electron transport from plastocyanin to ferredoxin in photosystem I. Chls (*blue*), quinines (*black*), the copper atom of PC (*blue*), and Fe (*red balls*) and S (*green balls*) of the three Fe4-S4 clusters and the Fd Fe2-S2 are depicted. Two tryptophan residues (*light-blue and light-pink space-filling structures*) that might be involved in electron transport from PC to P700 are also shown in the context of their secondary structural environment.

port in PSI come from optical spectroscopy in wild-type organisms (148); these studies suggest that fast absorption changes are associated with PsaB quinone reoxidation. This hypothesis was based on the observation that mutations in the PsaA quinone-binding site have substantial effects only on the ∼200 ns reoxidation rate, whereas symmetrical mutations in the PsaB quinone-binding site affect only the ~20 ns reoxidation rate (122). In a very recent discussion of the sidedness in PSI electron transfer with the phylloquinones bound to either the PsaA or the PsaB subunits (255), the partial reaction in the electron transfer chain that could not be simulated is the phylloquinone (A_1) reoxidation reaction. In order to simulate measured rates of the biphasic decay (approximately 20 and 200 ns), a novel model was presented that suggests that the redox potentials of the quinones are almost isoenergetic with that of the iron sulfur center, F_X. Therefore, the only substantially irreversible electron-transfer reactions would be the reoxidation of A_0 on both electron transfer branches and the reduction of F_A by F_X. This hypothesis, along with future ultrafast measurements and high resolution studies of wild-type and mutated PSI, are likely to elucidate the mechanism of electron transfer in PSI.

Electron Acceptors

Fd's function as the principle PSI electron-acceptor plays a significant role in determining the enthalpy on earth. Fd reduces $NADP^+$ via FNR for various reductive biosynthetic pathways, thioredoxin via Fd-thioredoxin reductase for redox regulation, and also enzymes such as acyl carrier protein (ACP) desaturase, nitrite reductase, and glutamic acid synthase. Fd also reduces the cyt b_6f complex or plastoquinone in a cyclic electron transfer pathway around PSI that generates a proton gradient and, hence, ATP synthesis (52, 141, 153, 195, 196) (see below). Fd is a soluble protein with one 2Fe-2S cluster that accepts electrons from the F_B cluster on the stromal side of the PSI complex. In certain organisms, this reaction takes place under extreme conditions such as high temperature (103, 217). The Fd-PSI interaction involves the PsaC, D, and E subunits (10, 190, 204). The reduction of Fd by F_B involves three first-order components with $t_{1/2}$ values of 500 ns, 13–20 μs, and 100–123 μs

(266, 267). The 500 ns phase corresponds to electron transfer from F_A/F_B to Fd. Based on kinetic arguments, it has been proposed that a PsaE-dependent, transient tertiary complex containing PSI, Fd, and FNR forms during linear electron transport (288). **Figure 6** depicts a model of such a tertiary complex that is based on the structures of plant PSI (28), the Fd-FNR complex (177), and cross-linking data (101, 102, 183, 265). The Fd-FNR structure was fitted to the most likely contact sites that (*a*) obey the structural constraints and (*b*) place the electron carrier at distances that allow for the observed kinetics of electron transport (**Figure 6**). Although the two structures could not be fitted in a way that places Fd close enough to F_B to obtain the necessary rate of electron transfer between them, the model allows oxidized Fd to toggle towards F_B and close the gap between them. Upon reduction, Fd returns to its initial position, close enough to the FNR flavin for efficient electron transfer. Obviously, the actual structures of PSI-Fd and PSI-Fd-FNR supercomplexes are needed to better understand the mechanism of electron transport between F_B and $NADP^+$. The recent report of a cyanobacterial crystal of a 1:1 PSI:Fd complex (109) that diffracts to 7–8 Å may be the first step in this direction. Fd-mediated electron transport is not the only reaction that can occur on the reducing side of PSI. Cyanobacteria grown under iron-depleted conditions synthesize a flavoprotein (flavodoxin) that replaces Fd functionally in most, but not all, reactions (199, 225).

Light-Harvesting and Excitation Migration in Plant Photosystem I

PSI maintains a quantum yield of approximately one in all its forms in various organisms (219, 220). This efficiency persisted for 3.5 billion years of evolution and survived an enormous number of potential mutations. Not surprisingly, the sequences of genes encoding PsaA and B exhibit very high amino acid sequence conservation, in particular for the amino acids that are likely to coordinate

Chl (29, 30, 151, 262). Other factors are also important for Chl binding, however. The plant PSI structure revealed that only 3 of the 96 Chl molecules reported in the model of the cyanobacterial PSI RC are missing: two bound to PsaM and PsaX, and one bound to PsaJ (**Table 1**). Of the remaining 93 Chl, 92 are found at the same position in the plant RC; these Chls include 15 that have their Mg^{2+} coordinated by H_2O (28). Only one of these (B33) had a significantly changed position; this change was due to the insertion in plant PSI of a three-amino-acid loop that coordinates this Chl, whose novel position resulted in loss of the long wavelength (730 nm) "red trap" of cyanobacterial PSI. A few other minor alterations, mainly in chromophore orientation, were also observed (28). Thus, to adapt the plant RC to utilize energy from the LHCI antenna required the addition of only 10 Chl molecules at three contact regions (17, 210). It is not clear whether the exact position and coordination of each Chl molecule contributes to the almost perfect quantum yield of the system, and, if so, how a deleterious mutation in the system would be detected and corrected (220).

Structural information on the geometry of the Chl molecules in PSI permits the construction of microscopic models for an excitation-transfer network of PSI (56, 72, 118, 158, 200, 263, 264, 310). Once the location and orientation of pigments are determined, excitation-transfer rates between pigments are described by Forster theory (105, 251), or, for strong couplings and fast timescales, by Redfield theory (310). Thus, excitation-transfer pathways among the pigments of cyanobacterial and plant PSI can be defined as an excitation-transfer network (262). This approach yielded computations of kinetic parameters (average excitation lifetimes, overall quantum efficiency) to a reasonable accuracy, as well as the construction of stochastic models whose robustness (error tolerance) and optimality (high relative fitness) allow probing of the network by comparing the pigment network geometry with alternative geometries (289). These models must ultimately be verified experimentally.

Structure of Photosystem II

In the case of plant PSII, a three-dimensional model of the plant PSII supercomplex obtained by cryoelectron microscopy and single particle analysis is available (223), but the only available crystal structures are of the PsbP and PsbQ extrinsic subunits, at 1.6 and 1.95 Å resolution, respectively (58, 138) These structures are presented in **Figure 9**. The larger subunit is composed mainly of β-sheets, and does not appear to have any structural features in common with its cyanobacterial counterpart (PsbV). The structure of PsbQ likewise has no counterpart among cyanobacterial subunits. The core of this protein is a four-helix bundle, but the N-terminal 45 residues are mobile and are not resolved in the structure shown in the figure. This flexible domain of PsbQ is believed to be involved in binding to PSII (261). Attempts to crystallize PsbO failed, possibly because it is intrinsically disordered (191). Attempts to produce diffraction quality crystals of intact plant PSII were difficult (107) due to proteolysis of samples during crystallization (D.F. Ghanotakis, personal communication). This problem was not encountered in attempts to crystallize PSII from thermophilic cyanobacteria (i.e., *T. elongatus*, *T. vulcanus*) (95, 155, 322). The protein complex forms dimers in the crystals, and the resolution of the structures ranges from 3.8 to 3.5 Å; a more recent report gave a resolution of 3.2 Å (37), and further improvements may appear before this review is published.

Stromal and sideview models of PSII structure based on the data presented by Ferriera et al. (95) are shown in **Figures 10** and **11**. Such models are satisfying because many of their features coincide with predictions derived from biochemical and spectroscopic probing experiments; however, they also provide enhanced structural details regarding placement of the individual subunits and the orientations of pigments associated

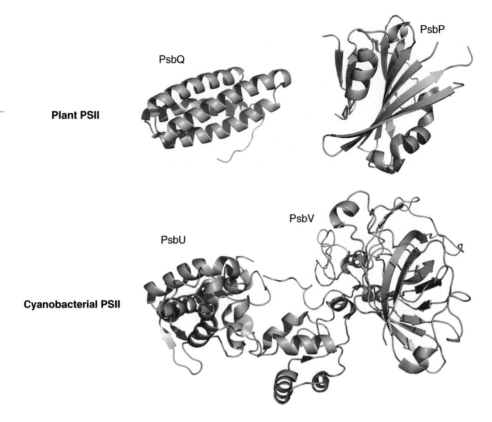

Figure 9

Structures of the smaller extrinsic polypeptides of photosystem II (PSII). The plant PSII subunit structures are taken from crystals of the isolated proteins (58, 138). Structural data are from PDB: PsbQ-1NZE and PsbP - 1V2B. The cyanobacterial structure shows the interaction between PsbU and PsbV, taken from the *T. elongatus* structure (PDB: PSII-1S5L) (95).

with the RC and its antenna system. In all of the structures now available, it can be seen that membrane-spanning helices of the PsbA and PsbD RC subunits are in close proximity to one another. RC chromophores (comprising six Chl, two Pheo$_a$, the plastoquinones Q_A and Q_B, and the redox-active tyrosines Y_Z and Y_D) are bound to these subunits, as expected. The PsbC subunit is close to PsbA, and PsbD is in close proximity to PsbB. The disposition of Chl molecules in PsbB and C are now better resolved; 14 Chl a are bound to PsbB, and 16 are bound to PsbC. For 23 Chl, the ligand to the central Mg^{2+} atom of the chlorin ring is a His-imidazole nitrogen. Seven β-carotenes are resolved in the structure; one of these connects cyt b$_{559}$, Chl$_{zD1}$, and P680, the RC Chl of photosystem II (37). The large extrinsic loops of PsbB and C are readily visible as significant protrusions into the lumenal space above the membrane-spanning α-helices of these large subunits. Accessory subunits (i.e., PsbH, I, J,

K, L, M, N, T, X, and Z) are modeled into the structure; L, M, and T are suggested to be involved in formation of PSII dimers, whereas I and X are proposed to stabilize binding of the fifth and sixth Chl molecules, Chl$_{ZD1}$ and Chl$_{ZD2}$, that are bound to PsbA and D, respectively. The PsbJ, K, N, and Z subunits are clustered near PsbC, and are hypothesized to be involved in carotenoid binding (95). On the stromal side of the structure, the Q_A binding site is composed of amino acid residues contributed by PsaD; for the Q_B site, the ligands are donated by PsbA. A nonheme iron ligated between these sites completes a structure that is quite similar, but not identical, to the quinone sites in photosynthetic bacteria (160). A summary of this information, including the proposed subunit-cofactor interactions, is presented in **Table 2**.

As predicted from biochemical and mutagenesis experiments (46), the large extrinsic loops of PsbB and C provide binding sites for

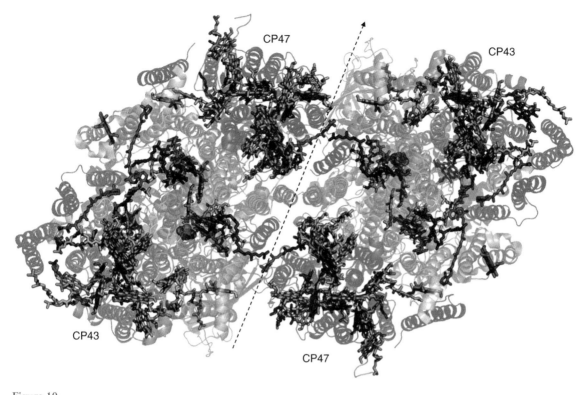

Figure 10

A stromal side view of the structure of the cyanobacterial photosystem II (PSII) dimer. The polypeptide chains are shown at lower contrast to reveal the chromophores; PsbB (*PsbB*) and PsbC (*PsbC*) are labeled, and the boundary between the monomeric RCs is indicated (*dashed arrow*). Chl a (*green*), carotenoids (*red*), and plastoquinones (*blue*) are also shown. The structure is based on PSII PDB-1S5L.

attachment of PsbO, which is visible on the lumenal side of the complex as an elongated structure containing β-sheets, consistent with predictions from physical characterizations of the soluble protein (34, 191, 192, 272, 307, 323). In the structural model, the N terminus of the protein is bound to the extrinsic loop of PsbC, whereas a loop in the PSbO structure makes contact with the extrinsic domain of PsbB. The structure gives no evidence for the interaction detected in plant PSII between the PsbO N terminus and the extrinsic loop of PsbB (227). The presence of two copies of PsbO in plants (306) may be responsible for the extra PsbO-PsbB interaction in spinach. Although PsbO stabilizes the inorganic ion cluster, the 3.5 Å model predicts that no PsbO ligands bind to the Mn atoms. How-

ever, a loop in PsbO extends in the direction of the Mn cluster, and this loop is proposed to function as a hydrophilic pathway between the lumen and the inorganic ion cluster (95). The smaller extrinsic subunits of cyanobacterial PSII appear to bind through interactions with PsbO and with one another; a model of the PsbU-PsbV subunits is given in **Figure 9**. A comparison of this structure with that of the two plant subunits, as shown in **Figure 9**, points to the substantial differences between these pairs of proteins. The plant subunits either contain a four-helix bundle (PsbQ) or are rich in β-sheets (PsbP), features that are absent from the structures of PsbU and V. The presence of a heme in PsbV gives further evidence for the marked differences between the prokaryotic and eukaryotic subunits.

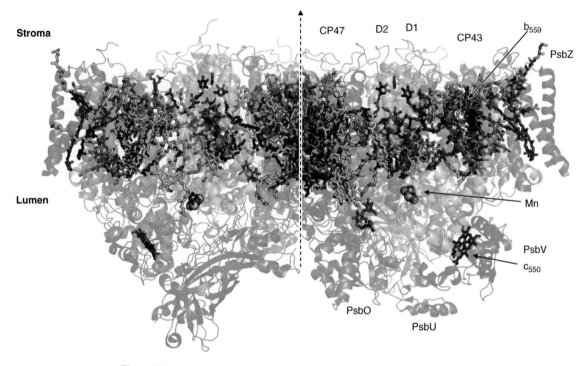

Figure 11

Side view of the structure of cyanobacterial photosystem II. Positions of the extrinsic polypeptides are indicated, along with the intrinsic subunits PsbA-D and the small intrinsic accessory subunit, PsbZ. The chromophore colors are as given in **Figure 10**; the c_{550} and b_{559} hemes (*red*) and the Mn cluster (*blue*) are highlighted. The pseudo-C_2-symmetry axis between the monomeric subunits of the homodimer is also indicated (*vertical dashed arrow*).

Caution is advisable in drawing firm conclusions about the structure of PSII from the available structures. Limited resolution (3.8–3.2 Å) requires some interpretive modeling to build structures as, for example, with the amino acid side chains (37). A major issue concerns the structure of the inorganic ion cluster itself. All models to date propose a monomer-trimer arrangement of the Mn atoms in the cluster, in agreement with spectroscopic experiments (236). In the detailed model of Ferreira et al. (95), three Mn atoms and an atom of Ca^{2+} form a distorted cube-like structure; an isolated Mn atom may be positioned to play a role in H_2O oxidation, which we discuss below. Unfortunately, high X-ray energies and exposure times used to obtain diffraction data resulted in radiation damage that reduced the Mn atoms, probably to all Mn^{2+}, in contrast to the native Mn^{3+} and Mn^{4+} oxidation states (164, 248). It is likely that Mn^{2+} has dissociated from native ligands, causing some rearrangement of the amino acid residues in the binding site (76). This possibility is also suggested by Fourier Transfer Infra Red spectoscopy (FTIR) experiments on *Synechocystis* 6803 PSII that showed that the carboxyl terminus of PsbA (Ala344) is a ligand to the Mn cluster (63, 207, 279). The most detailed model based on the crystal structure places this residue near the Ca^{2+} atom but not as a Mn ligand. These reservations should not detract from the enormous achievement of obtaining a crystal structure of PSII; however, more data, obtained at shorter exposure times, are required to validate current models of the inorganic ion cluster.

Electron Transport in Photosystem II

Characterizations of PSII by a variety of methods summarized in References 78, 89, 90, 117, and 203 identified the electron transport cofactors in PSII, including Mn, Ca^{2+}, and Cl^- in H_2O oxidation and their stoichiometries (i.e., four Mn, one Ca^{2+}, and one Cl^- per RC) (1, 179, 187, 271, 315). The identification of redox-active tyrosines, one of which (Y_Z) mediates electron transfer from the inorganic ion cluster to P680 in the RC, was a significant advance in understanding PSII electron transfer (21). A functional analogy between PSII and the bacterial RC formed the basis for the current model of electron transfer (89). Therefore, the pathway of electron transfer in PSII is generally agreed to be as follows: $H_2O \rightarrow [Mn_4CaCl] \rightarrow Yz/Y_Z^\bullet \rightarrow P680/P680^+ \rightarrow Pheo_a/Pheo_a^- \rightarrow Q_A/Q_A^- \rightarrow Q_B/Q_B^-$. Double reduction and protonation of Q_B^- releases Q_BH_2 from its PSII binding site in exchange for an oxidized quinone (89). It is now clear from mutagenesis of the heme-binding pocket of cyt b_{559} that it is not required for O_2-evolution activity (209), although cyt b_{559} is necessary for assembly of stable PSII complexes and may function in a cyclic reaction around PSII (290).

The estimated redox potentials of intermediates in the PSII electron transfer pathway depend on the potential (E'_m) of the primary oxidant, $P680^+/P680$, which was set at +1.12 V based on a potential of −0.64 V for the Pheo a/Pheo a- couple (90). Other potentials are as follows: (*a*) O_2/H_2O, +0.93V; (*b*) $Y_Z^\bullet/Y_Z$, +0.97 V; (*c*) Q_A^-/Q_A, −0.03 V; and (*d*) Q_B/Q_B^-, +0.030V (89, 287). A reevaluation of the P680 and Pheo$_a$ reduction potentials are in order (71, 244), based on new results that suggest a more positive potential (+1.27 V) for $P680^+/P680$ and therefore for Pheo a/a- and for intermediate redox states in the H_2O-oxidizing reaction as well. The kinetics of electron-transfer reactions have been worked out in detail. The rate-limiting step in H_2O-oxidation is approximately 1.4 ms;

Table 2 Chlorophylls, transmembrane helices, and cofactors of O_2-evolving PSII RCs from cyanobacteria and plants[1]

Subunits	Transmembrane helices		Chlorophylls		Other cofactors
	Cyano	Plant	Cyano	Plant	
A	5	5	3	3	Y_Z, 4Mn, Pheo a, Q_B
B	6	6	16	16 (?)	
C	6	6	14	14 (?)	
D	5	5	3	3	Y_D, Q_A
E	1	1			Cyt b_{559} heme
F	1	1			Cyt b_{559} heme
H	1	1			
I	1	1			
J	1	1			
K	1	1			
L	1	1			
M	1	1			
O	0	0			
P[2]	—	0			
Q[2]	—	0			
S	—	4			
T	1				
U[3]	0	—			
V[3]	0	—			Cyt c_{550} heme
X	1	1			
Y	1	1			
Z	2	2		—	
...	...	...	...	....	
	35	38 (?)	36	36 (?)	

[1] The number given for transmembrane helices in cyanobacteria is taken from the models constructed from crystallographic data (95, 155, 160, 322), but should be viewed as provisional until higher-resolution data become available (37). For higher plants, hydropathy plotting was used to predict the number of transmembrane helices.
[2] An extrinsic subunit unique to plant PSII.
[3] Extrinsic subunits unique to cyanobacteria.

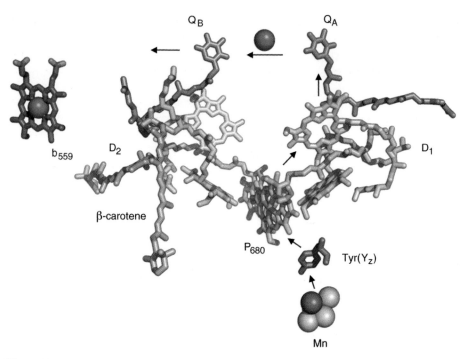

Figure 12

Structure of the photosystem II (PSII) electron transfer chain. The direction of electron transfer down the right (D1 or PsbA) side from P690 to Q_A is indicated (*arrows*). The following cofactors are shown: Chl a (*green*), Pheo a (*light blue*), plastoquinones (*purple*), cyt b_{559} heme and reducing-side nonheme iron (*red*), carotenoids (*orange*), Ca^{2+} (*magenta*), and Mn atoms (*blue*); one Mn atom is obscured in the structure. The structure is based on PDB: PSII-1S5L.

electron transfer from Y_Z to $P680^+$ occurs in the ns to μs time domain, and electron transfer from P680 to $Pheo_a$ occurs in approximately 3 ps. Reduction of Q_A by Pheo a- occurs in 250–300 ps, and the $Q_A^- \rightarrow Q_B$ reaction has a half-time of approximately 100 μs (89, 90).

The crystal structures of PSII have revealed more exact details of the organization of electron transfer cofactors (95, 155, 322); a model is presented in **Figure 12** in which the accessory Chls (Chl_{ZD1} and Chl_{ZD2}) are omitted for clarity. The bifurcated electron transfer pathway comprised of Chl a, Pheo a, and plastoquinones is similar to the arrangement of cofactors of the RC of purple photosynthetic bacteria (80). A notable difference is the spacing of the two Chl molecules that are presumed to make up P680. In PSII this distance is estimated to be 8.3 Å (95) rather than

the 7.6 Å in bacteria. The longer distance is in accord with the proposal that, in PSII, the entire array of RC pigments might be able to function as a multimeric RC (83), even though a localized Chl cation radical is present in the charge-separated state (90). The structural model shows that the cofactors are separated by relatively short distances: 10.6 Å for P680-Chl a [PsbA(D1)] and for Chl a [PsbA (D1)]-Pheo a, and 14 Å for Pheo a -Q_A (160). These distances are consistent with the rapid rates of electron transfer that have been measured. The two carotenoids shown in the model presented in **Figure 12** include the pigment that, along with the accessory Chl molecule (Chl_{ZD1}) and cyt b_{559}, may be involved in a cyclic electron-transfer pathway from b_{559} on the reducing side of PSII back to the oxidizing side (90, 290). The Y_Z-Mn cluster complex is shown at the bottom of the figure.

The model, a monomer-trimer arrangement of Mn atoms, is similar to the structure derived from magnetic resonance experiments (236, 281). The distance between the tyrosine and the metal center is approximately 7 Å; this observation is in agreement with the distance derived from magnetic resonance experiments (50, 182). Mn ligands proposed in the model (D170, E189, E333, E354, H337, H332, and D342) (95) are all donated by PsbA. These ligands include residues identified as possible ligands by either site-directed mutagenesis (79, 88) or pulsed-magnetic-resonance spectroscopy (51). All models based on either crystal structures or on spectroscopic measurements (64, 163) predict a close interaction (3.5–4.5 Å) between Mn atoms and the Ca^{2+} in the metal cluster.

Mechanism of O_2 Evolution

The model for O_2 evolution invokes a set of oxidation states ("S" states) (172) to explain the period-four release of O_2 from thylakoids exposed to short ($<10 \mu s$) flashes of light. The reaction is a linear sequence of photocatalyzed oxidations, beginning in dark-adapted material from the S_1 state; the S_4 state decomposes spontaneously to release O_2 and form the S_0 state. The entire sequence may be written as: $2H_2O + S_0 \rightarrow S_1 \rightarrow S_2 \rightarrow S_3 \rightarrow S_4 \rightarrow S_0 + O_2 + 4 H^+$. Because Mn is the only redox-active metal in the site of H_2O oxidation, considerable effort has gone into probing its behavior. Spectroscopic experiments (164, 236, 248) as well as reductive titrations (176) give Mn oxidation states for S_1 of $2 Mn^{3+}/2 Mn^{4+}$. Results of several spectroscopic experiments (75, 81, 233, 236) point to Mn oxidation on each S-state advancement up to S_3. The rapid decay of the S_4 state ($t_{1/2} = \sim 1.4$ ms) prohibits characterization of the step in which O_2 is formed and released from PSII. Speculations about the identity of the terminal oxidant in the mechanism include $Y_Z^{\bullet}$ and a Mn^{5+} species as possible candidates (136, 235, 294, 295). The identity of the terminal oxidant is a critical issue that must be resolved for a full understanding of the chemistry of H_2O oxidation.

The roles of Cl^- and Ca^{2+} in H_2O oxidation are also topics of great interest. Removal of either ion from PSII blocks S-state advancement at S_2 (42, 187, 234). In the case of Cl^-, it has been shown that the anion is required for the $S_4 \rightarrow S_0$ transition and that its binding to the oxygen-evolving complex (OEC) is weaker in the higher S-states (302, 303). Evidence for a close proximity of Cl^- to the Mn cluster has also been presented (67, 182), and some models of the OEC show it as a ligand to Mn (286, 295), although this status has not been definitively confirmed by spectroscopic methods (127). Calcium has been shown to stabilize the ligand environment of the Mn cluster (198, 249); however, the requirement for Ca^{2+} to advance the S-states beyond S_2 suggests that it may play a more direct role in the mechanism of H_2O oxidation as well.

Critical questions about the mechanism of H_2O oxidation focus on (a) the steps at which substrate oxidation occurs and (b) the roles of Mn, Ca^{2+}, and Cl^- in this process. Experiments employing time-resolved mass spectrometry and isotopically-labeled H_2O indicate that the substrate binds in S_0 and S_3 (131). Advancements of the S-states are accompanied by H^+ release; the prevailing notion is that H^+ release follows a 1:0:1:2 pattern starting from S_0 (259). The origin of the protons released into the medium continues to be a subject of debate (see Reference 90); H_2O is the ultimate source, but the phenolic H^+ of Y_Z may form part of a H^+-transfer network. Another question concerns the pathway(s) by which H^+ exits the site of H_2O oxidation. Evidence that His190 of the PsbA subunit is involved, perhaps by hydrogen-bonding to the phenolic proton of Y_Z as a first step in H^+ transfer network, has been presented, but this observation has not been confirmed by spectroscopic methods (79). A proposal, based on the 3.5 Å structure, suggesting that some lumenal residues of PsbA participate in a proton transfer pathway (95), has not been tested experimentally. Regardless of the pathway, proton transfer coupled to electron transfer from the Mn cluster to $Y_Z^{\bullet}$ is an essential component of H_2O-oxidation chemistry. An uncompensated positive charge increase on the Mn cluster would generate an energetic barrier to subsequent oxidation reactions; this would be avoided by coupling of electron and H^+ transfer, or by the transfer of H-atoms. The latter mechanism is the basis of the proposal that the mechanism of H_2O oxidation proceeds by H-atom transfer (136, 286). This hypothesis provided the impetus for renewed interest in electron-transfer mechanisms on the oxidizing side of PSII. The Y_Z-Mn distance ($\sim$7 Å) measured in PSII crystals is too long for H-atom transfer (95), but this observation needs to be reevaluated in light of the evidence that the Mn cluster in these crystals is damaged.

The complexity of the H_2O-oxidation site in PSII has presented an enormous challenge to the development of hypothetical mechanisms for the reaction. A real chemical intermediate in S_3 has been detected at high O_2 pressures (20 bar) (65). Three substrate binding sites for such an intermediate are the two redox-active Mn atoms and Ca^{2+}, which has been proposed to be a H_2O-binding site because it generally accommodates two or more bound H_2O molecules as ligands in other protein systems (253, 314). This aspect of Ca^{2+} chemistry forms the basis for including the metal in proposed mechanisms for H_2O oxidation (235, 295). These mechanisms utilize Ca^{2+} as a Lewis acid to deprotonate a bound H_2O; the resulting Ca^{2+}-bound OH^- is used as a nucleophile to attack an $O=Mn^{+5}$ to form the O-O bond that leads to O_2 formation and reduction of the cluster to S_0. Of all of the metals that can occupy the PSII Ca^{2+} site, only Sr^{2+} can restore O_2-evolution activity in place of Ca^{2+}, but at much lower rates (314). This observation correlates with the Lewis acidity of both Sr^{2+} and Ca^{2+}, both of which have higher acidities than other metals that bind to PSII but are ineffective in restoration of activity (295).

Although many questions remain, substantial progress has been made towards a better understanding of the mechanism of H_2O oxidation. The role of Mn as a redox-active catalyst has been established in all but the final step of the mechanism, and there are rational proposals for the function of Ca^{2+} in the mechanism. What is now required is a structure of the undamaged inorganic ion cluster at higher resolution, as well as additional experiments to characterize both possible reaction intermediates and the oxidation states of Mn in S_4.

Light Harvesting and Excitation Transfer in Photosystem II

Isolated plant PSII supercomplexes retain the light harvesting apparatus, which comprises trimeric LHCII complexes (82); the number of LHC per RC is reported to vary between two and four trimers (38, 39), whereas core dimers of PSII contain approximately eight LHC trimers (237). Monomeric LHCII contains 8 Chl a and 6 Chl b, so approximately 170 Chl per monomeric PSII RC are associated with this protein (188, 276). Less abundant Chl a-binding proteins such as LHCb4, LHCb5, and LHCb6 are also present as monomers in PSII. A summary of the structural evidence to date indicates that LHCb4 is located close to PsbB, LHCb5 is near PsbC, and LHCb6 makes contact with LHCb4. Strongly bound LHCII trimers are in close contact with the RC polypeptides of PSII whereas a second population of these complexes makes contact with LHCb4 and LHCb6 (82). Based on structural models, the pathway of energy transfer in PSII can be formulated as follows: Direct energy transfer from strongly-bound LHCII and from LHCb5 to PsbC is to be expected from the proximity of these subunits to one another and to the RC. Energy transfer to PsbB is believed to occur by a pathway from a less-tightly-bound population of LHCII to LHCb6, and then through LHCb4, which is in close contact with PsbB. The exact size of the pool of LHCII associated with each PSII super-complex is fluid due to state transitions (304), which we discuss in the next section.

Exciton transfer from the Chl a bound to PsbB and PsbC to the RC itself constitutes the final step in energy transfer. In this case, the recent crystal structures have been useful in providing estimates of the distance (approximately 20 Å) between the RC Chl and the nearest antenna pigments in PsbB and PsbC. This placement has the advantage of protecting the antennae Chl from oxidation by $P680^+$, but also has little effect on fast-excitation transfer to the RC, which in the case of PsbB has been estimated to occur in approximately 20 ps (15). Competing models for the kinetics of energy transfer propose that either (a) exciton transfer is rapid, and formation of the charge separated state is rate limiting, or (b) energy transfer between antennae and the RC is slow and constitutes the rate-limiting step (77, 202). There is evidence to support either model at the present time (90).

MOLECULAR BIOLOGY AND PHYSIOLOGY OF PHOTOSYSTEMS I AND II

Cyclic Electron Transport and State Transitions

Cyclic electron transport around PSI, first described 50 years ago by Arnon et al. (16), required relatively high Fd concentrations. The early evidence for cyclic activity was demonstrated first under nonphysiological conditions in isolated chloroplasts and then in vivo (106). It was later shown that cyclic electron flow might be induced by CO_2 depletion, drought, and other stress conditions (for review, see Reference 25). Cyclic electron flow was also observed in dark-adapted leaves at the onset of illumination (147, 149, 150) and also on the basis of measurements of PSI-dependent energy storage by photoacoustic methods (144). Two parallel paths of cyclic electron transport have been identified by dif-

ferences in antimycin sensitivity, saturation characteristics, and substrate specificity (257). A mutation in the PGR5 protein causes decreased PSI cyclic activity (216); PGR5 is membrane bound, but has no extensive hydrophobic sequence. PGR5 is therefore unlikely to be intrinsic to the thylakoid or to fulfill the function of a Fd-cyt b_6f or Fd-plastoquinone oxidoreductase. Nevertheless, PGR5 is thought to have a role in electron transport from FNR to the cyt b_6f complex (216) [FNR was proposed to be a genuine subunit of the complex (320), but this proposal is not supported by the cyt b_6f structure (280)]. It was shown that Fd reduction of plastoquinone is PGR5 dependent (216); this reduction could be direct (through an unknown Fd-plastoquinone oxidoreductase), or indirect (through the cyt b_6f complex). An Arabidopsis mutant with a conditional defect in Q-cycle activity, pgr1, showed no difference in PGR5-dependent plastoquinone reduction by Fd; this observation suggests direct reduction of plastoquinone (229). This result forces one to reconsider direct reduction by Fd of the cyt b_6f complex. The recent structures of cyt b_6f revealed a unique heme, termed heme x, that is high-spin five-coordinate with no strong field ligand. It is positioned close to the intramembrane heme b(n) that is occupied by the n-side bound quinone in the cyt bc_1 complex of the mitochondrial respiratory chain. Thus, heme x could function in Fd-dependent cyclic electron transport (70, 178, 280). Tight binding of FNR to the cyt b_6f complex would provide a possible Fd-binding site for F_D and would provide a pathway for electron flow from the acceptor side of PSI to plastoquinone via Fd, FNR, and heme x in the cyt b_6f complex. From plastoquinone, electrons would follow the normal pathway (i.e., via cyt f and PC) to P700. At the present time there is no experimental evidence for such a pathway, so the structural basis for cyclic electron transport remains unknown.

Cyclic photophosphorylation is an essential component of state transitions, which are used by photosynthetic organisms to adapt to changes in light quality by redistributing excitation energy between the two photosystems to enhance photosynthetic yield (24). At high light intensities, LHCII migrates from PSII to PSI (7). This movement is correlated with protein phosphorylation and an increase in the 77 K fluorescence signal from PSI at 735 nm relative to that at 685 nm from PSII (180). It was concluded that phosphorylation of a population of granal LHCII caused migration of these pigment proteins from the PSII-rich appressed membranes into the PSI-enriched unstacked regions. Numerous experiments, including single particle analysis (69), conducted in higher plants supported this model, but the detailed mechanism of state transitions was unclear (113, 318, 319). The existence of LHCII migration at high light intensity was challenged by experiments using pea plants (168), but isolation of photoautotrophic *Chlamydomonas* mutants that were deficient in state transitions moved the debate to firmer grounds (96, 104). The *stt*7 mutant cannot undergo state transitions and is blocked in state I. This mutant displays the same deficiency in LHCII phosphorylation as cyt b_6f mutants that cannot undergo state transitions (100). A thylakoid-associated serine-threonine protein kinase, Stt7, has been identified (86) and was shown to be required for phosphorylation of the major light-harvesting protein (LHCII) and for state transitions (293). *Arabidopsis* state transitions and light adaptation require a thylakoid protein kinase STN7 (24), so a protein kinase governs state transitions in both algae and higher plants.

Crosslinking experiments to analyze PSI-LHCII interactions showed that LHCII is situated in close proximity to the PsaI, L, and H subunits (189, 321). However, attempts to fit LHCII monomer or trimer structures into PSI in a way that satisfied the crosslinking data were only partially successful (31). None of the configurations tested would fit LHCII into the supercomplex so that it would be in simultaneous contact with the three subunits and also provide efficient energy transfer to the RC. A model for the binding of a

LHCII trimer on the PsaA side of plant PSI was proposed (31), but it is not clear whether trimeric, rather than monomeric LHCII, actually binds to PSI, or if phosphorylated LHCII is even needed for binding (124, 321). It is nevertheless clear that supercomplexes of PSI-LHCII form under stress, and a high-resolution structure of such a supercomplex will clarify the nature of PSI-LCHII interactions.

State transitions in higher plants are limited. In state II, additional light harvesting by PSI does not exceed 20% (6). In contrast, PSI light harvesting in *Chlamydomonas* almost doubles; approximately 80% of the LHCII associates with PSI (85), and, as a result, PSI of *Chlamydomonas* has to accommodate a greater number of LHCII complexes in state II. Whereas addition of a single LHCII trimer could explain the 20% increase in state II light harvesting of plant PSI, a much larger number is required for the state II capacity in *Chlamydomonas*. The model proposed for binding of a LHCII trimer on the PsaA side of plant PSI (31) was supported by a single particle analysis of state II-enriched PSI (173). In addition, several observations using single particle analysis of PSI in *Chlamydomonas* demonstrated the presence of additional LHCII trimers, and probably monomers as well, attached to PSI (114, 156, 282, 224).

State transitions and cyclic phosphorylation activity are mutually regulated in ways that are unique to organisms inhabiting different ecological niches (6, 24, 145). For example, under state II conditions, a large fraction of ATP synthesis is coupled to cyclic electron transport, whereas, under state I conditions, no evidence for cyclic flow has been obtained (97). In *Chlamydomonas*, the State I-State II transition induces a switch from linear to cyclic electron flow; this switch reveals a strict cause-and-effect relationship between the redistribution of antenna complexes and the onset of cyclic electron flow (98). In C4 plants, in which PSII is largely absent from bundle sheath cells, cyclic electron transport is dominant (22). In C3 plants, the existence of simultaneous cyclic and linear transport reactions was questioned, even after one component of the cyclic electron flow pathway was characterized (216). Now it has been shown that cyclic electron transport not only occurs in C3 plants, but is essential for growth (215). A mutant that lacks both the principal pathways of cyclic electron transport is grossly impaired in growth and development. Thus, cyclic electron transport in conjunction with state transitions constitutes a vital mechanism for adaptations to a changing environment.

CONCLUDING REMARKS

At an earlier point in our careers, we were privileged to work at the same time in the laboratory of Ephraim Racker at Cornell University. Ef was justifiably famous for his groundbreaking work on membrane-protein complexes of the mitochondrial inner membrane, among many other significant accomplishments. This research had given him a world-wise view of this branch of science. Ef was also famous for his brief aphorisms, which were liberally applied to his research team, particularly complaining postdocs. One of the most famous of these was "Troubles are good for you," which was handed out when a preparative procedure went bad or a tricky reconstitution experiment failed to yield the expected result. Indeed, troubles lie in the path of anyone who takes on the challenges of working with the intricate membrane-protein complexes that catalyze the reactions of oxygenic photosynthesis. Isolation of active enzymes, the discovery of double-digit polypeptide contents, and crystals that grow slowly, if at all, are at the head of a long list of difficulties. And yet, here we are, at the start of a new century with the structures of all the membrane complexes laid out before us. This scenario would have delighted Ef, who spent his career cleaning up enzymes. Perhaps his most famous aphorism was "Don't waste clean thoughts on dirty enzymes." Now, with structures, techniques, and models proliferating at an incredible rate, we think that it is time for a revised aphorism: *Don't use your dirty thoughts on clean enzymes!*

ACKNOWLEDGMENTS

The authors gratefully acknowledge support for their own research from the Israel Science Foundation (N.N.) and the Molecular Biochemistry Program of the National Science Foundation (C.Y.). We thank Omri Drory for excellent technical assistance in the preparation of the figures used in this review.

LITERATURE CITED

1. Adelroth P, Lindberg K, Andreasson LE. 1995. Studies of Ca^{2+} binding in spinach photosystem II using $^{45}Ca^{2+}$. *Biochemistry* 34:9021–27
2. Akerlund H-E, Jansson C, Andersson B. 1982. Reconstitution of photosynthetic water splitting in insideout thylakoid vesicles and identification of a participating polypeptide. *Biochim. Biophys. Acta* 681:1–10
3. Albertsson PA. 2001. A quantitative model of the domain structure of the photosynthetic membrane. *Trends Plant Sci.* 6:349–58
4. Albertsson PA, Andreasson E. 2004. The constant proportion of grana and stroma lamellae in plant chloroplasts. *Physiol Plant.* 121:334–42
5. Albertsson PA, Andreasson E, Svensson P. 1990. The domain organization of the plant thylakoid membrane. *FEBS Lett.* 273:36–40
6. Allen JF. 2003. Cyclic, pseudocyclic and noncyclic photophosphorylation: new links in the chain. *Trends Plant Sci.* 8:15–19

7. Allen JF, Bennett J, Steinback KE, Arntzen CJ. 1981. Chloroplast protein phosphorylation couples plastoquinone redox state to distribution of excitation energy between photosystems. *Nature* 291:25–29

8. Allen JP, Feher G, Yeates TO, Komiya H, Rees DC. 1987. Structure of the reaction center from Rhodobacter sphaeroides R-26: the protein subunits. *Proc. Natl. Acad. Sci. USA* 84:6162–66

9. Amunts A, Ben-Shem A, Nelson N. 2005. Solving the structure of plant photosystem I – biochemistry is vital. *Photochem. Photobiol. Sci.* 4:1011–15

10. Andersen B, Scheller HV, Moller BL. 1992. The Psi-E subunit of Photosystem-I binds ferredoxin-NADP+ oxidoreductase. *FEBS Lett.* 311:169–73

11. Anderson J, Boardman N. 1966. Fractionation of the photochemical systems of photosynthesis. I. Chlorophyll contents and photochemical activities of particles isolated from spinach chloroplasts. *Biochim. Biophys. Acta* 112:403–21

12. Anderson JM. 1980. P-700 content and polypeptide profile of chlorophyll-protein complexes of spinach and barley thylakoids. *Biochim. Biophys. Acta* 591:113–26

13. Anderson JM. 1999. Insight into consequences of grana stacking of thylakoid membranes in vascular plants: a personal perspective. *Aust. J. Plant Physiol.* 26:625–39

14. Anderson JM. 2002. Changing concepts about the distribution of Photosystems I and II between grana-appressed and stroma exposed thylakoid membranes. *Photosynth. Res.* 73:157–64

15. Andrizhiyevskaya EG, Frolov D, van Grondelle R, Dekker JP. 2004. On the role of the CP47 core antenna in the energy transfer and trapping dynamics of Photosystem II. *Phys. Chem. Chem. Phys.* 6:4810–19

16. Arnon DI, Allen MB, Whatley B. 1954. Photosynthesis by isolated chloroplasts. *Nature* 174:394–96

17. Ballottari M, Govoni C, Caffarri S, Morosinotto T. 2004. Stoichiometry of LHCI antenna polypeptides and characterization of gap and linker pigments in higher plants Photosystem I. *Eur. J. Biochem.* 271:4659–65

18. Barber J. 2002. Photosystem II: a multisubunit membrane protein that oxidises water. *Curr. Opin. Struct. Biol.* 12:523–30

19. Barber J, Nield J. 2002. Organization of transmembrane helices in photosystem II: comparison of plants and cyanobacteria. *Philos. Trans. R Soc. London Ser.* 357:1329–35

20. Barber J, Nield J, Morris EP, Hankamer B. 1999. Subunit positioning in photosystem II revisited. *Trends Biochem. Sci.* 24:43–45

21. Barry BA. 1993. The role of redox-active amino acids in the photosynthetic water-oxidizing complex. *Photochem. Photobiol.* 57:179–88

22. Bassi R, dal Belin Peruffo A, Barbato R, Ghisi R. 1985. Differences in chlorophyll–protein complexes and composition of polypeptides between thylakoids from bundle sheaths and mesophyll cells in maize. *Eur. J. Biochem.* 146:589–95

23. Bassi R, Simpson D. 1987. Chlorophyll-protein complexes of barley photosystem I. *Eur. J. Biochem.* 163:221–30

24. Bellafiore S, Barneche F, Peltier G, Rochaix JD. 2005. State transitions and light adaptation require chloroplast thylakoid protein kinase STN7. *Nature* 433:892–95

25. Bendall DS, Manasse RS. 1995. Cyclic photophosphorylation and electron transport. *Biochim. Biophys. Acta* 1229:23–38

26. Bengis C, Nelson N. 1975. Purification and properties of the photosystem I reaction center from chloroplasts. *J. Biol. Chem.* 250:2783–88

27. Bengis C, Nelson N. 1977. Subunit structure of chloroplast photosystem I reaction center. *J. Biol. Chem.* 252:4564–69

28. Ben-Shem A, Frolow F, Nelson N. 2003. The crystal structure of plant photosystem I. *Nature* 426:630–35

29. Ben-Shem A, Frolow F, Nelson N. 2004. Evolution of photosystem I – from symmetry through pseudosymmetry to assymmetry. *FEBS Lett.* 564:274–80

30. Ben-Shem A, Frolow F, Nelson N. 2004. Light-harvesting features revealed by the structure of plant photosystem I. *Photosynth. Res.* 81:239–50

31. Ben-Shem A, Nelson N. 2005. System biology of Photosystem I – Formation of supper-complexes. In *Proc. XIII Int. Congr. Photosynth.*, ed. D Bruce, A van der Est pp. 770–72

32. Ben-Shem A, Nelson N, Frolow F. 2003. Crystallization and initial X-ray diffraction studies of higher plant photosystem I. *Acta Cryst. D* 59:1824–27

33. Berthold DA, Babcock GT, Yocum CF. 1981. A highly resolved oxygen-evolving Photosystem II preparation from spinach thylakoid membranes. *FEBS Lett.* 134:231–34

34. Betts SD, Ross JR, Pichersky E, Yocum CF. 1997. Mutation Val235Ala weakens binding of the 33-kDa manganese stabilizing protein of photosystem II to one of two sites. *Biochemistry* 36:4047–53

35. Bibby TS, Mary I, Nield J, Partensky F, Barber J. 2003. Low-light-adapted Prochloro-coccus species possess specific antennae for each photosystem. *Nature* 424:1051–54

36. Bibby TS, Nield J, Barber J. 2001. Iron deficiency induces the formation of an antenna ring around trimeric photosystem I in cyanobacteria. *Nature* 412:743–45

37. Biesiadka J, Loll B, Kern J, Irrgang KD, Zouni A. 2004. Crystal structure of cyanobacterial photosystem II at 3.2 Å resolution: a closer look at the Mn-cluster. *Phys. Chem. Chem. Phys.* 6:4733–36

38. Boekema EJ, Jensen PE, Schlodder E, van Breemen JF, van Roon H, et al. 2001 Green plant photosystem I binds light-harvesting complex I on one side of the complex. *Biochemistry* 40:1029–36

39. Boekema EJ, van Roon H, Calkoen F, Bassi R, Dekker JP. 1999. Multiple types of association of photosystem II and its light harvesting antenna in partially solubilized photosystem II membranes. *Biochemistry* 38:2233–39

40. Boekema EJ, van Roon H, van Breemen JF, Dekker JP. 1999. Supramolecular organization of photosystem II and its light-harvesting antenna in partially solubilized photosystem II membranes. *Eur. J. Biochem.* 266:444–52

41. Boudreaux BF, MacMillan C, Teutloff R, Agalarov F, Gu S, et al. 2001. Mutations in both sides of the photosystem I reaction center identify the phylloquinone observed by electron paramagnetic resonance spectroscopy. *J. Biol. Chem.* 276:37299–306

42. Boussac A, Rutherford AW. 1988. Nature of the inhibition of the oxygen-evolving enzyme of photosystem-II induced by NaCl washing and reversed by the addition of Ca^{2+} or Sr^{2+}. *Biochemistry* 27:3476–83

43. Breton J, Nabedryk E, Leibl W. 1999. FTIR study of the primary electron donor of photosystem I (P700) revealing delocalization of the charge in P700+ and localization of the triplet character in 3P700. *Biochemistry* 38:11585–92

44. Brettel K. 1997. Electron transfer and arrangement of the redox cofactors in photosystem I. *Biochim. Biophys. Acta* 1318:322–73

45. Brettel K, Leibl W. 2001. Electron transfer in photosystem I. *Biochim. Biophys. Acta* 1507:100–14

46. Bricker TM, Frankel LK. 2002. The structure and function of CP47 and CP43 in photosystem II. *Photosynth. Res.* 72:131–46

47. Bricker TM, Frankel LK. 2003. Carboxylate groups on the manganese-stabilizing protein are required for efficient binding of the 24 kDa extrinsic protein to photosystem II. *Biochemistry* 42:2056–61

48. Bricker TM, Ghanotakis DF. 1996. Introduction to oxygen evolution and the oxygen-evolving complex. See Ref. 234a, pp. 113–36
49. Bricker TM, Morvant J, Masri N, Sutton HM, Frankel LK. 1998. Isolation of a highly active photosystem II preparation from *Synechocystis* 6803 using a histidine-tagged mutant of CP 47. *Biochim. Biophys. Acta* 1409:50–57
50. Britt RD, Peloquin JM, Campbell KA. 2000. Pulsed and parallel-polarization EPR characterization of the photosystem II oxygen-evolving complex. *Annu. Rev. Biophys. Biomol. Struct.* 29:463–95
51. Britt RD, Tang XS, Gilchrist ML, Lorigan GA, Larsen BS, et al. 1994. Histidine at the catalytic site of the photosynthetic oxygen-evolving complex. *Biochem. Soc. Trans.* 22:343–47
52. Buchanan BB, Balmer Y. 2005. Redox regulation: A broadening horizon. *Annu. Rev. Plant Biol.* 56:187–220
53. Burnap RL, Sherman LA. 1991. Deletion mutagenesis in *Synechocystis* sp PCC6803 indicates that the Mn-stabilizing protein of photosystem II is not essential for O_2 evolution. *Biochemistry* 30:440–46
54. Büttner M, Xie D-L, Nelson H, Pinther W, Hauska G, Nelson N. 1992. Photosynthetic reaction center genes in green sulfur bacteria and in Photosystem 1 are related. *Proc. Natl. Acad. Sci. USA* 89:8135–39
55. Büttner M, Xie D-L, Nelson H, Pinther W, Hauska G, Nelson N. 1992. The photosystem I-like P840-reaction center of green S-bacteria is a homodimer. *Biochim. Biophys. Acta* 1101:154–56
56. Byrdin M, Jordan P, Krauss N, Fromme P, Stehlik D, Schlodder E. 2002. Light harvesting in photosystem I: modeling based on the 2.5 Å structure of photosystem I from Synechococcus elongatus. *Biophys. J.* 83:433–57
57. Caffarri S, Frigerio S, Olivieri E, Righetti PG, Bassi R. 2005. Differential accumulation of Lhcb gene products in thylakoid membranes of Zea mays plants grown under contrasting light and temperature conditions. *Proteomics* 5:758–68
58. Calderone V, Trabucco M, Vujicic A, Battistutta R, Giacometti GM, et al. 2003. Crystal structure of the PsbQ protein of photosystem II from higher plants. *EMBO Rep.* 4:900–5
59. Chen M, Bibby TS, Nield J, Larkum AW, Barber J. 2005. Structure of a large photosystem II supercomplex from Acaryochloris marina. *FEBS Lett.* 579:1306–10
60. Chitnis PR. 2001. Photosystem I: Function and physiology. *Annu. Rev. Plant Physiol. Mol. Biol.* 52:593–626
61. Chitnis PR, Purvis D, Nelson N. 1991. Molecular cloning and targeted mutagenesis of the gene psaF encoding subunit III of photosystem I from the cyanobacterium Synechocystis sp. PCC 6803. *J. Biol. Chem.* 266:20146–51
62. Chitnis PR, Xu Q, Chitnis VP, Nechushtai R. 1995. Function and organization of photosystem I polypeptides. *Photosynth. Res.* 44:23–40
63. Chu HA, Hillier W, Debus RJ. 2004. Evidence that the C-terminus of the D1 polypeptide of photosystem II is ligated to the manganese ion that undergoes oxidation during the S1 to S_2 transition: an isotope-edited FTIR study. *Biochemistry* 43:3152–66
64. Cinco RM, Holman KLM, Robblee JH, Yano J, Pizarro SA, et al. 2002. Calcium EXAFS establishes the Mn-Ca cluster in the oxygen-evolving complex of photosystem II. *Biochemistry* 41:12928–33
65. Clausen J, Junge W. 2004. Detection of an intermediate of photosynthetic water oxidation. *Nature* 430:480–83
66. Clayton RK, Haselkorn R. 1972. Protein components of bacterial photosynthetic membranes. *J. Mol. Biol.* 68:97–105

67. Clemens KL, Force DA, Britt RD. 2002. Acetate binding at the photosystem II oxygen evolving complex: An S_2 state multiline signal ESEEM study. *J. Am. Chem. Soc.* 124:10921–33

68. Cohen RO, Shen G, Golbeck JH, Xu W, Chitnis PR, et al. 2004. Evidence for asymmetric electron transfer in cyanobacterial photosystem I: analysis of a methionine to leucine mutation of the ligand to the primary electron acceptor A_0. *Biochemistry* 43:4741–54

69. Consoli E, Croce R, Dunlap DD, Finzi L. 2005. Diffusion of light-harvesting complex II in the thylakoid membranes. *EMBO Rep.* 6:782–86

70. Cramer WA, Zhang H, Yan J, Kurisu G, Smith JL. 2004. Evolution of photosynthesis: time-independent structure of the cytochrome b6f complex. *Biochemistry* 43:5921–29

71. Cuni A, Xiong L, Sayre R, Rappaport F, Lavergne J. 2004. Modification of the pheophytin midpoint potential in Photosystem II: modulation of the quantum yield of charge separation and of charge recombination pathways. *Phys. Chem. Chem. Phys.* 6:4825–31

72. Damjanovic A, Vaswani HM, Fromme P, Fleming GR. 2002. Chlorophyll excitations in photosystem I of Synechococcus elongatus. *J. Phys. Chem. B* 106:10251–62

73. Danielsson R, Albertsson PA, Mamedov F, Styring S. 2004. Quantification of photosystem I and II in different parts of the thylakoid membrane from spinach. *Biochim. Biophys. Acta* 1608:53–61

74. Dashdorj N, Xu W, Cohen RO, Golbeck JH, Savikhin S. 2005. Asymmetric electron transfer in cyanobacterial Photosystem I: charge separation and secondary electron transfer dynamics of mutations near the primary electron acceptor A0. *Biophys. J.* 88:1238–49

75. Dau H, Iuzzolino L, Dittmer J. 2001. The tetra-manganese complex of photosystem II during its redox cycle - X-ray absorption results and mechanistic implications. *Biochim. Biophys. Acta* 1503:24–39

76. Dau H, Liebisch P, Haumann M. 2004. The structure of the manganese complex of Photosystem II in its dark-stable S_1-state-EXAFS results in relation to recent crystallographic data. *Phys. Chem. Chem. Phys.* 6:4781–92

77. Dau H, Sauer K. 1996. Exciton equilibration and photosystem II exciton dynamics—fluorescence study on photosystem II membrane particles of spinach. *Biochim. Biophys. Acta* 1273:175–90

78. Debus RJ. 1992. The manganese and calcium ions of photosynthetic oxygen evolution. *Biochim. Biophys. Acta* 1102:269–52

79. Debus RJ. 2001. Amino acid residues that modulate the properties of tyrosine Y-Z and the manganese cluster in the water oxidizing complex of photosystem II. *Biochim. Biophys. Acta* 1503:164–86

80. Deisenhofer J, Michel H. 1989. Nobel lecture. The photosynthetic reaction centre from the purple bacterium Rhodopseudomonas viridis. *EMBO J.* 8:2149–70

81. Dekker JP. 1992. Optical studies on the oxygen-evolving complex of photosystem II. In *Manganese Redox Enzymes*, ed. VL Pecoraro, pp. 85–104. New York: VCH

82. Dekker JP, Boekema EJ. 2005. Supramolecular organization of thylakoid membrane proteins in green plants. *Biochim. Biophys. Acta* 1706:12–39

83. Dekker JP, Van Grondelle R. 2000. Primary charge separation in photosystem II. *Photosynth. Res.* 63:195–208

84. Delepelaire P, Chua NH. 1981. Electrophoretic purification of chlorophyll a/b-protein complexes from Chlamydomonas reinhardtii and spinach and analysis of their polypeptide compositions. *J. Biol. Chem.* 256:9300–7

85. Delosme R, Olive J, Wollman F-A. 1996. Changes in light energy distribution upon state transitions: an in vivo photoacoustic study of the wild type and photosynthesis mutants from Chlamydomonas reinhardtii. *Biochim. Biophys. Acta* 1273:150–58

86. Depege N, Bellafiore S, Rochaix JD. 2003. Role of chloroplast protein kinase Stt7 in LHCII phosphorylation and state transition in Chlamydomonas. *Science* 299:1572–75

87. Dexter DL. 1953. A theory of sensitized luminescence in solids. *J. Chem. Phys.* 21:836–50

88. Diner BA. 2001. Amino acid residues involved in the coordination and assembly of the manganese cluster of photosystem II. Proton-coupled electron transport of the redox-active tyrosines and its relationship to water oxidation. *Biochim. Biophys. Acta* 1503:147–63

89. Diner BA, Babcock GT. 1996. Structure, dynamics and energy conversion efficiency in photosystem II. See Ort & Yocum 1996, pp. 213–47

90. Diner BA, Rappaport F. 2002. Structure, dynamics, and energetics of the primary photochemistry of photosystem II of oxygenic photosynthesis. *Annu. Rev. Plant Biol.* 53:551–80

91. Dominici P, Caffarri S, Armenante F, Ceoldo S, Crimi M, Bassi R. 2002. Biochemical properties of the PsbS subunit of photosystem II either purified from chloroplast or recombinant. *J. Biol. Chem.* 277:22750–58

92. Eaton-Rye JJ, Murata N. 1989. Evidence that the amino-terminus of the 33 kDa extrinsic protein is required for binding to the photosystem II complex. *Biochim. Biophys. Acta* 977:219–26

93. Eisen JA, Nelson KE, Paulsen IT, Heidelberg JF, Wu M, et al. 2002. The complete genome sequence of Chlorobium tepidum TLS, a photosynthetic, anaerobic, green-sulfur bacterium. *Proc. Natl. Acad. Sci. USA* 99:9509–14

94. Fairclough WV, Forsyth A, Evans MC, Rigby SE, Purton S, Heathcote P. 2003. Bidirectional electron transfer in photosystem I: electron transfer on the PsaA side is not essential for phototrophic growth in Chlamydomonas. *Biochim. Biophys. Acta* 1606:43–55

95. Ferreira KN, Iverson TM, Maghlaoui K, Barber J, Iwata S. 2004. Architecture of the photosynthetic oxygen-evolving center. *Science* 303:1831–38

96. Finazzi G. 2004. The central role of the green alga Chlamydomonas reinhardtii in revealing the mechanism of state transitions. *J. Exp. Bot.* 56:383–88

97. Finazzi G, Furia A, Barbagallo RP, Forti G. 1999. State transitions, cyclic and linear electron transport and photophosphorylation in Chlamydomonas reinhardtii. *Biochim. Biophys. Acta* 1413:117–29

98. Finazzi G, Rappaport F, Furia A, Fleischmann M, Rochaix JD, et al. 2002. Involvement of state transitions in the switch between linear and cyclic electron flow in Chlamydomonas reinhardtii. *EMBO Rep.* 3:280–85

99. Finazzi G, Sommer F, Hippler M. 2005. Release of oxidized plastocyanin from photosystem I limits electron transfer between photosystem I and cytochrome b6f complex in vivo. *Proc. Natl. Acad. Sci. USA* 102:7031–36

100. Finazzi G, Zito F, Barbagallo RP, Wollman FA. 2001. Contrasted effects of inhibitors of cytochrome b6f complex on state transitions in *Chlamydomonas reinhardtii*: the role of Qo site occupancy in LHCII kinase activation. *J. Biol. Chem.* 276:9770–77

101. Fischer N, Hippler M, Setif P, Jacquot JP, Rochaix JD. 1998. The PsaC subunit of photosystem I provides an essential lysine residue for fast electron transfer to ferredoxin. *EMBO J.* 17:849–58

102. Fischer N, Setif P, Rochaix JD. 1999. Site-directed mutagenesis of the PsaC subunit of photosystem I. F(b) is the cluster interacting with soluble ferredoxin. *J. Biol. Chem.* 274:23333–40

103. Fish A, Danieli T, Ohad I, Nechushtai R, Livnah O. 2005. Structural basis for the thermostability of ferredoxin from the cyanobacterium *Mastigocladus laminosus*. *J. Mol. Biol.* 350:599–608

104. Fleischmann MM, Ravanel S, Delosme R, Olive J, Zito F, et al. 1999. Isolation and characterization of photoautotrophic mutants of *Chlamydomonas reinhardtii* deficient in state transition. *J. Biol. Chem.* 274:30987–94

105. Forster T. 1948. Zwischen molekular energiewanderung und fluoreszenz. *Ann. Phys.* 2:55–75

106. Forti G, Parisi B. 1963. Evidence for the occurrence of cyclic photophosphorylation in vivo. *Biochim. Biophys. Acta* 71:1–6

107. Fotinou C, Kokkinidis M, Fritzsch G, Haase W, Michel H, Ghanotakis DF. 1993. Characterization of a photosystem II core and its three-dimensional crystals. *Photosynth. Res.* 37:41–48

108. Frigaard NU, Bryant DA. 2004. Seeing green bacteria in a new light: genomics-enabled studies of the photosynthetic apparatus in green sulfur bacteria and filamentous anoxygenic phototrophic bacteria. *Arch. Microbiol.* 182:265–76

109. Fromme P, Bottin H, Krauss N, Setif P. 2002. Crystallization and electron paramagnetic resonance characterization of the complex of photosystem I with its natural electron acceptor ferredoxin. *Biophys. J.* 83:1760–73

110. Fromme P, Jordan P, Krauss N. 2001. Structure of photosystem I. *Biochim. Biophys. Acta* 1507:5–31

111. Fromme P, Witt HT, Schubert W-D, Klukas O, Saenger W, Krauss N. 1996. Structure of Photosystem I at 4.5 Å resolution: a short review including evolutionary aspects. *Biochim. Biophys. Acta* 1275:76–83

112. Funk C, Schroder WP, Green BR, Renger G, Andersson B. 1994. The intrinsic 22 kDa protein is a chlorophyll-binding subunit of photosystem II. *FEBS Lett.* 342:261–66

113. Garab G, Cseh Z, Kovacs L, Rajagopal S, Varkonyi Z, et al. 2002. Light-induced trimer to monomer transition in the main light-harvesting antenna complex of plants: thermo-optic mechanism. *Biochemistry* 41:15121–29

114. Germano M, Yakushevska AE, Keegstra W, van Gorkom HJ, Dekker JP, Boekema EJ. 2002. Supramolecular organization of photosystem I and light-harvesting complex I in *Chlamydomonas reinhardtii*. *FEBS Lett.* 525:121–25

115. Ghanotakis DF, Topper JN, Babcock GT, Yocum CF. 1984. Water-soluble 17-kDa and 23-kDa polypeptides restore oxygen evolution activity by creating a high-affinity binding-site for Ca^{2+} on the oxidizing side of photosystem II. *FEBS Lett.* 170:169–73

116. Ghanotakis DF, Topper JN, Yocum CF. 1984. Structural organization of the oxidizing side of photosystem II- exogenous reductants reduce and destroy the Mn-complex in photosystem II membranes depleted of the 17 and 23 kDa polypeptides. *Biochim. Biophys. Acta* 767:524–31

117. Ghanotakis DF, Yocum CF. 1990. Photosystem II and the oxygen-evolving complex. *Annu. Rev. Plant Phys. Plant Mol. Biol.* 41:255–76

118. Gobets B, van Grondelle R. 2001. Energy transfer and trapping in photosystem I. *Biochim. Biophys. Acta* 1507:80–99

119. Golding AJ, Joliot P, Johnson GN. 2005. Equilibration between cytochrome f and P700 in intact leaves. *Biochim. Biophys. Acta* 1706:105–9

120. Gong XM, Agalarov R, Brettel K, Carmeli C. 2003. Control of electron transport in photosystem I by the iron-sulfur cluster FX in response to intra- and intersubunit interactions. *J. Biol. Chem.* 278:19141–50

121. Green BR, Durnford DG. 1996. The chlorophyll-carotenoid proteins of oxygenic photosynthesis. *Annu. Rev. Plant Physiol. Plant Mol. Biol.* 47:685–714

122. Guergova-Kuras M, Boudreaux B, Joliot A, Joliot P, Redding K. 2001. Evidence for two active branches for electron transfer in photosystem I. *Proc. Natl. Acad. Sci. USA* 98:4437–42

123. Gupta R, He Z, Luan S. 2002. Functional relationship of cytochrome c6 and plastocyanin in *Arabidopsis*. *Nature* 417:567–71

124. Haldrup A, Jensen PE, Lunde C, Scheller HV. 2001. Balance of power: a view of the mechanism of photosynthetic state transitions. *Trends Plant Sci.* 6:301–5

125. Hankamer B, Barber J, Boekema EJ. 1997. Structure and membrane organization of photosystem II in green plants. *Annu. Rev. Plant Physiol. Plant Mol. Biol.* 48:541–71

126. Hankamer B, Morris E, Nield J, Gerle C, Barber J. 2001. Three-dimensional structure of the photosystem II core dimer of higher plants determined by electron microscopy. *J. Struct. Biol.* 135:262–69

127. Hasegawa K, Kimura Y, Ono TA. 2002. Chloride cofactor in the photosynthetic oxygen-evolving complex studied by Fourier transform infrared spectroscopy. *Biochemistry* 41:13839–50

128. Hauska G, Schoedl T, Remigy H, Tsiotis G. 2001. The reaction center of green sulfur bacteria. *Biochim. Biophys. Acta* 1507:260–77

129. Heathcote P, Jones MR, Fyfe PK. 2003. Type I photosynthetic reaction centres: Form and function. *Philos. Trans. R. Soc. London Ser. B* 358:231–43

130. Heinemeyer J, Eubel H, Wehmhoner D, Jansch L, Braun HP. 2004. Proteomic approach to characterize the supramolecular organization of photosystems in higher plants. *Pytochemistry* 65:1683–92

131. Hillier W, Wydrzynski T. 2000. The affinities for the two substrate water binding sites in the O_2 evolving complex of photosystem II vary independently during S-state turnover. *Biochemistry* 39:4399–405

132. Hippler M, Drepper F, Haehnel W, Rochaix JD. 1998. The N-terminal domain of PsaF: precise recognition site for binding and fast electron transfer from cytochrome c6 and plastocyanin to photosystem I of *Chlamydomonas reinhardtii*. *Proc. Natl. Acad. Sci. USA* 95:7339–44

133. Hippler M, Drepper F, Rochaix JD, Muhlenhoff U. 1999. Insertion of the N-terminal part of PsaF from *Chlamydomonas reinhardtii* into photosystem I from *Synechococcus elongatus* enables efficient binding of algal plastocyanin and cytochrome c6. *J. Biol. Chem.* 274:4180–88

134. Hippler M, Klein J, Fink A, Allinger T, Hoerth P. 2001. Towards functional proteomics of membrane protein complexes: analysis of thylakoid membranes from *Chlamydomonas reinhardtii*, *Plant J.* 28:595–606

135. Hippler M, Reichert J, Sutter M, Zak E, Altschmied L, et al. 1996. The plastocyanin binding domain of photosystem I. *EMBO J.* 15:6374–84

136. Hoganson CW, Babcock GT. 1997. A metalloradical mechanism for the generation of oxygen from water in photosynthesis. *Science* 277:1953–56

137. Horton P, Ruban AV, Walters RG. 1996. Regulation of light harvesting in green plants. *Annu. Rev. Plant Physiol. Plant Mol. Biol.* 47:655–84

138. Ifuku K, Nakatsu T, Kato H, Sato F. 2004. Crystal structure of the PsbP protein of photosystem II from Nicotiana tabacum. *EMBO Rep.* 5:362–67

139. Ihalainen JA, Jensen PE, Haldrup A, van Stokkum IH, van Grondelle R, et al. 2002. Pigment organization and energy transfer dynamics in isolated photosystem I (PSI)

complexes from *Arabidopsis thaliana* depleted of the PSI-G, PSI-K, PSI-L, or PSI-N subunit. *Biophys. J.* 83:2190–201

140. Jackowski G, Olkiewicz P, Zelisko A. 2003. The acclimative response of the main light-harvesting chlorophyll a/b-protein complex of photosystem II (LHCII) to elevated irradiances at the level of trimeric subunits. *J. Photochem. Photobiol. B* 70:163–70

141. Jagendorf AT. 1967. Acid-base transitions and phosphorylation by chloroplasts. *Fed. Proc.* 26:1361–69

142. Jensen PE, Haldrup A, Rosgaard L, Scheller HV. 2003. Molecular dissection of photosystem I in higher plants: topology, structure and function. *Physiol. Plant.* 119:313–21

143. Jensen PE, Haldrup A, Zhang S, Scheller HV. 2004. The PSI-O subunit of plant photosystem I is involved in balancing the excitation pressure between the two photosystems. *J. Biol. Chem.* 279:24212–17

144. Joet T, Cournac L, Peltier G, Havaux M. 2002. Cyclic electron flow around photosystem I in C3 plants: in vivo control by the redox state of chloroplasts and involvement of the NADH-dehydrogenase complex. *Plant Physiol.* 128:760–69

145. Johnson GN. 2005. Cyclic electron transport in C3 plants: fact or artefact? *J. Exp. Bot.* 56:407–16

146. Johnson TW, Shen G, Zybailov B, Kolling D, Reategui R, et al. 2000. Recruitment of a foreign quinone into the A1 site of photosystem I. Genetic and physiological characterization of phylloquinone biosynthetic pathway mutants in *Synechocystis* sp. PCC6803. *J. Biol. Chem.* 275:8523–30

147. Joliot P, Beal D, Joliot A. 2004. Cyclic electron flow under saturating excitation of dark-adapted Arabidopsis leaves. *Biochim. Biophys. Acta* 1656:166–76

148. Joliot P, Joliot A. 1999. In vivo analysis of the electron transfer within photosystem I: are the two phylloquinones involved? *Biochemistry* 38:11130–36

149. Joliot P, Joliot A. 2002. Cyclic electron transfer in plant leaf. *Proc. Natl. Acad. Sci. USA* 99:10209–14

150. Joliot P, Joliot A. 2005. Quantification of cyclic and linear flows in plants. *Proc. Natl. Acad. Sci. USA* 102:4913–18

151. Jolley C, Ben-Shem A, Nelson N, Fromme P. 2005. Structure of plant photosystem I revealed by theoretical modeling. *J. Biol. Chem.* 280:33627–36

152. Jordan P, Fromme P, Witt HT, Klukas O, Saenger W, Krauss N. 2001. Three-dimensional structure of cyanobacterial photosystem I at 2.5 A resolution. *Nature* 411:909–17

153. Junge W. 1999. ATP synthase and other motor proteins. *Proc. Natl. Acad. Sci. USA* 96:4735–37

154. Kaftan D, Brumfeld V, Nevo R, Scherz A, Reich Z. 2002. From chloroplasts to photosystems: in situ scanning force microscopy on intact thylakoid membranes. *EMBO J.* 21:6146–53

155. Kamiya N, Shen JR. 2003. Crystal structure of oxygen-evolving photosystem II from *Thermosynechococcus vulcanus* at 3.7-Å resolution. *Proc. Natl. Acad. Sci. USA* 100:98–103

156. Kargul J, Nield J, Barber J. 2003. Three-dimensional reconstruction of a light-harvesting complex I-photosystem I (LHCI-PSI) supercomplex from the green alga *Chlamydomonas reinhardtii*. Insights into light harvesting for PSI. *J. Biol. Chem.* 278:16135–41

157. Kashino Y, Lauber WM, Carroll JA, Wang Q, Whitmarsh J, et al. 2002. Proteomic analysis of a highly active photosystem II preparation from the cyanobacterium *Synechocystis* sp. PCC 6803 reveals the presence of novel polypeptides. *Biochemistry* 41:8004–12

158. Kennis JTM, Gobets B, van Stokkum IHM, Dekker JP, van Grondelle R, Fleming GR. 2001. Light harvesting by chlorophylls and carotenoids in the photosystem I core complex of Synechococcus elongatus: A fluorescence upconversion study. *J. Phys. Chem. B* 105:4485–94

159. Kerfeld CA, Krogmann DW. 1998. Photosynthetic cytochromes c in cyanobacteria, algae and plants. *Annu. Rev. Plant Physiol. Plant Mol. Biol.* 49:397–425

160. Kern J, Loll B, Zouni A, Saenger W, Irrgang KD, Biesiadka J. 2005. Cyanobacterial Photosystem II at 3.2 A resolution - the plastoquinone binding pockets. *Photosynth. Res.* 84:153–59

161. Kim EH, Chow WS, Horton P, Anderson JM. 2005. Entropy-assisted stacking of thylakoid membranes. *Biochim. Biophys. Acta* 1708:187–95

162. Kim S, Sandusky P, Bowlby NR, Aebersold R, Green BR, et al. 1992. Characterization of a spinach Psbs cDNA encoding the 22 kDa protein of photosystem II. *FEBS Lett.* 314:67–71

163. Kim SH, Gregor W, Peloquin JM, Brynda M, Britt RD. 2004. Investigation of the calcium-binding site of the oxygen evolving complex of photosystem II using [87]Sr ESEEM spectroscopy. *J. Am. Chem. Soc.* 126:7228–37

164. Klein MP, Sauer K, Yachandra VK. 1993. Perspectives on the structure of the photosynthetic oxygen-evolving manganese complex and its relation to the Kok cycle. *Photosynth. Res.* 38:265–77

165. Klein SM, Vernon LP. 1977. Composition of a photosystem I chlorophyll protein complex from *Anabaena flos-aquae*. *Biochim. Biophys. Acta* 459:364–75

166. Klukas O, Schubert WD, Jordan P, Krauss N, Fromme P, et al. 1999. Photosystem I, an improved model of the stromal subunits PsaC, PsaD, and PsaE. *J. Biol. Chem.* 274:7351–60

167. Knoetzel J, Mant A, Haldrup A, Jensen PE, Scheller HV. 2002. PSI-O, a new 10-kDa subunit of eukaryotic photosystem I. *FEBS Lett.* 510:145–48

168. Kohorn BD, Yakir D. 1990. Movement of newly imported light-harvesting chlorophyll-binding protein from unstacked to stacked thylakoid membranes is not affected by light treatment or absence of amino-terminal threonines. *J. Biol. Chem.* 265:2118–23

169. Kok B. 1957. Absorption changes induced by the photochemical reaction of photosynthesis. *Nature* 179:583–84

170. Kok B. 1961 Partial purification and determination of oxidation-reduction potential of the photosynthetic chlorophyll complex absorbing at 700 nm. *Biochim. Biophys. Acta* 48:527–33

171. Kok B, Cheniae GM. 1966. Kinetics and intermediate steps of the oxygen evolving step in photosynthesis. In *Current Topics in Bioenergetics*, ed. DR Sanadi, 1:1–97. New York: Academic

172. Kok B, Forbush B, McGloin M. 1970. Cooperation of charges in photosynthetic O_2 evolution. 1. A linear 4-step mechanism. *Photochem. Photobiol.* 11:457–75

173. Kouril R, van Oosterwijk N, Yakushevska AE, Boekema EJ. 2005. Photosystem I: a search for green plant trimers. *Photochem. Photobiol. Sci.* 4:1091–94

174. Krabben L, Schlodder E, Jordan R, Carbonera D, Giacometti G, et al. 2000. Influence of the axial ligands on the spectral properties of P700 of photosystem I: a study of site-directed mutants. *Biochemistry* 39:13012–25

175. Kuhlbrandt W, Wang DN, Fujiyoshi Y. 1994. Atomic model of plant light-harvesting complex by electron crystallography. *Nature* 367:614–21

176. Kuntzleman T, Yocum CF. 2005. Reduction-induced inhibition and Mn(II) release from the photosystem II oxygen evolving complex by hydroquinone or NH$_2$OH are consistent with a Mn(III0/Mn(III)(/Mn(IV)/Mn(IV) oxidation state for the dark-adapted enzyme. *Biochemistry* 44:2129–42

177. Kurisu G, Kusunoki M, Katoh E, Yamazaki T, Teshima K, et al. 2001. Structure of the electron transfer complex between ferredoxin and ferredoxin-NADP(+) reductase. *Nat. Struct. Biol.* 8:117–21

178. Kurisu G, Zhang H, Smith JL, Cramer WA. 2003. Structure of the cytochrome b6f complex of oxygenic photosynthesis: tuning the cavity. *Science* 302:1009–14

179. Kuwabara T, Murata N. 1983. Quantitative-analysis of the inactivation of photosynthetic oxygen evolution and the release of polypeptides and manganese in the photosystem II particles of spinach-chloroplasts. *Plant Cell Physiol.* 24:741–47

180. Kyle DJ, Staehelin LA, Arntzen CJ. 1983. Lateral mobility of the light-harvesting complex in chloroplast membranes controls excitation energy distribution in higher plants. *Arch. Biochem. Biophys.* 222:527–41

181. Laemmli UK. 1970. Cleavage of structural proteins during the assembly of the head of bacteriophage T4. *Nature* 227:680–85

182. Lakshmi KV, Eaton SS, Eaton GR, Brudvig GW. 1999. Orientation of the tetranuclear manganese cluster and tyrosine Z in the O$_2$-evolving complex of photosystem II: An EPR study of the S$_2$Y$_Z^\bullet$ state in oriented acetate-inhibited photosystem II membranes. *Biochemistry* 38:12758–67

183. Lelong C, Setif P, Lagoutte B, Bottin H. 1994. Identification of the amino acids involved in the functional interaction between photosystem I and ferredoxin from Synechocystis sp. PCC 6803 by chemical cross-linking. *J. Biol. Chem.* 269:10034–39

184. Leuschner C, Bricker TM. 1996. Interaction of the 33 kDa extrinsic protein with photosystem II: Rebinding of the 33 kDa extrinsic protein to photosystem II membranes which contain four, two, or zero manganese per photosystem II reaction center. *Biochemistry* 35:4551–57

185. Li XP, Gilmore AM, Caffarri S, Bassi R, Golan T, et al. 2004. Regulation of photosynthetic light harvesting involves intrathylakoid lumen pH sensing by the PsbS protein. *J. Biol. Chem.* 279:22866–74

186. Liebl U, Mockensturm-Wilson M, Trost JT, Brune DC, Blankenship RE, Vermaas W. 1993. Single core polypeptide in the reaction center of the photosynthetic bacterium *Heliobacillus mobilis*: structural implications and relations to other photosystems. *Proc. Natl. Acad. Sci. USA* 90:7124–28

187. Lindberg K, Vanngard T, Andreasson LE. 1993. Studies of the slowly exchanging chloride in Photosystem II of higher-plants. *Photosynth. Res.* 38:401–8

188. Liu Z, Yan H, Wang K, Kuang T, Zhang J, et al. 2004. Crystal structure of spinach major light-harvesting complex at 2.72 A resolution. *Nature* 428:287–92

189. Lunde CP, Jensen PE, Haldrup A, Knoetzel J, Scheller HV. 2000. The PSI-H subunit of photosystem I is essential for state transitions in plant photosynthesis. *Nature* 408:613–15

190. Lushy A, Verchovsky L, Nechushtai R. 2002. The stable assembly of newly synthesized PsaE into the photosystem I complex occurring via the exchange mechanism is facilitated by electrostatic interactions. *Biochemistry* 41:11192–99

191. Lydakis-Simantiris N, Betts SD, Yocum CF. 1999. Leucine 245 is a critical residue for folding and function of the manganese stabilizing protein of photosystem II. *Biochemistry* 38:15528–35

192. Lydakis-Simantiris N, Hutchison R, Betts SD, Barry BA, Yocum CF. 1999. Manganese stabilizing protein of photosystem II is a thermostable, natively unfolded polypeptide. *Biochemistry* 38:404–14

193. Markwell JP, Reinman S, Thornber JP. 1978. Chlorophyll-protein complexes from higher plants: a procedure for improved stability and fractionation. *Arch. Biochem. Biophys.* 190:136–41

194. Mayfield SP, Bennoun P, Rochaix JD. 1987. Expression of the nuclear encoded Oee1 protein is required for oxygen evolution and stability of photosystem II particles in Chlamydomonas reinhardtii. *EMBO J.* 6:313–18

195. McCarty RE, Evron Y, Johnson EA. 2000. The chloroplast ATP synthase: A rotary enzyme? *Annu. Rev. Plant Physiol. Plant Mol. Biol.* 51:83–109

196. McCarty RE, Racker E. 1966. Effect of a coupling factor and its antiserum on photophosphorylation and hydrogen ion transport. *Brookhaven Symp. Biol.* 19:202–14

197. McConnel MD, Ramesh VM, Wyndham I, van der Est A, Webber AN. 2004. Directionality of electron transport through Photosystem I of Chlamydomonas reinhardtii probed by transient electron paramagnetic resonance. In *13th Int. Congr. Photosynth.* Montreal, Canada: Humana

198. Mei R, Yocum CF. 1991. Calcium retards NH_2OH inhibition of O_2 evolution activity by stabilization of Mn^{2+} binding to photosystem II. *Biochemistry* 30:7836–42

199. Meimberg K, Fischer N, Rochaix JD, Muhlenhoff U. 1999. Lys35 of PsaC is required for the efficient photoreduction of flavodoxin by photosystem I from Chlamydomonas reinhardtii. *Eur. J. Biochem.* 263:137–44

200. Melkozernov AN, Lin S, Blankenship RE, Valkunas L. 2001. Spectral inhomogeneity of photosystem I and its influence on excitation equilibration and trapping in the cyanobacterium Synechocystis sp. PCC6803 at 77 K. *Biophys. J.* 81:1144–54

201. Merchant S, Sawaya MR. 2005. The light reactions: a guide to recent acquisitions for the picture gallery. *Plant Cell* 17:648–63

202. Merry SAP, Kumazaki S, Tachibana Y, Joseph DM, Porter G, et al. 1996. Subpicosecond equilibration of excitation energy in isolated photosystem II reaction centers revisited: time-dependent anisotropy. *J. Phys. Chem.* 100:10469–78

203. Miller AF, Brudvig GW. 1991. A guide to electron-paramagnetic resonance spectroscopy of photosystem-II membranes. *Biochim. Biophys. Acta* 1056:1–18

204. Minai L, Fish A, Darash-Yahana M, Verchovsky L, Nechushtai R. 2001. The assembly of the PsaD subunit into the membranal photosystem I complex occurs via an exchange mechanism. *Biochemistry* 40:12754–60

205. Miyao M, Murata N. 1984. Calcium ions can be substituted for the 24-kDa polypeptide in photosynthetic oxygen evolution. *FEBS Lett.* 168:118–20

206. Miyao M, Murata N. 1984. Role of the 33-kDa polypeptide in preserving Mn in the photosynthetic oxygen-evolution system and replacement by chloride ions. *FEBS Lett.* 170:350–54

207. Mizusawa N, Yamanari N, Kimura Y, Ishii A, Nakazawa S, Ono T-A. 2004. Changes in the functional and structural properties of the Mn cluster induced by replacing the side group of the c-terminus of the D1 protein of photosystem II. *Biochemistry* 43:14644–52

208. Molina-Heredia FP, Wastl J, Navarro JA, Bendall DS, Hervas M, et al. 2003. A new function for an old cytochrome? *Nature* 424:33–34

209. Morais F, Kuhn K, Stewart DH, Barber J, Brudvig GW, Nixon PJ. 2001. Photosynthetic water oxidation in cytochrome b_{559} mutants containing a disrupted heme-binding pocket. *J. Biol. Chem.* 276:31986–93

210. Morosinotto T, Ballottari M, Klimmek F, Jansson S, Bassi R. 2005. The association of antenna system to photosystem 1 in higher plants: Cooperative interactions stabilizes the supramolecular complex and enhance red-shifted spectral forms. *J. Biol. Chem.* 280:31050–58

211. Moseley JL, Allinger T, Herzog S, Hoerth P, Wehinger E, et al. 2002. Adaptation to Fe-deficiency requires remodeling of the photosynthetic apparatus. *EMBO J.* 21:6709–20

212. Moseley JL, Quinn J, Eriksson M, Merchant S. 2000. The Crd1 gene encodes a putative di-iron enzyme required for photosystem I accumulation in copper deficiency and hypoxia in *Chlamydomonas reinhardtii. EMBO J.* 19:2139–51

213. Muhiuddin IP, Heathcote P, Carter S, Purton S, Rigby SEJ, et al. 2001. Evidence from time resolved studies of the radical pair for photosynthetic electron transfer on both the PsaA and PsaB branches of the Photosystem I reaction centre. *FEBS Lett.* 503:56–60

214. Mullet JE, Burke JJ, Arntzen CJ. 1980. Chlorophyll proteins of photosystem I. *Plant Physiol.* 65:814–22

215. Munekage Y, Hashimoto M, Miyake C, Tomizawa K, Endo T, et al. 2004. Cyclic electron flow around photosystem I is essential for photosynthesis. *Nature* 429:579–82

216. Munekage Y, Hojo M, Meurer J, Endo T, Tasaka M, Shikanai T. 2002. PGR5 is involved in cyclic electron flow around photosystem I and is essential for photoprotection in *Arabidopsis. Cell* 110:361–71

217. Nechushtai R, Muster P, Binder A, Liveanu V, Nelson N. 1983. Photosystem I reaction center from the thermophilic cyanobacterium-Mastigocladus laminosus. *Proc. Natl. Acad. Sci. USA* 80:1179–83

218. Nelson N, Ben-Shem A. 2002. Photosystem I reaction center: Past and future. *Photosyth. Res.* 73:193–206

219. Nelson N, Ben-Shem A. 2004. The complex architecture of oxygenic photosynthesis. *Nat. Rev. Mol. Cell Biol.* 5:971–82

220. Nelson N, Ben-Shem A. 2005. Structure, function and regulation of plant photosystem I. In *Photosystem I*, ed. JH Golbeck. Dordrecht, The Neth.: Kluwer Acad. In press

221. Nelson N, Ben-Shem A. 2005. The structure of photosystem I and evolution of photosynthesis. *BioEssays* 27:914–22

222. Nelson N, Sacher A, Nelson H. 2002. The significance of molecular slips in transport systems. *Nat. Rev. Mol. Cell Biol.* 3:876–81

223. Nield J, Orlova EV, Morris EP, Gowen B, van Heel M, Barber J. 2000. 3D map of the plant photosystem II supercomplex obtained by cryoelectron microscopy and single particle analysis. *Nat. Struct. Biol.* 7:44–47

224. Nield J, Redding K, Hippler M. 2004. Remodeling of light-harvesting protein complexes in chlamydomonas in response to environmental changes. *Eukaryot. Cell* 3:1370–80

225. Nogues I, Hervas M, Peregrina JR, Navarro JA, de la Rosa MA, et al. 2005. Anabaena flavodoxin as an electron carrier from photosystem I to ferredoxin-NADP+ reductase. Role of flavodoxin residues in protein-protein interaction and electron transfer. *Biochemistry* 44:97–104

226. Noren GH, Boerner RJ, Barry BA. 1991. EPR characterization of an oxygen-evolving photosystem II preparation from the transformable cyanobacterium *Synechocystis* 6803. *Biochemistry* 30:3943–50

227. Odom WR, Bricker TM. 1992. Interaction of Cpa-1 with the manganese-stabilizing protein of photosystem II - identification of domains cross-linked by 1-ethyl-3-[3-(dimethylamino)propyl]carbodiimide. *Biochemistry* 31:5616–20

228. Okamura MY, Steiner LA, Feher G. 1974. Characterization of reaction centers from photosynthetic bacteria. I. Subunit structure of the protein mediating the primary photochemistry in *Rhodopseudomonas spheroides* R-26. *Biochemistry* 13:1394–403

229. Okegawa Y, Tsuyama M, Kobayashi Y, Shikanai T. 2005. The pgr1 mutation in the Rieske subunit of the cytochrome b6f complex does not affect PGR5-dependent cyclic electron transport around photosystem I. *J. Biol. Chem.* 280:28332–36

230. Okkels JS, Nielsen VS, Scheller HV, Moller BL. 1992. A cDNA clone from barley encoding the precursor from the photosystem I polypeptide PSI-G: sequence similarity to PSI-K. *Plant Mol. Biol.* 18:989–94

231. Olesen K, Ejdeback M, Crnogorac MM, Kostic NM, Hansson O. 1999. Electron transfer to photosystem 1 from spinach plastocyanin mutated in the small acidic patch: ionic strength dependence of kinetics and comparison of mechanistic models. *Biochemistry* 38:16695–705

232. Olive J, Vallon O. 1991. Structural organization of the thylakoid membrane: freeze-fracture and immunocytochemical analysis. *J. Electron Microsc. Tech.* 18:360–74

233. Ono T, Noguchi T, Inoue Y, Kusunoki M, Matsushita T, Oyanagi H. 1992. X-ray-detection of the period-4 cycling of the manganese cluster in photosynthetic water oxidizing enzyme. *Science* 258:1335–37

234. Ono T, Zimmermann JL, Inoue Y, Rutherford AW. 1986. Electron paramagnetic resonance evidence for a modified S-state transition in chloride-depleted photosystem II. *Biochim. Biophys. Acta* 851:193–201

234a. Ort DR, Yocum CF, eds. 1996. *Oxygenic Photosynthesis: The Light Reactions.* Dordrecht, The Neth.: Kluwer Acad.

235. Pecoraro VL, Baldwin MJ, Caudle MT, Hsieh W-Y, Law NA. 1998. A proposal for water oxidation in photosystem II. *Pure Appl. Chem.* 70:925–29

236. Peloquin JM, Campbell KA, Randall DW, Evanchik MA, Pecoraro VL, et al. 2000. Mn-55 ENDOR of the S_2 state multiline EPR signal of photosystem II: Implications on the structure of the tetranuclear Mn cluster. *J. Am. Chem. Soc.* 122:10926–42

237. Peter JF, Thornber JP. 1991. Biochemical composition and organization of higher plant photosystem II light-harvesting pigment proteins. *J. Biol. Chem.* 266:16745–54

238. Pichersky E, Jansson S. 1996. The light-harvesting chlorophyll a/b-binding polypeptides and their genes in angiosperm and gymnosperm species. See Ref. 234a, pp. 507–21

239. Popelkova H, Im MM, Yocum CF. 2002. N-terminal truncations of manganese stabilizing protein identify two amino acid sequences required for binding of the eukaryotic protein to photosystem II and reveal the absence of one binding-related sequence in cyanobacteria. *Biochemistry* 41:10038–45

240. Popelkova H, Im MM, Yocum CF. 2003. Binding of manganese stabilizing protein to photosystem II: Identification of essential N-terminal threonine residues and domains that prevent nonspecific binding. *Biochemistry* 42:6193–200

241. Purton S, Stevens DR, Muhiuddin IP, Evans MC, Carter S, et al. 2001. Site-directed mutagenesis of PsaA residue W693 affects phylloquinone binding and function in the photosystem I reaction center of *Chlamydomonas reinhardtii*. *Biochemistry* 40:2167–75

242. Pushkar YN, Karyagina I, Stehlik D, Brown S, van der Est A. 2005. Recruitment of a foreign quinone into the A1 site of photosystem I. Consecutive forward electron transfer from A0 TO A1 to FX with anthraquinone in the A1 site as studied by transient EPR. *J. Biol. Chem.* 280:12382–90

243. Ramesh VM, Gibasiewicz K, Lin S, Bingham SE, Webber AN. 2004. Bidirectional electron transfer in photosystem I: accumulation of A0- in A-side or B-side mutants of the axial ligand to chlorophyll A0. *Biochemistry* 43:1369–75

244. Rappaport F, Guergova-Kuras M, Nixon PJ, Diner BA, Lavergne J. 2002. Kinetics and pathways of charge recombination in photosystem II. *Biochemistry* 41:8518–27

245. Redinbo MR, Yeates TO, Merchant S. 1994. Plastocyanin: Structural and functional analysis. *J. Bioenerg. Biomembr.* 26:49–66

246. Rhee K-H. 2001. Photosystem II: The solid structural era. *Annu. Rev. Biophys. Biomol. Struct.* 30:307–28

247. Rigby SE, Muhiuddin IP, Evans MC, Purton S, Heathcote P. 2002. Photoaccumulation of the PsaB phyllosemiquinone in photosystem I of *Chlamydomonas reinhardtii*. *Biochim. Biophys. Acta* 1556:13–20

248. Riggs PJ, Mei R, Yocum CF, Penner-Hahn JE. 1992. Reduced derivatives of the manganese cluster in the photosynthetic oxygen-evolving complex. *J. Am. Chem. Soc.* 114:10650–51

249. Riggs-Gelasco PJ, Mei R, Yocum CF, Penner-Hahn JE. 1996. Reduced derivatives of the Mn cluster in the oxygen-evolving complex of photosystem II: An EXAFS study. *J. Am. Chem. Soc.* 118:2387–99

250. Rintamaki E, Martinsuo P, Pursiheimo S, Aro EM. 2000. Cooperative regulation of light-harvesting complex II phosphorylation via the plastoquinol and ferredoxin-thioredoxin system in chloroplasts. *Proc. Natl. Acad. Sci. USA* 97:11644–49

251. Ritz T, Park S, Schulten K. 2001. Kinetics of excitation migration and trapping in the photosynthetic unit of purple bacteria. *J. Phys. Chem. B* 105:8259–67

252. Rosgaard L, Zygadlo A, Scheller HV, Mant A, Jensen PE. 2005. Insertion of the plant photosystem I subunit G into the thylakoid membrane. *FEBS J.* 272:4002–10

253. Rutherford AW. 1989. Photosystem II, the water-splitting enzyme. *Trends Biochem. Sci.* 14:227–32

254. Saha S, Ouitrakul R, Izawa S Good NE. 1971. Electron transport and photophospho-rylation as a function of the electron acceptor. *J. Biol. Chem.* 246:3204–9

255. Santabarbara S, Kuprov I, Fairclough WV, Purton S, Hore PJ, et al. 2005. Bidirectional electron transfer in photosystem I: determination of two distances between P700+ and A1- in spin-correlated radical pairs. *Biochemistry* 44:2119–28

256. Satoh K. 1996. Introduction to the photosystem II reaction center-isolation and biochemcial and biophysical characterization. See Ref. 234a, pp. 193–211

257. Scheller HV. 1996. In vitro cyclic electron transport in barley thylakoids follows two independent pathways. *Plant Physiol.* 110:187–94

258. Scheller HV, Jensen PE, Haldrup A, Lunde C, Knoetzel J. 2001. Role of subunits in eukaryotic Photosystem I. *Biochim. Biophys. Acta* 1507:41–60

259. Schlodder E, Witt HT. 1999. Stoichiometry of proton release from the catalytic center in photosynthetic water oxidation - Reexamination by a glass electrode study at pH 5.5–7.2. *J. Biol. Chem.* 274:30387–92

260. Schubert WD, Klukas O, Saenger W, Witt HT, Fromme P, Krauss N. 1998. A common ancestor for oxygenic and anoxygenic photosynthetic systems: a comparison based on the structural model of photosystem I. *J. Mol. Biol.* 280:297–314

261. Seidler A. 1996. The extrinsic polypeptides of Photosystem II. *Biochim. Biophys. Acta* 1277:35–60

262. Sener MK, Jolley C, Ben-Shem A, Fromme P, Nelson N, Schulten K. 2005. Evolution of excitation migration pathways of photosystem I from cyanobacteria to plants. *Biophys J.* 88:A510

263. Sener MK, Lu D, Ritz T, Park S, Fromme P, Schulten K. 2002. Robustness and opti-mality of light harvesting in cyanobacterial photosystem I. *J. Phys. Chem. B* 106:7948–60

264. Sener MK, Park S, Lu D, Damjanovic A, Ritz T, et al. 2004. Excitation migration in trimeric cyanobacterial photosystem I. *J. Chem. Phys.* 120:11183–95

265. Setif P, Fischer N, Lagoutte B, Bottin H, Rochaix JD. 2002. The ferredoxin docking site of photosystem I. *Biochim. Biophys. Acta* 1555:204–9

266. Setif PQ, Bottin H. 1994. Laser flash absorption spectroscopy study of ferredoxin reduction by photosystem I in Synechocystis sp. PCC 6803: evidence for submicrosecond and microsecond kinetics. *Biochemistry* 33:8495–504

267. Setif PQ, Bottin H. 1995. Laser flash absorption spectroscopy study of ferredoxin reduction by photosystem I: spectral and kinetic evidence for the existence of several photosystem I-ferredoxin complexes. *Biochemistry* 34:9059–70

268. Shen JR, Ikeuchi M, Inoue Y. 1997. Analysis of the psbU gene encoding the 12-kDa extrinsic protein of photosystem II and studies on its role by deletion mutagenesis in *Synechocystis* sp. PCC 6803. *J. Biol. Chem.* 272:17821–26

269. Shen JR, Inoue Y. 1993. Binding and functional-properties of 2 new extrinsic components, cytochrome-C550 and a 12-kDa protein, in cyanobacterial photosystem II. *Biochemistry* 32:1825–32

270. Shen JR, Qian M, Inoue Y, Burnap RL. 1998. Functional characterization of *Synechocystis* sp. PCC 6803 ΔpsbU and ΔpsbV mutants reveals important roles of cytochrome c-550 in cyanobacterial oxygen evolution. *Biochemistry* 37:1551–58

271. Shen JR, Satoh K, Katoh S. 1988. Calcium content of oxygen-evolving photosystem-II preparations from higher plants - effects of NaCl treatment. *Biochim. Biophys. Acta* 933:358–64

272. Shutova T, Irrgang KD, Shubin V, Klimov VV, Renger G. 1997. Analysis of pH-induced structural changes of the isolated extrinsic 33 kilodalton protein of photosystem II. *Biochemistry* 36:6350–58

273. Simpson DJ, Knoetzel J. 1996. Light-harvesting complexes of plants and algae: introduction, survey and nomenclature. See Ref. 234a, pp. 493–506

274. Sommer F, Drepper F, Haehnel W, Hippler M. 2004. The hydrophobic recognition site formed by residues PsaA-Trp651 and PsaB-Trp627 of photosystem I in *Chlamydomonas reinhardtii* confers distinct selectivity for binding of plastocyanin and cytochrome c6. *J. Biol. Chem.* 279:20009–17

275. Sommer F, Drepper F, Hippler M. 2002. The luminal helix l of PsaB is essential for recognition of plastocyanin or cytochrome c6 and fast electron transfer to photosystem I in *Chlamydomonas reinhardtii*. *J. Biol. Chem.* 277:6573–81

276. Standfuss J, Terwisscha van Scheltinga AC, Lamborghini M, Kuhlbrandt W. 2005. Mechanisms of photoprotection and nonphotochemical quenching in pea light-harvesting complex at 2.5 A resolution. *EMBO J.* 24:919–28

277. Stauber EJ, Fink A, Markert C, Kruse O, Johanningmeier U, Hippler M. 2003. Proteomics of Chlamydomonas reinhardtii light-harvesting proteins. *Eukaryot. Cell* 2:978–94

278. Stockel J, Oelmuller R. 2004. A novel protein for photosystem I biogenesis. *J. Biol. Chem.* 279:10243–51

279. Strickler MA, Walker LM, Hillier W, Debus RJ. 2005. Evidence from biosynthetically incorporated strontium and FTIR difference spectroscopy that the C-terminus of the D1 polypeptide of photosystem II does not ligate calcium. *Biochemistry* 44:8571–77

280. Stroebel D, Choquet Y, Popot JL, Picot D. 2003. An atypical haem in the cytochrome b(6)f complex. *Nature* 426:413–18

281. Svensson B, Tiede DM, Nelson DR, Barry BA. 2004. Structural studies of the manganese stabilizing subunit in photosystem II. *Biophys. J.* 86:1807–12

282. Takahashi Y, Yasui T-A, Stauber EJ, Hippler M. 2004. Comparison of the subunit compositions of the PSI–LHCI supercomplex and the LHCI in the green alga *Chlamydomonas reinhardtii*. *Biochemistry* 43:7816–23

283. Thornton LE, Ohkawa H, Roose JL, Kashino Y, Keren N, Pakrasi HB. 2004. Homologs of Plant PsbP and PsbQ proteins are necessary for regulation of photosystem II activity in the cyanobacterium *Synechocystis* 6803. *Plant Cell* 16:2164–67

284. Thornton LE, Roose JL, Pakrasi HB, Ikeuchi M. 2005. The low molecular weight proteins of photosystem II. In *Photosystem II: The Water/Plastoquinone Oxido-Reductase in Photosynthesis*, ed. T Wydrzynski, K Satoh, pp.121–38. Dordrecht, The Neth.: Springer

285. Tohri A, Dohmae N, Suzuki T, Ohta H, Inoue Y, Enami I. 2004. Identification of domains on the extrinsic 23 kDa protein possibly involved in electrostatic interaction with the extrinsic 33 kDa protein in spinach photosystem II. *Eur. J. Biochem.* 271:962–71

286. Tommos C, Babcock GT. 1998. Oxygen production in nature: A light-driven metalloradical enzyme process. *Acc. Chem. Res.* 31:18–25

287. Tommos C, Babcock GT. 2000. Proton and hydrogen currents in photosynthetic water oxidation. *Biochim. Biophys. Acta* 1458:199–219

288. van Thor JJ, Geerlings TH, Matthijs HC, Hellingwerf KJ. 1999. Kinetic evidence for the PsaE-dependent transient ternary complex photosystem I/Ferredoxin/Ferredoxin:NADP(+) reductase in a cyanobacterium. *Biochemistry* 38:12735–46

289. Vasil'ev S, Bruce D. 2004. Optimization and evolution of light harvesting in photosynthesis: The role of antenna chlorophyll conserved between photosystem II and photosystem I. *Plant Cell* 16:3059–68

290. Vasil'ev S, Brudvig GW, Bruce D. 2003. The X-ray structure of photosystem II reveals a novel electron transport pathway between P680, cytochrome b559 and the energy-quenching cation, ChlZ+. *FEBS Lett.* 543:159–63

291. Vermaas W. 1993. Molecular biological approaches to analyze the structure and function of photosystem II. *Annu. Rev. Plant Physiol. Plant Mol. Biol.* 44:457–81

292. Vernon LP, Shaw ER. 1971. Subchloroplast fragments: Triton X-100 method. In *Methods in Enzymology*, ed. A San Pietro, 23:277–89. New York: Academic Press

293. Vink M, Zer H, Alumot N, Gaathon A, Niyogi K, et al. 2004. Light-modulated exposure of the light-harvesting complex II (LHCII) to protein kinase(s) and state transition in *Chlamydomonas reinhardtii* xanthophyll mutants. *Biochemistry* 43:7824–33

294. Vrettos JS, Limburg J, Brudvig GW. 2001. Mechanism of photosynthetic water oxidation: combining biophysical studies of photosystem II with inorganic model chemistry. *Biochim. Biophys. Acta* 1503:229–45

295. Vrettos JS, Stone DA, Brudvig GW. 2001. Quantifying the ion selectivity of the Ca2+ site in photosystem II: Evidence for direct involvement of Ca^{2+} in O_2 formation. *Biochemistry* 40:7937–45

296. Wastl J, Bendall DS, Howe CJ. 2002. Higher plants contain a modified cytochrome c6. *Trends Plant Sci.* 7:244–45

297. Webber AN, Su H, Bingham SE, Kass H, Krabben L, et al. 1996. Site-directed mutations affecting the spectroscopic characteristics and midpoint potential of the primary donor in photosystem I. *Biochemistry* 35:12857–63

298. Weber K, Osborn M. 1969. The reliability of molecular weight determinations by dodecyl sulfate-polyacrylamide gel electrophoresis. *J. Biol. Chem.* 244:4406–12

299. Wedel N, Klein R, Ljungberg U, Andersson B, Herrmann RG. 1992. The single copy gene psbS codes for a phylogenetically intriguing 22 kDa polypeptide of photosystem II. *FEBS Lett.* 314:61–66

300. Weigel M, Pesaresi P, Leister D. 2003. Tracking the function of the cytochrome c6-like protein in higher plants. *Trends Plant Sci.* 8:513–17

301. Weigel M, Varotto C, Pesaresi P, Finazzi G, Rappaport F, et al. 2003. Plastocyanin is indispensable for photosynthetic electron flow in *Arabidopsis thaliana*. *J. Biol. Chem.* 278:31286–89

302. Wincencjusz H, van Gorkom HJ, Yocum CF. 1997. The photosynthetic oxygen evolving complex requires chloride for its redox state $S_2 \rightarrow S_3$ and $S_3 \rightarrow S_0$ transitions but not for $S_0 \rightarrow S_1$ or $S_1 \rightarrow S_2$ transitions. *Biochemistry* 36:3663–70

303. Wincencjusz H, Yocum CF, van Gorkom HJ. 1998. S-state dependence of chloride binding affinities and exchange dynamics in the intact and polypeptide-depleted O2 evolving complex of photosystem II. *Biochemistry* 37:8595–604

304. Wollman FA. 2001. State transitions reveal the dynamics and flexibility of the photosynthetic apparatus. *EMBO J.* 20:3623–30

305. Wollman FA, Minai L, Nechushtai R. 1999. The biogenesis and assembly of photosynthetic proteins in thylakoid membranes. *Biochim. Biophys. Acta* 1411:21–85

306. Xu Q, Bricker TM. 1992. Structural organization of proteins on the oxidizing side of photosystem II - 2 molecules of the 33-kDa manganese-stabilizing proteins per reaction center. *J. Biol. Chem.* 267:25816–21

307. Xu Q, Nelson J, Bricker TM. 1994. Secondary structure of the 33 kDa extrinsic protein of photosystem II - a far-UV circular dichroism study. *Biochim. Biophys. Acta* 1188:427–31

308. Xu W, Chitnis PR, Valieva A, van der Est A, Brettel K, et al. 2003. Electron transfer in cyanobacterial photosystem I: II. Determination of forward electron transfer rates of site-directed mutants in a putative electron transfer pathway from A0 through A1 to FX. *J. Biol. Chem.* 278:27876–87

309. Xu W, Chitnis PR, Valieva A, van der Est A, Pushkar YN, et al. 2003. Electron transfer in cyanobacterial photosystem I: I. Physiological and spectroscopic characterization of site-directed mutants in a putative electron transfer pathway from A0 through A1 to FX. *J. Biol. Chem.* 278:27864–75

310. Yang M, Damjanovic A, Vaswani HM, Flemming GR. 2003 Energy transfer in photosystem I of cyanobcateria Synechococcus eleongatus: Model study with structure-based semi-emperical Hamiltonian and experimental spectral density. *Biophys. J.* 85:140–58

311. Yang M, Fleming GR. 2002. Influence of phonons on exciton transfer dynamics: comparison of the Redfield, Forster, and modified Redfield equations. *Chem. Phys.* 282:1163–80

312. Yang MN, Fleming GR. 2003. Construction of kinetic domains in energy trapping processes and application to a photosynthetic light harvesting complex. *J. Chem. Phys.* 119:5614–22

313. Yi X, McChargue M, Laborde S, Fankel LK, Bricker TM. 2005. The manganese-stabilizing protein is required for photosystem II assembly/stability and photoautotrophy in higher plants. *J. Biol. Chem.* 280:16170–74

314. Yocum CF. 1991. Calcium activation of photosynthetic water oxidation. *Biochim. Biophys. Acta* 1059:1–15

315. Yocum CF, Yerkes CT, Blankenship RE, Sharp RR, Babcock GT. 1981. Stoichiometry, inhibitor sensitivity, and organization of manganese associated with photosynthetic oxygen evolution. *Proc. Natl. Acad. Sci. USA* 78:7507–11

316. Yu JP, Shen GZ, Wang T, Bryant DA, Golbeck JH, McIntosh L. 2003. Suppressor mutations in the study of photosystem I biogenesis: sll0088 is a previously unidentified gene involved in reaction center accumulation in Synechocystis sp. strain PCC 6803. *J. Bacteriol.* 185:3878–87

317. Zeng MT, Gong XM, Evans MC, Nelson N, Carmeli C. 2002. Stabilization of iron-sulfur cluster F(X) by intra-subunit interactions unraveled by suppressor and second site-directed mutations in PsaB of Photosystem I. *Biochim. Biophys. Acta* 1556:254–64

318. Zer H, Vink M, Keren N, Dilly-Hartwig HG, Paulsen H, et al. 1999. Regulation of thylakoid protein phosphorylation at the substrate level: reversible light-induced conformational changes expose the phosphorylation site of the light-harvesting complex II. *Proc. Natl. Acad. Sci. USA* 96:8277–82

319. Zer H, Vink M, Shochat S, Herrmann RG, Andersson B, Ohad I. 2003. Light affects the accessibility of the thylakoid light harvesting complex II (LHCII) phosphorylation site to the membrane protein kinase(s). *Biochemistry* 42:728–38

320. Zhang H, Whitelegge JP, Cramer WA. 2001. Ferredoxin: NADP oxidoreductase is a subunit of the chloroplast cytochrome b6 f complex. *J. Biol. Chem.* 276:38159–65

321. Zhang S, Scheller HV. 2004. Light-harvesting complex II binds to several small subunits of photosystem I. *J. Biol. Chem.* 279:3180–87

322. Zouni A, Witt HT, Kern J, Fromme P, Krauss N, et al. 2001. Crystal structure of photosystem II from *Synechococcus elongatus* at 3.8 angstrom resolution. *Nature* 409:739–43

323. Zubrzycki IZ, Frankel LK, Russo PS, Bricker TM. 1998. Hydrodynamic studies on the manganese-stabilizing protein of photosystem II. *Biochemistry* 37:13553–58

324. Zybailov B, van der Est A, Zech SG, Teutloff C, Johnson TW, et al. 2000. Recruitment of a foreign quinone into the A1 site of photosystem I. II. Structural and functional characterization of phylloquinone biosynthetic pathway mutants by electron paramagnetic resonance and electron-nuclear double resonance spectroscopy. *J. Biol. Chem.* 275:8531–39

Glycosyltransferases of Lipophilic Small Molecules

Dianna Bowles, Eng-Kiat Lim, Brigitte Poppenberger, and Fabián E. Vaistij

Center for Novel Agricultural Products, Department of Biology, University of York, York YO10 5DD, United Kingdom; email: djb32@york.ac.uk, ekl100@york.ac.uk, bp7@york.ac.uk, fv4@york.ac.uk

Annu. Rev. Plant Biol. 2006. 57:567–97

The *Annual Review of Plant Biology* is online at plant.annualreviews.org

doi: 10.1146/ annurev.arplant.57.032905.105429

First published online as a Review in Advance on March 3, 2006

1543-5008/06/0602-0567$20.00

Key Words

detoxification, homeostasis, hormones, secondary metabolites, stress responses

Abstract

Glycosyltransferases of small molecules transfer sugars to a wide range of acceptors, from hormones and secondary metabolites to biotic and abiotic chemicals and toxins in the environment. The enzymes are encoded by large multigene families and can be identified by a signature motif in their primary sequence, which classifies them as a subset of Family 1 glycosyltransferases. The transfer of a sugar onto a lipophilic acceptor changes its chemical properties, alters its bioactivity, and enables access to membrane transporter systems. In vitro studies have shown that a single gene product can glycosylate multiple substrates of diverse origins; multiple enzymes can also glycosylate the same substrate. These features suggest that in a cellular context, substrate availability is a determining factor in enzyme function, and redundancy depends on the extent of coordinate gene regulation. This review discusses the role of these glycosyltransferases in underpinning developmental and metabolic plasticity during adaptive responses.

Contents

1. INTRODUCTION

Plants have evolved an extraordinary capacity to perceive changes in their external environments and adapt rapidly to maximize opportunity and minimize risk. This plasticity depends on the integration of growth, development, and metabolism, and the evolution of diverse mechanisms to regulate cellular homeostasis. Increasing evidence suggests that glycosylation is one of these mechanisms, with the identification of large multigene families of glycosyltransferases (GTs) able to recognize hormones, secondary metabolites, and biotic and abiotic chemicals and toxins in the environment. This review focuses on the class of GTs that recognize small molecules and describes their biochemical features and the evidence that has accumulated concerning their catalytic activities and functions in plants.

GTs that typically transfer sugars onto lipophilic small-molecule acceptors are grouped into Family 1 of a classification scheme that now describes more than 78 distinct families of GTs (**http://afmd.cnrs-mrs. fr/CAZY/acc.html**). Approximately 50% of the GT1 family contains a signature motif in their amino acid sequences, which is now a defining feature of this class of GTs, found in viruses and throughout the plant and animal kingdoms. A nomenclature system was established (77) on the basis of the phylogeny of gene sequences (67, 77, 108, 120). In plants, most GT1 enzymes contain the signature motif (67, 108). For example, in the completed genome of *Arabidopsis thaliana*, 107 open-reading frames contain the motif, in addition to 10 pseudogenes with frame-shift mutations, whereas only three GT1 enzymes do not have this feature (120).

The activated sugar donor of plant GTs is typically UDP-glucose (UDP-Glc), although UDP-rhamnose (UDP-Rha), UDP-galactose (UDP-Gal), UDP-xylose (UDP-Xyl), and UDP-glucuronic acid (UDP-GlcUA) have also been identified as activated sugars for the transfer reactions. Single or multiple glycosylation of the acceptors can occur at $-OH$, $-COOH$, $-NH_2$, $-SH$, and C–C groups. These reactions have been reviewed extensively (8, 49, 53, 70, 111, 145). Addition of a sugar onto a lipophilic acceptor will make the compound more polar and prevent any further possibility of its free diffusion across lipid bilayers and between intracellular compartments. To date, with the exception of three GTs that have both the signature motif and a hydrophobic sequence (92, 97, 154), plant enzyme sequences do not have obvious targeting information (67). This suggests the GTs function in the cytosol, but this may involve association with the cytosolic face of membrane compartments and, for those involved in secondary metabolism, location within multiprotein complexes (14).

Although the GT transfer reactions are cytosolic, the glycoside products that are formed gain access to membrane-bound transporter systems that recognize the glycosyl residues. Scientists have identified a carrier of glucosides for both endogenous metabolites and xenobiotics in tonoplast membranes, and ATP binding cassette (ABC) transporters have also been implicated in glycosylated xenobiotic transport (4, 118). Studies have documented the accumulation of glycosylated compounds in the vacuolar compartment (84). Glycosides and glycosidases of small lipophilic molecules have also been identified in the apoplast (21, 121), although their exit route was not defined. The clearance of glycosylated acceptors from the cytosol underpins the view that GTs are involved in detoxification, as both the vacuolar and apoplastic space can accommodate many different products that accumulate with low rates of turnover.

The above points highlight that glycosylation alters the solubility of compounds and their movement within the cell. There is also evidence, such as the spontaneous breakdown of glucosinolates on deglycosylation by myrosinase, that glycosylation can stabilize compounds (24). In relation to hormones, as well as defense-related small molecules of plant and nonplant origin, glycosylation/deglycosylation can directly affect bioactivity (99). Therefore, the action of GTs of small molecules impacts a multitude of events in plants because their substrates are ubiquitous and have diverse functions or activities, and the consequences of glycosylation can be manyfold.

2. THE RELATEDNESS OF GLYCOSYLTRANSFERASE STRUCTURE AND SEQUENCE TO SUBSTRATE RECOGNITION

Structural information is crucial to the fundamental understanding of protein evolution, as well as to the understanding of catalytic enzyme mechanisms. Prior to 2005, only three GT1 protein structures were available in the public domain (100, 101, 102). All of these were bacterial GTs involved in antibiotic biosynthesis. The structures consisted of two Rossmann folds, each constructed with a central sheet of several β-strands flanked on either side by α-helices. Results from the cocrystallization of these proteins with their ligands indicated that residues in the N-terminal half of the protein were responsible for acceptor binding, whereas those in the C-terminal half were involved mainly in donor interactions. Owing to the low sequence sim-

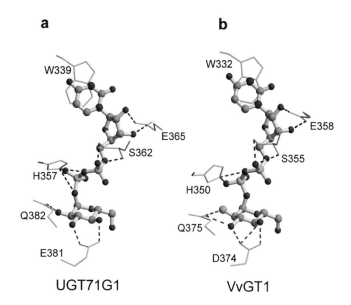

a   **b**

UGT71G1   VvGT1

ilarity between the bacterial GTs and plant GTs, as well as the lack of a signature motif in the bacterial sequences, few studies used the published structures to model plant enzymes (34, 140).

As of writing two plant GT1 enzymes have been crystallized and their three-dimensional structures solved independently by two research groups (128; G.J. Davies, unpublished data). In both studies the results show that plant proteins also contain two Rossmann folds and acceptors bind to residues in the N-terminal half, whereas activated donor sugars bind mainly to amino acids in the C-terminal region. The *Medicago truncatula* UGT71G1 was crystallized with the donor UDP-Glc, and the structure was solved at 2.6 Å (128). In contrast, a nonhydrolysable donor, UDP-2-deoxy-2-fluoro-Glc, was used in the crystallization of *Vitis vinifera* (Vv) GT1 with the acceptor kaempferol; this structure was solved at 1.9 Å (G.J. Davies, unpublished data).

The structures of both GTs clearly illustrate the role of the signature motif and, as illustrated in **Figure 1**, identify the residues that constitute the donor-sugar binding pocket. Thus, tryptophan (residue 332 in VvGT1 and residue 339 in UGT71G1) forms the hydrophobic platform that stacks

Figure 1

The three-dimensional structures of (*a*) *Medicago truncatula* UGT71G1 with UDP-glucose and (*b*) *Vitis vinifera* (Vv) GT1 with UDP-2-deoxy-2-fluoro-glucose illustrate the commonality of donor-sugar binding.

with the uracil base of UDP-Glc. Glutamate (residue 358 in VvGT1 and residue 365 in UGT71G1) binds the two hydroxyls of ribose. Histidine (residue 350 in VvGT1 and residue 357 in UGT71G1) interacts with the O2 of the β-phosphate of UDP, and serine (residue 355 in VvGT1 and residue 362 in UGT71G1) interacts with the equivalent atom of the α-phosphate. Aspartate (residue 374 in VvGT1)/glutamate (residue 381 in UGT71G1) and glutamine (residue 375 in VvGT1 and residue 382 in UGT71G1) play key roles in recognizing the hydroxyl at the C2, C3, and C4 positions of the Glc moiety (**Figure 1**).

As additional plant GT1 structures are solved, predictive modeling of more individuals within the multigene families becomes possible. This modeling can build on the considerable biochemical data available on the activities of plant GTs in vitro. Most of the studies we review in Section 3 include in vitro assays of recombinant GTs and their genes, cloned from a wide range of plant species. These studies include examples in which there is clear evidence that a single gene product can recognize multiple acceptors in vitro. As illustrated in **Figure 2**, the structures and metabolic relatedness of known acceptors of GTs include plant metabolites and xenobiotics, including shikimic acid derivatives and alkaloids; mevalonate derivatives, including terpenoids and steroids; as well as polyketides; amino acid derivatives; and man-made chemicals not found in nature.

Although a single GT can recognize multiple substrates, there is now also good evidence that multiple GTs within the genome of a single plant species can recognize the same substrate. This has been demonstrated in biochemical analyses of the entire multigene family of GTs from *Arabidopsis*. Gene sequences containing the signature motif were cloned, expressed as recombinant proteins in *Escherichia coli*, and screened for activity toward a broad range of compounds in vitro using UDP-Glc as the activated sugar donor. The data were analyzed within the context of gene phylogeny and evolution of catalytic activities (69).

Researchers have identified certain compounds recognized by many different GTs throughout the phylogenetic tree (69). An example is the hydroxycoumarin esculetin, which can be glucosylated at either the 6-OH or 7-OH position, and which is recognized by 48 *Arabidopsis* GTs belonging to six phylogenetic groups (B, D, E, F, H, and L). Interestingly, although multiple GTs recognized the substrate, regioselective glucosylation occurred in distinct branches in each phylogenetic group, with evidence of changes in regioselectivity during evolution of the ancestral genes (**Figure 3**). It is not yet known whether the GTs with the same regioselectivity interact with esculetin in identical ways.

Screening the panel of recombinant *Arabidopsis* GTs also produced examples of compounds with features recognized by only a small number of highly homologous GT sequences belonging to single phylogenetic groups or clades within a group. Thus, regioselective glucosylation at the –COOH position of hydroxybenzoic acids and phenylpropanoic acids was restricted to eight GTs of group L (72); N-glucosylation of cytokinins to two GTs, UGT76C1 and UGT76C2 in group H (48); and 4-OH glucosylation of monolignols to three GTs of the UGT72E clade (73). An interesting anomaly was salicylic acid (SA), recognized by the highly homologous UGT74F1 and UGT74F2 (82% amino acid identity) but glucosylated at the 2-OH and –COOH positions, respectively (72).

In the above examples, regioselectivity and substrate recognition were reflected in gene phylogeny. However, there were other compounds, such as abscisic acid (ABA) and quercetin, with structural features recognized by different GTs from many different phylogenetic groups of the *Arabidopsis* tree (68, 71). Regioselective glucosylation of quercetin at the 3-OH position was achieved by 11 individual GTs from three different phylogenetic groups (D, E, and F). Again, it will be

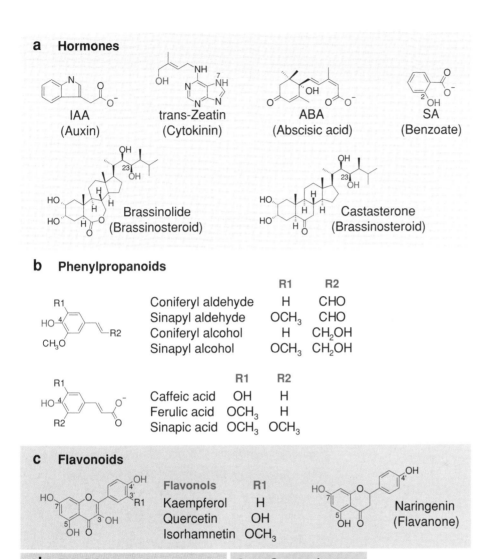

a Hormones

IAA
(Auxin)

trans-Zeatin
(Cytokinin)

ABA
(Abscisic acid)

SA
(Benzoate)

Brassinolide
(Brassinosteroid)

Castasterone
(Brassinosteroid)

b Phenylpropanoids

	R1	R2
Coniferyl aldehyde	H	CHO
Sinapyl aldehyde	OCH_3	CHO
Coniferyl alcohol	H	CH_2OH
Sinapyl alcohol	OCH_3	CH_2OH

	R1	R2
Caffeic acid	OH	H
Ferulic acid	OCH_3	H
Sinapic acid	OCH_3	OCH_3

c Flavonoids

Flavonols	R1
Kaempferol	H
Quercetin	OH
Isorhamnetin	OCH_3

Naringenin
(Flavanone)

d Betalains

Betanidin

e Coumarins

Scopoletin

Figure 2

(a–i) The chemical structures of plant metabolites are shown in these panels, with their glycosylation sites highlighted. (j) The metabolic relatedness of the compounds is illustrated.

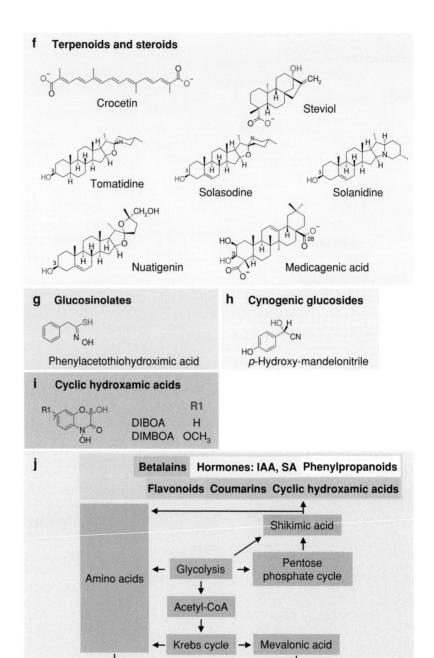

f   Terpenoids and steroids

Crocetin

Steviol

Tomatidine

Solasodine

Solanidine

Nuatigenin

Medicagenic acid

g   Glucosinolates

Phenylacetothiohydroximic acid

h   Cynogenic glucosides

p-Hydroxy-mandelonitrile

i   Cyclic hydroxamic acids

	R1
DIBOA	H
DIMBOA	OCH$_3$

j

Betalains   Hormones: IAA, SA   Phenylpropanoids

Flavonoids   Coumarins   Cyclic hydroxamic acids

Shikimic acid

Amino acids

Glycolysis

Pentose phosphate cycle

Acetyl-CoA

Krebs cycle → Mevalonic acid

Glucosinolates   Cytokinins

Cyanogenic glucosides

Terpenoids and steroids (including brassinosteroids and ABA)

Figure 2

(*Continued*)

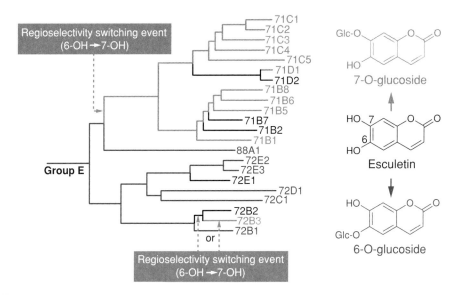

Figure 3

Glycosylation of esculetin by *Arabidopsis* glycosyltransferases (GTs) in phylogenetic group E. The regioselective glycosylation of esculetin falls into two subsets within group E, with the exception of UGT72B1 and UGT72B3, which suggests that a regioselectivity switching event has occurred during the gene's evolution. GTs not analyzed are labeled in black.

interesting to determine whether these diverse GTs interact with the flavonoid in identical ways.

In vitro biochemical studies reveal that (*a*) multiple GTs in a genome have the capacity to glycosylate the same substrate and (*b*) an individual GT has the capacity to glycosylate multiple substrates. Whether these insights become general principles will emerge as more plant genomes are sequenced completely and systematic biochemical analyses are undertaken, informed by a structural understanding of the GTs.

The key question is the extent to which any of these in vitro biochemical studies are useful for increasing our awareness of GT activity and physiological function in planta. In vitro there is an absence of factors influencing GT activity and its kinetic properties in the cell, such as cofactors, protein-protein interactions, metabolite channeling, and the effects of crowding. There is also the problem that UDP-Rha is not yet commercially available, and UDP-Glc and UDP-Gal are

typically used as the activated sugar donors in vitro. It is clear, however, from in vitro studies that substrate availability may be a major determining factor of GT activity in plants. If the native enzyme has the capacity to recognize multiple substrates in vivo, their availability to act as acceptors at any one time will be all-important. Similarly, functional redundancy of GTs capable of recognizing the same substrate will depend on whether their genes are coordinately regulated in cells of the plant, and indeed, whether those same substrates are recognized in a cellular context. It is thus essential to examine the consequences of changing GT expression in planta, whether developmental or metabolic- or stress/defense-related. Silencing multiple GTs may also be necessary to reveal clear phenotypes if redundancy is an issue. When analyzed in wild-type, unchallenged plants, GT enzyme activities are generally low, and this has also been reflected in GT transcript abundance. Challenges, particularly those related to stress conditions upregulate the expression of many GTs. Microarray databases are available at **https://www.genevestigator.ethz.ch/**, **http://genome-www5.stanford.edu/**, and **http://affymetrix.arabidopsis.info/narrays/experimentbrowse.pl**. The following section reviews current information on GT activities and the associated plant studies.

3. ACCEPTORS OF FAMILY 1 PLANT GLYCOSYLTRANSFERASES

Phytochemical studies throughout the twentieth century have demonstrated the number and complexity of small-molecule glycosides in higher plants. Often these molecules exist in numerous glycoforms, regioselectively glycosylated at different positions and carrying single sugars or multiple sugars linked as monosaccharides or as di-, tri-, and higher oligosaccharides. For example, from a total of 5000 different flavonoids, 300 different glycosides of a single flavonol, quercetin, have been identified (37). Glycosides of small molecules are the products of the GT1 family of enzymes, and the widespread occurrence, diversity, and complexity of the glycosides throughout the plant kingdom indicate a broad functionality for the GT1 enzymes.

3.1. Acceptors of Plant Origin

3.1.1. Hormones. Many compounds in a plant influence developmental processes and enable rapid adaptation in response to changes in the external environment. In this context, the homeostasis of hormones is critical, and a wide range of mechanisms has evolved to control precisely the levels of different hormones in plant cells and tissues. Glycosylation is thought to be one of these mechanisms, and all classical hormones, with the exception of ethylene, occur as glycosides in planta. This form of conjugation has been well studied, with many early biochemical papers describing GT activities toward different hormones, as well as profiling the existence

of hormone glycosides in plant extracts. This early work has been reviewed (58), along with reviews focusing on each hormone class (19, 27, 95, 126, 131, 155). These reviews discuss evidence that glycosylation can be either reversible or irreversible, depending on the individual hormone, and that the glycoside conjugates have different bioactivities from the free forms of the hormones. Results from applying hormone glycosides to cell culture/explants are difficult to interpret, given uptake issues as well as the likely occurrence of apoplastic glycosidases (16, 22). It should be noted that there are also many other hormone conjugates, including, for example, those that involve amides and fatty acids, as well as many additional factors that regulate hormone levels and their activities. The genetic tools to explore the relative importance of glycosylation and the other homeostatic mechanisms are becoming available. Recent work describing genes encoding GTs that glycosylate hormones are discussed below. Most of these studies involve only in vitro assays of recombinant GTs, but some studies have expanded to investigate the potential roles of those GTs in planta. GTs involved in gibberellin and jasmonate glycosylation have not been identified.

Auxins. The conjugation of indole-3-acetic-acid (IAA) is complex, with different plant species having distinct profiles of amide and glycoside conjugates; in vegetative tissues, *Arabidopsis* maintains approximately 90% of IAA in amide linkages, with 10% as ester-linked conjugates and only 1% as free IAA (155). The first gene to be identified encoding a GT of IAA was the maize *IAGLU* (135). More recently, screening recombinant GTs of *Arabidopsis* in vitro revealed that UGT84B1 synthesized 1-O-indole acetyl glucose ester (IAGlc), and overexpression of that GT led to a phenotype consistent with auxin deficiency (50, 51). The altered root phenotype of the transgenic lines was not recovered by application of IAA but was rescued by the auxin analogue 2,4-dichlorophenoxyacetic acid

(2,4-D), a compound not glucosylated in vitro by UGT84B1. Metabolic profiling of the overexpressor lines showed high levels of the IAGlc, but surprisingly, the levels of free IAA also increased, which suggests that overproduction of an IAA-conjugating enzyme leads to complex changes in auxin homeostasis (50).

Brassinosteroids. Feeding studies with many different brassinosteroids (BRs) and related metabolites have identified a wide range of glycosides (27). In mung beans, when brassinolide (BL), the most biologically active BR, was applied, the 23-O-glucoside was the most abundant metabolite formed (133). Recently, studies identified an *Arabidopsis* GT capable of catalyzing the 23-O-glucosylation of BL and its biosynthetic precursor, castasterone (114). Overexpression of UGT73C5 resulted in BR-deficient phenotypes, as well as reduced levels of active BRs in transgenic plants, which suggests that glucosylation of BRs reduces their bioactivity. Silencing the GT led to a reduction of BL-23-O-glucosylation activity below the detection limit in the seedlings used in BL feeding studies, confirming that UGT73C5 is involved in BL glucosylation in planta.

Cytokinins. Glycosylation of cytokinins involves O-glucosylation, O-xylosylation, and N-glucosylation (95). Genes encoding GTs that recognize cytokinins have been identified from several plant species; including ZOG1, a *trans*-zeatin-O-glucosyltransferase from *Phaseolus lunatus* (83); ZOX1, a *trans*-zeatin-O-xylosyltransferase from *Phaseolus vulgaris* (82); and two *cis*-zeatin-O-glucosyltransferases from *Zea mays* (81, 142). The genes were expressed in *E. coli*, and activities of the recombinant enzymes were determined in vitro. In addition, the effect of overexpressing *ZOG1* in transgenic tobacco was investigated (80). Compared with controls, plant tissues constitutively overexpressing the GT were capable of converting exogenous zeatin to high levels of zeatin-O-glucoside. An inducible promoter was used to drive *ZOG1* ex-

pression in transgenic leaf disc cultures; on inducible expression of the GT, a 10-fold higher zeatin level was required for the formation of shoots and callus compared with controls, which suggests increased inactivation of the hormone.

Screening of recombinant GTs from *Arabidopsis* in vitro also revealed enzymatic activities toward this class of hormones (48). The first two GTs with N-glucosyltransferase activity toward cytokinins UGT76C1 and UGT76C2 were identified. When *trans*-zeatin was applied to transgenic lines constitutively overexpressing UGT76C1, an increased accumulation of *trans*-zeatin-7-N-glucoside was detected (48).

Abscisic acid. Several glycosides of ABA have been identified in many plant species and the glucose ester is typically the most abundant conjugate (126). A recombinant enzyme from a GT gene of *Vigna angularis* converted 2-*trans*-(+)-ABA to its glucose ester in vitro (156). Eight recombinant GTs of *Arabidopsis* were recently found to recognize ABA in vitro, with only one, UGT71B6, showing enantioselective glucosylation toward the naturally occuring *cis*-S-(+)-ABA (71). The ability of UGT71B6 to glucosylate a wide range of ABA analogues was determined (116). Three bioactive analogues, PBI-514, PBI-524, and PBI-401, specifically designed as mechanism-based inhibitors of the 8′-hydroxylase of ABA, were not recognized by UGT71B6.

Salicylic acid. Two glucosylated forms of SA have been identified in plant species: the glucose ester and the 2-O-glucoside (143). Several publications have shown the elevation of SA and increased levels of the glucose ester and glucoside during biotic or abiotic stress/pathogen responses (32). When SA is applied to plants, the expression of a number of defense/stress-related genes is elevated, including those that encode GTs. In this context, *Nicotiana* species have been well studied and have revealed many SA-inducible GTs, including the *Tobacco* genes *Is5a* and *Is10a* (45, 46); *TOGT1* and *TOGT2*, which are identical to the former two genes (except for three and one nucleotides, respectively) (25); *SAGT* (65); and *NtGT1a* and *NtGT1b* (136); as well as the tomato gene *Twi1* (106). When recombinant enzymes encoded by these genes were assayed in vitro, their substrate recognition was broad (25, 65), and in one instance, SA was not an acceptor (136). Screening *Arabidopsis* GTs with SA and other benzoates in vitro revealed that only two GTs, UGT74F1 and UGT74F2, were active toward SA, and both these GTs also recognized benzoic acid (72). UGT74F2 was identified separately in an unrelated mutant screen (117) when the GT expressed activity toward anthranilate, a molecule structurally similar to SA and involved in tryptophan biosynthesis.

3.1.2. Secondary metabolites.
The sedentary lifestyle of plants has led to the evolution of a vast multitude of molecules that are synthesized for environmental adaptation and to influence other living organisms that cohabit the biosphere, both below and above ground. Many of these molecules are products of secondary metabolism. This section focuses on those secondary metabolites whose activity may be affected by glycosylation. For some metabolites, particularly those functioning in defense responses, glycosylation stabilizes the molecule in plants, and removal of the sugar leads to degradation and the formation of new breakdown products that are bioactive and often toxic. For other metabolites, the glycosides are bioactive, and removal of the sugars, such as by pathogen hydrolases, reduces toxicity. In the following sections, each class of secondary metabolites is considered in turn, often because each class has multiple functions, whether in development or defense, and the effect of glycosylation is related to each function.

Phenylpropanoids. The phenylpropanoid pathway leads from phenylalanine to a vast complex of secondary metabolites with a multitude of functions in plants (22, 23). GT activities toward metabolites of the general phenylpropanoid pathway have been investigated in relation mainly to sinapate ester formation in the Brassicaceae family, with some studies also focusing on monolignols. In members of the Brassicaceae family, 1-O-sinapoylglucose (SG) is an intermediate in the synthesis of sinapoylmalate, a putative ultraviolet protectant in foliar tissue, and sinapoylcholine, made during seed development and degraded during germination to provide sinapic acid and choline for the seedling. The *Arabidopsis* genes encoding enzymes involved in the conversion of SG to sinapoylmalate and SG to sinapoylcholine have been identified (66, 129) and reveal that both encode serine carboxypeptidase–like proteins and each is capable of catalyzing a *trans*-esterification reaction rather than hydrolysis. It has been suggested that serine carboxypeptidase–like proteins may have acquired novel functions during the evolution of plant secondary metabolism, and their action on SG reflects the use of the high-energy Glc ester as an activated sinapate donor (129). In the context of this review, SG is formed by a GT on sinapic acid, and genes encoding enzymes capable of this transfer reaction have been identified in both oil seed rape (*Brassica napus*) and in *Arabidopsis* (74, 89, 90, 91). The oil seed rape BnSGT, assayed as a recombinant enzyme preparation in vitro, displayed highest relative activity toward sinapate (90). Decreasing the expression of BnSGT in transgenic rape plants using RNA silencing led to a reduction in many different sinapate esters, including Glc, gentiobiose, and kaempferol glycoside, as well as sinapoylcholine and sinapoylmalate (5). These data support the view that SG plays a central role as an activated sinapate donor and that serine carboxypeptidase–like proteins acting as acyltransferases may occur in oil seed rape as well as *Arabidopsis* (66, 129).

Three closely related GTs from *Arabidopsis* (UGT84A1–A3), assayed as recombinant proteins in vitro, displayed activity toward hydroxycinnamic acids (74). Of the three, UGT84A2 had the highest activity toward sinapic acid, compared with ferulic, caffeic, p-coumaric, and cinnamic acids. In the same study, UGT72E2 and UGT72E3 were identified with activity toward phenylpropanoids, in particular, the coniferyl and sinapyl alcohols. More recently, researchers determined the specificity of a recombinant UGT72E1 and analyzed activities of the entire UGT72E clade toward coniferaldehyde and sinapyldehyde (73). Given the recent and unexpected finding that oxidation of the aldehydes likely plays an important role in the synthesis of their corresponding hydroxycinnamic acids (103), it will be interesting to determine whether glucosylation of the aldehydes plays a role in substrate availability in planta. Researchers recently discovered that the accumulation of glucosides of coniferyl alcohol and sinapyl alcohol in roots of *Arabidopsis* is light-dependent (40).

Flavonoids: flavonols. Flavonoids have been detected in the pollen of many plant species and account for a large percentage (2%–5%) of their dry weight. In petunia pollen, the major flavonoids are the flavonols kaempferol and quercetin 3-O-glycosides, whereas maize pollen, the other well-studied system in this context, contain at least 10 glycosides of kaempferol, quercetin, and isorhamnetin (139). Although not a universal requirement, evidence from some plant species suggests that flavonols play an important role in pollen function and that glycosylation of these compounds may be influential. Chalcone synthase (CHS) catalyzes the initial step in flavonoid biosynthesis: maize and petunia *chs* mutants were not only deficient in flavonoid production, but males were also sterile (104). Sterility arises from a failure to produce a functional pollen tube, which suggests that flavonoids are required for pollen fertility (138). The defect could be overcome by supplying kaempferol (93, 146). In petunia, adding the aglycones to flavonoid-deficient pollen led to flavonol 3-O-diglycoside production (147). GT activities

were identified in detergent-soluble pollen extracts, which suggests their association with membranes. Two GT activities, F3GalT and F2″GT, were defined. F3GalT transferred Gal to the 3-OH of the flavonol, and F2″GT formed a disaccharide Glc-(1→2)-Gal. The sequence of F3GalT was used to identify the gene encoding the GT and its activity toward UDP-Gal, and flavonol substrates were confirmed by a detailed biochemical analysis in vitro (92).

Two studies combining in vitro analyses and in planta metabolite profiling have identified a number of interesting GTs involved in flavonol glycoside biosynthesis in *Arabidopsis* (52, 141). Metabolite profiling of T-DNA insertion lines for UGT73C6 and UGT78D1 enabled a detailed comparison of mutant and wild-type leaf and floral tissues to identify the impact of the gene knock-outs on kaempferol and quercetin glycosides (52). The greatest impact was observed for UGT78D1 knock-outs. Parallel in vitro assays using the recombinant enzymes showed that UGT78D1 could synthesize the 3-O-rhamnoside of both quercetin and kaempferol, whereas UGT73C6 displayed higher activity toward a quercetin 3-O-rhamnoside, which suggests the flavonol glycosides rather than the aglycones may be the preferred substrates.

In a different study (141), *Arabidopsis* plants overexpressing the *PAP1* gene encoding a MYB transcription factor and leading to elevated levels of anthocyanins were used in a comprehensive transcriptomic and metabolomic analysis to identify novel genes involved in flavonoid metabolism. The expression of three GTs (UGT79B1, UGT75C1, and UGT78D2) was upregulated in the *PAP1* overexpressor lines. Detailed metabolic profiling of T-DNA insertion mutants *ugt78d2* and *ugt75c1* suggested acceptor specificity in planta, which was further analyzed by in vitro assays. Thus, UGT78D2 glucosylated both anthocyanins and flavonols at the 3-OH position, whereas UGT75D1 transferred glucose to the 5-OH position of anthocyanins. Interestingly, UGT78D1 and UGT78D2, the genes described in the two studies, were highly homologous, but their specificity for donor sugars was different, with UGT78D1 using UDP-Rha and UGT78D2 using UDP-Glc (52, 141).

Flavonoids: anthocyanidins. The pigmentation of flowers and fruits is due to the accumulation of flavonoids, carotenoids, and betalains. This field of study has been reviewed extensively in References 96 and 151. This section addresses anthocyanins and focuses mainly on recent genetic studies involving GTs.

Anthocyanins determine red, blue, and purple pigmentation. All flavonoids carry a hydroxyl group at the 4′ position of the B-ring of the molecule, as well as the possibility of hydroxylation at the 3′ position (or at the 3′ and 5′ positions) by flavonoid 3′-hydroxylase or flavonoid 3′5′ hydroxylase, respectively (42). The hydroxylation pattern is a major determinant of the color of the pigments and is dependent on genetic background. At least three enzymic steps are then required to convert the colorless dihydroflavonols to anthocyanins. The first is a reduction step to form leucoanthocyanidins, followed by further oxidation, dehydration, and glucosylation to produce the corresponding 3-O-glucosides of pelargonidin (brick-red), cyanidin (red), and delphinidin (blue). These may be further modified in many plant species by glycosylation, methylation, and acylation; the extent and type of modification depend on both plant species and variety. Anthocyanins are targeted for accumulation in the vacuole, and entry across the tonoplast is thought to involve transport via the glutathione pump(s) (79). The color of anthocyanins is affected by the presence of metal ions, vacuolar pH, and copigments such as flavonols and flavones. Glycosylation is considered to play a major role in both the solubility and stability of the pigments.

The best-characterized GTs are those that catalyze the first 3-O-glucosylation event common to the biosynthetic pathway of all an-

thocyanins (see Reference 28). This step was thought to precede subsequent glycosylation events. However, recently, a single GT that synthesized the cyanidin 5-O-glucoside first, followed by the cyanidin 3,5-di-O-glucoside, was identified in *Rosa hybrida* (**Figure 4a**) (107). The activity was confirmed to reside in a single gene product by in vitro assay of the recombinant enzyme (RhGT1), which could use either anthocyanidin or anthocyanidin 5-O-glucoside as an acceptor, but not the anthocyanidin 3-O-glucoside. Phylogenetic analyses revealed that RhGT1 differed significantly from other anthocyanidin 3- and 5-GT subfamilies.

A GT that catalyzed the 3′-O-glucosylation of the B-ring to synthesize gentiodelphin (a derivative of an anthocyanin 3,5,3′-tri-O-glucoside) involved in the deep-blue pigmentation of the flowers was purified from *Gentiana triflora* (**Figure 4b**) (28). In vitro assay of the recombinant enzyme confirmed the activity and indicated that the 3′-GT strictly required three OH groups on the B-ring for substrate recognition.

Flowers of wild-type Japanese morning glory (*Ipomoea nil*) are red or blue, whereas flowers of the *dusky* mutants are reddish-brown or purplish-gray. Recently, each of the mutant phenotypes was found to correlate with a frame-shift mutation at the 3′ coding region of a gene encoding a GT (98). The absence of the GT activity in the mutants led to the accumulation of anthocyanidin 3-O-glucoside derivatives rather than the 3-O-sophorosides found in wild-type petals (**Figure 4c**). The specificity of the GT (3GGT) was supported by in vitro studies of the recombinant enzyme and by overexpression in transgenic petunia that led to reduced levels of the predicted substrate. Another recent study has identified the first GT capable of transferring GlcUA from UDP-GlcUA to anthocyanidin 3-O-glucosides in the red daisy flower *Bellis perennis* (**Figure 4d**) (123). The native enzyme was isolated, its gene cloned, and the recombinant protein expressed in yeast was purified to homogeneity

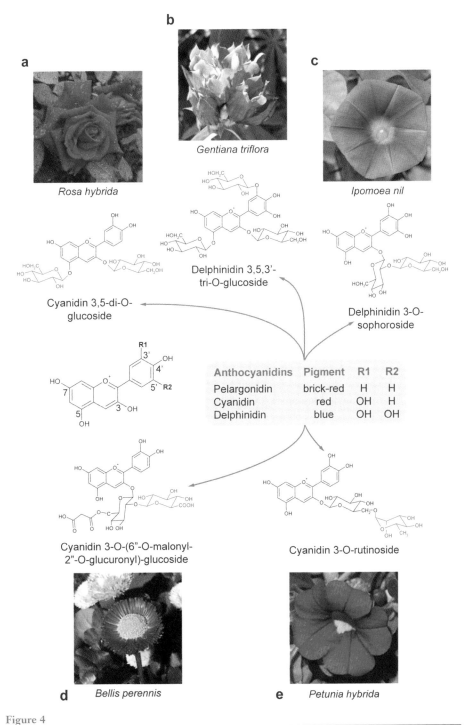

a *Rosa hybrida*

b *Gentiana triflora*

c *Ipomoea nil*

Cyanidin 3,5-di-O-glucoside

Delphinidin 3,5,3'-tri-O-glucoside

Delphinidin 3-O-sophoroside

Anthocyanidins	Pigment	R1	R2
Pelargonidin	brick-red	H	H
Cyanidin	red	OH	H
Delphinidin	blue	OH	OH

Cyanidin 3-O-(6"-O-malonyl-2"-O-glucuronyl)-glucoside

Cyanidin 3-O-rutinoside

d *Bellis perennis*

e *Petunia hybrida*

Figure 4

Representative glycoforms of anthocyanidins that determine the flower color of different plant species.

and assayed in vitro to confirmed donor and acceptor specificity. These two studies add to earlier genetic analyses, such as the identification of the GT transferring Rha to the Glc moiety of cyanidin 3-O-glucoside in petunia (**Figure 4e**) (13, 62).

Flavonoids: flavanone. In bitter *Citrus* species such as grapefruit, the sensation of bitterness is caused by flavanone glycosides in which the regiospecificity of Rha attachment to the naringenin 7-O-glucoside determines the bitter flavor. If the 2-OH position of the Glc is rhamnosylated, the resulting compound, naringin, is bitter; when the 6-OH position is rhamnosylated, the resulting diglycoside, narirutin, is tasteless. Although these properties have been recognized for many years, the GT responsible for the 2-OH glycosylation was recently purified, its gene cloned, and its activity confirmed using heterologous expression in a transgenic tobacco cell culture (26). This study complements an earlier work on limonoid glycosylation, which is responsible for the so-called delayed bitterness of both bitter and nonbitter *Citrus* species (57).

Betalains. In the Caryophyllales, the chromogenic anthocyanins are replaced by fruit and flower pigments of the betalains, comprised of betacyanins (red and purple) and betaxanthins (yellow), synthesized in the shikimic acid pathway. Although not studied as extensively as the flavonoid pigments, a number of studies have focused on the synthesis of betacyanins and particularly their glycosylation. Following the partial purification of two betanidin GTs (5-GT and 6-GT) from *Dorotheanthus bellidiformis* (148), the gene encoding the 5-GT was cloned, and the highest activity of the recombinant protein in vitro was shown toward betanidin, with regiospecific transfer of Glc to the 5-OH position (144). The enzyme also recognized *o*-dihydroxylated flavonoids, including quercetin, transferring Glc to the 4'-OH (85%) and the 7-OH (15%) positions,

which illustrates a commonality in structural features of the betanidin and flavonoids (**Figure 3**). Recently, a GT from *Beta vulgaris* (red beet) was also identified and its activity toward betanidin investigated by assaying, in parallel, the relative accumulation of the glycoside and the pigmentation of red beet leaves (127).

Coumarins. As described in the section above on plant hormones, the expression of two tobacco genes encoding GTs was induced by SA (25, 45, 46), as well as by a number of other defense-related compounds and by biotic challenge. In vitro substrate recognition by the recombinant TOGTs/Is5a and Is10a (25), as well as NtGT1a and NtGT1b (136), was found to be broad, with highest activity toward the hydroxycoumarin, scopoletin, as well as hydroxycinnamic acids. The consequences of changing the expression of the *TOGT1/Is5a* on the course of a pathogen response has been analyzed in three recent studies involving transgenic tobacco (16, 29, 85). The first study, reducing expression of the two TOGTs by an antisense strategy (16), decreased levels of both scopoletin glucoside and the aglycone were observed, together with weakened resistance to Tobacco Mosaic Virus (TMV). The same group also overexpressed *TOGT1* and surprisingly did not find any enhanced resistance to TMV, although there was an increased blue fluorescence surrounding the TMV lesions under ultraviolet light (29). In contrast, the third study, by Matros & Mock (85), also overexpressed *TOGT1* in transgenic tobacco and showed enhanced resistance to Potato Virus Y. Both groups discuss their data in relation to the significance of scopoletin in defense responses to viruses and other plant pathogens given that the glucoside could be a preformed antimicrobial agent, deglycosylated during spread of the pathogen to release the bioactive glycone. Changing the activity of TOGT would therefore modulate the kinetics of glycoside formation and produce the complex phenotypes observed (29, 85).

Terpenoids and steroids. The plastid is the site of carotenoid biosynthesis, but modification of the apocarotenoid cleavage products takes place largely outside the plastidial compartment, prior to accumulation of water-soluble metabolites in the vacuole (6). Saffron, the dried red styles of *Crocus sativus*, contains three major apocarotenoids responsible for bitter taste, aroma, and pigmentation (7). The final biosynthetic steps in the formation of the crocin yellow pigment includes glucosylation of the insoluble aglycone crocetin leading to enhanced stability and water solubility. Cloning of a *C. sativus* GT (UGTCs2), expressed in stigma tissue, that recognizes crocetin was recently reported (97). The N terminus of UGTCs2 has a hydrophobic region, which suggests association of the GT with membranes.

The Sweet Honey Leaf (*Stevia rebaudiana*) accumulates a mixture of intensely sweet compounds in its leaves. These are different diterpenoid glycosides in which the extent and regioselectivity of glycosylation influence taste perception. The most abundant of these compounds are the triglucoside, stevioside, and the tetraglucoside rebaudioside A. The initial steps of stevioside biosynthesis occur in plastids, followed by further modifications in which glucosylation of the C-4 carboxyl position of steviolbioside is thought to be critical for transport of the stevioside into the vacuole. Recently, three GTs (UGT74G1, UGT76G1, and UGT85C2) were identified and cloned from *Stevia* leaves (119); and their regioselective glucosylation of steviol was confirmed through in vitro analyses of the recombinant enzymes.

Saponins are glycosylated triterpenoids, steroids, or steroidal alkaloids and are found in many plant species (36, 47, 99). The molecules are characterized by an oligosaccharide chain, consisting of up to five sugars, typically Glc, Gal, Ara, GlcUA, Xyl, or Rha, attached at the C-3 position. Some saponins may also have a single Glc attached at C-26 or C-28. In oat leaves, the steroidal avenacosides A and B are biologically inactive but are converted into antifungal compounds upon tissue damage or pathogen invasion by a plant glucosidase specific for the C-26 position. This is an example in which bioactivity is revealed by deglycosylation, and both the compound and the hydrolase are made by the plant. The sugar chain attached to C-3 is thought to be critical for both the membrane-permeabilizing and antifungal properties of saponins as removal of these sugar residues often results in loss of bioactivity. Interestingly, the C-3 oligosaccharide is the target for hydrolases produced by invading fungal pathogens leading to saponin detoxification. For example, the oat root–infecting pathogen *Gaeumannomyces graminis* produces avenacinase, a β-glucosidase that detoxifies the triterpenoid avenicin saponins by removing the terminal Glc from the C-3 chain. The same strategy is used in the detoxification of steroidal glycoalkaloids, found primarily in the Solanaceae family, including tomato and potato. For example, the oligosaccharide at the C-3 of α-tomatine is a target for detoxification by the hydrolases produced by many tomato pathogens (122).

By contrast to the substantial literature available on the glycosidases of saponins, there are comparatively few reports of the GTs involved in glycosylation at either the C-3 or C-26/28 position. In this context, three studies in which genes encoding GTs involved in saponin biosynthesis in *Solanum* species have been published recently and have emphasized the importance of in planta analysis to confirm and extend understanding gained from in vitro assays. A potato GT (SGT1) was identified from screening a wound-induced potato tuber cDNA library in yeast and selecting clones on the basis of the higher toxicity of a steroidal alkaloid aglycone relative to its glycoside (94). In vitro assays with the recombinant GT indicated SGT1 could transfer Glc to a number of acceptors, with higher activity toward tomatidine and solasodine compared with solanidine. However, reduced expression of SGT1, using an antisense strategy in transgenic tobacco, led to a massive shift in steroidal glycoalkaloid profile and a surprising reduction in α-solanine accumulation (Gal at C-3) rather than the predicted reduction in α-chaconine (Glc at C-3) (87). On re-assaying the GT in vitro, a strong preference of SGT1 for UDP-Gal rather then UDP-Glc was demonstrated, in accord with the metabolic profile of the antisense lines. Another *Solanum* species GT (SaGT4A), as yet analyzed only in vitro, used UDP-Glc as a donor and catalyzed the 3-O-glucosylation of steroidal sapogenins, such as nuatigenin, as well as steroidal alkaloids, such as solanidine (59).

Using a very different approach, GTs that glycosylate triterpene saponins have recently been identified in the model legume *M. truncatula* (1). Methyl jasmonate had been shown previously to induce the accumulation of saponins and genes encoding early enzymes of triterpene aglycone formation in cell suspension cultures of *M. truncatula* (132, 134). Transcriptomic analysis revealed a number of potential GT transcripts upregulated in response to methyl jasmonate, and their coexpression relative to that of β-amyrin synthase led to nine candidate GTs of the triterpene aglycones. These were expressed as recombinant proteins in *E. coli* and assayed for activity against a wide range of acceptors. Two GTs, UGT73K1 and UGT71G1, were functionally characterized in vitro using UDP-Glc, UDP-Gal, or UDP-GlcUA as donors and a wide variety of saponin aglycone and phenolic acceptors. Both GTs used UDP-Glc as a donor and glucosylated a number of triterpenoids. Although UGT71G1 also glycosylated quercetin and certain isoflavones with higher efficiency than triterpenes in vitro, transcript and metabolite profiling of elicited cell cultures supported its role in terpenoid biosynthesis. Achnine et al. (1) emphasized that the most critical factor in determining the activity of GTs in planta would be the availability of suitable substrates in cells and tissues of plants.

Glucosinolates and cyanogenic glucosides.
Glucosinolates are found almost exclusively in the Brassicacae family and represent a diverse class of products defined by a common glucone comprising a sulfonated oxime and a β-thioglucose residue, with a variable side chain responsible for glucosinolate chemical diversity (24). Upon tissue damage, the compounds stored in the vacuole come into contact with the plant thioglucosidase myrosinase, and hydrolysis occurs leading to unstable intermediates that spontaneously rearrange to form bioactive compounds including isothiocyanates, thiocyanates, and nitriles. Cyanogenic glycosides are found much more widely in the plant kingdom and are synthesized by conversion of amino acid precursors to oximes (157). Upon disruption of cell integrity, the glycosides come into contact with glycosidases and are hydrolyzed to release toxic hydrogen cyanide and an aldehyde or ketone (115). Therefore, in both instances the action of the glycosidase triggers the production of bioactive molecules.

The first gene encoding a thiohydroximate S-glucosyltransferase (S-GT) was cloned from *B. napus* and the activity of the recombinant enzyme partially characterized in vitro (78). Recently, the *Arabidopsis* homologue to the S-GT, UGT74B1 was identified and the substrate specificity of its recombinant protein determined in vitro (31). The role of UGT74B1 was also analyzed in planta using a T-DNA insertional mutant when significantly decreased levels of glucosinolates were observed together with chlorosis along the leaf veins, suggested to be caused by toxicity from the build up of thiohydroximates. Phenotypes reminiscent of auxin overproduction were also observed, and levels of IAA were threefold higher than in wild type, suggesting that knocking out UGT74B1 impacted auxin metabolism, a feature also observed in other mutants of glucosinolate synthesis.

Mandelonitrile was used as substrate to purify a GT (sbHMNGT) from *Sorghum bicolor*, and its sequence used to clone a gene whose recombinant product was assayed in vitro for activity against a range of acceptors (35, 54). The data showed a broad substrate recognition for the recombinant enzyme, which included conversion of *p*-hydroxymandelonitrile to synthesize the cyanogenic glycoside dhurrin. Dhurrin accumulation was achieved in transgenic *Arabidopsis* by transferring the gene encoding the GT (renamed UGT85B1) co-expressed with those encoding two multifunctional cytochrome P450 enzymes (137). This study was recently complemented by a detailed analysis in which different genes of the dhurrin pathway were introduced separately and together (61). Introduction of UGT85B1 overcame the pleiotropic and deleterious effects observed in transgenic plants expressing only CYP79A1 and CYP71E1, suggesting that this could be owing to the formation of a multienzyme complex involving the GT that facilitated channeling of intermediates during synthesis, thereby preventing their toxic effects.

Cyclic hydroxamic acids. 1,4-benzoxazinones are cyclic hydroxamic acids occurring constitutively as glucosides in certain members of the Gramineae family (105). The glucosides are located in vacuoles and become available for hydrolysis by plastid glycosidases when cell integrity is lost in response to tissue damage or pathogen invasion. The resulting aglycones in rye, 2,4-dihydroxy-1,4-benzoxazin-3-one (DIBOA), and in maize and wheat, 2,4-dihydroxy-7-methoxy-1,4-benzoxazin-3-one (DIMBOA), decompose rapidly with a liberation of formic acid. Both the benzoxazinone aglycones and their degradation products exhibit multifunctional bioactivities, whereas their parent glucosides are inactive (130). Two GTs, BX8 and BX9, were purified from maize seedlings using UDP-Glc as a donor and DIMBOA and DIBOA as acceptors; sequencing enabled their genes to be cloned, and steady-state kinetic constants for recombinant enzyme activities in vitro were determined. For both GTs, DIMBOA was the preferred substrate. Overexpression of either GT BX8 or GT BX9 in *Arabidopsis* reduced the toxic effects of DIBOA and DIMBOA application on the transgenic plants (149). Because it is known that these aglycones also act as allelochemicals in the rhizosphere (3, 110), the GTs may also function in detoxifying the impact of exogenous benzoxazinones delivered through root exudates of neighboring plants. There is additional evidence for GTs in downregulating the impact of allelochemicals in field communities (125). In allelopathy, the glycosylation events involve plant enzymes and substrates, but from neighboring plants.

3.1.3. Undefined plant acceptors.

Root factors. Root caps, attached to root apices of many species, play a number of roles, including protection of the apical meristem, perception of gravity, and the production of border cells (which play a key role in influencing interactions of the plant within the rhizosphere) (38). Using peas as a model system, the removal of border cells triggered mitosis in the root cap meristem (12). Because the system could be synchronized, genes whose expression was rapidly upregulated at the onset of cell division in the root cap could be identified, and one of these was found to be a GT (154). The donor specificity of the recombinant GT, assayed in cellular extracts from transformed *Neurospora crassa*, was UDP-GlcUA, with no activity demonstrated toward either UDP-Glc or UDP-Gal. The GlcUA was transferred to an unknown acceptor present in boiled pea tissue extract (154). When a GT-His gene fusion was overexpressed in a hairy root culture, the fusion protein was located mainly in microsomal membranes, and this correlated with the presence of an N-terminal signal peptide in the amino acid sequence of the GT. When PsUGT1 expression was constitutively downregulated using an antisense strategy in alfalfa, renewed border-cell production did not occur. These data suggest that expression of the GT was required for the root cap meristem activity that led to the replacement of border cells (154). In this system, the glucuronsylated product of PsUGT1 appears to be the bioactive factor necessary for root cap meristem cell division, with an inactive aglycone (as yet unknown). When the PsUGT1 was constitutively overexpressed in *Arabidopsis*, multiple effects were observed, including early senescence; as that model does not have a root cap, it was not possible to analyze its impact on border-cell renewal (152). Using the antisense PsUGT1 transgenic alfalfa roots as a model, the absence of border cells was found to increase the susceptibility (>90%) of the root tip to infection by a fungal pathogen and decrease the frequency (fourfold lower) of nodulation by a bacterial symbiont (154).

Cell plate factors. Phragmoplastin, a protein involved in cell plate formation, was used as bait in a two-hybrid screening system to analyze interacting proteins from *Arabidopsis* (44). The screen identified a GT, UGT1 (UGT75B1), that was also capable as a recombinant fusion protein in pulling down the SA2 domain of phragmoplastin in vitro. A UGT1-green fluorescence protein fusion was used to study the localization of the GT in tobacco BY2 suspension cultures, which are synchronized in cell division. The results confirmed that the GT reporter fusion was associated with the developing cell plate. A product entrapment procedure was used to show that both UGT1 and callose synthase were core-covered, suggesting that the GT may play a role in the synthesis of callose during cell plate formation (44). Interaction of the GT with callose synthase was demonstrated in a yeast two-hybrid system (43).

3.2. Acceptors of Nonplant Origin

3.2.1. Biotic compounds: pathogen toxins.
Invading pests and pathogens use a wide repertoire of mechanisms in their battle against plant defenses, including the production and secretion of toxins into the cells of the plant under invasion. Inactivation of these toxins by the plant is likely critical, and in this context, glycosylation has evolved as an important means for their detoxifica-

tion. There have been numerous publications in which clear evidence was presented that fungal phytotoxins can be modified in planta (56). For example, destruxin B, produced by *Alternaria brassicae*, was hydroxylated and glucosylated by *Sinapis alba*, a plant species resistant to the blackspot fungus (109). Interestingly, in that example, the hydroxylated product also induced the biosynthesis of phytoalexins in the resistant plant species. To date, only one plant GT capable of recognizing a fungal toxin has been identified, its gene cloned, and the ability of its recombinant gene product to detoxify the compound demonstrated (113). The trichothecene deoxynivalenol (DON) is produced by fungi of the genus *Fusarium*, which causes destructive diseases on many small grain cereal species such as wheat, barley, and rye, as well as maize (30). These mycotoxins are harmful if present in food or feed products, and DON is also considered a virulence factor in the fungal pathogenesis (86). UGT73C5 was identified by screening an Arabidopsis cDNA library expressed in yeast for an enhanced resistance to DON. The recombinant GT catalyzed the formation of DON-3-O-glucoside in yeast cells and, when overexpressed in transgenic *Arabidopsis*, conferred enhanced tolerance to DON (113). Interestingly, as summarized in the hormone section, UGT73C5 also glucosylates the 23-OH position of BRs (114), which suggests the GT may play a dual role in the plant, glucosylating endogenous and exogenous acceptors.

3.2.2. Abiotic compounds: organic and inorganic pollutants.
Extensive literature is available on the ability of plants to detoxify non-natural chemical compounds in their environments, and researchers have long considered their potential for phytoremediation (33, 112, 124). Typically, detoxification can occur in two phases in the plant or animal kingdoms (17, 18). When necessary, phase I activates the chemical for detoxification through introducing functional groups such as via hydroxylation or carboxylation. Phase II enzymes

conjugate hydrophilic molecules, such as through the addition of a glycosyl, malonyl, or glutathione residue to those functional groups. In plants, this modification leads to their elimination from the cytosol via membrane-bound transporters and into the vacuolar or apoplastic space. Evidence suggests that the carriers for transport of glycosylated and glutathionylated xenobiotics across the tonoplast are different, the former using a carrier system energetically coupled to the transmembrane H^+ gradient, the latter transported by ABC transporter(s) directly energized by ATP (4). There are many studies describing partial purification of GT activities toward exogenous chemical compounds (10, 11, 64, 111), and xenobiotics have been included in screens of recombinant GT activities (39, 136).

Three recent publications have focused on defined plant GTs and have analyzed in detail the activity of recombinant proteins in vitro toward xenobiotics (75, 88), as well as the effect of decreasing the expression of the GT in planta on the metabolism of xenobiotics (9). In one study, recombinant GTs of *Arabidopsis*, already known to exhibit in vitro activities toward a variety of endogenous plant compounds, were further assayed for their activities in vitro toward the xenobiotics 2,4,5-trichlorophenol (TCP) (88). The analysis included UGT72E1, UGT75D1, UGT84A1, UGT84A2, UGT84B1, UGT75B1, and UGT80A2; all the GTs recognized TCP, with the exception of UGT80A2. Competition studies showed that TCP affected the activities toward naturally occurring substrates and vice versa, suggesting that cross-talk between detoxification of xenobiotics and endogenous metabolites may occur in planta, depending on the presence of GTs and competing substrates.

Another group using a different strategy found that the pollutant 3,4-dichloroaniline (DCA) was rapidly detoxified by root cultures of *Arabidopsis*, with the N-glucosyl-DCA exported into the medium (75). The native N-glucosyltransferase was purified, identified as UGT72B1, and following cloning of its gene, in vitro activity of the recombinant protein was determined toward DCA and other substrates. Interestingly, the recombinant enzyme displayed both N-glucosylation activity toward DCA (10.7 nmol s^{-1} mg^{-1}) but also O-glucosylation activity toward chlorinated phenols, with the highest specific activity toward TCP (5.2 nmol s^{-1} mg^{-1}). No activity was detected toward naturally occurring substrates except 4-hydroxyphenylpyruvic acid (0.18 nmol s^{-1} mg^{-1}). The study was extended to examine a T-DNA insertion line in which UGT72B1 was knocked out (9). Cell extracts from the knock-out line displayed reduced GT activity in vitro toward DCA and TCP. However, feeding either radiolabeled DCA or TCP to root cultures/whole plants showed a differential response that was dependent on the xenobiotic. The data suggest that although UGT72B1 was the primary enzyme responsible for DCA conjugation, other GTs in *Arabidopsis* could compensate for TCP conjugation in the knock-out. Surprisingly, although glucosylation of DCA was severely compromised in the knockout, the plants were nevertheless more resistant to the compound, which suggested that the accumulation of nonextractable residues from radiolabeled DCA observed in cell wall residues of the knock-out may be a more effective detoxification route than glucosylation and vacuolar compartmentation of glycosides.

4. APPLICATIONS OF PLANT GLYCOSYLTRANSFERASES

A principle feature of plant GTs of small molecules is their ability to glycosylate acceptors in a regioselective manner. Many different GTs recognize the same acceptor but transfer glycosyl residues to different sites on the molecule. Often these different glycosides of the aglycone possess different chemical properties, functionalities in the plant, and bioactivities, such as efficacy as antioxidants and nutraceuticals. An example involves the regioselective glucosylation of quercetin, which leads to different quercetin monoglucosides, each possessing different levels of chemical reactivity and hydrophilicity (20, 68). Regioselective glycosylation using classical chemical synthesis is difficult because appropriate blocking reagents are required to mask other reactive sites on the molecule, and these must be removed following site-specific modification. Various approaches are being taken to solve this problem for industrial applications, such as the design of glycosynthases (76), but the use of GTs, their biochemical activities in vitro, and the availability of large numbers of plant GT sequences that recognize compounds beyond those naturally occuring in plants provide a good basis for the development of regioselective biocatalysts, either through structure-based protein engineering or through semirational mutagenesis.

With the recent solution of three-dimensional structures of two plant GTs, it becomes more straightforward, for example, to engineer changed, activated sugar donor specificity. As illustrated in **Figure 1**, replacing aspartate 374 and glutamine 375 of VvGT1 may result in mutants that recognize sugars with different chemical features at the C2 and C4 positions. Interestingly, preceding the structural data, the potential to change donor specificity was already demonstrated in the engineering of an *Aralia* species anthocyandin GT that used UDP-Gal as donor sugar (63). When histidine 374 of the *Aralia* GT (which is equivalent to glutamine 375 of VvGT1 in sequence alignment) was mutated to glutamine by site-directed mutagenesis, the resulting mutant preferred UDP-Glc to UDP-Gal. Note that the two donor sugars are different at the C4 position of the sugar moiety.

An alternative engineering strategy involves semirational generation of mutants, such as the random mutation of the ligand binding pocket. The success of this strategy was proven in the mutagenesis study of a bacterial GT1 enzyme involved in urdamycin biosynthesis (41). The sequence encoding a 13-amino-acid segment of the acceptor binding pocket was randomly mutated and yielded a number of mutants displaying different regioselectivity in the transfer reactions. Given that structures of two plant GTs are now solved, the information available on their acceptor binding pockets provide an important foundation for modeling other plant GTs and engineering changed acceptor specificity and affinity.

Applications involving plant GTs are likely to be developed in the fields of biocatalysis and metabolic engineering of crop plants. When used as biocatalysts, the applications involve GTs functioning as isolated enzymes or within whole-cell fermentation using prokaryotic or eukaryotic cells. An interesting application of an immobilized GT involved the use of an enzyme from pummelo to debitter citrus juice through converting limanoids into tasteless glycosides (55). The major constraint in the application of isolated GTs is the requirement of supplementary donor sugars for the transfer reactions. Use of GTs in whole-cell biocatalysis systems can solve this problem because endogenous donor sugars in the host cell systems are accessible for use by the recombinant GTs (2, 60, 68, 150). The use of plant cell systems for biotransformation of small molecules has more than 30 years of history, and both naturally occurring metabolites as well as non-natural compounds have been glycosylated in plant whole-cell systems (60). Because the glycosides are typically sequestered in vacuoles, cell disruption and extraction is required for product recovery. More recent studies have developed several new bacterial whole-cell biocatalysis systems expressing plant GTs (2, 68, 150). An interesting finding was that the aglycones added to the culture medium were taken up by the bacterial cells and the glycosides formed were transported back into the culture medium. As a result, the product recovery was simple (68). Combinatorial whole-cell biocatalysis of small molecules can also be carried out using bacterial cells expressing different recombinant enzymes. This was demonstrated in the synthesis of polymethylated quercetin glycosides using a bacterial system expressing plant methyltransferases and plant GTs (149). The stereoselectivity of GTs has also been exploited in the chiral separation of (+)-ABA from (±)-ABA using a whole-cell biocatalysis system (68).

This review has emphasized the range of acceptors and regioselectivity of plant GTs. Although these features underpin biocatalyst design, they also provide the basis for applications in crop plants. These may involve, for example, modification of changed sensitivity to hormones and their agrochemical analogues, changed flower color, and changed tolerance to biotic and abiotic stresses. There is also the possibility that increasing the glycosylation of secondary metabolites may lead to increased yield of their corresponding glycosides. If the reactions are cytosolic, but the glycosylated products are transported out of the cytosol, it may be possible to increase flux by removing the product from the reaction mix. In terms of metabolic engineering applications such as those involving the production of monomers in crop plant factories for postharvest polymerization, this could prove to have utility.

CONCLUSION

Phytochemical studies have provided detailed information on the existence, diversity, and complexity of small-molecule glycosides. The low abundance of many of the enzymes involved in glycoside production and the unavailability of appropriate donor sugars and purified acceptors for many years slowed progress on identifying the GTs involved. Increasingly, the genetic tools to define the activities of this class of enzymes and the impact of these activities on the life of the plant are becoming available. The multiplicity of GTs, both in numbers of enzymes and potential acceptors, is considerable, making in planta studies complicated but essential to undertake. Through integrating biochemical knowledge with genetic tools, the role of small-molecule glycosylation in underpinning developmental and metabolic plasticity is becoming apparent. The coming years will continue to provide increasing clarity of this fascinating group of enzymes.

SUMMARY POINTS

1. GTs of small lipophilic molecules transfer sugars regioselectively from activated sugar donors to acceptors that include hormones, secondary metabolites, biotic toxins, and abiotic chemicals in the environment.

2. Plant genomes contain a large number of genes encoding GTs of small lipophilic molecules, some of which have the capacity to recognize common features on multiple acceptors in vitro and others more specific to individual compounds.

3. Most GT sequences of small molecules do not have obvious targeting information, and their reactions are thought to occur in the cytosol, possibly in association with multiprotein complexes attached to membranes.

4. Glycosylation of the lipophilic acceptors changes their chemical properties, increasing their solubility in aqueous environments and often changing their bioactivity and stability and enabling access to membrane-bound energized carriers that transport the glycosides out of the cytosol, such as into the vacuole for detoxification.

5. In planta, specificity of the catalytic activity of the GTs will be determined by (*a*) substrate availability, with access to different potential acceptors defining the product pattern, and (*b*) coordinate regulation of GT gene expression dictating potential functional redundancy.

6. The multiplicity of GT genes and catalytic activities in each plant species has the potential to provide a mechanism for cellular homeostasis through enabling developmental and metabolic plasticity during adaptive responses to environmental change.

ACKNOWLEDGMENTS

The authors would like to thank the United Kingdom Biotechnology and Biological Science Research Council, the Garfield Weston Foundation, and the Austrian Science Fund (Erwin-Schrödinger Fellowship to B.P.) for funding support. Xiaoqiang Wang (Noble Laboratory) and Gideon J. Davies (York Structural Biology Laboratory) are thanked for providing G structural data ahead of publication. The Rose Gallery, Shigeru Iida Laboratory, and Noriko Hamakko are thanked for providing illustrations. Members of D.B.'s group at the Center for Novel Agricultural Products are thanked for their support: Jean Sheridan for secretarial assistance, and Rick Dixon and the Samuel Roberts Noble Foundation for their help and hospitality.

LITERATURE CITED

GTs glycosylating triterpene saponins in *Medicago truncatula* were identified and in vitro activities were compared with metabolite profiling of cell cultures to determine acceptor specitificity.

1. **Achnine L, Huhman DV, Farag MA, Sumner LW, Blount JW, Dixon RA. 2005. Genomics-based selection and functional characterization of triterpene glycosyltransferases from the model legume *Medicago truncatula*. *Plant J*. 41:875–87**

2. Arend J, Warzecha H, Hefner T, Stockigt J. 2001. Utilizing genetically engineered bacteria to produce plant-specific glucosides. *Biotechnol. Bioeng.* 76:126–31

3. Barnes JP, Putnam AR. 1987. Role of benzoxazinones in allelopathy by rye (*Secale-cereale* L). *J. Chem. Ecol.* 13:889–906

4. Bartholomew DM, Van Dyk DE, Lau SMC, O'Keefe DP, Rea PA, Viitanen PV. 2002. Alternate energy-dependent pathways for the vacuolar uptake of glucose and glutathione conjugates. *Plant Physiol.* 130:1562–72

5. Baumert A, Milkowski C, Schmidt J, Nimtz M, Wray V, Strack D. 2005. Formation of a complex pattern of sinapate esters in *Brassica napus* seeds, catalyzed by enzymes of a serine carboxypeptidase-like acyltransferase family? *Phytochemistry* 66:1334–45

6. Bouvier F, Isner JC, Dogbo O, Camara B. 2005. Oxidative tailoring of carotenoids: a prospect towards novel functions in plants. *Trends Plant Sci.* 10:187–94

7. Bouvier F, Suire C, Mutterer J, Camara B. 2003. Oxidative remodeling of chromoplast carotenoids: identification of the carotenoid dioxygenase *CsCCD* and *CsZCD* genes involved in crocus secondary metabolite biogenesis. *Plant Cell* 15:47–62

8. Bowles D, Isayenkova J, Lim EK, Poppenberger B. 2005. Glycosyltransferases: managers of small molecules. *Curr. Opin. Plant Biol.* 8:254–63

9. Brazier-Hicks M, Edwards R. 2005. Functional importance of the Family 1 glucosyltransferase UGT72B1 in the metabolism of xenobiotics in *Arabidopsis thaliana*. *Plant J.* 42:556–66

10. Brazier M, Cole DJ, Edwards R. 2002. O-glucosyltransferase activities toward phenolic natural products and xenobiotics in wheat and herbicide-resistant and herbicide-susceptible black-grass (*Alopecurus myosuroides*). *Phytochemistry* 59:149–56

11. Brazier M, Cole DJ, Edwards R. 2003. Partial purification and characterisation of a 2,4,5 trichlorophenol detoxifying O-glucosyltransferase from wheat. *Phytochemistry* 64:419–24

12. Brigham LA, Woo HH, Wen F, Hawes MC. 1998. Meristem-specific suppression of mitosis and a global switch in gene expression in the root cap of pea by endogenous signals. *Plant Physiol.* 118:1223–31

13. Brugliera F, Holton TA, Stevenson TW, Farcy E, Lu CY, Cornish EC. 1994. Isolation and characterization of a cDNA clone corresponding to the Rt locus of *Petunia hybrida*. *Plant J.* 5:81–92

14. Burbulis IE, Winkel-Shirley B. 1999. Interactions among enzymes of the *Arabidopsis* flavonoid biosynthetic pathway. *Proc. Natl. Acad. Sci. USA* 96:12929–34

15. Chen ZX, Malamy J, Henning J, Conrath U, Sanchezcasas P, et al. 1995. Induction, modification, and transduction of the salicylic-acid signal in plant defense responses. *Proc. Natl. Acad. Sci. USA* 92:4134–37

16. Chong J, Baltz R, Schmitt C, Beffa R, Fritig B, Saindrenan P. 2002. Downregulation of a pathogen-responsive tobacco UDP-Glc: phenylpropanoid glucosyltransferase reduces scopoletin glucoside accumulation, enhances oxidative stress, and weakens virus resistance. *Plant Cell* 14:1093–107

17. Cole DJ, Edwards R. 2000. Secondary metabolism of agrochemicals in plants. In *Agrochemicals and Plant Protection*, ed. TR Roberts, pp. 107–54. Chichester, UK: Wiley & Sons

18. Coleman JOD, BlakeKalff MMA, Davies TGE. 1997. Detoxification of xenobiotics by plants: chemical modification and vacuolar compartmentation. *Trends Plant Sci.* 2:144–51

19. Creelman RA, Mullet JE. 1997. Biosynthesis and action of jasmonates in plants. *Annu. Rev. Plant Physiol. Plant Mol. Biol.* 48:355–81

20. Day AJ, Bao YP, Morgan MRA, Williamson G. 2000. Conjugation position of quercetin glucuronides and effect on biological activity. *Free Radic. Biol. Med.* 29:1234–43

21. Dietz KJ, Sauter A, Wichert K, Messdaghi D, Hartung W. 2000. Extracellular beta-glucosidase activity in barley involved in the hydrolysis of ABA glucose conjugate in leaves. *J. Exp. Bot.* 51:937–44

22. Dixon RA, Achnine L, Kota P, Liu CJ, Reddy MSS, Wang LJ. 2002. The phenylpropanoid pathway and plant defence—a genomics perspective. *Mol. Plant Pathol.* 3:371–90

23. Dixon RA, Chen F, Guo DJ, Parvathi K. 2001. The biosynthesis of monolignols: a "metabolic grid," or independent pathways to guaiacyl and syringyl units? *Phytochemistry* 57:1069–84

24. Fahey JW, Zalcmann AT, Talalay P. 2001. The chemical diversity and distribution of glucosinolates and isothiocyanates among plants. *Phytochemistry* 56:5–51

25. Fraissinet-Tachet L, Baltz R, Chong J, Kauffmann S, Fritig B, Saindrenan P. 1998. Two tobacco genes induced by infection, elicitor and salicylic acid encode glucosyltransferases acting on phenylpropanoids and benzoic acid derivatives, including salicylic acid. *FEBS Lett.* 437:319–23

26. Frydman A, Weisshaus O, Bar-Peled M, Huhman DV, Sumner LW, et al. 2004. Citrus fruit bitter flavors: isolation and functional characterization of the gene Cm1,2RhaT encoding a 1,2 rhamnosyltransferase, a key enzyme in the biosynthesis of the bitter flavonoids of citrus. *Plant J.* 40:88–100

27. Fujioka S, Yokota T. 2003. Biosynthesis and metabolism of brassinosteroids. *Annu. Rev. Plant Biol.* 54:137–64

28. Fukuchi-Mizutani M, Okuhara H, Fukui Y, Nakao M, Katsumoto Y, et al. 2003. Biochemical and molecular characterization of a novel UDP-glucose: anthocyanin

3'-O-glucosyltransferase, a key enzyme for blue anthocyanin biosynthesis, from gentian. *Plant Physiol.* 132:1652–63

29. Gachon C, Baltz R, Saindrenan P. 2004. Over-expression of a scopoletin glucosyltransferase in *Nicotiana tabacum* leads to precocious lesion formation during the hypersensitive response to tobacco mosaic virus but does not affect virus resistance. *Plant Mol. Biol.* 54:137–46

30. Gale LR. 2003. Population structure of fusarium species causing head blight of grain crops. In *Fusarium Head Blight of Wheat and Barley*, ed. KJ Leonard, WR Bushnell, pp. 120–43. St. Paul, MN: Am. Phytopathol. Soc.

31. Grubb CD, Zipp BJ, Ludwig-Muller J, Masuno MN, Molinski TF, Abel S. 2004. Arabidopsis glucosyltransferase UGT74B1 functions in glucosinolate biosynthesis and auxin homeostasis. *Plant J.* 40:893–908

32. Hammondkosack KE, Silverman P, Raskin I, Jones JDG. 1996. Race-specific elicitors of *Cladosporium fulvum* induce changes in cell morphology and the synthesis of ethylene and salicylic acid in tomato plants carrying the corresponding Cf disease resistance gene. *Plant Physiol.* 110:1381–94

33. Hannink NK, Rosser SJ, Bruce NC. 2002. Phytoremediation of explosives. *CRC Crit. Rev. Plant Sci.* 21:511–38

34. Hans J, Brandt W, Vogt T. 2004. Site-directed mutagenesis and protein 3D-homology modelling suggest a catalytic mechanism for UDP-glucose-dependent betanidin 5-O-glucosyltransferase from *Dorotheanthus bellidiformi*s. *Plant J.* 39:319–33

35. Hansen KS, Kristensen C, Tattersall DB, Jones PR, Olsen CE, et al. 2003. The in vitro substrate regiospecificity of recombinant UGT85B1, the cyanohydrin glucosyltransferase from *Sorghum bicolor*. *Phytochemistry* 64:143–51

36. Haralampidis K, Trojanowska M, Osbourn AE. 2002. Biosynthesis of triterpenoid saponins in plants. *Adv. Biochem. Eng. Biotechnol.* 75:31–49

37. Harborne JB, Baxter H. 1999. *The Handbook of Natural Flavonoids.* Vol. 1. Chichester, UK: Wiley

38. Hawes MC, Brigham LA, Wen F, Woo HH, Zhu Z. 1998. Function of root border cells in plant health: pioneers in the rhizosphere. *Annu. Rev. Phytopathol.* 36:311–27

39. Hefner T, Arend J, Warzecha H, Siems K, Stockigt J. 2002. Arbutin synthase, a novel member of the NRD1beta glycosyltransferase family, is a unique multifunctional enzyme converting various natural products and xenobiotics. *Bioorg. Med. Chem.* 10:1731–41

40. Hemm M, Rider S, Ogas J, Murry D, Chapple C. 2004. Light induces phenylpropanoid metabolism in Arabidopsis roots. *Plant J.* 38:765–78

41. Hoffmeister D, Wilkinson B, Foster G, Sidebottom PJ, Ichinose K, Bechthold A. 2002. Engineered urdamycin glycosyltransferases are broadened and altered in substrate specificity. *Chem. Biol.* 9:287–95

42. Holton TA, Cornish EC. 1995. Genetics and biochemistry of anthocyanin biosynthesis. *Plant Cell* 7:1071–83

43. Hong Z, Delauney AJ, Verma DP. 2001. A cell plate-specific callose synthase and its interaction with phragmoplastin. *Plant Cell* 13:755–68

44. Hong Z, Zhang Z, Olson JM, Verma DP. 2001. A novel UDP-glucose transferase is part of the callose synthase complex and interacts with phragmoplastin at the forming cell plate. *Plant Cell* 13:769–79

45. Horvath DM, Chua NH. 1996. Identification of an immediate-early salicylic acid-inducible tobacco gene and characterization of induction by other compounds. *Plant Mol. Biol.* 31:1061–72

A T-DNA insertion mutant of Arabidopsis *UGT74B1* indicated the GT functioned in glucosinolate biosynthesis.

46. Horvath DM, Huang DJ, Chua NH. 1998. Four classes of salicylate-induced tobacco genes. *Mol. Plant Microbe Interact.* 11:895–905

47. Hostettmann KA, Marston A. 1995. *Saponins*. Cambridge, UK: Cambridge Univ. Press

48. Hou B, Lim EK, Higgins GS, Bowles DJ. 2004. N-glucosylation of cytokinins by glycosyltransferases of *Arabidopsis thaliana*. *J. Biol. Chem.* 279:47822–32

49. Ikan R. 1999. *Naturally Occurring Glycosides*. Chichester, UK: Wiley

50. Jackson RG, Kowalczyk M, Li Y, Higgins G, Ross J, et al. 2002. Over-expression of an Arabidopsis gene encoding a glucosyltransferase of indole-3-acetic acid: phenotypic characterisation of transgenic lines. *Plant J.* 32:573–83

51. Jackson RG, Lim EK, Li Y, Kowalczyk M, Sandberg G, et al. 2001. Identification and biochemical characterization of an Arabidopsis indole-3-acetic acid glucosyltransferase. *J. Biol. Chem.* 276:4350–56

52. Jones P, Messner B, Nakajima J, Schaffner AR, Saito K. 2003. UGT73C6 and UGT78D1, glycosyltransferases involved in flavonol glycoside biosynthesis in *Arabidopsis thaliana*. *J. Biol. Chem.* 278:43910–18

53. Jones P, Vogt T. 2001. Glycosyltransferases in secondary plant metabolism: tranquilizers and stimulant controllers. *Planta* 213:164–74

54. Jones PR, Moller BL, Hoj PB. 1999. The UDP-glucose:p-hydroxymandelonitrile-O-glucosyltransferase that catalyzes the last step in synthesis of the cyanogenic glucoside dhurrin in *Sorghum bicolor*. Isolation, cloning, heterologous expression, and substrate specificity. *J. Biol. Chem.* 274:35483–91

55. Karim MR, Hashinaga F. 2002. Preparation and properties of immobilized pummelo limonoid glucosyltransferase. *Process Biochem.* 38:809–14

56. Karlovsky P. 1999. Biological detoxification of fungal toxins and its use in plant breeding, feed and food production. *Nat. Toxins* 7:1–23

57. Kita M, Hirata Y, Moriguchi T, Endo-Inagaki T, Matsumoto R, et al. 2000. Molecular cloning and characterization of a novel gene encoding limonoid UDP-glucosyltransferase in Citrus. *FEBS Lett.* 469:173–78

58. Kleczkowski K, Schell J. 1995. Phytohormone conjugates: nature and function. *CRC Crit. Rev. Plant Sci.* 14:283–98

59. Kohara A, Nakajima C, Hashimoto K, Ikenaga T, Tanaka H, et al. 2005. A novel glucosyltransferase involved in steroid saponin biosynthesis in *Solanum aculeatissimum*. *Plant Mol. Biol.* 57:225–39

60. Kren V, Thiem J. 1997. Glycosylation employing bio-systems: from enzymes to whole cells. *Chem. Soc. Rev.* 26:463–73

61. Kristensen C, Morant M, Olsen CE, Ekstrom CT, Galbraith DW, et al. 2005. Metabolic engineering of dhurrin in transgenic Arabidopsis plants with marginal inadvertent effects on the metabolome and transcriptome. *Proc. Natl. Acad. Sci. USA* 102:1779–84

62. Kroon J, Souer E, de Graaff A, Xue Y, Mol J, Koes R. 1994. Cloning and structural analysis of the anthocyanin pigmentation locus Rt of *Petunia hybrida*: characterization of insertion sequences in two mutant alleles. *Plant J.* 5:69–80

63. Kubo A, Arai Y, Nagashima S, Yoshikawa T. 2004. Alteration of sugar donor specificities of plant glycosyltransferases by a single point mutation. *Arch. Biochem. Biophys.* 429:198–203

64. Lao SH, Loutre C, Brazier M, Coleman JO, Cole DJ, et al. 2003. 3,4-dichloroaniline is detoxified and exported via different pathways in Arabidopsis and soybean. *Phytochemistry* 63:653–61

65. Lee HI, Raskin I. 1999. Purification, cloning, and expression of a pathogen inducible UDP-glucose: salicylic acid glucosyltransferase from tobacco. *J. Biol. Chem.* 274:36637–42

66. Lehfeldt C, Shirley AM, Meyer K, Ruegger MO, Cusumano JC, et al. 2000. Cloning of the SNG1 gene of Arabidopsis reveals a role for a serine carboxypeptidase-like protein as an acyltransferase in secondary metabolism. *Plant Cell* 12:1295–306

67. Li Y, Baldauf S, Lim EK, Bowles DJ. 2001. Phylogenetic analysis of the UDP-glycosyltransferase multigene family of *Arabidopsis thaliana*. *J. Biol. Chem.* 276:4338–43

68. Lim EK, Ashford DA, Hou B, Jackson RG, Bowles DJ. 2004. Arabidopsis glycosyltransferases as biocatalysts in fermentation for regioselective synthesis of diverse quercetin glucosides. *Biotechnol. Bioeng.* 87:623–31

69. Lim EK, Baldauf S, Li Y, Elias L, Worrall D, et al. 2003. Evolution of substrate recognition across a multigene family of glycosyltransferases in Arabidopsis. *Glycobiology* 13:139–45

70. Lim EK, Bowles DJ. 2004. A class of plant glycosyltransferases involved in cellular homeostasis. *EMBO J.* 23:2915–22

71. Lim EK, Doucet CJ, Hou B, Jackson RG, Abrams SR, Bowles DJ. 2005. Resolution of (+)-abscisic acid using an Arabidopsis glycosyltransferase. *Tetrahedron Asymmetry* 16:143–47

72. Lim EK, Doucet CJ, Li Y, Elias L, Worrall D, et al. 2002. The activity of Arabidopsis glycosyltransferases toward salicylic acid, 4-hydroxybenzoic acid, and other benzoates. *J. Biol. Chem.* 277:586–92

73. Lim EK, Jackson RG, Bowles DJ. 2005. Identification and characterisation of Arabidopsis glycosyltransferases capable of glucosylating coniferyl aldehyde and sinapyl aldehyde. *FEBS Lett.* 579:2802–6

74. Lim EK, Li Y, Parr A, Jackson R, Ashford DA, Bowles DJ. 2001. Identification of glucosyltransferase genes involved in sinapate metabolism and lignin synthesis in Arabidopsis. *J. Biol. Chem.* 276:4344–49

75. Loutre C, Dixon DP, Brazier M, Slater M, Cole DJ, Edwards R. 2003. Isolation of a glucosyltransferase from *Arabidopsis thaliana* active in the metabolism of the persistent pollutant 3,4-dichloroaniline. *Plant J.* 34:485–93

76. Mackenzie LF, Wang QP, Warren RAJ, Withers SG. 1998. Glycosynthases: mutant glycosidases for oligosaccharide synthesis. *J. Am. Chem. Soc.* 120:5583–84

77. Mackenzie PI, Owens IS, Burchell B, Bock KW, Bairoch A, et al. 1997. The UDP glycosyltransferase gene superfamily: recommended nomenclature update based on evolutionary divergence. *Pharmacogenetics* 7:255–69

78. Marillia EF, MacPherson JM, Tsang EW, Van Audenhove K, Keller WA, GrootWassink JW. 2001. Molecular cloning of a *Brassica napus* thiohydroximate S-glucosyltransferase gene and its expression in *Escherichia coli*. *Physiol. Plant* 113:176–84

79. Marrs KA, Alfenito MR, Lloyd AM, Walbot V. 1995. A glutathione-S-transferase involved in vacuolar transfer encoded by the maize gene bronze-2. *Nature* 375:397–400

80. Martin RC, Mok DWS, Smets R, van Onckelen HA, Mok MC. 2001. Development of transgenic tobacco harbouring a zeatin O-glucosyltransferase gene from *Phaseolus*. *In vitro Cell. Dev. Biol. Plant* 37:354–60

81. Martin RC, Mok MC, Habben JE, Mok DW. 2001. A maize cytokinin gene encoding an O-glucosyltransferase specific to *cis*-zeatin. *Proc. Natl. Acad. Sci. USA* 98:5922–26

82. Martin RC, Mok MC, Mok DW. 1999. A gene encoding the cytokinin enzyme zeatin O-xylosyltransferase of *Phaseolus vulgaris*. *Plant Physiol.* 120:553–58

Regioselectivity of glucosylation of a model substrate was analyzed across the entire Family1 GT gene family of Arabidopsis, determining relatedness of sequence similarity to substrate recognition.

UGT72B1 from Arabidopsis was able to carry out N- and O-glucosylation of chlorinated aniline and phenolic xenobiotic compounds.

83. Martin RC, Mok MC, Mok DW. 1999. Isolation of a cytokinin gene, ZOG1, encoding zeatin O-glucosyltransferase from *Phaseolus lunatus*. *Proc. Natl. Acad. Sci. USA* 96:284–89

84. Martinoia E, Klein M, Gesser M, Sanchez-Hernandez R, Rea PA. 2001. Vacuolar transport of secondary metabolites and xenobiotics. In *Vacuolar Compartments*, ed. D Robinson, J Rogers, pp. 221–53. Sheffield, UK: Sheffield Acad.

85. Matros A, Mock HP. 2004. Ectopic expression of a UDP-glucose: phenylpropanoid glucosyltransferase leads to increased resistance of transgenic tobacco plants against infection with Potato Virus Y. *Plant Cell Physiol.* 45:1185–93

86. McCormick SM. 2003. The role of DON in pathogenicity. In *Fusarium Head Blight of Wheat and Barley*, ed. KJ Leonard, WR Bushnell, pp. 165–83. St. Paul, MN: Am. Phytopathol. Soc.

87. McCue KF, Shepherd LVT, Allen PV, Maccree MM, Rockhold DR, et al. 2005. Metabolic compensation of steroidal glycoalkaloid biosynthesis in transgenic potato tubers: using reverse genetics to confirm the in vivo enzyme function of a steroidal alkaloid galactosyltransferase. *Plant Sci.* 168:267–73

88. Messner B, Thulke O, Schaffner AR. 2003. Arabidopsis glucosyltransferases with activities toward both endogenous and xenobiotic substrates. *Planta* 217:138–46

89. Milkowski C, Baumert A, Schmidt D, Nehlin L, Strack D. 2004. Molecular regulation of sinapate ester metabolism in *Brassica napus*: expression of genes, properties of the encoded proteins and correlation of enzyme activities with metabolite accumulation. *Plant J.* 38:80–92

90. Milkowski C, Baumert A, Strack D. 2000. Cloning and heterologous expression of a rape cDNA encoding UDP-glucose: sinapate glucosyltransferase. *Planta* 211:883–86

91. Milkowski C, Baumert A, Strack D. 2000. Identification of four Arabidopsis genes encoding hydroxycinnamate glucosyltransferases. *FEBS Lett.* 486:183–84

92. Miller KD, Guyon V, Evans JN, Shuttleworth WA, Taylor LP. 1999. Purification, cloning, and heterologous expression of a catalytically efficient flavonol 3-O-galactosyltransferase expressed in the male gametophyte of *Petunia hybrida*. *J. Biol. Chem.* 274:34011–19

93. Mo YY, Nagel C, Taylor LP. 1992. Biochemical complementation of chalcone synthase mutants defines a role for flavonols in functional pollen. *Proc. Natl. Acad. Sci. USA* 89:7213–17

94. Moehs CP, Allen PV, Friedman M, Belknap WR. 1997. Cloning and expression of solanidine UDP-glucose glucosyltransferase from potato. *Plant J.* 11:227–36

95. Mok DWS, Mok MC. 2001. Cytokinin metabolism and action. *Annu. Rev. Plant Physiol. Plant Mol. Biol.* 52:89–118

96. Mol J, Grotewold E, Koes R. 1998. How genes paint flowers and seeds. *Trends Plant Sci.* 3:212–17

97. Moraga AR, Nohales PF, Perez JA, Gomez-Gomez L. 2004. Glucosylation of the saffron apocarotenoid crocetin by a glucosyltransferase isolated from *Crocus sativus* stigmas. *Planta* 219:955–66

98. **Morita Y, Hoshino A, Kikuchi Y, Okuhara H, Ono E, et al. 2005. Japanese morning glory *dusky* mutants displaying reddish-brown or purplish-gray flowers are deficient in a novel glycosylation enzyme for anthocyanin biosynthesis, UDP-glucose: anthocyanidin 3-O-glucoside-2″-O-glucosyltransferase, due to 4-bp insertions in the gene. *Plant J.* 42:353–63**

99. Morrissey JP, Osbourn AE. 1999. Fungal resistance to plant antibiotics as a mechanism of pathogenesis. *Microbiol. Mol. Biol. Rev.* 63:708–24

Changes in flower color in naturally occurring mutants were linked to 4-bp insertions in a gene encoding an anthocyanidin-specific GT.

100. Mulichak AM, Losey HC, Lu W, Wawrzak Z, Walsh CT, Garavito RM. 2003. Structure of the TDP-epi-vancosaminyltransferase GtfA from the chloroeremomycin biosynthetic pathway. *Proc. Natl. Acad. Sci. USA* 100:9238–43

101. Mulichak AM, Losey HC, Walsh CT, Garavito RM. 2001. Structure of the UDP-glucosyltransferase GtfB that modifies the heptapeptide aglycone in the biosynthesis of vancomycin group antibiotics. *Structure (Camb.)* 9:547–57

102. Mulichak AM, Lu W, Losey HC, Walsh CT, Garavito RM. 2004. Crystal structure of vancosaminyltransferase GtfD from the vancomycin biosynthetic pathway: interactions with acceptor and nucleotide ligands. *Biochemistry* 43:5170–80

103. Nair RB, Bastress KL, Ruegger MO, Denault JW, Chapple C. 2004. The *Arabidopsis thaliana* reduced epidermal fluorescence1 gene encodes an aldehyde dehydrogenase involved in ferulic acid and sinapic acid biosynthesis. *Plant Cell* 16:544–54

104. Napoli C, Lemieux C, Jorgensen R. 1990. Introduction of a chimeric chalcone synthase gene into petunia results in reversible co-suppression of homologous genes in trans. *Plant Cell* 2:279–89

105. Niemeyer HM. 1988. Hydroxamic acids (4-hydroxy-1,4-benzoxazin-3-ones), defense chemicals in the gramineae. *Phytochemistry* 27:3349–58

106. O'Donnell P J, Truesdale MR, Calvert CM, Dorans A, Roberts MR, Bowles DJ. 1998. A novel tomato gene that rapidly responds to wound- and pathogen-related signals. *Plant J.* 14:137–42

107. Ogata J, Kanno Y, Itoh Y, Tsugawa H, Suzuki M. 2005. Anthocyanin biosynthesis in roses. *Nature* 435:757–58

108. Paquette S, Moller BL, Bak S. 2003. On the origin of Family 1 plant glycosyltransferases. *Phytochemistry* 62:399–413

109. Pedras MSC, Zaharia IL, Gai Y, Zhou Y, Ward DE. 2001. In planta sequential hydroxylation and glycosylation of a fungal phytotoxin: avoiding cell death and overcoming the fungal invader. *Proc. Natl. Acad. Sci. USA* 98:747–52

110. Perez FJ, Ormenonunez J. 1993. Weed growth interference from temperate cereals - the effect of a hydroxamic-acids-exuding rye (*Secale-cereale* L.) cultivar. *Weed Res.* 33:115–19

111. Pflugmacher S, Sandermann H. 1998. Taxonomic distribution of plant glucosyltransferases acting on xenobiotics. *Phytochemistry* 49:507–11

112. Pilon-Smits E. 2005. Phytoremediation. *Annu. Rev. Plant Biol.* 56:15–39

113. Poppenberger B, Berthiller F, Lucyshyn D, Sieberer T, Schuhmacher R, et al. 2003. Detoxification of the fusarium mycotoxin deoxynivalenol by a UDP-glucosyltransferase from *Arabidopsis thaliana*. *J. Biol. Chem.* 278:47905–14

114. Poppenberger B, Fujioka S, Soeno K, George GL, Vaistij FE, et al. 2005. The UGT73C5 of Arabidopsis thaliana glucosylates brassinosteroids. *Proc. Natl. Acad. Sci. USA* 102:15253–58

115. Poulton JE. 1988. Localization and catabolism of cyanogenic glycosides. *Ciba Found. Symp.* 140:67–91

116. Priest DM, Jackson RG, Ashford DA, Abrams SR, Bowles DJ. 2005. The use of abscisic acid analogues to analyse the substrate selectivity of UGT71B6, a UDP-glycosyltransferase of *Arabidopsis thaliana*. *FEBS Lett* 579:4454–58

117. Quiel JA, Bender J. 2003. Glucose conjugation of anthranilate by the Arabidopsis UGT74F2 glucosyltransferase is required for tryptophan mutant blue fluorescence. *J. Biol. Chem.* 278:6275–81

118. Rea PA. 1999. MRP subfamily ABC transporters from plants and yeast. *J. Exp. Bot.* 50:895–913

The first GT involved in glucosylation of anthocyanidins that recognized, sequentially, the 5-OH and then the 3-OH positions.

UGT73C5 from Arabidopsis recognized a fungal toxin and overexpression of the GT increases tolerance.

119. Richman A, Swanson A, Humphrey T, Chapman R, McGarvey B, et al. 2005. Functional genomics uncovers three glucosyltransferases involved in the synthesis of the major sweet glucosides of *Stevia rebaudiana*. *Plant J.* 41:56–67

120. Ross J, Li Y, Lim E, Bowles DJ. 2001. Higher plant glycosyltransferases. *Genome Biol.* 2:3004.1–6

121. Samuels AL, Rensing KH, Douglas CJ, Mansfield SD, Dharmawardhana DP, Ellis BE. 2002. Cellular machinery of wood production: differentiation of secondary xylem in *Pinus contorta* var. latifolia. *Planta* 216:72–82

122. Sandrock RW, VanEtten HD. 1998. Fungal sensitivity to and enzymatic degradation of the phytoanticipin alpha-tomatine. *Phytopathology* 88:137–43

123. Sawada S, Suzuki H, Ichimaida F, Yamaguchi MA, Iwashita T, et al. 2005. UDP-glucuronic acid: anthocyanin glucuronosyltransferase from red daisy (*Bellis perennis*) flowers: enzymology and phylogenetics of a novel glucuronosyltransferase involved in flower pigment biosynthesis. *J. Biol. Chem.* 280:899–906

124. Schäffner A, Messner B, Langebartels C, Sandermann H. 2002. Genes and enzymes for in-planta phytoremediation of air, water and soil. *Acta Biotechnol.* 22:141–51

125. Schulz M, Wieland I. 1999. Variation in metabolism of BOA among species in various field communities—biochemical evidence for co-evolutionary processes in plant communities? *Chemoecology* 9:133–41

126. Schwartz SH, Zeevaart JAD. 2004. Abscisic acid biosynthesis and metabolism. In *Plant Hormones, Biosynthesis, Signal Transduction, Action*, ed. PJ Davies, pp. 137–55. Dordrecht, Netherlands: Kluwer Acad.

127. Sepulveda-Jimenez G, Rueda-Benitez P, Porta H, Rocha-Sosa M. 2005. A red beet (*Beta vulgaris*) UDP-glucosyltransferase gene induced by wounding, bacterial infiltration and oxidative stress. *J. Exp. Biol.* 56:605–11

128. Shao H, He X, Achnine L, Blount JW, Dixon RA, Wang X. 2005. Crystal structures of a multifunctional triterpene/flavonoid glycosyltransferase from *Medicago truncatula*. *Plant Cell* 17:3141–54

129. Shirley AM, McMichael CM, Chapple C. 2001. The *sng2* mutant of Arabidopsis is defective in the gene encoding the serine carboxypeptidase-like protein sinapoylglucose: choline sinapoyltransferase. *Plant J.* 28:83–94

130. Sicker D, Frey M, Schulz M, Gierl A. 2000. Role of natural benzoxazinones in the survival strategy of plants. *Int. Rev. Cytol.* 198:319–46

131. Sponsel VM, Hedden P. 2004. Gibberellin biosynthesis and inactivation. In *Plant Hormones, Biosynthesis, Signal Transduction, Action!* ed. PJ Davies, pp. 63–94. Dordrecht, Netherlands: Kluwer Acad.

132. Suzuki H, Achnine L, Xu R, Matsuda SPT, Dixon RA. 2002. A genomics approach to the early stages of triterpene saponin biosynthesis in *Medicago truncatula*. *Plant J.* 32:1033–48

133. Suzuki H, Kim SK, Takahashi N, Yokota T. 1993. Metabolism of castasterone and brassinolide in mung bean explant. *Phytochemistry* 33:1361–67

134. Suzuki H, Reddy MSS, Naoumkina M, Aziz N, May GD, et al. 2005. Methyl jasmonate and yeast elicitor induce differential transcriptional and metabolic re-programming in cell suspension cultures of the model legume *Medicago truncatula*. *Planta* 220:696–707

135. Szerszen JB, Szczyglowski K, Bandurski RS. 1994. *IAGLU*, a gene from *Zea mays* involved in conjugation of growth hormone indole-3-acetic acid. *Science* 265:1699–701

136. Taguchi G, Yazawa T, Hayashida N, Okazaki M. 2001. Molecular cloning and heterologous expression of novel glucosyltransferases from tobacco cultured cells that have broad substrate specificity and are induced by salicylic acid and auxin. *Eur. J. Biochem.* 268:4086–94

The first plant GT1 protein structure solved at 2.6 Å with the donor UDP-Glc present in the binding pocket.

137. Tattersall DB, Bak S, Jones PR, Olsen CE, Nielsen JK, et al. 2001. Resistance to an herbivore through engineered cyanogenic glucoside synthesis. *Science* 293:1826–28

138. Taylor LP, Jorgensen R. 1992. Conditional male-fertility in chalcone synthase-deficient petunia. *J. Hered.* 83:11–17

139. Taylor LP, Strenge D, Miller KD. 1998. The role of glycosylation in flavonol-induced pollen germination. In *Flavonoids In The Living System*, ed. J Manthey, B Buslig, pp. 35–44. New York: Plenum

140. Thorsoe KS, Bak S, Olsen CE, Imberty A, Breton C, Lindberg Moller B. 2005. Determination of catalytic key amino acids and UDP sugar donor specificity of the cyanohydrin glycosyltransferase UGT85B1 from Sorghum bicolor. Molecular modeling substantiated by site-specific mutagenesis and biochemical analyses. *Plant Physiol.* 139:664–73

141. Tohge T, Nishiyama Y, Hirai MY, Yano M, Nakajima J, et al. 2005. Functional genomics by integrated analysis of metabolome and transcriptome of Arabidopsis plants over-expressing an MYB transcription factor. *Plant J.* 42:218–35

142. Veach YK, Martin RC, Mok DW, Malbeck J, Vankova R, Mok MC. 2003. O-glucosylation of *cis*-zeatin in maize. Characterization of genes, enzymes, and endogenous cytokinins. *Plant Physiol.* 131:1374–80

143. Verberne MC, Budi Muljono AB, Verpoorte R. 1999. Salicylic acid biosynthesis. In *Biochemistry and Molecular Biology of Plant Hormones*, ed. K Libbenga, M Hall, PJJ Hooykaas, pp. 295–314. London: Elsevier

144. Vogt T, Grimm R, Strack D. 1999. Cloning and expression of a cDNA encoding betanidin 5-O-glucosyltransferase, a betanidin- and flavonoid-specific enzyme with high homology to inducible glucosyltransferases from the Solanaceae. *Plant J.* 19:509–19

145. Vogt T, Jones P. 2000. Glycosyltransferases in plant natural product synthesis: characterization of a supergene family. *Trends Plant Sci.* 5:380–86

146. Vogt T, Pollak P, Tarlyn N, Taylor LP. 1994. Pollination- or wound-induced kaempferol accumulation in petunia stigmas enhances seed production. *Plant Cell* 6:11–23

147. Vogt T, Taylor LP. 1995. Flavonol 3-O-glycosyltransferases associated with petunia pollen produce gametophyte-specific flavonol diglycosides. *Plant Physiol.* 108:903–11

148. Vogt T, Zimmermann E, Grimm R, Meyer M, Strack D. 1997. Are the characteristics of betanidin glucosyltransferases from cell-suspension cultures of *Dorotheanthus bellidiformis* indicative of their phylogenetic relationship with flavonoid glucosyltransferases? *Planta* 203:349–61

149. von Rad U, Huttl R, Lottspeich F, Gierl A, Frey M. 2001. Two glucosyltransferases are involved in detoxification of benzoxazinoids in maize. *Plant J.* 28:633–42

150. Willits MG, Giovanni M, Prata RTN, Kramer CM, De Luca V, et al. 2004. Biofermentation of modified flavonoids: an example of in vivo diversification of secondary metabolites. *Phytochemistry* 65:31–41

151. Winkel-Shirley B. 2001. Flavonoid biosynthesis. A colorful model for genetics, biochemistry, cell biology, and biotechnology. *Plant Physiol.* 126:485–93

152. Woo HH, Faull KF, Hirsch AM, Hawes MC. 2003. Altered life cycle in Arabidopsis plants expressing PsUGT1, a UDP-glucuronosyltransferase-encoding gene from pea. *Plant Physiol.* 133:538–48

153. Woo HH, Hirsch AM, Hawes MC. 2004. Altered susceptibility to infection by *Sinorhizobium meliloti* and *Nectria haematococca* in alfalfa roots with altered cell cycle. *Plant Cell Rep.* 22:967–73

154. Woo HH, Orbach MJ, Hirsch AM, Hawes MC. 1999. Meristem-localized inducible expression of a UDP-glycosyltransferase gene is essential for growth and development in pea and alfalfa. *Plant Cell* 11:2303–15

Metabolomics, transcriptomics, in vitro studies, and characterization of T-DNA Arabidopsis mutants defined the activities of two GTs involved in flavonoid biosynthesis.

A *Pisum sativum* GT required for root cap meristematic activity.

155. Woodward AW, Bartel B. 2005. Auxin: regulation, action, and interaction. *Ann. Bot.* 95:707–35
156. Xu ZJ, Nakajima M, Suzuki Y, Yamaguchi I. 2002. Cloning and characterization of the abscisic acid-specific glucosyltransferase gene from adzuki bean seedlings. *Plant Physiol.* 129:1285–95
157. Zagrobelny M, Bak S, Rasmussen AV, Jorgensen B, Naumann CM, Moller BL. 2004. Cyanogenic glucosides and plant-insect interactions. *Phytochemistry* 65:293–306

Protein Degradation Machineries in Plastids

Wataru Sakamoto

Research Institute for Bioresources, Okayama University, Kurashiki,
Okayama 710-0046, Japan; email: saka@rib.okayama-u.ac.jp

Annu. Rev. Plant Biol.
2006. 57:599–621

The *Annual Review of
Plant Biology* is online at
plant.annualreviews.org

doi: 10.1146/
annurev.arplant.57.032905.105401

First published online as a
Review in Advance on
February 7, 2006

1543-5008/06/
0602-0599$20.00

Key Words

protease, ATP-dependent proteolysis, plastid and chloroplast,
photosynthesis and oxidative damage, thylakoid membranes

Abstract

Plastids undergo drastic morphological and physiological changes
under different developmental stages and in response to environmental conditions. A key to accomplishing these transitions and
maintaining homeostasis is the quality and quantity control of many
plastid proteins by proteases and chaperones. Although a limited
number of plastid proteases have been identified by biochemical approaches, recent progress in genome information revealed various
plant proteases that are of prokaryotic origin and that are localized in
chloroplasts. Of these, ATP-dependent proteases such as Clp, FtsH,
and Lon are considered the major enzymes involved in processive
degradation (gradual degradation to oligopeptides and amino acids).
The basic architecture of plant ATP-dependent proteases is very
similar to the architechture of bacterial enzymes, such as those in
Escherichia coli, but plastid enzymes apparently have extraordinary
numbers of isomers. Recent molecular genetic characterization in
Arabidopsis has identified differential roles of these isomers. This review covers what is currently known about the types and function of
plastid proteases together with our new observations.

Contents

INTRODUCTION

Proteins in living organisms can exist in various forms, either as monomeric or multimeric, soluble or membrane-bound, activated by processing or modification, properly assembled, or as a complex. Each protein thus has its own lifetime, but generally does not exist beyond the lifetime of the organism. This means that most of the proteins are destined to turnover and that protein quality control is physiologically essential for sustaining life (30, 127). The mechanism involved requires protein degradation and regeneration by proteases and chaperone activities, respectively.

Plastids, which are derived from endosymbiosis of photosynthetic bacteria, are plant organelles whose morphology dynamically changes in response to developmental status and the abiotic environment. Examples of plastids are chloroplasts in leaves under light, etioplasts in leaves in darkness, amyloplasts in roots, and chromoplasts in fruits. Accumulating evidence indicates that proteases play an

essential role in the transition of one plastid type into others (1, 3). Moreover, the photosynthetic apparatus in chloroplasts undergoes constant photooxidative damage under light, and damaged proteins must be removed by proteases involved in the repair cycle (10, 11, 68, 78; see also 7).

The function of proteases is often vital and versatile. Some proteases act as a chaperone whose activity is inducible under specific conditions. Also, protease activity itself can be regulated in a specific manner such as by endopeptidic processing. Thus, regulated proteolysis can be regarded as fine tuning at the last step of gene expression (30, 125). The ubiquitin-dependent degradation pathway through 26S proteasomes provides a regulatory circuit with many developmental phenomena in plants (72, 113). In contrast, plastids do not possess 26S proteasomes but instead carry prokaryote-related ATP-dependent proteolytic machinery. While there have been many biochemical attempts to identify the factors involved in plastid protein degradation, only a few have been successful. In the past decade, however, the sequencing of many plant genomes has revealed genes encoding prokaryotic-like proteases that have been well characterized in *Escherichia coli*, *Synechocystis*, and other model microorganisms. In this article, I focus on protease families recently identified in plastids of *Arabidopsis* and other higher plants. I emphasize the prokaryotic ATP-dependent proteases that have been characterized in genomics and molecular genetic approaches. Readers also should refer to recent reviews for chloroplasts (1, 3) and for cyanobacteria (90, 116). Other reviews (4, 20, 41, 94, 114) are also recommended for specific proteases.

TYPES AND FUNCTIONS OF PLASTID PROTEASES: A GENERAL OVERVIEW

How many types of proteases are found in plastids? Although a limited number of proteases have been identified in biochemical methods, novel protease homologs that are targeted to plastids can be predicted based on the complete genome information from model plant species. Using four programs to predict plastid targeting, Richly & Leister (91) estimated that in *Arabidopsis*, approximately 2200 proteins constitute chloroplasts along with those encoded in the chloroplast genome. The functions of approximately 5% of these proteins are thought to be related to protein fate. As described below and in **Figure 1**, at least 11 different types of

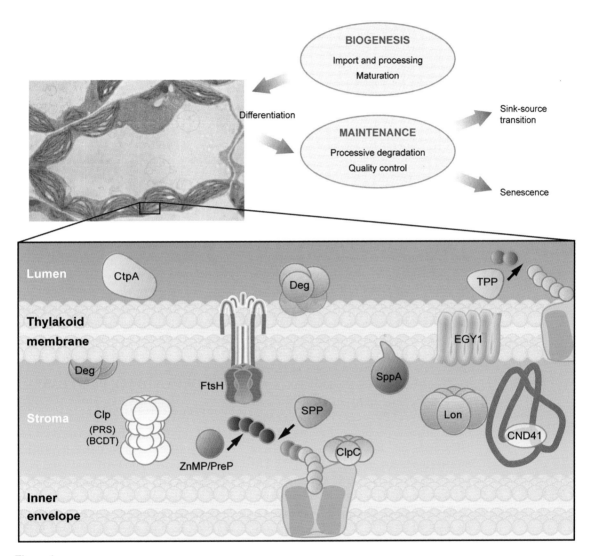

Figure 1

Schematic view of types and functions of proteases in plastids. The upper part shows an electron microscopic image of *Arabidopsis* chloroplasts. Biogenesis of chloroplasts from proplastids through membrane fission requires import of cytosolic proteins as a precursor and concomitant processing. Once chloroplasts are formed, quality control of proteins is accomplished mainly by ATP-dependent proteases and is crucial for its maintenance. Processive degradation is needed for the transition between plastid types, particularly at sink-source transition and senescence. The bottom part is a schematic representation of proteases present in chloroplasts.

Transit peptide:
N-terminal amino
acid residue of a
precursor protein
that is synthesized in
the cytosol and
imported via Toc/Tic
translocon into
chloroplasts

PSII: Photosystem
II

Processive
degradation:
continued hydrolysis
of peptide bonds of a
polypeptide to
generate
oligopeptides or free
amino acids

LHCII: light
harvesting complex
II

peptidase or protease families encoded in more than 50 genes are found, representing roughly 2.3% of the constituent proteins. The different types of proteases include serine, metallo-, and possibly cysteine, and aspartic proteases, and some of their reaction requires ATP. Most of the peptidases identified in cyanobacteria have paralogs in *Arabidopsis*, suggesting that the majority of the protease components are of prokaryotic origin (65).

Proteases (or peptidases) in plastids have two types of function. The first function is a positive action of proteases mainly by endopeptidic activities. Some processing peptidases that have been well characterized are stromal and thylakoidal processing peptidases and their related peptidases (94). Plastid-targeted proteins encoded in the nuclear genome are usually synthesized in the cytosol as a precursor with an N-terminal extension (transit peptide). Precursor proteins imported into the stroma undergo maturation by a metallopeptidase termed stroma processing peptidases (SPPs) to remove the transit peptide (71, 92, 93, 134). Further degradation of transit peptides in the stroma involves another type of zinc metalloproteases (termed Zn-MP/PreP) (14, 71). Proteins imported into the thylakoid lumen undergo a similar processing by a peptidase in the thylakoid membrane named [thylakoidal processing peptidase (TPP)] (16, 106). Another type of the processing occurs in the maturation of D1 protein, one of the two reaction center proteins in Photosystem II (PSII) (7, 79). The processing event in which the C-terminal part of D1 is cleaved off by CtpA (C-terminal processing peptidase) appears to be involved in the proper assembly of the PSII reaction center (42, 95). CtpA is a serine protease with a catalytic dyad (57).

The second function of the plastid proteases is the processive (gradual) degradation of unnecessary proteins to free amino acids. This type of degradation machinery is required for removal of unnecessary proteins that are generated by expression in excess, by

error in synthesis and assembly, or by heat denature or photo-oxidative damage. Proteins that have fulfilled their roles may also need to be degraded properly. Plants have developed elaborate machinery for quality control of photosynthetic proteins (particularly the reaction center of PSII), because the chloroplast is where a large number of reactive oxygen species are generated and where the repair of the damaged proteins through degradation and reassembly is crucial for photoprotection (10, 11, 78). Some studies have suggested the plastidic proteases involved in this process are nucleotide-dependent (33, 62, 117). A similar thylakoid-attached proteolytic activity is reported to be involved in degrading the abundant Lhcb proteins in the light harvesting complex of PSII (LHCII) in vitro (25, 28, 129). Degradation of Lhcb and its related proteins is needed to adjust the antenna capacity to light acclimation and also in senescence (5, 60, 135). As implicated in these works, most energy-dependent proteases identified in the past decade possess an ATPase domain that forms a ring structure (see below) and that possibly acts as an unfoldase. I therefore focus on these prokaryotic ATP-dependent proteases in the following sections.

ATP-DEPENDENT PROTEASES

Common Features

Table 1 lists three ATP-dependent proteases experimentally shown to reside in plastids. These proteases, Clp, FtsH, and Lon, share a conserved ATP-binding motif but possess a different catalytic domain for proteolysis. They are all prokaryotic and were originally identified and characterized in *E. coli* (29). Eukaryotic organisms have homologs of these proteases in plastids and mitochondria. The importance of ATP-dependent proteases in plastids is shown by the fact that chloroplast genomes of not only alga but also higher plants contain a gene potentially encoding ClpP, a protease subunit of Clp (66). Subsequently, ClpP was also discovered in the

Table 1 Subunits and isomers of ATP-dependent proteases in plastids of *Arabidopsis*

Subunit or isomer	AGI number	Function	Length (amino acid)[a]	Expression in high light[b]	Mutant phenotype	Reference(s)
Clp Protease core						
ClpP1	Atcg00670 (Chloroplast gene)	Serine protease	196	N.D.	Lethal (heteroplasmy in tobacco and *Chlamydomonas*)	(40, 54, 108)
ClpP3	At1g66670	Serine protease	309	+	N.D.	
ClpP4	At5g45390	Serine protease	292	+	N.D.	
ClpP5	At1g02560	Serine protease	298	+	N.D.	
ClpP6	At1g11750	Serine protease	271	+	N.D.	
ClpR1	At1g49970	Clp-like (no cat. triad)	387	+/−	Pale yellow	(20)
ClpR2	At1g12410	Clp-like (no cat. triad)	279	+	Pale yellow[c]	
ClpR3	At1g09130	Clp-like (no cat. triad)	330	+	N.D.	
ClpR4	At4g17040	Clp-like (no cat. triad)	305	+	Seedling lethal[c]	
ClpS1	At4g25370	Unknown	238	N.D.	N.D.	
ClpS2	At4g12060	Unknown	241	N.D.	N.D.	
Clp chaperone						
ClpB3	At5g15450	AAA	968	N.D.	Pale yellow[d]	
ClpC1 (Hsp93)	At5g50920	AAA	929	+	Pale yellow	(22a, 51b, 112)
ClpC2	At3g48870	AAA	952	+	No visible phenotype Suppression of *var2*	(20, 84)
ClpD (ERD1)	At5g51070	AAA	945	+	No visible phenotype	(20)
ClpT	At1g68660	Unknown	159	N.D.	No visible phenotype	(20)
FtsH isomer						
FtsH1	At1g50250	AAA and metalloprotease	716	+/−	No visible phenotype	(101, 132a)
FtsH2 (VAR2)	At2g30950	AAA and metalloprotease	695	+	Yellow variegated	(19, 122, 132a)
FtsH5 (VAR1)	At5g42270	AAA and metalloprotease	704	+	Yellow variegated	(100, 132a)
FtsH6	At5g15250	AAA and metalloprotease	687	+/−	No visible phenotype	(101)
FtsH7	At3g47060	AAA and metalloprotease	802	+/−	N.D.	
FtsH8	At1g06430	AAA and metalloprotease	685	+++	No visible phenotype	(101, 132a)
FtsH9	At5g58870	AAA and metalloprotease	806	+	N.D.	
FtsH11	At5g53170	AAA and metalloprotease	806	+	No visible phenotype[e]	
FtsH12	At1g79560	AAA and metalloprotease	1008	+	N.D.	
Lon isomer						
Lon4	At3g05790	AAA and serine protease	942	−	N.D.	

[a]The numbers of amino acids were based on gene annotation and contain transit peptide sequences.

[b]Expression at the transcript level is based on oligonucleotide microarray analysis by Sinvany-Villalobo et al. (111). -, no induction; +/−, moderate induction; +++, very strong induction. N.D., not determined.

[c]Personal communication by K. van Wijk.

[d]Personal communication by F. Myouga and K. Shinozaki.

[e]Personal communication by H. Janska.

nuclear genome (115). The overall architecture of the Clp complex resembles that of the multimeric 26S proteasome in the cytosol, suggesting that these ATP-dependent proteases are evolutionarily related and are the main protein degradation machineries in plastids (20, 127). A membrane-bound ATP-dependent protease, FtsH, is also encoded in the chloroplast genome in the red algae *Cyanidioschyzon merolae* (44).

The conserved ATPase domain in the aforementioned proteases includes the so-called AAA domain (9, 55, 85). Proteins containing these domains comprise a large protein family called AAA$^+$ (ATPases associated with various cellular activities plus) (76, 80). Among the AAA$^+$ proteins is a subfamily (called AAA proteins) that contains an additional C-terminal conserved domain [second region of homology (SRH)] (47). FtsH is also called AAA protease. AAA$^+$ proteins are universally found in prokaryotes and eukaryotes with various cellular functions (26). The protease domain of Clp is of the serine type and consists of a catalytic triad. Similarly, Lon is a serine-type protease and a recent structural analysis indicates that the catalytic center is a dyad. FtsH is a metalloprotease and the catalytic center is composed of a conserved zinc-binding motif. All three proteases exist as a protein complex, with the ATPase domain forming a hexameric or heptameric core ring structure. Although the precise action of the energy-dependent process with respect to proteolysis is not fully understood, in Clp the ATPase complex recruits and simultaneously unfolds a substrate protein through the ring, and then delivers it into the proteolytic chamber for degradation (127). Although the basic architecture of each protease established in *E. coli* and cyanobacteria has been described, here I only deal with plastid homologs.

Some ATP-dependent proteases in plastids (e.g., Clp and Lon) are involved in protein degradation in stroma, and others (e.g., FtsH) are involved in protein degradation in thylakoid membranes. Other proteases like Deg may be also involved in the thylakoidal lumen. The presence of these bacterial proteases was initially demonstrated by immunological analysis (83). In chloroplasts, protein complexes undergo complete degradation when lacking either one of the subunits by mutation (128). Accumulation of precursor proteins imported into chloroplasts is usually undetectable in vivo. These proteases may have roles in degrading precursors, excess subunit proteins, and photooxidatively damaged proteins (63, 82). Recent molecular genetic char-

acterization in *Arabidopsis* has demonstrated the fundamental roles of ATP-dependent proteases, which I describe in detail below.

Multiplication of Protease Components

One important feature of plastid proteases as opposed to proteases in other compartments is that their subunits and isoforms exist as multiple copies (**Table 1**). Although the genes encoding Clp subunits, FtsH, and Lon exist as single copies in *E. coli* and most eubacteria, the corresponding genes exist as multiple copies in photosynthetic bacteria, unicellular alga, and higher plants (2, 116). Given that some isoforms of these proteases are also present in mitochondria, one should carefully distinguish which ones indeed function in plastids. Prediction programs are available, but the actual location needs to be confirmed experimentally. Two in vivo ways to localize different homologs in either plastids or mitochondria have been reported by (*a*) green fluorescent protein (GFP) transient assay using putative N-terminal transit peptide (101), and (*b*) proteome analysis and determination of the polypeptide in plastid fraction (86, 87, 111, 130). The finding that the number of the subunits and isoforms is greater in higher plants than in unicellular alga and cyanobacteria implies that the diversification occurred during the evolution of photosynthetic organisms. Because many isomers are found in Clp subunits, FtsH, and Lon in *Arabidopsis* and other plants, we should clarify the nomenclature for these proteins. Efforts have been made to unify their nomenclature, but it should be updated. In addition to the nomenclature proposed by Adam et al. (2), I followed Clarke et al. (20) for Clp, and Huesgen et al. (41) for Deg (previously termed as DegP).

Clp PROTEASE

Basic Structure

Clp is a multisubunit enzyme in which the catalytic domain for proteolysis and the

ATPase domain are split in different subunits. In *E. coli*, the protease subunit ClpP forms a heptameric ring with a narrow central pore (126). Two of the rings associate with each other on one side and result in forming a tetradecameric barrel-like structure. This has an internal central proteolytic chamber composed of a catalytic triad conferring serine-protease activity. Another complex of the AT-Pase subunits, which consists of either ClpA or ClpX (containing two or one AAA domains, respectively), is connected further outside of this proteolytic complex at one or both ends (32, 39). ClpA and ClpX independently form a homo-hexameric ring characteristic of AAA$^+$ proteins, and can act, per se, as a chaperone. In combination with ClpP, ClpA/P, and ClpX/P holo enzymes perform protein degradation, in a way that ClpA or ClpX provide an ATP-dependent unfoldase activity and act as a gateway to recruit the unfolded substrates into the narrow proteolytic chamber of ClpP (127). This unfolding-coupled processive degradation is a common mechanism shared with the eukaryotic 26S proteasome and partially with other ATP-dependent proteases, such as FtsH and Lon.

E. coli has other Clp proteins called ClpB and ClpC that do not associate with the ClpP protease complex but comprise the Clp/HSP100 protein family together with ClpA. In chloroplasts, homologs of ClpB and ClpC, but not ClpA, are present and form a complex with ClpP (34, 107). In addition, an *E. coli* subunit called ClpS regulates the activity of the Clp complex (23, 61). A homolog of the bacterial ClpS is also present in *Arabidopsis* but is instead termed ClpT. This is because plastids contain two novel subunits, termed ClpS1 and S2, that are not found in *E. coli* (86, 87). ClpS1 and S2 are predominantly present only in chloroplasts, and their N-terminal part shares homology with ClpA/C. Furthermore, there is a novel subunit called ClpR that appears to be specific to photosynthetic organisms (90, 103). ClpR is homologous and thus redundant to ClpP, except that it lacks either one or all of the conserved amino acids of the catalytic triad and does not act as a protease. Thus, Clp subunits and isomers are diversely distributed among different organisms. Note that the subunit names are based mostly on homologies, and not necessarily on function.

Subunits and Gene Family

In *Arabidopsis*, about two dozen genes encoding subunits of Clp have been found (20, 116): Only ClpP1 is encoded in the chloroplast genome and all other genes are in the nuclear genome (**Table 1**). Earlier studies using immunological detection demonstrated the in vivo presence of a complex formed by a protease subunit and a chaperone subunit showing ATP-dependent proteolytic activity (81, 115). Peltier et al. (86) recently identified the component of the Clp protease core complex (325–350 kDa) that resides in stroma and showed that it contains five ClpP isomers (ClpP1, P3, P4, P5, P6), four proteolytically inactive subunits ClpR1 to ClpR4, and two plant-specific subunits ClpS1 and S2. Characterization of the complex in different tissues suggested that the overall composition appears to be similar in different plastid types. The Clp protease complex in plastids, likely forming an authentic tetradecamer, thus is hetero-oligomeric rather than homo-oligomeric. In addition, ClpS1 and S2 peripherally attach to the twin-barrel structure of the core, likely acting as a regulator of the interaction with the chaperone complex. Although the function of ClpR remains unknown, a three-dimensional model of the hetero complex implies that the inclusion of ClpR in the plastid complex may control access of the substrate to the catalytic chamber.

Compared with the protease complex, the chaperone (ATPase) complex is less understood. Nevertheless, plastids contain homologs related to *E. coli* ClpA, termed ClpB3, ClpC1, ClpC2, and ClpD, all of which have two AAA domains and belong to the Clp/HSP100 family, but do not contain homologs related to *E. coli* ClpX (20, 86, 116). Instead, ClpX1-3 appears to reside in

Unfoldase activity: enzymatic activity of unfolding proteins that are natively folded or denatured by stress and making these proteins accessible to proteolytic or refolding processes

mitochondria exclusively (35), although the prediction programs suggest the possibility that all three are localized in plastids. ClpD was originally identified as a gene highly responsive to draught stress and senescence (75). ClpC (also termed Hsp93) was independently shown to be associated with the translocon Tic of the inner envelope (77). In contrast to plastids, the Clp complex structure in mitochondria seems rather homogeneous and resembles the *E. coli* ClpX/P. The protease core in mitochondria of *Arabidopsis* contains only ClpP2 and the ATPase complex consists only of ClpX (X1, X2, X3) (86). Homogeneity of the mitochondrial Clp also illustrates that the plastid Clp has exceptional subunit compositions and an extraordinary number of isomers, providing an intriguing question of the relationship between Clp diversity and the evolution of photosynthesis.

Expression and Genetic Analysis

ClpP is dispensable in *E. coli*, but its expression is affected by certain stress conditions like heat shock and carbon starvation (29). Similar observations have been reported in *Bacillus subtilis* and other nonphotosynthetic bacteria. In contrast, ClpP in *Synechococcus* is not responsive to heat shock, but rather plays roles in steady-state growth and acclimation to high-light condition (21, 89). In *Arabidopsis*, most of the Clp genes showed increased transcript levels under high light but were less responsive to temperature shifts (111, 133). These results together with the proteome analysis imply that all isomers constituting the protease core complex substantially accumulate in all plastid types, and that regulation of the proteolytic activity of the complex may depend on regulatory subunits.

Reverse genetic approaches have been taken to further decipher the Clp function in plastids, despite the presence of many isomers (**Table 1**). Inactivation of ClpP1, encoded in the chloroplast genome, was reported to result in heteroplasmy between the mutated and wild-type genes in tobacco (54,

108) and *Chlamydomonas* (40), demonstrating that ClpP1 is essential for cell viability. A tobacco plant that retained *clpP1* heteroplasmy showed defective development in mesophyll-containing chloroplasts with disrupted inner membrane structures. No information is presently available on the effects of knockout of nuclear-encoded ClpPs. On the other hand, knockdown of ClpP4 by antisense methods caused severely reduced growth with chlorotic leaf tissues (20). This may mean that each isomer is required for the functional protease core, supporting the hetero-oligomeric composition proposed by Peltier et al. (86), but further genetic evidence is needed. As for other subunits, visible phenotypes such as yellow and pale green have been reported on the knockout or knockdown mutants of ClpR1, ClpR2, ClpR4, ClpC1, and ClpB3, whereas no clear phenotypes were observed on those of ClpC2, ClpD, and ClpT (20, 22a, 51b, 112). Interestingly, a mutation at the *ClpC2* locus was recently shown to suppress a variegated phenotype caused by loss of an FtsH (84). Although the mechanism involved in this genetic suppression remains unclear, it demonstrates the interaction of the Clp regulatory components with other protease members.

FtsH PROTEASE

Basic Structure

FtsH (also called HflB) was originally identified in *E. coli* as an essential protein (123) and was shown to degrade various short-lived proteins (6, 38, 124; see 43 for review). In contrast to multisubunit-composed Clp, FtsH has both ATPase and protease domains in one polypeptide and forms a homo-oligomeric complex. The homologs of FtsH have also been studied in detail in yeast mitochondria, in which three homologs (Yta10-12p) are present in inner membranes (55). Based on an X-ray crystallographic analysis, the ATPase domain of *E. coli* FtsH was proposed to constitute a hexameric ring that contains conserved aromatic residues facing the ring structure and the ATP-binding pocket is located between the neighboring protomers (53). The AAA domain of FtsH in plastids is almost identical in *E. coli*, implying a similar hexameric structure in plastid FtsHs.

E. coli FtsH has two transmembrane domains at the N terminus that anchor it in plasma membrane, and the protease domain at the C terminus faces the cytoplasm (43). FtsH exists as a very large complex by interacting with other membrane proteins such as HflKC (43, 97). In chloroplasts, all FtsH homologs are located in thylakoid membranes and the protease domain faces the stroma (19, 59, 101). FtsH also exists in plant mitochondria (51). However, yeast has two kinds of AAA proteins, one with a single transmembrane domain (Yta11p) and the others with two (Yta10p and Yta12p). These two proteins have different topologies with respect to the mitochondrial inner membrane: the protease domain faces either the intermembrane space (i-AAA) or the matrix (m-AAA) (9, 55). The two m-AAA proteins form a large hetero complex with other components called prohibitins (8, 120).

Gene Family

Multiplication of the genes coding for FtsH is much greater in photosynthetic organisms than in nonphotosynthetic bacteria and mitochondria of eukaryotes (64). Four isomers of FtsH have been identified in *Synechocystis* sp. PCC 6803. Inactivation of two of these isomers is lethal and so these isomers appear to be essential (64). Loss of one of the remaining two isomers, slr0228, leads to a dramatic sensitivity to high-light exposure and deficiency in the photosynthetic apparatus in thylakoid membranes, particularly in PSII (110, 51a). FtsH seems to be the main protease factor involved in the repair cycle of PSII, particularly the repair of D1 protein (12, 78). *Arabidopsis* has twelve *FtsH* genes (*FtsH1-12*). In addition, four other genes apparently encode proteins homologous to FtsH, but these are not re-

garded as FtsH because they lack a conserved zinc-binding motif, which presumably renders them inactive for proteolysis (116). Nine of the 12 FtsHs reside in chloroplasts (FtsH1, 2, 5, 6, 7, 8, 9, 11, 12), and the remaining three reside in mitochondria (FtsH3, 4, 10), based on our GFP transient assays (101). However, FtsH11, which contains only one transmembrane domain, is highly homologous to yeast mitochondrial Yta11, and was recently suggested to be located in both chloroplasts and mitochondria (37, 124a). For all the FtsHs immunologically detected in thylakoid membranes, the proteolytic domain was shown to face the stroma (59).

The importance of FtsH in chloroplasts was originally revealed by immunological detection of FtsH homologs in spinach chloroplasts, followed by isolation of the corresponding cDNA in *Arabidopsis* (59). In an in vitro import assay where a precursor of Rieske Fe-S protein was used with isolated chloroplasts, the precursors that remained in the stroma were promptly degraded, whereas the responsible protease appeared to have characteristics similar to FtsH and its degradation was inhibited by an FtsH antibody (82). As in *Synechocystis*, FtsH in chloroplasts apparently plays an important role in the degradation of photo-oxidatively damaged D1 and other proteins in PSII. Lindahl et al. (58) reported that in isolated spinach thylakoid membranes exposed to high light, D1 is degraded in two distinct steps (during generation of the intermediate products and during subsequent degradation). They found that a recombinant FtsH1 fusion protein expressed by *E. coli* can act on the lateral step. Tobacco DS9 is a homolog of FtsH and is the most similar to *Arabidopsis* FtsH2 (105). It was identified as a protein that was dramatically reduced at the transcript in response to the *N* gene-mediated hypersensitive response to tobacco mosaic virus. These observations indicate that FtsH in chloroplasts has multiple cellular functions, as is the case in *E. coli* and other microorganisms.

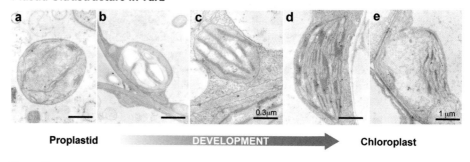

Plastid Ultrastructure in *var2*

Proplastid   DEVELOPMENT   Chloroplast

Figure 2

Arabidopsis leaf-variegated mutants called *yellow variegated* (*var*). (*Top panel*) Photographs of wild-type Columbia and *var1-1*, *var2-6*, and a suppressor mutant of *var2* (*sup52*). Leaf variegation in *var1* and *var2* is a result of loss of FtsH5 and FtsH2, respectively. Degree of leaf variegation is generally higher in young leaves than in lateral leaves, and also higher in *var2* than in *var1*. (*Bottom panel*) Ultrastructures of plastids in *var2* at the different developmental stages. A proplastid in shoot meristem (*a*) appears normal, whereas differentiation into chloroplasts in leaf primordia results in abberant plastid morphologies with vacuolated inner structures (*b* and *c*). In mesophylls of variegated leaves, normal-appearing chloroplasts accumulate in green tissues (*d*), whereas plastids with collapsed inner membrane structures are detected in white tissues (*e*). Bar: 0.3 μm in *a*, *b*, and *c*; 1 μm in *d* and *e*.

Expression and Genetic Analysis

FtsHs in chloroplasts are one of the best-characterized proteases in terms of molecular genetics. This is because a mutation at genes encoding some FtsHs shows a typical leaf-variegated phenotype that has long been known in *Arabidopsis* (98). The mutants are called *yellow variegated1* (*var1*) and *var2* (shown in **Figure 2**), and the corresponding loci in the wild type have been shown to encode FtsH5 and FtsH2, respectively, by Steve Rodermel's group and my group (19, 100, 122). Knockout mutations of the other chloroplastic FtsHs such as FtsH1, 6, and 8 did not result in any visible phenotypes (101). Two important observations here are that (*a*) loss of one FtsH does not cause lethality because of the functional interchangeability among the FtsH homologs, and (b) despite this redundancy, the variegation that is specifically detected as a result of the loss of either FtsH2 or FtsH5 implies that their expression could be coordinately regulated. In fact, immunological detection in which FtsH2 and FtsH5 were distinguished by specific antibodies showed that the lack of either one resulted in the concomitant decrease of the other (101). A concomitant decrease of FtsH5 in var2 was also observed in a proteomics analysis (130). Regulation likely occurs at the post-translational level. FtsH2 and FtsH5 were found to form a hetero complex of ~400 kDa.

Proteomic analysis of isolated thylakoids in *Arabidopsis* demonstrated that the FtsH complex had the highly related homologs FtsH1 and FtsH8, in addition to FtsH2 and FtsH5, which shows that these are the four major FtsHs constituting the FtsH complex (27, 111, 130). Stoichiometry of each isomer in the complex remained unclear, although the relative amount estimated at the protein level is FtsH2>FtsH5>(FtsH1, FtsH8) (111). The variegated phenotype observed in var1 (weak) and var2 (severe) seems to correlate well with this observation (**Figure 2**). Phylogenetic analysis clearly indicates that FtsH homologs can be grouped into at least several clusters. Besides the mitochondrial isomers, two clades can be drawn from this, one with FtsH1 and FtsH5 and the other with FtsH2 and FtsH8. Interestingly, the existence of this pair appears well conserved in unicellular alga (69, 70) as well as in higher plants (*Arabidopsis* and rice, see 131). Leaf variegation in var2(ftsh2) was rescued by overexpressing *FtsH8* cDNA (130, 131). Similarly, leaf variegation in var1(ftsh5) was rescued by overexpressing *FtsH1* cDNA but not *FtsH2* cDNA (131), suggesting that FtsH proteins in each clade are functionally redundant. Detailed characterization of the knockout mutants indicated that the appearance of white tissues were more intense in *ftsh1/ftsh5* and *ftsh2/ftsh8* double mutants than in *ftsh2/ftsh5* double mutants (132a).

Yu et al. (131) also demonstrated that antisense repression of FtsH1 in *var1(ftsh5)* background results in albino-like phenotypes. Together, these observations provide an interesting possibility that at least one isomer in each pair may be required for proper function.

Most of the variegated mutants isolated so far turned out to be alleles of *var2* (99). A fundamental question is why a distinct variegated phenotype can be observed only with the simultaneous loss of FtsH2 and FtsH5. The appearance of variegated sectors is higher at the juvenile leaf stage than at the later developmental stages. Expression of other chloroplastic proteins such as other FtsHs and ClpC seemed to increase in the late developmental stages (132). Leaf variegation can be suppressed by *trans*-action of a second-site mutation. These suppressors have been isolated and one has been assigned to the *ClpC2* locus (84). We also recently cloned one of the suppressors and assigned it to be the locus of the gene encoding a plastidic translation initiation factor (unpublished results; see **Figure 2**). Although these data still do not explain the mechanism leading to leaf variegation, they imply that the function of FtsH in chloroplasts is associated with various photosynthetic activities.

Expression of FtsH isomers at the transcription level indicates that some chloroplastic FtsHs, such as FtsH8, are highly inducible by high light (111). However, the overall FtsH protein levels do not substantially respond to stress conditions. A notable role of FtsH in chloroplasts is its involvement in the PSII repair cycle. In *Synechocystis*, FtsH has been copurified with PSII complexes (48, 110). Chlorophyll fluorescence induction analysis in green sectors of *var1* and *var2* showed that these mutants greatly reduce PSII activity when irradiated under high light (12, 100, 132). In fact, high-light-dependent degradation of D1 did occur in the wild-type leaves but not in *var2-2* leaves (12, 19). These observations, together with the data provided in cyanobacteria, demonstrate that FtsH is a

Leaf variegation: a category of genetic mutation in plants in which a leaf segregates into green and white sectors

Chlorophyllic SC cell

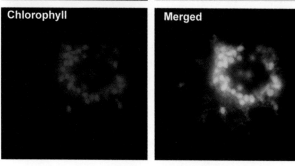

Lon4-GFP

20 µm

Chlorophyll

Merged

Non-chlorophyllic SL cell

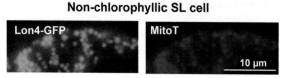

Lon4-GFP

MitoT

10 µm

Figure 3

GFP-transient assay using suspension-cultured tobacco cells with a *Lon4-GFP* fusion gene. (*Top panel*) A protoplast of chlorophyllic SC cells was transformed with a *GFP* gene fused to a putative transit peptide from *Arabidopsis Lon4*. GFP signals were colocalized with chlorophyll autofluorescence, suggesting that Lon4 targets chloroplasts. In addition, GFP signals were detected as granule bodies that likely corresponded to mitochondria. (*Bottom panel*) In fact, Lon4-GFP expressed in non-chlorophyllic SL cells colocalized with the signal from a mitochondria-specific probe, MitoTracker.

crucial factor in the PSII repair cycle. Based on genetic, biochemical, and physiological analyses, FtsH is proposed to be involved in two functions: (*a*) photoprotection as a major protease factor for the PSII repair, and (*b*) thylakoid formation at an early step of chloroplast development (19, 100, 132).

Lon PROTEASE

Lon was the first ATP-dependent protease found in *E. coli*. Deficiency of Lon results in accumulation of abnormal proteins and elevated sensitivity to DNA damage (31). Like FtsH, it contains the AAA and protease domains in one polypeptide but no transmembrane domain (96). Characteristic to Lon is its affinity to DNA, although the domain required for DNA binding is unknown (121). A ring-like structure with heptamer has been suggested in yeast mitochondria (119). Lon is therefore considered to form a complex typical of AAA proteins. A crystal structure of *E. coli* Lon was also determined recently and shown to form a hexameric ring with a catalytic Serine-Lysine dyad (15).

Homologs of Lon have been identified in higher plants (13, 102). In *Arabidopsis*, four genes have been detected as potentially encoding Lon based on a homology search (Lon1-4) (46). One of the four Lon proteins, Lon1, is specifically involved in the degradation of mitochondrial proteins during tapetum formation in anthers (102). Lon2 has a consensus-targeting signal to peroxisomes at the C terminus (called PTS1) and is phylogenetically associated with animal paralogs that were recently shown to reside in peroxisomes. A GFP assay using Lon2 targeted the protein into peroxisomes (A. Kato, unpublished results). A gene encoding Lon is not found in the genome sequence of *Synechocystis* sp. PCC 6803. Thus, whether Lon is present in chloroplasts remains controversial. However, a transient assay in my laboratory using tobacco cells with an N-terminal sequence from Lon4 (encoded in At3g05790) fused to GFP showed that Lon4 can be targeted to both chloroplasts and mitochondria (**Figure 3**). This result, together with immunological detection of Lon homologs in the stroma, indicates that Lon4 is most likely present in plastids and plays roles in protein degradation.

OTHER PROTEASES

E. coli has another type of ATP-dependent protease, HslUV, but no homologs of HslUV have been detected in photosynthetic organisms. Besides Clp, FtsH, and Lon,

ATP-independent protease of the Deg family play roles in protein degradation in plastids (41). DegP is a serine protease that forms a homotrimeric oligomer in *E. coli* and human (22). Two of the trimers further dimerize to form a hexamer (52). *E. coli* has three Deg proteases, Deg P, Q, S, each of which has one or two characteristic PDZ domains toward the C terminus (one in DegS and two in DegP and DegQ) that are necessary for protease-protease interactions and that possibly regulate recognition of substrate proteins. DegP also has a chaperone activity, and the switch between protease and chaperone activities can be accomplished by a temperature shift (24, 118). Similar to AAA proteases, Deg homologs are organized as a protein family in photosynthetic organisms (50, 109), with 16 homologs found in *Arabidopsis* based on the genome information (41, 116). Four of the *Arabidopsis* Deg homologs (Deg1, 2, 5, 8) are located in chloroplasts (17, 36), where they are peripherally attached to the thylakoid membrane. Deg1, 5, and 8 have been located on the luminal side and Deg2 has been located on the stromal side (36, 45, 104). No reports have been made so far on the effects of homozygous knockout mutations in any *Deg* genes in *Arabidopsis*. Expression of Deg proteins seems to be increased by abiotic stress such as salts, light, and temperature. Deg1 and Deg2 have been studied in detail in *Arabidopsis* (17, 36). In particular, DegP2 has been proposed to play a role in PSII repair through degrading photodamaged D1 in combination with FtsH, although genetic data confirming this role is lacking. Deg appears to play an indirect role in D1 degradation in *Synechocystis*. However, a mutant lacking all Deg proteases shows a slight sensitivity to high light (109), which raises the possibility that the PSII repair system in *Synechocystis* is different from that in *Arabidopsis* (78).

Other proteases have been identified in plastids, but their roles in protein degradation are poorly understood. EGY1 is an ATP-independent metalloprotease that is involved in chloroplast development (18). EGY1 has eight putative transmembrane domains presumably located in thylakoid membranes, and more interestingly, its catalytic center, represented by a zinc-binding motif, seems to be embedded inside the membrane. The function of EGY1 may be similar or equivalent to that of Rhomboid protease in yeast mitochondria (67), although homologs of Rhomboid other than EGY1 and EGY2 have been detected in *Arabidopsis*. Both cyanobacteria and chloroplasts possess homologs of bacterial SppA tightly associated with thylakoid membranes (56, 88, 114). SppA is an ATP-independent serine protease whose expression appears to be upregulated by light. CND41 is a tobacco protein identified as comprising nucleoid (it has an affinity for DNA and is located in the stroma) in suspension-cultured cells (74). It has aspartic protease activity and is induced by senescence (49, 73). *Arabidopsis* has two homologs whose functions are currently unclear. A stromal glutamyl endopeptidase (GEP) that can cleave in vitro a short peptide corresponding to the N-terminal part of Lhcb1 was recently found in pea (25). A protein homolog of GEP is present in *Arabidopsis* and appears to have a potential triad for serine proteases.

FUTURE PERSPECTIVES

As described in this review, the recent availability of genome information in model plant species has made it possible to determine the overall architecture of the proteolytic machineries in plastids, without knowing the substrates and biochemical properties the proteases involved. The identified proteases substantially accumulate in plastids at the basal level, meaning that their proteolytic activities must be strictly regulated. A combination of genetic and biochemical approaches, such as the use of T-DNA insertion mutants and suppressors, should greatly elucidate the regulatory mechanism. The phenotypes of these mutants (especially those without obvious phenotypes) need to be observed under different growth conditions and at different

Photodamage: oxidative damage to protein, DNA, and lipids, resulting from excess photochemical energy in the form of reactive oxygen species that are generated through photosynthetic electron transfer

development stages. Some questions that need to be answered are (*a*) does the lack of any one or multiple proteases affect plant growth under certain temperature/light conditions, and (*b*) can a protease act as a regulator of specific plastid types in different tissues? In addition, a comparison of the sequences and functions of the protease components in unicellular and multicellular organisms other than *Arabidopsis* will show how these machineries have evolved or have been conserved.

Many questions need to be answered. Although the basic structure of plastidic complexes is known, the proteolytic action of ATP-dependent proteases is poorly understood, mainly due to their low proteolytic activity in vitro. Determining the substrates of the proteases, and whether they are specific substrates is a challenging but important task. For example, FtsH is known to degrade photodamaged D1, but how it recognizes photodamaged or denatured substrates is unclear. Apparently, turnover of abundant proteins in chloroplasts such as Rubisco and Lhcb must be taken into consideration. If FtsH or Clp specifically degrades one of the sigma transcription factors in plastids, then these proteins may regulate chloroplast development. To fully understand the regulatory mechamism, characterization of protein profiles in the knockout mutants and in the different plastid types will help to identify the proteins involved in the key processes.

SUMMARY POINTS

1. Plastids contain more than 11 types of proteases. In *Arabidopsis*, these proteases are encoded by more than 50 genes.

2. Plastids contain three prokaryotic ATP-dependent proteases, Clp, FtsH, and Lon, as major enzymes for processive degradation.

3. Many isoforms of Clp subunits are present in plastids and some are plant-specific. The Clp protease core complex is heteromeric and each isomer seems to be required for plant viability.

4. Twelve FtsH isoforms are present in *Arabidopsis* plastids and form a hetero/homo complex. FtsH is involved in the repair cycle of Photosystem II.

5. Four FtsH isoforms (FtsH1, 2, 5, 8) are the major ones, and the presence of either FtsH1 or FtsH5 as well as either FtsH2 or FtsH8 is necessary for thylakoid development. Loss of FtsH2 and FtsH5 leads to a leaf-variegated phenotype.

FUTURE ISSUES TO BE RESOLVED

1. Multiple mutants for protease subunits or isomers need to be characterized, particularly under different environmental conditions. Substrates for each ATP-dependent protease and the mechanism of substrate recognition should be determined.

2. Differential functions of each isoform, especially those specific to plastids (such as ClpR and ClpS), should be examined.

3. Factors affecting proteolytic activity and/or associated with protease complexes need to be identified.

NOTE ADDED IN PROOF

Involvement of FtsH6 in the degradation of LHCII during high-light acclimation and senescence was recently reported by Želisko et al.

ACKNOWLEDGMENTS

The author thanks Dr. Ryo Matsushima for a critical reading of the manuscript, Eiko Miura for her help with preparing the figures, and Drs. Zach Adam, Adrian Clarke, Fumiyoshi Myouga, and Klaas van Wijk for sharing unpublished data on the mutants. The work from our group was supported by Grants-In-Aid for Scientific Research from MEXT (No. 16085207), the Okayama University scientific program "Establishment of Plant Health Science," and the Oohara Foundation.

LITERATURE CITED

1. Adam Z. 2000. Chloroplast proteases: possible regulators of gene expression? *Biochimie* 82:647–54

2. Adam Z, Adamska I, Nakabayashi K, Ostersetzer O, Haussuhl K, et al. 2001. Chloroplast and mitochondrial proteases in Arabidopsis. A proposed nomenclature. *Plant Physiol.* 125:1912–18

3. Adam Z, Clarke AK. 2002. Cutting edge of chloroplast proteolysis. *Trends Plant Sci.* 7:451–56

4. Adam Z, Zaltsman A, Sinvany-Villalobo G, Sakamoto W. 2005. FtsH proteases in chloroplasts and cyanobacteria. *Physiol. Plant* 123:386–90

5. Adamska I, Lindahl M, Roobol-Boza M, Andersson B. 1996. Degradation of the light-stress protein is mediated by an ATP-independent, serine-type protease under low-light conditions. *Eur. J. Biochem.* 236:591–99

6. Akiyama Y, Kihara A, Tokuda H, Ito K. 1996. FtsH (HflB) is an ATP-dependent protease selectively acting on SecY and some other membrane proteins. *J. Biol. Chem.* 271:31196–201

7. Anbudurai PR, Mor TS, Ohad I, Shestakov SV, Pakrasi HB. 1994. The *ctpA* gene encodes the C-terminal processing protease for the D1 protein of the photosystem II reaction center complex. *Proc. Natl. Acad. Sci. USA* 91:8082–86

8. Arlt H, Tauer R, Feldmann H, Neupert W, Langer T. 1996. The YTA10-12 complex, an AAA protease with chaperone-like activity in the inner membrane of mitochondria. *Cell* 85:875–85

9. Arnold I, Langer T. 2002. Membrane protein degradation by AAA proteases in mitochondria. *Biochim. Biophys. Acta* 1592:89–96

10. Aro EM, Virgin I, Andersson B. 1993. Photoinhibition of Photosystem II. Inactivation, protein damage and turnover. *Biochim. Biophys. Acta* 1143:113–34

11. Asada K. 1999. The water-water cycle in chloroplasts: Scavenging of active oxygens and dissipation of excess photons. *Annu. Rev. Plant Physiol. Plant Mol. Biol.* 50:601–39

12. Bailey S, Thompson E, Nixon PJ, Horton P, Mullineaux CW, et al. 2002. A critical role for the Var2 FtsH homologue of *Arabidopsis thaliana* in the photosystem II repair cycle in vivo. *J. Biol. Chem.* 277:2006–11

13. Barakat S, Pearce DA, Sherman F, Rapp WD. 1998. Maize contains a Lon protease gene that can partially complement a yeast *pim1*-deletion mutant. *Plant Mol. Biol.* 37:141–54

14. Bhushan S, Stahl A, Nilsson S, Lefebvre B, Seki M, et al. 2005. Catalysis, subcellular localization, expression and evolution of the targeting peptides degrading protease, AtPreP2. *Plant Cell Physiol.* 46:985–96

15. Botos I, Melnikov EE, Cherry S, Tropea JE, Khalatova AG, et al. 2004. The catalytic domain of *Escherichia coli* Lon protease has a unique fold and a Ser-Lys dyad in the active site. *J. Biol. Chem.* 279:8140–48

16. Chaal BK, Mould RM, Barbrook AC, Gray JC, Howe CJ. 1998. Characterization of a cDNA encoding the thylakoidal processing peptidase from *Arabidopsis thaliana*. Implications for the origin and catalytic mechanism of the enzyme. *J. Biol. Chem.* 273:689–92

17. Chassin Y, Kapri-Pardes E, Sinvany G, Arad T, Adam Z. 2002. Expression and characterization of the thylakoid lumen protease DegP1 from Arabidopsis. *Plant Physiol.* 130:857–64

18. Chen G, Bi YR, Li N. 2005. *EGY1* encodes a membrane-associated and ATP-independent metalloprotease that is required for chloroplast development. *Plant J.* 41:364–75

19. **Chen M, Choi Y, Voytas DF, Rodermel S. 2000. Mutations in the Arabidopsis *VAR2* locus cause leaf variegation due to the loss of a chloroplast FtsH protease. *Plant J.* 22:303–13**

20. Clarke AK, MacDonald TM, Sjögren LLE. 2005. The ATP-dependent Clp protease in chloroplasts of higher plants. *Physiol. Plant* 123:406–12

21. Clarke AK, Schelin J, Porankiewicz J. 1998. Inactivation of the *clpP1* gene for the proteolytic subunit of the ATP-dependent Clp protease in the cyanobacterium *Synechococcus* limits growth and light acclimation. *Plant Mol. Biol.* 37:791–801

22. Clausen T, Southan C, Ehrmann M. 2002. The Htr family of proteases: implications for protein composition and cell fate. *Mol. Cell* 10:443–55

22a. Constan D, Froehlich JE, Rangarajan S, Keegstra K. 2004. A stromal Hsp100 protein is required for normal chloroplast development and function in Arabidopsis. *Plant Physiol.* 136:3605–15

23. Dougan DA, Reid BG, Horwich AL, Bukau B. 2002. ClpS, a substrate modulator of the ClpAP machine. *Mol. Cell* 9:673–83

24. Ehrmann M, Clausen T. 2004. Proteolysis as a regulatory mechanism. *Annu. Rev. Genet.* 38:709–24

25. Forsberg J, Ström J, Kiesekbach T, Larsson H, Alexciev K, et al. 2005. Protease activities in the chloroplast capable of cleaving an LHCII N-terminal peptide. *Physiol. Plant* 123:21–29

26. Frickey T, Lupas AN. 2004. Phylogenetic analysis of AAA proteins. *J. Struct. Biol.* 146:2–10

27. **Friso G, Giacomelli L, Ytterberg AJ, Peltier JB, Rudella A, et al. 2004. In-depth analysis of the thylakoid membrane proteome of *Arabidopsis thaliana* chloroplasts: new proteins, new functions, and a plastid proteome database. *Plant Cell* 16:478–99**

28. Georgakopoulos JH, Sokolenko A, Arkas M, Sofou G, Herrmann RG, Argyroudi-Akoyunoglou JH. 2002. Proteolytic activity against the light-harvesting complex and the D1/D2 core proteins of Photosystem II in close association to the light-harvesting complex II trimer. *Biochim. Biophys. Acta* 1556:53–64

29. Gottesman S. 1996. Proteases and their targets in *Escherichia coli*. *Annu. Rev. Genet.* 30:465–506

30. Gottesman S, Wickner S, Maurizi MR. 1997. Protein quality control: triage by chaperones and proteases. *Genes Dev.* 11:815–23

One of the first reports on cloning *VAR2* locus-encoding FtsH2, whose mutation results in leaf variegation.

This paper describes a proteomic analysis of thylakoid proteins and other information on plastid protein database.

31. Gottesman S, Zipser D. 1978. Deg phenotype of *Escherichia coli lon* mutants. *J. Bacteriol.* 133:844–51

32. Grimaud R, Kessel M, Beuron F, Steven AC, Maurizi MR. 1998. Enzymatic and structural similarities between the *Escherichia coli* ATP-dependent proteases, ClpXP and ClpAP. *J. Biol. Chem.* 273:12476–81

33. Halperin T, Adam Z. 1996. Degradation of mistargeted OEE33 in the chloroplast stroma. *Plant Mol. Biol.* 30:925–33

34. Halperin T, Ostersetzer O, Adam Z. 2001. ATP-dependent association between subunits of Clp protease in pea chloroplasts. *Planta* 213:614–19

35. Halperin T, Zheng B, Itzhaki H, Clarke AK, Adam Z. 2001. Plant mitochondria contain proteolytic and regulatory subunits of the ATP-dependent Clp protease. *Plant Mol. Biol.* 45:461–68

36. Haußühl K, Andersson B, Adamska I. 2001. A chloroplast DegP2 protease performs the primary cleavage of the photodamaged D1 protein in plant photosystem II. *EMBO J.* 20:713–22

37. Heazlewood JL, Tonti-Filippini JS, Gout AM, Day DA, Whelan J, Millar AH. 2004. Experimental analysis of the Arabidopsis mitochondrial proteome highlights signaling and regulatory components, provides assessment of targeting prediction programs, and indicates plant-specific mitochondrial proteins. *Plant Cell* 16:241–56

38. Herman C, Thevenet D, D'Ari R, Bouloc P. 1995. Degradation of sigma 32, the heat shock regulator in *Escherichia coli*, is governed by HflB. *Proc. Natl. Acad. Sci. USA* 92:3516–20

39. Hoskins JR, Pak M, Maurizi MR, Wickner S. 1998. The role of the ClpA chaperone in proteolysis by ClpAP. *Proc. Natl. Acad. Sci. USA* 95:12135–40

40. Huang C, Wang S, Chen L, Lemieux C, Otis C, et al. 1994. The *Chlamydomonas* chloroplast *clpP* gene contains translated large insertion sequences and is essential for cell growth. *Mol. Gen. Genet.* 244:151–9

41. Huesgen RF, Schuhmann H, Adamska I. 2005. The family of Deg proteases in cyanobacteria and chloroplasts of higher plants. *Physiol. Plant* 123:413–20

42. Inagaki N, Maitra R, Satoh K, Pakrasi HB. 2001. Amino acid residues that are critical for in vivo catalytic activity of CtpA, the carbox5yl-terminal processing protease for the D1 protein of photosystem II. *J. Biol. Chem.* 276:30099–105

43. Ito K, Akiyama Y. 2005. Cellular Functions, mechanism of action, and regulation of FtsH protease. *Annu. Rev. Microbiol.* 59:211–31

44. Itoh R, Takano H, Ohta N, Miyagishima S, Kuroiwa H, Kuroiwa T. 1999. Two *ftsH*-family genes encoded in the nuclear and chloroplast genomes of the primitive red alga *Cyanidioschyzon merolae*. *Plant Mol. Biol.* 41:321–37

45. Itzhaki H, Naveh L, Lindahl M, Cook M, Adam Z. 1998. Identification and characterization of DegP, a serine protease associated with the luminal side of the thylakoid membrane. *J. Biol. Chem.* 273:7094–98

46. Janska H. 2005. ATP-dependent proteases in plant mitochondria: What do we know about them today? *Physiol. Plant* 123:399–405

47. Karata K, Inagawa T, Wilkinson AJ, Tatsuta T, Ogura T. 1999. Dissecting the role of a conserved motif (the second region of homology) in the AAA family of ATPases. Site-directed mutagenesis of the ATP-dependent protease FtsH. *J. Biol. Chem.* 274:26225–32

48. Kashino Y, Lauber WM, Carroll JA, Wang Q, Whitmarsh J, et al. 2002. Proteomic analysis of a highly active photosystem II preparation from the cyanobacterium *Synechocystis* sp. PCC 6803 reveals the presence of novel polypeptides. *Biochemistry* 41:8004–12

49. Kato Y, Murakami S, Yamamoto Y, Chatani H, Kondo Y, et al. 2004. The DNA-binding protease, CND41, and the degradation of ribulose-1,5-bisphosphate carboxylase/oxygenase in senescent leaves of tobacco. *Planta* 220:97–104

50. Kieselbach T, Funk C. 2003. The family of Deg/HtrA proteases: from *Escherichia coli* to *Arabidopsis*. *Physiol. Plant* 119:337–46

51. Kolodziejczak M, Kolaczkowska A, Szczesny B, Urantowka A, Knorpp C, et al. 2002. A higher plant mitochondrial homologue of the yeast m-AAA protease. Molecular cloning, localization, and putative function. *J. Biol. Chem.* 277:43792–98

51a. Komenda J, Barker M, Kuviková S, de Vries R, Mullineaux CW, et al. 2006. The FtsH protease, Slr0228, is important for quality control of Photosystem II in the thhylakoid membrane of *Synechocystis* PCC 6803. *J. Biol. Chem.* In press

51b. Kovacheva S, Bedard J, Patel R, Dudley P, Twell D, et al. 2005. *In vivo* studies on the roles of Tic110, Tic40 and Hsp93 during chloroplast protein import. *Plant J.* 41:412–28

52. Krojer T, Garrido-Franco M, Huber R, Ehrmann M, Clausen T. 2002. Crystal structure of DegP (HtrA) reveals a new protease-chaperone machine. *Nature* 416:455–59

53. Krzywda S, Brzozowski AM, Verma C, Karata K, Ogura T, Wilkinson AJ. 2002. The crystal structure of the AAA domain of the ATP-dependent protease FtsH of Escherichia coli at 1.5 Å resolution. *Structure* 10:1073–83

54. Kuroda H, Maliga P. 2003. The plastid *clpP1* protease gene is essential for plant development. *Nature* 425:86–89

55. Langer T. 2000. AAA proteases: cellular machines for degrading membrane proteins. *Trends Biochem. Sci.* 25:247–51

56. Lensch M, Herrmann RG, Sokolenko A. 2001. Identification and characterization of SppA, a novel light-inducible chloroplast protease complex associated with thylakoid membranes. *J. Biol. Chem.* 276:33645–51

57. Liao DI, Qian J, Chisholm DA, Jordan DB, Diner BA. 2000. Crystal structures of the photosystem II D1 C-terminal processing protease. *Nat. Struct. Biol.* 7:749–53

58. Lindahl M, Spetea C, Hundal T, Oppenheim AB, Adam Z, Andersson B. 2000. The thylakoid FtsH protease plays a role in the light-induced turnover of the photosystem II D1 protein. *Plant Cell* 12:419–31

59. **Lindahl M, Tabak S, Cseke L, Pichersky E, Andersson B, Adam Z. 1996. Identification, characterization, and molecular cloning of a homologue of the bacterial FtsH protease in chloroplasts of higher plants. *J. Biol. Chem.* 271:29329–34**

60. Lindahl M, Yang DH, Andersson B. 1995. Regulatory proteolysis of the major light-harvesting chlorophyll *a/b* protein of photosystem II by a light-induced membrane-associated enzymic system. *Eur. J. Biochem.* 231:503–9

61. Lupas AN, Koretke KK. 2003. Bioinformatic analysis of ClpS, a protein module involved in prokaryotic and eukaryotic protein degradation. *J. Struct. Biol.* 141:77–83

62. Majeran W, Olive J, Drapier D, Vallon O, Wollman FA. 2001. The light sensitivity of ATP synthase mutants of *Chlamydomonas reinhardtii*. *Plant Physiol.* 126:421–33

63. Majeran W, Wollman FA, Vallon O. 2000. Evidence for a role of ClpP in the degradation of the chloroplast cytochrome b_6f complex. *Plant Cell* 12:137–50

64. Mann NH, Novac N, Mullineaux CW, Newman J, Bailey S, Robinson C. 2000. Involvement of an FtsH homologue in the assembly of functional photosystem I in the cyanobacterium *Synechocystis* sp. PCC 6803. *FEBS Lett* 479:72–77

65. Martin W, Rujan T, Richly E, Hansen A, Cornelsen S, et al. 2002. Evolutionary analysis of Arabidopsis, cyanobacterial, and chloroplast genomes reveals plastid phylogeny and thousands of cyanobacterial genes in the nucleus. *Proc. Natl. Acad. Sci. USA* 99:12246–51

The first report on the identification of an FtsH homolog in chloroplasts.

66. Maurizi MR, Clark WP, Kim SH, Gottesman S. 1990. ClpP represents a unique family of serine proteases. *J. Biol. Chem.* 265:12546–52

67. McQuibban GA, Saurya S, Freeman M. 2003. Mitochondrial membrane remodelling regulated by a conserved rhomboid protease. *Nature* 423:537–41

68. Melis A. 1999. Photosystem-II damage and repair cycle in chloroplasts: what modulates the rate of photodamge *in vivo*? *Trends Plant Sci.* 4:130–35

69. Minagawa J, Takahashi Y. 2004. Structure, function and assembly of Photosystem II and its light-harvesting proteins. *Photosynth. Res.* 82:241–63

70. Misumi O, Matsuzaki M, Nozaki H, Miyagishima SY, Mori T, et al. 2005. *Cyanidioschyzon merolae* genome. A tool for facilitating comparable studies on organelle biogenesis in photosynthetic eukaryotes. *Plant Physiol.* 137:567–85

71. Moberg P, Stahl A, Bhushan S, Wright SJ, Eriksson A, et al. 2003. Characterization of a novel zinc metalloprotease involved in degrading targeting peptides in mitochondria and chloroplasts. *Plant J.* 36:616–28

72. Moon J, Parry G, Estelle M. 2004. The ubiquitin-proteasome pathway and plant development. *Plant Cell* 16:3181–95

73. Murakami S, Kondo Y, Nakano T, Sato F. 2000. Protease activity of CND41, a chloroplast nucleoid DNA-binding protein, isolated from cultured tobacco cells. *FEBS Lett* 468:15–18

74. Nakano T, Murakami S, Shoji T, Yoshida S, Yamada Y, Sato F. 1997. A novel protein with DNA binding activity from tobacco chloroplast nucleoids. *Plant Cell* 9:1673–82

75. Nakashima K, Kiyosue T, Yamaguchi-Shinozaki K, Shinozaki K. 1997. A nuclear gene, *erd1*, encoding a chloroplast-targeted Clp protease regulatory subunit homolog is not only induced by water stress but also developmentally up-regulated during senescence in *Arabidopsis thaliana*. *Plant J.* 12:851–61

76. Neuwald AF, Aravind L, Spouge JL, Koonin EV. 1999. AAA⁺: A class of chaperone-like ATPases associated with the assembly, operation, and disassembly of protein complexes. *Genome Res.* 9:27–43

77. Nielsen E, Akita M, Davila-Aponte J, Keegstra K. 1997. Stable association of chloroplastic precursors with protein translocation complexes that contain proteins from both envelope membranes and a stromal Hsp100 molecular chaperone. *EMBO J.* 16:935–46

78. Nixon PJ, Barker M, Boehm M, de Vries R, Komenda J. 2005. FtsH-mediated repair of the photosystem II complex in response to light stress. *J. Exp. Bot.* 56:357–63

79. Oelmuller R, Herrmann RG, Pakrasi HB. 1996. Molecular studies of CtpA, the carboxyl-terminal processing protease for the D1 protein of the photosystem II reaction center in higher plants. *J. Biol. Chem.* 271:21848–52

80. Ogura T, Wilkinson AJ. 2001. AAA⁺ superfamily ATPases: common structure–diverse function. *Genes Cells* 6:575–97

81. Ostersetzer O, Adam Z. 1996. Effects of light and temperature on expression of ClpC, the regulatory subunit of chloroplastic Clp protease, in pea seedlings. *Plant Mol. Biol.* 31:673–76

82. Ostersetzer O, Adam Z. 1997. Light-stimulated degradation of an unassembled Rieske FeS protein by a thylakoid-bound protease: the possible role of the FtsH protease. *Plant Cell* 9:957–65

83. Ostersetzer O, Tabak S, Yarden O, Shapira R, Adam Z. 1996. Immunological detection of proteins similar to bacterial proteases in higher plant chloroplasts. *Eur. J. Biochem.* 236:932–36

84. Park S, Rodermel SR. 2004. Mutations in ClpC2/Hsp100 suppress the requirement for FtsH in thylakoid membrane biogenesis. *Proc. Natl. Acad. Sci. USA* 101:12765–70

85. Patel S, Latterich M. 1998. The AAA team: related ATPases with diverse functions. *Trends Cell Biol.* 8:65–71

This reports on the detailed proteomic analysis of the Clp protease complex in chloroplasts and mitochondria.

86. Peltier JB, Ripoll DR, Friso G, Rudella A, Cai Y, et al. 2004. Clp protease complexes from photosynthetic and non-photosynthetic plastids and mitochondria of plants, their predicted three-dimensional structures, and functional implications. *J. Biol. Chem.* 279:4768–81

87. Peltier JB, Ytterberg J, Liberles DA, Roepstorff P, van Wijk KJ. 2001. Identification of a 350-kDa ClpP protease complex with 10 different Clp isoforms in chloroplasts of *Arabidopsis thaliana. J. Biol. Chem.* 276:16318–27

88. Pojidaeva E, Zinchenko V, Shestakov SV, Sokolenko A. 2004. Involvement of the SppA1 peptidase in acclimation to saturating light intensities in *Synechocystis* sp. strain PCC 6803. *J. Bacteriol.* 186:3991–99

89. Porankiewicz J, Schelin J, Clarke AK. 1998. The ATP-dependent Clp protease is essential for acclimation to UV-B and low temperature in the cyanobacterium *Synechococcus. Mol. Microbiol.* 29:275–83

90. Porankiewicz J, Wang J, Clarke AK. 1999. New insights into the ATP-dependent Clp protease: *Escherichia coli* and beyond. *Mol. Microbiol.* 32:449–58

91. Richly E, Leister D. 2004. An improved prediction of chloroplast proteins reveals diversities and commonalities in the chloroplast proteomes of Arabidopsis and rice. *Gene* 329:11–16

92. Richter S, Lamppa GK. 1998. A chloroplast processing enzyme functions as the general stromal processing peptidase. *Proc. Natl. Acad. Sci. USA* 95:7463–68

93. Richter S, Lamppa GK. 2003. Structural properties of the chloroplast stromal processing peptidase required for its function in transit peptide removal. *J. Biol. Chem.* 278:39497–502

94. Richter S, Zhong R, Lamppa G. 2005. Function of the stromal processing peptidase in the chloroplast import pathway. *Physiol. Plant* 123:362–68

95. Roose JL, Pakrasi HB. 2004. Evidence that D1 processing is required for manganese binding and extrinsic protein assembly into photosystem II. *J. Biol. Chem.* 279:45417–22

This paper describes the cloning of the *VAR1* locus encoding FtsH5, whose mutation results in leaf variegation.

96. Rotanova TV, Melnikov EE, Khalatova AG, Makhovskaya OV, Botos I, et al. 2004. Classification of ATP-dependent proteases Lon and comparison of the active sites of their proteolytic domains. *Eur. J. Biochem.* 271:4865–71

97. Saikawa N, Akiyama Y, Ito K. 2004. FtsH exists as an exceptionally large complex containing HflKC in the plasma membrane of *Escherichia coli. J. Struct. Biol.* 146:123–29

98. Sakamoto W. 2003. Leaf-variegated mutations and their responsible genes in *Arabidopsis thaliana. Genes Genet. Syst.* 78:1–9

99. Sakamoto W, Miura E, Kaji Y, Okuno T, Nishizono M, Ogura T. 2004. Allelic characterization of the leaf-variegated mutation *var2* identifies the conserved amino acid residues of FtsH that are important for ATP hydrolysis and proteolysis. *Plant Mol. Biol.* 56:705–16

This paper describes the presence of nine FtsH homologs in chloroplasts by GFP assay and describes the formation of the homo/hetero FtsH complexes.

100. Sakamoto W, Tamura T, Hanba-Tomita Y, Murata M. 2002. The *VAR1* locus of *Arabidopsis* encodes a chloroplastic FtsH and is responsible for leaf variegation in the mutant alleles. *Genes Cells* 7:769–80

101. Sakamoto W, Zaltsman A, Adam Z, Takahashi Y. 2003. Coordinated regulation and complex formation of YELLOWVARIEGATED1 and YELLOWVARIEGATED2, chloroplastic FtsH metalloproteases involved in the repair cycle of photosystem II in Arabidopsis thylakoid membranes. *Plant Cell* 15:2843–55

102. Sarria R, Lyznik A, Vallejos CE, Mackenzie SA. 1998. A cytoplasmic male sterility-associated mitochondrial peptide in common bean is post-translationally regulated. *Plant Cell* 10:1217–28

103. Schelin J, Lindmark F, Clarke AK. 2002. The *clpP* multigene family for the ATP-dependent Clp protease in the cyanobacterium *Synechococcus*. *Microbiology* 148:2255–65

104. Schubert M, Petersson UA, Haas BJ, Funk C, Schroder WP, Kieselbach T. 2002. Proteome map of the chloroplast lumen of *Arabidopsis thaliana*. *J. Biol. Chem.* 277:8354–65

105. Seo S, Okamoto M, Iwai T, Iwano M, Fukui K, et al. 2000. Reduced levels of chloroplast FtsH protein in tobacco mosaic virus-infected tobacco leaves accelerate the hypersensitive reaction. *Plant Cell* 12:917–32

106. Shackleton JB, Robinson C. 1991. Transport of proteins into chloroplasts. The thylakoidal processing peptidase is a signal-type peptidase with stringent substrate requirements at the -3 and -1 positions. *J. Biol. Chem.* 266:12152–56

107. Shanklin J, DeWitt ND, Flanagan JM. 1995. The stroma of higher plant plastids contain ClpP and ClpC, functional homologs of *Escherichia coli* ClpP and ClpA: an archetypal two-component ATP-dependent protease. *Plant Cell* 7:1713–22

108. Shikanai T, Shimizu K, Ueda K, Nishimura Y, Kuroiwa T, Hashimoto T. 2001. The chloroplast *clpP* gene, encoding a proteolytic subunit of ATP-dependent protease, is indispensable for chloroplast development in tobacco. *Plant Cell Physiol.* 42:264–73

109. Silva P, Choi YJ, Hassan HA, Nixon PJ. 2002. Involvement of the HtrA family of proteases in the protection of the cyanobacterium *Synechocystis* PCC 6803 from light stress and in the repair of photosystem II. *Philos. Trans. Roy. Soc. London Ser. B. Biol. Sci.* 357:1461–67

110. Silva P, Thompson E, Bailey S, Kruse O, Mullineaux CW, et al. 2003. FtsH is involved in the early stages of repair of photosystem II in Synechocystis sp PCC 6803. *Plant Cell* 15:2152–64

111. Sinvany-Villalobo G, Davydov O, Ben-Ari G, Zaltsman A, Raskind A, Adam Z. 2004. Expression in multigene families. Analysis of chloroplast and mitochondrial proteases. *Plant Physiol.* 135:1336–45

112. Sjögren LL, MacDonald TM, Sutinen S, Clarke AK. 2004. Inactivation of the *clpC1* gene encoding a chloroplast Hsp100 molecular chaperone causes growth retardation, leaf chlorosis, lower photosynthetic activity, and a specific reduction in photosystem content. *Plant Physiol.* 136:4114–26

113. Smalle J, Vierstra RD. 2004. The ubiquitin 26S proteasome proteolytic pathway. *Annu. Rev. Plant Biol.* 55:555–90

114. Sokolenko A. 2005. SppA peptidases: family diversity from heterotrophic bacteria to photoautotrophic eukaryotes. *Physiol. Plant* 123:391–98

115. Sokolenko A, Lerbs-Mache S, Altschmied L, Herrmann RG. 1998. Clp protease complexes and their diversity in chloroplasts. *Planta* 207:286–95

116. Sokolenko A, Pojidaeva E, Zinchenko V, Panichkin V, Glaser VM, et al. 2002. The gene complement for proteolysis in the cyanobacterium *Synechocystis* sp. PCC 6803 and *Arabidopsis thaliana* chloroplasts. *Curr. Genet.* 41:291–310

117. Spetea C, Hundal T, Lohmann F, Andersson B. 1999. GTP bound to chloroplast thylakoid membranes is required for light-induced, multienzyme degradation of the photosystem II D1 protein. *Proc. Natl. Acad. Sci. USA* 96:6547–52

118. Spiess C, Beil A, Ehrmann M. 1999. A temperature-dependent switch from chaperone to protease in a widely conserved heat shock protein. *Cell* 97:339–47

First report on the identification of the Clp subunit proteins in higher plant chloroplasts.

This paper describes extensive expression studies of protease genes in chloroplasts and mitochondria.

This describes protease genes in *Synechocystis* sp. PCC6803 and their homologs in *Arabidopsis*.

119. Stahlberg H, Kutejova E, Suda K, Wolpensinger B, Lustig A, et al. 1999. Mitochondrial Lon of *Saccharomyces cerevisiae* is a ring-shaped protease with seven flexible subunits. *Proc. Natl. Acad. Sci. USA* 96:6787–90

120. Steglich G, Neupert W, Langer T. 1999. Prohibitins regulate membrane protein degradation by the m-AAA protease in mitochondria. *Mol. Cell Biol* 19:3435–42

121. Suzuki CK, Rep M, van Dijl JM, Suda K, Grivell LA, Schatz G. 1997. ATP-dependent proteases that also chaperone protein biogenesis. *Trends Biochem. Sci.* 22:118–23

122. Takechi K, Sodmergen, Murata M, Motoyoshi F, Sakamoto W. 2000. The *YELLOW VARIEGATED (VAR2)* locus encodes a homologue of FtsH, an ATP-dependent protease in Arabidopsis. *Plant Cell Physiol.* 41:1334–46

123. Tomoyasu T, Yuki T, Morimura S, Mori H, Yamanaka K, et al. 1993. The *Escherichia coli* FtsH protein is a prokaryotic member of a protein family of putative ATPases involved in membrane functions, cell cycle control, and gene expression. *J. Bacteriol.* 175:1344–51

124. Tomoyasu T, Yuki T, Morimura S, Mori H, Yamanaka K, et al. 1995. *Escherichia coli* FtsH is a membrane-bound, ATP-dependent protease which degrades the heat shock transcription factor σ^{32}. *EMBO J.* 14:2551–60

124a. Urantowka A, Knorpp C, Olczak T, Kolodziejczak M, Janska H. 2005. Plant mitochondria contain at least two *i*-AAA-like complexes. *Plant Mol. Biol.* 59:239–52

125. Vierstra RD. 1996. Proteolysis in plants: mechanisms and functions. *Plant Mol. Biol.* 32:275–302

126. Wang J, Hartling JA, Flanagan JM. 1997. The structure of ClpP at 2.3 Å resolution suggests a model for ATP-dependent proteolysis. *Cell* 91:447–56

127. Wickner S, Maurizi MR, Gottesman S. 1999. Posttranslational quality control: folding, refolding, and degrading proteins. *Science* 286:1888–93

128. Wollman FA, Minai L, Nechushtai R. 1999. The biogenesis and assembly of photosynthetic proteins in thylakoid membranes1. *Biochim. Biophys. Acta* 1411:21–85

129. Yang DH, Webster J, Adam Z, Lindahl M, Andersson B. 1998. Induction of acclimative proteolysis of the light-harvesting chlorophyll *a/b* protein of photosystem II in response to elevated light intensities. *Plant Physiol.* 118:827–34

130. Yu F, Park S, Rodermel SR. 2004. The Arabidopsis FtsH metalloprotease gene family: interchangeability of subunits in chloroplast oligomeric complexes. *Plant J.* 37:864–76

131. Yu F, Park S, Rodermel SR. 2005. Functional redundancy of AtFtsH metalloproteases in thylakoid membrane complexes. *Plant Physiol.* 138:1957–66

132. Zaltsman A, Feder A, Adam Z. 2005. Developmental and light effects on the accumulation of FtsH protease in Arabidopsis chloroplasts - implications for thylakoid formation and photosystem II maintenance. *Plant J.* 42:609–17

132a. Zaltsman A, Ori N, Adam Z. 2005. Two types of FtsH protease subunits are required for chloroplast biogenesis and Photosystem II repair in Arabidopsis. *Plant Cell* 17:2782–90

133. Zheng B, Halperin T, Hruskova-Heidingsfeldova O, Adam Z, Clarke AK. 2002. Characterization of chloroplast Clp proteins in Arabidopsis: Localization, tissue specificity and stress responses. *Physiol. Plant* 114:92–101

134. Zhong R, Wan J, Jin R, Lamppa G. 2003. A pea antisense gene for the chloroplast stromal processing peptidase yields seedling lethals in Arabidopsis: survivors show defective GFP import in vivo. *Plant J.* 34:802–12

135. Żelisko A, Jackowski G. 2004. Senescence-dependent degradation of Lhcb3 is mediated by a thylakoid membrane-bound protease. *J Plant Physiol.* 161:1157–70

RELATED RESOURCES

Apel K, Hirt H. 2004. Reactive oxygen species: metabolism, oxidative stress, and signal transduction. *Annu. Rev. Plant Biol.* 55: 373–99

Gottesman S. 2003. Proteolysis in bacterial regulatory circuits. *Annu. Rev. Cell Dev. Biol.* 19: 565–87

Leon P, Arroyo A, Mackenzie S. 1998. Nuclear control of plastid and mitochondrial development in higher plants. *Annu. Rev. Plant Physiol. Plant Mol. Biol.* 49: 453–80

Merchant S, Dreyfuss BW. 1998. Posttranslational assembly of photosynthetic metalloproteins. *Annu. Rev. Plant Physiol. Plant Mol. Biol.* 49: 25–51

Molybdenum Cofactor Biosynthesis and Molybdenum Enzymes

Günter Schwarz and Ralf R. Mendel

Institute of Plant Biology, Technical University Braunschweig, 38023 Braunschweig, Germany; email: gschwarz@uni-koeln.de, r.mendel@tu-bs.de

Annu. Rev. Plant Biol.
2006. 57:623–47

The *Annual Review of Plant Biology* is online at plant.annualreviews.org

doi: 10.1146/
annurev.arplant.57.032905.105437

First published online as a
Review in Advance on
February 7, 2006

1543-5008/06/
0602-0623$20.00

Key Words

molybdopterin, nitrate reductase, sulfite oxidase, xanthine dehydrogenase, aldehyde oxidase

Abstract

The molybdenum cofactor (Moco) forms the active site of all eukaryotic molybdenum (Mo) enzymes. Moco consists of molybdenum covalently bound to two sulfur atoms of a unique tricyclic pterin moiety referred to as molybdopterin. Moco is synthesized from GTP by an ancient and conserved biosynthetic pathway that can be divided into four steps involving the biosynthetic intermediates cyclic pyranopterin monophosphate, molybdopterin, and adenylated molybdopterin. In a fifth step, sulfuration or bond formation between Mo and a protein cysteine result in two different catalytic Mo centers. There are four Mo enzymes in plants: (*1*) nitrate reductase catalyzes the first and rate-limiting step in nitrate assimilation and is structurally similar to the recently identified, (*2*) peroxisomal sulfite oxidase that detoxifies excessive sulfite. (*3*) Aldehyde oxidase catalyzes the last step of abscisic acid biosynthesis, and (*4*) xanthine dehydrogenase is essential for purine degradation and stress response.

Contents

Mo: molybdenum

Molybdenum
cofactor (Moco):
forms the active site
of all eukaryotic Mo
enzymes

MPT:
molybdopterin/
metal-binding pterin

INTRODUCTION

It has long been known that the transition element molybdenum (Mo) is an essential micronutrient for plants, animals, and microorganisms. With one exception, all Mo-dependent enzymes use the metal in the form of Mo cofactor (Moco), which consists of Mo covalently bound to the dithiolate moiety of a tricyclic pterin moiety referred to as molybdopterin (MPT) (**Figure 1**) (105). The other type of Mo-containing cofactor is exclusively found in nitrogenase, forming the so-called iron-Mo cofactor (FeMoco) (3). The task of the pterin is to position the catalytic Mo atom correctly within the active center, to control its redox behavior, and probably to partici-

pate in the electron transfer to or from the Mo atom.

Moco-containing enzymes catalyze important redox reactions in the global carbon, sulfur, and nitrogen cycles (41). More than 40—mostly bacterial—Mo enzymes are described in nature, but only four occur in plants. They are classified into two families depending on the coordination chemistry of the Mo ligand (40, 53) (**Figure 1**): Nitrate reductase (NR) catalyzes the first and rate-limiting step in nitrate assimilation (13) and together with sulfite oxidase (SO) forms a class of Mo enzymes in which the Mo atom is covalently bound to a strictly conserved cysteine residue (**Figure 1a**). Xanthine dehydrogenase (XDH) is involved in purine catabolism and, together with aldehyde oxidase (AO), belongs to a second class of Mo enzymes (26, 121) that share a third terminal sulfur ligand (**Figure 1b**). To complete the catalytic cycle, Mo enzymes harbor an intramolecular electron transport chain from or to the substrate using other prosthetic groups as cofactors and cosubstrates such as heme, Fe-S-clusters, FAD, or NADH.

Genetics of the Molybdenum Cofactor

The investigation of Mo metabolism started with the genetic analysis of mutants of the filamentous fungus *Aspergillus nidulans* (101) that were defective in NR. Cove & Pateman (17) isolated NR-deficient mutants that showed a simultaneous loss of two Mo-dependent enzymes, NR and XDH. As Mo was the only link between those two otherwise very different enzymes, the authors suggested that both enzymes share a common Mo-related cofactor. In the following years, similar mutants were described for *Escherichia coli* (27), *Drosophila melanogaster* (135), several higher plants (92), and humans (48). As in all organisms, up to six different genetic complementation groups have identified the existence of a multistep biosynthetic pathway of Moco was proposed (79).

a

Molybdenum cofactor

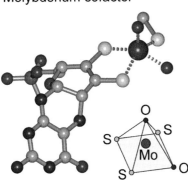

Nitrate reductase
Sulfite oxidase

b

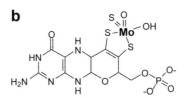

Molybdenum cofactor

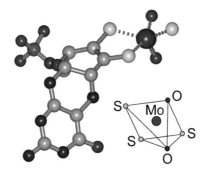

Xanthine dehydrogenase
Aldehyde oxidase

Figure 1

Structure and coordination of the molybdenum cofactor (Moco) in enzymes of the (*a*) nitrate reductase/sulfite oxidase (NR/SO) and (*b*) xanthine dehydrogenase/aldehyde oxidase (XDH/AO) family. Chemical structure and three-dimensional projection of Moco (ball-and-stick mode) as seen in the crystal structure of *Pichia angusta* NR Molybdenum (Mo) domain (24) and bovine xanthine oxidase (99). Due to the high conservation between animal and plant XDH (39), the Mo center in the plant enzyme should be similar to the bovine one. Both types of cofactors show a pyramidal geometry of the Mo center with the apical oxygen pointing upward in one case (NR/SO) or pointing downward in the other case (AO/XDH), as depicted by the cartoon under each structure.

A mutational block of Moco biosynthesis leads to the loss of essential metabolic functions because all enzymes that depend on Mo lose their activity, which ultimately causes the organism to die. In contrast to animals, Moco mutants of plants can be kept alive on media containing reduced nitrogen as a N-source, so one can argue that the loss of NR activity is more dramatic for the plant than the lack of the other three Mo enzymes (XDH, AO, SO). Moco mutants have been described in numerous plants, e.g., in tobacco (82), *Nicotiana plumbaginifolia* (92), *Arabidopsis* (11, 18), barley (54), and the green alga *Chlamydomonas reinhardtii* (23). The phenotype of plant Moco mutants was best studied in *N. plumbaginifolia*, where all six Moco-

specific genetic loci (*cnx*A-*cnx*F) showed a similar morphology strongly deviating from that of the wild type: stunted growth, chlorosis of leaves, and small, narrow, and crinkled leaves (25), which is probably caused by the impairment of the plants to synthesize the phytohormones abscisic acid (ABA) and indole acetic acid due to the loss of AO activities (121).

Among eukaryotes, the molecular, biochemical, and genetic analysis of Moco mutants was most advanced in higher plants. These results also formed the basis to decipher Moco biosynthesis in humans (108), where Moco deficiency is a severe genetic disease leading to death in early childhood (45). It turned out that the pathways of Moco

Nitrate reductase (NR): catalyzes the first and rate-limiting step in nitrate assimilation

Sulfite oxidase (SO): a peroxisomal enzyme that detoxifies excessive sulfite, thereby producing hydrogen peroxide

Xanthine dehydrogenase (XDH): essential for purine degradation and stress response

Aldehyde oxidase (AO): catalyzes the final step in the biosynthesis of the phytohormone abscisic acid

Moco biosynthesis: conserved and ancient biosynthetic pathway that starts from GTP and consists of four steps

ABA: abscisic acid

biosynthesis showed many similarities in both organisms and therefore we compare them whenever appropriate.

Chemistry of the Molybdenum Cofactor

Using the crude protein extract of the *Neurospora crassa nit-1* mutant (126), Nason and coworkers (51, 93, 94) provided the first biochemical evidence for the existence of a cofactor common to all Mo enzymes. They reconstituted the activity of inactive apo-NR by low-molecular-weight fractions derived from denatured Mo enzymes of plant, mammalian, or bacterial origin, demonstrating the incorporation of a ubiquitous and universal cofactor. Consequently, nitrogenase, as the only Mo-dependent enzyme that contains no Moco, did not release a *nit-1* positive activity (102) because of its unique FeMoco. The observed complementation of *nit-1* apo-NR by Moco from different sources served as the basis to develop a sensitive biological in vitro assay referred to as the *nit-1* assay for cofactor determination.

Nason et al. (94) found that the reconstituting activity released from diverse Mo enzymes was very labile, with a lifetime of a few minutes, indicating the oxygen-sensitive nature of Moco. The need to include an excess of molybdate (80, 81, 133) into the reconstitution mixture indicated a strong tendency of Moco to lose Mo whereas sulfhydryl re-

active agents totally inhibited Moco activity in the *nit-1* assay (2, 78, 81, 133), thus pointing sulfur's participation in metal coordination. Due to the labile nature of Moco and its high sensitivity to air oxidation, structural elucidation was done by using degradation or oxidation products of Moco, thereby revealing the pterin nature of Moco and its C6 substitution with a unique four-carbon side chain (46) that coordinates the metal via a dithiolate group (**Figure 1**). Crystal structures of different Mo enzymes confirmed the core structure of Moco and helped to clarify its redox state (53). Due to the formation of a third pyrano ring between the C3′ hydroxy group and the pterin C7 atom, a fully reduced hydrogenated pterin (tetrahydro state) is formed (96).

MOLYBDENUM COFACTOR BIOSYNTHESIS

Already in pregenomic times, a detailed mutant characterization contributed substantially to our understanding of the genetics and biochemistry of Moco biosynthesis in bacteria, plants, fungi, and humans. Investigations such as phenotype suppression by external molybdate or reconstitution experiments mixing cell-free protein extracts of different complementation groups provided evidence for two intermediates of the biosynthetic pathway. Furthermore, defects in molybdate uptake and processing could be assigned to

---

Figure 2

Biosynthesis of molybdenum cofactor (Moco). Shown are the known biosynthetic intermediates of eukaryotic Moco biosynthesis. Moco synthesis can be divided into four steps. For molybdopterin (MPT) and MPT-AMP, the ligands of the dithiolate sulfurs are indicated by an "R," as it is currently unknown at which state copper is bound to the dithiolate. Upon molybdenum (Mo) insertion, it is also not clear how many oxo ligands are bound to the metal. Therefore, two Mo-oxo ligands are depicted and a third line indicates an additional ligand. The plant proteins catalyzing each step are depicted. Functional properties like Fe-S-clusters (two oxygen-labile [4Fe-4S] clusters) in Cnx2, the use of S-adenosyl methionine (SAM), adenylation, and sulfuration of the small subunit of MPT synthase (Cnx7) are indicated, based on the functional characterization of homologous proteins from human and bacteria that are shown in red and black, respectively. All substrates/cosubstrates are indicated in blue. The in vivo source of MPT sulfur is not known yet. Steps three and four in plant and human are catalyzed by the individual domains of Cnx1 and Gephyrin (G and E).

specific mutants. The first model of Moco biosynthesis was derived from *E. coli*, for which five Moco-specific operons are known (105).

In all organisms studied so far, Moco is synthesized by a conserved biosynthetic pathway that can be divided into five steps, according to the biosynthetic intermediates cyclic pyranopterin monophophate, MPT, adenylated MPT, and Moco (**Figure 2**). In eukaryotes, always six gene products catalyzing Moco biosynthesis have been identified

cPMP: cyclic
pyranopterin
monophosphate

in plants (83), fungi (6, 85, 131, 132), and humans (107, 127, 128). Genes and gene products were named in plants according to the *cnx* nomenclature (cofactor for nitrate reductase and xanthine dehydrogenase) introduced for the fungal mutants with the mutants labeled by letters (*cnxA-F*) and the cDNAs labeled by numbers (*cnx1-3, cnx5-7*). For human Moco synthetic genes, Reiss and coworkers (107) introduced a different MOCS (molybdenum cofactor synthesis) nomenclature.

Moco biosynthesis was studied in different depths using proteins from plant, bacterial, and human sources. In general, steps 1 and 2 are intensively studied in bacteria and humans whereas the last two steps as well as Moco maturation are best studied in the plant system.

Step 1: Conversion of GTP into cPMP

MPT is the only four-carbon side chain substituted pterin known so far, and several other pteridines such as biopterin have three-carbon side chains. Two pathways are known for the synthesis of pteridines (130) and flavins (8) that start with the conversion of GTP by the enzymes cyclohydrolyse I and II, respectively, whereas Moco synthesis depends on a third route also starting with GTP. Based on labeling studies in *E. coli*, a complex reaction sequence (138) starting from GTP (32) generates the first stable intermediate cyclic pyranopterin monophosphate (cPMP). The main difference in Moco synthesis is that the C8 atom of the purine base is inserted between the 2′ and 3′ ribose carbon atoms, thus forming the four-carbon atoms (all derived from the ribose) of the pyrano ring (109, 138).

In *A. thaliana*, cPMP synthesis is catalyzed by Cnx2 and Cnx3 (**Figure 2**). Both *cnx2* and *cnx3* were identified using the approach of functional complementation of *E. coli* Moco mutants *moaA* and *moaC*, thus demonstrating the functional conservation between bacterial and plant Moco synthesis (43). Cnx2 and homologs belong to the family of S-adenosyl methionine (SAM)-dependent radical enzymes. Members of this large family catalyze the formation of protein and/or substrate radicals by reductive cleavage of SAM by a [4Fe-4S] cluster (125). Although biochemical and structural data on the function of Cnx2-homologous proteins MoaA and MOCS1A were accumulated during the past few years, nothing is known about the function of Cnx3 and its homologs. Bacterial MoaC forms hexamers with a hypothetical active site at the interface of two monomers (137). Cnx2 and Cnx3 are larger than their bacterial counterparts, which is attributed to N-terminal extensions carrying hypothetical targeting motifs for mitochondrial or chloroplast transport. However, import studies could not demonstrate the transport of Cnx2 or Cnx3 in any of the two organelles (43). The fact that Cnx2 should have an [4Fe-4S] cluster similar to MOCS1A (31) makes it a feasible candidate for mitochondrial import as this is the major site of eukaryotic Fe-S-cluster synthesis (68).

Functional characterization of proteins involved in the first step of Moco biosynthesis started with human MOCS1A and MOCS1B (33), which are derived from a bicistronic cDNA that is spliced in a complex way (28, 107). The human homologs can also restore bacterial Moco synthesis, similar to Cnx2 and Cnx3 (33). Interestingly, Cnx2 and homologous proteins contain a conserved C-terminal double-glycine motif. Deletions or mutations in this motif result in the loss of MOCS1A function, indicating a crucial role in the catalytic mechanism (33). Structural information is available for the bacterial MoaA protein (32) forming an incomplete triosephosphate isomerase barrel, which binds an N-terminal [4Fe-4S] cluster typical for SAM-dependent radical enzymes. The lateral opening of the incomplete barrel is covered by the C-terminal part containing a second, MoaA-specific [4Fe-4S] cluster. Both [4Fe-4S] clusters are extremely oxygen sensitive (31), and each one is coordinated by three conserved cysteine residues. The fourth ligand of the N-terminal cluster is SAM and the substrate 5′ GTP coordinates one nonligated Fe in the C-terminal cluster.

The reaction product of Cnx2 and Cnx3 is cPMP. Originally, the first intermediate of Moco synthesis was named precursor Z (139a). Recently, its chemical structure was clarified by mass spectrometry and ^{1}H NMR spectroscopy (111). It was demonstrated that the first intermediate of Moco biosynthesis is indeed a pyranopterin, similar to Moco, and carries a geminal diol in the C1′ position of the side chain. Therefore, precursor Z was renamed 1′,1′-dihydoxy 2′, 4′ cyclic pyranopterin monophosphate according to the IUPAC nomenclature. For simplification, cyclic pyranopterin monophosphate (cPMP) is used. The geminol diol might have an additional protective function for cPMP and could also drive the subsequent sulfur transfer reaction in a particular direction.

Step 2: Synthesis of the Molybdopterin Dithiolate

The MPT dithiolate is formed by incorporating two sulfur atoms into cPMP during the second step of Moco biosynthesis (**Figure 2**). This reaction is catalyzed by MPT synthase, a heterotetrameric complex of two small and two large subunits that stoichiometrically converts cPMP into MPT. Plant MPT synthase is encoded by *cnx6* (large subunit: 23.8 kDa) and *cnx7* (small subunit: 10.5 kDa). In contrast to the first step of Moco synthesis, the approach of functional reconstitution of bacterial mutants was not successful in cloning the genes involved in the second step. Whereas the large subunit of *A. thaliana* MPT synthase was identified based on homologies to its bacterial counterpart MoaE, cloning of the small subunit (*cnx7*) was achieved in a yeast two-hybrid screen by using the assumed protein-protein interaction between both subunits (30). However, using a direct approach for reconstitution as well as biochemical studies demonstrated that the large subunit Cnx6 can replace the function

of MoaE in vivo and in vitro (G. Schwarz, unpublished data). Similar results were found for human MPT synthase (62) encoded by a bicisctronic mRNA (*MOCS2*) (127).

Cnx7 and homologous proteins are only conserved in their C-terminal region, which includes a double-glycine motif also found in ubiquitin, a crucial protein in eukaryotic protein degradation (38). Biochemical studies using in vitro assembled MPT synthase from individually expressed and purified subunits demonstrated that the C terminus of the small subunit carries the sulfur as thiocarboxylate (30, 62). The functional importance of this thiocarboxylate was also demonstrated in the crystal structure of *E. coli* MPT synthase, which shows that the C terminus of MoaD is deeply inserted into the large subunit to form the active site (110). The tetramer is formed by dimerization of two large subunits forming two clearly separated active sites (**Figure 2**). Due to the fact that each small subunit of MPT synthase carries a single sulfur atom, a two-step mechanism for the formation of the MPT dithiolate has been proposed, which involves the formation of a mono-sulfurated intermediate (30, 139).

The Source of the Dithiolate Sulfurs

In a separate reaction, which is catalyzed by one or more proteins, sulfur is transferred to the small subunit of MPT synthase (**Figure 2**). In bacteria, the MoeB protein is crucial for the activity of MPT synthase as *moeB* mutants contain a sulfur-free MPT synthase (103). MoeB is homologous in its entire region to the N-terminal part of the ubiquitin-activating enzyme UbA1 from *Saccharomyces cereviseae* (37, 77). As UbA1 catalyzes the adenylylation of ubiquitin, MoeB catalyzes the adenylylation of its target protein, the small subunit MoaD, by using Mg-ATP as a substrate (65). Crystal structures of MoeB in complex with MoaD have been determined in its apo, ATP-bound, and MoaD-adenylate forms (61), presenting a conserved mechanism of the acyl-adenylate formation in ubiquitin activation, thiamin, and Moco biosynthesis. MoeB alone is not sufficient to reactivate carboxylated MoaD. Free sulfide- or persulfide-loaded cysteine desulfurases (IscS, CSD, or CsdB/SufS) are needed to cleave the acyl-adenylate of MoaD, thus forming a thiocarboxylated small subunit (64). The in vivo source of sulfur is still unknown, but a redundant function of separate persulfide-generating systems is possible (64).

The plant homolog of MoeB is Cnx5, which was identified based on homology on the primary sequence level (95). However, in contrast to Cnx2, Cnx3, and Cnx6, no functional reconstitution of the corresponding *moeB* mutants was achieved (95). Similar results were found for the human homolog MOCS3 (76). As Cnx7 and MOCS2A (plant and human small subunits) are also not active in *E. coli*, one can argue that the sulfur transfer mechanism is not conserved between pro- and eukaryotes.

In addition to a conserved MoeB domain, Cnx5 and homologous eukaryotic proteins are characterized by large C-terminal extensions forming a rhodanese-like domain (RLD). Rhodaneses (thiosulfate:cyanide sulfurtransferases) are widespread enzymes that catalyze in vitro the transfer of a sulfane sulfur atom from thiosulfate to cyanide. The biological role of rhodaneses is still unknown as their in vivo substrates have not been identified. In the active form, the sulfur is bound to a conserved cysteine residue as persulfide and this cysteine is also conserved in the RLDs of Cnx5 (95) and MOCS3 (76). Studies with human RLD of MOCS3 demonstrated its ability to catalyze the transfer of sulfur from thiosulfate to cyanide (76). In a defined in vitro assay generating MPT from cPMP, the sulfurated form of MOCS3-RLD provided the sulfur for the thiocarboxylation of the small subunit of human MPT synthase (76). Mutation of the putative persulfide-forming active-site Cys412 abolished the sulfurtransferase activity of MOCS3 completely. Recently, the presence of a persulfide bound to the catalytically active Cys412 was demonstrated (75). There-

fore, MOCS3, Cnx5, and other eukaryotic homologs can be seen as multifunctional proteins combining the adenylylation of the small subunit (MoeB domain) with the subsequent sulfur transfer reaction (RLD).

Molybdenum Uptake and Insertion

After synthesis of MPT, the chemical backbone is ready to bind and coordinate the Mo atom. One of the first observations of Moco mutants was the identification of molybdate-repairable phenotypes pointing to a defect in molybdate uptake or Mo insertion (5). *E. coli* mutants with a complete suppression of their phenotype were found to have a defect in the *mod* locus encoding a high-affinity ABC-type uptake system (29). In contrast to the well-studied molybdate transport and homeostasis in bacteria, eukaryotic molybdate transport is still poorly understood. In *C. rheinhardtii*, genetic evidence suggested the existence of a distinct molybdate uptake system (69), and very recently a molybdate transporter was cloned (E. Fernandez, personal communication). In parallel, in *A. thaliana*, a molybdate transporter has been cloned and characterized (T. Fujiwara, personal communication).

A key question of Moco biosynthesis was whether it is molybdate that serves as the donor for insertion of Mo into MPT or whether molybdate has to undergo an intracellular processing prior to insertion. Plant (25), fungal (17), and mammalian molybdate-repairable mutants (22) showed a mutation in one of the two conserved domains of proteins Cnx1 (117), CnxE (85), or gephyrin (128), respectively. They are two-domain proteins containing a G domain homologous to the *E. coli* protein MogA and an E domain homologous to bacterial MoeA. The modular nature of these proteins pointed to a functional "cooperation" between their domains, such as product-substrate channeling as they combine functions of proteins that are separately expressed in *E. coli*. Again the approach of functional complementation of bacterial mutants was successful to clone the corresponding plant (*cnx1*) as well as the fungal gene (*cnxE*). However, only the function of MogA could be reconstituted by the corresponding G domain (117), indicating differences in the metal-insertion process between bacteria and eukaryotes. Based on recent biochemical and structural studies with plant Cnx1 (57, 70), substantial progress has been made in understanding the metal transfer mechanism. A novel biosynthetic intermediate, adenylated MPT (MPT-AMP), was identified (**Figure 2**) and consequently Mo insertion was divided into two separate reactions (steps 3 and 4) (57).

Step 3: Adenylylation of MPT

Molybdate-repairable mutants were found to accumulate MPT (49) and consequently a binding of the hypothetical substrate MPT to the Cnx1 G domain (Cnx1G) was demonstrated (115). Subsequent studies using Cnx1G variants indicated functions in MPT binding and catalysis (59). However, molybdate binding could not be detected (117). The crystal structure of Cnx1G (116) was determined and functionally important residues were mapped to a large surface depression, indicating a clear separation between MPT binding and residues important for catalysis (60). Crystal structures of Cnx1G wild-type and mutant variants in complex with MPT confirmed the proposed binding of MPT (57), whereas the structure of a variant (S583A) revealed a novel intermediate in Moco biosynthesis as an adenosine was covalently bound via a pyrophosphate bond to the C4′ carbon of MPT, thereby forming adenylylated MPT (57). Subsequently, the Mg^{2+}- and ATP-dependent in vitro synthesis of MPT-AMP using purified Cnx1G was demonstrated (70) (**Figures 2 and 3**).

An unexpected observation in the substrate- and product-bound Cnx1G structures was the identification of copper bound to the MPT dithiolate sulfurs (57) (**Figure 3**). The function of this novel MPT ligand is presently unknown, but copper might play a

role in sulfur transfer to cPMP, in protecting the MPT dithiolate from oxidation, and/or in presenting a suitable leaving group for Mo insertion. In vitro studies with Cnx1G-bound MPT-AMP revealed an inhibition of Moco synthesis in the presence of excess copper, providing a link between Mo and copper metabolism (57). As copper is always found in a protein-bound state, it might be that Cnx1 interacts with a copper chaperone when the metal is released during Mo insertion. Recently, an interaction using a split-ubiquitin-based two-hybrid approach was identified with a CCH-homologous protein (G. Schwarz, unpublished data).

Step 4: The Metal-Insertion Reaction

In the final steps of Moco biosynthesis, MPT-AMP has to be converted into mature Moco. As Cnx1G catalyzes MPT adenylation, the other Cnx1 E domain (Cnx1E) should be involved in further processing the product of Cnx1G, thereby building a product-substrate channel. In vitro experiments using MPT-AMP-loaded Cnx1G demonstrated Mg-dependent synthesis of Moco (57). This activity was significantly increased in the presence of Cnx1E, suggesting its participation in the metal-insertion reaction. In vivo studies based on transcriptional regulation of the *E. coli mod* operon showed that Cnx1 can bind molybdate in an MPT-dependent manner (58). Recently, we found a molybdate-dependent hydrolysis of MPT-AMP (G. Schwarz, unpublished data). Cleavage of AMP was coupled to the metal exchange reaction where bound copper was released and Mo was transferred to MPT, thus yielding mature Moco (**Figures 2 and 3**).

For the Cnx1E-corresponding *E. coli moeA* mutant, a suppression of Moco deficiency was found in a low-sulfur medium (34). Under those conditions genes encoding proteins of the sulfate assimilation pathway are induced (56). Molybdate acts as a substrate analog of ATP sulfurylase [molybdolysis (122)], the first

Cnx1G: Cnx1 G domain

Copper: binds to the MPT dithiolate sulfurs

Cnx1E: Cnx1 E domain

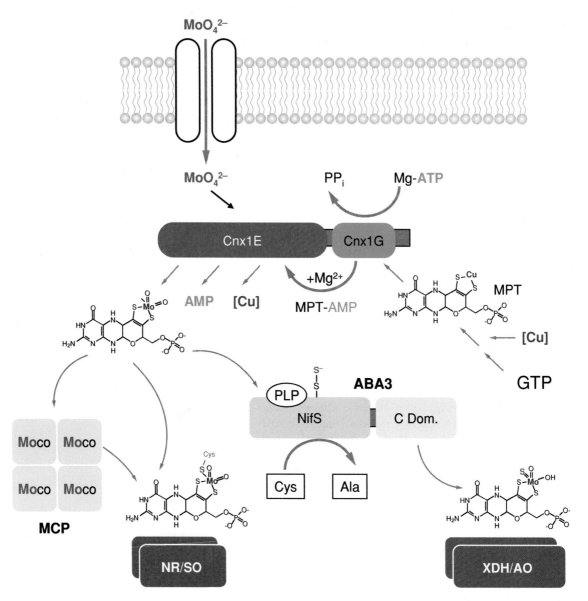

Figure 3

Organization of molybdenum cofactor (Moco) biosynthesis and Moco maturation. Shown are the final steps of plant Moco biosynthesis. Due to subcellular localization and functional homology to human gephyrin, Cnx1 is believed to be in close proximity to the plasma membrane, where it might interact with the hypothetical molybdate anion channel. The individual reactions of Cnx1 and its products (Moco, pyrophosphate, AMP, copper) are indicated. Copper is shown in brackets as its oxidation state prior to incorporation and after release is not known yet. Mature Moco can be either bound to a Moco carrier protein (MCP, shown as tetramer), to nitrate reductase (NR) and sulfite oxidase (SO) (dimers), or upon sulfuration by the ABA3 protein to xanthine dehydrogenase (XDH) or aldehyde oxidase (AO) (dimers). ABA3 forms a protein-bound persulfide, which is the source of the terminal sulfur ligand in Moco in enzymes of the XDH/AO family.

enzyme in this pathway catalyzing the adenylylation of sulfate (9). Under sulfur starvation ATP sulfurylase is highly expressed, which could result in molybdolysis and thus transient formation of adenylylated molybdate, a species that is supposed to be highly reactive. Therefore, it might be proposed that during MPT-AMP hydrolysis adenylylated molybdate is formed as a reaction intermediate, which is subsequently used as the Mo source for Moco formation.

Finally, Cnx1 is essential for stabilizing the newly formed Moco (59). Cnx1 is also able to bind to actin filaments of the cell skeleton of plants via its N-terminal domain and is localized next to the plasma membrane (117). What could be the functional significance of cytoskeleton binding of Cnx1 in terms of Moco biosynthesis? We assume that during evolution it became important to facilitate product-substrate flow, which could result in microcompartmentalization of a hypothetical Moco biosynthetic multienzyme complex ensuring the fast and protected transfer of the labile intermediates within the reaction sequence from GTP to Moco. Therefore, anchoring to cellular structures like the cytoskeleton might help organize and stabilize such a biosynthetic machinery and would bring it close to the molybdate transporter (anion channel), thus providing the metal for Moco synthesis (**Figure 3**).

Step 5: Maturation of Molybdenum Cofactor

Moco biosynthesis is completed once the metal is incorporated into the pterin moiety (83). However, additional modifications must occur before the cofactor is inserted into the appropriate apoenzyme and/or Moco is able to promote catalysis. Mo enzymes of the NR/SO family provide a sulfur of a conserved cysteine to covalently link Mo to the apoprotein (42) (**Figure 1a**), whereas in enzymes of the XDH/AO family this essential sulfur ligand (**Figure 1b**) does not originate from the apoprotein nor does it come from the Moco

moiety. Rather, it must be added in a final maturation step in order to activate the Mo enzyme (**Figure 3**).

For rat and fly, early work of Wahl et al. (134) demonstrated that in vitro this sulfur can be spontaneously lost or can be removed from AO and XDH by cyanide treatment generating an inactive enzyme. The reaction, however, is reversible and the enzyme can be reactivated by sulfide treatment under reducing conditions. In vivo, this terminal sulfur has to be added by a separate enzymatic reaction, catalyzed by a Moco sulfurase (MCSU). MCSU activities were described for *Drosophila melanogaster* [Ma-l (134)], *A. nidulans* [HxB (113)], plants [ABA3 (66)], and humans [MCSU (44)]. Only for the plant enzyme ABA3 are biochemical data available (10), providing evidence on how Moco sulfurases catalyze the activation of enzymes of the XDH/AO family (**Figure 3**). It is still unclear whether ABA3 sulfurates Moco in vivo before or after insertion into apoenzymes, whereas under in vitro conditions ABA3 can act directly on an enzyme-bound Moco. The N terminus of ABA3 shares significant homologies to the bacterial cysteine sulfurases SufS, IscS, and NifS (10). In a pyridoxal phosphate-dependent mechanism of *trans*-sulfuration, an ABA3-bound persulfide, resulting from the desulfuration of free L-cysteine, is likely transferred to the Mo center (36) (**Figure 3**). The C-terminal domain of ABA3 is probably responsible for mediating the contact between XDH or AO and the *trans*-sulfurase domain of ABA3 (4, 10). The terminal sulfuration step is an interesting regulatory switch point because the activity of ABA3 could control the amount of functional XDH/AO molecules in the cell that, in turn, would control cellular levels of, e.g., hormones in case of plant AO. In fact, transcription of the *aba3* gene is inducible by drought and salt stress in plants (10) as well as by ABA (140).

Regarding Moco insertion into NR or SO, nothing is known about a specific mechanism leading to the covalent attachment of the

Moco sulfurase (MCSU) ABA3: adds sulfur to the Mo center of aldehyde oxidase and xanthine dehydrogenase, thereby activating these enzymes

metal to the enzyme-specific and conserved cysteine residue that forms the third sulfur ligand of Moco. At least in vitro, NR as well as SO can bind Moco very efficiently, with reconstitution times of less than an hour (63). Regarding the mechanism of Moco ligation to NR and SO, it is also important to state that the oxygen coordination of Moco as it is generated by the action of Cnx1E is unknown. It is possible that due to the proposed nucleotide-assisted metal-transfer mechanism three oxygen atoms remain bound in mature Moco where one of them is replaced by the terminal sulfur ligand in XO/AO whereas in SO/NR this position is occupied by a cysteine.

Storage and Transfer of Molybdenum Cofactor

After synthesis and maturation Moco has to be incorporated into the appropriate apoenzyme. As Moco is labile and oxygen sensitive (105), it was assumed that there is no free Moco occurring in the cell, and it was suggested that Moco should be transferred immediately after biosynthesis to the apoenzyme or that it could be bound to a carrier protein that protects and stores Moco until further use. Among eukaryotes, first in the green alga *C. rheinhardtii*, an activity of a Moco carrier protein (MCP) was described (1). Later the activity was purified and a 16-kDa protein was identified (**Figure 3**) that was able to bind and protect Moco against oxidation (136). MCP activity was measured with the *nit-1* reconstitution assay without any denaturing procedure, indicating that bound Moco is delivered to apo-NR. It is unknown whether MCP is also able to donate Moco to Mo enzymes other than NR. *C. rheinhardtii* MCP forms a homotetramer (**Figure 3**) in solution and is homologous to bacterial proteins with unknown function that contain a predicted nucleotide-binding Rossman fold (7).

Among plants, there are proteins with low sequence similarity that are classified as lysine decarboxylase-like proteins forming a multigene family in *A. thaliana* with up to eight

highly conserved members. The availability of sufficient amounts of Moco is essential for the cell to meet its changing demand for synthesizing Mo enzymes; therefore, the existence of MCP would provide a way to buffer the supply and demand of Moco.

MOLYBDENUM ENZYMES

More than 40 different Mo enzymes are described in nature so far, but only four of them occur in eukaryotes and are all found in plants (NR, SO, XDH, AO). The alignment of primary sequences enables one to define regions and domains that are well conserved among different Mo enzymes and other regions that are highly variable in sequence, mostly serving as interdomains called "hinge" regions (**Figure 4**). The first crystal structures of Mo enzymes from eukaryotes combined with the wealth of sequence knowledge were a great leap forward for Mo enzyme research in recent years. It is remarkable that the four Mo enzymes described in eukaryotes are all homodimeric proteins. They are inactive as monomers and dimerization depends on the presence of Moco. They harbor an electron transport chain from or to the substrate involving different prosthetic groups (FAD, heme, Fe-S clusters) that are bound to separate domains identified on the enzyme's monomer (**Figure 4**). According to sequence homology and cofactor coordination, eukaryotic enzymes are classified in two families: One is the NR/SO family, where the Moco is covalently bound to a fully conserved active site cysteine, and the other is the XO/XDH/AO family, where a third sulfur ligand is formed by terminal sulfur.

Nitrate Reductase

NR (EC 1.6.6.1) is a cytoplasmic enzyme with a mass of about 200 kDa (dimer). There are several reviews about different aspects of NR research (12, 13), so only some points are given here. The NR monomer contains three regions associated with the Mo center,

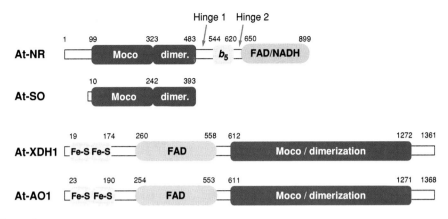

Figure 4

Domain structure of plant molybdenum (Mo) enzymes. The molybdenum cofactor (Moco) domains of nitrate reductase/sulfite oxidase and xanthine dehydrogenase/aldehyde oxidase (XDH/AO) show no significant homologies. Additional redox active domains [FAD, heme b_5 (b_5), [2Fe-2S] cluster (Fe-S)] involved in intramolecular electron transfer are indicated. Domain boundaries are depicted by the residue numbers above the domain. XDH1 and AO1 were chosen as representative members of both families, as there are two XDH and four AO proteins known so far in *A. thaliana*.

the Fe-heme of the cytochrome b_5 domain, and a C-terminal domain associated with a FAD cofactor (**Figure 4**). NR dimerization is mediated by the Mo-containing domain, which can be further subdivided into the N-terminal Moco-binding and C-terminal dimerization domains. The cytochrome b_5 domain is separated from the dimerization domain by a solvent-exposed linker region, named hinge 1, whereas the linker between the cytochrome domain and the FAD domain is referred to as hinge 2 (**Figure 4**). In plants, hinge 1 bears a regulatory Ser residue that mediates the inhibition of NR by a 14-3-3 protein upon phosphorylation (50, 74). The Moco domain is preceded by an N-terminal extension rich in acidic residues that varies between 7 and 121 residues that might be involved in post-transcriptional regulation (98).

NR occurs in three different forms: NADH-specific forms are frequently present in higher plants and algae, NADPH-specific forms are unique to fungi, and NAD(P)H-bispecific forms are found in all aforementioned organisms and are most common in fungi (14). The catalytic cycle of NR can be divided into three parts: a reductive half-reaction in which NAD(P)H reduces FAD,

electron transfer via the intermediate cytochrome b_5 domain, and an oxidative half-reaction in which the Mo center transfers its electrons onto nitrate, thereby forming nitrite and hydroxide/water (123). The rates of intramolecular electron transfer between the domains in *A. thaliana* NR are similar (123). Several fragments of NR have been recombinantly expressed, each of which possesses partial catalytic activity or characteristic spectral properties of the holo-enzyme (71, 104, 106).

The primary structure of NR is conserved among plants, algae, and fungi whereas they are completely different from bacterial NR regarding sequence similarity and structural composition (129). Plant NR belongs to the NR/SO family of Mo enzymes for which the first crystal structure was determined for chicken SO (52). For eukaryotic NR the individual structure of the corn FAD domain (72, 73) has been determined. Recently, the crystal structure of the catalytic domain of a first representative member of eukaryotic NR became available. Fischer et al. (24) determined crystal structures of the Mo-containing nitrate-reducing N-terminal fragment (residues 1–484) of yeast NAD(P)H:NR (NR-Mo) from *Pichia angusta* at 1.7 and 2.6

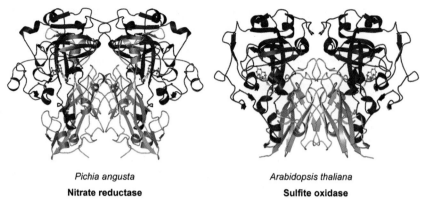

Pichia angusta
Nitrate reductase

Arabidopsis thaliana
Sulfite oxidase

Figure 5

Structure of yeast (*Pichia angusta*) nitrate reductase catalytic domain (24) and plant sulfite oxidase (114). Molybdenum cofactor (Moco) domains are shown in dark red, dimerization domains are in orange, and nonconserved linker regions are highlighted in gray. The bound Moco is shown in ball-and-stick mode.

Å resolution (**Figure 5a**). The overall fold of the butterfly-shaped dimeric NR-Mo is characterized by a mixed $\alpha+\beta$ structure and a clear separation between the Moco-binding domain and dimerization domain. Dimerization is mainly mediated by the C-terminal domain with some additional interactions between the Moco domains. Despite the similarity to SO, differences occur in the N- and C-terminal parts, and in an additional loop, as well as near the active site. In the 1.7 Å structure, a bound sulfate caused several conformational changes in the active site as compared to apo-NR-Mo, and four ordered water molecules were found in close proximity to Mo. Based on these water molecules, a mechanism for nitrate reduction catalyzed by NR involving nitrate binding, formation of a penta-coordinated reaction intermediate, and release of the products nitrite and water has been proposed (24).

Sulfite Oxidase

The existence of SO in plants was shown only recently by the identification of a cDNA from *A. thaliana* encoding a functional plant SO (PSO) (21). SO is widespread and highly conserved within the plant kingdom: The SO gene is found in higher plants, algae and mosses, and the encoded protein seems to be highly conserved because antibodies directed against *Arabidopsis* SO detect proteins of similar size in a wide range of herbaceous and also woody plants (21). PSO has unique properties that are different from animal SOs. Whereas animal SOs contain a Moco and a heme domain (15), PSO lacks the heme domain (21) (**Figure 4**). Thus, among eukaryotes, PSO is the simplest Mo enzyme and possesses only one redox center. Oxygen serves as the terminal electron acceptor for plant SO (EC 1.8.3.1) and becomes reduced to hydrogen peroxide (31a). The latter finding explains the peroxisomal localization of PSO (21, 97), which is different from the localization of animal SO, which is found in the mitochondria (15). Animal SO is mainly found in liver, where it catalyzes the terminal step in the oxidative degradation of cysteine, methionine, and membrane components such as sulfatides (47) by the reduction of cytochrome *c*.

Because PSO is not found in the chloroplasts, one can assume that the function of PSO is not related to the chloroplast-based sulfur assimilation pathway (67). Rather, PSO has a sulfite-detoxifying function; sulfite is a toxic metabolite that has to be removed in order to protect the cell against a surplus of sulfite derived from SO_2 gas in the atmosphere (acid rain) (35) or during the decomposition of sulfur-containing amino acids. The compartmentalization of sulfur assimilation

PSO: plant sulfite oxidase

and sulfite oxidation in different organelles allows plants to coregulate these opposing metabolic demands. The biochemical properties of PSO have been analyzed, and despite the missing heme-containing domain, UV-visible spectra, electron paramagnetic resonance spectra, as well as K_M values were comparable (6a, 21).

The crystal structure of chicken SO was the first atomic structure (52) of a eukaryotic Mo enzyme. Recently, the crystal structure of *Arabidopsis* PSO was determined at 2.6 Å (114), revealing remarkable structural conservation between the plant and animal enzymes (**Figure 5b**). Like all eukaryotic Mo enzymes, PSO forms a dimer with a molecular mass of approximately 90 kDa. It can be divided into the N-terminal Moco domain and C-terminal dimerization domain. Comparisons of conserved surface residues and charge distributions between plant and animal SO revealed major differences near the entrance to both active sites. The different levels of sequence conservation in plant and animal SOs strengthen a proposed rearrangement of the cytochrome b_5 domain in animal SO and underscore the different terminal electron acceptors. Arg374 has been identified as an important residue for substrate binding due to its conformational change in the PSO apostructure (114) compared to the sulfate-bound structure of chicken SO (52). Comparison to the catalytic domain of NR illustrates the common fold of enzymes of the NR/SO family with only a few differences in the boundaries of the enzymes and very important changes within the active site that are believed to determine substrate specificity and catalytic properties (24).

Xanthine Dehydrogenase

In plants, XDH (EC 1.1.1.204), but not the oxidase form, was identified in a variety of organisms and tissues. The enzyme was purified from leaves of wheat (89) and legumes (90, 112) and showed highest affinities for xanthine and hypoxanthine as substrates but also accepted purines and pterines at much lower rates. Plant XDH is homodimeric with a molecular mass of around 300 kDa (**Figure 4**). In *Arabidopsis*, two XDH genes were found in tandem orientation and were shown to be differentially regulated: Only AtXDH1 responded to stresses like drought, cold, and salinity, and also to natural senescence (39). Besides purine degradation, plant XDH is supposed to play a role in important cellular processes: (*a*) plant-pathogen interactions between phytopathogenic fungi and legumes and cereals (86, 87), (*b*) cell death associated with hypersensitive response (88, 91), and (*c*) natural senescence (100). As all these processes require the formation of reactive oxygen species, XDH was supposed to be able to produce superoxide anions and/or hydrogen peroxide (100). Recently, this assumption was confirmed: Purified recombinant *Arabidopsis* XDH was proven to produce superoxide radicals (39). The native enzyme was also shown to produce superoxide radicals, but not H_2O_2 in response to water stress (141). The subcellular location of XDH is still not clear; it was suggested that XDH is associated to peroxisomes because pea leaf peroxisomes contain XDH activity, which catabolizes xanthine to uric acid inside the organelles (16). However, immunocytochemistry of XDH in cowpea nodules demonstrated a cytoplasmic location (20), and no targeting signal is found in the XDH sequence of *Arabidopsis*.

Aldehyde Oxidase

AO (EC 1.2.3.1) is a cytoplasmic enzyme with an apparent molecular mass of 300 kDa, containing FAD, iron, and Moco as prosthetic groups with a stoichiometry of 4:1:1 (55). AO and XDH have very similar amino acid sequences so it is suggested that they evolved from a common ancestor (42). The domain arrangement of AO (**Figure 4**) shows that the redox-active iron is incorporated in the form of [2Fe-2S] centers that are localized on the N-terminal part. In *Arabidopsis*, four AO cDNAs were found and physically mapped to different chromosomes (118). The encoded enzyme isoforms have relatively broad substrate specificity for several aldehydes including abscisic-aldehyde, indole-3-aldehyde, indole-3-acetaldehyde, naphthy-laldehyde, and benzaldehyde. From the substrate specificity, mutant analysis, and tissue distribution, it can be concluded that *Arabidopsis* AO3 catalyzes the conversion of abscisic-aldehyde to ABA (121), the final step in ABA biosynthesis (reviewed in 120). A different line of experimental approaches linked AO activity to the biosynthesis of the plant hormone indole-3-acetic acid (IAA), where it catalyzes the conversion of indole-3-acetaldehyde to IAA: AO1 activity is five times higher in the IAA-overproducing mutant *sur1* as compared to the *Arabidopsis* wild type (119). Recently it was shown that AO is also involved in auxin signaling (19).

Plant AOs form a multigene family whose members catalyze the final step in biosynthesis of the phytohormones ABA and auxins, namely IAA and 1-naphthalene acetic acid. These two functions are sufficient to assign an important role in plant development and adaptation to environmental stresses to AOs, although there are also other pathways for the synthesis of both hormones (84, 124). The broad substrate specificity of AO makes it likely that AOs are involved in additional metabolic reactions other than phytohormone synthesis. Detoxification reactions and pathogen response may be good candidates for these additional functions. Recently it was shown that plant AOs produce H_2O_2 in response to drought stress and ABA treatment (141).

SUMMARY POINTS

1. Moco forms the active site of all eukaryotic Mo enzymes. Moco consists of Mo covalently bound to two sulfur atoms of a unique pterin referred to as molybdopterin.

2. There are four enzymes in plants that contain Moco: nitrate reductase, sulfite oxidase, aldehyde oxidase, and xanthine dehydrogenase.

3. Moco is synthesized from GTP by an ancient and conserved biosynthetic pathway that can be divided into four steps. If any of these steps is blocked by a mutation all Mo enzymes lose their acivity, which is lethal for the organism.

4. Copper is involved in Moco biosynthesis. It seems to hold the place for the subsequent insertion of Mo.

5. In a final maturation step, sulfur is added to the Mo center of aldehyde oxidase and xanthine dehydrogenase. This reaction is catalyzed by the Moco sulfurase ABA3.

6. Structures for the catalytic domains of nitrate reductase and sulfite oxidase have been determined. They form the molecular basis for the understanding of substrate specificity and reaction mechanism.

7. Aldehyde oxidases are important for phytohormone biosynthesis, and xanthine dehydrogenase is essential for purine degradation and stress response.

FUTURE ISSUES

1. Although the synthesis of pteridines and folates is well known, the chemistry underlying cPMP formation is still enigmatic and proposed theories have to be proven. Here the role of S-adenosylmethionine and the unique [4Fe-4S] clusters in catalysis is of great interest.

2. What is the role of copper in Moco synthesis and what proteins donate/accept copper during Moco formation? When and how is the copper incorporated into MPT?

3. How is Moco inserted into apo-Mo enzymes? Is there a general mechanism or is it associated with the different modifications found?

4. At which cellular compartment is Moco synthesized and how is Moco biosynthesis regulated to meet the changing demands of the cell for Moco?

ACKNOWLEDGMENTS

We thank the many people who worked with us over the years on molybdenum metabolism. In particular we are grateful to Dr. Florian Bittner and Dr. Robert Hänsch for many critical discussions during the preparation of this review. Our research was consistently supported by the Deutsche Forschungsgemeinschaft, which we gratefully acknowledge. We are also grateful to the European Union, the Fonds der Chemischen Industrie, the Thyssen Stiftung, and the International Graduate Program of the Technical University of Braunschweig for finances.

LITERATURE CITED

1. Aguilar M, Kalakoutskii K, Cardenas J, Fernandez E. 1992. Direct transfer of molybdopterin cofactor to aponitrate reductase from a carrier protein in *Chlamydomonas reinhardtii*. *FEBS Lett.* 307:162–63

2. Alikulov ZA, Mendel RR. 1983. Molybdenum cofactor from tobacco cell cultures and milk xanthine oxidase: involvement of sulfhydryl groups in dimerization activity of cofactor. *Biochem. Physiol. Pflanzen.* 179:693–705

3. Allen RM, Chatterjee R, Madden MS, Ludden PW, Shah VK. 1994. Biosynthesis of the iron-molybdenum cofactor of nitrogenase. *Crit. Rev. Biotechnol.* 14:225–49

4. Amrani L, Primus J, Glatigny A, Arcangeli L, Scazzocchio C, Finnerty V. 2000. Comparison of the sequences of the *Aspergillus nidulans hxB* and *Drosophila melanogaster ma-l* genes with *nifS* from *Azotobacter vinelandii* suggests a mechanism for the insertion of the terminal sulphur atom in the molybdopterin cofactor. *Mol. Microbiol.* 38:114–25

5. Amy NK. 1981. Identification of the molybdenum cofactor in chlorate-resistant mutants of *Escherichia coli*. *J. Bacteriol.* 148:274–82

6. Appleyard MV, Sloan J, Kana'n GJ, Heck IS, Kinghorn JR, Unkles SE. 1998. The *Aspergillus nidulans cnxF* gene and its involvement in molybdopterin biosynthesis. Molecular characterization and analysis of in vivo generated mutants. *J. Biol. Chem.* 273:14869–76

6a. Astashkin AV, Hood BL, Feng C, Hille R, Mendel RR, et al. 2005. Structures of the Mo(V) forms of sulfite oxidase from *Arabidopsis thaliana* by pulsed EPR spectroscopy. *Biochemistry* 44:13274–81

7. Ataya FS, Witte CP, Galvan A, Igeno MI, Fernandez E. 2003. Mcp1 encodes the molybdenum cofactor carrier protein in *Chlamydomonas reinhardtii* and participates in protection, binding, and storage functions of the cofactor. *J. Biol. Chem.* 278:10885–90

8. Bacher A, Eberhardt S, Eisenreich W, Fischer M, Herz S, et al. 2001. Biosynthesis of riboflavin. *Vitam. Horm.* 61:1–49

9. Bick JA, Leustek T. 1998. Plant sulfur metabolism–the reduction of sulfate to sulfite. *Curr. Opin. Plant Biol.* 1:240–44

10. Bittner F, Oreb M, Mendel RR. 2001. ABA3 is a molybdenum cofactor sulfurase required for activation of aldehyde oxidase and xanthine dehydrogenase in *Arabidopsis thaliana*. *J. Biol. Chem.* 276:40381–84

11. Braaksma FJ, Feenstra WJ. 1982. Isolation and characterization of nitrate reductase-deficient mutants of *Arabidopsis thaliana*. *Theor. Appl. Genet.* 64:83–90

12. Campbell WH. 1999. Nitrate reductase structure, function and regulation: bridging the gap between biochemistry and physiology. *Annu. Rev. Plant Physiol. Plant Mol. Biol.* 50:277–303

13. Campbell WH. 2001. Structure and function of eukaryotic NAD(P)H:nitrate reductase. *Cell. Mol. Life Sci.* 58:194–204

14. Campbell WH, Kinghorn KR. 1990. Functional domains of assimilatory nitrate reductases and nitrite reductases. *Trends Biochem. Sci.* 15:315–19

15. Cohen HJ, Betcher-Lange S, Kessler DL, Rajagopalan KV. 1972. Hepatic sulfite oxidase. Congruency in mitochondria of prosthetic groups and activity. *J. Biol. Chem.* 247:7759–66

16. Corpas FJ, Colina C, Sanchez-Rasero F, Rio LA. 1997. A role of leaf peroxisomes in the catabolism of purines. *J. Plant Physiol.* 151:246–50

17. Cove DJ, Pateman JA. 1963. Independently segregating genetic loci concerned with nitrate reductase activity in *Aspergillus nidulans*. *Nature* 198:262–63

18. Crawford NM. 1992. Study of chlorate resistant mutants of *Arabidopsis*: insights into nitrate assimilation and ion metabolism of plants. In *Genetic Engineering, Principles and Methods*, ed. JK Setlow, pp. 89–98. New York: Plenum Press

19. Dai X, Hayashi K, Nozaki H, Cheng Y, Zhao Y. 2005. Genetic and chemical analyses of the action mechanisms of sirtinol in Arabidopsis. *Proc. Natl. Acad. Sci. USA* 102:3129–34

20. Datta DB, Triplett EW, Newcomb EH. 1991. Localization of xanthine dehydrogenase in cowpea root nodules: implications for the interaction between cellular compartments during ureide biogenesis. *Proc. Natl. Acad. Sci. USA* 88:4700–2

21. Eilers T, Schwarz G, Brinkmann H, Witt C, Richter T, et al. 2001. Identification and biochemical characterization of *Arabidopsis thaliana* sulfite oxidase. A new player in plant sulfur metabolism. *J. Biol. Chem.* 276:46989–94

22. Falciani F, Terao M, Goldwurm S, Ronchi A, Gatti A, et al. 1994. Molybdenum(VI) salts convert the xanthine oxidoreductase apoprotein into the active enzyme in mouse L929 fibroblastic cells. *Biochem. J.* 298:69–77

23. Fernandez E, Matagne RF. 1986. In vivo complementation analysis of nitrate reductase-deficient mutants in *Chlamydomonas reinhardtii*. *Curr. Genet.* 10:397–403

24. Fischer K, Barbier GG, Hecht H-J, Mendel RR, Campbell WH, Schwarz G. 2005. Crystal structure of the yeast nitrate reductase molybdenum domain provides insight into eukaryotic nitrate assimilation. *Plant Cell* 17:1167–79

25. Gabard J, Pelsy F, Marion-Poll A, Caboche M, Saalbach I, et al. 1988. Genetic analysis of nitrate reductase deficient mutants of *Nicotiana plumbaginifolia*: Evidence for six complementation groups among 70 classified molybdenum cofactor deficient mutants. *Mol. Gen. Genet.* 213:275–81

26. Garattini E, Mendel R, Romao MJ, Wright R, Terao M. 2003. Mammalian molybdo-flavoenzymes, an expanding family of proteins: structure, genetics, regulation, function and pathophysiology. *Biochem. J.* 372:15–32

27. Glaser JH, DeMoss JA. 1971. Phenotypic restoration by molybdate of nitrate reductase activity in chlD mutants of *Escherichia coli*. *J. Bacteriol.* 108:854–60

28. Gray TA, Nicholls RD. 2000. Diverse splicing mechanisms fuse the evolutionarily conserved bicistronic MOCS1A and MOCS1B open reading frames. *RNA* 6:928–36

29. Grunden AM, Shanmugam KT. 1997. Molybdate transport and regulation in bacteria. *Arch. Microbiol.* 168:345–54

30. Gutzke G, Fischer B, Mendel RR, Schwarz G. 2001. Thiocarboxylation of molybdopterin synthase provides evidence for the mechanism of dithiolene formation in metal-binding pterins. *J. Biol. Chem.* 276:36268–74

31. Haenzelmann P, Hernandez HL, Menzel C, Garcia-Serres R, Huynh BH, et al. 2004. Characterization of MOCS1A, an oxygen-sensitive iron-sulfur protein involved in human molybdenum cofactor biosynthesis. *J. Biol. Chem.* 279:34721–32

31a. Hänsch R, Lang C, Riebeseel E, Lindigkeit R, Gessler A, et al. 2006. Plant sulfite oxidase as novel producer of H_2O_2: combination of enzyme catalysis with a subsequent non-enzymatic reaction step. *J. Biol. Chem.* In press

32. Hänzelmann P, Schindelin H. 2004. Crystal structure of the S-adenosylmethionine-dependent enzyme MoaA and its implications for molybdenum cofactor deficiency in humans. *Proc. Natl. Acad. Sci. USA* 101:12870–75

33. Hänzelmann P, Schwarz G, Mendel RR. 2002. Functionality of alternative splice forms of the first enzymes involved in human molybdenum cofactor biosynthesis. *J. Biol. Chem.* 277:18303–12

34. Hasona A, Ray RM, Shanmugam KT. 1998. Physiological and genetic analyses leading to identification of a biochemical role for the moeA (molybdate metabolism) gene product in *Escherichia coli*. *J. Bacteriol.* 180:1466–72

35. Heber U, Hüve K. 1998. Action of SO_2 on plants and metabolic detoxification of SO_2. *Intl. Rev. Cytol.* 177:255–86

36. Heidenreich T, Wollers S, Mendel RR, Bittner F. 2005. Characterization of the NifS-like domain of ABA3 from *Arabidopsis thaliana* provides insight into the mechanism of molybdenum cofactor sulfuration. *J. Biol. Chem.* 280:4213–18

37. Hershko A, Ciechanover A. 1992. The ubiquitin system for protein degradation. *Annu. Rev. Biochem.* 61:761–807

38. Hershko A, Ciechanover A. 1998. The ubiquitin system. *Annu. Rev. Biochem.* 67:425–79

39. Hesberg C, Hansch R, Mendel RR, Bittner F. 2004. Tandem orientation of duplicated xanthine dehydrogenase genes from *Arabidopsis thaliana*: differential gene expression and enzyme activities. *J. Biol. Chem.* 279:13547–54

40. Hille R. 1996. The mononuclear molybdenum enzymes. *Chem. Rev.* 96:2757–816

41. Hille R. 2002. Molybdenum and tungsten in biology. *Trends Biochem. Sci.* 27:360–67

42. Hille R. 2002. Molybdenum enzymes containing the pyranopterin cofactor: an overview. *Met. Ions Biol. Syst.* 39:187–226

43. Hoff T, Schnorr KM, Meyer C, Caboche M. 1995. Isolation of two Arabidopsis cDNAs involved in early steps of molybdenum cofactor biosynthesis by functional complementation of *Escherichia coli* mutants. *J. Biol. Chem.* 270:6100–7

44. Ichida K, Matsumura T, Sakuma R, Hosoya T, Nishino T. 2001. Mutation of human molybdenum cofactor sulfurase gene is responsible for classical xanthinuria type II. *Biochem. Biophys. Res. Commun.* 282:1194–200

45. Johnson JL, Duran M. 2001. Molybdenum cofactor deficiency and isolated sulfite oxidase deficiency. In *The Metabolic and Molecular Bases of Inherited Disease*, ed. C Scriver, A Beaudet, W Sly, D Valle, pp. 3163–77. New York: McGraw-Hill

46. Johnson JL, Hainline BE, Rajagopalan KV, Arison BH. 1984. The pterin component of the molybdenum cofactor. Structural characterization of two fluorescent derivatives. *J. Biol. Chem.* 259:5414–22

47. Johnson JL, Rajagopalan KV. 1979. The oxidation of sulphite in animals systems. *Ciba Found. Symp.* 72:119–33

48. Johnson JL, Waud WR, Rajagopalan KV, Duran M, Beemer FA, Wadman SK. 1980. Inborn errors of molybdenum metabolism: combined deficiencies of sulfite oxidase and xanthine dehydrogenase in a patient lacking the molybdenum cofactor. *Proc. Natl. Acad. Sci. USA* 77:3715–19

49. Joshi MS, Johnson JL, Rajagopalan KV. 1996. Molybdenum cofactor biosynthesis in Escherichia coli mod and mog mutants. *J. Bacteriol.* 178:4310–12

50. Kaiser WM, Huber SC. 2001. Post-translational regulation of nitrate reductase: mechanism, physiological relevance and environmental triggers. *J. Exp. Bot.* 52:1981–89

51. Ketchum PA, Cambier HY, Frazier WA 3rd, Madansky CH, Nason A. 1970. In vitro assembly of Neurospora assimilatory nitrate reductase from protein subunits of a Neurospora mutant and the xanthine oxidizing or aldehyde oxidase systems of higher animals. *Proc. Natl. Acad. Sci. USA* 66:1016–23

52. Kisker C, Schindelin H, Pacheco A, Wehbi WA, Garrett RM, et al. 1997. Molecular basis of sulfite oxidase deficiency from the structure of sulfite oxidase. *Cell* 91:973–83

53. Kisker C, Schindelin H, Rees DC. 1997. Molybdenum-cofactor-containing enzymes: structure and mechanism. *Annu. Rev. Biochem.* 66:233–67

54. Kleinhofs A, Warner RL, Lawrence JM, Jeter JM, Kudrna DA. 1989. Molecular genetics of nitrate reductase in barley. In *Molecular and Genetic Aspects of Nitrate Assimilation*, ed. JL Wray, JR Kinghorn, pp. 197–211. Oxford: Oxford Univ. Press

55. Koshiba T, Saito E, Ono N, Yamamoto N, Sato M. 1996. Purification and properties of flavin- and molybdenum containing aldehyde oxidase from coleoptyles of maize. *Plant Physiol.* 110:781–89

56. Kredich NM. 1996. Biosynthesis of cysteine. In *Escherichia coli and Salmonella typhimurium: Cellular and Molecular Biology*, ed. FC Neidhardt, R Curtiss III, JL Ingraham, ECC Lin, KB Low, et al., pp. 514–27. Washington, DC: ASM Press

57. Kuper J, Llamas A, Hecht HJ, Mendel RR, Schwarz G. 2004. Structure of molybdopterin-bound Cnx1G domain links molybdenum and copper metabolism. *Nature* 430:803–6

58. Kuper J, Meyer zu Berstenhorst S, Vodisch B, Mendel RR, Schwarz G, Boxer DH. 2003. In vivo detection of molybdate-binding proteins using a competition assay with ModE in *Escherichia coli*. *FEMS Microbiol. Lett.* 218:187–93

59. Kuper J, Palmer T, Mendel RR, Schwarz G. 2000. Mutations in the molybdenum cofactor biosynthetic protein Cnx1G from *Arabidopsis thaliana* define functions for molybdopterin bind, Mo-insertion and molybdenum cofactor stabilization. *Proc. Natl. Acad. Sci. USA* 97:6475–80

60. Kuper J, Winking J, Hecht HJ, Mendel RR, Schwarz G. 2003. The active site of the molybdenum cofactor biosynthetic protein domain Cnx1G. *Arch. Biochem. Biophys.* 411:36–46

61. Lake MW, Wuebbens MM, Rajagopalan KV, Schindelin H. 2001. Mechanism of ubiquitin activation revealed by the structure of a bacterial MoeB-MoaD complex. *Nature* 414:325–29

62. Leimkuhler S, Freuer A, Araujo JA, Rajagopalan KV, Mendel RR. 2003. Mechanistic studies of human molybdopterin synthase reaction and characterization of mutants identified in group B patients of molybdenum cofactor deficiency. *J. Biol. Chem.* 278:26127–34

63. Leimkuhler S, Rajagopalan KV. 2001. In vitro incorporation of nascent molybdenum cofactor into human sulfite oxidase. *J. Biol. Chem.* 276:1837–44

64. Leimkuhler S, Rajagopalan KV. 2001. A sulfurtransferase is required in the transfer of

cysteine sulfur in the in vitro synthesis of molybdopterin from precursor Z in *Escherichia coli*. *J. Biol. Chem.* 276:22024–31

65. Leimkühler S, Wuebbens MM, Rajagopalan KV. 2001. Characterization of *Escherichia coli* MoeB and its involvement in the activation of molybdopterin synthase for the biosynthesis of the molybdenum cofactor. *J. Biol. Chem.* 276:34695–701

66. Leon-Klooserziel KM, Gil MA, Ruijs GJ, Jacobsen SE, Olszewski NE, et al. 1996. Isolation and characterization of abscisic acid-deficient *Arabidopsis* mutants at two new loci. *Plant J.* 10:655–61

67. Leustek T, Saito K. 1999. Sulfate transport and assimilation in plants. *Plant Physiol.* 120:637–44

68. Lill R, Muhlenhoff U. 2005. Iron-sulfur-protein biogenesis in eukaryotes. *Trends Biochem. Sci.* 30:133–41

69. Llamas A, Kalakoutskii KL, Fernandez E. 2000. Molybdenum cofactor amounts in *Chlamydomonas reinhardtii* depend on the *Nit5* gene function related to molybdate transport. *Plant Cell Environ.* 23:1247–55

70. Llamas A, Mendel RR, Schwarz G. 2004. Synthesis of adenylated molybdopterin: an essential step for molybdenum insertion. *J. Biol. Chem.* 279:55241–46

71. Lu G, Campbell W, Lindqvist Y, Schneider G. 1992. Crystallization and preliminary crystallographic studies of the FAD domain of corn NADH: nitrate reductase. *J. Mol. Biol.* 224:277–79

72. Lu G, Campbell WH, Schneider G, Lindqvist Y. 1994. Crystal structure of the FAD-containing fragment of corn nitrate reductase at 2.5 Å resolution: relationship to other flavoprotein reductases. *Structure* 2:809–21

73. Lu G, Lindqvist Y, Schneider G, Dwivedi U, Campbell W. 1995. Structural studies on corn nitrate reductase: refined structure of the cytochrome b reductase fragment at 2.5 Å, its ADP complex and an active-site mutant and modeling of the cytochrome b domain. *J. Mol. Biol.* 248:931–48

74. MacKintosh C, Meek SE. 2001. Regulation of plant NR activity by reversible phosphorylation, 14–3–3 proteins and proteolysis. *Cell. Mol. Life Sci.* 58:205–14

75. Matthies A, Nimtz M, Leimkuhler S. 2005. Molybdenum cofactor biosynthesis in humans: identification of a persulfide group in the rhodanese-like domain of MOCS3 by mass spectrometry. *Biochemistry* 44:7912–20

76. Matthies A, Rajagopalan KV, Mendel RR, Leimkuhler S. 2004. Evidence for the physiological role of a rhodanese-like protein for the biosynthesis of the molybdenum cofactor in humans. *Proc. Natl. Acad. Sci. USA* 101:5946–51

77. McGrath JP, Jentsch S, Varshavsky A. 1991. *UBA1*: an essential yeast gene encoding ubiquitin-activating enzyme. *EMBO J.* 10:227–36

78. Mendel RR. 1983. Release of molybdenum co-factor from nitrate reductase and xanthine oxidase by heat treatment. *Phytochemistry* 22:817–19

79. Mendel RR. 1992. The plant molybdenum cofactor (MoCo) - its biochemical and molecular genetics. In *Plant Biotechnology and Development - Current Topics in Plant Molecular Biology*, ed. PM Gresshoff, pp. 11–16. Boca Raton and London: CRC Press

80. Mendel RR, Alikulov ZA, Lvov NP, Müller AJ. 1981. Presence of the molybdenum-cofactor in nitrate reductase-deficient mutant cell lines of *Nicotiana tabacum*. *Mol. Gen. Genet.* 181:395–99

81. Mendel RR, Buchanan RJ, Wray JL. 1984. Characterization of a new type of molybdenum cofactor-mutant in cell cultures of *Nicotiana tabacum*. *Mol. Gen. Genet.* 195:186–89

82. Mendel RR, Müller AJ. 1976. A common genetic determinant of xanthine dehydrogenase and nitrate reductase in *Nicotiana tabacum*. *Biochem. Physiol. Pflanzen* 170:538–41

83. Mendel RR, Schwarz G. 2002. Biosynthesis and molecular biology of the molybdenum cofactor (Moco). *Met. Ions Biol. Syst.* 39:317–68
84. Milborrow BV. 2001. The pathway of biosynthesis of abscisic acid in vascular plants: a review of the present state of knowledge of ABA biosynthesis. *J. Exp. Bot.* 52:1145–64
85. Millar LJ, Heck IS, Sloan J, Kana'n GJ, Kinghorn JR, Unkles SE. 2001. Deletion of the cnxE gene encoding the gephyrin-like protein involved in the final stages of molybdenum cofactor biosynthesis in Aspergillus nidulans. *Mol. Genet. Genomics* 266:445–53
86. Montalbini P. 1992. Inhibition of hypersensitive response by allopurinol applied to the host in the incompatible relationship between *Phaseolus vulgaris* and *Uromyces phaseoli*. *J. Phytopathol.* 134:218–28
87. Montalbini P. 1992. Ureides and enzymes of ureide synthesis in wheat seeds and leaves and effect of allopurinol on *Puccinia recondita* f.sp. *tritici* infection. *Plant Sci.* 87:225–31
88. Montalbini P. 1995. Effect of rust infection on purine catabolism enzyme levels in wheat leaves. *Phys. Mol. Plant Path.* 46:275–92
89. Montalbini P. 1998. Purification and some properties of xanthine dehydrogenase from wheat leaves. *Plant Sci.* 134:89–102
90. Montalbini P. 2000. Xanthine dehydrogenase from leaves of leguminous plants: Purification, characterization and properties of the enzyme. *J. Plant Physiol.* 156:3–16
91. Montalbini P, Della Torre G. 1996. Evidence of a two-fold mechanism responsible for the inhibition by allopurinol of the hypersensitive response induced in tobacco by tobacco necrosis virus. *Phys. Mol. Plant Path.* 48:273–87
92. Müller AJ, Mendel RR. 1989. Biochemical and somatic cell genetics of nitrate reductase in *Nicotiana*. In *Molecular and Genetic Aspects of Nitrate Assimilation*, ed. JL Wray, JR Kinghorn, pp. 166–85. Oxford: Oxford Univ. Press
93. Nason A, Antoine AD, Ketchum PA, Frazier WA 3rd, Lee DK. 1970. Formation of assimilatory nitrate reductase by in vitro inter-cistronic complementation in *Neurospora crassa*. *Proc. Natl. Acad. Sci. USA* 65:137–44
94. Nason A, Lee KY, Pan SS, Ketchum PA, Lamberti A, DeVries J. 1971. Invitro formation of assimilatory reduced nicotinamide adenine dinucleotide phosphate: nitrate reductase from a Neurospora mutant and a component of molybdenum-enzymes. *Proc. Natl. Acad. Sci. USA* 68:3242–46
95. Nieder J, Stallmeyer B, Brinkmann H, Mendel RR. 1997. Identification of *A. thaliana* cDNAs homologous to the *E. coli* sulphotransferase MoeB. In *Sulphur Metabolism in Higher Plants*, ed. WJ Cram, LJ De Kok, I Stulen, C Brunold, H Rennenberg. Leiden: Backhuys Publ.
96. Nieter Burgmayer SJ, Pearsall DL, Blaney SM, Moore EM, Sauk-Schubert C. 2004. Redox reactions of the pyranopterin system of the molybdenum cofactor. *J. Biol. Inorg. Chem.* 9:59–66
97. Nowak K, Luniak N, Witt C, Wustefeld Y, Wachter A, et al. 2004. Peroxisomal localization of sulfite oxidase separates it from chloroplast-based sulfur assimilation. *Plant Cell Physiol.* 45:1889–94
98. Nussaume L, Vincentz M, Meyer C, Boutin JP, Caboche M. 1995. Post-transcriptional regulation of nitrate reductase by light is abolished by an N-terminal deletion. *Plant Cell* 7:611–21
99. Okamoto K, Matsumoto K, Hille R, Eger BT, Pai EF, Nishino T. 2004. The crystal structure of xanthine oxidoreductase during catalysis: implications for reaction mechanism and enzyme inhibition. *Proc. Natl. Acad. Sci. USA* 101:7931–36
100. Pastori GM, Rio LA. 1997. Natural senescence of pea leaves: an activated oxygen-mediated function for peroxisomes. *Plant Physiol.* 113:411–18

101. Pateman JA, Cove DJ, Rever BM, Roberts DB. 1964. A common cofactor for nitrate reductase and xanthine dehydrogenase which also regulates the synthesis of nitrate reductase. *Nature* 201:58–60

102. Pienkos PT, Shah VK, Brill WJ. 1977. Molybdenum cofactors from molybdoenzymes and in vitro reconstitution of nitrogenase and nitrate reductase. *Proc. Natl. Acad. Sci. USA* 74:5468–71

103. Pitterle DM, Johnson JL, Rajagopalan KV. 1993. In vitro synthesis of molybdopterin from precursor Z using purified converting factor. Role of protein-bound sulfur in formation of the dithiolene. *J. Biol. Chem.* 268:13506–9

104. Pollock VV, Conover RC, Johnson MK, Barber MJ. 2002. Bacterial expression of the molybdenum domain of assimilatory nitrate reductase: production of both the functional molybdenum-containing domain and the nonfunctional tungsten analog. *Arch. Biochem. Biophys.* 403:237–48

105. Rajagopalan KV, Johnson JL. 1992. The pterin molybdenum cofactors. *J. Biol. Chem.* 267:10199–202

106. Ratnam K, Shiraishi N, Campbell WH, Hille R. 1997. Spectroscopic and kinetic characterization of the recombinant cytochrome c reductase fragment of nitrate reductase. Identification of the rate-limiting catalytic step. *J. Biol. Chem.* 272:2122–28

107. Reiss J, Cohen N, Dorche C, Mandel H, Mendel RR, et al. 1998. Mutations in a polycistronic nuclear gene associated with molybdenum cofactor deficiency. *Nat. Genet.* 20:51–53

108. Reiss J, Johnson JL. 2003. Mutations in the molybdenum cofactor biosynthetic genes MOCS1, MOCS2, and GEPH. *Hum. Mutat.* 21:569–76

109. Rieder C, Eisenreich W, O'Brien J, Richter G, Götze E, et al. 1998. Rearrangement reactions in the biosynthesis of molybdopterin - An NMR study with multiply ^{13}C/^{15}N labelled precursors. *Eur. J. Biochem.* 255:24–36

110. Rudolph MJ, Wuebbens MM, Rajagopalan KV, Schindelin H. 2001. Crystal structure of molybdopterin synthase and its evolutionary relationship to ubiquitin activation. *Nat. Struct. Biol.* 8:42–46

111. Santamaria-Araujo JA, Fischer B, Otte T, Nimtz M, Mendel RR, et al. 2004. The tetrahydropyranopterin structure of the sulfur-free and metal-free molybdenum cofactor precursor. *J. Biol. Chem.* 279:15994–99

112. Sauer P, Frebortova J, Sebela M, Galuszka P, Jacobsen S, et al. 2002. Xanthine dehydrogenase of pea seedlings: a member of the plant molybdenum oxidoreductase family. *Plant Physiol. Biochem.* 40:393–400

113. Scazzocchio C, Holl FB, Foguelman AI. 1973. The genetic control of molybdoflavoproteins in *Aspergillus nidulans*. Allopurinol-resistant mutants constitutive for xanthine-dehydrogenase. *Eur. J. Biochem.* 36:428–45

114. Schrader N, Fischer K, Theis K, Mendel RR, Schwarz G, Kisker C. 2003. The crystal structure of plant sulfite oxidase provides insights into sulfite oxidation in plants and animals. *Structure* 11:1251–63

115. Schwarz G, Boxer DH, Mendel RR. 1997. Molybdenum cofactor biosynthesis. The plant protein Cnx1 binds molybdopterin with high affinity. *J. Biol. Chem.* 272:26811–14

116. Schwarz G, Schrader N, Mendel RR, Hecht HJ, Schindelin H. 2001. Crystal structures of human gephyrin and plant Cnx1 G domains: comparative analysis and functional implications. *J. Mol. Biol.* 312:405–18

117. Schwarz G, Schulze J, Bittner F, Eilers T, Kuper J, et al. 2000. The molybdenum cofactor biosynthetic protein Cnx1 complements molybdate-repairable mutants, transfers

molybdenum to the metal binding pterin, and is associated with the cytoskeleton. *Plant Cell* 12:2455–72

118. Sekimoto H, Seo M, Kawakami N, Komano T, Desloire D, et al. 1998. Molecular cloning and characterization of aldehyde oxidases in *Arabidopsis thaliana*. *Plant Cell Physiol.* 39:433–42

119. Seo M, Akaba S, Oritani T, Delarue M, Bellini C, et al. 1998. Higher activity of an aldehyde oxidase in the auxin-overproducing superroot1 mutant of *Arabidopsis thaliana*. *Plant Physiol.* 116:687–93

120. Seo M, Koshiba T. 2002. Complex regulation of ABA biosynthesis in plants. *Trends Plant Sci.* 7:41–48

121. Seo M, Peeters AJ, Koiwai H, Oritani T, Marion-Poll A, et al. 2000. The arabidopsis aldehyde oxidase 3 (AAO3) gene product catalyzes the final step in abscisic acid biosynthesis in leaves. *Proc. Natl. Acad. Sci. USA* 97:12908–13

122. Seubert PA, Grant PA, Christie EA, Farley JR, Segel IH. 1979. Kinetic and chemical properties of ATP sulphurylase from Penicillin chrysogenum. *Ciba Found. Symp.* 72:19–47

123. Skipper L, Campbell WH, Mertens JA, Lowe DJ. 2001. Pre-steady-state kinetic analysis of recombinant Arabidopsis NADH:nitrate reductase: rate-limiting processes in catalysis. *J. Biol. Chem.* 276:26995–7002

124. Slovin JP, Bandurski RS, Cohen JD. 1999. Auxin. In *Biochemistry and Molecular Biology of Plant Hormones*, ed. PJJ Hooykaas, MA Hall, KR Libbenga, pp. 115–40. Amsterdam: Elsevier Sci.

125. Sofia HJ, Chen G, Hetzler BG, Reyes-Spindola JF, Miller NE. 2001. Radical SAM, a novel protein superfamily linking unresolved steps in familiar biosynthetic pathways with radical mechanisms: functional characterization using new analysis and information visualization methods. *Nucleic Acids Res.* 29:1097–106

126. Sorger GJ, Giles NH. 1965. Genetic control of nitrate reductase in *Neurospora crassa*. *Genetics* 52:777–88

127. Stallmeyer B, Drugeon G, Reiss J, Haenni AL, Mendel RR. 1999. Human molybdopterin synthase gene: identification of a bicistronic transcript with overlapping reading frames. *Am. J. Hum. Genet.* 64:698–705

128. Stallmeyer B, Schwarz G, Schulze J, Nerlich A, Reiss J, et al. 1999. The neurotransmitter receptor-anchoring protein gephyrin reconstitutes molybdenum cofactor biosynthesis in bacteria, plants, and mammalian cells. *Proc. Natl. Acad. Sci. USA* 96:1333–38

129. Stolz JF, Basu P. 2002. Evolution of nitrate reductase: molecular and structural variations on a common function. *Chem. Biochem.* 3:198–206

130. Thony B, Auerbach G, Blau N. 2000. Tetrahydrobiopterin biosynthesis, regeneration and functions. *Biochem. J.* 347(Pt. 1):1–16

131. Unkles SE, Heck IS, Appleyard MV, Kinghorn JR. 1999. Eukaryotic molybdopterin synthase. Biochemical and molecular studies of *Aspergillus nidulans* cnxG and cnxH mutants. *J. Biol. Chem.* 274:19286–93

132. Unkles SE, Smith J, Kanan GJ, Millar LJ, Heck IS, et al. 1997. The *Aspergillus nidulans* cnxABC locus is a single gene encoding two catalytic domains required for synthesis of precursor Z, an intermediate in molybdenum cofactor biosynthesis. *J. Biol. Chem.* 272:28381–90

133. Wahl RC, Hageman RV, Rajagopalan KV. 1984. The relationship of Mo, molybdopterin, and the cyanolyzable sulfur in the Mo cofactor. *Arch. Biochem. Biophys.* 230:264–73

134. Wahl RC, Warner CK, Finnerty V, Rajagopalan KV. 1982. Drosophila melanogaster ma-1 mutants are defective in the sulfuration of desulfo Mo hydroxylases. *J. Biol. Chem.* 257:3958–62

135. Warner CK, Finnerty V. 1981. Molybdenum hydroxylases in *Drosophila*. II Molybdenum cofactor in xanthine dehydrogenase, aldehyde oxidase and pyridoxal oxidase. *Mol. Gen. Genet.* 184

136. Witte CP, Igeno MI, Mendel R, Schwarz G, Fernandez E. 1998. The *Chlamydomonas reinhardtii* MoCo carrier protein is multimeric and stabilizes molybdopterin cofactor in a molybdate charged form. *FEBS Lett.* 431:205–9

137. Wuebbens MM, Liu MTW, Rajagopalan KV, Schindelin H. 2000. Insights into molybdenum cofactor deficiency provided by the crystal structure of the molybdenum cofactor biosynthesis protein MoaC. *Structure* 8:709–18

138. Wuebbens MM, Rajagopalan KV. 1995. Investigation of the early steps of molybdopterin biosynthesis in *Escherichia coli* through the use of in vivo labeling studies. *J. Biol. Chem.* 270:1082–87

139. Wuebbens MM, Rajagopalan KV. 2003. Mechanistic and mutational studies of *Escherichia coli* molybdopterin synthase clarify the final step of molybdopterin biosynthesis. *J. Biol. Chem.* 278:14523–32

139a. Wuebbens MM, Rajagopalan KV. 1993 Structural characterization of a molybdopterin precursor. *J. Biol. Chem.* 268:13493–98

140. Xiong L, Ishitani M, Lee H, Zhu JK. 2001. The Arabidopsis LOS5/ABA3 locus encodes a molybdenum cofactor sulfurase and modulates cold stress- and osmotic stress-responsive gene expression. *Plant Cell* 13:2063–83

141. Yesbergenova Z, Yang G, Oron E, Soffer D, Fluhr R, Sagi M. 2005. The plant Mo-hydroxylases aldehyde oxidase and xanthine dehydrogenase have distinct reactive oxygen species signatures and are induced by drought and abscisic acid. *Plant J.* 42:862–76

Peptide Hormones in Plants

Yoshikatsu Matsubayashi and Youji Sakagami

Graduate School of Bio-Agricultural Sciences, Nagoya University Chikusa, Nagoya 464-8601 Japan; email: matsu@agr.nagoya-u.ac.jp

Annu. Rev. Plant Biol.
2006. 57:649–74

The *Annual Review of Plant Biology* is online at
plant.annualreviews.org

doi: 10.1146/
annurev.arplant.56.032604.144204

First published online as a
Review in Advance on
February 7, 2006

Key Words

peptide signaling, ligand-receptor interaction, receptor kinase, post-translational processing, post-translational modification

Abstract

In recent years, numerous biochemical and genetic studies have demonstrated that peptide signaling plays a greater than anticipated role in various aspects of plant growth and development. A substantial proportion of these peptides are secretory and act as local signals mediating cell-to-cell communication. Specific receptors for several peptides were identified as being membrane-localized receptor kinases, the largest family of receptor-like molecules in plants. These findings illustrate the importance of peptide signaling in the regulation of plant growth, functions that were previously ascribed to the combined action of small lipophilic compounds referred to as "traditional plant hormones." Here, we outline recent advances in the current understanding of biologically active peptides in plants, currently regarded as a new class of plant hormones.

Contents

INTRODUCTION

Cell-to-cell interaction is very important for the development of multicellular organization and for the function of most organ systems. Extensive research on animal systems has revealed that this intercellular communication is largely mediated by steroids, peptides, and other small bioactive compounds. Peptides are the most common mediators of cell-to-cell interaction in animals, probably because of the diversity of their sequence and length, which are further diversified by post-translational modifications.

In higher plants, cell-to-cell interaction is mainly mediated by small lipophilic compounds (so-called plant hormones) such as auxins, cytokinins, gibberellins, abscisic acid, ethylene, brassinosteroids, and jasmonates. These compounds mediate comprehensive cell-to-cell communication in many developmental stages. Recent findings indicate that many secretory and nonsecretory peptide signals are also involved in various aspects of plant growth regulation including defense responses, callus growth, meristem organization, self-incompatibility (SI), root growth, leaf-shape regulation, nodule development, and organ abscission. Most of these peptides have been identified by biochemical purification and genetic studies. Also, in silico genome analysis has revealed the presence of many genes encoding short open reading frames homologous to these peptides. In this review, we summarize current knowledge about the structures, functions, genes, and signal transduction properties of peptide hormones in plants, with a brief discussion about prospects for future studies of peptide ligands in plants.

SYSTEMINS

Background

Many higher plants respond to wounds from insect attacks by producing defense proteins in leaves and stems (32, 95). The best-characterized defense proteins are serine protease inhibitor proteins (protease inhibitors I and II) that have been detected in leaves of solanaceous plants such as tomato and potato (32, 88). These proteinase inhibitors interfere with the protein digestion of attacking pests and retard their growth and development

(95). Interestingly, protease inhibitors I and II rapidly accumulate not only in wounded leaves but also in undamaged leaves far from the damage sites, indicating that long-distance signal transmission induces a systemic defense response.

Isolation of Tomato Systemin (TomSys)

Supplying young excised tomato plants with water extracts of wounded tomato leaves induces production of proteinase inhibitors I and II, suggesting that this extract contains specific induction factors (94). Biochemical purification of these factors based on their proteinase inhibitor-inducing activity led to the identification of oligogalacturonides derived from the plant cell wall (6) and an 18-amino acid peptide (87). When supplied at fmol/plant levels via cut stems, the 18-amino acid peptide induced expression of proteinase inhibitors in the leaves of young tomato plants. When [^{14}C]-labeled 18-amino acid peptide was applied to wound sites, radioactivity was subsequently detected in the wounded leaves and upper leaves, indicating that the peptide is mobile in plants (77, 87). In contrast, the oligogalacturonides did not move to distal leaves when applied to leaf wounds, suggesting that they are only involved in local wound responses (1). The 18-amino acid peptide was named systemin (tomato systemin, TomSys) because of its systemic nature (**Figure 1**). However, several recent studies suggest that wound-induced release of TomSys into the vascular system activates jasmonic acid biosynthesis in surrounding vascular tissues, and that the resulting jasmonic acid acts as a long-distance signal inducing a systemic wound response (110) (discussed below).

Precursor Protein for TomSys

TomSys is produced by proteolytic processing of the C terminus of a 200-residue precursor called tomato prosystemin (67, 68) (**Figure 1**).

Prosystemin orthologs have only been detected in solanaceous species, such as potato, black nightshade, and bell pepper (23), suggesting that the systemin-mediated wound response is species specific. Prosystemin does not have the N-terminal signal sequence typical of secreted peptides, and it has been detected in the cytosol of vascular parenchyma cells in wounded tissues by immunochemical analysis (78). However, the mechanisms by which TomSys is produced from prosystemin and released into the vascular system have not been established.

Low constitutive expression of prosystemin has been detected in unwounded tomato leaves, but levels in both wounded and unwounded leaves significantly increase in response to wounding (67). Prosystemin has only been detected in vascular phloem parenchyma cells of minor veins and midribs of leaves, and in the bicollateral phloem bundles of petioles and stems of tomato (43, 78). Antisense inhibition of TomSys translation in tomato plants markedly reduces systemic induction of proteinase inhibitor expression (67, 82). In contrast, overexpression of prosystemin results in constitutive expression of defense response proteins, as if the plant were in a permanently wounded state (66).

Action of TomSys

It has long been believed that wounding causes TomSys to be processed from prosystemin, loaded into the phloem, and transported to unwounded tissues where it activates genes responsible for wound responses. However, recent genetic analysis and grafting experiments have produced novel insights into the mechanism by which TomSys activates systemic wound responses in distal leaves (52, 53, 55, 56, 96, 108, 110). The first TomSys-insensitive mutant to be characterized was *def-1* (40, 55, 57). This mutant is deficient in biosynthesis of jasmonic acid, suggesting that jasmonic acid signaling is involved in the effects of TomSys (40, 55). Further screening

Systemins

TomSys precursor

```
MGTPSYDIKNKGDDMQEEPKVKLHHEKGGDEKEKIIEKETPSQDINNKDTISSYVLRDDTQEIPKMEHEBGGYVKEKIVEKETISQYIIKIEGDDDAQEKLKVEYEEEEYEKEKIVEKETPSQDINNKGDDAQE
KPKVEHEEGDDKETPSQDIIKMEGEGALEITKVVCEKIIVREDIAVQSKPPSKRDPPKMQTDNNKL 200
```

TobHypSys precursor

```
MRVLFLIYLILSPFGAEARTLLENHEGLNVGSGYGRGANLPPPSPASSPPSKEVSNSVSPTRTDEKTSENTELVMTTIAQGENINQLFSFPTSADNYYQLASFKKLFISYLLPVSYVWNLIGSSSFDHDLVDIF
DSKSDERYWNRKPLSPPSPKPADGQRPLHSY 165
```

Hydroxyprolination
Glycosylation
↓

Hydroxyprolination
Glycosylation
↓

RGANLPOOSOASSOOSKE
TobHypSys I

NRKPLSOOSOKPADGQRP
TobHypSys II

TomHypSys precursor

```
MISFFRAFFLIIIISFLIFVGAQARTLLGNYHDDEMLIELKLESGNYGRTPYKTPPPPTSSSPTHQEIVNGRHDSVLPPPSPKTDPIIGQLTTITTTPHHDDTVAAPPVGGRHDYVASPPPPKPQDEQRQIIIT
SSSSTLPLQASY 146
```

Hydroxyprolination
Glycosylation
↓

Hydroxyprolination
Glycosylation
↓

Hydroxyprolination
Glycosylation
↓

RTOYKTOOOOTSSSOTHQ
TomHypSys I

GRHDSVLPOOSOKTD
TomHypSys III

GRHDYVASOOOOKPQDE
TomHypSys II

Phytosulfokine

```
PSK1 MKTKSEVLIFFFTLVLLLSMASSVILRE---DGFAP------PKPSPTTHEKASTK-G---DRDGV---ECKNSDSEEEC-LVKKTVA-AHTDYIYTQDLNLSP 86
PSK2 M---ANVSALL-TIALLL--CSTLMCT----ARPEPAISISITTAADPCNMEKKIE-GKLDDMHMVD-ENC-GAD-DEDC-LMRRTLV-AHTDYIYTQKKKH-P 87
PSK3 M---KQSLCLA-VLFLILSTSSSAIRRGKEDQEINPLV-----SATSVEEDSVNKLM-G-------ME--YC-GEG-DEEC-LRRRMMTESHLDYIYTQHHK--H 81
PSK4 M---GKFTTIF-IMALLL--CSTLTYA-----ARLTPTT----TTALSRENSVKEIE-G---DK--VEEESCNGIG-EEEC-LIRRSLV-LHTDYIYTQNHK--P 79
PSK5 M---VKFTTFLCIIALLL--CSTLTHAS---ARLNP------TSVYPEENSFKKLEQG---E---V---ICEGVG-EEECFLIRRTLV-AHTDYIYTQNHN--P 77
       *    :  :  :  *:*  .*:        *      .      .     *      :  * . . :*:* * :: :. * ***** .:
```

Sulfation
↓

sYIsYTQ

Figure 1

Deduced amino acid sequences of precursor proteins for systemins, phytosulfokine, SCR/SP11, SCRL, RALF, and RALFL. Domains encoding mature peptides are highlighted in yellow, and predicted N-terminal signal sequences are underlined in blue. Identical amino acid residues are indicated by an asterisk, and similar amino acid residues are indicated by a colon. Some of the systemins are glycosylated and contain hydroxyproline (one-letter abbreviation: O) residues. PSK is tyrosine sulfated (one-letter abbreviation: sY).

---

of suppressor mutants of 35S::prosystemin-mediated constitutive proteinase expression phenotypes resulted in identification of the TomSys-insensitive mutants *spr1* and *spr2* (41, 55). *spr1* has a mutation in a TomSys perception or downstream signaling component (52), whereas *spr2* is deficient in jasmonate biosynthesis. *Spr1* scion can perceive the graft-transmissible signal, resulting in systemic induction of proteinase inhibitor production when grafted onto wounded wild-type root stock (52). Combined with the fact that wounded *spr1* root stock failed to induce

a systemic response in wild-type scion, these findings suggest that TomSys is not the long-distance mobile signal but rather is a key regulator of the production of the signal (52). The available evidence indicates that jasmonic acid or a related compound is the transmissible systemic signal in this wound response (53, 56, 108, 110). This is consistent with the finding that the jasmonic acid-insensitive mutant *jai1* does not respond to the systemic signal when grafted onto wounded wild-type root stock, and with the finding that the jasmonic acid biosynthesis mutant *spr2* does not

SCR/SP11 and SCRL

```
SP11-S8   MKSAVYALLCFIFIVSGHIQEL-EANL-MKRCTRGFRKLGKCTTLEEEKCKTLY--P--R---GQCTCSDSKMNIHS-CDCKS-C--- 74
SCR-S6    MKSAIYALLCFIFLVSSHGQEV-EANL-KKNCVGKTRLPGPCGDSGASSCRDLYN-QTEKTMPVSCRCVPT--G--R-CFCSL-CK-- 77
SCR-S13   MKSAVYALLCFIFIVSGHIQEV-EANL-MMPCG-SF-MFGNCRNIGARECEKLNS-PGKRK-PSHCKCTDTQMGTYS-CDCKL-C--- 77
SP11-S9   MKSAIYALLCFIFIVSSHVQEV-EANL-RKTCVHRLNSGGSCGKSGQHDCEAFYTNKTNQK-AFYCNCTSP-FRTRY-CDCAIKCKVR 83
SP11-S12  MKSAIYALLCFIFIILSRSQEL/TEVGADKQQCKKNF--PGHCETS-ER-CENTYK-RLNKK-VFDCHC-QP-FGRRRLCTCK--C--- 75
          ****:.********:: .: **:.  *       * * *   *.       * . : * *.    * * *
```

Disulfide bond formation

$$---C_1---C_2---C_3---C_4-C_5---C_6-C_7-C_8-$$

```
SCRL1   MKYGVLFMVSCGVM-FLILSHV---EE----VEAMKKFGCNTT-HPFPGKCGNNGKSSWVSDMKKLPSAPKNRD-IRCECSDRPSLARGMPGER-VCRC-DYDC- 92
SCRL2   MKCGVLEMISCLLITFLVLSHV---RE----VESKTKWGCDMN-RPFPGKCGTNGKDTCISDIKKMPGAPKDLV-VRCECSQR-FVWKGYPPER-LCKC-QYDC- 92
SCRL3   MKSAILLMVSCVFM-FLVVSYI---QD----VEGANK-RCHLN-QMFTGKCGNDKACLGDFKNK-RFRYDL----CQCTDATQISPSLPPQR-VCNC-SRPC- 87
SCRL4   MKFAAILLVTCVLF-SLLPSHLSQGEESSMNIDAQRRPWCPSKKQVFGGSCGNDGAQQCLNNLLSTWDPSVRLSPVSCNCTP-------QPNNNILCSCPNMICP 97
SCRL5   MKFVAIFLVTCVLF-SLFPSHLSQGEESRMNINAERRPWCPSKIQMFDTNCEVDGAKQCLDLLISTWDPSVRLTRVSCICSD-------FPYRNMMCSCPNMICP 97
        **  ::::::*  :. *. *.:: .:   ::. : * . :.* .* :*.  :.: .           * *:       *  ..:* * .  *
```

RALF and RALFL

```
RALF     MG----VP--SGLILCVLIGAF-FIS---MAA--AGDSG-AYDWVMPARSG--GGCKGSIGEC-I-AE-----------E--EEFE--LDSESNRRIILAT-KKYISYGALQKNSVPCSR 86
RALFL1   MD----KS--FTLFLTLTILVVFIISSPPVQAGFANDLG-GVAWATTGDNG--SGCHGSIAEC-IGAE-----------E--EEM----DSEINRRILAT-TKYISYQSLKRNSVPCSR 91
RALFL4   MG----VK--MLLIFGLLILAM--VA----KS--VNA-----TYPLT-KS-----CING-QGC-I-GE-----------D--DELESLMDSETNRRQLARGRRYIGYDALKKNNVPCSR 78
RALFL19  MG----IK--ILLILGLLTLAV--VA----ES--ANA-----TWTLT-KS-----CVNG-QGC-I-GE-----------D--GELDYLMDSETNRRQLAARRSYISYGALRKNNVPCSR 78
RALFL22  MT----NT--RAIYAVIAILAI-VISA--VES--TGDFGDSLDFVRAGSSSLFSGCTGSIAEC-I-AE-----------E--EEME--FDSDISRRILAQ-KKYISYGAMRRNSVPCSR 90
RALFL23  MRGLSRNSGAAAIFAILLILAVHNWSVA-VSSQ-STEFA-G-DFP-PFETE---CRGTIAECSVSAALGDGGDLFYGGGEMGEEFE--MDSEINRRILAT-RRYISYGALRRNTIPCSR 108
         *      :         :     :.        :     :.    .  *.
```

```
RALF     RGASYYNCKPGAQANPYSRGCSAITRC-RS-- 115
RALFL1   RGASYYNCQNGAQANPYSRGCSKIARC-RS-- 120
RALFL4   RGRSYYDCKKRRRNNPYRRGCSAITHCYRYAR 110
RALFL19  RGRSYYDCKKRKRANPYRRGCSVITHCYRQTS 110
RALFL22  RGASYYNCQRGAQANPYSRGCSTITRC-RR-- 119
RALFL23  RGASYYNCRRGAQANPYSRGCSAITRC-RRS- 138
         ** ***:*:  :  *** **** *::* *
```

Figure 1

(*Continued*)

---

produce a graft-transmissible systemic signal (56).

Thus, upon wounding, TomSys is produced from tomato prosystemin in phloem parenchyma cells via an unknown mechanism (43, 78), and is translocated into vascular bundles where it binds to a membrane receptor (described below). TomSys then triggers various events including modulation of ion fluxes (25, 73), an increase in cytoplasmic calcium (72), upregulation of calmodulin gene expression (4), inactivation of plasma membrane H^+-ATPase activity (via calcium-dependent phosphorylation) (97), and activation of mitogen activated protein kinase (MAPK) (39, 111), leading to activation of phospholipase A (76) and allene oxide cyclase (108), which mediate release of linolenic acid from membrane lipids and formation of the jasmonic

acid intermediate 12-*oxo*-phytodienoic acid (OPDA), respectively. Activating these signaling pathways in vascular bundles leads to increased production of jasmonic acid, which further upregulates expression of the prosystemin gene (43, 108), resulting in a further increase in the level of jasmonic acid in vascular bundles, via a positive feedback loop. Finally, jasmonic acid or a related compound moves through the phloem and ultimately induces production of defensive proteins in the target leaves (22, 95).

Systemin-Like Peptides with Distinct Sequences

Tobacco plants, which, like tomato, belong to the solanaceous family, exhibit a systemic wound response similar to that of tomato

LRR-RLK:
leucine-rich repeat
receptor-like kinase

plants, but no TomSys ortholog has been found in tobacco plants. TomSys causes alkalinization of the culture medium of tomato suspension cells by modulating plasma membrane H$^+$-ATPase activity (97), and other peptides with the same effect have been detected in tobacco plants. In biochemical purification studies, two hydroxyproline-rich glycopeptides, TobHypSys I and II, were detected in wounded tobacco leaves (84) (**Figure 1**). TobHypSys I and II each contain 18 residues, and they have no sequence similarity with tomato systemin, but they each exhibit tobacco-trypsin inhibitor-inducing activity similar to that of TomSys. These findings suggest that different peptides have similar functions in different plant species. Interestingly, the tobacco peptides are produced from a single 165-residue precursor protein that has a secretion signal sequence at its N terminus (84). Purification studies show that tomato plants contain three novel hydroxyproline-rich glycopeptides (TomHypSys I, II, and III, with lengths of 20, 18, and 15 amino acids, respectively) that signal the activation of defense genes (86) (**Figure 1**). TomHypSys I, II, and III are derived from a single precursor peptide. Recently, it has been reported that this precursor protein is synthesized in phloem parenchyma cells in response to wounding and sequestered in the cell wall matrix, where TomHypSys I, II, and III are generated by proteolytic processing by processing peptidases (77a).

TomSys Receptor

Binding analysis using a [^{125}I]TomSys analog revealed the presence of a high-affinity TomSys-binding protein (SR160) in tomato cell membranes (69). The binding is rapid, saturable, and reversible, with a dissociation constant of approximately 1 nM (69, 100). Photoaffinity labeling using a [^{125}I]labeled photoactivatable analog of TomSys showed that the molecular size of SR160 is 160 kD (100). SR160 was purified by preparative SDS-PAGE and ConA column chro-

matography, and was identified as a member of the leucine-rich repeat receptor-like kinase (LRR-RLK) family, which is the largest family of plant receptor-like kinases (RLKs) (101). SR160 has a high percentage of amino acid identity with the brassinolide receptor BRI1 in *Arabidopsis* (54), and it is identical to the tomato brassinolide receptor Cu-3 (now called tBRI1) (71). On tomato brassinolide receptor mutant *cu-3* plants, all leaves other than the apical leaves are insensitive to TomSys (98). Specific interaction between tBRI1/SR160 and TomSys was also confirmed by the finding that tBRI1/SR160 overexpressed in tobacco cells is specifically photoaffinity labeled by TomSys (98). Furthermore, when tBRI1/SR160 was overexpressed in tobacco cells, in which no TomSys orthologs have been identified, transformants acquired the ability to respond to TomSys (98). These results indicate that brassinolide and systemin signaling in tomato plants use the same cell surface receptor.

It is unclear how TomSys and brassinolide can bind to a single receptor (tBRI1/SR160). Recently, it was reported that brassinolide binds a bacterially expressed small recombinant protein comprising the island domain and LRR22 (within the extracellular domain) of *Arabidopsis* BRI1 (48). This finding strongly suggests that the region comprising this recombinant protein contains the brassinolide binding site of *Arabidopsis* BRI1, and probably the brassinolide binding site of tBRI1/SR160. However, brassinolide does not compete with systemin for binding to tBRI1/SR160, suggesting that they have distinct binding sites within the same protein (101). In contrast, brassinolide competitively inhibits TomSys-induced proteinase inhibitor synthesis in leaves of excised tomato plants (98). Because the general model of receptor-mediated signal transduction involves ligand-induced changes in the global receptor conformation, the available evidence suggests that tBRI1/SR160 can exist in two distinct conformations depending on the bound ligands, and that binding of either ligand prevents the receiver from assuming the conformation induced by binding of the alternative ligand.

PHYTOSULFOKINE

Background

Lines of evidence suggest that relative rates of callus formation from plant explants and successive proliferation in vitro are highly dependent on initial cell population size. Callus formation and proliferation progress rapidly at high cell density, but significantly less rapidly at low cell density. This dependence is greater for more mature explant cells. Diluting mechanically dispersed asparagus mesophyll cells in excess culture medium significantly reduces the rate of callus formation, even if sufficient amounts of growth regulators and nutrients are supplied (60). To promote cellular growth at low cell populations, several researchers have successfully used specialized culture techniques such as nurse cultures (89), in which target cells are grown close to but physically separated from high-density nurse cells, suggesting that cell-to-cell communication mediated by a chemical factor is involved in cell growth.

Isolation of Phytosulfokine

From the 1980s until the mid-1990s, the chemical properties of the above-described factor, which is often called the "conditioning factor," were only partially characterized. In maize cell cultures, it was found to be a highly hydrophilic, neutral molecule (5), and was also highly hydrophilic, and relatively heat stable, in a carrot cell line (2).

Although low cell density inhibited proliferation of fully differentiated mesophyll cells, growth of those cells was significantly promoted by adding conditioned medium derived from asparagus cell culture (60). Using this bioassay system, the active factor was purified from the conditioned medium and identified as a sulfated peptide composed of only five amino acids (**Figure 1**). Due to the presence of sulfate esters, the peptide was named phytosulfokine (PSK) (60). Chemically synthesized PSK induces cellular dedifferentiation and proliferation of dispersed asparagus mesophyll cells, even at nanomolar concentrations. PSK is present, with an identical structure, in conditioned medium derived from cell lines of many plants, including asparagus (60), rice (64), maize (64), *Zinnia* (63), carrot (34), and *Arabidopsis* (130), indicating that it is widely distributed among higher plants.

In addition to promoting cell proliferation, PSK triggers tracheary element (TE) differentiation of dispersed *Zinnia* mesophyll cells at nanomolar concentrations (63). This phenomenon is not a secondary effect caused by increased cell density, because a high proportion of TEs differentiate directly from dispersed mesophyll cells without intervening cell division. It has also been demonstrated that PSK promotes various stages of plant growth including somatic embryogenesis (34, 42, 49), adventitious bud formation (127), adventitious root formation (128), and pollen germination (14). When PSK is applied to plant seedlings at high concentrations, it retards senescence under heat-stress condition (126).

PSK Precursor Peptides

PSK is produced by enzymatic processing of an ~80-amino acid precursor peptide that has a secretion signal at its N terminal (129) (**Figure 1**). PSK precursor genes are redundantly distributed throughout the genome (five genes in *Arabidopsis*) (130), and are found in a variety of angiosperm and gymnosperm plant species (58). The only conserved amino acids within PSK precursors are the five-amino acid PSK domain and several conserved residues immediately upstream of the PSK domain (including dibasic amino acid residues).

In *Arabidopsis*, expression of *PSK* genes is not limited to tissues in which cells actively divide and differentiate, and it has been detected in most plant parts including mature leaves, stems, roots, and calluses (130 and unpublished observation). This suggests that PSK is not a simple mitogen or differentiation initiator, and is consistent with the finding that overexpression of the *PSK* precursor gene causes no apparent changes in plant growth or development under normal growth conditions (unpublished observation). Another important observation is that rapidly proliferating suspension cells and immature cells from young tissues often grow in the absence of PSK even when they are diluted with excess medium. These observations sharply contrast with the finding that PSK is necessary for initiation of proliferation and/or transdifferentiation of fully differentiated mature cells. Thus, the available evidence suggests that plant cells gradually lose the potential to restart proliferation and/or differentiation during cellular maturation, and that PSK reactivates this potential, which is a prerequisite for initiation of in vitro culture.

PSK Receptor

Specific binding sites for [^{35}S]PSK or [^{3}H]PSK have been detected on the surface of suspension-cultured cells and in plasma-membrane-enriched fractions of various plants (61, 64). Scatchard analysis using [^{3}H]PSK detected a PSK-binding site with an affinity of approximately 150 fmol per mg of microsomal proteins and a dissociation constant (K_d) of 4.2 nM. This PSK receptor protein has been visualized by photoaffinity labeling of carrot plasma membrane fractions using a photoactivatable ^{125}I-labeled PSK analog (62). SDS-PAGE (sodium dodecyl sulfate-polyacrylamide gel electrophoresis) analysis of the labeled proteins indicates that a 120-kD protein and a minor 150-kD protein specifically interact with PSK.

The PSK-binding protein was purified from microsomal fractions of carrot cells by detergent solubilization and ligand-based affinity chromatography using a PSK-Sepharose column (59). Based on the internal sequence of the PSK-binding protein, the 120-kD and 150-kD proteins were identified as LRR-RLKs derived from a single gene. The difference in their molecular sizes is likely due to differences in post-translational modification such as glycosylation and/or truncation of part of the peptide backbone. Compared with control cells, transgenic carrot cells overexpressing the PSK-binding LRR-RLK exhibited accelerated growth and a significant increase in PSK-binding sites on their cell membranes. These findings indicate that this LRR-RLK is a component of a functional PSK receptor that directly interacts with PSK (59). The PSK-binding LRR-RLK is named PSKR1. Expression of *PSKR1* has been detected throughout tissues of the leaves, apical meristem, hypocotyl, and root of carrot seedlings, although much higher expression has been detected in cultured carrot cells. *PSKR1* antisense calluses can survive and proliferate, but their growth stops within a short time after inoculation, resulting in formation of a smaller callus than the wild type. However, *PSKR1* antisense calluses can still regenerate morphologically normal shoots and roots.

Studies revealing the in vitro function of PSK and the molecular basis of ligand-receptor interaction in PSK signaling have paved the way for research aimed at characterization of the in vivo role of PSK and its downstream signaling pathway in plants. The carrot PSK receptor, PSKR1, exhibits high-percentage amino acid identity with several LRR-RLKs found in *Arabidopsis*. The in vivo function of PSK is currently being studied using knockout mutants of the genes for those LRR-RLKs.

SCR/SP11

Background

Many flowering plants possess self-incompatibility (SI) systems in which pollen from closely related individuals is recognized and rejected by the pistil to prevent inbreeding and maintain genetic diversity within a species. A recent review of SI in plants published in the *Annual Review of Plant Biology* is recommended for readers requiring a comprehensive review of SI (115). Here, we briefly highlight SI in the genus *Brassica* to illustrate peptide ligand-receptor interaction during the initial stages of self- or nonself- recognition.

Classical genetic analyses have revealed that SI is controlled by a single multiallelic locus named the sterility locus (*S*-locus). When pollen and pistil share the same allele, a molecular interaction between the male and female determinants triggers an SI response in which metabolic activation of the pollen grain and subsequent growth of the pollen tube are completely inhibited. The fact that these SI responses occur immediately after primary contact between the pollen grain and the stigma surface strongly suggests the involvement of specific cell surface molecules in SI systems. During the past two decades, SI determinants in *Brassica* species have been identified through molecular cloning of *S*-locus genes whose products are expressed specifically in the stigma, pollen, or anther.

Ligand-Receptor Pair Involved in a Self-Incompatibility Response

Molecular and biochemical studies have identified two *S*-locus-derived proteins, *S*-locus glycoprotein (SLG) and *S*-locus receptor-like kinase (SRK), that are specifically expressed on the stigma surface. *SLG* was the first gene identified in the *S*-locus and encodes a cell wall-localized extracellular glycoprotein containing polymorphic regions (79, 116). However, the physiological role of SLG in the SI response is still not well understood and instances in which SLG expression in the stigma of certain *Brassica* species is absent, but in which the plants nonetheless exhibit an SI response, have been reported (113). The other *S*-locus gene, *SRK*, encodes a typical RLK, consisting of an SLG-like extracellular domain, a single transmembrane domain, and a cytoplasmic Ser/Thr kinase domain (107).

It has been established that SRK is a central component of the female SI response. Transformation with an *SRK* transgene results in acquisition of the corresponding SI specificity and is manifested as rejection of pollen that has an the same *S* haplotype as that of the transgene (106, 114).

Further comprehensive analysis of the *S*-locus region directed toward the identification of genes encoding ligands for SRK has revealed the presence of a small gene specifically expressed in the tapetum cells of the anther and pollen (103, 112, 117). This gene encodes a highly polymorphic secretory peptide, *S*-locus cysteine-rich protein (SCR) or *S*-locus protein 11 (SP11), and the open reading frame is composed of 74–81 amino acid residues reflecting *S*-haplotype-associated polymorphism (**Figure 1**). Several findings have confirmed that the SCR/SP11 gene product is the pollen determinant of SI. The pollen of *Brassica* plants transformed with a certain *SCR/SP11* haplotype acquired the SI specificity encoded by the transgene. Recombinant or chemically synthesized SCR/SP11 peptide applied to the stigma at concentrations as low as 50 fmol per stigma inhibited the hydration of compatible pollen (117). Furthermore, *S*-haplotype-specific ligand-receptor interactions between SCR/SP11 and SRK have been detected using ^{125}I-labeled SCR/SP11 (118) or Flag-tagged SCR/SP11 (46). The ^{125}I-SCR/SP11 binding experiments detected both high-affinity (K_d = 0.7 nM, Bmax = 180 fmol/mg protein) and low-affinity (K_d = 250 nM, Bmax = 3 pmol/mg protein) binding sites in the stigmatic microsomal membranes of the same *S*-haplotype (118). Bound SCR/SP11 induces *S*-haplotype-specific autophosphorylation of SRK (118).

As opposed to the other known peptides, no further post-translational processing, except for the removal of signal peptide, is required to yield mature SCR/SP11 peptide. Instead, correct disulfide bond formation is a prerequisite for SCR/SP11 activity. Four disulfide bonds between eight conserved cysteine amino acids (C1–C8, C2–C5, C3–C6, and C4–C7) stabilize the structure and form a loop in the C3–C4 region of the protein (70). This C3–C4 region forms a hypervariable domain depending on each *S*-haplotype and is considered one of the determinants affecting binding specificity to SRK. Another important domain was identified by site-directed mutagenesis, by which it was observed that the C3–C4 and C5–C6 regions contribute to this ligand-receptor interaction (15). The *Arabidopsis* genome also includes the large *SCR-related* (*SCRL*) gene family, which is homologous to *SCR/SP11* (123). The *SCRL* family consists of 28 homologous genes encoding 4.4–9.5 kD basic and hydrophilic peptides that have the N-terminal signal peptide and the eight conserved cysteine residues (**Figure 1**). Some *SCRLs* are expressed in various tissues including flower buds, roots, stems, and leaves, but their functions remain to be characterized.

The signal cascade downstream of SRK has not yet been elucidated, but *M* locus protein kinase (MLPK) and Armadillo-repeat-containing 1 (ARC1) are thought to be involved. MLPK is a membrane-anchored cytoplasmic kinase that may form a signaling complex with SRK (74). ARC1 is an E3 ubiquitin ligase that binds to the kinase domain of SRK in a phosphorylation-dependent manner and may target unknown substrates for ubiquitination, leading to pollen rejection (109).

CLV3

Background

As opposed to the basic body plan of animals, the body plan of higher plants is characterized by the continuous formation of new undifferentiated cells in the meristems. This reservoir of progeny cells has the potential to differentiate into many organ types. The shoot apical meristem (SAM), for example, generates all of the aboveground organs such as leaves, buds, stems, vasculature, flowers, and fruits. Despite continued cell division and cell

differentiation, the meristem retains its size and shape for the duration of the plant's life, suggesting a mechanism of balance between cell differentiation and cell division in the meristem.

The *Arabidopsis* SAM is composed of three cell layers, the epidermal cell layer (L1), the subepidermal cell layer (L2), and the underlying cell layers (L3) (see photos and illustrations in Reference 10). Although the development of each is flexible, the L1 develops into epidermis of shoots, leaves, and flowers, the L2 produces ground tissues, and L3 develops into vascular tissues and the internal tissues of leaves. The SAM cell layers can be divided into three zones according to their functions. The peripheral zone (PZ), will form the lateral organs, and the rib zone (RZ), will become the stem core. The central zone (CZ), characterized by relatively slow rates of cell division, functions as the source of cells for the PZ and RZ. This highly coordinated regulation of the SAM structure is thought to rely on an elaborate signaling network. To understand how this is achieved, genetic analyses have been undertaken to elucidate which genes are responsible for regulating meristematic functions (see Reference 28).

Identification and Functions of *CLV3*

CLAVATA (*CLV*) are a group of genes that are important in regulating SAM growth (16). Mutations in three distinct loci, *clv1*, *clv2*, and *clv3*, produce similar phenotypes related to enlargement of the vegetative and inflorescence meristems (17, 18, 47). The genes derive their name from the Latin word for club shaped, *clavata*, because the floral meristems of these mutants often form numerous extra club-like carpels. *CLV1* encodes a receptor-like serine/threonine kinase with an extracellular domain composed of leucine-rich repeats, a transmembrane domain, and a cytoplasmic kinase domain (19). *CLV2* encodes a receptor-like protein that is similar to *CLV1* except that it only has a small intracellular domain lacking a kinase (44). It has been

CLV3 and CLE

```
CLV3 MDSKSFVLLLLLFCF-LFL--HDASDLT-QAHAHVQGLSN-RKM-MMMK--MESEW-VGANGEAEKAKTKG----LG--LHEELRTVPSGPDPLHHHVNPPRQPRNNFQLP 96
CLE1 MAN-----LKFLLCLFLIC--VSLSRSS-ASRP-MFPNADGIKRGRMMI--EAEEV-LKAS--MEKLMERG----FN---ESM-RLSPGGPDP-RHH------------- 74
CLE2 MAK-----LSFTFCFLLFLL-LSS-IAA-GSRP-LEG-AR-VGV-KVRG--LSPSI-EATSPTVEDDQAAGS---HG--KSPE-RLSPGGPDP-QHH------------- 75
CLE3 MAS-----LKLWVCLVLLLV-LELTSVH-ECRP-LVAEERFSGSSRLKK--IRREL-FERLKEMKGRS-EGEETILGNTLDSK-RLSPGGPDP-RHH------------- 83
CLE4 MAS-----FKLWVCLILLL--LEF-SVH-QCRP-LVAEESPSDSGNIRK--IMREL-LKRSEELKVRSKDGQ-TVLG-TLDSK-RLSPGGPDP-RHH------------- 80
CLE5 MAT-----LILKQTLIILLIIFSLQTLSSQARI-LRSYRA-VSMGNMDSQVLLHELGFDLS-KFKGHNERR----FL--VSSD-RVSPGGPDP-QHH------------- 81
          *   .     ::  :  :::   .        .:  :       :         .     :           *  *.****  :**
                                                                                    ‾‾‾‾‾‾‾‾‾‾‾‾‾‾
                                                                                       Conserved
                                                                                        domain
```

IDA and IDL

```
IDA  M---APC--RTM----M------VLLC-FVLFLAASSSCVAA--ARIG---------ATMEM---K-KN----IKR---------LTFKNSHIFGYLPKGVPIPPSAPSKRHNSF-VNS-LPH--- 77
IDL1 MN--LSH--KTM----F------MTL--YIVFLLIFGSYNAT--ARIGPI-----KLSETEIVQTRSRQEI--IGG---------FTFKG-RVFHSFSKRVLVPPSGPSMRHNSV-VNN-LKH--- 86
IDL2 MS-SRNQ--RSRITSSFFVSFFTRTI--LLLLILLLGFCNG---ARTNTN-----VFN-SKPH--KKHNDA--VSS---------STK--QFLGFLPRHFPVPASGPSRKHNDIGLLSWHRS-SP 95
IDL3 MS-SRSH--RSR---KY--Q-LTRTIPILVLLLVLLSCCNG---ART-TN-----VFNTSSP--PKQKDV--VSPPHDHVHHQVQDHKSVQFLGSLPRQFPVPTSGPSRKHNEIGLSS-TKT--- 99
IDL4 MYPTRPHYWRRR----LSIN-RPQAFLLLILCLFFIHHCDA---SRFSSSS----VFY-RNP---NYDH---SNN---------TVRRGHFLGFLPRHLPVPASAPSRKHNDIGIQALLSP--- 93
IDL5 M---GNK--RIK---AM------MILVVMIMMVFSWRICEADSLRRYSSSSRPQRFFKVRRPNPRNHHHQNQGFNG---------DDYPPESFSGFLPKTLPIPHSAPSRKHNVYGLQSTNSHRCP 103
         *          :            :  ::  :      .    *            :            .  .:  . :* *.** .**  :
                                                                                 ‾‾‾‾‾‾‾‾‾‾‾‾‾‾‾‾‾‾‾‾
                                                                                    Conserved
                                                                                     domain
```

POLARIS

```
POLARIS
MKPRLCFNFRRRSISPCYISISYLLVAKLFKLFKIH 36
```

ENOD40

```
ENOD40 A                ENOD40 B
MELCWLTTIHGS 12         MMVLEEAWRERGVRGEGAHSSHSLT 24
```

ROT4 and DVL

```
ROT4 MAP-----EENGTCEPCK-TFGQKCSHVVKKQRAKFYILRRCIAMLVCWHDQNHDRKDS 53
DVL1 MEMKRVMMSSAERSKEKKRSISRRLGKYMKEQKGRIYIIRRCMVMLLCSHD-------- 51
DVL2 MES---IMS-LKR-KEKK-SQSRRLGKYLKEQKGRIYIIRRCVMMLLCSHD-------- 45
DVL3 MKG-----T-----KKKT-PCNKKLGGYLKEQKGRLYIIRRCVVMLICWHD-------- 40
DVL4 MK-------MGG-SKRR-VSSKGLGAVLKEQRAKLYIIRRCVVMLLCWHD-------- 41
DVL5 MKT---TGSSVGG-TKRK-MWSRGVGGVVREQKAKLYIIRRCVVMLLCWHD-------- 46
       *            .:  .  :::*:.::**:***: **:* **
```

Figure 2

Deduced amino acid sequences of CLV3, CLE, IDA, IDL, POLARIS, ROT4/DVL, and ENOD40.
Domains encoding mature peptides are shown, and predicted N-terminal signal sequences are
underlined in blue. Identical amino acid residues are indicated by an asterisk, and similar amino acid
residues are indicated by a colon.

suggested that CLV1 forms a heterodimer with CLV2, stabilized by disulfide bond(s) (122).

Conversely, *CLV3* encodes a 96-amino acid peptide including a secretory signal peptide at the N terminal (29) (**Figure 2**). Given that the phenotype of the *clv1* mutant resembles that of *clv3*, both appear to function in the same signal transduction pathway and the CLV3 peptide is therefore thought to be a ligand for the CLV1/CLV2 receptor complex. This hypothesis is further supported by the expression patterns of each gene; *CLV3* is expressed in the surface L1 and L2 cell layers of the central zone, whereas *CLV1* is expressed in the inner L3 layer of the same zone (19, 29). In addition, CLV3 is transported through the secretory pathway and extracellular secretion is required for successfully activating the CLV1/CLV2 receptor complex (93). This side-by-side expression of the CLV1 RLK and CLV3 secretory peptides suggests that the CLV3 peptide synthesized in the overlying cell layers moves to activate the CLV1 expressed in the underlying cell layers, although further biochemical studies are required to confirm this proposed ligand-receptor interaction.

The activated CLV1 signal results in the downregulation of *WUSCHEL* (*WUS*) (102), a homeodomain transcription factor that promotes stem cell activity (65). It has been demonstrated that overexpression of *WUS* leads to uncontrolled proliferation of stem cells, whereas mutations in the *WUS* gene make the stem cells undergo differentiation. Consequently, in *clv* mutants, the overexpression of *WUS* results in the overproliferation of stem cells. By contrast, whereas ectopic *WUS* expression can induce ectopic *CLV3* expression, no *CLV3* expression occurs in *wus* mutants, indicating that *WUS* positively regulates *CLV3* expression (7). Because *CLV3* acts as a negative regulator of *WUS* expression, a feedback regulatory loop exists in which *WUS* expression promotes the expression of *CLV3*, which in turn activates a signal transduction pathway that negatively regulates *WUS* expression. This feedback loop is essential for maintaining an optimal balance of stem cells in the SAM. Interestingly, overexpression of *CLV3* results in a loss of meristem function in the root apical meristem (RAM) as well as the SAM, indicating that activation of a CLV-like signaling pathway may also control cell fate in roots (38), and that the CLV3-like peptide might also be involved in regulating RAM growth.

CLE, a Gene Family Encoding CLV3-Like Peptides

The maize embryo-surrounding region protein (*ESR*) genes are expressed in a specific zone of the developing endosperm and encode secreted polypeptides (81). Although the entire sequences of CLV3 and ESR genes are different, they share a short conserved 14-amino acid sequence at the carboxy terminal region. This region is important for CLV3 peptide function, because two independently isolated mutant *CLV3* alleles (*clv3–1* and *clv3–5*) contain a mutation within this conserved region (29). Based on these observations, a database search was conducted for sequences related to the conserved 14-amino

acid region, and 25 genes encoding small secretory polypeptides were found in *Arabidopsis* (20) (**Figure 2**). These genes were named *CLAVATA3/ESR related* (*CLE*) and, in contrast to the SAM-specific expression of *CLV3*, most of the CLE peptides are expressed in various tissues throughout the development of the plant (104).

Several studies have suggested that some of the *CLE* genes can function in the SAM and/or the RAM by activating the *CLV* signaling pathway. Because *CLE40* can act as a substitute for *CLV3* in the activation of *CLV* signaling in the shoot by promoter swapping, *CLV3* and *CLE40* are considered functionally equivalent proteins that differ mainly in their expression patterns (38). *CLE40* is expressed in all tissues including the roots, and *cle40* mutant roots have a well-defined wavy appearance, suggesting a role for *CLE40* in a signaling pathway controlling taxis of the root tip. Misexpression of *CLE19* in *Arabidopsis* also resulted in dramatic consumption of the root meristem, the formation of pin-shaped pistils, and vascular islands by overactivating an endogenous CLV-like pathway involved in root meristem maintenance (11, 27).

Although the majority of CLE peptides are characterized by conservation of the 14-amino acid region near their C terminal, marked intrafamilial sequence diversity is observed in other domains. There is evidence that processing of secreted signaling polypeptides occurs in plants and it has been demonstrated that the majority of CLE peptides contain a potential dibasic processing site that could be recognized by subtilases (3). The fact that mutations in a putative Zn^{2+}-carboxypeptidase result in the suppression of the *CLE19* overexpression phenotypes supports the involvement of post-translational processing during the maturation step of CLE peptides (11). If the more divergent regions of the proteins do not constitute part of the final mature gene product, this may partially explain the high level of sequence divergence in these regions. This hypothesis is supported by findings obtained from experiments involving the direct application of synthetic peptides to *Arabidopsis* roots (26). Treatment of *Arabidopsis* roots with synthetic peptides derived from the conserved 14-amino acid region of CLV3, CLE19, and CLE40 mimics their overexpression phenotype. Interestingly, *clv2* did not respond to peptide treatment, suggesting that the CLV2 receptor-like protein is involved in CLE peptide signaling. This circumstantial evidence indicates that CLE peptides (as well as the CLV3 peptide) are translated as precursor peptides and secreted after posttranslational processing, yielding mature peptides encoded within the conserved 14-amino acid region. These mature peptides bind to a CLV2 receptor-like protein, which forms a heterodimer with CLV1 RLK, and ultimately activate the CLV signaling pathway.

RAPID ALKALINIZATION FACTOR

When mechanically wounded cells are added to suspension-cultured tomato cells, the culture medium becomes alkalinized (25). This indicates that some of the substance(s) produced by wounded cells can modulate proton efflux of intact cells. Based on such findings, substances implicated in wound responses were tested for their effect on medium alkalinization, and the results indicated that the wound hormone systemin causes a measurable increase in the pH of the culture medium (25). Because of the simplicity of this bioassay system, it was later used to screen for systemins in tobacco plants (84). During purification of tobacco systemins, a 49-amino acid peptide that causes rapid medium alkalinization but does not activate a defense response was identified in tobacco leaves (85) (**Figure 1**). This peptide was named rapid alkalinization factor (RALF). RALF peptides with similar sequences have also been found in tomato and alfalfa. RALF induces rapid activation of MAPK activity when added to cells at nanomolar concentrations (85). When supplied to *Arabidopsis* seedlings, synthetic tomato RALF peptide causes immediate arrest of root growth and

slight enlargement of meristem cells. However, the fundamental in vivo role and target of RALF signaling remains unknown.

Tomato RALF precursor cDNA encodes a 115-amino acid polypeptide containing a signal sequence at its N terminal and the RALF peptide at its C terminal (85). It is not known how mature RALF peptide is produced from its precursor, but a dibasic amino acid motif (typical of recognition sites of processing enzymes in yeast and animals) is located two residues upstream from the N terminus of mature RALF. *RALF*-like genes have been identified in many plant species, and are expressed in various tissues including roots, suggesting that the peptide has basic physiological roles in plants other than arrest of root growth (30, 85). In *Arabidopsis*, 34 genes encoding putative RALF-like peptides have been identified (80) (**Figure 1**). However, there have been no reports of gain-of-function or loss-of-function experiments involving *RALF* genes.

A putative RALF receptor has been detected in plasma membranes. Scatchard analysis using a photoaffinity-labeled RALF analog, ^{125}I-azido-RALF, revealed the presence of a single-affinity class of binding sites on the surface of cells, with a K_d of 0.8 nM (99). When UV irradiated, this photoaffinity ligand specifically cross-linked with a 25-kDa protein and 120-kDa protein in tomato cell membranes (99). Although the relationships between these two protein species in ligand reception and signal transduction are unclear, the biochemical evidence suggests that the two proteins are components of a RALF receptor complex. Because RALF precursor genes form a highly redundant family, it is difficult to perform genetic analysis of RALF signaling using the ligand. Molecular cloning of the RALF receptor and analysis of its loss-of-function mutants should provide direct clues as to the function of RALF in plants.

ENOD40

Most legume plants can engage in symbiosis with nitrogen-fixing bacteria (rhizobia) to form root nodules. Rhizobia induce nodule development on the plant by producing lipo-chito oligosaccharides called Nod factors, which trigger the initial stages of nodule development, including root hair deformation and curling, cortical cell division, and expression of several nodulin genes. Nodulin genes are classified as early nodulin (ENOD) and late nodulin (LNOD) genes, according to the timing of their induction.

Expression of one of the early nodulin genes, *ENOD40* (24, 50, 131), is rapidly induced by rhizobia in the root pericycle and in the dividing cortical cells of the nodule primordium. Knockdown of *ENOD40* arrests functional nodule development, and its overexpression accelerates nodulation, indicating that this gene plays a central role in nodule development (13). However, overexpression of *ENOD40* causes no apparent aberration of plant growth, suggesting that this gene does not directly trigger cell division, but rather sensitizes cells to division-inducing signals. *ENOD40* expression has also been detected in nonsymbiotic organs of legumes (83), and its homologs have been found in nonlegumes (51, 124). In rice, expression of *ENOD40* has been detected in stems, especially in parenchyma cells surrounding the protoxylem, suggesting that *ENOD40* plays a role in the development of vascular bundles. These findings indicate that *ENOD40* was originally involved in another plant developmental pathway, and was then recruited into the symbiotic nodulation pathway. However, a maize knockout mutant of an *ENOD40* homolog showed no phenotypic aberrations in plant growth or development (21).

ENOD40 mRNA lacks a long open reading frame (ORF) and instead contains several short ORFs. There has been great controversy over whether peptides encoded by these short ORFs function as hormones (91, 92), or whether the mRNA itself possesses biological activity (9, 33). Several studies support the former theory, but the available evidence does not exclude the latter theory. It is also possible that *ENOD40* encodes a biologically active RNA molecule that requires the peptide products for full activity.

Seven possible ORFs that may encode very small peptides have been found within the soybean *ENOD40* gene. In vitro translation of soybean *ENOD40* mRNA in wheat germ extracts resulted in the formation of a 12-amino acid peptide and a 24-amino acid peptide (peptides A and B) from overlapping ORFs (92) (**Figure 2**). Peptides A and B interact with the 93-kD subunit of sucrose synthase. Peptide-mapping experiments showed that peptide A covalently binds to Cys_{264} of soybean sucrose synthase via a disulfide bond (91), but the target of peptide B is not known. Sucrose synthase catalyzes the reversible conversion of sucrose and uridine diphosphate (UDP) into UDP-glucose and -fructose, respectively, and plays a major role in sucrose metabolism in several plant organs (119). Breakdown of sucrose is a key step in nitrogen fixation, and is a prerequisite for normal nodule development (31). Modifying sucrose synthase by peptide A leads to the activation of its sucrose cleavage activity (91). Binding of peptides A and B also reduces the rate of CDPK-dependent phosphorylation of sucrose synthase, and reduced phosphorylation of sucrose synthase increases its stability against proteasome-mediated degradation (36). However, the lack of sequence conservation of one of these peptides in several legume species makes its unlikely that it is involved in a general mechanism of *ENOD40* activity (9). In addition, the cysteine residue targeted by peptide A is not conserved in the sucrose synthase of barley, carrot, or tobacco. Because all of these binding experiments were performed in vitro, it is unclear to what extent such protein modification occurs in vivo and whether the expression of *ENOD40* modulates net sucrose cleavage activity of sucrose synthase in plants.

POLARIS

The *POLARIS* (*PLS*) gene was identified in an exhaustive analysis of a promoter trap transgenic line in which reporter gene expression is observed predominantly in roots. Expression of *PLS* has been detected in embryonic root from the heart stage, and in seedling primary and lateral root tips (121). *PLS* encodes a short transcript of ~500 nucleotides, which contains a short ORF encoding a peptide with a predicted length of 36 amino acids and a predicted molecular mass of 4.6 kD (12) (**Figure 2**). Mutation of the initiation ATG codon of this ORF causes a complete loss of *PLS* gene function, indicating that *PLS* encodes a functional polypeptide rather than a biologically active RNA molecule. The predicted 36-amino acid peptide has no secretion signal, suggesting that it functions in the cytoplasm, although no direct evidence of intracellular localization has been reported. The PLS peptide has not yet been biochemically isolated, despite attempts using protein gel blot analysis combined with immunological methods.

PLS mutant plants have reduced primary root length, due to reduced longitudinal cell expansion and increased radial expansion. Vascularization of the rosette leaves is also reduced in *PLS* mutant plants, with fewer higher-order veins arising from the major strands. These phenotypes may be partly due to changes in the hormonal sensitivity of *PLS*, because *pls* mutants exhibit hyperresponsiveness to exogenous cytokinin and reduced responsiveness to auxin, two hormones required for correct root growth and leaf vascular development. Overexpression of *PLS* reduces inhibition of root growth by exogenous cytokinins and increases leaf vascularization. Based on this circumstantial evidence, it has been proposed that *PLS* is required for correct auxin-cytokinin homeostasis, although the direct target of the PLS peptide has not been identified.

IDA

Abscission is a physiologically determined program of cell separation that enables plants to shed unwanted organs such as old leaves or floral organs. Abscission begins with formation of the abscission zone, which divides the plant body from the organs to be shed. Within several days after anthesis, *Arabidopsis* plants shed intact turgid flower petals, sepals, and stamens in a developmentally programmed manner.

An *Arabidopsis* mutant called *inflorescence deficient in abscission* (*ida*), which retains its floral organs indefinitely, was identified during screening for mutants with delayed floral abscission (8). Senesced dry floral parts of *ida* plants remained attached, even after the shedding of mature seeds. The *IDA* gene encodes a 77-amino acid peptide with an N-terminal secretion signal peptide (**Figure 2**). Promoter analysis has shown that *IDA* is expressed in the floral organ abscission zone throughout the floral abscission process. Studies have also identified five genes paralogous to *IDA*, named *IDL1-5*, in *Arabidopsis*. Sequence alignment of the deduced peptides of this family indicate the presence of a highly conserved domain flanked by basic amino acid residues near the C terminal, which is similar to the structures of the PSK and CLV3/CLE (discussed below) precursor peptides (**Figure 2**). This structure suggests that ligands are encoded within the conserved domain.

The available evidence suggests that a small peptide encoded by IDA is a ligand for HAESA, which is an *Arabidopsis* plasma membrane-associated LRR-RLK that is involved in controlling floral organ abscission (45). *HAESA* is expressed at the base of petioles and pedicels, as well as in abscission zones of floral organs. Antisense inhibition of *HAESA* causes defects in floral organ abscission, similar to the phenotype of *ida*. Structural identification of mature IDA ligands should greatly aid characterization of their ligand-receptor interaction.

ROT4/DVL1

The *ROTUNDIFOLIA4* (*ROT4*) gene was identified during screening of activation-tagged populations of Arabidopsis for isolation of leaf-shape mutants (75). *rot4-1D* is a dominant mutant that exhibits misexpression of *ROT4* due to insertion of T-DNA carrying 35S enhancers, and *rot4-1D* plants have short and rounded leaves, short floral organs, and short inflorescence stems. The phenotype is due to reduced cell proliferation, specifically in the longitudinal axis of the organs, suggesting that the *ROT4* gene controls polar cell proliferation.

The *DEVIL1* (*DVL1*) gene was identified in an activation tagging pool at around the same time that *ROT4* was identified (125). *dvl1-1D* has rounder leaves, shortened petioles, shortened siliques, and moderately horned fruit tips. This phenotype is very similar to that of *rot4-1D*.

The *ROT4* and *DVL1* genes have small ORFs that encode a 53- and 51-amino acid peptide, respectively, whose amino acid sequences are highly homologous with each other (**Figure 2**). Database searches revealed that *ROT4* and *DVL1* are members of an *Arabidopsis* gene family consisting of 23 small genes that potentially encode short peptides. Overexpression of the ROT4-GFP fusion rescues the *rot4-1D* phenotype, suggesting that expression of this small ORF is sufficient for its function. Frameshift or point mutations within *DVL1* alter the plant phenotype. Other members of this gene family seem to have a function similar to that of *ROT4/DVL1*, as indicated by the phenotypes of individual overexpressors. Functional redundancy of the *ROT4/DVL1* family is also consistent with the finding that disruption of only one member of the family causes no obvious phenotypic change.

Expression of *ROT4* has been detected by RT-PCR in the shoot apex and young leaves of wild-type *Arabidopsis* plants, although ROT4 peptide has not been biochemically detected in those tissues. In contrast, expression patterns and levels differ among members of this gene family. Like *ROT4*, *DVL1* is predominantly expressed in leaves, whereas some other members of the *ROT4/DVL1* family are expressed in flowers and roots.

Thus, the *ROT4/DVL1* family encodes small peptides that appear to be involved in regulation of polar cell proliferation during various developmental stages. Although the functional redundancy of the *ROT4/DVL1* family makes it difficult to perform loss-of-function studies, it is expected that further analysis will clarify the intrinsic function of these unique peptides.

DISCUSSION

In this review, we summarize the sequences and functions of currently known biologically active peptides in plants. The mature sequences of only four of those peptides (the systemins, PSK, SCR/SP11, and RALF) have been biochemically characterized. The remaining genes encode putative peptides whose mature form remains to be elucidated. Obviously, it is very important to identify whether these putative peptides undergo post-translational modification and/or processing before they are released from the endoplasmic reticulum (ER) or Golgi apparatus. In this discussion, we briefly summarize what is known about post-translational modification and processing of these peptides, and we discuss the possibility of identifying new peptide ligands based on the available genetic information.

Post-Translational Processing

In animals and yeasts, synthesis of biologically active peptides and proteins often involves post-translational proteolysis of precursors. Examination of the primary sequences of many animal peptide hormones has shown that cleavage of a precursor to produce mature peptide occurs on the C-terminal side of a group of basic amino acids. In animals, this cleavage is catalyzed by subtilisin/kexin-like prohormone convertases (90).

PSK, several systemins, and RALF, which are derived from larger precursor peptides, are apparently produced via the above-described post-translational processing pathway.

Sequence alignment of known PSK precursors derived from a variety of plant species indicates that the 5-amino acid PSK domain is located near the C terminal of the precursors, and that a single- or double-basic –amino acid motif is located several residues upstream from the 5-amino acid PSK domain (typically at aa –8, relative to the first residue of PSK). This basic motif is perfectly conserved in all PSK precursors, strongly suggesting that initial cleavage occurs at that point. However, subsequent aminopeptidase and carboxypeptidase cleavage is required to remove residual N-terminal extensions and C-terminal tails and thus produce mature PSK. These proposed PSK processing mechanisms sharply contrast with those of animal peptide hormones, in which the mature peptide is usually generated after initial processing on the C-terminal side of a group of basic amino acids and subsequent simple removal of terminal basic residues by carboxypeptidases. It is also unclear how these exopeptidases remove residual amino acids to specifically yield 5-amino acid PSK. One possibility is that the PSK domain escapes proteolysis due to sulfate modification of tyrosines, which often confers resistance to proteolytic digestion. Posttranslational processing of plant peptide hormones may involve regulatory mechanisms that are more complex than those of animals. Plant subtilases have greater structural similarity with prokaryotic degrading-type subtilases than with animal processing-type subtilases, due to the lack of the P-domain characteristic of the animal enzymes (3).

CLV3/CLE and IDA/IDL peptides have a conserved domain flanked by basic amino acid residues near their C terminal, but there is marked intrafamily sequence diversity in other domains, which is similar to the intrafamily sequence diversity of PSK precursor peptides. These sequence characteristics strongly suggest that small peptides encoded within the C-terminal conserved domains act as ligands for corresponding receptors. Biochemical identification of the mature sequences of these small peptides and characterization of their ligand-receptor interaction are needed to determine whether these putative secretory peptides function as hormones.

Post-Translational Modification

Some proteins must be modified in one or more ways before they can function in their mature active form. Hydroxyprolination, tyrosine sulfation, and glycosylation have been observed as post-translational modifications of plant secretory peptides.

4-Hydroxyproline has been detected in many plant glycoproteins, including extensins, proline-rich glycoproteins, and arabinogalactan proteins. This modification is necessary for glycosylation of proline residues. Formation of 4-hydroxyproline in proteins is catalyzed by the prolyl 4-hydroxylases localized in both the ER and Golgi apparatus (37, 120, 132). Recent amino acid substitution analysis revealed that hydroxylation of proline residues requires the 5-amino acid sequence [AVSTG]-Pro-[AVST]-[GAVPSTC]-[APS or acidic], although several single-amino acid substitutions are compatible with hydroxylation of proline (105). The Pro-Pro-Gly repeat and poly-Pro are also preferentially hydroxylated by these enzymes.

Several systemins undergo hydroxyprolination, although their modification patterns are unique in that not all consecutive Pro residues are converted to 4-hydroxyproline. Of the six prolines in TobHypSys I and II, five and three prolines are modified, respectively, indicating that prolyl 4-hydroxylases have complex substrate specificities. Consecutive Pro residues and/or a Pro-rich domain that generally fit the above motif have been found in the C-terminal conserved domain of CLV3/CLE and IDA/IDL peptides.

Sulfation of tyrosine residues is now recognized as a post-translational modification of plant proteins, and was discovered when sulfated PSK was first detected. The presence of an acidic residue at the −1 position of the target Tyr is a minimum requirement for sulfation (35), and recent studies using recombinant PSK precursor peptide indicate that multiple acidic residues widely distributed over the precursor peptide synergistically determine the sulfation efficiency (Y. Matsubayashi, Y. Ohnishi, M. Ogawa & Y. Sakagami, unpublished data). This unique acidic motif has not been found in any other peptide hormone precursors. Interestingly, this sulfation motif is distinct from those of sulfated animal peptides in that the plant tyrosine-sulfation enzyme recognizes a far larger domain than its animal equivalent. The computer program Sulfinator, which predicts tyrosine-sulfation sites using an algorithm based on sequences of known sulfated animal proteins, cannot detect sulfation sites within PSK precursor sequences. Tyrosylprotein sulfotransferase (TPST), which is a tyrosine sulfating enzyme, has been cloned in animals, but no ortholog of TPST has been found in the *Arabidopsis* genome, although tyrosine-sulfation activity has been detected in solubilized plant Golgi fractions. Thus, it is likely that plant TPST is structurally distinct from animal TPST and has unique substrate specificity.

Genes Encoding Putative Small Secretory Peptides

The sequencing of plant genomes has produced information that is useful for identifying genes with putative small ORFs. In addition, prediction of secretory proteins has been facilitated by advances in bioinformatics technology such as Web-based programs including SignalP, TargetP, and PSORT. Several genes encoding putative small secretory peptides have been identified using a combination of these computational techniques.

RALFLs are an example of genes that have been identified using such in silico methods (80). *RALFLs* were identified during a systematic search for short secretory peptides involving examination of records of all predicted proteins from *Arabidopsis* chromosomes 2 and 4. Using SignalP, annotated putative proteins with a length of less than 200 amino acids were analyzed for the presence of a signal peptide. Proteins likely to contain a signal peptide were further analyzed using BLAST (basic local alignment search tool) as part of the search for additional homologous sequences in *Arabidopsis*.

An advantage of the above approach is that novel genes encoding small secretory peptides can be identified irrespective of their functional redundancy and phenotypes (including silent phenotypes). However, this methodology is only applicable to gene families in which at least one member has been annotated, and in studies using this method, small genes encoding peptides are frequently overlooked by prediction programs. In fact, 20 of the 34 known *RALFL* genes have not been annotated, and have only been identified in TBLASTN searches of the C-terminal conserved region of RALFLs. Given the recent improvements in the prediction accuracy of gene prediction programs, it appears that in silico methods will continue to aid identification of secretory peptides.

Perspective

Despite the enormous importance of peptide signaling in animals, researchers largely ignored peptide signaling in plants for many years because of the prominent roles played by six lipophilic nonpeptide plant hormones in plant growth and development. It is now clear that small peptides also play important roles in intercellular and intracellular signaling in plants. The current research aimed at identification of novel peptide ligands and their signal transduction pathways should eventually produce a paradigm for hormone function in plants, and will clarify the differences and similarities in peptide signal transduction between plants and animals.

SUMMARY POINTS

1. In addition to lipophilic nonpeptide plant hormones, recent findings indicate that many secretory and nonsecretory peptide signals are involved in various aspects of plant growth regulation.

2. Some secretory peptides undergo post-translational processing and/or modification before secretion.

3. Sequencing of plant genomes has revealed the presence of many genes with putative small open reading frames encoding secretory and nonsecretory peptides with unknown functions.

FUTURE DIRECTIONS/UNRESOLVED ISSUES

1. Biochemical identification of the mature sequences of putative secretory peptides and characterization of their ligand-receptor interaction are needed to determine whether these peptides function as hormones.

2. Combining the plant genome database with in silico bioinformatic analysis can be effective in identifying peptide genes potentially involved in plant cell-to-cell communication.

LITERATURE CITED

1. Baydoun EA, Fry SC. 1985. The immobility of pectic substances in injured tomato leaves and its bearing on the identity of the wound hormone. *Planta* 165:269–76

2. Bellincampi D, Morpurgo G. 1987. Conditioning factor affecting growth in plant cells in culture. *Plant Sci.* 51:83–91

3. Berger D, Altmann T. 2000. A subtilisin-like serine protease involved in the regulation of stomatal density and distribution in *Arabidopsis thaliana*. *Genes Dev.* 14:1119–31

4. Bergey DR, Ryan CA. 1999. Wound- and systemin-inducible calmodulin gene expression in tomato leaves. *Plant Mol. Biol.* 40:815–23

5. Birnberg PR, Somers DA, Brenner ML. 1988. Characterization of conditioning factors that increase colony formation from black Mexican sweet corn protoplasts. *J. Plant Physiol.* 132:316–21

6. Bishop PD, Pearce G, Bryant JE, Ryan CA. 1984. Isolation and characterization of the proteinase inhibitor-inducing factor from tomato leaves. Identity and activity of poly- and oligogalacturonide fragments. *J. Biol. Chem.* 259:13172–77

7. Brand U, Grunewald M, Hobe M, Simon R. 2002. Regulation of CLV3 expression by two homeobox genes in Arabidopsis. *Plant Physiol.* 129:565–75

8. Butenko MA, Patterson SE, Grini PE, Stenvik GE, Amundsen SS, et al. 2003. Inflorescence deficient in abscission controls floral organ abscission in Arabidopsis and identifies a novel family of putative ligands in plants. *Plant Cell* 15:2296–307

9. Campalans A, Kondorosi A, Crespi M. 2004. Enod40, a short open reading frame-containing mRNA, induces cytoplasmic localization of a nuclear RNA binding protein in Medicago truncatula. *Plant Cell* 16:1047–59

10. Carles CC, Fletcher JC. 2003. Shoot apical meristem maintenance: the art of a dynamic balance. *Trends Plant Sci.* 8:394–401

11. Casamitjana-Martinez E, Hofhuis HF, Xu J, Liu CM, Heidstra R, Scheres B. 2003. Root-specific CLE19 overexpression and the sol1/2 suppressors implicate a CLV-like pathway in the control of Arabidopsis root meristem maintenance. *Curr. Biol.* 13:1435–41

12. Casson SA, Chilley PM, Topping JF, Evans IM, Souter MA, Lindsey K. 2002. The POLARIS gene of Arabidopsis encodes a predicted peptide required for correct root growth and leaf vascular patterning. *Plant Cell* 14:1705–21

13. Charon C, Sousa C, Crespi M, Kondorosi A. 1999. Alteration of enod40 expression modifies Medicago truncatula root nodule development induced by Sinorhizobium meliloti. *Plant Cell* 11:1953–66

14. Chen YF, Matsubayashi Y, Sakagami Y. 2000. Peptide growth factor phytosulfokine-α contributes to the pollen population effect. *Planta* 211:752–55

15. Chookajorn T, Kachroo A, Ripoll DR, Clark AG, Nasrallah JB. 2004. Specificity determinants and diversification of the Brassica self-incompatibility pollen ligand. *Proc. Natl. Acad. Sci. USA* 101:911–17

16. Clark SE. 2001. Cell signalling at the shoot meristem. *Nat. Rev. Mol. Cell Biol.* 2:276–84

17. Clark SE, Running MP, Meyerowitz EM. 1993. CLAVATA1, a regulator of meristem and flower development in Arabidopsis. *Development* 119:397–418

18. Clark SE, Running MP, Meyerowitz EM. 1995. CLAVATA3 is a specific regulator of shoot and floral meristem development affecting the same processes as CLAVATA1. *Development* 121:2057–67

19. Clark SE, Williams RW, Meyerowitz EM. 1997. The CLAVATA1 gene encodes a putative receptor kinase that controls shoot and floral meristem size in Arabidopsis. *Cell* 89:575–85

20. Cock JM, McCormick S. 2001. A large family of genes that share homology with CLAVATA3. *Plant Physiol.* 126:939–42

21. Compaan B, Ruttink T, Albrecht C, Meeley R, Bisseling T, Franssen H. 2003. Identification and characterization of a Zea mays line carrying a transposon-tagged ENOD40. *Biochim. Biophys. Acta* 1629:84–91

22. Constabel CP, Bergey DR, Ryan CA. 1995. Systemin activates synthesis of wound-inducible tomato leaf polyphenol oxidase via the octadecanoid defense signaling pathway. *Proc. Natl. Acad. Sci. USA* 92:407–11

23. Constabel CP, Yip L, Ryan CA. 1998. Prosystemin from potato, black nightshade, and bell pepper: primary structure and biological activity of predicted systemin polypeptides. *Plant Mol. Biol.* 36:55–62

24. Crespi MD, Jurkevitch E, Poiret M, d'Aubenton-Carafa Y, Petrovics G, et al. 1994. enod40, a gene expressed during nodule organogenesis, codes for a non-translatable RNA involved in plant growth. *EMBO J.* 13:5099–112

25. Felix G, Boller T. 1995. Systemin induces rapid ion fluxes and ethylene biosynthesis in Lycopersicon peruvianum cells. *Plant J.* 7:381–89

26. Fiers M, Golemiec E, Xu J, van der Geest L, Heidstra R, et al. 2005. The 14-amino acid CLV3, CLE19, and CLE40 peptides trigger consumption of the root meristem in Arabidopsis through a CLAVATA2-dependent pathway. *Plant Cell* 17:2542–53

27. Fiers M, Hause G, Boutilier K, Casamitjana-Martinez E, Weijers D, et al. 2004. Misexpression of the CLV3/ESR-like gene CLE19 in Arabidopsis leads to a consumption of root meristem. *Gene* 327:37–49

28. Fletcher JC. 2002. Shoot and floral meristem maintenance in arabidopsis. *Annu. Rev. Plant Biol.* 53:45–66

29. Fletcher JC, Brand U, Running MP, Simon R, Meyerowitz EM. 1999. Signaling of cell fate decisions by CLAVATA3 in Arabidopsis shoot meristems. *Science* 283:1911–14

30. Germain H, Chevalier E, Caron S, Matton DP. 2005. Characterization of five RALF-like genes from Solanum chacoense provides support for a developmental role in plants. *Planta* 220:447–54

31. Gordon AJ, Minchin FR, James CL, Komina O. 1999. Sucrose synthase in legume nodules is essential for nitrogen fixation. *Plant Physiol.* 120:867–78

32. Green TR, Ryan CA. 1972. Wound-induced proteinase inhibitor in plant leaves: a possible defense mechanism against insects. *Science* 175:776–77

33. Guzzo F, Portaluppi P, Grisi R, Barone S, Zampieri S, et al. 2005. Reduction of cell size induced by enod40 in *Arabidopsis thaliana*. *J. Exp. Bot.* 56:507–13

34. Hanai H, Matsuno T, Yamamoto M, Matsubayashi Y, Kobayashi T, et al. 2000. A secreted peptide growth factor, phytosulfokine, acting as a stimulatory factor of carrot somatic embryo formation. *Plant Cell Physiol.* 41:27–32

35. Hanai H, Nakayama D, Yang H, Matsubayashi Y, Hirota Y, Sakagami Y. 2000. Existence of a plant tyrosylprotein sulfotransferase: novel plant enzyme catalyzing tyrosine O-sulfation of preprophytosulfokine variants in vitro. *FEBS Lett.* 470:97–101

36. Hardin SC, Tang GQ, Scholz A, Holtgraewe D, Winter H, Huber SC. 2003. Phosphorylation of sucrose synthase at serine 170: occurrence and possible role as a signal for proteolysis. *Plant J.* 35:588–603

37. Hieta R, Myllyharju J. 2002. Cloning and characterization of a low molecular weight prolyl 4-hydroxylase from *Arabidopsis thaliana*. Effective hydroxylation of proline-rich, collagen-like, and hypoxia-inducible transcription factor alpha-like peptides. *J. Biol. Chem.* 277:23965–71

38. Hobe M, Muller R, Grunewald M, Brand U, Simon R. 2003. Loss of CLE40, a protein functionally equivalent to the stem cell restricting signal CLV3, enhances root waving in Arabidopsis. *Dev. Genes Evol.* 213:371–81

39. Holley SR, Yalamanchili RD, Moura DS, Ryan CA, Stratmann JW. 2003. Convergence of signaling pathways induced by systemin, oligosaccharide elicitors, and ultraviolet-B radiation at the level of mitogen-activated protein kinases in Lycopersicon peruvianum suspension-cultured cells. *Plant Physiol.* 132:1728–38

40. Howe GA, Lightner J, Browse J, Ryan CA. 1996. An octadecanoid pathway mutant (JL5) of tomato is compromised in signaling for defense against insect attack. *Plant Cell* 8:2067–77

41. Howe GA, Ryan CA. 1999. Suppressors of systemin signaling identify genes in the tomato wound response pathway. *Genetics* 153:1411–21

42. Igasaki T, Akashi N, Ujino-Ihara T, Matsubayashi Y, Sakagami Y, Shinohara K. 2003. Phytosulfokine stimulates somatic embryogenesis in Cryptomeria japonica. *Plant Cell Physiol.* 44:1412–16

43. Jacinto T, McGurl B, Franceschi V, Delano-Freier J, Ryan CA. 1997. Tomato prosystemin promotor confers wound-inducible, vascular bundle-specific expression of the beta-glucoronidase gene in transgenic tomato plants. *Planta* 203:406–12

44. Jeong S, Trotochaud AE, Clark SE. 1999. The Arabidopsis CLAVATA2 gene encodes a receptor-like protein required for the stability of the CLAVATA1 receptor-like kinase. *Plant Cell* 11:1925–34

45. Jinn TL, Stone JM, Walker JC. 2000. HAESA, an Arabidopsis leucine-rich repeat receptor kinase, controls floral organ abscission. *Genes Dev.* 14:108–17

46. Kachroo A, Schopfer CR, Nasrallah ME, Nasrallah JB. 2001. Allele-specific receptor-ligand interactions in Brassica self-incompatibility. *Science* 293:1824–26

47. Kayes JM, Clark SE. 1998. CLAVATA2, a regulator of meristem and organ development in Arabidopsis. *Development* 125:3843–51

48. Kinoshita T, Cano-Delgado A, Seto H, Hiranuma S, Fujioka S, et al. 2005. Binding of brassinosteroids to the extracellular domain of plant receptor kinase BRI1. *Nature* 433:167–71

49. Kobayashi T, Eun C, Hanai H, Matsubayashi Y, Sakagami Y, Kamada H. 1999. Phytosulphokine-a, a peptidyl plant growth factor, stimulates somatic embryogenesis in carrot. *J. Exp. Bot.* 50:1123–28

50. Kouchi H, Hata S. 1993. Isolation and characterization of novel nodulin cDNAs representing genes expressed at early stages of soybean nodule development. *Mol. Gen. Genet.* 238:106–19

51. Kouchi H, Takane K, So RB, Ladha JK, Reddy PM. 1999. Rice ENOD40: isolation and expression analysis in rice and transgenic soybean root nodules. *Plant J.* 18:121–29

52. Lee GI, Howe GA. 2003. The tomato mutant spr1 is defective in systemin perception and the production of a systemic wound signal for defense gene expression. *Plant J.* 33:567–76

53. Li C, Liu G, Xu C, Lee GI, Bauer P, et al. 2003. The tomato suppressor of prosystemin-mediated responses2 gene encodes a fatty acid desaturase required for the biosynthesis of jasmonic acid and the production of a systemic wound signal for defense gene expression. *Plant Cell* 15:1646–61

54. Li J, Chory J. 1997. A putative leucine-rich repeat receptor kinase involved in brassinosteroid signal transduction. *Cell* 90:929–38

55. Li L, Li C, Howe GA. 2001. Genetic analysis of wound signaling in tomato. Evidence for a dual role of jasmonic acid in defense and female fertility. *Plant Physiol.* 127:1414–17

56. Li L, Li C, Lee GI, Howe GA. 2002. Distinct roles for jasmonate synthesis and action in the systemic wound response of tomato. *Proc. Natl. Acad. Sci. USA* 99:6416–21

57. Lightner J, Pearce G, Ryan CA, Browse J. 1993. Isolation of signaling mutants of tomato (*Lycopersicon esculentum*). *Mol. Gen. Genet.* 241:595–601

58. Lorbiecke R, Sauter M. 2002. Comparative analysis of PSK peptide growth factor precursor homologs. *Plant Sci.* 163:321–32

59. **Matsubayashi Y, Ogawa M, Morita A, Sakagami Y. 2002. An LRR receptor kinase involved in perception of a peptide plant hormone, phytosulfokine.** *Science* **296:1470–72**

60. Matsubayashi Y, Sakagami Y. 1996. Phytosulfokine, sulfated peptides that induce the proliferation of single mesophyll cells of Asparagus officinalis L. *Proc. Natl. Acad. Sci. USA* 93:7623–27

61. Matsubayashi Y, Sakagami Y. 1999. Characterization of specific binding sites for a mitogenic sulfated peptide, phytosulfokine-alpha, in the plasma-membrane fraction derived from *Oryza sativa* L. *Eur. J. Biochem.* 262:666–71

62. Matsubayashi Y, Sakagami Y. 2000. 120- and 160-kDa receptors for endogenous mitogenic peptide, phytosulfokine-alpha, in rice plasma membranes. *J. Biol. Chem.* 275:15520–25

63. Matsubayashi Y, Takagi L, Omura N, Morita A, Sakagami Y. 1999. The endogenous sulfated pentapeptide phytosulfokine-alpha stimulates tracheary element differentiation of isolated mesophyll cells of zinnia. *Plant Physiol.* 120:1043–48

64. Matsubayashi Y, Takagi L, Sakagami Y. 1997. Phytosulfokine-alpha, a sulfated pentapeptide, stimulates the proliferation of rice cells by means of specific high- and low-affinity binding sites. *Proc. Natl. Acad. Sci. USA* 94:13357–62

65. Mayer KF, Schoof H, Haecker A, Lenhard M, Jurgens G, Laux T. 1998. Role of WUSCHEL in regulating stem cell fate in the Arabidopsis shoot meristem. *Cell* 95:805–15

This paper describes the identification of the phytosulfokine receptor by biochemical purification studies.

66. McGurl B, Orozco-Cardenas M, Pearce G, Ryan CA. 1994. Overexpression of the prosystemin gene in transgenic tomato plants generates a systemic signal that constitutively induces proteinase inhibitor synthesis. *Proc. Natl. Acad. Sci. USA* 91:9799–802

67. McGurl B, Pearce G, Orozco-Cardenas M, Ryan CA. 1992. Structure, expression, and antisense inhibition of the systemin precursor gene. *Science* 255:1570–73

68. McGurl B, Ryan CA. 1992. The organization of the prosystemin gene. *Plant Mol. Biol.* 20:405–9

69. Meindl T, Boller T, Felix G. 1998. The plant wound hormone systemin binds with the N-terminal part to its receptor but needs the C-terminal part to activate it. *Plant Cell* 10:1561–70

70. Mishima M, Takayama S, Sasaki K, Jee JG, Kojima C, et al. 2003. Structure of the male determinant factor for Brassica self-incompatibility. *J. Biol. Chem.* 278:36389–95

71. Montoya T, Nomura T, Farrar K, Kaneta T, Yokota T, Bishop GJ. 2002. Cloning the tomato curl3 gene highlights the putative dual role of the leucine-rich repeat receptor kinase tBRI1/SR160 in plant steroid hormone and peptide hormone signaling. *Plant Cell* 14:3163–76

72. Moyen C, Hammond-Kosack KE, Jones J, Knight MR, Johannes E. 1998. Systemin triggers an increase in cytoplasmic calcium in tomato mesophyll cells: Ca2+ mobilization from intra- and extracellular compartments. *Plant Cell Environ.* 21:1101–11

73. Moyen C, Johannes E. 1996. Systemin transiently depolarizes the tomato mesophyll cell membrane and antagonizes fusicoccin-induced extracellular acidification of mesophyll tissue. *Plant Cell Environ.* 19:464–70

74. Murase K, Shiba H, Iwano M, Che FS, Watanabe M, et al. 2004. A membrane-anchored protein kinase involved in Brassica self-incompatibility signaling. *Science* 303:1516–19

75. Narita NN, Moore S, Horiguchi G, Kubo M, Demura T, et al. 2004. Overexpression of a novel small peptide ROTUNDIFOLIA4 decreases cell proliferation and alters leaf shape in *Arabidopsis thaliana*. *Plant J.* 38:699–713

76. Narvaez-Vasquez J, Florin-Christensen J, Ryan CA. 1999. Positional specificity of a phospholipase A activity induced by wounding, systemin, and oligosaccharide elicitors in tomato leaves. *Plant Cell* 11:2249–60

77. Narvaez-Vasquez J, Pearce G, Orozco-Cardenas ML, Franceschi VR, Ryan CA. 1995. Autoradiographic and biochemical evidence for the systemic translocation of systemin in tomato plants. *Planta* 195:593–600

77a. Narvaez-Vasquez J, Pearce G, Ryan CA. 2005. The plant cell wall matrix harbors a precursor of defense signaling peptides. *Proc. Natl. Acad. Sci. USA* 102:12974–77

78. Narvaez-Vasquez J, Ryan CA. 2004. The cellular localization of prosystemin: a functional role for phloem parenchyma in systemic wound signaling. *Planta* 218:360–69

79. Nasrallah JB, Kao T-h, Chen C-H, Goldberg ML, Nasrallah ME. 1987. Amino-acid sequence of glycoproteins encoded by three alleles of the S locus of *Brassica oleracea*. *Nature* 326:617–19

80. Olsen AN, Mundy J, Skriver K. 2002. Peptomics, identification of novel cationic Arabidopsis peptides with conserved sequence motifs. *In Silico Biol.* 2:441–51

81. Opsahl-Ferstad HG, Le Deunff E, Dumas C, Rogowsky PM. 1997. ZmEsr, a novel endosperm-specific gene expressed in a restricted region around the maize embryo. *Plant J.* 12:235–46

82. Orozco-Cardenas M, McGurl B, Ryan CA. 1993. Expression of an antisense prosystemin gene in tomato plants reduces resistance toward Manduca sexta larvae. *Proc. Natl. Acad. Sci. USA* 90:8273–76

83. Papadopoulou K, Roussis A, Katinakis P. 1996. Phaseolus ENOD40 is involved in symbiotic and non-symbiotic organogenetic processes: expression during nodule and lateral root development. *Plant Mol. Biol.* 30:403–17

84. Pearce G, Moura DS, Stratmann J, Ryan CA. 2001. Production of multiple plant hormones from a single polyprotein precursor. *Nature* 411:817–20

85. Pearce G, Moura DS, Stratmann J, Ryan CA. 2001. RALF, a 5-kDa ubiquitous polypeptide in plants, arrests root growth and development. *Proc. Natl. Acad. Sci. USA* 98:12843–47

86. Pearce G, Ryan CA. 2003. Systemic signaling in tomato plants for defense against herbivores. Isolation and characterization of three novel defense-signaling glycopeptide hormones coded in a single precursor gene. *J. Biol. Chem.* 278:30044–50

87. Pearce G, Strydom D, Johnson S, Ryan CA. 1991. A polypeptide from tomato leaves activates the expression of proteinase inhibitor genes. *Science* 253:895–97

88. Plunkett G, Senear DF, Zuroske G, Ryan CA. 1982. Proteinase inhibitors I and II from leaves of wounded tomato plants: purification and properties. *Arch. Biochem. Biophys.* 213:463–72

89. Raveh D, Hubermann E, Galun E. 1973. In vitro culture of tobacco protoplasts: use of feeder techniques to support division of cells plated at low densities. *In Vitro* 9:216–22

90. Rehemtulla A, Kaufman RJ. 1992. Protein processing within the secretory pathway. *Curr. Opin. Biotechnol.* 3:560–65

91. Röhrig H, John M, Schmidt J. 2004. Modification of soybean sucrose synthase by S-thiolation with ENOD40 peptide A. *Biochem. Biophys. Res. Commun.* 325:864–70

92. Röhrig H, Schmidt J, Miklashevichs E, Schell J, John M. 2002. Soybean ENOD40 encodes two peptides that bind to sucrose synthase. *Proc. Natl. Acad. Sci. USA* 99:1915–20

93. Rojo E, Sharma VK, Kovaleva V, Raikhel NV, Fletcher JC. 2002. CLV3 is localized to the extracellular space, where it activates the Arabidopsis CLAVATA stem cell signaling pathway. *Plant Cell* 14:969–77

94. Ryan CA. 1974. Assay and biochemical properties of the proteinase inhibitor inducing factor, a wound hormone. *Plant Physiol.* 54:328–32

95. Ryan CA. 1990. Proteinase inhibitors in plants: genes for improving defenses against insects and pathogens. *Annu. Rev. Phytopathol.* 28:425–49

96. Ryan CA, Moura DS. 2002. Systemic wound signaling in plants: a new perception. *Proc. Natl. Acad. Sci. USA* 99:6519–20

97. Schaller A, Oecking C. 1999. Modulation of plasma membrane H+-ATPase activity differentially activates wound and pathogen defense responses in tomato plants. *Plant Cell* 11:263–72

98. Scheer JM, Pearce G, Ryan CA. 2003. Generation of systemin signaling in tobacco by transformation with the tomato systemin receptor kinase gene. *Proc. Natl. Acad. Sci. USA* 100:10114–17

99. Scheer JM, Pearce G, Ryan CA. 2005. LeRALF, a plant peptide that regulates root growth and development, specifically binds to 25 and 120 kDa cell surface membrane proteins of *Lycopersicon peruvianum*. *Planta* 221:667–74

100. Scheer JM, Ryan CA. 1999. A 160-kD systemin receptor on the surface of Lycopersicon peruvianum suspension-cultured cells. *Plant Cell* 11:1525–36

101. **Scheer JM, Ryan CA Jr. 2002. The systemin receptor SR160 from *Lycopersicon peruvianum* is a member of the LRR receptor kinase family. *Proc. Natl. Acad. Sci. USA* 99:9585–90**

This paper describes the identification of the systemin receptor by biochemical purification studies.

102. Schoof H, Lenhard M, Haecker A, Mayer KF, Jurgens G, Laux T. 2000. The stem cell population of Arabidopsis shoot meristems is maintained by a regulatory loop between the CLAVATA and WUSCHEL genes. *Cell* 100:635–44

103. Schopfer CR, Nasrallah ME, Nasrallah JB. 1999. The male determinant of self-incompatibility in Brassica. *Science* 286:1697–700

104. Sharma VK, Ramirez J, Fletcher JC. 2003. The Arabidopsis CLV3-like (CLE) genes are expressed in diverse tissues and encode secreted proteins. *Plant Mol. Biol.* 51:415–25

105. Shimizu M, Igasaki T, Yamada M, Yuasa K, Hasegawa J, et al. 2005. Experimental determination of proline hydroxylation and hydroxyproline arabinogalactosylation motifs in secretory proteins. *Plant J.* 42:877–89

106. Silva NF, Stone SL, Christie LN, Sulaman W, Nazarian KA, et al. 2001. Expression of the S receptor kinase in self-compatible *Brassica napus* cv. Westar leads to the allele-specific rejection of self-incompatible *Brassica napus* pollen. *Mol. Genet. Genomics* 265:552–59

107. Stein JC, Howlett B, Boyes DC, Nasrallah ME, Nasrallah JB. 1991. Molecular cloning of a putative receptor protein kinase gene encoded at the self-incompatibility locus of *Brassica oleracea. Proc. Natl. Acad. Sci. USA* 88:8816–20

108. Stenzel I, Hause B, Maucher H, Pitzschke A, Miersch O, et al. 2003. Allene oxide cyclase dependence of the wound response and vascular bundle-specific generation of jasmonates in tomato-amplification in wound signalling. *Plant J.* 33:577–89

109. Stone SL, Anderson EM, Mullen RT, Goring DR. 2003. ARC1 is an E3 ubiquitin ligase and promotes the ubiquitination of proteins during the rejection of self-incompatible Brassica pollen. *Plant Cell* 15:885–98

110. Stratmann JW. 2003. Long distance run in the wound response–jasmonic acid is pulling ahead. *Trends Plant Sci.* 8:247–50

111. Stratmann JW, Ryan CA. 1997. Myelin basic protein kinase activity in tomato leaves is induced systemically by wounding and increases in response to systemin and oligosaccharide elicitors. *Proc. Natl. Acad. Sci. USA* 94:11085–89

112. Suzuki G, Kai N, Hirose T, Fukui K, Nishio T, et al. 1999. Genomic organization of the S locus: identification and characterization of genes in SLG/SRK region of S(9) haplotype of *Brassica campestris* (syn. rapa). *Genetics* 153:391–400

113. Suzuki T, Kusaba M, Matsushita M, Okazaki K, Nishio T. 2000. Characterization of Brassica S-haplotypes lacking S-locus glycoprotein. *FEBS Lett.* 482:102–8

114. Takasaki T, Hatakeyama K, Suzuki G, Watanabe M, Isogai A, Hinata K. 2000. The S receptor kinase determines self-incompatibility in Brassica stigma. *Nature* 403:913–16

115. Takayama S, Isogai A. 2005. Self-incompatibility in plants. *Annu. Rev. Plant Biol.* 56:467–89

116. Takayama S, Isogai A, Tsukamoto C, Ueda Y, Hinata K, et al. 1987. Sequences of S-glycoproteins, products of *Brassica campestris* self-incompatibility locus. *Nature* 326:102–5

117. Takayama S, Shiba H, Iwano M, Shimosato H, Che FS, et al. 2000. The pollen determinant of self-incompatibility in Brassica campestris. *Proc. Natl. Acad. Sci. USA* 97:1920–25

118. Takayama S, Shimosato H, Shiba H, Funato M, Che FS, et al. 2001. Direct ligand-receptor complex interaction controls Brassica self-incompatibility. *Nature* 413:534–38

This paper demonstrates the direct ligand-receptor interaction involved in the self-incompatible response.

119. Thummler F, Verma DP. 1987. Nodulin-100 of soybean is the subunit of sucrose synthase regulated by the availability of free heme in nodules. *J. Biol. Chem.* 262:14730–36

120. Tiainen P, Myllyharju J, Koivunen P. 2005. Characterization of a second *Arabidopsis thaliana* prolyl 4-hydroxylase with distinct substrate specificity. *J. Biol. Chem.* 280:1142–48

121. Topping JF, Lindsey K. 1997. Promoter trap markers differentiate structural and positional components of polar development in Arabidopsis. *Plant Cell* 9:1713–25

122. Trotochaud AE, Hao T, Wu G, Yang Z, Clark SE. 1999. The CLAVATA1 receptor-like kinase requires CLAVATA3 for its assembly into a signaling complex that includes KAPP and a Rho-related protein. *Plant Cell* 11:393–406

123. Vanoosthuyse V, Miege C, Dumas C, Cock JM. 2001. Two large *Arabidopsis thaliana* gene families are homologous to the *Brassica* gene superfamily that encodes pollen coat proteins and the male component of the self-incompatibility response. *Plant Mol. Biol.* 46:17–34

124. Vleghels I, Hontelez J, Ribeiro A, Fransz P, Bisseling T, Franssen H. 2003. Expression of ENOD40 during tomato plant development. *Planta* 218:42–49

125. Wen J, Lease KA, Walker JC. 2004. DVL, a novel class of small polypeptides: overexpression alters Arabidopsis development. *Plant J.* 37:668–77

126. Yamakawa S, Matsubayashi Y, Sakagami Y, Kamada H, Satoh S. 1999. Promotive effects of the peptidyl plant growth factor, phytosulfokine-alpha, on the growth and chlorophyll content of Arabidopsis seedlings under high night-time temperature conditions. *Biosci. Biotechnol. Biochem.* 63:2240–43

127. Yamakawa S, Sakurai C, Matsubayashi Y, Sakagami Y, Kamada H, Satoh S. 1998. The promotive effects of a peptidyl plant growth factor, phytosulfokine, on the formation of adventitious roots and expression of a gene for a root-specific cystatin in cucumber hypocotyls. *J. Plant Res.* 111:453–58

128. Yamakawa S, Sakuta C, Matsubayashi Y, Sakagami Y, Kamada H, Satoh S. 1998. The promotive effects of a peptidyl plant growth factor, phytosulfokine-a, on the formation of adventitious roots and expression of a gene for a root-specific cystatin in cucumber hypocotyls. *J. Plant Res.* 111:453–58

129. Yang H, Matsubayashi Y, Nakamura K, Sakagami Y. 1999. *Oryza sativa* PSK gene encodes a precursor of phytosulfokine-alpha, a sulfated peptide growth factor found in plants. *Proc. Natl. Acad. Sci. USA* 96:13560–65

130. Yang H, Matsubayashi Y, Nakamura K, Sakagami Y. 2001. Diversity of Arabidopsis genes encoding precursors for phytosulfokine, a peptide growth factor. *Plant Physiol.* 127:842–51

131. Yang WC, Katinakis P, Hendriks P, Smolders A, de Vries F, et al. 1993. Characterization of *GmENOD40*, a gene showing novel patterns of cell-specific expression during soybean nodule development. *Plant J.* 3:573–85

132. Yuasa K, Toyooka K, Fukuda H, Matsuoka K. 2005. Membrane-anchored prolyl hydroxylase with an export signal from the endoplasmic reticulum. *Plant J.* 41:81–94

Sugar Sensing and Signaling in Plants: Conserved and Novel Mechanisms

Filip Rolland,[1] Elena Baena-Gonzalez,[2] and Jen Sheen[2]

[1] Department of Molecular Microbiology, Flanders Interuniversity Institute for Biotechnology (VIB10), and Laboratory of Molecular Cell Biology K.U. Leuven, 3001 Heverlee-Leuven, Belgium; email: filip.rolland@bio.kuleuven.be

[2] Department of Molecular Biology, Massachusetts General Hospital and Department of Genetics, Harvard Medical School, Boston, Massachusetts 02114; email: baena@molbio.mgh.harvard.edu, sheen@molbio.mgh.harvard.edu

Annu. Rev. Plant Biol. 2006. 57:675–709

The *Annual Review of Plant Biology* is online at plant.annualreviews.org

doi: 10.1146/ annurev.arplant.57.032905.105441

Key Words

glucose, sucrose, trehalose, *Arabidopsis*, hexokinase, Snf1-related protein kinase

Abstract

Sugars not only fuel cellular carbon and energy metabolism but also play pivotal roles as signaling molecules. The experimental amenability of yeast as a unicellular model system has enabled the discovery of multiple sugar sensors and signaling pathways. In plants, different sugar signals are generated by photosynthesis and carbon metabolism in source and sink tissues to modulate growth, development, and stress responses. Genetic analyses have revealed extensive interactions between sugar and plant hormone signaling, and a central role for hexokinase (HXK) as a conserved glucose sensor. Diverse sugar signals activate multiple HXK-dependent and HXK-independent pathways and use different molecular mechanisms to control transcription, translation, protein stability and enzymatic activity. Important and complex roles for Snf1-related kinases (SnRKs), extracellular sugar sensors, and trehalose metabolism in plant sugar signaling are now also emerging.

Contents

INTRODUCTION

Life on earth largely depends on the photosynthetic fixation of carbon and light energy in energy-rich sugar molecules and the concomitant production of oxygen. Consistent with their importance as the prime carbon and energy sources for most cell types, sugars, in addition, have acquired important regulatory functions early in evolution, controlling metabolism, stress resistance, growth, and development in bacteria, yeasts, plants, and animals. The regulatory roles of sugars (and nutrients in general) are most explicit in free-living microorganisms that are challenged by a constantly, often dramatically changing environment. The yeast *Saccharomyces cerevisiae* (baker's or brewer's yeast) is a particularly well-studied eukaryotic model system for sugar sensing and signaling, not in the least because of the numerous applications of alcoholic fermentation. In multicellular organisms, maintenance of nutrient and energy homeostasis within cells and tissues is of vital importance and requires the constant monitoring and adjusting of nutrient availability. Failure to do so can have dramatic consequences that cause life-threatening diseases, such as diabetes, in mammals. In photosynthetic, sugar-producing, and sessile organisms like plants, maintenance of energy homeostasis requires even more sophisticated and flexible regulatory mechanisms to account for the amazing physiological and developmental plasticity seen in plants. In recent years, a pivotal role of sugars as signaling molecules and their dramatic effects on plant growth and development have become apparent. Still, a great deal remains to be learned about the precise molecular mechanisms involved. There have been comprehensive reviews on various aspects of sugar regulation in plants (43, 67, 76, 111, 123). This review intends to provide an overview of the latest evidence supporting the central roles of sugar signals and signaling in plant life. A comparison of conserved and novel sugar regulation mechanisms in the yeast and plant model systems is presented. Promising future research directions and emerging new pathways and mechanisms are discussed.

YEAST AS A MODEL SYSTEM

In general, yeast has proven very useful as a model and experimental tool for reverse genetics approaches of eukaryotic cell biology. *Saccharomyces cerevisiae* is a facultative anaerobic organism but, even in the presence of oxygen, prefers the fermentation of sugars like glucose, fructose and sucrose to far more energy-efficient respiration. Rapid proliferation and reusable ethanol production during fermentation apparently offers a selective advantage over less ethanol-tolerant microorganisms. This yeast therefore has developed a whole array of glucose sensing and signaling pathways to enable the optimal and exclusive use of this carbon source. In view of the ancient and possibly conserved nature of cellular sugar sensing and signaling mechanisms in eukaryotes, the pathways elucidated in yeast are introduced concisely (**Figure 1**) (reviewed in 112 and 113).

An important pathway, responsible for transcriptional repression of a large number of genes involved in respiration, gluconeogenesis and the uptake and metabolism of alternative carbon-sources, is the "main glucose repression pathway" (**Figure 1***a*). Glucose activation of this pathway involves the glycolytic enzyme and sensor Hexokinase2 (Hxk2), which interacts with the Glc7-Reg1 protein phosphatase 1 (PP1) complex that dephosphorylates and inactivates a key protein kinase (PK), Sucrose nonfermenting1 (Snf1). In addition, Hxk2, in response to glucose, translocates to the nucleus, where it interacts with Mig1 [a zinc-finger DNA-binding transcription factor (TF)] to form a stable complex that recruits co-repressor proteins (91). Based on extensive random mutagenesis, it was concluded that the role of Hxk2 in glucose repression was tightly associated with its catalytic activity. However, a regulatory role for Hxk2 as a glucose sensor is recently substantiated by

the isolation and characterization of new *hxk2* mutants with uncoupled catalytic and signaling activities (112, 113).

The Snf1 PK, an ortholog of mammalian AMP-activated PK (AMPK), is required for derepression of gene expression under low glucose and starvation conditions through phosphorylation of Mig1, which causes Mig1 to dissociate from the repressor complex and subsequently undergo nuclear export.

Due to low energy efficiency, fermentative metabolism requires a high metabolic flux through glycolysis. Therefore, in the presence of glucose, the expression of hexose transporters (HXTs) with appropriate affinity and capacity is upregulated through the action of a second glucose signaling pathway (**Figure 1***b*). Two catalytically inactive Hxt homologs, Snf3 and Rgt2, function as high- and low-affinity sensors, respectively, for extracellular glucose and activate casein kinase 1 (Yck1). This HXT-induction pathway inactivates the Rgt1 transcription repressor through SCF^{GRR1} (ubiquitin E3 ligase)- and proteasome-mediated degradation of the Rgt1-interacting and -regulating proteins Std1 and Mth1. Yck1 presumably phosphorylates Std1 and Mth1, which are tethered from the nucleus to the C-terminal tails of the glucose sensors, thereby targeting them for ubiquitination and degradation (61).

The third sugar-regulatory pathway involves cAMP-PKA signaling, which enables the fast growth rate on fermentable carbon sources through a phosphorylation cascade (−). Remarkably, glucose activation of cAMP synthesis by adenylate cyclase (AC) involves a dual mechanism. Extracellular glucose or sucrose is sensed by the G-protein coupled receptor (GPCR) system (75), consisting of the Gpr1 receptor, Gpa2 (a heterotrimeric Gα-protein), and Rgs2, a negative regulator of G-protein signaling. However, activation also strictly depends on glucose uptake and phosphorylation (but no further metabolism). Some evidence again suggests a rather regulatory role for multiple hexose kinases [Hxk1 and 2 or Glucokinase1 (Glk1)], possibly

HXK: hexokinase

PK: protein kinase

TF: transcription factor

GPCR: G-protein coupled receptor

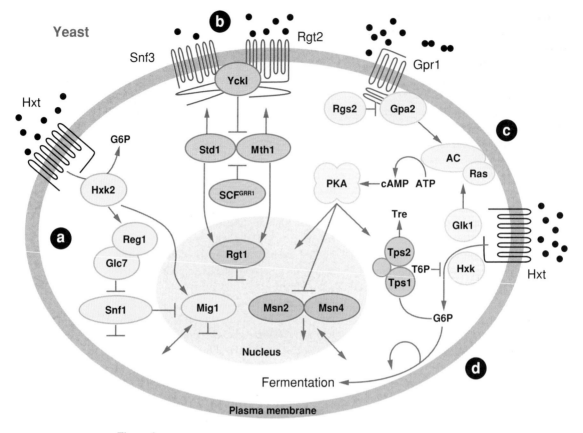

Yeast

Figure 1

Glucose sensing and signaling pathways in yeast. (*a*) The main glucose repression pathway. Hexokinase 2 (Hxk2) acts as a sensor and translocates to the nucleus in response to glucose. Sucrose nonfermenting 1 (Snf1) is required for derepression of gene expression under starvation conditions. (*b*) The HXT induction pathway. Two hexose transporter homologs, Snf3 and Rgt2, function as glucose sensors at the plasma membrane, where they activate Casein kinase I (Yck1). (*c*) The cAMP-dependent Protein Kinase A (PKA) pathway with a dual sensing system for glucose activation: extracellular glucose (and sucrose) sensing by the G-protein coupled receptor (GPCR) system and intracellular hexose phosphorylation. (*d*) Glycolytic activity and gene expression are controlled by metabolic intermediates, including trehalose-6-P (T6P), which inhibits Hxk2 activity. High and low levels of glucose (*black dots*) and sucrose (*double dots*) are indicated. See text for details.

through activation of the small Ras G-proteins, which are required for (basal) AC activity. In addition to stimulating glycolytic activity and mobilization of reserve carbohydrates and ribosomal protein gene expression, PKA activity also dramatically reduces stress resistance during growth on glucose through inactivation (phosphorylation and cytoplasmic translocation) of the Msn2 and Msn4 TFs. These TFs, isolated as multicopy-suppressors of the *snf1* mutant phenotype,

activate gene expression in the absence of high glucose levels by binding to stress response elements (STRE) in the promoters of stress-regulated genes. PKA also integrates signaling by other essential nutrients such as phosphate, sulphate, and nitrogen sources.

Finally, metabolic intermediates are involved in expression and (allosteric) activity regulation of glycolytic enzymes (**Figure 1*d***). Unexpectedly, mutant alleles conferring a general glucose-sensing defect are affected in the trehalose-6-P (T6P) synthase gene *TPS1*. Trehalose has a dual function as a storage carbohydrate and stress protectant in microorganisms and is accumulated mainly during starvation conditions. In addition, trehalose metabolism plays a vital role in controlling yeast glycolysis, at least in part through the allosteric inhibition of T6P on HXK activity.

Numerous regulatory interactions between these different pathways enable exquisite fine-tuning of the cell's response to glucose availability. Interestingly, Hxk2, PKA, and Snf1 signaling have also been implicated in yeast longevity control, and analogous ancient pathways appear to exist in mammals and plants.

SUGAR SIGNALS IN PLANTS

Sugar regulation is necessarily far more complex in plants. First, multicellular organisms need both long-distance and tissue- or even cell-type-specific signaling mechanisms and coordination with both development and physiological and environmental changes. As autotrophic, photosynthetic organisms, plants are made up of sugar exporting (source) and sugar importing (sink) tissues and organs, and sugar signals are generated from different sources at different locations (**Figure 2**). Sugar metabolism is a very dynamic process, and metabolic fluxes and sugar concentrations alter dramatically both during development and in response to environmental signals such as diurnal changes and biotic and abiotic stress (11, 12, 108, 124, 146). Integration of environmental signals with metabolism is particularly important for sessile organisms. Not surprisingly, intricate regulatory interactions with plant hormones are an essential part of the sugar sensing and signaling network. Finally, photosynthesis and carbon metabolism and allocation are themselves subject to rigorous feedback regulation and a prime target of sugar signaling.

In general, source activities like photosynthesis, nutrient mobilization, and export are upregulated under low sugar conditions, whereas sink activities like growth and storage are upregulated when carbon sources are abundantly available. Photosynthesis and sink demand need to be rigorously coordinated, and this coordination involves both metabolic (substrate and allosteric) regulation and specific sugar-signaling mechanisms. Although sucrose is the major photosynthetic product and transport sugar in plants, many sugar-signaling effects on growth and metabolism

a)

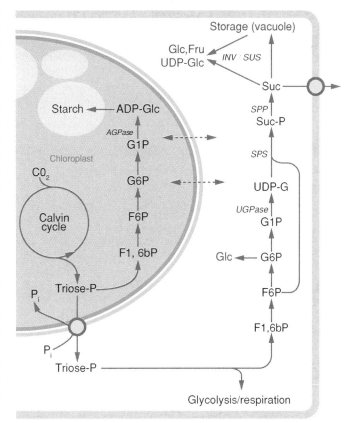

Figure 2

Sugar signals in source and sink cells. Simplified model of the major carbon fluxes and sugar signal generation by photosynthesis, transport and hydrolysis in photosynthetic source cells during the day (*a*) and night (*b*) and in sink tissue (*c*). See text for details. SPS, sucrose-P synthase; SPP, sucrose-P phosphatase; AGPase, ADP-glc pyrophosphorylase; UGPase, UDP-glucose pyrophosphorylase; INV, invertase; C-INV, cytosolic INV; CW-INV, cell wall INV; V-INV, vacuolar INV; SUS, sucrose synthase

T6P: trehalose-6-P

TPS: trehalose-6-P synthase

b)

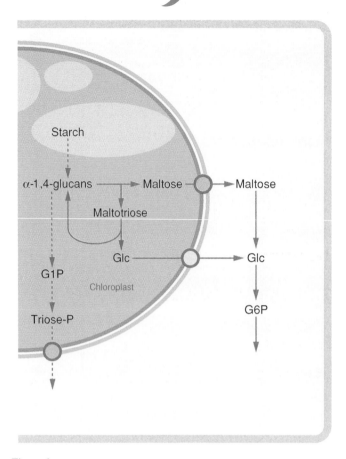

Figure 2
(*Continued*)

CW-INV: cell wall invertase

AGPase: ADP-glc pyrophosphorylase

C-INV: cytosolic invertase

SUS: sucrose synthase

V-INV: vacuolar invertase

G6P: glucose-6-P

or import of sucrose depends on the source or sink status of the leaf cells. Biotic or abiotic stress and hormonal signals can also induce cell wall invertase (CW-INV) expression and sink formation in leaf tissue (7, 109). Excess photosynthate is transiently stored as starch in the chloroplast during the day. ADP-glucose pyrophosphorylase (AGPase), a key enzyme in starch synthesis, is highly regulated by sugars (28, 42, 69). A major source for glucose signals is transitory starch breakdown from chloroplasts in leaf cells during the night (mainly via maltose and glucose export; **Figure 2***b*) and from plastids (amyloplasts) in starch-storing organs (124, 145).

In sink tissues (**Figure 2***c*), sucrose can be imported into cells through plasmodesmata (symplastic transport) or the cell wall (apoplastic transport). Intracellular sucrose is cleaved by cytoplasmic INV (C-INV), generating glucose and fructose, or by sucrose synthase (SUS) producing fructose and UDP-glucose. Sucrose can also be imported and stored in the vacuole, and vacuolar INV (V-INV) is a major intracellular source of hexoses in expanding tissues. In the apoplast, extracellular sucrose is hydrolysed by CW-INV, a major driving force in sugar unloading and gradient maintenance and therefore sink strength. These enzymes generate high levels of extracellular glucose and fructose that are taken up by hexose transporters, which are coexpressed and coordinately regulated with CW-INV (109).

It is clear that sucrose transport and hydrolysis play key regulatory roles in carbon allocation and sugar signal generation. The extensive feedback regulation of the INVs and SUS by sugar signaling generates a very sensitive self-regulatory system (67). The actual situation is more complex with transport of sugars and intermediates in and out of plastids (145) and vacuoles. Interestingly, substantial direct glucose-6-P (G6P) to glucose conversion by glucose-6-phosphatase activity is also observed in maize root tips (2). Besides photosynthesis and breakdown of sucrose and starch, the hydrolysis of cell wall

can be attributed to the action of its hydrolytic hexose products, glucose and fructose (or their downstream metabolic intermediates). However, recent studies suggest that sucrose and trehalose (or T6P) regulate specific responses that are not affected by hexoses (see below).

A current, simplified model of the major carbon fluxes in plants shows where sucrose and hexose signals can be generated and perceived in source and sink cells (**Figure 2**). In photosynthetic (source) cells (**Figure 2***a*), photosynthate generated in the Calvin cycle is exported, mainly as triose-phosphates, from the chloroplast to the cytosol, where it is used in glycolysis (and subsequently in respiration or biosynthesis) or converted to sucrose for local use or export to sink tissues. Net export

polysaccharides also likely generates sugar signals. Several cell wall glycosyl hydrolases are upregulated under stress conditions such as dark, sugar depletion, senescence and infection (23, 40, 74; J. Sheen, unpublished observations). Sugar signaling also needs to be integrated with the availability of other essential nutrients, such as nitrogen, phosphate and sulfate. Diurnal changes in nutrient availability are anticipated by the plant, and circadian regulation of enzymes involved in carbon allocation contributes significantly to an optimal use of the available resources. Moreover, recent studies have offered strong evidence for the critical role of sugar signaling in the actual regulation of diurnal gene expression (11, 33).

SUGAR CONTROL OF GROWTH AND DEVELOPMENT

Seed Development and Germination

Our understanding of sugar regulation of growth and development has benefited from studies on (mainly legume and especially bean) embryo and seed development. These processes are characterized by well-defined developmental and metabolic transitions (146). For example, during early seed development, high maternal CW-INV activity generates high hexose levels that promote embryo growth by cell division. High-resolution histographical mapping reveals a clear correlation between free glucose concentrations (present in spatial gradients) and mitotic activity in developing cotyledons (13). This role for glucose as a developmental trigger or even "morphogen" is possibly mediated by sugar (and cytokinin) control of cyclinD gene expression (107). D-type cyclins are involved in the G1/S transition, which in yeast and mammals is also controlled by nutrient availability. CYCD3;1 expression appears to be associated primarily with proliferating tissues and downregulation of CYCD3;1 might be an important factor in mitotic cell cycle exit and

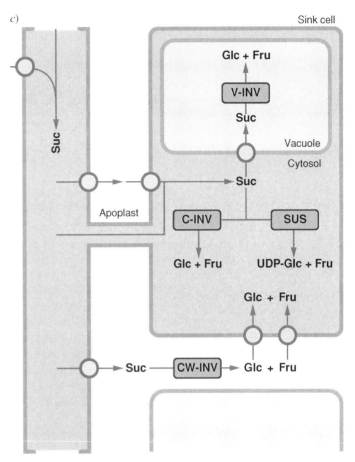

c)

Sink cell

Figure 2
(Continued)

the onset of cellular expansion and differentiation (31). In the moss *Physcomitrella patens*, targeted *cycD* gene knockouts exhibit developmental progression independent of sugar supply but have no obvious morphological phenotype (83). During the so-called transition phase, the embryo switches from a mainly mitotic growth to differentiation and growth driven by cell expansion. This switch is associated with a strong transient increase in sucrose uptake and the establishment of embryo sink strength. During this phase, free hexose levels decrease dramatically and the metabolic flux is redirected to storage product accumulation (mainly starch and nitrogen in the case of pea seeds). Sucrose, in general, appears to be rather associated with the regulation of storage- and differentiation-related

ABA: ABSCISIC
ACID
(SYNTHESIS)

GIN: GLUCOSE
INSENSITIVE

processes, in part through the regulation of metabolic enzyme gene expression and activity (146). The transition phase is also marked by a shift from high maternal CW-INV activity to high filial SUS activity.

Arabidopsis seed development follows a similar format with the major difference that it stores mainly lipids. A recent microarray study has initiated the dissection of the contrapuntal networks of gene expression during seed filling (115). Interestingly, the *wrinkled1* mutant, that has a severely reduced seed oil content, is deficient in a putative APETALA2 (AP2)-type TF that controls glycolytic gene expression and activity necessary for the conversion of sucrose into triacylglycerol biosynthesis precursors (16). Remarkably, loss-of-function mutations in the AP2 TF itself, best known for its involvement in flower development, increase seed mass and yield (60, 94). The increased cell size and number in the mutant embryos is associated with an increased hexose to sucrose ratio throughout embryo development (94); this observation suggests that this TF exerts its effect by modulating sugar metabolism and thereby signaling and development. In the storage stage of *Arabidopsis* embryogenesis, trehalose metabolism also plays an essential role (35; see below).

Although supplementation of exogenous sugars relieves the inhibition of germination by added ABA or mannose, glucose inhibits *Arabidopsis* seed germination (30, 105). Glucose-delayed seed germination is ABA-dependent but not caused by an increase in cellular ABA concentrations. This delay is rather associated with a slowing down of the decline in endogenous ABA important for the last stage of seed maturation and dessication. It appears that glucose and ABA interactions vary when their concentrations change. In addition, some sugar and ABA signaling mutants display normal germination kinetics (105), suggesting the involvement of specific signaling pathways in germination and differential responsiveness to sugars depending on the developmental stage.

Sugar and Hormone Signaling in Early Seedling Development

Positive interactions between sugar and ABA signaling are more obvious during early seedling development (43, 76). ABA mediates a postgermination developmental arrest checkpoint that enables the germinated embryos to cope with new, adverse growth conditions (82). During *Arabidopsis* early seedling development, high levels of exogenous sugars similarly repress hypocotyl elongation, cotyledon greening and expansion, and shoot development.

The developmental arrest phenotype has enabled different groups using somewhat different screening conditions to isolate a number of sugar-insensitive and sugar-hypersensitive mutants in *Arabidopsis*. These mutants are often allelic, and their characterization has revealed extensive and intimate connections between sugar and plant hormone signaling pathways (**Figure 3**) (reviewed in 43, 76, and 111). Notably, several of the sugar mutants isolated turned out to be allelic to known *ABA synthesis* (*aba*) and *ABA insensitive* (*abi*) mutants. A central role for ABA in plant sugar signaling was substantiated by the characterization of *glucose insensitive5* (*gin5*) and *gin6/sucrose uncoupling6* (*sun6*)*/sugar insensitive5* (*sis5*) as mutant alleles of *ABA3* and the gene that encodes the AP2-type transcription factor ABI4, respectively (3, 43, 76). The glucose-insensitive *sis4/gin1* mutants are allelic to *aba2*, which is deficient in a short-chain dehydrogenase/reductase (SDR1) required for ABA synthesis (21, 43, 76). Exogenous glucose specifically increased both (*a*) expression of ABA synthesis and signaling genes and (*b*) endogenous ABA levels (21). This suggests that glucose-specific accumulation of ABA is required for glucose signaling during early seedling development. The fact that not all *abi* mutants are glucose insensitive during early seedling development indicates that there are multiple pathways for glucose and ABA signaling (3).

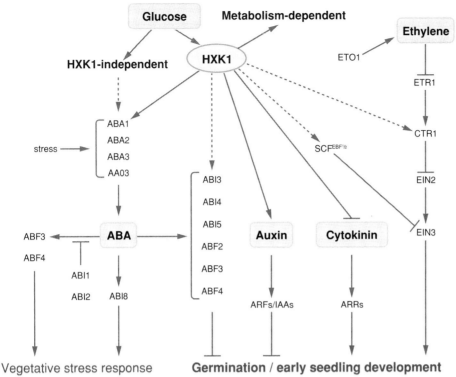

Figure 3

Model of genetic interactions between sugar and hormone signaling. HXK1-mediated glucose signaling that controls seedling development involves an increase in ABA and induces both ABA synthesis and ABA signaling gene expression. Glucose and ethylene signaling converge on the ETHYLENE INSENSITIVE3 (EIN3) TF to differentially regulate its protein stability. Finally, HXK-signaling interacts positively and negatively with auxin and cytokinin signaling, respectively. Hypothetical connections are shown (*dashed lines*). See References 43, 76, 111, and text for more details.

Another hormone that clearly interacts with sugar signals in controlling seedling development is ethylene (**Figure 3**). Treatment of wild-type seedlings with the ethylene precursor 1-aminocyclopropane-1-carboxylic acid (ACC) copies the *gin* phenotype, and epistatic analysis puts GIN1/ABA2 downstream of the ethylene receptor ETR1 (156). Whereas ethylene insensitive mutants, *etr1-1* and *ethylene insensitive2* (*ein2*), exhibit glucose hypersensitivity (156), *gin4* and *sis1* are mutant alleles of *CONSTITUTIVE TRIPLE RE-SPONSE1* (*CTR1*), a negative regulator of ethylene signaling (21, 43, 76). A molecular link between glucose and ethylene signaling is provided by the finding that glucose and ethy-lene antagonistically regulate protein stability of the EIN3 TF (152).

Mutant screens for altered sugar respon-siveness of germination and seedling devel-opment are not saturated, and new mutants are still being identified. The *glucose hypersen-sitive1* (*ghs1*) mutant contains a T-DNA in-sertion in a plastid ribosomal protein gene (93). However, because of the extensive inter-actions between sugar and other pathways, it is expected that more components will be iden-tified in screens and studies of other responses. The *bls1* mutant, for example, was isolated in a screen for photomorphogenic mutants and uncovers interactions between brassinos-teroid, light and sugar (bls) responses (73).

SnRK: Snf1-related kinase

Still, many sugar mutants identified by other screens are involved in the ABA pathway. Several sugar-insensitive and salt, low temperature, and osmotic stress-resistant mutants, for example, are allelic to *aba3* or *abi4* (reviewed in Reference 111). In addition, ABF2, an ABA response element (ABRE) binding basic leucine zipper (bZIP) TF, is an essential component of glucose signaling (65), and overexpression of ABF3 and ABF4 also increases glucose sensitivity (64). Whereas most ABA response mutants have only subtle defects in the absence of stress, the glucose-insensitive *abi8* mutant displays severely stunted growth and male sterility (14). Interestingly, the mutant has reduced expression of *V-INV*, *C-INV*, and *SUS* genes, and glucose supplementation improves viability and root growth. Consistent with the predominant expression of ABI8 in the root elongation zone, *abi8* is allelic with two dwarf mutants defective in root meristem maintenance and cell elongation (14).

Vegetative and Reproductive Development

Local sink establishment, carbon metabolism and sugar accumulation appear to play important roles in vegetative plant growth and development, presumably in part through sugar signal generation (**Figure 2**). Several lines of evidence point to a crucial role for carbon metabolism and especially the sucrose-cleaving enzymes in plant growth and development (109). A particularly remarkable finding is the spatially regulated expression of genes that encode carbon metabolic proteins like SUS, AGPase, and Snf1-related kinases (SnRK) in the tomato apical meristem; these genes serve as markers for early leaf development (101). Transgenic expression of the *Arabidopsis thaliana* homeobox leucine zipper transcription factor ATHB13, also revealed a sugar-dependent control of cotyledon and leaf shape through the specific modulation of lateral expansion of epidermal cells (51). These observations support a role for

sugar metabolism and signaling in vegetative organogenesis. Interestingly, source strength appears to determine the timing of fixed developmental programs. Decreased photosynthetic rates by antisense suppression of the RUBISCO Small subunit (RBCS) in tobacco, for example, specifically delayed early shoot morphogenesis and increased the shoot/root ratio. These results suggest that plants have a source strength threshold for full, adult shoot morphogenetic growth (137). However, metabolic control of cell growth also allows remarkable flexibility in the response to changing growth conditions, as exemplified by the gravity response of maize internodal pulvinal cells. Auxin redistribution asymmetrically increases invertase expression and activity, and this increase results in the asymmetrical accumulation of hexoses and differential cell elongation across the pulvinus (80). In dark-grown *Arabidopsis* seedlings, exogenous sucrose can induce adventitious root formation (128). Many *Arabidopsis* sugar mutants, such as *gin1*, *gin2* and *gaolaozhuangren2* (*glz2*), exhibit abnormal growth and development (20, 21, 89). Recent exciting studies have also demonstrated the critical role of *Arabidopsis* TPS1 and T6P in vegetative growth and flowering (6, 117, 118, 141).

In addition to vegetative development, carbon allocation and sugar signals also control reproductive development. Induction of flowering is associated with starch mobilization and a transient increase in leaf carbohydrate export to the shoot apical meristem, suggesting that phloem carbohydrates are a critical factor. More specifically, the C/N ratio of the phloem sap increased markedly and early during induction (24). Sucrose availability on the aerial part of the plant promotes morphogenesis and flowering of *Arabidopsis* in the dark, and supplementation with 1% exogenous sucrose rescues the late-flowering phenotype of several mutants (110). However, higher concentrations of exogenous sugars delay the transition in both wild-type and late-flowering mutants by extending the late-vegetative phase. The concomitant delay in activation of LEAFY suggests that sugars can control the expression of floral meristem identity genes (95). Interestingly, a glycosyl hydrolase, SUS, and asparagine synthase are putative direct targets for the LEAFY TF, which is essential for flower development. Expression of a CW-INV under a meristem-specific promoter causes accelerated flowering and enhanced branching of the inflorescence and seed yield, whereas the C-INV causes delayed flowering and both reduced seed yield and branching. These results emphasize the importance of the exact source, nature, and location of the sugar signals (55). More evidence for an essential role of accurate carbon allocation in reproductive development comes from the male-sterility phenotypes in tobacco with tissue-specific antisense suppression of a CW-INV (48) and antisense *SnRK* transgenic barley (155). The *Arabidopsis* sugar-insensitive mutant *glz2* shows delayed flowering, aberrant flowers and fruits, and completely sterile gynoecium (20).

Senescence and Stress

After reproduction, the final stage in plant life is senescence, which is a highly regulated stepwise process controlled by complex developmental programs and environmental signals. Leaf senescence typically coincides with a decline in chlorophyll content and photosynthetic activity. The repressive effect of sugars on photosynthetic gene expression and activity and the correlation between HXK expression and the rate of leaf senescence (29, 89, 151) are indicative of an important role for HXK-dependent sugar signaling in leaf senescence. Although this is consistent with observations in other eukaryotic organisms, there has been some controversy about the senescence-inducing effect of sugars. This controversy is mainly due to the observation that dark-treatment of leaves, and concomitant chlorophyll breakdown and starvation, can induce senescence. However, dark incubation of whole plants delays senescence, and, although some senescence-associated genes

(*SAG/SEN*) are induced by dark-incubation and repressed by sugars, a recent microarray analysis found significant differences in gene expression between dark/starvation-induced and developmental senescence (15). Moreover, leaf senescence is induced by high light and long days and is associated with hexose accumulation (32). More research is needed to explain the apparent contradiction between starvation responses and sugar accumulation during senescence.

The exact source of the sugar accumulation during senescence is not clear. In castor bean leaves, sieve tube occlusions and carbohydrate back-up seem to precede chlorophyll degradation during natural senescence (62). This observation suggests that phloem blockage by stress-induced callose deposition is the cause there. However, senescence is generally associated with massive nutrient (especially nitrogen) remobilization and export from deteriorating leaves, implying that basic cellular metabolism and phloem transport remain functional until the later stages of senescence. Although it is possible that a high sugar-to-nitrogen ratio is the trigger for senescence and nitrogen remobilisation from older leaves (103, 150), analysis of *Arabidopsis* recombinant inbred lines shows that late-senescing lines appear to mobilize glutamine, asparagine, and sulfate more efficiently than early-senescing lines (32).

Although ABA is known to promote senescence, a recent study (103) suggests that ABA is not required for the sugar-dependent induction of leaf senescence. Cytokinins, on the other hand, can delay plant senescence, and studies with *gin2* show that sugars and cytokinins work antagonistically (89). Interestingly, cytokinin-induced CW-INV expression is an essential downstream component of cytokinin-mediated local delay (green islands) of leaf senescence (7).

Senescence is also associated with the expression of *pathogenesis-related* (*PR*) genes. Both exogenous sugars and overexpression of a yeast INV in the plant vacuole or cell wall can induce *PR* gene expression (54, 130, 151).

In addition to regulating carbon partitioning, plant development, and hormone responses, INVs have an important role in stress responses as central signal integrators and modulators (109). CW-INV is induced by both abiotic stress and pathogen infection to locally increase respiratory sink activity and can be regarded as a PR protein. However, PK inhibitor studies indicate that sugars and stress regulate source and sink metabolism and defense responses through different pathways (36, 108). The *Arabidopsis* hypersenescing mutant *hys1* provides the clearest link between sugar, senescence, and stress signaling. This mutant is not only hypersensitive to sugar inhibition of seedling development and gene expression, but also allelic to *constitutive expressor of pathogenesis-related genes5* (*cpr5*) (153).

Sugar Starvation

As well as being able to sense and optimally exploit carbohydrate availability, plants need to be able to cope with carbohydrate depletion. In addition to natural diurnal fluctuations, variations in other environmental conditions can result in sugar starvation conditions. In general, plants deal with such conditions by arresting growth and by redirecting cellular activity towards basic metabolism and respiration based on protein, amino acid, and lipid catabolism rather than glycolysis. Energy-consuming biosynthetic processes, including protein synthesis, are switched off (11, 23, 58, 154). As in yeast and animal cells, starvation conditions also trigger proteolysis and autophagy in plants. *Arabidopsis* orthologs of the yeast AUTOPHAGY (ATG) protein system are induced by sucrose starvation and have been shown to be essential for nutrient recycling and senescence (23, 132).

Starvation conditions are, however, difficult to manipulate experimentally in whole plants. Cell cultures or excised roots and leaves have often been used to study starvation effects, including derepression of α-amylase gene expression (in rice suspension-cultured cells), the coordinated induction of the glyoxylate cycle (malate synthase and isoc-

itrate lyase) gene expression (in cucumber cell cultures), activation of a β-methylcrotonyl-coenzyme A carboxylase (MCCase) subunit gene (in sycamore cell suspension cultures), increased mitochondrial fatty acid β-oxidation, and increased proteolysis and nitrogen distribution (in excised maize root tips) (reviewed in Reference 154). Interestingly, induction of a number of *DARK INDUCED* (*DIN*) genes in detached leaves is inhibited by sucrose supplementation. This indicates that sugar deprivation is the key factor in the induction of these genes. Consistent with this hypothesis, *DIN* gene expression is induced by addition of a photosynthesis inhibitor and in sucrose-depleted *Arabidopsis* cell culture and tobacco BY-2 cells (40). Most *DIN* genes encode proteins involved in amino acid and carbohydrate catabolism, and some are associated with leaf senescence (40). *DIN6/ASPARAGINE SYNTHASE1* (*ASN1*), which encodes a glutamine-dependent asparagine synthase, appears to be a particularly good reporter gene for sugar starvation conditions (11, 23, 71, 104, 134). In *Arabidopsis* culture cells, sucrose deprivation leads to structural changes in mitochondria, a decrease in mitochondrial volume, a reduction in the rate of cellular respiration, and global gene expression changes (23, 45). Recent detailed analysis of the molecular events of dark-induced leaf senescence also revealed a prominent increase in asparagine levels and *ASN1* gene expression, and mitochodrial amino acid catabolism (58, 78). The clever use of an *Arabidopsis* starchless *phosphoglucomutase* (*pgm*) mutant with larger diurnal changes of endogenous sugar levels has facilitated the identification of genes controlled by low sugar conditions and the circadian clock in whole plants (11, 131).

SUGAR SENSORS

The Roles of the Hexokinase Glucose Sensor

Recent isolation and characterization of the *Arabidopsis gin2* mutants clearly identify hexokinase (AtHXK1) as a core component in plant sugar sensing and signaling (89, 152). Initial evidence for a function of plant HXK as a glucose sensor came from studies with different sugars, sugar analogs, and metabolic intermediates in a mesophyll-protoplast transient expression system and phenotypic analyses of transgenic *Arabidopsis* (59). HXK genetically functions upstream of GIN1/ABA2 in the glucose-signaling pathway (156). In order to study the function of AtHXK1 in a more physiological context, plants were grown under various light intensities that altered endogenous sugar levels and signals. Whereas increased energy supply under high light accelerated wild-type plant growth, *gin2/hxk1* mutant plants remained small with reduced cell expansion. In addition to modulating developmental arrest in the presence of high exogenous glucose, AtHXK1 has an important role in growth promotion as well. Analyses of a possible link with growth hormones revealed that *gin2* mutant hypocotyl explants are relatively insensitive to auxin-induction of cell proliferation and root formation, but hypersensitive to shoot induction by cytokinin. Consistent with this observation, seedling development of the auxin-resistant mutants *auxin resistant1* (*axr1*), *axr2*, and *transport inhibitor response1* (*tir1*), and plants with a constitutive cytokinin response or supplemented with exogenous cytokinin is insensitive to high glucose levels (**Figure 3**). The *gin2* mutant plants also display a clear delayed-senescence phenotype and reduced fertility. These effects parallel the effects of calorie restriction and mutations in signaling components on longevity in other eukaryotes (89).

Most interestingly, the *gin2* mutants still have 50% of the wild-type glucose kinase activity and accumulate normal sugar phosphate levels. Moreover, there is no clear correlation between glucose kinase activity and glucose reduction of chlorophyll content and photosynthetic gene expression. Uncoupling of metabolic and signaling activity is confirmed by the construction and analysis of two catalytically inactive *AtHXK1* alleles. Although deficient in ATP binding and phosphoryl transfer, respectively, these alleles sustain wild-type growth, repression of photosynthetic gene expression, and auxin and cytokinin responsiveness when expressed in a *gin2* background (89). Future functional characterization of the high-molecular-weight protein complexes that harbor the AtHXK1 protein will shed light on the molecular details of its regulatory interactions (Y. Cho & J. Sheen, unpublished observations).

The glucose kinase activity still present in the *gin2* mutants is probably not solely due to the presence of AtHXK2. *Arabidopsis* encodes four more hexokinase-like (AtHKL) proteins, one of which has detectable kinase activity (therefore dubbed AtHXK3) (B. Moore & J. Sheen, unpublished observations). HXK and HXL protein localization is expected to play an important role in their functions (**Figure 4a**). A completely functional glycolytic metabolon is found on the outside of the *Arabidopsis* mitochondrial membrane (44). This enables both optimal substrate availability and coordination of glucose metabolism with cellular energy demand. AtHXK1 protein indeed appears to be predominantly associated with mitochondria (B. Moore & J. Sheen, unpublished observations). A regulatory role for HXK in metabolic control of cell death similar to the situation in mammals is therefore also possible. HXK activities have also been detected in the cytosol and associated with plastids (148). Consistent with the fact that photosynthetic cells generate glucose mainly from starch breakdown, the major glucose-phosphorylating enzyme in the moss *Physcomytrella patens* is a novel type of chloroplast stromal kinase (96). Such an inner-plastidic HXK has also recently been identified in tobacco (46). Plants in general appear to contain two types of HXKs: type A kinases (such as PpHxk1 and two *Arabidopsis* HKLs), which have a predicted chloroplast transit peptide, and type B kinases (such as AtHXK1 and AtHXK2), which have a membrane anchor (96; B. Moore & J. Sheen, unpublished observations).

HKL: hexokinase-like protein

Metabolon: an enzyme complex enabling transfer of biosynthetic intermediates between catalytic sites without diffusion, thereby maximizing metabolic flux and avoiding interference

Plant

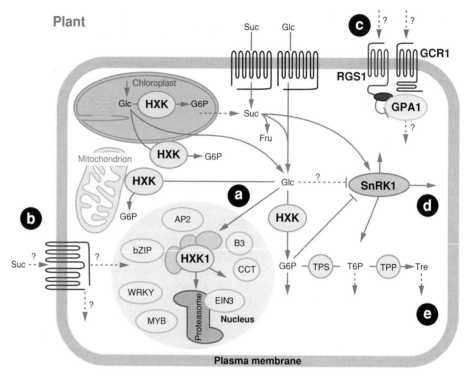

Figure 4

Model of sugar-sensing mechanisms in plants. (*a*) The HXK1 glucose sensor is mainly associated with mitochondria, possibly as part of a glycolytic metabolon. In addition, HXK1 is found in high-molecular-weight complexes in the nucleus where it controls transcription and proteasome-mediated degradation of the EIN3 TF. Other HXK and HKL proteins are also associated with the outer membrane of plastids, including chloroplasts, or cytosol. HXK can also be found in the chloroplast stroma. (*b*) Sucrose (and other disaccharides) appears to be sensed at the plasma membrane, possibly by transporter homologs. Monosaccharide transporters might have similar functions as membrane sensors. (*c*) G-protein coupled receptor signaling by RGS1 and GPA1 is involved in glucose control of seed germination and seedling development, possibly in a hexokinase-independent way. (*d*) SnRK1 proteins play an important role in plant sugar and starvation signaling, although the significance of the regulation of these proteins by sucrose (*Suc*) and G6P is still unclear. (*e*) Important regulatory effects are reported for trehalose (*Tre*) and T6P, apparently downstream of SnRK1. In the nucleus, several types of transcription factors are involved in sugar-regulated transcription. See text for more details.

Surprisingly, AtHXK1 can translocate to the nucleus as well (**Figure 4*a***) (152). More complex functions of HXK are anticipated in rice, in which ten functional HXK homologs have been identified (J.S. Jeon, personal communication). In addition to HXKs, plants also contain several fructokinases, some of which might also be involved in sugar sensing (98). Surprisingly, the *gin2* mutants are insensitive to glucose but still sensitive to fructose and

sucrose (W. Cheng & J. Sheen, unpublished observations).

Cell Surface Receptors

In yeast, extracellular glucose and sucrose are detected by the Gpr1-Gpa2 system, one of only two GPCR systems, the other one being involved in pheromone detection. Animals use different GPCR combinations to function as sweet taste receptors. Remarkably, proteins of the Type 1 Receptor (T1R) family are also expressed in the intestinal tract and enteroendocrine cells (34), where they could be involved in sugar sensing. In striking contrast to animals, where GPCRs constitute one of the major mechanisms for extracellular signal detection, plants apparently contain only one canonical G-protein α-subunit (encoded by *GPA1* and *RGA1* in *Arabidopsis* and rice, respectively). These proteins and the associated β and γ subunits have been implicated in a wide variety of developmental, light, phospholipid, and hormone responses (100), oxidative stress response, and fungal disease resistance. As the yeast proteins are involved in sensing the most vital signals (sugar and sex), one is intuitively tempted to speculate about the involvement of hetero-trimeric G-proteins in plant sugar sensing (**Figure 4b**). Interestingly, GPA1 interacts with two putative receptor proteins: G-protein coupled receptor1 (GCR1), a seven-transmembrane domain protein with some homology to classical GPCRS, and Regulator of G-protein signaling1 (RGS1), an unusual hybrid seven-transmembrane domain protein with a C-terminal RGS-box (19). RGS proteins typically negatively regulate heterotrimeric G-proteins by accelerating their intrinsic GTPase-activity. Consistent with such a function, loss of RGS1 increases GPA1 activity, which results in increased cell elongation in hypocotyls in darkness and increased cell production in roots grown in light (19). The *rgs1* mutant seedlings display insensitivity to 6% glucose, whereas RGS1 overexpressors are hypersensitive (18, 19). Based on the use of different sugars and sugar-analogs, it is suggested that AtRGS1 functions in an HXK-independent glucose signaling pathway (18). The *gpa1* mutants are hypersensitive to ABA and sugar inhibition of germination (139). Glucose addition also causes a rapid transient increase in the interaction of AtRGS1 with AtGPA1 at the plasma membrane and its subsequent internalization, possibly as a desensitization mechanism (P. Taylor & A. Jones, personal communication). It will be interesting to identify the targets and processes downstream of RGS1 and GPA1.

Another potential extracellular glucose or sucrose detection system in plants may involve proteins analogous to the yeast glucose transporter-like sensors, Snf3 and Rgt2 (**Figure 4c**) (70). More specifically, the *Arabidopsis* and tomato SUT2 sucrose transporter homologs, which do not have detectable transport activity, are characterized by a long central cytoplasmic loop reminiscent of the Snf3/Rgt2 structure. This observation suggests that these proteins may have a role in sucrose sensing (8). However, conclusive evidence for a membrane sugar sensor probably requires extensive mutant analysis. The use of nonmetabolizable disaccharides has provided useful information. For example, structure-function analysis indicates that the fructose moiety is needed for sensing nonmetabolized lactulose, palatinose, and turanose disaccharide and α−amylase repression in barley embryos (84). In addition, monosaccharide transporters with extended cytoplasmic loops are encoded in the *Arabidopsis* genome, and the monosaccharide sugar transporter STP13 acts as a heterologous multicopy suppressor of the yeast *snf4Δ* mutant growth phenotype (66).

MOLECULAR MECHANISMS OF SUGAR REGULATION

Distinct Sugar Signaling Pathways Regulate Gene Expression

Based on the role of HXK1, three distinct glucose signal transduction pathways are defined in plants (151). In the first HXK1-dependent pathway, gene expression is correlated with the HXK1-mediated signaling function. A major effect of this pathway is the repression of photosynthetic gene expression. Target genes in this pathway can now be defined genetically by the *gin2* mutants and catalytically inactive alleles (89, 151; E. Baena-Gonzalez & F. Rolland, unpublished results). A second pathway is glycolysis-dependent and can also be sustained by heterologous yeast Hxk2 activity. An example is the glucose induction of *PR1* and *PR5* gene expression (151). Finally, there is evidence for HXK1-independent signaling pathways. Glucose induction of *CHS*, *PAL1* and genes encoding AGPase as well as glucose repression of *ASN1* are observed independent of sense and antisense overexpression of *Arabidopsis* HXK1 or overexpression of yeast Hxk2 (151). Transcriptional responses to nonphosphorylated glucose analogs have been observed in *Chenopodium* cell suspension cultures, *Chlorella*, and transgenic *Arabidopsis*, although one should be cautious about possible nonspecific effects of such chemicals. The glucose analog 3-OMG, not perceived as a sugar signal, is still phosphorylated by HXK with low catalytic efficiency, and the product, 3-OMG-6-phosphate, accumulates in these cells (25). Conversely, none of the 200 glucose-responsive *Arabidopsis* genes identified in a recent study responds to 3-OMG or 6DOG (142).

There are a number of selected genes [e.g., a gene that encodes a sugar beet proton-sucrose symporter (141a)], whose expression is regulated by sucrose but not glucose or fructose; this observation points to an HXK-independent, sucrose-specific signaling pathway. Interestingly, nonmetabolizable sucrose-analogs such as palatinose and turanose can also affect carbohydrate metabolism and gene expression. This observation suggests the existence of a di-saccharide sensing system at the plasma membrane (**Figure 4**) (5, 38, 84, 135). However, such analogs again have no physiological relevance and can elicit distinct responses consistent with their perception as stress-related stimuli.

Transcription Control

Over the years, a large number of plant genes have been found to be transcriptionally regulated by sugars, consistent with the coordinated regulation of source and sink activities. Importantly, several genes that encode

metabolic proteins involved in sugar signal generation undergo transcriptional feedback-regulation by their own products. Repression of photosynthesis gene promoters, for example, has been studied in mesophyll protoplasts and transgenic seedlings. As well as photosynthesis genes, the *INV* and *SUS* genes are also extensively regulated by sugar availability (67). Also, when sugar levels are high, carbohydrate storage through starch synthesis is upregulated by the induction of genes that encode AGPase (28).

Many sugar-regulated genes and promoters have been used to screen for *Arabidopsis* mutants with potential defects in transcription control (reviewed in References 43 and 111). A screen using the regulatory sequences of the sugar-inducible AGPase large subunit (*APL3*) gene fused to a negative selection marker has identified several *impaired sucrose induction* (*isi*) mutants. Another screen based on the activity of a luciferase (LUC) reporter gene under the control of the *APL3* promoter yielded *high sugar-response* (*hsr*) mutants that exhibited elevated LUC activity and *APL3* expression in response to low sugar concentrations. The screen using sugar-regulated expression of an *Arabidopsis* β-amylase generated *low beta amylase* (*lba*) and *high beta amylase* (*hba*) mutants with altered sugar-regulation of a subset of genes. *Arabidopsis reduced sugar response* (*rsr*) mutants were selected using the sucrose-activated promoter of patatin, a potato tuber storage protein. Molecular analysis of the mutants will bring new information on the mechanisms underlying sugar-mediated transcription control.

Genome-Wide Expression Analyses

From the examples described above, it is clear that our knowledge about sugar-regulated gene expression largely comes from data from a variety of species, mutants, tissues, developmental stages, and treatments. The new microarray technologies now enablE genome-wide expression analyses of *Arabidopsis* sugar and starvation responses. Soil-grown adult

Arabidopsis phosphorus-deficient3 (*pho3*) mutant plants are used specifically to study the genomic response to sugar accumulation (79). This mutant is affected in the SUCROSE TRANSPORTER2 (SUC2), and therefore accumulates soluble sugars, starch, and anthocyanins. High expression levels of genes that encode sucrose phosphate synthases (SPS), the plastid glucose G6P/phosphate translocator (characteristically expressed only in heterotrophic tissues), and the AGPase large subunits are consistent with the starch accumulation in the mutant. Also consistent with the phenotype, there is a large increase in the expression of TFs and enzymes involved in anthocyanin biosynthesis. Apparently, secondary metabolism is also an important target for transcription regulation by sugars. Using a more comprehensive approach, the short-term effects of glucose and nitrogen in global gene expression in the dark have been studied in liquid-grown *Arabidopsis* seedlings (104). The use of the protein synthesis inhibitor cycloheximide shows that glucose repression is a more direct process than glucose induction, which often requires de novo protein synthesis. TFs with sugar-regulated expression profiles are likely regulators of the broad transcriptional response to sugars.

Several global gene expression studies have been published on sugar starvation responses. Using cDNA macroarrays and seedlings grown in the presence or absence of sucrose, a small number of (mostly carbohydrate and amino acid metabolism) genes were shown to be upregulated in concert during sugar depletion (74). A more detailed analysis of nutrient mobilization in response to sucrose starvation in *Arabidopsis* cells cultured in suspension has been carried out using the ATH1 GeneChip (23). Consistent with extensive nutrient recycling for cell survival, genes that were upregulated are involved in carbohydrate, amino acid, protein and lipid catabolism and autophagy. Although these cultures were nonphotosynthetic, several photosynthesis-associated genes were also upregulated upon starvation. Genes that were downregulated

are involved in metabolism (biosynthesis), protein synthesis, and cell division. Similar expression profiles were observed in the responses of *Arabidopsis* rosettes to an extended night period and a starchless *pgm* mutant at the end of the night (11, 131). These studies also introduce the use of MAPMAN, a practical and informative tool to display complex genomic data in diagrams of metabolic and regulatory pathways. Interestingly, the molecular events in dark-induced senescence of *Arabidopsis* leaves (analyzed using a combination of cDNA microarray and biochemical analyses) exhibited extensive similarities with the sugar starvation response. Many TF genes were identified as putative regulators (78). However, a comparative microarray study reveals significant differences in gene expression and signaling pathways between developmental and dark/starvation-induced senescence (15).

Extended dark treatment causes a starvation condition that overrides the transcriptional regulation by circadian rhythm. However, in addition to energizing sugar production and (re)setting the clock, light can also directly affect gene expression through light-specific mechanisms. In a recent study, the effects of both light and sugar were examined. The results reveal that the majority of affected genes are co-regulated by both stimuli (133, 134). More extensive time-course gene expression analyses using wild-type and the *pgm* mutant plants under a 12 h photoperiod provide a clear picture of the essential roles of sugar signals for a large set of circadian regulated genes (11).

Coordination between sugar and other nutrient metabolic pathways is essential to optimize the use of energy resources. A number of genes involved in N-assimilation are co-regulated by sugars, and N-availability extensively regulates carbon-metabolic-gene expression (26, 116, 144). Sugar responses in general depend significantly on the N-status of the plant. Sugar repression of photosynthetic gene expression, chlorophyll accumulation and seedling development are antagonized by nitrate (89). Complex interactions are observed between C and N signaling (116, 144). The effects of nitrogen and a combination of both glucose and nitrogen have been recently analyzed (104). Interestingly, most of the nitrogen responses seem to require the presence of a carbon source. A combination of microarray and extensive informatics analyses, classification, and modeling provides evidence for combined carbon and nitrogen signaling, especially in the control of metabolism and energy and protein synthesis, even suggesting the existence of a single CN-responsive regulatory cis-element for a subset of genes (97).

Oxygen availability also affects sugar signaling, especially the regulation of sucrose metabolism (68). A recent microarray analysis provides more insights into the effects of sucrose on gene expression in *Arabidopsis* seedlings under anoxia conditions (85).

Promoter Elements and Transcription Factors

The large genomic datasets generated in microarray experiments provide an excellent opportunity to identify conserved DNA elements in the promoters of co-regulated genes. Currently, most information on regulatory cis-elements involved in sugar signaling comes from a few selected genes, encoding sweet potato tuber and cereal seed proteins, and proteins involved in maize photosynthesis.

Studies on sugar activation of sweet potato tuber class I *patatin*, *SUS*, *sporamin* and *β-amylase* promoters identified several sucrose-responsive cis-elements, including the Sucrose-responsive element (SURE), A- and B-boxes, the TGGACGG element, an SP8 motif, and an SP8-binding protein, SPF1 (reviewed in Reference 111). SPF1 is a WRKY -type sucrose-repressed negative regulator with putative orthologs in other species, including *Arabidopsis*. These factors typically bind to (T)TGAC(C/T) W-boxes, also found in defense-related gene pro-

moters. A sugar-induced WRKY-type TF, SUSIBA2 that is expressed in barley endosperm binds to the SURE and W-box, but not the SP8a element, to activate the barley *isoamylase1* (*iso1*) promoter (127). In addition, a novel DNA-binding protein, designated STOREKEEPER (STK), specifically recognizes the B-box motif to control sucrose-induced patatin expression in potato tubers (157). A more recent dissection analysis of the sugar/ABA-induced sweet potato *sporamin A* promoter in transgenic tobacco has yielded a minimal promoter (Spo^{min}) that contains negatively acting regions and two carbohydrate metabolite signal responsive elements (CMSRE), CMSRE-1 (TGGACGG) and CMSRE-2, in addition to the SP8a motif (92).

The most recent and fruitful studies of transcription control have been obtained by analyzing the sugar-inducible promoter of a sporamin gene that encodes the most abundant protein in sweet potato storage roots. Two putative TFs, WRI1 (activator of Spo^{min}::LUC1; ASML1) and a novel CCT-domain protein (ASML2) were isolated recently by enhancer activation-tagging of an *Arabidopsis* line carrying the LUC reporter under control of a short, minimal sugar/ABA-inducible *sporamin* promoter. Several sugar-regulated genes, including *βAMY* and, in the case of ASML2, *APL3*, are activated in the transgenic lines (87, 88). Both TF genes are also specifically induced by high sugar concentrations. Apparently, the WRI1 TF plays an important role in directing the carbon flow towards storage when sugar levels are high. The *hsi2* mutant displays high Spo^{min}::LUC1 reporter activity even in noninducing conditions and is deficient in a novel B3 domain transcriptional repressor (138).

Sugars also modulate hormone signaling at the transcriptional level. Most obviously, glucose induces *ABA* and *ABI* gene expression as a core mechanism of its signal transduction (4, 21). A detailed analysis of three factors involved in sugar signaling, ABI4, ABI5, and CTR1, documents their specific and differential regulation by glucose, ABA, stress, and developmental stage (4). Glucose repression of several ethylene biosynthesis and signal transduction genes suggests that interactions between sugar and ethylene signaling take place in part at the transcriptional level (104). Transcriptional regulation of other hormone signaling components by sugars is also likely.

Studies with several maize photosynthetic gene promoters (119, 120) suggest the involvement of different regulatory elements in sugar repression and negative control of positive cis-elements. Extensive studies of sugar repression and starvation induction of transcription have also been carried out on the promoters of rice genes that encode α-amylases (αAMY), involved in seed starch degradation. In a study with a minimal αAMY3 promoter, a sugar response sequence (SRS) was identified with three essential elements for high sugar starvation-induced expression: the GC-box, the G-box, and the TATCCA element. Interestingly, three novel MYB proteins with a single DNA-binding domain (OsMYBS1-3) specifically bind to the TATCCA element to regulate αAMY expression (86).

The identification of G-box cis-elements provides a link between nutrient stress and other environmental stress responses. The G-box motif (CACGTG) is, for example, involved in phytochrome-mediated light control of gene expression and is very similar to ABRE (CCACGTGG). The ABRE-binding factors ABF2, ABF3 and ABF4 have also been implicated in sugar signaling (64, 65). Analysis of a conserved minimal light-responsive module (CMA5) recently revealed an ABI4-dependent sugar and ABA repression mechanism involving a novel element conserved in several RBCS promoters (1). This S-box element (CACCTCCA) is an ABI4-binding site and is typically closely associated with the G-box in light-regulated promoters. Novel bioinformatics and experimental approaches will be required to use fully the large number of publicly available microarray data to un-cover new regulatory elements and TF functions in sugar regulation.

Transcript Stability and Processing

The abundance of mRNA is not only the result of transcription control. Several important regulatory effects of sugars appear to operate at the post-transcriptional level. Sugar repression of rice αAMY3 involves control of both transcription and mRNA stability. Specific sequences in the 3′ untranslated region (UTR) of the transcript can control sugar-dependent mRNA stability (17). Using the transcription blocker actinomycin D to study mRNA half-life, several other growth- and stress-related genes have been shown to be controlled by sugars at the level of mRNA stability (56). Expression of the maize CW-INV gene Incw1 is also differentially regulated by sugars in a complex manner. In a maize cell suspension culture, both metabolizable and nonmetabolizable sugars induce Incw1 expression. However, only the sucrose- or glucose-induced increase in steady state abundance of a smaller transcript (divergent in the 3′UTR) results in increased protein expression and enzyme activity (22). Although the exact mechanisms are not clear, the 3′UTR of the Incw1 gene can be considered a sensor for sugar starvation that links sink metabolism to cellular mRNA processing and translation (22).

Translation

Another level of expression regulation controlled by stress and nutrient starvation conditions is selective mRNA translation. One such mechanism involves the presence of micro-open reading frames (μORFs) in the 5′UTR; these μORFs positively or negatively affect the translation efficiency of the downstream coding sequence (CDS)/ORF. For example, transcription of the Arabidopsis S-class bZIP TF ATB2/bZIP11 is stimulated by light and sugars, but its subsequent translation is repressed by higher levels of sucrose. Interestingly, specific sucrose-induced repression of translation (SIRT) is dependent on the unusually long 5'UTR of the ATB2/bZIP11 transcript (114). Detailed analysis has now identified four μORFs in the 5'UTR, one of which (μORF2) is necessary and sufficient for translational regulation (147). Consistent with the differential expression regulation of ATB2/bZIP11 by sugars and its specific expression pattern in vascular tissues of fertilized ovules (funiculi), seedlings, and young vascular tissues, a regulatory role for ATB2/bZIP11 in resource allocation to newly established sinks has been proposed (114). The sucrose control μORF (SC-μORF) is also conserved in four other *Arabidopsis* and several more (often stress- and hormone-induced) mono- and dicot S-class bZIP TF UTRs. In at least one other case (AtbZIP2) the SC-μORF is essential for SIRT. This suggests that the use of μORFs is a general regulatory feature for a subset of plant bZIP TFs (147). The molecular details of this type of regulation and its exact physiological importance, however, are still unclear.

Protein Stability

Once a protein is synthesized, its activity can still be regulated in many ways. Recent bioinformatic analyses suggest that over 5% of the *Arabidopsis* proteome may be involved in ubiquitin-and 26S proteasome-dependent protein degradation. Consistently, protein stability and selective proteolysis have emerged as major regulatory mechanisms in plant signaling and development, rivaling transcription control and protein phosphorylation (122). It is not surprising that sugar signaling pathways also make use of these mechanisms. Consistent with the glucose oversensitive (*glo*) phenotype for the ethylene insensitive (*etr1*, *ein2* and *ein3*) mutants and the *gin* phenotype for constitutive ethylene signaling (*ctr1/gin4*) mutants (**Figure 3**), glucose antagonizes ethylene signaling by enhancing proteasome-dependent degradation of the key downstream transcriptional regulator EIN3 in the nucleus (152). Ethylene on the other hand, enhances EIN3 stability (152,

41). Interestingly, the glucose response is dependent on AtHXK1, which can also be found in the nucleus. Interactions with auxin and even cytokinin signaling could involve similar mechanisms. Two specific EIN3-binding F-box proteins, EBF1 and EBF2, that form SCF complexes to repress ethylene action and promote growth by directing EIN3 degradation, have been identified (41). The precise molecular link of these proteins with the sugar signaling pathway remains to be elucidated. Interestingly, EBF1 and EBF2 are most related to the yeast F-box protein Glucose repression resistant1 (Grr1), which has been implicated in controlling and possibly coupling sugar sensing and the cell cycle. Many key components in light, biotic and abiotic stress, and hormone responses, as well as developmental programs (such as flowering and senescence) and cell cycle control are indeed well-known targets for controlled proteolysis in plants (122). As in other eukaryotes, the half-life of many plant cyclin-dependent kinase (CDK) modulators is regulated by the proteasome (122). Interestingly, the D-type cyclin CYCD3;1, which is transcriptionally upregulated by sucrose or glucose and cytokinins to enable the G1/S transition (107), appears to be a highly unstable protein and is degraded by a proteasome-dependent mechanism upon sucrose depletion (102). Moreover, CYCD3;1 is phosphorylated in sugar starvation conditions, and a hyperphosphorylated form accumulates in the presence of a proteasome inhibitor. These observations suggest that phosphorylation is involved in targeting CYCD3;1 for destruction (102). Changes in the expression and the enzymatic properties of the 20S proteasome mediated by oxidation have been observed in sugar-starved maize roots (9).

SNF1-RELATED PROTEIN KINASES

A Large Superfamily of CDPK-SnRK

Protein phosphorylation and dephosphorylation are key regulatory mechanisms in controlling protein function and activity. Experiments with specific inhibitors indicate the involvement of a variety of different PKs and protein phosphatases (PPs) in plant sugar signaling. Higher plants encode a particularly large superfamily of calcium-dependent PKs (CDPKs) and SnRKs. Several CDPKs are specifically induced by sucrose, and both pharmacological studies and observations of sugar-induced Ca^{2+}-fluxes have suggested the involvement of Ca^{2+} as a second messenger in sugar signaling.

The SnRK family consists of three subgroups, based on sequence similarity and domain structure. The SnRK1 proteins are most closely related to yeast Snf1 and mammalian AMPK (50). There are three members in *Arabidopsis*, only two of which, AKIN10 and AKIN11, are expressed (10; F. Rolland & E. Baena-Gonzalez, unpublished observations). The SnRK2 and SnRK3 (also termed CBL-interacting PK or CIPK) groups are probably unique to plants (50). SnRK1 homologs from various plant species can complement the yeast *snf1*Δ mutant phenotype, suggesting an evolutionary conservation in function. However, the best defined SnRK1 regulation and functions are mostly plant-specific and include activation by sucrose, phosphorylation of plant enzymes, and activation of starch synthesis in potato tubers (50). Possibly because of a key role in starch accumulation, SnRK1 silencing by DNA bombardment causes abnormal pollen development and male sterility in transgenic barley (155). Remarkably, significant differences appear to exist between the activation mechanisms for plant SnRKs, yeast Snf1, and mammalian AMPKs (50).

Modulation of Enzymatic Activity and Protein Degradation

Two SnRKs from spinach leaf can, in vitro, phosphorylate and inactivate 3-hydroxy-3-methylglutaryl-CoA reductase, nitrate reductase (NR), and SPS, enzymes involved in isoprenoid synthesis, nitrogen assimilation,

and sucrose biosynthesis, respectively (126). The activation state of NR is associated with photosynthetic activity and sugar availability. This observation offers a mechanism for SnRKs to coordinate carbon and nitrogen metabolism. SnRK1s have overlapping substrate specificities with CDPKs, and detailed phosphorylation studies with synthetic peptides have defined the minimal recognition sequence and the differential effects of specific residues and their positions on activity and specificity (57). Phosphorylation by SnRKs or CDPKs is, however, not always sufficient for enzyme inactivation. Phosphorylation of NR creates a phosphopeptide motif for 14-3-3 protein binding. This motif is responsible for the actual reversible inhibition of enzyme activity under stress conditions. Several other metabolic enzymes have been shown to bind 14-3-3 proteins, including a TPS (90), and 14-3-3 proteins have been implicated in cell survival under stress conditions. Several key metabolic enzymes, like NR, have rather short half-lives and phosphorylation and 14-3-3 protein binding appears to be important in controlling protein degradation as well. However, there are contradictory results and interpretations as to the exact function of 14-3-3 protein binding in protein degradation (63). Although some evidence indicates that 14-3-3 protein binding initiates and/or accelerates NR degradation, selective loss of 14-3-3 protein binding appears to regulate cleavage of their binding partners, including NR and SPS, in sugar-starved *Arabidopsis* cells (27).

In addition to phosphorylation or dephosphorylation and protein stability or breakdown, redox regulation is emerging as another important post-translational mechanism in sugar control of plant metabolism. This mechanism is well known to be involved in reversible light-activation of key photosynthetic enzymes, but is now also found to regulate plastid enzymes in nongreen heterotrophic organs as well. Studies with potato tuber AGPase demonstrated that redox activation of the enzyme (by reducing a disulphide bond between two subunits of the

Redox regulation: signals generated by the photosynthetic electron transport chain, transmitted to thioredoxins, can modify target enzymes by disulphide bond reduction

tetrameric protein) regulates starch synthesis in response to sucrose import (135). Redox activation of AGPase is also observed after supplying exogenous sucrose to *Arabidopsis* leaves in the dark, or in a sugar accumulating *pgm* mutant (53). Two different signaling pathways have been proposed for sucrose and glucose, involving SnRK1 and HXK, respectively (42, 135). Glucose feeding, through HXK–dependent metabolism (e.g., the oxidative pentose-P cycle), increases the overall NADPH/NADP$^+$ ratio, which then most likely increases the reduction state of the plastid thioredoxins. Unlike glucose, sucrose activation of AGPase is strongly attenuated in SnRK1-antisense potato tubers and can be mimicked by the nonmetabolizable sucrose-analog, palatinose. Although the exact signaling mechanism is not clear, this phenomenon appears to be another sucrose-specific signaling effect.

Gene Expression Regulation

SnRK1, like Snf1 and AMPK, also affects gene expression. Antisense knockdown of SnRK1 in potato, for example, causes a significant reduction in *SUS4* gene expression in tubers and loss of *SUS4* sucrose-inducibility in leaves (106). This result is, however, not consistent with a role for SnRK1 in sugar starvation. It is proposed that SnRK1 can be activated by high cellular sucrose and/or low cellular glucose levels (50), although sucrose is hydrolyzed to glucose and fructose in plant cells. Expression of the wheat *αAMY2*, is induced by carbon starvation in cultured embryos, and SnRK1 antisense silencing represses transient *αAMY2* promoter activity (72). Although a prominent role for SnRK1 in plant metabolic signaling is now generally accepted, there are often seemingly conflicting results. Possibly, SnRK1 regulation and function differ depending on the cell or tissue type, developmental stage, and on the interactions with other signaling mechanisms.

Regulation of SnRK1

SnRK1 kinase activity is controlled by phosphorylation of a conserved threonine in the so-called activation or "T-loop" of the catalytic subunit. No upstream kinases or phosphatases have been identified in plants yet. Unlike AMPK, SnRK1 is not allosterically activated by AMP. However, T-loop dephosphorylation and consequent inactivation is inhibited by binding of low, physiological concentrations of 5′-AMP to SnRK1 (125). Also consistent with a role in sugar starvation conditions, sugar phosphates, especially G6P, can inhibit SnRK1 activity (136). Similar to the yeast Snf1 and mammalian AMPKs, SnRK1s are heterotrimeric proteins. The association of the catalytic α-subunits in complexes with different regulatory β- and γ-subunits, differentially regulated by hormonal and environmental signals, cell and tissue type, and developmental stage, offers another mechanism for complex and dynamic activity regulation and signal integration.

In plants, SnRK1s interact with several more proteins. Pleiotropic Regulatory Locus1 (PRL1) is a nuclear WD (Trp Asp) repeat protein that interacts with the *Arabidopsis* SnRK1s (10). The *prl1* mutant displays complex phenotypes, including transcriptional derepression of glucose-responsive genes but hypersensitivity to sugar and multiple hormones as well as hyperaccumulation of free sugars and starch. In a kinase assay using immunoprecipitated protein complexes from *Arabidopsis* and an SPS peptide substrate, both sucrose and the *prl1* mutation increased SnRK1 activity. These data again challenge the idea for a role of SnRK1 in sugar starvation conditions. An in vitro assay with purified proteins confirms that PRL1 indeed acts as a negative regulator of SnRK1. However, although low glucose levels enhance the yeast two-hybrid interaction with PRL1, the sucrose regulation of SnRK1 activity is unaffected in *prl1* mutant plants (10). Apparently, other factors or regulatory mechanisms are also involved.

Partly explaining the complex and pleiotropic phenotypes, and possibly providing a direct mechanistic link with metabolic regulation of protein degradation, the *Arabidopsis* SnRK1 is found to interact with both the SCF ubiquitin E3 ligase subunit SKP1/ASK1 and the SKP1/ASK1-binding 26S proteasome subunit α4/PAD1 (37). SKP1/ASK1 is also found in SCF complexes involved in the regulation of auxin and jasmonate signaling and senescence (122). In vitro, binding of SKP1/ASK1 to SnRK1 increases under low glucose conditions and competes with PRL1 binding to the same regulatory domain of SnRK1. In vivo, however, they do not seem to occur in common SnRK1 complexes (37). Further experiments confirm that SnRK1 associates with the 26S proteasome. The exact relevance of this interaction is not clear.

Diverse SnRK1-interacting proteins (SnIPs) have been identified using yeast two-hybrid screening. It remains to be learned whether these SnIPs are regulators or targets. A novel protein tyrosine phosphatase (PTP), dubbed PTPKIS, has been shown to interact with SnRK1 via a kinase interaction sequence (KIS) domain (39). The barley endosperm class I heat shock protein BHSP17 is a phosphorylation substrate of spinach leaf and barley endosperm SnRK1 (121), providing an obvious link with a general stress response. More specifically, the geminivirus proteins AL2 and L2 interact with and inactivate tobacco SnRK1. The metabolic alterations mediated by SnRK1 may be a component of the plant's antiviral defense mechanism (52).

In a screen for heterologous multicopy suppressors of the yeast *snf4* (Snf1 regulatory protein) deficiency, several proteins including a plant casein kinase I ortholog and two Msn2/4-type zinc-finger factors, AZF2 and ZAT10, involved in stress responses, were isolated in addition to the *Arabidopsis* Snf4 ortholog (66).

The moss *Physcomitrella patens* (*Pp*) is an excellent model system for functional genomics based on targeted gene knockouts. A moss *Pp-snf1a Ppsnf1b* double knockout mutant, which lacks all SnRK1 activity, displays abnormal development with premature senescence, hypersensitivity to auxin, and hyposensitivity to cytokinin. The mutant is unable to grow in low light or day/night light cycles, but the growth defect can be partially rescued by supplementation of an external carbon source, indicating that the moss SnRK1 is required for survival under low-energy conditions (129). The function of SnRK1 in legume seeds is also being characterized by gene silencing and microarrays (146). Recent analysis of *akin10 akin11* double knockout in *Arabidopsis* leaves has revealed a central role of SnRK1 as a master regulator in the stress and starvation signaling network (F. Rolland, E. Baena-Gonzalez & J. Sheen, unpublished observations). Although a conserved function for Snf1/AMPK/SnRK1 in eukaryotic nutrient stress signaling appears to be established, their regulation, downstream targets, and interactions with other pathways are likely more divergent. More research is needed to resolve the complex issues of SnRK1 regulation and functions in flowering plants.

TREHALOSE

It is often difficult to determine at which level sugar metabolism affects signal transduction (112). In plants, as in yeast and mammals, metabolic intermediates or alterations in cellular energy or redox state can also act as signals.

The ample examples of substrate and allosteric feedback and feed-forward regulation of carbon metabolism by metabolic intermediates, although important, are not a topic of this review. However, trehalose metabolism, a small side-branch of the major carbon flux in bacterial, yeast, and plant cells, has recently drawn a lot of attention because of its intriguing regulatory effects on plant growth, development, and stress resistance. The disaccharide trehalose is typically synthesized in a two-step reaction: T6P is first synthesized from G6P and UDP-Glc by TPS, and then

TPP: trehalose-6-P phosphatase

dephosphorylated to trehalose by a T6P phosphatase (TPP). T6P levels are tightly regulated in yeast by a complex of the TPS (Tps1) and TPP (Tps2) proteins, together with a regulatory protein (redundantly encoded by *TSL1* and *TPS3*). In *Arabidopsis*, addition of even fairly low amounts of external trehalose to the growth medium results in a significant inhibition of seedling root elongation (149). Although its specificity is not well defined, the potent trehalase inhibitor validamycin has been used to exclude possible effects of trehalose hydrolysis to glucose. The growth defect on external trehalose is associated with a strong induction of the AGPase gene *APL3*, increased AGPase activity, and concomitant hyperaccumulation of starch in the cotyledons. This suggests that a failing allocation of photosynthate to the roots is causing the growth defect (149). Consistent with that hypothesis, addition of metabolizable sugars can suppress the growth inhibition by trehalose.

In contrast to microorganisms, and with the exception of some desert resurrection plants like the pteridophyte *Selaginella lepidophylla* [in which the high trehalose concentrations (up to 15% of the dry weight) have been associated with extreme drought tolerance], plants in general do not accumulate trehalose at all. This can be explained partly by the high trehalase activity that is likely also involved in exogenous trehalose breakdown during symbiotic and pathogenic interactions with microorganisms. However, introduction of yeast and bacterial trehalose synthesis genes can improve abiotic stress resistance significantly, albeit without increasing endogenous trehalose concentrations to the extend found in microorganisms; thus, this result is inconsistent with a function for trehalose as a compatible solute/stress protectant (reviewed in Reference 99). In addition, whereas heterologous alteration of trehalose metabolism typically leads to clear morphological changes, regulated bacterial TPS-TPP coexpression or expression of a bacterial TPSP (TPS-TPP) fusion construct abolishes these morpholog-

ical side effects (99). These observations all point to an important regulatory function.

Current attention has shifted to endogenous plant trehalose metabolism and its role in growth and development, and heterologous yeast *tps1Δ* mutant complementation has identified functional plant TPS genes Remarkably, *AtTPS1* is essential for embryo maturation. *Arabidopsis tps1* knockout mutants are developmentally arrested in the torpedo stage, a phase in embryo development that is generally associated with an increase in sucrose levels and initiation of storage reserve accumulation (35). It has been proposed that trehalose metabolism may be important for the regulation of storage reserve accumulation. However, using reserve protein promoter-reporters and transcriptomic, metabolite, and microscopic analyses, it is found that the actual cellular differentiation of the torpedo stage *tps1* embryos resembles that of a equally old, cotyledon-stage wild-type embryo. This observation indicates that morphogenesis (cell growth and division) is affected but uncoupled from differentiation (49). Expression of a bacterial TPS (OtsA) but not the addition of trehalose could rescue the embryo-lethal mutants (117), pointing to the importance of the T6P intermediate in development.

Controlled alterations of T6P levels by expressing combinations of *E. coli* trehalose metabolism genes clearly demonstrate that T6P is indispensable for carbohydrate utilization for growth in *Arabidopsis* (117). Moreover, dexamethasone-induced expression of TPS1 allows recovery of mature homozygous *tps1* mutant plants, showing that T6P is essential for both normal vegetative growth and the transition to flowering (141). Trehalose-mediated growth inhibition of seedlings is also likely due to T6P accumulation (118). The exact mechanism of T6P action, however, is still unclear, since, unlike in yeast, T6P is not an inhibitor of plant HXK activity (35).

Surprisingly, but consistent with an important regulatory role in growth and development, a plethora of trehalose metabolism genes is now being uncovered in plants (77, 118, 143). There are four *TPS1* (class I *TPS*; *AtTPS1-4*) and seven TPS2 (class II *TPS* with two C-terminal phosphatase boxes; *AtTPS5-11*) homologs in *Arabidopsis*. No TPS or TPP activity has been detected yet for the class II proteins. Ten putative T6P phosphatase (*AtTPPA-AtTPPJ*) genes are annotated that basically contain only the phosphatase box domain. Although some have been shown to complement a yeast *tps2Δ* mutant, it is not clear how specific they are. Plants do not appear to have a TSL1-TPS3-like regulatory subunit, required for complex formation in yeast. Interestingly, expression of the trehalose metabolism genes is differentially regulated during embryo development and senescence and by nitrogen and sugar availability, hypoxia, circadian rhythm, ABA, and external trehalose. A microarray analysis of the plant's response to exogenous trehalose (118) has identified target genes mostly involved in stress signaling. *AKIN11* is also upregulated by trehalose, and its expression seems to correlate with T6P levels. Interestingly, T6P regulates starch synthesis via redox activation of AGPase downstream of SnRK1 (69). Several *Arabidopsis* TPS proteins possess multiple SnRK1 phosphorylation sites revealed by a recent study using a novel multiparallel kinase target assay (47). *AKIN10* overexpression also induces class II *TPS* gene expression (F. Rolland & E. Baena-Gonzalez, unpublished observations).

TPS and *TPP* expression occurs in a wide range of tissues. Remarkably, the *Arabidopsis* class II *TPS* genes show a cell layer-specific expression in root and shoot apical meristems (M. Ramon, personal communication). This suggests a prominent role in growth regulation. It remains unclear how trehalose metabolism affects growth and development and stress resistance. As in yeast, trehalose metabolism likely interferes with sugar signaling in plants. *Arabidopsis* plants overexpressing the yeast *TPS1* are drought tolerant and insensitive to sugar and ABA, suggesting a role for *TPS1* or its product in downregu-

lating HXK-dependent signaling (6). In addition to trehalose, some plant and bacterial species accumulate fructose oligomers and polymers, called fructans, as a reserve carbohydrate that can enhance plant cold and drought tolerance. The occurence of fructan exohydrolases (FEHs) in non-fructan-accumulating plants such as *Arabidopsis* similarly suggests a defense-related role for these enzymes (by acting on bacterial fructans) or the presence of undetected low amounts of endogenous fructans with a role as signaling molecules (140).

CONCLUSIONS AND PERSPECTIVES

Sugars are finally being recognized as important regulatory molecules with signaling functions in plants and other organisms. Whereas the power of yeast genetics has enabled the rapid and detailed elucidation of diverse sugar sensing and signaling pathways, plant sugar signaling has proven more difficult to study due to the complexity of source-sink interactions, responses to diverse sugar signals and metabolites, and the intimate integration of a web-like signaling network governed by plant hormones, nutrients, and environmental conditions. The use of different experimental systems, including isolated cells, excised tissues, cell cultures, whole plants, and mutants under different environmental and nutrient conditions at various developmental stages is critical in dissecting the plethora of sugar responses and their connections in plants. Microarray and clustering analysis are new, powerful genomic tools to provide a global view on the transcript dynamics controlled by different sugar responses and identify novel regulatory components and target genes. The sharing of the massive data sets is beginning to provide new insights into the extent and mechanisms of sugar-regulated gene expression and interactions with other signals. The molecular details of signal transduction pathways and their crosstalk with other pathways will be revealed by using a combination of genomic proteomic and genetic approaches. Current technology limits the ability to visualize and quantify the precise location and concentration of various sugar molecules and metabolites in living cells. Novel molecular sensors and fluorescence resonance energy transfer (FRET)-based imaging (81) will hopefully circumvent this limitation and provide critical information to facilitate the elucidation of intracellular sugar signal transduction pathways.

SUMMARY POINTS

1. Yeast is an excellent model and tool to study the conserved mechanisms of eukaryotic sugar sensing and signaling.

2. In plants, sugars control metabolism, growth, stress responses, and development from embryogenesis to senescence.

3. Plant sugar regulation is mediated by diverse sugar signals, which are generated at different locations depending on environmental conditions and developmental stage. Sucrose transport and hydrolysis play key regulatory roles in sugar signal generation.

4. Plant-specific sugar signaling mechanisms involve extensive interactions with plant hormone signaling.

5. HXKs are evolutionarily conserved eukaryotic glucose sensors. Plants may also use membrane receptors for extracellular sugar sensing.

6. Sugars regulate cellular activity at mutiple levels, from transcription and translation to protein stability and activity.

7. SnRK1s appear to play a conserved role in starvation responses, but are likely regulated differently in yeast, mammals and plants. Future studies will clarify the unique regulation of SnRK1s by sucrose and their critical role in cellular stress signaling, as well as novel functions in the regulation of the daily cycle of carbon metabolism in plants.

8. Trehalose metabolism is emerging as a novel, important regulator of plant growth, metabolism, and stress resistance.

ACKNOWLEDGMENTS

We would like to thank Malcolm Campbell, Mark Stitt, Chris Leaver, Kenzo Nakamura, Wolf Frommer, Hai Huang, Jong-Seong Jeon, Alan Jones, Matthew Ramon, Brandon Moore, Young-Hee Cho, Sang-Dong Yoo, Qi Hall, and Wan-Hsing Cheng for sharing information. We apologize for not citing many publications due to space limitations and refer to previous reviews and more recent papers for detailed information. Research on sugar sensing and signaling in the Sheen lab is currently supported by the NSF (IBN-02,17191) and NIH (R01 GM060493) grants. F.R. is supported by a return grant from the Belgian Office for Scientific, Technical and Cultural Affairs and a fellowship from the Research Foundation – Flanders (FWO – Vlaanderen).

LITERATURE CITED

1. Acevedo-Hernández GJ, León P, Herrera-Estrella LR. 2005. Sugar and ABA responsiveness of a minimal *RBCS* light-responsive unit is mediated by direct binding of ABI4. *Plant J.* 43:506–19

2. Alonso AP, Vigeolas H, Raymond P, Rolin D, Dieuaide-Noubhani M. 2005. A new substrate cycle in plants. Evidence for a high glucose-phosphate-to-glucose turnover from in vivo steady-state and pulse-labeling experiments with [13C]glucose and [14C]glucose. *Plant Physiol.* 138:2220–32

3. Arenas-Huertero F, Arroyo A, Zhou L, Sheen J, Leon P. 2000. Analysis of Arabidopsis glucose insensitive mutants, *gin5* and *gin6*, reveals a central role of the plant hormone ABA in the regulation of plant vegetative development by sugar. *Genes Dev.* 14:2085–96

4. Arroyo A, Bossi F, Finkelstein RR, Leon P. 2003. Three genes that affect sugar sensing (abscisic acid insensitive 4, abscisic acid insensitive 5, and constitutive triple response 1) are differentially regulated by glucose in Arabidopsis. *Plant Physiol.* 133:231–42

5. Atanassova R, Leterrier M, Gaillard C, Agasse A, Sagot E, et al. 2003. Sugar-regulated expression of a putative hexose transport gene in grape. *Plant Physiol.* 131:326–34

6. Avonce N, Leyman B, Mascorro-Gallardo JO, Van Dijck P, Thevelein JM, Iturriaga G. 2004. The Arabidopsis trehalose-6-P synthase *AtTPS1* gene is a regulator of glucose, abscisic acid, and stress signaling. *Plant Physiol.* 136:3649–59

7. Balibrea Lara ME, Gonzalez Garcia MC, Fatima T, Ehness R, Lee TK, et al. 2004. Extracellular invertase is an essential component of cytokinin-mediated delay of senescence. *Plant Cell* 16:1276–87

8. Barker L, Kuhn C, Weise A, Schulz A, Gebhardt C, et al. 2000. SUT2, a putative sucrose sensor in sieve elements. *Plant Cell* 12:1153–64

9. Basset G, Raymond P, Malek L, Brouquisse R. 2002. Changes in the expression and the enzymic properties of the 20S proteasome in sugar-starved maize roots, evidence for an in vivo oxidation of the proteasome. *Plant Physiol.* 128:1149–62

10. Bhalerao RP, Salchert K, Bako L, Okresz L, Szabados L, et al. 1999. Regulatory interaction of PRL1 WD protein with Arabidopsis SNF1-like protein kinases. *Proc. Natl. Acad. Sci. USA* 96:5322–27

11. Bläsing OE, Gibon Y, Günther M, Höhne M, Morcuende R, et al. 2005. Sugars and circadian regulation make major contributions to the global regulation of diurnal gene expression in Arabidopsis. *Plant Cell.* 17:3257–81

12. Borisjuk L, Rolletschek H, Wobus U, Weber H. 2003. Differentiation of legume cotyledons as related to metabolic gradients and assimilate transport into seeds. *J. Exp. Bot.* 54:503–12

13. Borisjuk L, Walenta S, Weber H, Mueller-Klieser W, Wobus U. 1998. High-resolution histographical mapping of glucose concentrations in developing cotyledons of *Vicia faba* in relation to mitotic activity and storage processes: glucose as a possible developmental trigger. *Plant J.* 15:583–91

14. Brocard-Gifford I, Lynch TJ, Garcia ME, Malhotra B, Finkelstein RR. 2004. The Arabidopsis thaliana ABSCISIC ACID-INSENSITIVE8 encodes a novel protein mediating abscisic acid and sugar responses essential for growth. *Plant Cell* 16:406–21

15. Buchanan-Wollaston V, Page T, Harrison E, Breeze E, Lim PO, et al. 2005. Comparative transcriptome analysis reveals significant differences in gene expression and signalling pathways between developmental and dark/starvation-induced senescence in Arabidopsis. *Plant J.* 42:567–85

16. Cernac A, Benning C. 2004. WRINKLED1 encodes an AP2/EREB domain protein involved in the control of storage compound biosynthesis in Arabidopsis. *Plant J.* 40:575–85

17. Chan MT, Yu SM. 1998. The 3' untranslated region of a rice alpha-amylase gene functions as a sugar-dependent mRNA stability determinant. *Proc. Natl. Acad. Sci. USA* 95:6543–47

Using an extremely comprehensive approach, this study dissects how sugars, nitrogen, light, water deficit, and clock regulation interact to control plant diurnal gene expression.

Evidence for the involvement of a GPCR (RGS1) in sugar regulation of seedling development, opening up the possibility that plants also contain receptors for extracellular sugar signals.

18. Chen JG, Jones AM. 2004. AtRGS1 function in *Arabidopsis thaliana*. *Methods Enzymol.* 389:338–50

19. Chen JG, Willard FS, Huang J, Liang J, Chasse SA, et al. 2003. A seven-transmembrane RGS protein that modulates plant cell proliferation. *Science* 301:1728–31

20. Chen M, Xia X, Zheng H, Yuan Z, Huang H. 2004. The GAOLAOZHUANGREN2 gene is required for normal glucose response and development of Arabidopsis. *J. Plant Res.* 117:473–76

21. Cheng WH, Endo A, Zhou L, Penney J, Chen HC, et al. 2002. A unique short-chain dehydrogenase/reductase in Arabidopsis glucose signaling and abscisic acid biosynthesis and functions. *Plant Cell* 14:2723–43

22. Cheng WH, Taliercio EW, Chourey PS. 1999. Sugars modulate an unusual mode of control of the cell-wall invertase gene (Incw1) through its 3′ untranslated region in a cell suspension culture of maize. *Proc. Natl. Acad. Sci. USA* 96:10512–17

23. Contento AL, Kim SJ, Bassham DC. 2004. Transcriptome profiling of the response of Arabidopsis suspension culture cells to Suc starvation. *Plant Physiol.* 135:2330–47

24. Corbesier L, Bernier G, Perilleux C. 2002. C:N ratio increases in the phloem sap during floral transition of the long-day plants *Sinapis alba* and *Arabidopsis thaliana*. *Plant Cell Physiol.* 43:684–88

25. Cortes S, Gromova M, Evrard A, Roby C, Heyraud A, et al. 2003. In plants, 3-o-methylglucose is phosphorylated by hexokinase but not perceived as a sugar. *Plant Physiol.* 131:824–37

26. Coruzzi GM, Zhou L. 2001. Carbon and nitrogen sensing and signaling in plants: emerging 'matrix effects'. *Curr. Opin. Plant Biol.* 4:247–53

27. Cotelle V, Meek SE, Provan F, Milne FC, Morrice N, MacKintosh C. 2000. 14-3-3s regulate global cleavage of their diverse binding partners in sugar-starved Arabidopsis cells. *EMBO J.* 19:2869–76

28. Crevillén P, Ventriglia T, Pinto F, Orea A, Merida A, Romero JM. 2005. Differential pattern of expression and sugar regulation of *Arabidopsis thaliana* ADP-glucose pyrophosphorylase-encoding genes. *J. Biol. Chem.* 280:8143–49

29. Dai N, Schaffer A, Petreikov M, Shahak Y, Giller Y, et al. 1999. Overexpression of Arabidopsis hexokinase in tomato plants inhibits growth, reduces photosynthesis, and induces rapid senescence. *Plant Cell* 11:1253–66

30. Dekkers BJ, Schuurmans JA, Smeekens SC. 2004. Glucose delays seed germination in *Arabidopsis thaliana*. *Planta* 218:579–88

31. Dewitte W, Riou-Khamlichi C, Scofield S, Healy JM, Jacqmard A, et al. 2003. Altered cell cycle distribution, hyperplasia, and inhibited differentiation in Arabidopsis caused by the D-type cyclin CYCD3. *Plant Cell* 15:79–92

32. Diaz C, Purdy S, Christ A, Morot-Gaudry JF, Wingler A, Masclaux-Daubresse C. 2005. Characterization of markers to determine the extent and variability of leaf senescence in Arabidopsis. A metabolic profiling approach. *Plant Physiol.* 138:898–908

33. Dodd AN, Salathia N, Hall A, Kevei E, Toth R, et al. 2005. Plant circadian clocks increase photosynthesis, growth, survival, and competitive advantage. *Science* 309:630–33

34. Dyer J, Salmon KS, Zibrik L, Shirazi-Beechey SP. 2005. Expression of sweet taste receptors of the T1R family in the intestinal tract and enteroendocrine cells. *Biochem. Soc. Trans.* 33:302–5

This paper for the first time demonstrated a conserved role of TPS in controlling plant growth and metabolism.

35. Eastmond PJ, van Dijken AJ, Spielman M, Kerr A, Tissier AF, et al. 2002. Trehalose-6-phosphate synthase 1, which catalyses the first step in trehalose synthesis, is essential for Arabidopsis embryo maturation. *Plant J.* 29:225–35

36. Ehness R, Ecker M, Godt DE, Roitsch T. 1997. Glucose and stress independently regulate source and sink metabolism and defense mechanisms via signal transduction pathways involving protein phosphorylation. *Plant Cell* 9:1825–41

37. Farras R, Ferrando A, Jasik J, Kleinow T, Okresz L, et al. 2001. SKP1-SnRK protein kinase interactions mediate proteasomal binding of a plant SCF ubiquitin ligase. *EMBO J.* 20:2742–56

38. Fernie AR, Willmitzer L. 2001. Molecular and biochemical triggers of potato tuber development. *Plant Physiol.* 127:1459–65

39. Fordham-Skelton AP, Chilley P, Lumbreras V, Reignoux S, Fenton TR, et al. 2002. A novel higher plant protein tyrosine phosphatase interacts with SNF1-related protein kinases via a KIS (kinase interaction sequence) domain. *Plant J.* 29:705–15

40. Fujiki Y, Yoshikawa Y, Sato T, Inada N, Ito M, et al. 2001. Dark-inducible genes from Arabidopsis thaliana are associated with leaf senescence and repressed by sugars. *Physiol. Plant.* 111:345–52

41. Gagne JM, Smalle J, Gingerich DJ, Walker JM, Yoo SD, et al. 2004. Arabidopsis EIN3-binding F-box 1 and 2 form ubiquitin-protein ligases that repress ethylene action and promote growth by directing EIN3 degradation. *Proc. Natl. Acad. Sci. USA* 101:6803–8

42. Geigenberger P, Kolbe A, Tiessen A. 2005. Redox regulation of carbon storage and partitioning in response to light and sugars. *J. Exp. Bot.* 56:1469–79

43. Gibson SI. 2005. Control of plant development and gene expression by sugar signaling. *Curr. Opin. Plant Biol.* 8:93–102

44. Giege P, Heazlewood JL, Roessner-Tunali U, Millar AH, Fernie AR, et al. 2003. Enzymes of glycolysis are functionally associated with the mitochondrion in Arabidopsis cells. *Plant Cell* 15:2140–51

45. Giege P, Sweetlove LJ, Cognat V, Leaver CJ. 2005. Coordination of nuclear and mitochondrial genome expression during mitochondrial biogenesis in Arabidopsis. *Plant Cell* 17:1497–512

46. Giese JO, Herbers K, Hoffmann M, Klosgen RB, Sonnewald U. 2005. Isolation and functional characterization of a novel plastidic hexokinase from *Nicotiana tabacum*. *FEBS Lett.* 579:827–31

47. Glinski M, Weckwerth W. 2005. Differential multisite phosphorylation of the trehalose-6-phosphate synthase gene family in *Arabidopsis thaliana*: a mass spectrometry-based process for multiparallel peptide library phosphorylation analysis. *Mol. Cell. Proteomics* 4:1614–25

48. Goetz M, Godt DE, Guivarc'h A, Kahmann U, Chriqui D, Roitsch T. 2001. Induction of male sterility in plants by metabolic engineering of the carbohydrate supply. *Proc. Natl. Acad. Sci. USA* 98:6522–27

49. Gomez LD, Baud S, Graham IA. 2005. The role of trehalose-6-phosphate synthase in Arabidopsis embryo development. *Biochem. Soc. Trans.* 33:280–82

50. Halford NG, Hey S, Jhurreea D, Laurie S, McKibbin RS, et al. 2003. Metabolic signalling and carbon partitioning: role of Snf1-related (SnRK1) protein kinase. *J. Exp. Bot.* 54:467–75

51. Hanson J, Johannesson H, Engstrom P. 2001. Sugar-dependent alterations in cotyledon and leaf development in transgenic plants expressing the HDZhdip gene ATHB13. *Plant Mol. Biol.* 45:247–62

52. Hao L, Wang H, Sunter G, Bisaro DM. 2003. Geminivirus AL2 and L2 proteins interact with and inactivate SNF1 kinase. *Plant Cell* 15:1034–48

53. Hendriks JH, Kolbe A, Gibon Y, Stitt M, Geigenberger P. 2003. ADP-glucose pyrophosphorylase is activated by posttranslational redox-modification in response to light and to sugars in leaves of Arabidopsis and other plant species. *Plant Physiol.* 133:838–49

54. Herbers K, Meuwly P, Frommer WB, Metraux JP, Sonnewald U. 1996. Systemic acquired resistance mediated by the ectopic expression of invertase: possible hexose sensing in the secretory pathway. *Plant Cell* 8:793–803

55. Heyer AG, Raap M, Schroeer B, Marty B, Willmitzer L. 2004. Cell wall invertase expression at the apical meristem alters floral, architectural, and reproductive traits in *Arabidopsis thaliana*. *Plant J.* 39:161–69

56. Ho S, Chao Y, Tong W, Yu S. 2001. Sugar coordinately and differentially regulates growth- and stress-related gene expression via a complex signal transduction network and multiple control mechanisms. *Plant Physiol.* 125:877–90

57. Huang JZ, Huber SC. 2001. Phosphorylation of synthetic peptides by a CDPK and plant SNF1-related protein kinase. Influence of proline and basic amino acid residues at selected positions. *Plant Cell Physiol.* 42:1079–87

58. Ishizaki K, Larson TR, Schauer N, Fernie AR, Graham IA, Leaver CJ. 2005. The critical role of Arabidopsis electron-transfer flavoprotein: ubiquinone oxidoreductase during dark-induced starvation. *Plant Cell* 17:2587–600

59. Jang JC, Leon P, Zhou L, Sheen J. 1997. Hexokinase as a sugar sensor in higher plants. *Plant Cell* 9:5–19

60. Jofuku KD, Omidyar PK, Gee Z, Okamuro JK. 2005. Control of seed mass and seed yield by the floral homeotic gene *APETALA2*. *Proc. Natl. Acad. Sci. USA* 102:3117–22

61. Johnston M, Kim JH. 2005. Glucose as a hormone: receptor-mediated glucose sensing in the yeast *Saccharomyces cerevisiae*. *Biochem. Soc. Trans.* 33:247–52

62. Jongebloed U, Szederkenyi J, Hartig K, Schobert C, Komor E. 2004. Sequence of morphological and physiological events during natural ageing and senescence of a castor bean leaf: sieve tube occlusion and carbohydrate back-up precede chlorophyll degradation. *Physiol. Plant.* 120:338–46

63. Kaiser WM, Huber SC. 2001. Post-translational regulation of nitrate reductase: mechanism, physiological relevance and environmental triggers. *J. Exp. Bot.* 52:1981–89

64. Kang JY, Choi HI, Im MY, Kim SY. 2002. Arabidopsis basic leucine zipper proteins that mediate stress-responsive abscisic acid signaling. *Plant Cell* 14:343–57

65. Kim S, Kang JY, Cho DI, Park JH, Kim SY. 2004. ABF2, an ABRE-binding bZIP factor, is an essential component of glucose signaling and its overexpression affects multiple stress tolerance. *Plant J.* 40:75–87

66. Kleinow T, Bhalerao R, Breuer F, Umeda M, Salchert K, Koncz C. 2000. Functional identification of an Arabidopsis Snf4 ortholog by screening for heterologous multicopy suppressors of *snf4* deficiency in yeast. *Plant J.* 23:115–22

67. Koch KE. 2004. Sucrose metabolism: regulatory mechanisms and pivotal roles in sugar sensing and plant development. *Curr. Opin. Plant Biol.* 7:235–46

68. Koch KE, Ying Z, Wu Y, Avigne WT. 2000. Multiple paths of sugar-sensing and a sugar/oxygen overlap for genes of sucrose and ethanol metabolism. *J. Exp. Bot.* 51(Spec. Issue):417–27

69. **Kolbe A, Tiessen A, Schluepmann H, Paul M, Ulrich S, Geigenberger P. 2005. Trehalose 6-phosphate regulates starch synthesis via posttranslational redox activation of ADP-glucose pyrophosphorylase. *Proc. Natl. Acad. Sci. USA* 102:11118–23**

70. Lalonde S, Boles E, Hellmann H, Barker L, Patrick JW, et al. 1999. The dual function of sugar carriers. Transport and sugar sensing. *Plant Cell* 11:707–26

This work demonstrates the SnRK1-dependent posttranslational redox activation of AGPase by T6P, providing evidence for a regulatory role of T6P as a signaling molecule.

71. Lam HM, Hsieh MH, Coruzzi G. 1998. Reciprocal regulation of distinct asparagine synthetase genes by light and metabolites in *Arabidopsis thaliana*. *Plant J.* 16:345–53

72. Laurie S, McKibbin RS, Halford NG. 2003. Antisense SNF1-related (SnRK1) protein kinase gene represses transient activity of an alpha-amylase (alpha-Amy2) gene promoter in cultured wheat embryos. *J. Exp. Bot.* 54:739–47

73. Laxmi A, Paul LK, Peters JL, Khurana JP. 2004. Arabidopsis constitutive photomorphogenic mutant, *bls1*, displays altered brassinosteroid response and sugar sensitivity. *Plant Mol. Biol.* 56:185–201

74. Lee EJ, Koizumi N, Sano H. 2004. Identification of genes that are up-regulated in concert during sugar depletion in Arabidopsis. *Plant Cell Environ.* 27:337–45

75. Lemaire K, Van de Velde S, Van Dijck P, Thevelein JM. 2004. Glucose and sucrose act as agonist and mannose as antagonist ligands of the G protein-coupled receptor Gpr1 in the yeast *Saccharomyces cerevisiae*. *Mol. Cell* 16:293–99

76. Leon P, Sheen J. 2003. Sugar and hormone connections. *Trends Plant Sci.* 8:110–16

77. Leyman B, Van Dijck P, Thevelein JM. 2001. An unexpected plethora of trehalose biosynthesis genes in *Arabidopsis thaliana*. *Trends Plant Sci.* 6:510–13

78. Lin JF, Wu SH. 2004. Molecular events in senescing Arabidopsis leaves. *Plant J.* 39:612–28

79. Lloyd JC, Zakhleniuk OV. 2004. Responses of primary and secondary metabolism to sugar accumulation revealed by microarray expression analysis of the Arabidopsis mutant, *pho3*. *J. Exp. Bot.* 55:1221–30

80. Long JC, Zhao W, Rashotte AM, Muday GK, Huber SC. 2002. Gravity-stimulated changes in auxin and invertase gene expression in maize pulvinal cells. *Plant Physiol.* 128:591–602

81. **Looger LL, Lalonde S, Frommer WB. 2005. Genetically encoded FRET sensors for visualizing metabolites with subcellular resolution in living cells. *Plant Physiol.* 138:555–57**

82. Lopez-Molina L, Mongrand S, Chua NH. 2001. A postgermination developmental arrest checkpoint is mediated by abscisic acid and requires the ABI5 transcription factor in Arabidopsis. *Proc. Natl. Acad. Sci. USA* 98:4782–87

83. Lorenz S, Tintelnot S, Reski R, Decker EL. 2003. Cyclin D-knockout uncouples developmental progression from sugar availability. *Plant Mol. Biol.* 53:227–36

84. Loreti E, Alpi A, Perata P. 2000. Glucose and disaccharide-sensing mechanisms modulate the expression of alpha-amylase in barley embryos. *Plant Physiol.* 123:939–48

85. Loreti E, Poggi A, Novi G, Alpi A, Perata P. 2005. A genome-wide analysis of the effects of sucrose on gene expression in Arabidopsis seedlings under anoxia. *Plant Physiol.* 137:1130–38

86. Lu CA, Ho TH, Ho SL, Yu SM. 2002. Three novel MYB proteins with one DNA binding repeat mediate sugar and hormone regulation of alpha-amylase gene expression. *Plant Cell* 14:1963–80

87. Masaki T, Mitsui N, Tsukagoshi H, Nishii T, Morikami A, Nakamura K. 2005. ACTIVATOR of Spomin::LUC1/WRINKLED1 of *Arabidopsis thaliana* transactivates sugar-inducible promoters. *Plant Cell Physiol.* 46:547–56

88. Masaki T, Tsukagoshi H, Mitsui N, Nishii T, Hattori T, et al. 2005. Activation tagging of a gene for a protein with novel class of CCT-domain activates expression of a subset of sugar-inducible genes in *Arabidopsis thaliana*. *Plant J.* 43:142–52

89. **Moore B, Zhou L, Rolland F, Hall Q, Cheng WH, et al. 2003. Role of the Arabidopsis glucose sensor HXK1 in nutrient, light, and hormonal signaling. *Science* 300:332–36**

This paper discusses the development of molecular sensors for live imaging of metabolites, enabling the study of metabolic signaling with subcellular resolution.

The regulatory role of the AtHxk1 glucose sensor and interactions between sugar and auxin and cytokinin hormone signaling are demonstrated.

90. Moorhead G, Douglas P, Cotelle V, Harthill J, Morrice N, et al. 1999. Phosphorylation-dependent interactions between enzymes of plant metabolism and 14-3-3 proteins. *Plant J.* 18:1–12

91. Moreno F, Ahuatzi D, Riera A, Palomino CA, Herrero P. 2005. Glucose sensing through the Hxk2-dependent signalling pathway. *Biochem. Soc. Trans.* 33:265–68

92. Morikami A, Matsunaga R, Tanaka Y, Suzuki S, Mano S, Nakamura K. 2005. Two cis-acting regulatory elements are involved in the sucrose-inducible expression of the sporamin gene promoter from sweet potato in transgenic tobacco. *Mol. Genet. Genomics* 272:690–99

93. Morita-Yamamuro C, Tsutsui T, Tanaka A, Yamaguchi J. 2004. Knock-out of the plastid ribosomal protein S21 causes impaired photosynthesis and sugar-response during germination and seedling development in *Arabidopsis thaliana*. *Plant Cell Physiol.* 45:781–88

94. Ohto M, Fischer RL, Goldberg RB, Nakamura K, Harada JJ. 2005. Control of seed mass by APETALA2. *Proc. Natl. Acad. Sci. USA* 102:3123–28

95. Ohto M, Onai K, Furukawa Y, Aoki E, Araki T, Nakamura K. 2001. Effects of sugar on vegetative development and floral transition in Arabidopsis. *Plant Physiol.* 127:252–61

96. Olsson T, Thelander M, Ronne H. 2003. A novel type of chloroplast stromal hexokinase is the major glucose-phosphorylating enzyme in the moss *Physcomitrella patens*. *J. Biol. Chem.* 278:44439–47

97. Palenchar PM, Kouranov A, Lejay LV, Coruzzi GM. 2004. Genome-wide patterns of carbon and nitrogen regulation of gene expression validate the combined carbon and nitrogen (CN)-signaling hypothesis in plants. *Genome Biol.* 5:R91

98. Pego JV, Smeekens SC. 2000. Plant fructokinases: a sweet family get-together. *Trends Plant Sci.* 5:531–16

99. Penna S. 2003. Building stress tolerance through over-producing trehalose in transgenic plants. *Trends Plant Sci.* 8:355–57

100. Perfus-Barbeoch L, Jones AM, Assmann SM. 2004. Plant heterotrimeric G protein function: insights from Arabidopsis and rice mutants. *Curr. Opin. Plant Biol.* 7:719–31

101. Pien S, Wyrzykowska J, Fleming AJ. 2001. Novel marker genes for early leaf development indicate spatial regulation of carbohydrate metabolism within the apical meristem. *Plant J.* 25:663–74

102. Planchais S, Samland AK, Murray JA. 2004. Differential stability of Arabidopsis D-type cyclins: CYCD3;1 is a highly unstable protein degraded by a proteasome-dependent mechanism. *Plant J.* 38:616–25

103. Pourtau N, Mares M, Purdy S, Quentin N, Ruel A, Wingler A. 2004. Interactions of abscisic acid and sugar signalling in the regulation of leaf senescence. *Planta* 219:765–72

104. **Price J, Laxmi A, St Martin SK, Jang JC. 2004. Global transcription profiling reveals multiple sugar signal transduction mechanisms in Arabidopsis. *Plant Cell* 16:2128–50**

105. Price J, Li TC, Kang SG, Na JK, Jang JC. 2003. Mechanisms of glucose signaling during germination of Arabidopsis. *Plant Physiol.* 132:1424–38

106. Purcell PC, Smith AM, Halford NG. 1998. Antisense expression of a sucrose non-fermenting-1-related protein kinase sequence in potato results in decreased expression of sucrose synthase in tubers and loss of sucrose-inducibility of sucrose synthase transcripts in leaves. *Plant J.* 14:195–202

107. Riou-Khamlichi C, Menges M, Healy JM, Murray JA. 2000. Sugar control of the plant cell cycle: differential regulation of Arabidopsis D-type cyclin gene expression. *Mol. Cell. Biol.* 20:4513–21

One of the first comprehensive whole-genome microarray analyses of *Arabidopsis* glucose-regulated gene expression.

108. Roitsch T. 1999. Source-sink regulation by sugar and stress. *Curr. Opin. Plant Biol.* 2:198–206

109. Roitsch T, Gonzalez MC. 2004. Function and regulation of plant invertases: sweet sensations. *Trends Plant Sci.* 9:606–13

110. Roldan M, Gomez-Mena C, Ruiz-Garcia L, Salinas J, Martinez-Zapater JM. 1999. Sucrose availability on the aerial part of the plant promotes morphogenesis and flowering of Arabidopsis in the dark. *Plant J.* 20:581–90

111. Rolland F, Moore B, Sheen J. 2002. Sugar sensing and signaling in plants. *Plant Cell* 14(Suppl.):S185–205

112. Rolland F, Winderickx J, Thevelein JM. 2001. Glucose-sensing mechanisms in eukaryotic cells. *Trends Biochem. Sci.* 26:310–17

113. Rolland F, Winderickx J, Thevelein JM. 2002. Glucose-sensing and -signalling mechanisms in yeast. *FEMS Yeast Res.* 2:183–201

114. Rook F, Gerrits N, Kortstee A, van Kampen M, Borrias M, et al. 1998. Sucrose-specific signalling represses translation of the Arabidopsis ATB2 bZIP transcription factor gene. *Plant J.* 15:253–63

115. Ruuska SA, Girke T, Benning C, Ohlrogge JB. 2002. Contrapuntal networks of gene expression during Arabidopsis seed filling. *Plant Cell* 14:1191–206

116. Scheible WR, Morcuende R, Czechowski T, Fritz C, Osuna D, et al. 2004. Genome-wide reprogramming of primary and secondary metabolism, protein synthesis, cellular growth processes, and the regulatory infrastructure of Arabidopsis in response to nitrogen. *Plant Physiol.* 136:2483–99

117. Schluepmann H, Pellny T, van Dijken A, Smeekens S, Paul M. 2003. Trehalose 6-phosphate is indispensable for carbohydrate utilization and growth in *Arabidopsis thaliana. Proc. Natl. Acad. Sci. USA* 100:6849–54

118. Schluepmann H, van Dijken A, Aghdasi M, Wobbes B, Paul M, Smeekens S. 2004. Trehalose mediated growth inhibition of Arabidopsis seedlings is due to trehalose-6-phosphate accumulation. *Plant Physiol.* 135:879–90

119. Sheen J. 1990. Metabolic repression of transcription in higher plants. *Plant Cell* 2:1027–38

120. Sheen J. 1999. C4 gene expression. *Annu. Rev. Plant Physiol. Plant Mol. Biol.* 50:187–217

121. Slocombe SP, Beaudoin F, Donaghy PG, Hardie DG, Dickinson JR, Halford NG. 2004. SNF1-related protein kinase (snRK1) phosphorylates class I heat shock protein. *Plant Physiol. Biochem.* 42:111–16

122. Smalle J, Vierstra RD. 2004. The ubiquitin 26S proteasome proteolytic pathway. *Annu. Rev. Plant Biol.* 55:555–90

123. Smeekens S. 2000. Sugar-induced signal transduction in plants. *Annu. Rev. Plant Physiol. Plant Mol. Biol* 51:49–81

124. Smith AM, Zeeman SC, Smith SM. 2005. Starch degradation. *Annu. Rev. Plant Biol.* 56:73–98

125. Sugden C, Crawford RM, Halford NG, Hardie DG. 1999. Regulation of spinach SNF1-related (SnRK1) kinases by protein kinases and phosphatases is associated with phosphorylation of the T loop and is regulated by 5′-AMP. *Plant J.* 19:433–39

126. Sugden C, Donaghy PG, Halford NG, Hardie DG. 1999. Two SNF1-related protein kinases from spinach leaf phosphorylate and inactivate 3-hydroxy-3-methylglutaryl-coenzyme A reductase, nitrate reductase, and sucrose phosphate synthase in vitro. *Plant Physiol.* 120:257–74

127. Sun C, Palmqvist S, Olsson H, Boren M, Ahlandsberg S, Jansson C. 2003. A novel WRKY transcription factor, SUSIBA2, participates in sugar signaling in barley by binding to the sugar-responsive elements of the iso1 promoter. *Plant Cell* 15:2076–92

128. Takahashi F, Sato-Nara K, Kobayashi K, Suzuki M, Suzuki H. 2003. Sugar-induced adventitious roots in Arabidopsis seedlings. *J. Plant Res.* 116:83–91

129. Thelander M, Olsson T, Ronne H. 2004. Snf1-related protein kinase 1 is needed for growth in a normal day-night light cycle. *EMBO J.* 23:1900–10

130. Thibaud MC, Gineste S, Nussaume L, Robaglia C. 2004. Sucrose increases pathogenesis-related PR-2 gene expression in *Arabidopsis thaliana* through an SA-dependent but NPR1-independent signaling pathway. *Plant Physiol. Biochem.* 42:81–88

131. Thimm O, Blasing O, Gibon Y, Nagel A, Meyer S, et al. 2004. MAPMAN: a user-driven tool to display genomics data sets onto diagrams of metabolic pathways and other biological processes. *Plant J.* 37:914–39

132. Thompson AR, Vierstra RD. 2005. Autophagic recycling: lessons from yeast help define the process in plants. *Curr. Opin. Plant Biol.* 8:165–73

133. Thum KE, Shasha DE, Lejay LV, Coruzzi GM. 2003. Light- and carbon-signaling pathways. Modeling circuits of interactions. *Plant Physiol.* 132:440–52

134. Thum KE, Shin MJ, Palenchar PM, Kouranov A, Coruzzi GM. 2004. Genome-wide investigation of light and carbon signaling interactions in Arabidopsis. *Genome Biol.* 5:R10

135. Tiessen A, Prescha K, Branscheid A, Palacios N, McKibbin R, et al. 2003. Evidence that SNF1-related kinase and hexokinase are involved in separate sugar-signalling pathways modulating post-translational redox activation of ADP-glucose pyrophosphorylase in potato tubers. *Plant J.* 35:490–500

136. Toroser D, Plaut Z, Huber SC. 2000. Regulation of a plant SNF1-related protein kinase by glucose-6-phosphate. *Plant Physiol.* 123:403–12

137. Tsai CH, Miller A, Spalding M, Rodermel S. 1997. Source strength regulates an early phase transition of tobacco shoot morphogenesis. *Plant Physiol.* 115:907–14

138. Tsukagoshi H, Saijo T, Shibata D, Morikami A, Nakamura K. 2005. Analysis of a sugar response mutant of Arabidopsis identified a novel b3 domain protein that functions as an active transcriptional repressor. *Plant Physiol.* 138:675–85

139. Ullah H, Chen JG, Wang S, Jones AM. 2002. Role of a heterotrimeric G protein in regulation of Arabidopsis seed germination. *Plant Physiol.* 129:897–907

140. Van den Ende W, De Coninck B, Van Laere A. 2004. Plant fructan exohydrolases: a role in signaling and defense? *Trends Plant Sci.* 9:523–28

141. van Dijken AJ, Schluepmann H, Smeekens SC. 2004. Arabidopsis trehalose-6-phosphate synthase 1 is essential for normal vegetative growth and transition to flowering. *Plant Physiol.* 135:969–77

141a. Vaughn MW, Harrington GN, Bush DR. 2002. Sucrose-mediated transcriptional regulation of sucrose symporter activity in the phloem. *Proc. Natl. Acad. Sci. USA* 99:10876–80

142. Villadsen D, Smith SM. 2004. Identification of more than 200 glucose-responsive Arabidopsis genes none of which responds to 3-O-methylglucose or 6-deoxyglucose. *Plant Mol. Biol.* 55:467–77

143. Vogel G, Fiehn O, Jean-Richard-dit-Bressel L, Boller T, Wiemken A, et al. 2001. Trehalose metabolism in Arabidopsis: occurrence of trehalose and molecular cloning and characterization of trehalose-6-phosphate synthase homologues. *J. Exp. Bot.* 52:1817–26

144. Wang R, Okamoto M, Xing X, Crawford NM. 2003. Microarray analysis of the nitrate response in Arabidopsis roots and shoots reveals over 1,000 rapidly responding genes and new linkages to glucose, trehalose-6-phosphate, iron, and sulfate metabolism. *Plant Physiol.* 132:556–67

145. Weber AP, Schwacke R, Flugge UI. 2005. Solute transporters of the plastid envelope membrane. *Annu. Rev. Plant Biol.* 56:133–64

146. **Weber H, Borisjuk L, Wobus U. 2005. Molecular physiology of legume seed development. *Annu. Rev. Plant Biol.* 56:253–79**

147. **Wiese A, Elzinga N, Wobbes B, Smeekens S. 2004. A conserved upstream open reading frame mediates sucrose-induced repression of translation. *Plant Cell* 16:1717–29**

148. Wiese A, Groner F, Sonnewald U, Deppner H, Lerchl J, et al. 1999. Spinach hexokinase I is located in the outer envelope membrane of plastids. *FEBS Lett.* 461:13–18

149. Wingler A, Fritzius T, Wiemken A, Boller T, Aeschbacher RA. 2000. Trehalose induces the ADP-glucose pyrophosphorylase gene, ApL3, and starch synthesis in Arabidopsis. *Plant Physiol.* 124:105–14

150. Wingler A, Marès M, Pourtau N. 2004. Spatial patterns and metabolic regulation of photosynthetic parameters during leaf senescence. *New Phytol.* 161:781–89

151. Xiao W, Sheen J, Jang JC. 2000. The role of hexokinase in plant sugar signal transduction and growth and development. *Plant Mol. Biol.* 44:451–61

152. **Yanagisawa S, Yoo SD, Sheen J. 2003. Differential regulation of EIN3 stability by glucose and ethylene signalling in plants. *Nature* 425:521–25**

153. Yoshida S, Ito M, Nishida I, Watanabe A. 2002. Identification of a novel gene HYS1/CPR5 that has a repressive role in the induction of leaf senescence and pathogen-defence responses in *Arabidopsis thaliana*. *Plant J.* 29:427–37

154. Yu SM. 1999. Cellular and genetic responses of plants to sugar starvation. *Plant Physiol.* 121:687–93

155. Zhang Y, Shewry PR, Jones H, Barcelo P, Lazzeri PA, Halford NG. 2001. Expression of antisense SnRK1 protein kinase sequence causes abnormal pollen development and male sterility in transgenic barley. *Plant J.* 28:431–41

156. Zhou L, Jang JC, Jones TL, Sheen J. 1998. Glucose and ethylene signal transduction crosstalk revealed by an Arabidopsis glucose-insensitive mutant. *Proc. Natl. Acad. Sci. USA* 95:10294–99

157. Zourelidou M, de Torres-Zabala M, Smith C, Bevan MW. 2002. Storekeeper defines a new class of plant-specific DNA-binding proteins and is a putative regulator of patatin expression. *Plant J.* 30:489–97

A nice overview of the central regulatory role and dynamics of sugar metabolism during legume seed development, with important implications for sugar regulation of whole-plant development.

This study uncovered an intriguing novel mechanism of sucrose-specific translation control, involving a conserved upstream open reading frame.

This paper describes the molecular link between glucose and ethylene signaling and the remarkable observation that plant HXK1 can translocate to the nucleus.

Vitamin Synthesis in Plants: Tocopherols and Carotenoids

Dean DellaPenna[1] and Barry J. Pogson[2]

[1] Department of Biochemistry and Molecular Biology, Michigan State University, East Lansing, Michigan 48824; email: dellapen@msu.edu

[2] ARC Center of Excellence in Plant Energy Biology, School of Biochemistry and Molecular Biology, Australian National University, Canberra ACT 0200, Australia; email: barry.pogson@anu.edu.au

Annu. Rev. Plant Biol.
2006. 57:711–38

The *Annual Review of Plant Biology* is online at
plant.annualreviews.org

doi: 10.1146/
annurev.arplant.56.032604.144301

First published online as a
Review in Advance on
February 7, 2006

1543-5008/06/0602-
0711$20.00

Key Words

metabolic engineering, vitamin E, provitamin A, Arabidopsis,
chloroplast, photosynthesis

Abstract

Carotenoids and tocopherols are the two most abundant groups of lipid-soluble antioxidants in chloroplasts. In addition to their many functional roles in photosynthetic organisms, these compounds are also essential components of animal diets, including humans. During the past decade, a near complete set of genes required for the synthesis of both classes of compounds in photosynthetic tissues has been identified, primarily as a result of molecular genetic and biochemical genomics-based approaches in the model organisms *Arabidopsis thaliana* and *Synechocystis* sp. PCC6803. Mutant analysis and transgenic studies in these and other systems have provided important insight into the regulation, activities, integration, and evolution of individual enzymes and are already providing a knowledge base for breeding and transgenic approaches to modify the types and levels of these important compounds in agricultural crops.

Contents

INTRODUCTION: PLASTIDIC ISOPRENOID SYNTHESIS

Plastids contain sophisticated biochemical machinery producing an enormous array of compounds that perform vital plastidic and cellular functions. Many of these compounds are also important for agriculture and human nutrition. Plastidic isoprenoid synthesis represents a major source of such compounds and includes the two major groups of lipid-soluble antioxidants in photosynthetic tissues, the tocochromanols and carotenoids. The tocochromanols are a group of eight tocopherols and tocotrienols that collectively constitute vitamin E, an essential nutrient in the diet of all mammals. Carotenoids constitute a much larger group of over 700 structures (17) that provide fruit and flowers with distinctive red, orange, and yellow coloring and are the dietary source of pigmentation in the tissues of many fish, crustaceans, and birds. In some cases specific carotenoids are essential components of mammalian diets as precursors for vitamin A synthesis. Vitamin A deficiency remains a significant global health problem (121, 147a).

Both carotenoids and tocochromanols are synthesized in whole or in part from the plastidic isoprenoid biosynthetic pathway. The biosynthesis of isoprenoid precursors is covered in detail elsewhere (67). Briefly, two distinct pathways exist for isopetenylpyrophosphate (IPP) production: the cytosolic mevalonic acid pathway and the plastidic mevalonate-independent, methylerythritol 4-phosphate (MEP) pathway. The methylerythritol 4-phosphate pathway combines glyceraldehyde-3-phosphate and pyruvate to form deoxy-D-xylulose 5-phosphate, and a number of steps are then required to form IPP and dimethylallylpyrophosphate (DMAPP) (67). IPP is subject to a sequential series of condensation reactions to form geranylgeranyl diphosphate (GGDP), a key intermediate in the synthesis of carotenoids, tocochromanols, and many other plastidic isoprenoids (**Figure 1**).

The tocochromanol and carotenoid biosynthetic pathways are typical of many plant compounds in that the enzymes from plant sources have historically proven extremely difficult to purify and analyze. This is a result of a combination of properties, including membrane association, low specific activity and poor stability of the enzymes

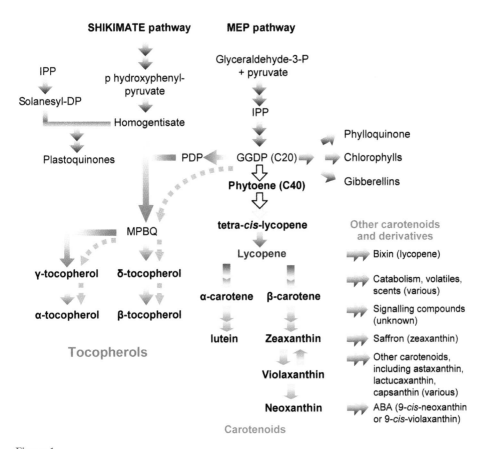

SHIKIMATE pathway   **MEP pathway**

Glyceraldehyde-3-P + pyruvate

IPP

p hydroxyphenyl-pyruvate

Solanesyl-DP

IPP

Homogentisate

Plastoquinones   PDP ← GGDP (C20) → → Phylloquinone

→ Chlorophylls

→ Gibberellins

Phytoene (C40)

MPBQ   tetra-*cis*-lycopene

Other carotenoids and derivatives

Lycopene

γ-tocopherol   δ-tocopherol   → Bixin (lycopene)

α-carotene   β-carotene   → Catabolism, volatiles, scents (various)

α-tocopherol   β-tocopherol   → Signalling compounds (unknown)

lutein   Zeaxanthin   → Saffron (zeaxanthin)

Tocopherols

Violaxanthin   → Other carotenoids, including astaxanthin, lactucaxanthin, capsanthin (various)

Neoxanthin   → ABA (9-*cis*-neoxanthin or 9-*cis*-violaxanthin)

Carotenoids

Figure 1

Overview of carotenoid and tocopherol biosynthesis in plants. The 2-C-methyl-D-erythritol-4-phosphate (MEP) pathway provides isopetenylpyrophosphate (IPP) for synthesis of the central intermediate geranylgeranyl diphosphate (GGDP). GGDP can be used for synthesis of phytoene, chlorophylls, and tocotrienols or reduced to phytyl-diphosphate (PDP) used for phylloquinone, chlorophyll, and tocopherol synthesis. Phytol released from chlorophyll degradation is also used for tocopherol synthesis (not shown, see text). The pathway shown by orange arrows provides the carotenoids found in leaves of most species. Other carotenoids and carotenoid cleavage/modification products are produced in certain species and/or particular tissues, and when known, the primary substrate for cleavage is given in parentheses. The pathway shown by green arrows is the synthesis of tocopherols from homogentisate, a product of the shikimate pathway. For clarity, only tocopherols are shown, but when GGDP is condensed with homogentisate, the corresponding tocotrienols are produced by the same pathway. ABA, abscisic acid; MPBQ, methyl-6-phytyl-1,4-benzoquinone.

during isolation as well as limitations in synthesizing or obtaining commercially available substrates for assays. Thus, much of our understanding of the genes and enzymes of tocochromanol and carotenoid biosynthesis has resulted from the increasing ease of integrating complementary comparative genomics, biochemical genetics, and molecular approaches. This review focuses on progress since the last reviews on these subjects in this series (30, 45). However, several recent reviews on aspects of the biosynthesis, function, and catabolism of these compounds are available, and readers are directed to these sources for additional information (29, 33, 38, 49, 74, 82–84, 104, 140, 144).

CAROTENOID BIOSYNTHESIS IN PLANTS

General Considerations and Early Steps in Biosynthesis

Carotenoids comprise a large isoprenoid family and most are C_{40} tetraterpenoids derived from phytoene. The carotenoid backbone is either linear or contains one or more cyclic β-ionone or ε-ionone rings or, less frequently, the unusual cyclopentane ring of capsanthin and capsorubin that imparts the distinct red color to peppers. Nonoxygenated carotenoids are referred to as carotenes, whereas their oxygenated derivatives are designated as xanthophylls. The most commonly occurring carotenes are β-carotene in chloroplasts and lycopene in chromoplasts of some flowers and fruits, e.g., tomatoes. The most abundant xanthophylls in photosynthetic plant tissues (lutein, violaxanthin, and neoxanthin) are key components of the light-harvesting complexes. Carotenoids are involved in photosystem assembly, light harvesting and photoprotection, photomorphogenesis, nonphotochemical quenching, lipid peroxidation and affect the size and function of the light-harvesting antenna and seed set (35, 47, 52, 62, 69, 93). As these topics have been reviewed extensively elsewhere (33, 51, 84), the roles of carotenoids in photosynthesis are not considered here.

The initial steps of plant carotenoid synthesis and their chemical properties have been thoroughly discussed in prior reviews, and readers are referred to these for more detail (28, 29, 33, 49, 104). Briefly, the first committed step in plant carotenoid synthesis is the condensation of two molecules of GGDP to produce phytoene (**Figure 2**) by the enzyme phytoene synthase (PSY). Phytoene is produced as a 15-*cis* isomer, which is subsequently converted to all-*trans* isomer derivatives. Two plant desaturases, phytoene desaturase (PDS) and ζ-carotene desaturase (ZDS), catalyze similar dehydrogenation reactions by introducing four double bonds to form lycopene. Desaturation requires a plastid terminal oxidase and plastoquinone in photosynthetic tissues (8, 21, 85). Bacterial desaturation differs from plants in that a single enzyme, *crtI* (phytoene desaturase), introduces four double bonds into phytoene to yield all-*trans*-lycopene (28).

Isomerizations During Carotenoid Desaturation

Until recently, the higher plant desaturases were assumed sufficient for the production of all-*trans*-lycopene. This conclusion was reached despite the accumulation of tetra-*cis*-lycopene in *tangerine* tomato and algal mutants (27, 135) and biochemical evidence to the contrary from daffodil (9). Recently, the carotenoid isomerase gene, *CRTISO*, was identified in Arabidopsis and tomato (55, 89). Intriguingly, the protein shows 20%–30% identity to the bacterial carotenoid desaturases; however it has no desaturase activity (89). Rather, the pathway to all-*trans*-lycopene proceeds via *cis* intermediates (16, 54): The PDS and ZDS enzymes introducing *cis*-carbon-carbon double bonds (5) (**Figure 2**) and CRTISO catalyze *cis-trans* isomerizations resulting in all-*trans*-lycopene (54, 89). There is evidence the desaturation and isomerization reactions can occur sequentially (16) or concurrently (54).

Mutant plants deficient in CRTISO activity accumulate various *cis*-isomer biosynthetic intermediates when dark-grown, but these intermediates can be photoisomerized in the light and yield viable plants, albeit with reduced lutein levels (89). If photoisomerization is sufficient, why are three genes required for the synthesis of *trans*-lycopene (*PDS*, *ZDS*, and *CRTISO*) in plants but only one (*crtI*) in bacteria? One possible explanation is CRTISO contributes to the regulation of the pathway, in that there is a delay in greening and a reduction in lutein in leaves of *crtISO* mutants (89). Consistent with this, expression of bacterial *crtI* in tobacco, Arabidopsis,

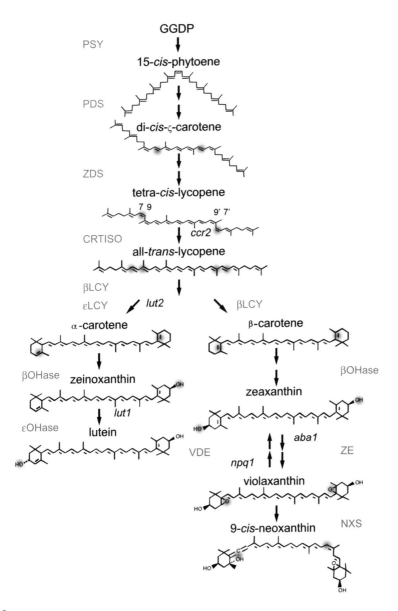

Figure 2

Carotenoid biosynthetic pathway in land plants. The pathway shows the primary steps found in nearly all plant species. The desaturases introduce a series of four double bonds in a *cis* configuration, which are isomerized to the all-*trans* conformations by the carotenoid isomerase. Although shown sequentially, there is evidence the carotenoid isomerase enzyme (CRTISO) may act in concert with the ζ–carotene desaturase (ZDS). Lycopene is cyclized to form α-carotene and β-carotene, which are subject to a series of oxygenation reactions to produce the xanthophylls typically found in chloroplasts. The abbreviation for the biosynthetic enzymes is given next to each step and Arabidopsis mutations are shown in italics (see **Table 1**). β-LCY, β-carotene cyclase; βOHase, β-carotene hydroxylase; εLCY, ε-cyclase; εOHase, ε-carotene hydroxylase; NXS, neoxanthin synthase; PDS, phytoene desaturase; PSY, phytoene synthase; VDE, violaxanthin deepoxidase; ZE, zeaxanthin epoxidase.

Table 1 Carotenoid biosynthetic enzymes in Arabidopsis and other selected plants

Enzyme (Genera)[a]	Abbreviation	Locus[b]	Gene ID[c]	Reference(s)
Early steps				
Phytoene synthase	PSY		At5g17230	(8)
Phytoene desaturase	PDS	PDS3	At4g14210	(28)
ζ-carotene desaturase	ZDS		At3g04870	(28)
Carotenoid isomerase	CRTISO	CCR2	At1g06820	(54, 89)
Cyclases				
β-carotene cyclase	βLCY1		At3g10230	(28)
β-carotene cyclase (*Lycopersicum*)	βLCY2	BETA	AF254793*	(102)
ε-cyclase	εLCY	LUT2	At5g57030	(28)
Xanthophyll enzymes				
β-carotene hydroxylase	βOHase1		At4g25700	(125)
	βOHase2		At5g52570	(132)
ε-carotene hydroxylase	εOHase	LUT1	At3g53130	(134)
Zeaxanthin epoxidase	ZE	ABA1	At5g67030	(28)
Violaxanthin deepoxidase	VDE	NPQ1	At1g08550	(28)
Neoxanthin synthase	NXS			
Other xanthophyll enzymes				
β-carotene 4-ketolase (*Adonis*)	AdKeto1		AAV85452*	(32)
	AdKeto2		AAV85453*	
Capsanthin/capsorubin synthase (*Capsicum*)	CCS		S71511*	(28)
Carotenoid cleavage and modifying enzymes				
9-*cis* epoxycarotenoid dioxygenase	NCED2	CCD2	At4g18350	(126)
	NCED3	CCD3	At3g14440	
	NCED5	CCD4	At1g30100	
	NCED6	CCD6	At3g24220	
	NCED9	CCD9	At1g78390	
Carotenoid cleavage dioxygenase	CCD1		At3g63520	(126)
	CCD4		At4g19170	
	CCD7	MAX3	At2g44990	(10)
	CCD8	MAX4	At4g32810	(122)
MORE AUXILLARY BRANCHING 1	MAX1		At2g26170	(11)
Carotenoid cleavage dioxygenase (*Crocus*)	CsCCD		AJ132927*	(15)
Zeaxanthin cleavage dioxygenase (*Crocus*)	CsZCD		AJ489276*	(15)
Crocin glucosyltransferase (*Crocus*)	CsGTase	UGTCs2	AY262037	(78)
Lycopene cleavage dioxygenase (*Bixa*)	BoLCD		CAD71148*	(13)

[a]Enzyme and genera in brackets if not *Arabidopsis*.
[b]Locus or alternate name. *CCR* = <u>C</u>HLOROPLAST and <u>C</u>AROTENOID <u>R</u>EGULATION; *BETA* = *BETA-CAROTENE*; *LUT* = <u>LUT</u>EIN; *ABA* = <u>ABA</u>CISIC <u>A</u>CID; *NPQ* = <u>N</u>ONPHOTOCHEMICAL <u>Q</u>UENCHING; *UGTCs* = UDP-GLUCOSYL TRANSFERASE from <u>C</u>rocus *sativuss*.
[c]*Arabidopsis thaliana* (At) gene identifier or * GenInfo identifier from Genbank.

and rice bypasses the native CRTISO activity and also results in reduced leaf lutein levels (76, 87, 149). Also in tomato fruit chromoplasts, CRTISO activity is needed for all-*trans*-lycopene accumulation as in the tomato *crtISO* mutant (*tangerine*) *cis*-lycopene is accumulated and appears resistant to photoisomerization (55). Thus, CRTISO is required for optimal carotenoid synthesis in etioplasts, chromoplasts, and chloroplasts.

β-Carotene Derived Xanthophyll Biosynthesis

β-carotene and zeaxanthin. The plant carotenoid biosynthetic pathway has two main branches after lycopene, distinguished by different cyclic end-groups. Two beta rings lead to the β,β branch (β-carotene and its derivatives: zeaxanthin, violaxanthin, antheraxanthin, and neoxanthin) whereas one beta and one epsilon ring define the β,ε branch (α-carotene and its derivatives). Although there is but a single *βLCY* gene in Arabidopsis, a second lycopene β-cyclase was identified in tomato (102). Expression of the second *βLCY* is low during wild-type fruit ripening but is dramatically elevated in the high β-carotene *Beta* mutant, demonstrating this gene's importance in determining fruit pigment composition (102). Interestingly, the second *βLCY* is only 53% identical to the first *βLCY* yet 86% identical to the capsanthin-capsorubin synthase from pepper (*Capsicum annum*), suggesting capsanthin-capsorubin synthase diverged from an ortholog of the second tomato *βLCY*.

Nearly all xanthophylls in higher plants have hydroxyl moieties on the carbon 3 of the cyclic β-ionone end-group. Although most other carotenoid pathway reactions are encoded by a single gene in Arabidopsis, multiple hydroxylase genes occur in Arabidopsis and tomato with distinct evolutionary backgrounds. Plant β-ring hydroxylases (β-OHs) share significant identity with bacterial β-ring hydroxylases (125) and are ferredoxin-dependent, nonheme dioxygenases with an iron-coordinating histidine cluster (14). The two Arabidopsis β-OHs are expressed in all tissues, albeit at different levels (132), whereas in tomato one β-OH is expressed in chloroplasts and the other in flowers (49). β-OH gene expression is strongly induced by excess light in Arabidopsis leaves (103) and is modulated by different intensities of white light during photomorphogenesis (147).

Violaxanthin and neoxanthin. An epoxide group is introduced into both rings of zeaxanthin by zeaxanthin epoxidase to form violaxanthin. Under high light stress, which acidifies the lumen, violaxanthin deepoxidase is activated, resulting in increased levels of zeaxanthin (84). Violaxanthin deepoxidase and zeaxanthin epoxidase were the first identified plant lipocalins, a class of β-barrel proteins that bind small hydrophobic molecules but are not usually catalytic (18).

Conversion of violaxanthin to neoxanthin is performed by the enzyme neoxanthin synthase (NXS). Genes encoding enzymes with limited NXS activity were identified in tomato and potato (1, 12), but whether they are the primary NXS in vivo remains a matter of debate, especially considering Arabidopsis lacks an ortholog for the potato and tomato enzymes but has NXS activity. The recent identification of mutants that lack neoxanthin in Arabidopsis (*Ataba4*) and tomato may lead to the resolution of this issue (A. Marion-Poll & J. Hirschberg, personal communication).

Lutein Biosynthesis

Both the β-cyclase and ε-cyclase enzymes (*βLCY* and *εLCY*, respectively) are required to form α-carotene and lutein (30, 92). Increasing or decreasing *εLCY* expression resulted in lutein levels ranging from 10% to 180% of wild type (94). Lettuce (*Lactuca sativa*) appears unique among higher plants in that its *εLCY* enzyme can catalyze formation of the bicyclic ε,ε-carotene (31, 90). In fact, a single amino-acid substitution, H457L in lettuce, was found sufficient for bicyclic to monocyclic ε-ring formation, with the converse occurring for L448H in Arabidopsis (31). Another interesting organism is the marine cyanobacterium *Prochlorococcus marinus* MED4, which contains a *βLCY* gene and an additional novel cyclase capable of forming both β- and ε-end-groups (124).

In contrast to the nonheme β-ring hydroxylases, the recently identified ε-ring hydroxylase was found to be a member of the cytochrome P450-type monooxygenase superfamily, and thus has a distinctly different enzymatic mechanism from the plant β-ring OHases described above (134). Arabidopsis mutant genotypes deficient in all three of the known carotene ring hydroxylases (β-hydroxylases 1 and 2 and the ε-ring hydroxylase) still produced at least 50% of the wild-type level of hydroxylated β-rings, primarily as the monohydroxy α-carotene derivative zeinoxanthin (133). One likely explanation for this result is the existence of a fourth carotenoid hydroxylase in Arabidopsis that has a major activity toward the β-ring of α-carotene (134). One possible candidate for this activity is CYP97A3, a putative cytochrome P450 with 50% identity to the ε-ring hydroxylase (133, 134).

Carotenoid Cleavage Products

The carotenoid cleavage enzymes are variously referred to as carotenoid cleavage dioxygenases (CCDs), related to carotenoid dioxygenase, or 9-*cis*-epoxycarotenoid dioxygenases (NCEDs), which was the first characterized member of this gene family (83). The CCD gene family is responsible for the formation of abscisic acid (ABA), vitamin A, volatiles used in the perfume industry such as β-ionone, colored food additives such as saffron and bixin, and novel classes of plant hormones (33, 74, 83). The expression and subcellular localization of five of the nine Arabidopsis CCDs were studied (126). All were targeted to the plastid, with AtNCED5 thylakoid bound, AtNCED2, AtNCED3, and AtNCED6 both thylakoid-bound and stromal, and AtNCED9 in the stroma (126). All CCDs tested to date act on carotenoids but do show differences in substrate specificity (113) and tissue distribution (126). The crystal structure of a cyanobacterial retinal-forming carotenoid oxygenase reveals a tunnel for holding the β-ionone ring during processing, and this structure will undoubtedly aid in future functional studies of the entire family of enzymes (61).

Abscisic acid. The pathway for synthesis of the plant hormone ABA involves NCEDs that cleave 9-*cis*-neoxanthin or 9-*cis*-violaxanthin to form xanthoxin. Xanthoxin is further modified to produce ABA (reviewed in 83).

Vitamin A. Vitamin A (retinaldehyde) is a C_{20} carotenoid cleavage product essential for animal survival as both a chromophore in vision (retinals) and a hormone (retinoic acids) that exerts most of the effects of vitamin A (144). Any carotenoid containing an unmodified β-ionone ring, such as β-carotene, has provitamin A activity and can be utilized by an animal carotene dioxygenase to produce retinaldehyde. Despite the importance of vitamin A in mammalian physiology, it was not until 2000 that a β-carotene 15,15'-dioxygenase was cloned from *Drosophila melanogaster* (145) and chicken (148) based on similarity to plant CCDs. Since then, progress in understanding vitamin A synthesis in animals has been rapid (144). These studies have shown isoprenoid processing enzymes are often encoded by related genes in plants and animals. These include CRTISO and RetSat (which saturates the 13–14 double bond of retinol), CYP707A (involved in ABA oxidation) and CYP26 (involved in retinoic acid oxidation), and RALDH1 (oxidizes retinaldehyde to retinoic acid) and its plant homolog that oxidizes ABA aldehyde to ABA (77).

Novel carotenoid cleavage products in plants. Evidence for the requirement of novel carotenoid-derived signaling compounds that regulate aspects of plant development, in particular apical dominance and branching, has been accumulating in recent years (6, 74). The Arabidopsis *more axillary growth* mutants (*max3* and *max4*), pea *ramosus* mutant (*rms1*), and petunia *decreased apical dominance* mutant (*dad1*) all cause increased branching of which *max4*, *rms1*, and *dad1* are disrupted in an orthologous carotenoid cleavage enzyme, CCD8, and *max3* in CCD7 (7, 10, 120, 122). CCD7 and CCD8 can sequentially cleave β-carotene to form the C_{18}

compound 13-apo-carotenone in vitro (112). Further modifications (11) are presumably required in vivo to produce the active, graft-transmissible compound that enables wild-type root stocks to complement *max* and *rms* shoots (7, 122, 138). Thus, there is growing evidence demonstrating a novel, mobile, carotenoid-derived hormone that acts downstream of auxin and inhibits shoot branching. Finally, another signal identifed by the *bypass1* mutation, which affects plant architecture, is apparently carotenoid derived and graft transmissible (142).

Carotenoid cleavage products (enzymatic and photooxidative derivatives) are also important in the food, fragrance, and cosmetic industries. Although other aroma constituents such as esters, terpenes, and pyrazines are usually also present (43), the C_9 to C_{13} carotenoid derivatives are often essential to the odor profile (119). Bixin (annatto) is a red-colored dicarboxylic monomethyl ester apocarotenoid, traditionally derived from the plant *Bixa orellana*. Bouvier et al. (13) identified a lycopene cleavage dioxygenase, bixin aldehyde dehydrogenase, and norbixin carboxyl methyltransferase that are required to produce bixin. Saffron, another commercially important colored compound from *Crocus sativus*, derives most of its characteristic color, flavor, and aroma from the accumulation of carotenoid derivatives. A crocus zeaxanthin 7,8(7',8')-cleavage dioxygenase was cloned and found to be targeted to the chromoplast where it initiated the production of the modified cleavage products (15), of which the final step is glucosylation (78).

Carotenoids in Nongreen Plastids

A substantial body of work exists on the biosynthesis and manipulation of carotenoids in chromoplasts (see 33, 49, 100, 128). During the chloroplast-to-chromoplast transformation process, carotenoids become localized in plastoglobuli before incorporation into the chromoplast (130). Carotenoids within plastoglobuli exhibit much higher light sta-

bility than carotenoids in chloroplast membranes, indicating pigments are better protected from light-mediated destruction in these structures (75). Carotenoids accumulated in fruits are important for protection of triacylglycerols, unsaturated lipids, proteins, membranes, and phenol quinones from photooxidation (75). Chromoplasts accumulate carotenoids in lipoprotein structures (39, 143). For example, in a novel cauliflower mutant with orange curd, β-carotene accumulates in the plastids of the pith and curd as sheets, ribbons, and crystals (66). Additionally, catabolism may also be an important component regulating carotenoid content in some tissues and developmental stages; for example, knockouts of *CCD1* increased total carotenoids in seeds by 40%, with some individual carotenoids increasing by three- to fivefold (3). Thus, carotenoid accumulation in nongreen plastids relies not only on the balance between carotenoid biosynthesis and degradation, but also on the development of structures capable of storing and retaining carotenoids.

Elaioplasts, which are specialized lipid-storing plastids in oil seeds, provide an ideal hydrophobic sink for accumulation of carotenoids. Seed-specific overexpression of PSY in canola resulted in an impressive 50-fold increase in total carotenoid content, in particular the provitamin A α- and β-carotenes (114). A similar approach in Arabidopsis seed resulted in a 43-fold increase in β-carotene and concomitant increases in other carotenoids and chlorophyll, but germination was delayed, reflecting higher levels of the carotenoid-derived hormone, ABA (68). Amyloplasts are "colorless" plastids specialized for storage of starch granules. Lutein is the predominant carotenoid present in many seed amyloplasts, including maize (56) and wheat (48). The antioxidant properties of carotenoids help to combat seed aging, with the loss of lutein subsequently accompanied by an increase in free radicals and reactive oxygen species and a loss of seed viability (20, 91).

The dark-grown etioplast is distinguished by the prolamellar body (PLB), a uniformly curved lattice of tubular membranes, which contains several of the biochemical building blocks required for the chloroplast including the xanthophylls, lutein, and violaxanthin. The Arabidopsis *ccr2* mutant accumulates tetra-*cis*-lycopene and lacks a PLB (89). The absence of this structure suggests that different carotenoids either directly or indirectly impede PLB formation, which results in a delay in photomorphogenesis (greening).

Engineering the Carotenoid Pathway to Benefit Human Health and Agriculture

An increasing body of work on the transgenic manipulation of carotenoids in food plants is emerging (for recent reviews see 100, 128). Because of the prevalence and dire consequences of vitamin A deficiency, provitamin A–carotenoid levels have been targeted for increase by plant breeding and genetic modification. One such example is the breeding of orange-fleshed sweet potato for local conditions in Kenya to provide a new source of β-carotene (46). The best-known example of carotenoid enhancement by molecular manipulation is Golden Rice. *PSY* from daffodil and the bacterial phytoene desaturase (*crtI*) from *Erwinia uredorva* were targeted for expression in rice endosperm (149). Both β-carotene and xanthophylls were produced indicating expression of later pathway enzymes normally occurs in rice endosperm (108). A second generation of Golden Rice has been produced using the maize PSY, which in conjunction with a larger population of transgenics enabled the elevation of carotenoids by up to 23-fold (87). Elite lines will be bred into local cultivars and subject to nutritional and risk assessment (26). In tomato, overexpressing the *Erwinia uredovora* PSY gene (*crtB*) resulted in a two- to fourfold increase in fruit carotenoids (42). Fruit-specific suppression of a photomorphogenic gene, *DET1*, in-

creased the carotenoid and flavonoid content in tomato fruit (36).

Lutein and zeaxanthin, which are important for photoprotection in plants, have been implicated in protecting against the leading cause of age-related blindness in the developed world, macular degeneration (33). Nontransgenic strains of a green alga, *Dunaliella salina*, were developed that accumulate zeaxanthin as the primary xanthophyll (57). *Dunaliella* is already cultivated as a source of β-carotene by the natural products industry. Potato, which usually accumulates lutein and violaxanthin, was genetically modified to accumulate zeaxanthin (101). Serendipitously, this resulted in elevated transcript levels of PSY and a concomitant two- to threefold increase in α-tocopherol (vitamin E) (101). Additional research has shown a correlation with transcript levels and genetic variability in carotenoid content across 20 potato cultivars (79). Intriguingly, overexpression of *PSY* in transgenic potatoes resulted in an increase in transcript for a protein known to function in carotenoid storage, fibrillin, in concert with an increase in carotenoid content (40).

Astaxanthin is a powerful antioxidant and hence a beneficial human dietary component. However, its main value is as a feed additive in aquaculture of salmon, which bioaccumulate astaxanthin in their flesh resulting in its characteristic pink color (71). Astaxanthin is expensive to synthesize chemically and is produced by a limited number of organisms (58); hence it is a target for biotechnological production. In plants, this includes expression of the ketocarotenoid biosynthetic enzyme(s), such as the *Haematococcus pluvialis* β-carotene ketolase (*CrtO*) gene in tobacco (73) and Arabidopsis seeds (123). Although only trace amounts of astaxanthin were produced in chloroplast-containing green tissue, astaxanthin esters were >20% of total carotenoids in chromoplasts of floral nectaries (73). A fusion protein produced from two astaxanthin biosynthetic genes from the bacterium *Paracoccus* expressed in tobacco nectaries resulted in a 10-fold increase in total carotenoid content, of which a small fraction was ketocarotenoids indicating the efficiency is affected by the high degree of esterification of xanthophyll precursors in this tissue (97). Astaxanthin biosynthesis is found in a limited number of plants, one being the flowers of *Adonis aestivalis*, which have an unexpected biosynthetic route to produce it (32). Two novel *Adonis aestivalis* enzymes with 60% sequence similarity to nonheme βOHases were identified, but neither enzyme displayed typical C3 β-hydroxylase activity and instead preferred to desaturate the 3,4-bond of the β-ring and hydroxylate the fourth carbon, resulting in the 4-keto-β-ring characteristic of astaxanthin and other ketocarotenoids (32).

The production of novel carotenoids has been made possible by innovative molecular shuffling of carotenoid biosynthetic genes. Random shuffling of bacterial phytoene desaturase (*crtI*) and β-cyclase (*crtY*) genes allowed the production of a variety of colored compounds, including the highly desaturated compound 3,4, 3′, 4′-tetra-dehydro-lycopene, despite limited knowledge of the enzymes' catalytic mechanisms (110). They also produced the monocyclic carotenoid, torulene, for the first time in *E. coli* by an entirely new metabolic route, different from any mechanism found in nature (110). A similar strategy enabled the creation of new bioactive compounds and the production of carotenoids otherwise inefficient to synthesize or extract (2, 64, 146).

TOCOCHROMANOL BIOSYNTHESIS IN CYANOBACTERIA AND PLANTS

General Considerations: Structures, Chemistry, and Vitamin E Activities

Tocochromanols are a group of four tocopherols and four tocotrienols produced at various levels and in different combinations by all plant tissues and some cyanobacteria. Tocochromanols are amphipathic molecules with the general structures shown in **Figure 3**.

The polar head group is derived from aromatic amino-acid metabolism whereas the saturated tail is derived from phytyl-diphosphate (phytyl-DP) or (GGDP) for tocopherols and tocotrienols, respectively. α-, β-, γ- and δ-tocochromanols differ only in the number and position of methyl substituents on the aromatic ring. Plant tissues vary enormously in their tocochromanol content and composition (45) with photosynthetic tissues generally containing low levels of total tocochromanols (<50 μ/gfw) and a high percentage of α-tocopherol whereas seeds contain 10–20 times this level of total tocochromanols, but α-tocopherol is most often a minor component. α-tocopherol content is especially important from a nutritional perspective as it has the highest vitamin E activity of all tocochromanols (**Figure 3**). This difference is a result of the preferential retention and distribution of α-tocopherol in animals, rather than differential absorption of tocochromanol species during digestion (136). Retention is mediated by a hepatic α-tocopherol transfer protein (α-TTP) with binding kinetics that correlate well with the relative vitamin E activity of each tocochromanol species (53). The importance of α-TTP binding for determining vitamin E activity is clear from the severe phenotypes of α-TTP knockout mice (129, 150). Although tocotrienol vitamin E activity is much lower than the corresponding tocopherols, dietary tocotrienols have been associated with other health benefits (131).

Although tocochromanols are only synthesized by photosynthetic organisms, most of our understanding of their chemistry and function comes from studies in artificial membranes and animal systems because of the vitamin E activity of tocochromanols in animal diets. From a chemical perspective, tocochromanols interact with polyunsaturated acyl groups and protect membrane lipids (especially polyunsaturated fatty acids) from oxidative damage by scavenging lipid peroxy radicals and quenching or chemically reacting with $^1O_2{}^*$ and other reactive oxygen species (ROS) (**Figure 4**) (reviewed in 111). Singlet

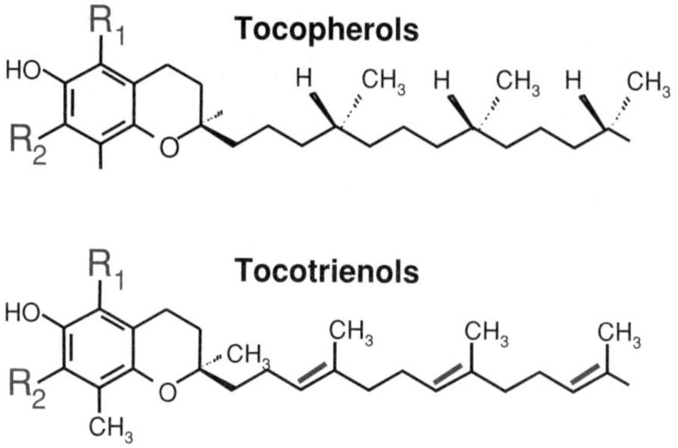

Figure 3

Tocochromanol structures and activities. Key differences in molecules are indicated in red. The table indicates the number and position of ring methyls in α-, β-, γ-, and δ-tocopherol and tocotrienols. The binding of each tocochromanol to an α-tocopherol transfer protein (α-TTP) (53, 88) and the vitamin E activity in the rat resorption-gestation assay (65) are expressed as a percent relative to α-tocopherol.

| | | | Activity versus α-tocopherol | |
Tocochromanol type	R_1	R_2	α-TPP binding	Vitamin E activity
α-tocopherol	CH_3	CH_3	100	100
α-tocotrienol	CH_3	CH_3	12.5	21-50
β-tocopherol	CH_3	H	38	25-50
β-tocotrienol	CH_3	H	nd	nm
γ-tocopherol	H	CH_3	9	8-19
γ-tocotrienol	H	CH_3	nd	nm
δ-tocopherol	H	H	1.5	<3
δ-tocotrienol	H	H	nd	nm

oxygen quenching occurs by a highly efficient charge-transfer mechanism. Termination of polyunsaturated fatty acid free radical chain reactions by tocochromanols occurs by donation of a hydrogen atom from the tocochromanol ring hydroxyl resulting in a "tocopherol radical." In mammals, the tocopherol radical is rapidly recycled back to the corresponding tocopherol allowing each tocopherol to participate in many lipid peroxidation chain-breaking events before being degraded. Whether a similar regeneration cycle occurs in plastids has not been demonstrated. Finally, tocochromanols can chemically scavenge various ROS and become converted to the corresponding quinone (and other derivatives), some of which have been shown to also participate in electron-transfer reactions (63, 118). Though it seems logical these quinones might be converted back to the corresponding tocopherols for additional rounds of scav-

enging, such reactions have not been reported in plants or animals. Biological functions of tocochromanols in mammalian systems and plants are discussed below.

The Tocochromanol Pathway Succumbs to Biochemical Genomics

The tocochromanol biosynthetic pathway (**Figure 5**) was elucidated from radiotracer studies in isolated chloroplasts and cyanobacteria in the mid-1980s (reviewed in 45). The tocochromanol pathway utilizes cytosolic aromatic amino-acid metabolism for head group synthesis and the plastidic deoxyxylulose 5-phosphate pathway for tail synthesis (phytyl-PP for tocopherols and GGDP for tocotrienols). The committed step in headgroup synthesis is the conversion of p-hydroxyphenylpyruvate (HPP) to homogentisic acid (HGA) by the enzyme HPP

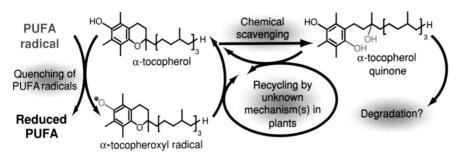

Figure 4

Polyunsaturated fatty acid (PUFA) quenching and reactive oxygen species (ROS) scavenging by tocopherols. Not all possible intermediates, reactions, or products are shown. Key differences in molecules are indicated in red.

dioxygenase (HPPD). Phytyl-PP or GGDP are condensed with HGA by a class of homogentisate prenyl transferases to yield 2-methyl-6-phytylplastoquinol (MPBQ) and 2-methyl-6-geranylgeranylplastoquinol (MGGBQ), respectively, the first committed intermediates in tocopherol and tocotrienol synthesis. The substrate specificity of this reaction is key for determining whether one or both tocochromanol classes are produced in a tissue. MPBQ and MGGBQ are methylated to form 2,3-dimethyl-5-phytyl-1, 4-benzoquinone (DMPBQ) or 2,3-dimethyl-5-geranylgeranyl-1, 4-benzoquinone (DMGGBQ), respectively. MPBQ and DMPBQ (or MGGBQ and DMGGBQ) are substrates for tocopherol cyclase to yield δ- and γ-tocopherols (and δ- and γ-tocotrienols), respectively. Finally, reaction with γ-tocopherol methyltransferase converts δ- and γ-tocopherols (and tocotrienols) to β- and α-tocopherols (and tocotrienols), respectively.

During the past decade our understanding of the molecular genetics of tocochromanol synthesis has become increasingly sophisticated. This is due to the directed application of "omics" and associated technologies to understand the synthesis of plant compounds important to human health and agriculture, an approach termed nutritional genomics (37). Several groups have targeted the tocochromanol pathway with this approach, such that all the core pathway enzymes have been isolated and studied in detail from Synechocystis sp. PCC6803 and Arabidopsis thaliana (19, 22, 23, 85, 86, 95, 105, 107, 109, 115, 116, 141). With the exception of MPBQ MT, the enzymes share significant sequence similarity between plants and cyanobacteria, which has facilitated genomics-driven ortholog isolation between the two organism groups. The sections below focus primarily on tocochromanol research in model photosynthetic organisms and highlight efforts, where appropriate, to use the knowledge obtained to manipulate tocochromanol levels in food crops.

Tocochromanol Aromatic Headgroup Synthesis

p-hydroxyphenylpyruvic acid dioxygenase (HPPD) was the first tocochromanol pathway enzyme to be cloned from Arabidopsis (86). HPPD catalyzes HGA synthesis, and mutation of the Arabidopsis locus (the PDS1 locus, At1g06590) conclusively demonstrated HPPD activity was essential for both tocopherol and plastoquinone biosynthesis in plants (85). Interestingly, disruption of the single HPPD in Synechocystis sp. PCC6803 (slr0090) only impacted tocopherol synthesis, indicating plastoquinone synthesis in Synechocystis sp. PCC6803 is HGA independent

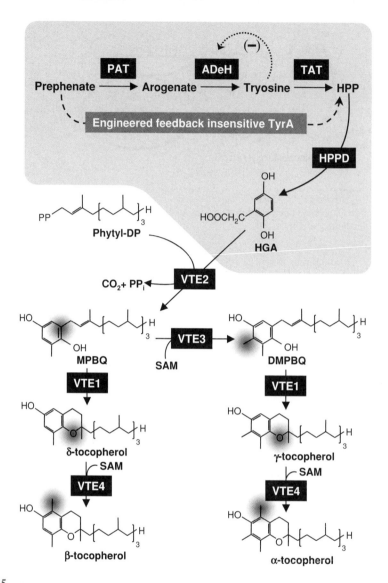

Figure 5

The tocopherol biosynthetic pathway in plants. The pathway and enzyme nomenclature, loci, and genes are in reference to studies in Arabidopsis, as described in detail in the text. Organisms that produce tocotrienols utilize the same pathway except the prenyltransferase reaction (VTE2) in these organisms can also utilize geranylgeranyl diphosphate (GGDP) in addition to or in place of phytyl-diphosphate (phytyl-DP). (*Yellow highlight*) Pathway leading from prephenate to homogentisic acid (HGA). Feedback inhibition of arogenate dehydrogenase (AdeH) by tyrosine is indicated by a dotted line. The activity of the feedback insensitive TyrA activity is indicated by a gray box and dashed line. α-tocopherol is the most abundant tocopherol produced in wild-type Arabidopsis leaves and in *Synechocystis* sp. PCC6803. γ-tocopherol is the most abundant tocopherol in Arabidopsis seed. The activity of VTE1, -2, -3, and -4 in generating the product for each step is highlighted in red on the relevant structure. DMPBQ, 2,3-dimethyl-5-phytyl-1, 4-benzoquinone; HPP, p-hydroxyphenylpyruvate; HPPD, HPP dioxygenase; PAT, prephenate amino transferase; SAM, S-adenosyl methionine; TAT, tyrosine amino transferase; VTE1, tocopherol cyclase; VTE2, homogentisate phyltransferase; VTE3, MPBQ methyltransferase; VTE4, γγ-tocopherol methyltransferase.

(34). Given the key location of HPPD in the tocochromanol pathway, it seemed a likely candidate regulating pathway flux. To test this hypothesis HPPD was overexpressed in Arabidopsis seed and leaves (137) resulting in more than a 20-fold increase in activity but only a 15% and 30% increase in seed and leaf tocopherols, respectively. Targeting overexpressed HPPD protein to either the cytosol or plastid of tobacco yielded similarly modest increases in seed tocochromanols (41). These data indicated that although HPPD is required, this activity alone is not a significant limitation to tocochromanol flux.

An alternative approach to engineering headgroup flux yielded unexpected results: greatly increased levels of tocotrienols in seed and leaves of various plants. The endogenous regulation of HPP production in plants, feedback inhibition of arogenate dehydrogenase by its product tyrosine, was bypassed by engineering a feedback insensitive, bifunctional prephenate dehydratase (TyrA) for overexpression in plants (60, 98). TyrA catalyzes HPP synthesis directly from prephenate but had little impact on tocochromanols when overexpressed alone. However, coexpression of TyrA with Arabidopsis HPPD in tobacco leaf resulted in an eightfold increase in total leaf tocochromanol levels, which occurred almost entirely because of increases in various tocotrienols normally only produced in tobacco seed (98). Similar results were obtained by seed-specific co-overexpression of TyrA and HPPD in Arabidopsis, canola, and soybean: two- to three fold increases in total seed tocochromanols, almost entirely because of increased tocotrienols (60). These results suggest flux to HGA is indeed limiting but requires both increased HPPD activity and increased flux to HPP. However, why co-overexpression of TyrA and HPPD specifically increases tocotrienols but not tocopherols remains unclear; perhaps the high HGA levels in the transgenics induce a GGDP-utilizing homogentisate prenyl transferase. It should be noted that seed

of TyrA/HPPD overexpressing Arabidopsis and soybean were black as a result of oxidative polymerization of HGA (present at 60- and 800-fold higher levels, respectively, than wild types), and germination was negatively impaired, an undesirable agronomic trait (60).

Prenylation of Homogentisic Acid

Homogentisate prenyl transferases catalyze the committed step in tocochromanol synthesis: condensation of phytyl-DP and HGA for tocopherols, and GGDP and HGA for tocotrienols. This class of hydrophobic, integral membrane proteins was cloned by approaches utilizing whole genome information from *Synechocystis* sp. PCC6803 and Arabidopsis (23, 107, 109). It was hypothesized that homogentisate prenyltransferases would show some level of similarity to related cyanobacterial and plant prenyltransferases that utilize similar prenyl-DPs as substrates. Chlorophyll synthesis involves one such enzyme: chlorophyll synthase (ChlG), which attaches PDP or GGDP to chlorophyllide (70). Query of the *Synechocystis* sp. PCC6803 genome database with the ChlG sequence identified several candidate genes including slr1736, which had ~20% protein identity with ChlG. Disruption of the slr1736 locus eliminated production of all tocopherols and pathway intermediates in *Synechocystis* sp. PCC6803. An Arabidopsis ortholog (At2g18950, the *VTE2* locus) was isolated, and both the *Synechocystis* sp. PCC6803 and Arabidopsis enzymes were expressed in *E. coli* and assayed. Both enzymes utilized phytyl-DP as a cosubstrate, but only the *Synechocystis* sp. PCC6803 enzyme could also utilize GGDP, which is intriguing, as *Synechocystis* sp. PCC6803 does not accumulate tocotrienols.

Mutation of the *VTE2* locus resulted in complete tocopherol deficiency in all tissues demonstrating it is the only activity for the synthesis of tocopherols in wild-type Arabidopsis (106). VTE2 was shown to be a limiting activity in unstressed

Arabidopsis as VTE2 overexpression increased total tocopherol levels up to fivefold and twofold in leaves and seeds, respectively (23, 107). VTE2 activity was also limiting for tocopherol synthesis during combined high light and nutrient stress (25). Isolation of paralogs (40%–50% protein identity to Arabidopsis VTE2) from various tocotrienol-producing monocots demonstrated the key role of the enzyme in determining the tocochromanol composition of a tissue (19). Active enzyme could not be produced in *E. coli* for direct analysis of substrate specificity. However, overexpression of a barley enzyme in Arabidopsis leaves and maize embryos increased tocotrienols up to 15-fold and sixfold of the total tocochromanol content of the respective wild-type tissues without impacting tocopherols. Because the bulk of the increase was γ-tocotrienol, which has low vitamin E activity (**Figure 3**), the vitamin E content of transgenics was increased less than 50% relative to wild-type tissues.

An Alternate Route for Phytyl-Tail Synthesis

It has long been assumed the phytyl tail of tocopherols is primarily derived from reduction of GGDP, and the phenotypes of tobacco and *Synechocystis* sp. PCC6803 lines with decreased GGDP reductase activity are consistent with this thinking (117, 127). However, the identification of a novel Arabidopsis mutant that reduces leaf and seed tocopherols 80% and 65%, respectively, relative to wild type indicates a second pathway provides an important source of phytyl-DP for tocopherol synthesis (139). The locus (VTE5, At5g04490) encodes a gene with similarity to yeast and Arabidopsis dolichol kinase, a polyisoprenoid substrate similar to phytol. VTE5 protein has phytol kinase activity when expressed in *E. coli*, and a second kinase in plants presumably acts on the phytyl monophosphate produced by VTE5 to yield phytyl-DP. The identification of VTE5 helps explain the inverse correlations between tocopherol levels and chlorophyll degradation during natural and induced leaf senescence (99) and canola-seed development (44). Although the relative contributions of phytyl-DP from GGDP and the VTE5-based recycling pathway to tocopherol synthesis have not been directly evaluated, this alternative source of phytyl-DP for tocopherol synthesis may help explain some surprising pathway-engineering results. Recall that expression of barley homogentisate geranylgeranyldiphosphate transferase (19) caused large increases in tocotrienols in Arabidopsis without negatively impacting tocopherol levels. This result could be readily explained if phytyl and geranylgeranyl tails were derived from separate precursor pools, with the majority of tocopherol phytyl tails coming from activation of free phytol rather than reduction of GGDP.

The Methyltransferases of Tocochromanol Synthesis

MPBQ MT and γ-TMT are key activities in determining the types of tocochromanols that accumulate in a tissue (**Figures 3** and **5**). *Synechocystis* sp. PCC6803 γ-TMT (slr0089) was the first pathway methyltransferase to be identified (reviewed in 45), in part because of its physical proximity to HPPD (slr0090) in the *Synechocystis* sp. PCC6803 genome (115). Briefly, disruption of slr0089 resulted in α-tocopherol deficiency and γ-tocopherol accumulation, consistent with loss of γ-TMT activity. Both slr0089 and the Arabidopsis γ-TMT ortholog (*VTE4*, At1g64970) were found to use δ- and γ-tocopherols as substrates to produce β- and α-tocopherols, respectively. Seed-specific overexpression of VTE4 in Arabidopsis resulted in the near-complete conversion of γ-tocopherol to α-tocopherol and a ninefold increase in vitamin E activity (115). Interestingly, VTE2 and VTE4 overexpression were additive in Arabidopsis leaves and seeds increasing total tocochromanols while simultaneously converting virtually all of the γ-tocopherol to α-tocopherol. In seed, this resulted in a nearly 12-fold increase in vitamin E activity (24).

Synechocystis sp. PCC6803 MPBQ MT (sll0418) was identified based on sequence similarity to γ-TMT and shown to use MPBQ but not δ- or β-tocopherols as substrates (22, 116). Disruption of the sll0418 gene only partially eliminated α-tocopherol accumulation suggesting an additional, partially redundant activity is present in Synechocystis sp. PCC6803 for this reaction. Surprisingly, unlike all other tocochromanol pathway steps, the SLL0418 protein sequence was not useful for identifying a plant ortholog. Instead, two groups used map-based cloning approaches to isolate ethyl methane sulfonate mutant alleles for Arabidopsis MPBQ MT (the VTE3 locus, At3g63410) (22, 141). Unlike the sll0418 mutant, the phenotypes of VTE3 mutants make it clear there are no redundant activities for the reaction in plants. VTE3 and SLL0418 have identical activities and substrate specificities in vitro but less than 20% amino-acid identity and represent a clear case of convergent evolution (22). Interestingly, the proteins with the highest identity to VTE3 are only present in Archaea (and other plants). The Chlamydomonas genome was unique in containing orthologs for both SLL0418 and VTE3.

VTE3 and VTE4 are key enzymes for metabolic engineering the tocochromanol content of crop plants because most crop plants accumulate δ-, β- and γ-tocochromanols (45). An outstanding example of the relevance of basic studies of metabolism in model systems to agricultural crops was reported by Van Eenennaam et al. (141) where coexpression of Arabidopsis VTE4 and VTE3 in soybean seed resulted in near-complete conversion of β-, γ-, and δ-tocopherols to α-tocopherol. The resulting fivefold increase in vitamin E activity of the transgenic soybean oil represents one of the clearest examples of nutritional genomics applied from a model plant to an agricultural crop.

The Tocopherol Cyclase Enzyme

The tocopherol cyclase gene (VTE1, At4g32770) was isolated by chromosome walking to mutations in Arabidopsis that eliminated the synthesis of tocopherols and caused accumulation of the pathway intermediate, DMPBQ (95, 105). The homologous Synechocystis sp. PCC6803 gene, slr1737, was present in a two open reading frame operon with slr1736, the Synechocystis sp. PCC6803 VTE2 ortholog. A maize tocopherol cyclase ortholog, whose activity was unknown at the time, had been previously cloned and studied based on the negative impact of mutating the locus on carbon translocation in germinating maize seedlings (96). The gene was originally designated SXD1 for sucrose export defective 1 and suggests tocopherols have impacts beyond acting as lipid-soluble antioxidants in plants, in this instance by somehow regulating carbon translocation from source tissues to sink tissues. The phenotype resulting from RNAi inhibition of tocopherol cyclase expression in potato was similar to maize sxd1 suggesting such functions for tocopherols may be conserved in plants (50).

Overexpression of VTE1 in Arabidopsis leaves produced surprising results (59). Total leaf tocochromanols increased several fold solely as a result of increased γ-tocopherol rather than α-tocopherol, the major tocopherol normally found in wild-type Arabidopsis leaves. This was interpreted as a limitation in VTE4 activity (59), which is puzzling as overexpression of VTE2 and VTE4, singly and in combination, clearly demonstrated VTE4 activity only becomes limiting when plants are stressed (24, 25, 115). Further, this conclusion does not address why ascorbate and glutathione levels were reduced 60% and 40%, respectively, relative to wild type in VTE1 overexpressing plants (59). Such decreases are especially significant as ascorbate and glutathione are present in 10^2 and 10^3 molar excesses, respectively, relative to tocopherols in wild type. A mechanistic explanation for the surprising and interesting consequences of VTE1 overexpression is still lacking.

Tocopherol Functions

As described above, because of their roles as vitamin E, tocochromanol functions have been studied most extensively in animal systems, and our understanding of plant tocochromanol functions pales by comparison. The antioxidant and radical scavenging roles of tocochromanols in animals are well-defined (111), and during the past decade additional nonantioxidant functions for specific tocochromanols have been described in a variety of animal systems (4, 151). Most often nonantioxidant functions are mediated by tocopherol-dependent alterations in the synthesis of lipid-derived signaling molecules, membrane-associated signaling pathways, and gene expression. Analogous nonantioxidant functions for tocochromanols have been proposed for plants (80–82), but this seems premature, as supporting evidence is nonexistent and tocochromanol biological functions may differ between the two kingdoms as a result of fundamental physiological differences.

The plant and cyanobacterial tocochromanol biosynthetic mutants described throughout this review will be essential tools for furthering understanding of tocochromanol functions in photosynthetic organisms. These mutants are already providing unanticipated results, the most obvious that, unlike tocopherol deficiency in animals, tocopherol deficiency in photosynthetic organisms is not lethal. Tocopherol-deficient *Synechocystis* sp. PCC6803 mutants and mature *vte4*, *vte2*, and *vte1* Arabidopsis plants show surprisingly robust phenotypes and are often virtually indistinguishable from wild-type counterparts in permissive conditions and several abiotic stresses, including high light (22, 23, 72, 109, 116). Indeed, the only well-defined tocochromanol function in plants to date is the protection of seed-storage lipids from oxidation during dormancy and germination in Arabidopsis (106). *vte2* but not *vte1* mutants exhibited massive oxidation of storage lipids during germination and severely reduced fitness, suggesting the DMPBQ accumulated by *vte1* can compensate for the lack of tocopherols in this regard. Once past germination, *vte1* and *vte2* are visually indistinguishable from wild type. This lack of readily observable phenotypes in tocopherol-deficient plants should not be taken as conclusive evidence against a vital role for tocochromanols in photoautotrophic plant tissues. The fact that the synthesis and presence of tocochromanols in photoautotrophic tissues are absolutely conserved throughout the plant kingdom argues for essential and conserved functions. Rather, the surprisingly subtle phenotypes of tocopherol-deficient mutants in plants and cyanobacteria suggest some of our long-held assumptions about tocochromanol functions in photosynthetic organisms need to be reassessed in an unbiased fashion, and this is certain to yield some surprises.

SUMMARY POINTS

1. Integrated molecular, genetic, and genomic approaches during the past decade have allowed isolation of the full set of core pathway genes for synthesis of tocochromanols and carotenoids in plants. This approach allows similar progress in many other previously recalcitrant areas of plant metabolism.

2. Metabolic engineering has demonstrated the feasibility of altering the levels of total and specific carotenoids and tocochromanols in agricultural crops to positively impact nutrition and human health.

3. The identification of novel functions for carotenoid derivatives from the Arabidopsis CCD gene family highlights the expanding and diverse roles of carotenoids beyond photosynthesis.

4. The unanticipated effects of some carotenoid and tocochromanol pathway mutants and transgenic experiments serve to highlight the complex regulation of these pathways at the molecular and biochemical levels.

5. Evolution of the plant carotenoid and tocochromanol pathways provides insight into the complex origins of plant metabolic pathways. The two pathways are a complex mix of genes with orthologs in photosynthetic and nonphotosynthetic bacteria and mammals combined with gene duplication and divergence within the plant kingdom.

FUTURE DIRECTIONS/ UNRESOLVED ISSUES

1. Although some carotenoid and tocochromanol enzymes have been cloned and studied for nearly a decade, our understanding of the overall biochemical and molecular regulation of these pathways in plants remains limited. Research to explain unanticipated results from biosynthetic mutants and metabolic engineering of the pathways promises novel insights into the regulation and integration of these pathways in plants.

2. Although intensive functional studies of carotenoids in photosynthetic tissues have highlighted important structure/function relationships, there is still considerable debate about the role(s) of individual carotenoids. In nonphotosynthetic tissues, carotenoid functions remain much less defined. The emerging roles of novel carotenoid derivatives in plant development and regulation of the pathway suggest many important functions beyond photosynthesis remain to be uncovered.

3. With the exception of germinating/dormant seedlings, tocochromanol functions in photosynthetic organisms remain an open question. The phenotypes of tocochromanol biosynthetic mutants are surprisingly similar to wild type and suggest long-held assumptions of tocochromanol functions in photosynthetic organisms need to be critically reassessed. Mutant and transgenic lines with altered tocochromanol levels and types will be important tools for these studies.

ACKNOWLEDGMENTS

We are grateful for support to B.J.P. by the Australian Research Council Center of Excellence in Plant Energy Biology (**www.plantenergy.uwa.edu.au**), ARC DP0343160 and DP0452148, and support to D.D. from NSF (IBN0131253, MCB0235929), Harvest Plus (**www.harvestplus.org**), and the Grand Challenges in Global Health Initiative (**www.grand challengesgh.org**). We thank all of our colleagues for years of stimulating discussion on the topics reviewed and dedicate this manuscript to one in particular, Dr. George Britton, whose guidance, enthusiasm, and good humor continue to inspire new generations of carotenoid researchers.

LITERATURE CITED

1. Al-Babili S, Hugueney P, Schledz M, Welsch R, Frohnmeyer H, et al. 2000. Identification of a novel gene coding for neoxanthin synthase from Solanum tuberosum. *FEBS Lett.* 485:168–72

2. Albrecht M, Takaichi S, Steiger S, Wang ZY, Sandmann G. 2000. Novel hydroxy-carotenoids with improved antioxidative properties produced by gene combination in *Escherichia coli. Nat. Biotech.* 18:843–46

3. Auldridge ME, Block A, Dabney-Smith C, Mila I, Bouzayen M, et al. 2006. Characterization of three members of the Arabidopsis carotenoid cleavage dioxygenase family demonstrates the divergent roles of this multifunctional enzyme family. *Plant J.* In press

4. Azzi A, Gysin R, Kempna P, Munteanu A, Negis Y, et al. 2004. Vitamin E mediates cell signaling and regulation of gene expression. *Ann. NY Acad. Sci.* 1031:86–95

5. Bartley GE, Scolnik PA, Beyer P. 1999. Two *Arabidopsis thaliana* carotene desaturases, phytoene desaturase and zeta-carotene desaturase, expressed in Escherichia coli, catalyze a poly-cis pathway to yield pro-lycopene. *Eur. J. Biochem.* 259:396–402

6. Beveridge CA, Gresshoff PM, Rameau C, Turnbull CGN. 2003. Additional signalling compounds are required to orchestrate plant development. *J. Plant Growth Regul.* 22:15–24

7. Beveridge CA, Symons GM, Murfet IC, Ross JJ, Rameau C. 1997. The rms1 mutant of pea has elevated indole-3-acetic acid levels and reduced root-sap zeatin riboside content but increased branching controlled by graft-transmissible signal(s). *Plant Physiol.* 115:1251–58

8. Beyer P. 1989. Carotene biosynthesis in daffodil chromoplasts: on the membrane-integral desaturation and cyclization reactions. In *Physiology, Biochemistry, and Genetics of Nongreen Plastids*, ed. CD Boyer, JC Shannon, RC Hardison, pp. 157–70. Rockville, MD: Am. Soc. of Plant Physiologists

9. Beyer P, Kroncke U, Nievelstein V. 1991. On the mechanism of the lycopene isomerase cyclase reaction in narcissus-pseudonarcissus L chromoplasts. *J. Biol. Chem.* 266:17072–78

10. Booker J, Auldridge M, Wills S, McCarty D, Klee H, Leyser O. 2004. MAX3/CCD7 is a carotenoid cleavage dioxygenase required for the synthesis of a novel plant signaling molecule. *Curr. Biol.* 14:1232–38

11. Booker J, Sieberer T, Wright W, Williamson L, Willett B, et al. 2005. MAX1 encodes a cytochrome P450 family member that acts downstream of MAX3/4 to produce a carotenoid-derived branch-inhibiting hormone. *Dev. Cell* 8:443–49

12. Bouvier F, D'Harlingue A, Backhaus RA, Kumagai MH, Camara B. 2000. Identification of neoxanthin synthase as a carotenoid cyclase paralog. *Eur. J. Biochem.* 267:6346–52

13. Bouvier F, Dogbo O, Camara B. 2003. Biosynthesis of the food and cosmetic plant pigment bixin (annatto). *Science* 300:2089–91

14. Bouvier F, Keller Y, D'Harlingue A, Camara B. 1998. Xanthophyll biosynthesis: molecular and functional characterization of carotenoid hydroxylases from pepper fruits (*Capsicum annuum* L.). *Biochim. Biophys. Acta* 1391:320–28

15. Bouvier F, Suire C, Mutterer J, Camara B. 2003. Oxidative remodeling of chromoplast carotenoids: identification of the carotenoid dioxygenase *CsCCD* and *CsZCD* genes involved in Crocus secondary metabolite biogenesis. *Plant Cell* 15:47–62

16. Breitenbach J, Sandmann G. 2005. zeta-Carotene cis isomers as products and substrates in the plant poly-cis carotenoid biosynthetic pathway to lycopene. *Planta* 220:785–93

Excellent, well-referenced short historical overview of nonantioxidant tocochromanol functions studies in animal systems since 1991.

17. Britton G, Liaaen Jensen S, Pfander H. 2004. *Carotenoids Handbook*. Basel: Birkauser Verlag

18. Bugos RC, Hieber AD, Yamamoto HY. 1998. Xanthophyll cycle enzymes are members of the lipocalin family, the first identified from plants. *J. Biol. Chem.* 273:15321–24

19. Cahoon EB, Hall SE, Ripp KG, Ganzke TS, Hitz WD, Coughlan SJ. 2003. Metabolic redesign of vitamin E biosynthesis in plants for tocotrienol production and increased antioxidant content. *Nat. Biotech.* 21:1082–87

20. Calucci L, Capocchi A, Galleschi L, Ghiringhelli S, Pinzino C, et al. 2004. Antioxidants, free radicals, storage proteins, puroindolines, and proteolytic activities in bread wheat (*Triticum aestivum*) seeds during accelerated aging. *J. Agric. Food Chem.* 52:4274–81

21. Carol P, Stevenson D, Bisanz C, Breitenbach J, Sandmann G, et al. 1999. Mutations in the Arabidopsis gene *immutans* cause a variegated phenotype by inactivating a chloroplast terminal oxidase associated with phytoene desaturation. *Plant Cell* 11:57–68

22. Cheng Z, Sattler S, Maeda H, Sakuragi Y, Bryant DA, DellaPenna D. 2003. Highly divergent methyltransferases catalyze a conserved reaction in tocopherol and plasto-quinone synthesis in cyanobacteria and photosynthetic eukaryotes. *Plant Cell* 15:2343–56

23. Collakova E, DellaPenna D. 2001. Isolation and functional analysis of homogenti-sate phytyltransferase from Synechocystis sp. PCC 6803 and Arabidopsis. *Plant Physiol.* 127:1113–24

24. Collakova E, DellaPenna D. 2003. Homogentisate phytyltransferase activity is limiting for tocopherol biosynthesis in Arabidopsis. *Plant Physiol.* 131:632–42

25. Collakova E, DellaPenna D. 2003. The role of homogentisate phytyltransferase and other tocopherol pathway enzymes in the regulation of tocopherol synthesis during abiotic stress. *Plant Physiol.* 133:930–40

26. Cuc Hoa TT, Al-Babili S, Schaub P, Potrykus I, Beyer P. 2003. Golden Indica and Japonica rice lines amenable to deregulation. *Plant Physiol.* 133:161–69

27. Cunningham F, Schiff J. 1985. Photoisomerization of delta-carotene stereoisomers in cells of *Euglena gracilis* mutant W₃BUL and in solution. *Photochem. Photobiol. Sci.* 42:295–307

28. Cunningham FX, Gantt E. 1998. Genes and enzymes of carotenoid biosynthesis in plants. *Annu. Rev. Plant Physiol. Plant Mol. Biol.* 49:557–83

29. Cunningham FX. 2002. Regulation of carotenoid synthesis and accumulation in plants. *Pure Appl. Chem.* 74:1409–17

30. Cunningham FX, Gantt E. 1998. Genes and enzymes of carotenoid biosynthesis in plants. *Annu. Rev. Plant Physiol. Plant Mol. Biol.* 49:557–83

31. Cunningham FX, Gantt E. 2001. One ring or two? Determination of ring number in carotenoids by lycopene epsilon-cyclases. *Proc. Nat. Acad. Sci. USA* 98:2905–10

32. Cunningham FX, Gantt E. 2005. A study in scarlet: enzymes of ketocarotenoid biosyn-thesis in the flowers of Adonis aestivalis. *Plant J.* 41:478–92

33. Cuttriss AJ, Pogson BJ. 2006. Carotenoids. In *The Structure and Function of Plastids*, ed. RR Wise, JK Hoober, pp. 315–34. Dordrecht, The Netherlands: Springer

34. Dahnhardt D, Falk J, Appel J, van der Kooij TA, Schulz-Friedrich R, Krupinska K. 2002. The hydroxyphenylpyruvate dioxygenase from Synechocystis sp. PCC 6803 is not required for plastoquinone biosynthesis. *FEBS Lett.* 523:177–81

35. Davison PA, Hunter CN, Horton P. 2002. Overexpression of beta-carotene hydroxylase enhances stress tolerance in Arabidopsis. *Nature* 418:203–6

An elegant study identifying critical amino acids that determine the function of carotenoid cyclase enzymes.

36. Davuluri GR, van Tuinen A, Fraser PD, Manfredonia A, Newman R, et al. 2005. Fruit-specific RNAi-mediated suppression of DET1 enhances carotenoid and flavonoid content in tomatoes. *Nat. Biotech.* 23:890–95

37. DellaPenna D. 1999. Nutritional genomics: manipulating plant micronutrients to improve human health. *Science* 285:375–79

38. DellaPenna D. 2005. A decade of progress in understanding vitamin E synthesis in plants. *J. Plant Physiol.* 162:729–37

39. Deruere J, Romer S, Dharlingue A, Backhaus RA, Kuntz M, Camara B. 1994. Fibril assembly and carotenoid overaccumulation in chromoplasts: a model for supramolecular lipoprotein structures. *Plant Cell* 6:119–33

40. Ducreux LJM, Morris WL, Hedley PE, Shepherd T, Davies HV, et al. 2005. Metabolic engineering of high carotenoid potato tubers containing enhanced levels of beta-carotene and lutein. *J. Exp. Bot.* 56:81–89

41. Falk J, Brosch M, Schafer A, Braun S, Krupinska K. 2005. Characterization of transplastomic tobacco plants with a plastid localized barley 4-hydroxyphenylpyruvate dioxygenase. *J. Plant Physiol.* 162:738–42

42. Fraser PD, Römer S, Shipton CA, Mills PB, Kiano JW, et al. 2002. Evaluation of transgenic tomato plants expressing an additional phytoene synthase in a fruit-specific manner. *Proc. Nat. Acad. Sci. USA* 99:1092–97

43. Gang DR. 2005. Evolution of flavors and scents. *Annu. Rev. Plant Biol.* 56:301–25

44. Goffman FD, Mollers C. 2000. Changes in tocopherol and plastochromanol-8 contents in seeds and oil of oilseed rape (Brassica napus L.) during storage as influenced by temperature and air oxygen. *J. Agric. Food Chem.* 48:1605–9

45. Grusak MA, DellaPenna D. 1999. Improving the nutrient composition of plants to enhance human nutrition and health. *Annu. Rev. Plant Physiol. Plant Mol. Biol.* 50:133–61

46. Hagenimana V, Anyango-Oyunga M, Low J, Njdroge SM, Gichuki ST, Kabira J. 1999. The effects of women farmers' adoption of orange-fleshed sweet potatoes: raising vitamin A intake in Kenya. *Rep. No. 3*, International Center for Research on Women, Washington DC

47. Havaux M, Niyogi KK. 1999. The violaxanthin cycle protects plants from photooxidative damage by more than one mechanism. *Proc. Nat. Acad. Sci. USA* 96:8762–67

48. Hentschel V, Kranl K, Hollmann J, Lindhauer MG, Bohm V, Bitsch R. 2002. Spectrophotometric determination of yellow pigment content and evaluation of carotenoids by high-performance liquid chromatography in durum wheat grain. *J. Agric. Food Chem.* 50:6663–68

49. Hirschberg J. 2001. Carotenoid biosynthesis in flowering plants. *Curr. Opin. Plant Biol.* 4:210–18

50. Hofius D, Hajirezaei MR, Geiger M, Tschiersch H, Melzer M, Sonnewald U. 2004. RNAi-mediated tocopherol deficiency impairs photoassimilate export in transgenic potato plants. *Plant Physiol.* 135:1256–68

51. Holt NE, Fleming GR, Niyogi KK. 2004. Toward an understanding of the mechanism of nonphotochemical quenching in green plants. *Biochemistry* 43:8281–89

52. Holt NE, Zigmantas D, Valkunas L, Li XP, Niyogi KK, Fleming GR. 2005. Carotenoid cation formation and the regulation of photosynthetic light harvesting. *Science* 307:433–36

53. Hosomi A, Arita M, Sato Y, Kiyose C, Ueda T, et al. 1997. Affinity for alpha-tocopherol transfer protein as a determinant of the biological activities of vitamin E analogs. *FEBS Lett.* 409:105–8

54. Isaacson T, Ohad I, Beyer P, Hirschberg J. 2004. Analysis in vitro of the enzyme CRTISO establishes a poly-cis-carotenoid biosynthesis pathway in plants. *Plant Physiol.* 136:4246–55

55. Isaacson T, Ronen G, Zamir D, Hirschberg J. 2002. Cloning of *tangerine* from tomato reveals a carotenoid isomerase essential for the production of beta-carotene and xanthophylls in plants. *Plant Cell* 14:333–42

56. Janick-Buckner D, Hammock JD, Johnson JM, Osborn JM, Buckner B. 1999. Biochemical and ultrastructural analysis of the y10 mutant of maize. *J. Hered.* 90:507–13

57. Jin ES, Feth B, Melis A. 2003. A mutant of the green alga *Dunaliella salina* constitutively accumulates zeaxanthin under all growth conditions. *Biotechnol. Bioeng.* 81:115–24

58. Johnson EA, Schroeder WA. 1995. Microbial carotenoids. *Adv. Biochem. Eng. Biotechnol.* 53:119–78

59. Kanwischer M, Porfirova S, Bergmuller E, Dormann P. 2005. Alterations in tocopherol cyclase activity in transgenic and mutant plants of Arabidopsis affect tocopherol content, tocopherol composition, and oxidative stress. *Plant Physiol.* 137:713–23

60. Karunanandaa B, Qi Q, Hao M, Baszis S, Jensen P, et al. 2005. Metabolically engineered oilseed crops with enhanced seed tocopherol. *Metab. Eng.* 7:384–400

61. Kloer DP, Ruch S, Al-Babili S, Beyer P, Schulz GE. 2005. The structure of a retinal-forming carotenoid oxygenase. *Science* 308:267–69

62. Kulheim C, Agren J, Jansson S. 2002. Rapid regulation of light harvesting and plant fitness in the field. *Science* 297:91–93

63. Lass A, Sohal RS. 1998. Electron transport-linked ubiquinone-dependent recycling of alpha-tocopherol inhibits autooxidation of mitochondrial membranes. *Arch. Biochem. Biophys.* 352:229–36

64. Lee PC, Momen AZR, Mijts BN, Schmidt-Dannert C. 2003. Biosynthesis of structurally novel carotenoids in *Escherichia coli. Chem. Biol.* 10:453–62

65. Leth T, Sondergaard H. 1977. Biological activity of vitamin E compounds and natural materials by the resorption-gestation test, and chemical determination of the vitamin E activity in foods and feeds. *J. Nutr.* 107:2236–43

66. Li L, Paolillo DJ, Parthasarathy MV, DiMuzio EM, Garvin DF. 2001. A novel gene mutation that confers abnormal patterns of β-carotene accumulation in cauliflower (*Brassica oleracea* var. botrytis). *Plant J.* 26:59–67

67. Lichtenthaler HK. 1999. The 1-deoxy-D-xylulose-5-phosphate pathway of isoprenoid biosynthesis in plants. *Annu. Rev. Plant Physiol. Plant Mol. Biol.* 50:47–65

68. Lindgren LO, Stalberg KG, Hoglund AS. 2003. Seed-specific overexpression of an endogenous Arabidopsis phytoene synthase gene results in delayed germination and increased levels of carotenoids, chlorophyll, and abscisic acid. *Plant Physiol.* 132:779–85

69. Lokstein H, Tian L, Polle JEW, DellaPenna D. 2002. Xanthophyll biosynthetic mutants of Arabidopsis thaliana: Altered nonphotochemical quenching of chlorophyll fluorescence is due to changes in Photosystem II antenna size and stability. *Biochim. Biophys. Acta* 1553:309–19

70. Lopez JC, Ryan S, Blankenship RE. 1996. Sequence of the bchG gene from Chloroflexus aurantiacus: relationship between chlorophyll synthase and other polyprenyltransferases. *J. Bacteriol.* 178:3369–73

71. Lorenz RT, Cysewski GR. 2000. Commercial potential for *Haematococcus* microalgae as a natural source of astaxanthin. *Trends Biotechnol.* 18:160–67

72. Maeda H, Sakuragi Y, Bryant DA, Dellapenna D. 2005. Tocopherols protect synechocystis sp. strain PCC 6803 from lipid peroxidation. *Plant Physiol.* 138:1422–35

Identification of an enzyme in plants postulated to exist for 50 years. See also Reference 89.

Most complete study describing the consequences of engineering up to six tocochromanol biosynthetic genes in different combinations in a single plant.

73. Mann V, Harker M, Pecker I, Hirschberg J. 2000. Metabolic engineering of astaxanthin production in tobacco flowers. *Nat. Biotech.* 18:888–92

74. McSteen P, Leyser O. 2005. Shoot branching. *Annu. Rev. Plant Biol.* 56:353–74

75. Merzlyak MN, Solovchenko AE. 2002. Photostability of pigments in ripening apple fruit: a possible photoprotective role of carotenoids during plant senescence. *Plant Sci.* 163:881–88

76. Misawa N, Masamoto K, Hori T, Ohtani T, Boger P, Sandmann G. 1994. Expression of an Erwinia phytoene desaturase gene not only confers multiple resistance to herbicides interfering with carotenoid biosynthesis but also alters xanthophyll metabolism in transgenic plants. *Plant J.* 6:481–89

77. Moise AR, von Lintig J, Palczewski K. 2005. Related enzymes solve evolutionarily recurrent problems in the metabolism of carotenoids. *Trends Plant Sci.* 10:178–86

78. Moraga A, Nohales P, Perez J, Gomez-Gomez L. 2004. Glucosylation of the saffron apocarotenoid crocetin by a glucosyltransferase isolated from Crocus sativus stigmas. *Planta* 219:955–66

79. Morris WL, Ducreux L, Griffiths DW, Stewart D, Davies HV, Taylor MA. 2004. Carotenogenesis during tuber development and storage in potato. *J. Exp. Bot.* 55:975–82

80. Munne-Bosch S. 2005. Linking tocopherols with cellular signaling in plants. *New Phytol.* 166:363–66

81. Munne-Bosch S. 2005. The role of alpha-tocopherol in plant stress tolerance. *J. Plant Physiol.* 162:743–48

82. Munne-Bosch S, Alegre L. 2002. The function of tocopherols and tocotrienols in plants. *Crit. Rev. Plant Sci.* 21:31–57

83. Nambara E, Marion-Poll A. 2005. Abscisic acid biosynthesis and catabolism. *Annu. Rev. Plant Biol.* 56:165–85

84. Niyogi KK. 1999. Photoprotection revisited: genetic and molecular approaches. *Annu. Rev. Plant Physiol. Plant Mol. Biol.* 50:333–59

85. Norris SR, Barrette TR, DellaPenna D. 1995. Genetic dissection of carotenoid synthesis in arabidopsis defines plastoquinone as an essential component of phytoene desaturation. *Plant Cell* 7:2139–49

86. Norris SR, Shen X, DellaPenna D. 1998. Complementation of the Arabidopsis *pds1* mutation with the gene encoding *p*-hydroxyphenylpyruvate dioxygenase. *Plant Physiol.* 117:1317–23

87. **Paine JA, Shipton CA, Chaggar S, Howells RM, Kennedy MJ, et al. 2005. Improving the nutritional value of Golden Rice through increased pro-vitamin A content. *Nat. Biotech.* 23:482–87**

88. Panagabko C, Morley S, Hernandez M, Cassolato P, Gordon H, et al. 2003. Ligand specificity in the CRAL-TRIO protein family. *Biochemistry* 42:6467–74

89. Park H, Kreunen SS, Cuttriss AJ, DellaPenna D, Pogson BJ. 2002. Identification of the carotenoid isomerase provides insight into carotenoid biosynthesis, prolamellar body formation, and photomorphogenesis. *Plant Cell* 14:321–32

90. Phillip D, Young AJ. 1995. Occurrence of the carotenoid lactucaxanthin in higher plant LHC II. *Photosynth. Res.* 43:273–82

91. Pinzino C, Nanni B, Zandomeneghi M. 1999. Aging, free radicals, and antioxidants in wheat seeds. *J. Agric. Food Chem.* 47:1333–39

92. Pogson B, McDonald K, Truong M, Britton G, DellaPenna D. 1996. Arabidopsis carotenoid mutants demonstrate lutein is not essential for photosynthesis in higher plants. *Plant Cell* 8:1627–39

Second-generation Golden Rice will allow provitamin A RDA to be obtained for many of those deficient in developing countries.

93. Pogson BJ, Niyogi KK, Bjorkman O, DellaPenna D. 1998. Altered xanthophyll compositions adversely affect chlorophyll accumulation and nonphotochemical quenching in Arabidopsis mutants. *Proc. Nat. Acad. Sci. USA* 95:13324–29

94. Pogson BJ, Rissler HM. 2000. Genetic manipulation of carotenoid biosynthesis and photoprotection. *Philos. Trans. R. Soc. Lond. B Biol. Sci.* 355:1395–403

95. Porfirova S, Bergmuller E, Tropf S, Lemke R, Dormann P. 2002. Isolation of an Arabidopsis mutant lacking vitamin E and identification of a cyclase essential for all tocopherol biosynthesis. *Proc. Nat. Acad. Sci. USA* 99:12495–500

96. Provencher LM, Miao L, Sinha N, Lucas WJ. 2001. Sucrose export defective 1 encodes a novel protein implicated in chloroplast-to-nucleus signaling. *Plant Cell* 13:1127–41

97. Ralley L, Enfissi EMA, Misawa N, Schuch W, Bramley PM, Fraser PD. 2004. Metabolic engineering of ketocarotenoid formation in higher plants. *Plant J.* 39:477–86

98. Rippert P, Scimemi C, Dubald M, Matringe M. 2004. Engineering plant shikimate pathway for production of tocotrienol and improving herbicide resistance. *Plant Physiol.* 134:92–100

99. Rise M, Cojocaru M, Gottlieb HE, Goldschmidt EE. 1989. Accumulation of α-tocopherol in senescing organs as related to chlorophyll degradation. *Plant Physiol.* 89:1028–30

100. Romer S, Fraser PD. 2005. Recent advances in carotenoid biosynthesis, regulation and manipulation. 221:305–8

101. Römer S, Lubeck J, Kauder F, Steiger S, Adomat C, Sandmann G. 2002. Genetic engineering of a zeaxanthin-rich potato by antisense inactivation and co-suppression of carotenoid epoxidation. *Metab. Eng.* 4:263–72

102. Ronen G, Carmel-Goren L, Zamir D, Hirschberg J. 2000. An alternative pathway to beta-carotene formation in plant chromoplasts discovered by map-based cloning of *Beta* and *old-gold* color mutations in tomato. *Proc. Nat. Acad. Sci. USA* 97:11102–7

103. Rossel JB, Wilson IW, Pogson BJ. 2002. Global changes in gene expression in response to high light in Arabidopsis. *Plant Physiol.* 130:1109–20

104. Sandmann G. 2002. Molecular evolution of carotenoid biosynthesis from bacteria to plants. *Physiol. Plantarum* 116:431–40

105. Sattler SE, Cahoon EB, Coughlan SJ, DellaPenna D. 2003. Characterization of tocopherol cyclases from higher plants and cyanobacteria. Evolutionary implications for tocopherol synthesis and function. *Plant Physiol.* 132:2184–95

106. **Sattler SE, Gilliland LU, Magallanes-Lundback M, Pollard M, DellaPenna D. 2004. Vitamin E is essential for seed longevity and for preventing lipid peroxidation during germination. *Plant Cell* 16:1419–32**

Demonstrates the essential role for tocopherols in limiting autocatalytic lipid oxidation during seed dormancy and germination.

107. Savidge B, Weiss JD, Wong YHH, Lassner MW, Mitsky TA, et al. 2002. Isolation and characterization of homogentisate phytyltransferase genes from Synechocystis sp PCC 6803 and Arabidopsis. *Plant Physiol.* 129:321–32

108. Schaub P, Al-Babili S, Drake R, Beyer P. 2005. Why is Golden Rice golden (yellow) instead of red? *Plant Physiol.* 138:441–50

109. Schledz M, Seidler A, Beyer P, Neuhaus G. 2001. A novel phytyltransferase from Synechocystis sp PCC 6803 involved in tocopherol biosynthesis. *FEBS Lett.* 499:15–20

110. Schmidt-Dannert C, Umeno D, Arnold FH. 2000. Molecular breeding of carotenoid biosynthetic pathways. *Nat. Biotech.* 18:750–53

111. Schneider C. 2005. Chemistry and biology of vitamin E. *Mol. Nutr. Food Res.* 49:7–30

112. Schwartz SH, Qin XQ, Loewen MC. 2004. The biochemical characterization of two carotenoid cleavage enzymes from Arabidopsis indicates that a carotenoid-derived compound inhibits lateral branching. *J. Biol. Chem.* 279:46940–45

113. Schwartz SH, Tan BC, McCarty DR, Welch W, Zeevaart JAD. 2003. Substrate specificity and kinetics for VP14, a carotenoid cleavage dioxygenase in the ABA biosynthetic pathway. *Biochim. Biophys. Acta* 1619:9–14

114. Shewmaker CK, Sheehy JA, Daley M, Colburn S, Ke DY. 1999. Seed-specific overexpression of phytoene synthase: increase in carotenoids and other metabolic effects. *Plant J.* 20:401–12

115. Shintani D, DellaPenna D. 1998. Elevating the vitamin E content of plants through metabolic engineering. *Science* 282:2098–100

116. Shintani DK, Cheng Z, DellaPenna D. 2002. The role of 2-methyl-6-phytylbenzoquinone methyltransferase in determining tocopherol composition in Synechocystis sp. PCC6803. *FEBS Lett.* 511:1–5

117. Shpilyov AV, Zinchenko VV, Shestakov SV, Grimm B, Lokstein H. 2005. Inactivation of the geranylgeranyl reductase (ChlP) gene in the cyanobacterium Synechocystis sp. PCC 6803. *Biochim. Biophys. Acta* 1706:195–203

118. Siegel D, Bolton EM, Burr JA, Liebler DC, Ross D. 1997. The reduction of alpha-tocopherolquinone by human NAD(P)H: quinone oxidoreductase: the role of alpha-tocopherolhydroquinone as a cellular antioxidant. *Mol. Pharmacol.* 52:300–5

119. Simkin AJ, Schwartz SH, Auldridge M, Taylor MG, Klee HJ. 2004. The tomato carotenoid cleavage dioxygenase 1 genes contribute to the formation of the flavor volatiles beta-ionone, pseudoionone, and geranylacetone. *Plant J.* 40:882–92

120. Snowden KC, Simkin AJ, Janssen BJ, Templeton KR, Loucas HM, et al. 2005. The decreased apical dominance 1/petunia hybrida carotenoid cleavage dioxygenase8 gene affects branch production and plays a role in leaf senescence, root growth, and flower development. *Plant Cell* 17:746–59

121. Sommer A, Davidson FR. 2002. Assessment and control of vitamin A deficiency: the Annecy Accords. *J. Nutr.* 132:S2845–50

122. Sorefan K, Booker J, Haurogne K, Goussot M, Bainbridge K, et al. 2003. *MAX4* and *RMS1* are orthologous dioxygenase-like genes that regulate shoot branching in Arabidopsis and pea. *Genes Dev.* 17:1469–74

123. Stalberg K, Lindgren O, Ek B, Hoglund AS. 2003. Synthesis of ketocarotenoids in the seed of Arabidopsis thaliana. *Plant J.* 36:771–79

124. Stickforth P, Steiger S, Hess WR, Sandmann G. 2003. A novel type of lycopene epsilon-cyclase in the marine cyanobacterium *Prochlorococcus marinus* MED4. *Arch. Microbiol.* 179:409–15

125. Sun ZR, Gantt E, Cunningham FX. 1996. Cloning and functional analysis of the beta-carotene hydroxylase of Arabidopsis thaliana. *J. Biol. Chem.* 271:24349–52

126. Tan BC, Joseph LM, Deng WT, Liu LJ, Li QB, et al. 2003. Molecular characterization of the Arabidopsis 9-cis epoxycarotenoid dioxygenase gene family. *Plant J.* 35:44–56

127. Tanaka R, Oster U, Kruse E, Rudiger W, Grimm B. 1999. Reduced activity of geranylgeranyl reductase leads to loss of chlorophyll and tocopherol and to partially geranylgeranylated chlorophyll in transgenic tobacco plants expressing antisense RNA for geranylgeranyl reductase. *Plant Physiol.* 120:695–704

128. Taylor M, Ramsay G. 2005. Carotenoid biosynthesis in plant storage organs: recent advances and prospects for improving plant food quality. *Physiol. Plantarum* 124:143–51

129. Terasawa Y, Ladha Z, Leonard SW, Morrow JD, Newland D, et al. 2000. Increased atherosclerosis in hyperlipidemic mice deficient in alpha-tocopherol transfer protein and vitamin E. *Proc. Natl. Acad. Sci. USA* 97:13830–34

130. Tevini M, Steinmuller D. 1985. Composition and function of plastoglobuli. II. Lipid composition of leaves and plastoglobuli during senescence. *Planta* 163:91–96

First study reporting engineering vitamin E content in plants. See also Reference 141.

Demonstrates that CCD8 is required for production of a novel signal that regulates apical dominance.

131. Theriault A, Chao JT, Wang Q, Gapor A, Adeli K. 1999. Tocotrienol: a review of its therapeutic potential. *Clin. Biochem.* 32:309–19

132. Tian L, DellaPenna D. 2001. Characterization of a second carotenoid beta-hydroxylase gene from Arabidopsis and its relationship to the LUT1 locus. *Plant Mol. Biol.* 47:379–88

133. Tian L, Magallanes-Lundback M, Musetti V, DellaPenna D. 2003. Functional analysis of beta- and epsilon-ring carotenoid hydroxylases in Arabidopsis. *Plant Cell* 15:1320–32

134. Tian L, Musetti V, Kim J, Magallanes-Lundback M, DellaPenna D. 2004. The Arabidopsis LUT1 locus encodes a member of the cytochrome P450 family that is required for carotenoid epsilon-ring hydroxylation activity. *Proc. Nat. Acad. Sci. USA* 101:402–7

135. Tomes ML, Quackenbush FL, Nelsom OE, North B. 1953. The inheritance of carotenoid pigment systems in the tomato. *Genetics* 38:117–27

136. Traber MG, Arai H. 1999. Molecular mechanisms of vitamin E transport. *Annu. Rev. Nutr.* 19:343–55

137. Tsegaye Y, Shintani DK, DellaPenna D. 2002. Overexpression of the enzyme *p*-hydroxyphenylpyruvate dioxygenase in Arabidopsis and its relation to tocopherol biosynthesis. *Plant Physiol. Biochem.* 40:913–20

138. Turnbull CGN, Booker JP, Leyser HMO. 2002. Micrografting techniques for testing long-distance signalling in Arabidopsis. *Plant J.* 32:255–62

139. Valentin HE, Lincoln K, Moshiri F, Jensen PK, Qi Q, et al. 2006. The Arabidopsis *vte5-1* mutant reveals a critical role for phytol kinase in seed tocopherol biosynthesis. *Plant Cell*. In press

140. Valentin HE, Qi Q. 2005. Biotechnological production and application of vitamin E: current state and prospects. *Appl. Microbiol. Biotechnol.* 68:436–44

141. Van Eenennaam AL, Lincoln K, Durrett TP, Valentin HE, Shewmaker CK, et al. 2003. Engineering vitamin E content: from Arabidopsis mutant to soy oil. *Plant Cell* 15:3007–19

142. Van Norman JM, Frederick RL, Sieburth LE. 2004. BYPASS1 negatively regulates a root-derived signal that controls plant architecture. *Curr. Biol.* 14:1739–46

143. Vishnevetsky M, Ovadis M, Vainstein A. 1999. Carotenoid sequestration in plants: the role of carotenoid-associated proteins. *Trends Plant Sci.* 4:232–35

144. von Lintig J, Hessel S, Isken A, Kiefer C, Lampert JM, et al. 2005. Towards a better understanding of carotenoid metabolism in animals. *Biochim. Biophys. Acta* 1740:122–31

145. von Lintig J, Vogt K. 2000. Molecular identification of an enzyme cleaving β-carotene to retinal. *J. Biol. Chem.* 275:11915–20

146. Wang CW, Liao JC. 2001. Alteration of product specificity of *Rhodobacter sphaeroides* phytoene desaturase by directed evolution. *J. Biol. Chem.* 276:41161–64

147. Woitsch S, Römer S. 2003. Expression of xanthophyll biosynthetic genes during light-dependant chloroplast differentiation. *Plant Physiol.* 132:1508–17

147a. World Health Organization. 2003. *Micronutrient deficiencies: combating vitamin A deficiency*. **http://www.who.int/nut/vad.htm**

148. Wyss A, Wirtz G, Woggon W, Brugger R, Wyss M, et al. 2000. Cloning and expression of β,β-carotene 15,15′-dioxygenase. *Biochem. Biophys. Res. Commun.* 271:334–36

149. Ye XD, Al-Babili S, Kloti A, Zhang J, Lucca P, et al. 2000. Engineering the provitamin A (β-carotene) biosynthetic pathway into (carotenoid-free) rice endosperm. *Science* 287:303–5

Demonstrates that ε-ring hydroxylation is catalyzed by a cytochrome P450 in plants and defines a new class of carotenoid ring hydroxylases in plants.

First report of Arabidopsis tocochromanol methyltransferases use to engineer vitamin E content in a major agricultural crop, soybean. See also Reference 115.

150. Yokota T, Igarashi K, Uchihara T, Jishage K, Tomita H, et al. 2001. Delayed-onset ataxia in mice lacking α-tocopherol transfer protein: model for neuronal degeneration caused by chronic oxidative stress. *Proc. Natl. Acad. Sci. USA* 98:15185–90

151. Zingg JM, Azzi A. 2004. Non-antioxidant activities of vitamin E. *Curr. Med. Chem.* 11:1113–33

APPENDIX

Compound Abbreviations

DMPBQ: 2,3-dimethyl-5-phytyl-1,4-benzoquinone
HGA: homogentisic acid
HPP: *p*-hydroxyphenylpyruvate
MPBQ: 2-methyl-6-phytyl-1,4-benzoquinone
phytyl-DP: phytyl-diphosphate
SAM: S-adenosyl methionine

Enzyme Abbreviations

AdeH: arogenate dehydrogenase
HPPD: HPP dioxygenase
PAT: prephenate amino transferase
TAT: tyrosine amino transferase
VTE1: tocopherol cyclase
VTE2: homogentisate phytyltransferase
VTE3: MPBQ methyltransferase
VTE4: γ-tocopherol methyltransferase

Plastid-to-Nucleus Retrograde Signaling

Ajit Nott,* Hou-Sung Jung,* Shai Koussevitzky,* and Joanne Chory

Plant Biology Laboratory and Howard Hughes Medical Institute, Salk Institute for Biological Studies, La Jolla, California 92037; email: nott@salk.edu, hjung@salk.edu, koussevitzky@salk.edu, chory@salk.edu

Annu. Rev. Plant Biol.
2006. 57:739–59

The *Annual Review of Plant Biology* is online at plant.annualreviews.org

doi: 10.1146/
annurev.arplant.57.032905.105310

First published online as a
Review in Advance on
February 7, 2006

1543-5008/06/0602-
0739$20.00

*These authors
contributed equally.

Key Words

Mg-ProtoporphyrinIX, redox signaling, *gun* mutants

Abstract

Plant cells store genetic information in the genomes of three organelles: the nucleus, plastid, and mitochondrion. The nucleus controls most aspects of organelle gene expression, development, and function. In return, organelles send signals to the nucleus to control nuclear gene expression, a process called retrograde signaling. This review summarizes our current understanding of plastid-to-nucleus retrograde signaling, which involves multiple, partially redundant signaling pathways. The best studied is a pathway that is triggered by buildup of Mg-ProtoporphyrinIX, the first intermediate in the chlorophyll branch of the tetrapyrrole biosynthetic pathway. In addition, there is evidence for a plastid gene expression-dependent pathway, as well as a third pathway that is dependent on the redox state of photosynthetic electron transport components. Although genetic studies have identified several players involved in signal generation, very little is known of the signaling components or transcription factors that regulate the expression of hundreds of nuclear genes.

Contents

INTRODUCTION

It is generally believed that plastids evolved from the endosymbiosis of a unicellular free-living photosynthetic bacterium by an ancient eukaryotic cell. The ancestral prokaryotic genome presumably contained all the information necessary to support an independent photoautotrophic lifestyle. However, over evolutionary time, subsequent to the endosymbiotic relationship that gave rise to green algae, and later to higher plants, the plastid genome has undergone progressive and drastic reduction in coding capacity. Several genes not necessary for the endosymbiotic existence may have been lost and a vast majority was transferred to the nuclear genome of the host. The present-day plastid genome of higher plants encodes fewer than 100 open reading frames, whereas the rest of the >3000 polypeptides found in the chloroplast, the differentiated photosynthetically active plastid, are transcribed from nuclear genes and imported post-translationally (1, 46). This division of labor presents a challenge to plant cells because essential photosynthetic and metabolic complexes, which are located in plastids, are composed of subunits encoded by both genomes. Such an arrangement necessitates tightly coordinated communication between plastids and the nucleus to ensure coregulated expression of genes whose products function together.

Plastid development and gene expression are largely under nuclear control (22, 47). The nucleus encodes most of the genes required for chloroplast gene expression, e.g., components of the transcription and translation machinery, as well as components of the protein import apparatus. In addition to such "antero-grade" control, "retrograde" control mechanisms have evolved by which chloroplast functional and developmental states can regulate expression of nuclear genes encoding plastid-localized proteins.

Control of nuclear gene expression in response to the developmental and functional state of plastids is critical for establishing the photoautotrophic lifestyle, and for efficiently allocating available resources under conditions of reduced organelle metabolic function. Later in development, retrograde signaling may be involved in fine-tuning nuclear gene expression in response to changes in chlorophyll biosynthetic flux, or for modulating nuclear gene expression in response to changes in photosynthetic flux or when chloroplasts are damaged in high light or by pathogens. Thus, intracellular communication between the organelles establishes the proper balance of gene expression in a changing environment.

Over 20 years ago, it was proposed that a plastid-generated factor could trigger such a retrograde signaling pathway. It is now clear, from both genetic and biochemical studies in a number of organisms, that there are several pathways of communication between chloroplasts and the nucleus. In this review we present a comprehensive discussion of our current understanding of chloroplast-to-nucleus signaling and provide a perspective for future work aimed at a complete understanding of the pathways.

HISTORICAL OVERVIEW

The first evidence for the existence of plastid signals controlling nuclear gene expression came from studies on the *albostrians* and *Saskatoon* mutants of barley (*Hordeum vulgare* L. cv. Haisa) (8). The recessive nuclear mutations in *albostrians* and *Saskatoon* prevent the accumulation of carotenoids, resulting in seedlings with either completely white leaves or white stripes (16). White areas in *albostrians* leaves contain undifferentiated small plastids that lack ribosomes, have only trace amounts of chlorophyll and as a result are photosynthetically inactive. Although the *albostrians* phenotype is caused by a recessive nuclear allele, the undifferentiated plastids are maternally inherited so mutant lines can contain green or white plas-

tids. Activity of two plastid-localized nuclear-encoded enzymes is significantly reduced in white sectors of the *albostrians* leaves (8), and expression of several nuclear genes encoding chloroplast-localized proteins, including the *Lhc* gene family (Light-harvesting chlorophyll *a/b*-binding protein), the small subunit of ribulose-1,5-bisphosphate carboxylase/oxygenase (RbcS), and Calvin cycle enzymes, is downregulated (26). Reduced levels of nuclear-encoded photosynthetic transcripts are not a result of phytochrome impairment, suggesting that a signal from developed plastids is required for the light induction of these genes (27).

Subsequent studies using mutant plants impaired in carotenoid biosynthesis, which causes photobleaching in plastids, have demonstrated that the expression of several nuclear-encoded photosynthetic genes is dramatically reduced in the absence of functional chloroplasts (51, 62, 63, 86). Similar observations have been made by inducing carotenoid deficiency by growing seedlings in the presence of norflurazon (NF), an inhibitor of the enzyme phytoene desaturase in the carotenoid biosynthesis pathway (62, 76).

In addition to photobleaching, arresting chloroplast development by inhibiting plastid gene expression (PGE) also leads to inhibition of nuclear photosynthetic gene expression. When mustard (*Sinapis alba* L.) seedlings are treated with chloramphenicol (CF), chloroplast development is inhibited, and so is the activity of nuclear-encoded chloroplast-localized enzymes (62). Activity of phytochrome-induced cytoplasmic enzymes like chalcone synthase is not affected and in some cases is even increased by the CF treatment (62). In pea (*Pisum sativum* L.), CF could inhibit both red- and blue-light-induced expression of a gene encoding for an Early Light-Induced Protein (ELIP) (3). Other inhibitors of chloroplast gene expression also inhibit expression of nuclear genes. These include tagetitoxin (75), lincomycin (an inhibitor of chloroplast protein translation), and nalidixic acid (an inhibitor of DNA

NF: norflurazon

PGE: plastid gene expression

CF: chloramphenicol

PET:
photosynthetic
electron transport

Mg-ProtoIX: Mg-
ProtoporphyrinIX

Mg-ProtoIXme:
Mg-
ProtoporphyrinIX
methyl ester

DP: dipyridyl

replication and transcription in the chloroplast) (23). A specific role for chloroplast gene expression in the generation of a plastid signal was demonstrated in pea using erythromycin applications, which specifically inhibit plastid protein translation but not mitochondrial protein translation (84).

Regulation of nuclear gene expression by the redox state of photosynthetic electron transport (PET) components in chloroplasts is also a proposed retrograde signaling pathway (17). Since the original observations in the unicellular green alga *Dunaliella tertiolecta* more than 10 years ago, several approaches have been taken to manipulate the chloroplast redox state in different species, including higher plants, to determine the effects of chloroplast redox states on nuclear gene expression. From these efforts, it has been shown that several nuclear-encoded photosynthesis-related and stress-responsive genes are regulated by chloroplast redox states (35, 49, 72).

Given the number of recent reviews written in the area of plastid-to-nucleus signaling, there is considerable interest in these signaling pathways, yet very little is actually known. Recent genetic and biochemical studies, in the unicellular green alga *Chlamydomonas reinhardtii* and the reference plant *Arabidopsis thaliana*, have identified one signal generated by photobleached plastids. Yet, signal transduction mechanisms are still unknown, and no mutants in signaling components have been reported. Identification of cytosolic and/or nuclear factors involved in these pathways is crucial to understand the signaling mechanisms and to determine possible interactions between the various proposed pathways.

CHLOROPHYLL BIOSYNTHETIC PRECURSORS IN RETROGRADE SIGNALING

One presumably important function of retrograde signaling is to coordinate the biosynthesis of chlorophyll with expression of nuclear-encoded chlorophyll-binding proteins (e.g., LHCA and LHCB proteins). It is not surprising then that considerable evidence over the years has implicated the chlorophyll biosynthetic precursors, Mg-ProtoporphyrinIX (Mg-ProtoIX) and Mg-ProtoporphyrinIX-methylesters (Mg-ProtoIXme), as regulators of nuclear gene expression (42, 83).

Chlorophyll Biosynthetic Precursors Regulate Nuclear Gene Expression in *C. reinhardtii*

The first evidence for the involvement of chlorophyll biosynthetic precursors in retrograde signaling came from work in *C. reinhardtii* (32, 33). In light-dark synchronized cultures of *C. reinhardtii*, *Lhcb* mRNA begins to accumulate about two hours after the transition to light, primarily due to transcriptional activation (31). Adding inhibitors of several early steps in chlorophyll biosynthesis to *C. reinhardtii* cultures does not inhibit *Lhcb* expression (**Figure 1**) (31–33). In contrast, treating algal cultures with dipyridyl (DP), which inhibits the conversion of ProtoIX to heme and also the conversion of Mg-ProtoIX to Protochlorophyllide (**Figure 1**), resulting in accumulation of Mg-ProtoIX and Mg-ProtoIXme (13), prevents *Lhcb* mRNA accumulation (33). *C. reinhardtii* cultures grown under anaerobic conditions also accumulate Mg-ProtoIXme (13) and prevent light induction of *Lhcb* and *RbcS* expression (32). These results strongly suggest that accumulation of porphyrin intermediates between ProtoIX and Mg-ProtoIXme is necessary for *Lhcb* repression. The *C. reinhardtii* mutant *brs-1*, defective in the H-subunit of Mg-chelatase (11), and consequently in the conversion of ProtoIX to Mg-ProtoIX, is impaired in light-induced *Lhcb* expression (33), suggesting that ProtoIX accumulation can also repress *Lhcb* transcription.

In *C. reinhardtii*, there is also evidence that the induction of HSP70 genes requires Mg-ProtoIX and Mg-ProtoIXme. The heat-shock

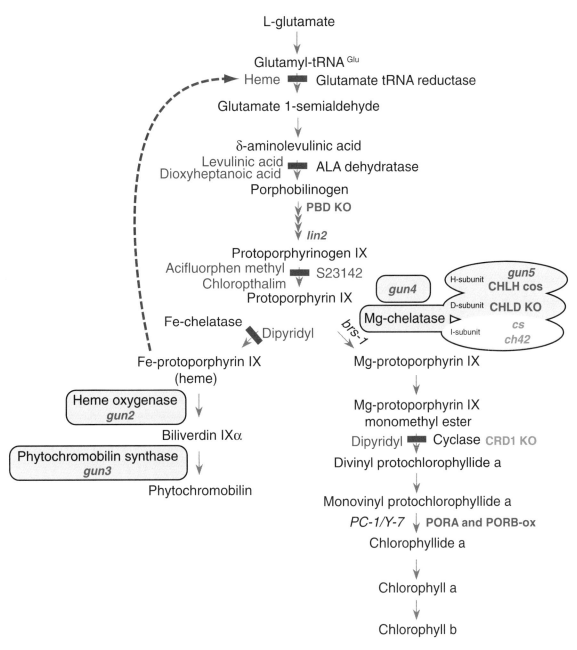

Figure 1

Tetrapyrrole biosynthetic pathway. Steps inhibited by specific inhibitors are indicated in red. Mutants with a *gun* phenotype are shown in blue, and mutants that do not show a *gun* phenotype are indicated in green. *brs-1* and *PC-1/Y-7* are *C. reinhardtii* mutants. PBD KO, T-DNA knockout of porphobilinogen deaminase; *lin2*, lesion in coproporphyrinogen oxidase; CHLD KO, T-DNA knockout of D-subunit of Mg-Chelatase; CHLH cos, cosuppression lines for H-subunit of Mg-Chelatase; CRD KO, T-DNA knockout of one subunit of the cyclase complex. *cs* and *ch42* are alleles of the I-subunit of Mg-Chelatase. PORA-ox and PORB-ox indicate overexpression of Protochlorophyllide oxidoreductase A and B, respectively.

genes *HSP70A* and *HSP70B*, encoding cytosolic and plastid-localized proteins respectively, can be induced by light via a pathway that is independent of heat-shock induction. Light induction of *HSP70* is impaired in the *brs-1* mutant (41, 42); however, *HSP70* light induction is normal in another chlorophyll biosynthesis mutant *PC-1/Y-7*, deficient in converting protochlorophyllide to chlorophyllide. These observations suggest that light induction of *HSP70* requires accumulation of Mg-ProtoIX (41). Indeed, addition of Mg-ProtoIX in the dark is sufficient to induce expression of *HSP70* genes (41). The effect is specific to Mg-ProtoIX because addition of ProtoIX, protochlorophyllide, or chlorophyllide is unable to substitute for light in *HSP70* induction (41). Interestingly, exogenously added ProtoIX is converted to Mg-ProtoIX and Mg-ProtoIXme, presumably within the chloroplast, but is still unable to elicit induction of *HSP70* in the dark (41). One possible explanation is that the Mg-ProtoIX made from exogenously added ProtoIX is sequestered within the chloroplasts, and is dependent on light for its release, whereas exogenously added Mg-ProtoIX has direct access to cytosolic and presumably the nuclear compartments to elicit the effect. This suggests that Mg-ProtoIX can function outside the chloroplast in this pathway and that light plays an additional role, perhaps in allowing plastidic Mg-ProtoIX to access the cytosol or the nucleus.

Other Studies Supporting a Role for Mg-ProtoIX as a Plastid-Generated Signal

Evidence for chlorophyll precursors in retrograde signaling also comes from studies on higher plants. Treating etiolated cress seedlings with thujaplicin inhibits protochlorophyllide synthesis and results in accumulation of Mg-ProtoIX and Mg-ProtoIXme and reduces the light-induced accumulation of *Lhcb* mRNA (66). Etiolated cress seedlings, when treated with δ-aminolevulinic acid

(ALA), accumulate 50% less *Lhcb* mRNA after light induction, compared to water-treated seedlings (38). Etiolated barley seedlings treated with amitrole, a carotenoid biosynthesis inhibitor, accumulate ALA, Mg-ProtoIX, and Mg-ProtoIXme and are impaired in light-induced *RbcS* and *Lhcb* expression (44). *Arabidopsis* lines overexpressing *PORA* or *PORB*, encoding isoforms of protochlorophyllide reductase, also fail to repress *Lhcb* in the presence of the herbicide NF, perhaps because these plants can metabolize Mg-ProtoIX more efficiently (**Figure 1**) (53). Lastly, lesions in specific enzymes in the tetrapyrrole biosynthetic pathway lead to loss of plastid control over nuclear *Lhcb* gene expression, as discussed below.

Arabidopsis gun (genomes uncoupled) Mutants

Using a genetic approach, Susek et al. (85) identified several nuclear-encoded genes required for plastid-to-nucleus signaling in *Arabidopsis*. An *Lhcb* promoter fused to both a selectable and screenable marker was integrated into the nuclear genome and seeds mutagenized with ethyl methanesulfonate (EMS). These lines were then used to isolate mutants in which *Lhcb* expression is uncoupled from the functional state of the chloroplast. Wild-type plants grown on NF, under continuous light, have low expression of reporters driven by the *Lhcb* promoter, owing to photobleaching of the chloroplast. In contrast, mutants have high levels of *Lhcb* expression on NF-containing medium, even though the chloroplasts are photobleached. From this initial screen, five nonallelic loci impaired in retrograde signaling were identified and named *genomes uncoupled* or *gun* mutants (85).

Four *gun* mutants have been characterized at the molecular level so far and all four involve lesions in plastid-localized enzymes that function in porphyrin biosynthesis. *gun2* and *gun3* are allelic to *hy1* and *hy2* and have mutations in the heme oxygenase and phytochromobilin synthase, respectively (**Figure 1**). These enzymes are involved in the synthesis of phytochromobilin; in their absence, plastids accumulate heme (56). Heme accumulation leads to negative feedback regulation of chlorophyll biosynthesis (**Figure 1**) (73, 87, 90). *gun5-1* has a point mutation in the *ChlH* gene encoding the porphyrin-binding subunit of the Mg-chelatase, the enzyme that introduces Mg^{2+} into ProtoporphyrinIX as the first committed step of chlorophyll biosynthesis (56). Lastly, *GUN4* encodes a Mg-ProtoIX-binding protein that can significantly stimulate the Mg-chelatase activity in vitro (45, 92). Thus, mutations in all four of these genes would lead to a decreased accumulation of Mg-ProtoIX. A second role for GUN4 in signaling or transport of Mg-ProtoIX has also been proposed because a significant portion of GUN4 is not associated with the Mg-chelatase (45).

The activities of the GUN2/3/4/5 (**Figure 1**) proteins indicate that accumulation of Mg-ProtoIX is important for repressing nuclear photosynthetic genes. Consistent with this idea, Strand and colleagues (83) observed that wild-type *Arabidopsis* seedlings grown on NF have about 15-fold more Mg-ProtoIX as compared to untreated controls, whereas *gun2* and *gun5* seedlings accumulate much less Mg-ProtoIX on NF. Lesions in other enzymes leading up to the synthesis of Mg-ProtoIX also impair plastid control of *Lhcb* expression. Mutations in porphobilinogen deaminase (PBD), in the D-subunit of the Mg-chelatase (CHLD), and in coproporphyrinogen oxidase (*lin2*) all impair retrograde signaling (**Figure 1**) (83). Additionally, a T-DNA knockout mutant in the CRD subunit of the cyclase complex that catalyzes the conversion of Mg-ProtoIXme to divinyl protochlorophyllide does not exhibit a gun phenotype when grown on NF (**Figure 1**) (Å. Strand, personal communication).

Contrary to expectation, retrograde signaling is not impaired in two *Arabidopsis* mutants, *cs* and *ch42*, that have lesions in the *ChlI* gene, which encodes the third subunit of Mg-Chelatase (56). *Lhcb* mRNA levels are similar to wild-type levels in *cs* mutants grown on NF, despite a demonstrably less active Mg-chelatase in *cs* than in *gun5-1* (56). The stronger allele, *ch42*, is albino but has a fully functional nuclear response (56). This suggests that GUN5 has a specific role in either sensing elevated Mg-ProtoIX levels or transmitting the signal, besides being required for its synthesis. Alternatively, sequence redundancy may provide an explanation for why *ChlI* mutants do not have a *gun* phenotype. A second *ChlI* gene (*ChlI2*) that is 82% similar to *ChlI1* exists in *Arabidopsis* (78). Although expression of *ChlI2* is not sufficient to support viable levels of chlorophyll synthesis in a *ChlI1* mutant background, it may be sufficient under conditions in which retrograde signaling has been measured (78).

Inhibitor feeding experiments in *Arabidopsis* seedlings also point to a key role for Mg-ProtoIX in retrograde signaling. Wild-type, *gun2*, and *gun5* seedlings grown on DP (see above) in the presence of NF are all able to repress *Lhcb* gene expression (83), likely because inhibition of later steps in chlorophyll biosynthesis allows *gun* mutant seedlings to accumulate enough Mg-ProtoIX (14). Indeed, combined addition of DP, NF, and a potent inhibitor of protoporphyrinogen oxidase, S23142, prevents accumulation of Mg-ProtoIX and restores the *gun* mutant phenotype (83). Finally, direct addition of Mg-ProtoIX to leaf protoplasts is sufficient to repress *Lhcb* gene expression, whereas addition of porphobilinogen, heme, or ProtoIX does not repress expression of a luciferase gene driven by the *Lhcb* promoter (83).

PLASTID GENE EXPRESSION-DEPENDENT SIGNALING

A second retrograde pathway that requires chloroplast gene expression has also been reported. Inhibition of chloroplast protein translation by CF or lincomycin results in repression of nuclear-encoded photosynthetic gene expression. The response to plastid gene expression occurs only early in seedling development, and it is light independent. This latter observation was first made using two constitutively photomorphogenetic mutants, the pea *lip1* and the *Arabidopsis cop1-4*. These mutants accumulate significant levels of the light-induced *Lhcb1.2* transcript when grown in the dark, but its levels are reduced when seedlings are exposed to lincomycin (84). Unlike the screens done on NF, no *gun* mutants have been reported from CF- or lincomycin-based genetic screens. However, *gun1* does have a phenotype on CF and lincomycin (23, 24, 85), suggesting that GUN1 has a role in the plastid gene expression-dependent pathway as well as the Mg-ProtoIX pathway. Genetic studies, using *gun1 gun4* and *gun1 gun5* double mutants, have implicated the existence of two separate but partially redundant pathways (56). In support of this interpretation, an early microarray study in *Arabidopsis* suggested that there was little overlap in the set of genes misregulated in *gun1* and *gun5* mutants (83). Recently, ABI4, an AP2-like transcription factor was implicated in the Mg-ProtoIX dependent pathway (2). ABI4, like GUN1, also appears to play a role in the PGE pathway (S. Koussevitzky, T. Mockler, F. Hong, Y. Huang & J. Chory, unpublished data). That GUN1 and ABI4 are required for both the gene expression-dependent and the Mg-ProtoIX pathways, suggests that these two signaling pathways converge. Consistent with this idea, analysis of many mutants and conditions using a gene-sequence-tag array of more than 2600 nuclear sequences encoding for chloroplast proteins suggests that a "master switch" controls the expression of many of these genes in response to the chloroplast signal (77). Based on gene expression patterns in these experiments, *gun1* and *gun5* cluster together, whereas a mutant in which *Lhcb* is underexpressed shows a complementary expression pattern (77).

RETROGRADE-RESPONSIVE *CIS*-ELEMENTS

Several studies have demonstrated that the *cis*-elements required for retrograde regulation are either identical to, or largely overlapping with, light-responsive elements, and in every case that has been examined the light- and plastid-responsive elements have been inseparable (7, 43, 81, 89). Minimal promoter regions from *Arabidopsis Lhcb* and *HEMA1* genes are sufficient for both light- and plastid-responsive expression (52). A 52-bp promoter element containing an I- and a G-box that was identified in the promoter of *rbcS 8B* in *Nicotiana plumbaginifolia* was able to confer phytochrome-, cryptochrome-, and retrograde-controlled reporter expression in *Arabidopsis* (48). In *C. reinhardtii*, the same promoter region is required for light- and Mg-ProtoIX-dependent expression of *HSP70* genes and it is distinct from the region required for heat-shock response (41). In *C. reinhardtii*, there are two *RbcS* genes, the light-inducible *RbcS1*, and light-independent *RbcS2*. Only the accumulation of *RbcS1* is affected in DP-treated cultures whereas *RbcS2* mRNA levels are unaffected (32). Even in the case of post-transcriptional regulation of the pea *PetE* in transgenic *Arabidopsis*, the same sequence in the 5′ untranslated region of the transcript is responsive to light and plastid signals (9).

Examination of individual promoter elements shows that tetramers of G-box or the GATA element, fused to a minimal nopaline synthase promoter (NOS), conferred light- and plastid-responsive expression, whereas another element that directed high-level expression in the dark did not respond to plastid signals (74). There are at least two well-characterized light-responsive elements in the *Lhcb* promoter, the CUF1 (cab upstream factor 1, CACGTA) element, which is similar to a G-box, and the GATA element. The CUF1 element is important for high-level expression in the light while being dispensable for phytochrome- and circadian-regulated *Lhcb* expression (5). When *gun5* seedlings were grown on NF, accumulation of luciferase driven by an *Lhcb1* promoter with a mutated CUF1 element was reduced to wild-type levels, clearly emphasizing a role for the G-box in retrograde signaling (83). The 5′ end of the CUF1 element contains a CCAC motif that resembles the recently identified S-box (2), an element important for sugar and ABA responsiveness in *rbcS 8B* promoter (2).

Conflicting results from other studies suggest that mutation or deletion of the G-box element alone does not completely abrogate light and plastid responsiveness. Transgenic tobacco plants expressing β-glucuronidase (GUS) driven by spinach *RbcS1* promoter fragment (−296/+80) fused to a 90-bp cauliflower mosaic virus minimal promoter (CaMV) showed light-inducible and plastid-responsive expression. Mutation of the conserved G-box element in this region, or truncation of the promoter fragment to exclude the G-box, dramatically reduced the expression of GUS but did not qualitatively

alter the dark repression or repression on NF (43).

MODEL FOR Mg-ProtoIX AND PLASTID GENE EXPRESSION-DEPENDENT RETROGRADE SIGNALING

The current model posits that reduced chloroplast function leads to an increase in accumulation of Mg-ProtoIX. Mg-ProtoIX then either diffuses or is actively transported to the cytoplasm, where it is bound by other, as yet unidentified, proteins that elicit regulation of nuclear gene expression (**Figure 2**) (82, 83). This is consistent with the proposed role for Mg-ProtoIX outside the chloroplast in *C. reinhardtii* (41). The fact that GUN4 is found in the stroma, thylakoid, and envelope fractions of the chloroplast suggests that GUN4 might be involved in intraplastidic transport of Mg-ProtoIX (45).

Indirect evidence indicates that at least some porphyrins are able to exit the chloroplast and export of some porphyrin

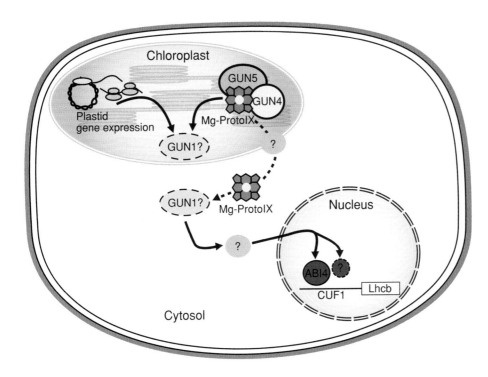

Figure 2

gun mutants in retrograde signaling. Because the identity of GUN1 is not yet known, its localization is depicted to be either in the plastid or the cytosol. GUN4 is found in stroma, thylakoid, and envelope fractions of chloroplasts. Other unidentified cytosolic components may also be involved in the signaling pathway.

compounds from isolated chloroplasts has been demonstrated (30). The initial steps in the biosynthesis of heme up to ProtoIX occur exclusively in plastids whereas the rest of the pathway can occur in both plastids and mitochondria. Presence of heme in the mitochondria implies that at least some intermediates are transported to the mitochondria from the chloroplasts. Also, phytochromobilin, the chromophore for phytochromes, is synthesized in chloroplasts and transported to the cytosol, where it binds phytochromes.

Evidence from other systems also supports a role for porphyrins outside the organelles in interorganelle signaling. Studies on mitochondrial retrograde signaling show that heme can modulate activator or repressor activity of bound proteins (20, 95). Heme can bind to the yeast transcription factor HapI and increase its affinity for DNA and its ability to activate transcription (28). Heme also binds to the bZIP transcription factor Bach1 and reduces its ability to activate transcription (64).

We do not yet know the signal in the gene expression-dependent pathway. Perhaps it is a plastid transcript, as suggested by Bradbeer and colleagues (8). It appears likely that the Mg-ProtoIX signal and the signal generated by the plastid gene expression-dependent pathway are integrated at some point prior to GUN1 (**Figure 2**). Presumably some as yet unidentified cytosolic components are involved in signal transduction. In the nucleus the retrograde signal activates a transcriptional repressor and/or inactivates a transcriptional activator, leading to repression of nucleus-encoded photosynthetic genes. One of the transcriptional repressors may be ABI4, but its weak *gun* phenotype suggests that there are other transcription factors that might act redundantly within the nucleus (**Figure 2**). Retrograde signaling culminates on promoter elements very close to, or on the, G-box itself, and perhaps binding of ABI4 to elements close to the G-box prevents light-dependent activation of nuclear genes.

CHLOROPLAST REDOX SIGNALS IN RETROGRADE SIGNALING

The reduction/oxidation (redox) states of PET components regulate gene expression within chloroplasts (71). Redox states of PET components have also been proposed as chloroplast signals influencing nuclear gene expression (17, 18, 70). Furthermore, reactive oxygen species (ROS) generated in chloroplasts also play a role in chloroplast redox signaling (35, 91). In the following sections, we discuss identified and possible chloroplast redox signals regulating nuclear gene expression, as well as the genes responding to these signals.

Linear photosynthetic electron transport begins in photosystem II (PSII) and electrons are delivered to the cytochrome b_6f complex (cyt b_6f) through the plastoquinone (PQ) pool (**Figure 3**). Plastocyanin (PC) mediates electron transport from cyt b_6f to photosystem I (PSI). The electrons are then transferred to ferredoxin (FD) and finally delivered to $NADP^+$ to generate NADPH (**Figure 3**). During this PET, protons (H^+) are pumped to the thylakoid lumen to generate a proton gradient that is then utilized for ATP synthesis. Oxygen molecules (O_2), instead of $NADP^+$, can accept electrons from PSI to form superoxide ($O_2^{\bullet-}$). In addition, excited chlorophyll can transfer energy to O_2 to create singlet oxygen ($^1O_2$) (6, 60). These ROS must be removed to prevent oxidative stress. $O_2^{\bullet-}$ is detoxified by superoxide dismutase (SOD) to hydrogen peroxide (H_2O_2) and then reduced to H_2O by various types of peroxidases in chloroplasts. $^1O_2$ returns to its ground state after energy transfer to antioxidants such as carotenoids (60).

Photosynthetic Electron Transport Components as Redox Signals

The involvement of redox states of PET components in nuclear gene expression has been shown in several different ways.

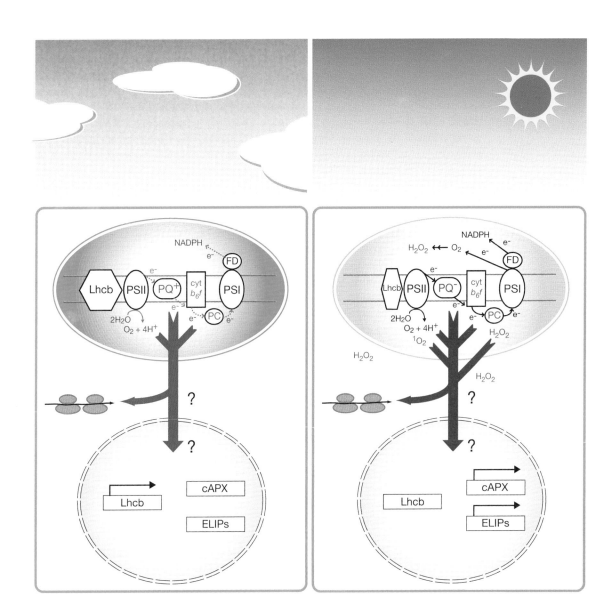

Figure 3

Under low light (*lefthand figure*), the rate of photosynthetic electron transport (PET) is low and most PET components are in oxidized states, e.g., the plastoquinone (PQ) pool is in an oxidized state (PQ^+). In contrast, in high-light conditions (*righthand figure*), due to higher excitation pressure, PET components are generally in reduced states, e.g., the PQ pool is in a reduced state (PQ^-). In addition to PET components, changes in cellular redox states are caused by different levels of reactive oxygen species (ROS) such as $O_2^{\bullet-}$ and H_2O_2 (34). Under low light (*lefthand figure*), ROS are seldom generated and, even if they are generated, most of them are detoxified by antioxidant systems (6). Under high light, however, much more ROS are generated than the antioxidant systems can deal with. These redox states may report the functional states of chloroplasts to the nucleus.

Low-light-grown plants were transiently exposed to high light or vice versa to change redox states of PET components (17, 34, 35, 49). PSII- or PSI-specific light and a shift between these PS-specific light conditions have also been utilized to adjust the redox states of PET components (72). In addition, other environmental conditions such as low temperature, sugar starvation, and/or reduced levels of electron acceptors such as O_2 and CO_2 have been used to determine the effects of the chloroplast redox states on nuclear gene expression (50, 58, 67). Furthermore, herbicides 3-(3,4-dichlorophenyl)-1,1-dimethylurea (DCMU), and 2,5-dibromo-3-methyl-6-isopropyl-p-benzoquinone (DBMIB) have been applied directly to plants or in combination with other treatments mentioned above to manipulate the redox states (17, 49, 72). These herbicides specifically block electron transport before (DCMU) or after (DBMIB) the PQ pool (88), mimicking the effect of low- or high-light intensities, respectively. The PQ pool is mostly oxidized in DCMU-treated plants and mostly reduced in DBMIB-treated plants.

The redox state of the PQ pool is one of the major determinants of PET-derived retrograde signaling (17, 35, 36, 72). Genes that are induced by high light are also induced by DBMIB treatment in the absence of high light; in contrast, DCMU treatment inhibits high-light-induced gene expression (17, 35, 36, 49). In addition, modifying the redox state of the PQ pool by shifting from PSI- to PSII-specific light causes an opposite effect on nuclear gene expression compared to a shift from PSII- to PSI-specific light (72).

The importance of the redox state of PET as a source of chloroplast signal(s) to the nuclear compartment was recently corroborated by gene expression analyses of 2661 genes encoding chloroplast proteins and 631 genes encoding nonchloroplast proteins in *Arabidopsis* (19). Using very strict environmental conditions, including PS-specific light and DCMU, genes responsive to PET redox state were identified. Among the tested genes, 286 genes were identified as directly regulated by the redox state of PET. It would be interesting to see how many among these 286 genes are specifically regulated by the redox state of the PQ pool. The total complement of nuclear genes controlled by the PET redox state is yet to be determined.

Among the PET components, the redox state of the PQ pool seems to be the most obvious source of retrograde signal(s) (17, 49, 67, 72). However, in at least one case, reduction or oxidation of the PQ pool by DCMU, DBMIB, or PS-specific light quality shows similar effects, i.e., DCMU and DBMIB both reduce nuclear gene expression (72). This suggests that the overall redox states of PET components other than the PQ pool can also generate retrograde signals.

Reactive Oxygen Species as Retrograde Signals

Besides the redox states of PET components, ROS can also function as chloroplast redox signals. Photochemical reactions in chloroplasts generate ROS and this helps relieve excitation pressure of PET components under high-light stress (6, 61). Among ROS, H_2O_2 and singlet oxygen ($^1O_2$) generated in chloroplasts by high light could act as chloroplast redox signals (**Figure 3**). H_2O_2 can be reduced to H_2O by chloroplast ascorbate peroxidases (APXs) and excess H_2O_2 diffuses through the chloroplast envelopes to the cytoplasm. Owing to its highly reactive nature, most $^1O_2$ appears to be exclusively inside of chloroplasts (39). External H_2O_2 treatment can induce expression of nuclear genes related to stress responses such as the *cytosolic APX* (*cAPX*) whose expression is also upregulated by high light (35, 37). H_2O_2 generated in chloroplasts by high light seems to play a role in nuclear gene expression. This was shown by infiltration into high-light-exposed leaves in which catalase abolished the induction of *APX2*, an *Arabidopsis cAPX*, by high light, whereas SOD did not (35).

In addition, a correlation between *Arabidopsis APX2* expression and H_2O_2 generation was shown by comparing the expression pattern of a luciferase gene driven by the *APX2* promoter and H_2O_2-specific staining pattern under high light (21). Thus, H_2O_2 could be a retrograde signaling molecule under high-light conditions.

H_2O_2 is also generated in other organelles and by other stimuli such as pathogen attack (54). However, a specific role for chloroplast-generated H_2O_2 has been shown by using transgenic tobacco plants expressing catalase or thylakoid-type APX in chloroplasts and by using methyl viologen (MV), which accelerates the generation of $O_2^{\bullet -}$ and H_2O_2 in chloroplasts (93). In the transgenic plants, cellular H_2O_2 levels under high light were significantly lower than in wild-type, and the *cAPX* gene induction was saturated much earlier than in wild type. In addition, *cAPX* expression pattern correlated with cellular H_2O_2 generated by MV. Thus, it is clear that chloroplast-generated H_2O_2 can be a redox signal that induces *cAPX* expression in the nucleus.

$^1O_2$ is most likely retained exclusively within chloroplasts considering its short lifetime and distances traveled (39, 55); however, $^1O_2$ generated in plastids can also influence nuclear gene expression. In the *Arabidopsis flu* mutant, the chlorophyll biosynthetic precursor protochlorophyllide accumulates as a free pigment and it is possible to increase the amount of $^1O_2$ without affecting the amount of other ROS such as H_2O_2 (65). Accumulation of $^1O_2$ significantly changes the expression of a number of nuclear genes. This implies that $^1O_2$ initiates a retrograde signal from the plastids. The details of the signal transduction mechanisms initiated by H_2O_2 and $^1O_2$ still need to be determined. Recently, the *Arabidopsis* EXECUTER 1 (EX1) protein was identified as a component in the $^1O_2$-mediated signaling pathway (91). Characterization of EX1 may help determine the $^1O_2$ mediated chloroplast-to-nucleus signal transduction pathway.

Nuclear Genes Regulated by Chloroplast Redox Signals

A number of nuclear genes encoding chloroplast-localized proteins are regulated by the chloroplast redox state. Under certain environmental conditions, photosynthesis-related genes are regulated to ensure efficient photosynthesis (4, 60). Under extreme conditions such as high light, the *Lhc* genes are downregulated to reduce the size of the light-harvesting complex as a protection mechanism. In addition, plants respond to the same conditions by accumulating more antioxidant molecules and by expressing stress-response proteins, both of which protect plants from harmful effects of reactive molecules (60). Thus, chloroplast redox signals are crucial not only for efficient metabolism, but also for photoprotection.

Photosynthesis-Related Genes

In *Dunaliella*, transcript levels of the *Lhcb* and the *chlorophyll a oxygenase* (*CAO*) are regulated by chloroplast redox states (12, 17, 49, 50). The effect of PET inhibitors, DCMU and DBMIB, indicate that the redox state of the PQ pool is the initial signal for regulating *Lhcb* and *CAO* expression (12, 17, 49), with possible involvement of other signals such as *trans*-thylakoid membrane potential (12).

Unlike green algae, the redox-dependent response in higher plants is more complicated. The reduced and oxidized PQ pool differentially regulates spinach *PetE* promoter activity. In contrast, the promoter activities of spinach *PsaD* and *PsaF* decreased in both DCMU and DBMIB treatments. These results indicate that spinach *PetE* expression is regulated by the redox state of the PQ pool, while the *PsaD* and *PasF* genes are regulated by the redox state of PET components other than PQ pool (72).

The *Lhcb* gene is also under the control of the chloroplast redox state in higher plants (58, 67, 94). Surprisingly, different treatments that generate the same chloroplast redox state result in different expression levels, suggesting a strong effect of experimental conditions (58, 67). For example, in barley, high-light-induced reduced state decreases *Lhcb* mRNA levels, whereas a reduced state generated by low amount of electron acceptors does not affect transcript levels (58). In addition, sugar starvation induces the *Arabidopsis Lhcb* and *PetE* genes in mature leaves, whereas sugar does not affect *PetE* accumulation in PS-specific light shift experiments (67, 72). Furthermore, the spinach *PetH* gene encoding ferredoxin-NADP$^+$-oxidoreductase (FNR) does not respond to the redox signal (72), whereas the *Arabidopsis PetH2* gene is responsive to the chloroplast redox state (19). In conclusion, although the redox state of PET generates a signal that controls the expression of several nuclear photosynthetic genes, the specific genes affected vary between species and experimental conditions.

It seems that not all photosynthesis-related genes are regulated by chloroplast redox signals at the transcriptional level (49). The redox states of chloroplasts can influence post-transcriptional steps including stability and polyribosome loading of mRNAs of several photosynthesis-related genes (15, 68, 69, 79). The stability and polyribosome association of pea *ferredoxin* (*Fed-1*) mRNA are PET dependent (68, 69). It remains to be seen if other photosynthesis-related genes are also regulated post-transcriptionally by the chloroplast redox state.

Stress-Response Genes

Among stress-response genes induced by high light, the *Arabidopsis cAPX* and *ELIP* are best characterized. Chloroplast-type *APXs* are constitutively expressed, whereas expression of *cAPXs* is highly responsive to environmental conditions (80). DCMU and DBMIB treatments show that the expression of an *Arabidopsis cAPX* gene, *APX2*, is under the control of the redox state of the PQ pool (34, 35). The *ELIP* genes encode chloroplast proteins that

are similar to members of the LHC protein family (57). Under high light, expression of *ELIP* is induced, whereas most LHC genes are repressed (25). This is consistent with a proposed photoprotective function for ELIPs (29). Similar to *APX2*, the expression of *Arabidopsis ELIP2* is also regulated by the redox state of the PQ pool (36). Interestingly, both *APX2* and *ELIP2* are induced by H_2O_2 in addition to the reduced PQ pool (35, 37). A recent report shows two phases in the induction of tobacco *cAPX*. Early response is induced by the reduced PQ pool and the later response is mediated by the cellular level of H_2O_2 (93). This suggests that the two signals can be temporally separated. It would be interesting to determine whether the induction of *Arabidopsis APX2* and *ELIP2* can be divided into similar phases.

POSSIBLE CHLOROPLAST REDOX SIGNAL TRANSDUCTION PATHWAYS

Very little is known about how chloroplast redox signals are delivered to the nucleus. One clue comes from pharmacological approaches, which indicate that a phospho-relay signaling pathway may be involved. In *Dunaliella*, it was shown that protein phosphatase inhibitors block a low-light acclimation process controlled by the redox state of the PQ pool (17). In addition, a protein kinase inhibitor also prevents *Dunaliella Lhcb* and *CAO* induction following high to low-light shift (49). In tobacco, it has been demonstrated that GUS reporter gene expression driven by the spinach *PsaF* promoter, which is regulated by the PET redox state (72), is affected by both kinase and phosphatase inhibitors (10).

ROS-mediated chloroplast-to-nucleus signal transduction also appears to involve protein phosphorylation. H_2O_2 activates mitogen-activated protein kinases (MAPKs) in *Arabidopsis* protoplasts (40) although it still needs to be determined whether $^1O_2$ can also activate a protein phosphorylation cascade. The fact that NPR1 (nonexpressor of <u>PR</u>

genes1) activates pathogen-related (PR) gene expression and that its activation is mediated by reduction of NPR1 to a monomeric form by cellular redox components suggests a mechanism by which the chloroplast redox signal might regulate nuclear gene expression (59). Taken together, these results strongly implicate a protein phosphorylation cascade in chloroplast-to-nucleus signal transduction initiated by the redox states of PET components. Identifying specific protein targets for the proposed phosphorylation relay will lead to a better understanding of redox-dependent retrograde signal transduction.

CONCLUSIONS AND PERSPECTIVES

Our understanding of plastid-to-nucleus retrograde signaling pathways is still rudimentary. We know a handful of proteins and one signaling intermediate involved in the pathway, but do not know any cytoplasmic signaling components. Importantly, we do not know how signals get out of the plastids. Several questions need to be addressed. Does Mg-ProtoIX exit the plastids or does accumulation of Mg-ProtoIX result in a secondary signal? If Mg-ProtoIX is transported, what are the specific transport proteins required? Is GUN4 involved in such transport? Where and how

are the Mg-ProtoIX and PGE signals integrated? What are the other signal transduction components between GUN1 and ABI4?

Identifying GUN1 will further our understanding of the plastid gene expression-dependent pathway and its relation to the Mg-ProtoIX-dependent pathway. Identifying proteins that interact, genetically or physically, with the known GUN proteins may reveal important new components. Biochemical identification of transcription factors that can bind to specific DNA elements required for retrograde signaling should uncover new proteins that are perhaps redundantly encoded and which have eluded identification by genetic means. The redox pathway has thus far not been amenable to genetic screens. The identification of robust redox-responsive genes should allow large-scale screening for mutants using selectable reporters. Several different approaches, including genetic screens for suppressors, interacting protein screens, and identification of putative porphyrin-binding proteins, will no doubt lead to identification of novel components and a better understanding of the plastid-to-nucleus retrograde signaling pathways. Together, these approaches should elucidate the mechanisms by which plants respond to changing, and often stressful, environments.

SUMMARY POINTS

1. Plastids emit signals that can control the expression of hundreds of nuclear genes.

2. Accumulation of Mg-ProtoporphyrinIX is one signal that elicits a nuclear response.

3. Functional plastid gene expression during the transition from heterotrophic to photoautotrophic growth modes is required for expression of nuclear-encoded photosynthetic genes.

4. Photosynthetic electron transport components and several reactive oxygen species have been proposed as putative redox-dependent retrograde signaling molecules.

5. Retrograde signals impinge on the same promoter elements that confer light-responsive gene expression.

6. Retrograde signaling pathways are crucial for allowing plants to respond to changing, often stressful, environments.

ACKNOWLEDGMENTS

Our work on retrograde signaling is supported by grants from the Department of Energy (J.C.) and the Howard Hughes Medical Institute (J.C.), by Damon Runyon Cancer Research Foundation (A.N.), and by a long-term fellowship from the European Molecular Biology Organization (S.K.). We would like to thank Jennifer Nemhauser and Jesse Woodson for critical comments and Sheila Moles for help in preparing the manuscript.

LITERATURE CITED

1. Abdallah F, Salamini F, Leister D. 2000. A prediction of the size and evolutionary origin of the proteome of chloroplasts of Arabidopsis. *Trends Plant Sci.* 5:141–42

2. Acevedo-Hernandez GJ, Leon P, Herrera-Estrella LR. 2005. Sugar and ABA responsiveness of a minimal RBCS light-responsive unit is mediated by direct binding of ABI4. *Plant J.* 43:506–19

3. Adamska I. 1995. Regulation of early light-inducible protein gene expression by blue and red light in etiolated seedlings involves nuclear and plastid factors. *Plant Physiol.* 107:1167–75

4. Anderson JM. 1986. Photoregulation of the composition, function, and structure of thylakoid membranes. *Annu. Rev. Plant Physiol.* 37:93–136

5. Anderson SL, Teakle GR, Martino-Catt SJ, Kay SA. 1994. Circadian clock- and phytochrome-regulated transcription is conferred by a 78 bp cis-acting domain of the Arabidopsis CAB2 promoter. *Plant J.* 6:457–70

6. Apel K, Hirt H. 2004. Reactive oxygen species: metabolism, oxidative stress, and signal transduction. *Annu. Rev. Plant Biol.* 55:373–99

7. Bolle C, Kusnetsov VV, Herrmann RG, Oelmüller R. 1996. The spinach AtpC and AtpD genes contain elements for light-regulated, plastid-dependent and organ-specific expression in the vicinity of the transcription start sites. *Plant J.* 9:21–30

8. Bradbeer JW, Atkinson YA, Börner T, Hagemann R. 1979. Cytoplasmic synthesis of plastid polypeptide may be controlled by plastid-synthesized RNA. *Nature* 279:816–17

9. Brown NJ, Sullivan JA, Gray JC. 2005. Light and plastid signals regulate the expression of the pea plastocyanin gene through a common region at the 5′ end of the coding region. *Plant J.* 43:541–52

10. Chandok MR, Sopory SK, Oelmüller R. 2001. Cytoplasmic kinase and phosphatase activities can induce *PsaF* gene expression in the absence of functional plastids: evidence that phosphorylation/dephosphorylation events are involved in interorganellar crosstalk. *Mol. Gen. Genomics* 264:819–26

11. Chekounova E, Voronetskaya V, Papenbrock J, Grimm B, Beck CF. 2001. Characterization of *Chlamydomonas* mutants defective in the H subunit of Mg-chelatase. *Mol. Genet. Genomics* 266:363–73

12. Chen YB, Durnford DG, Koblizek M, Falkowski PG. 2004. Plastid regulation of Lhcb1 transcription in the chlorophyte alga *Dunaliella tertiolecta*. *Plant Physiol.* 136:3737–50

13. Crawford MS, Wang W. 1983. Metabolism of magnesium protoporphyrin monomethyl ester in *Chlamydomonas reinhardtii*. *Plant Physiol.* 71:303–6

14. Duggan J, Gassman M. 1974. Induction of porphyrin synthesis in etiolated bean leaves by chelators of iron. *Plant Physiol.* 68:206–15

15. Eguchi S, Takano H, Ono K, Takio S. 2002. Photosynthetic electron transport regulates the stability of the transcript for the protochlorophyllide oxidoreductase gene in the liverwort, *Marchantia paleacea* var. diptera. *Plant Cell Physiol.* 43:573–77

16. Emanuel C, Weihe A, Graner A, Hess WR, Börner T. 2004. Chloroplast development affects expression of phage-type RNA polymerases in barley leaves. *Plant J.* 38:460–72

17. Escoubas J, Lomas M, LaRoche J, Falkowski PG. 1995. Light intensity regulation of cab gene transcription is signaled by the redox state of the plastoquinone pool. *Proc. Natl. Acad. Sci. USA* 92:10237–41

18. Fey V, Wagner R, Brautigam K, Pfannschmidt T. 2005. Photosynthetic redox control of nuclear gene expression. *J. Exp. Bot.* 56:1491–98

19. Fey V, Wagner R, Brautigam K, Wirtz M, Hell R, et al. 2005. Retrograde plastid redox signals in the expression of nuclear genes for chloroplast proteins of *Arabidopsis thaliana*. *J. Biol. Chem.* 280:5318–28

20. Forsburg SL, Guarente L. 1989. Communication between mitochondria and the nucleus in regulation of cytochrome genes in the yeast *Saccharomyces cerevisiae*. *Annu. Rev. Cell Biol.* 5:153–80

21. Fryer MJ, Ball L, Oxborough K, Karpinski S, Mullineaux PM, Baker NR. 2003. Control of ascorbate peroxidase 2 expression by hydrogen peroxide and leaf water status during excess light stress reveals a functional organization of *Arabidopsis* leaves. *Plant J.* 33:691–705

22. Goldschmidt-Clermont M. 1998. Coordination of nuclear and chloroplast gene expression in plant cells. *Int. Rev. Cytol.* 177:115–80

23. Gray JC, Sornarajah R, Zabron AA, Duckett CM, Khan MS. 1995. Chloroplast control of nuclear gene expression. In *Photosynthesis: From Light to Biosphere*, ed. P Mathis, pp. 543–50. The Netherlands: Kluwer Acad.

24. Gray JC, Sullivan JA, Wang JH, Jerome CA, MacLean D. 2003. Coordination of plastid and nuclear gene expression. *Philos. Trans. R. Soc. London Ser. B. Biol. Sci.* 358:135–44; discussion 44–45

25. Heddad M, Adamska I. 2000. Light stress-regulated two-helix proteins in *Arabidopsis thaliana* related to the chlorophyll a/b-binding gene family. *Proc. Natl. Acad. Sci. USA* 97:3741–46

26. Hess WR, Muller A, Nagy F, Borner T. 1994. Ribosome-deficient plastids affect transcription of light-induced nuclear genes: genetic evidence for a plastid-derived signal. *Mol. Gen. Genet.* 242:305–12

27. Hess WR, Schendel R, Börner T, Rüdiger W. 1991. Reduction of mRNA level for two nuclear encoded light regulated genes in the barley mutant *albostrians* is not correlated with phytochrome content and activity. *J. Plant Physiol.* 138:292–98

28. Hon T, Hach A, Tamalis D, Zhu Y, Zhang L. 1999. The yeast heme-responsive transcriptional activator Hap1 is a preexisting dimer in the absence of heme. *J. Biol. Chem.* 274:22770–74

29. Hutin C, Nussaume L, Moise N, Moya I, Kloppstech K, Havaux M. 2003. Early light-induced proteins protect *Arabidopsis* from photooxidative stress. *Proc. Natl. Acad. Sci. USA* 100:4921–26

30. Jacobs JM, Jacobs NJ. 1993. Porphyrin accumulation and export by isolated Barley (*Hordeum vulgare*) plastids (effect of diphenyl ether herbicides). *Plant Physiol.* 101:1181–87

31. Jasper F, Quednau B, Kortenjann M, Johanningmeier U. 1991. Control of cab gene expression in synchronized *Chlamydomonas reinhardtii* cells. *J. Photochem. Photobiol. B* 11:139–50

32. Johanningmeier U. 1988. Possible control of transcript levels by chlorophyll precursors in Chlamydomonas. *Eur. J. Biochem.* 177:417–24

33. Johanningmeier U, Howell SH. 1984. Regulation of light-harvesting chlorophyll-binding protein mRNA accumulation in *Chlamydomonas reinhardi*. Possible involvement of chlorophyll synthesis precursors. *J. Biol. Chem.* 259:13541–49

34. Karpinski S, Escobar C, Karpinska B, Creissen G, Mullineaux PM. 1997. Photosynthetic electron transport regulates the expression of cytosolic ascorbate peroxidase genes in Arabidopsis during excess light stress. *Plant Cell* 9:627–40

35. Karpinski S, Reynolds H, Karpinska B, Wingsle G, Creissen G, Mullineaux P. 1999. Systemic signaling and acclimation in response to excess excitation energy in Arabidopsis. *Science* 284:654–57

36. Kimura M, Manabe K, Abe T, Yoshida S, Matsui M, Yamamoto YY. 2003. Analysis of hydrogen peroxide-independent expression of the high-light-inducible *ELIP2* gene with the aid of the *ELIP2* promoter-luciferase fusions. *Photochem. Photobiol.* 77:668–74

37. Kimura M, Yoshizumi T, Manabe K, Yamamoto YY, Matsui M. 2001. *Arabidopsis* transcriptional regulation by light stress via hydrogen peroxide-dependent and -independent pathways. *Genes Cells* 6:607–17

38. Kittsteiner U, Brunner H, Rudiger W. 1991. The greening process in cress seedlings. II. Complexing agents and 5-aminolevulinate inhibit accumulation of *cab* messenger RNA coding for the light-harvesting chloropyll a/b protein. *Physiol. Plant* 81:190–96

39. Kochevar IE. 2004. Singlet oxygen signaling: from intimate to global. *Sci. STKE* 2004:pe7

40. Kovtun Y, Chiu W-L, Tena G, Sheen J. 2000. Functional analysis of oxidative stress-activated mitogen-activated protein kinase cascade in plants. *Proc. Natl. Acad. Sci. USA* 97:2940–45

41. Kropat J, Oster U, Rudiger W, Beck CF. 1997. Chlorophyll precursors are signals of chloroplast origin involved in light induction of nuclear heat-shock genes. *Proc. Natl. Acad. Sci. USA* 94:14168–72

42. Kropat J, Oster U, Rudiger W, Beck CF. 2000. Chloroplast signaling in the light induction of nuclear *HSP70* genes requires the accumulation of chlorophyll precursors and their accessibility to cytoplasm/nucleus. *Plant J.* 24:523–31

43. Kusnetsov V, Bolle C, Lubberstedt T, Sopory S, Herrmann RG, Oelmüller R. 1996. Evidence that the plastid signal and light operate via the same cis-acting elements in the promoters of nuclear genes for plastid proteins. *Mol. Gen. Genet.* 252:631–39

44. La Rocca N, Rascio N, Oster U, Rudiger W. 2001. Amitrole treatment of etiolated barley seedlings leads to deregulation of tetrapyrrole synthesis and to reduced expression of *Lhc* and *RbcS* genes. *Planta* 213:101–8

45. Larkin RM, Alonso JM, Ecker JR, Chory J. 2003. GUN4, a regulator of chlorophyll synthesis and intracellular signaling. *Science* 299:902–6

46. Leister D. 2003. Chloroplast research in the genomic age. *Trends Genet.* 19:47–56

47. Leon P, Arroyo A, Mackenzie S. 1998. Nuclear control of plastid and mitochondrial development in higher plants. *Annu. Rev. Plant Physiol. Plant Mol. Biol.* 49:453–80

48. Martinez-Hernandez A, Lopez-Ochoa L, Arguello-Astorga G, Herrera-Estrella L. 2002. Functional properties and regulatory complexity of a minimal *RBCS* light-responsive unit activated by phytochrome, cryptochrome, and plastid signals. *Plant Physiol.* 128:1223–33

49. Masuda T, Tanaka A, Melis A. 2003. Chlorophyll antenna size adjustments by irradiance in Dunaliella salina involve coordinate regulation of chlorophyll a oxygenase (*CAO*) and *Lhcb* gene expression. *Plant Mol. Biol.* 51:757–71

50. Maxwell DP, Laudenbach DE, Huner NPA. 1995. Redox regulation of light-harvesting complex II and *cab* mRNA abundance in *Dunaliella salina*. *Plant Physiol.* 109:787–95

51. Mayfield SP, Taylor WC. 1984. Carotenoid-deficient maize seedlings fail to accumulate light-harvesting chlorophyll *a/b* binding protein (LHCP) mRNA. *Eur. J. Biochem.* 144:79–84

52. McCormac AC, Fischer A, Kumar AM, Soll D, Terry MJ. 2001. Regulation of *HEMA1* expression by phytochrome and a plastid signal during de-etiolation in *Arabidopsis thaliana*. *Plant J.* 25:549–61

53. McCormac AC, Terry MJ. 2004. The nuclear genes *Lhcb* and *HEMA1* are differentially sensitive to plastid signals and suggest distinct roles for the GUN1 and GUN5 plastid-signaling pathways during de-etiolation. *Plant J.* 40:672–85

54. Mittler R. 2002. Oxidative stress, antioxidants and stress tolerance. *Trends Plant Sci.* 7:405–10

55. Moan J. 1990. On the diffusion length of singlet oxygen in cells and tissues. *J. Photochem. Photobiol.* 6:343–47

56. Mochizuki N, Brusslan JA, Larkin R, Nagatani A, Chory J. 2001. *Arabidopsis* genomes uncoupled 5 (*GUN5*) mutant reveals the involvement of Mg-chelatase H subunit in plastid-to-nucleus signal transduction. *Proc. Natl. Acad. Sci. USA* 98:2053–58

57. Montane MH, Kloppstech K. 2000. The family of light-harvesting-related proteins (LHCs, ELIPs, HLIPs): was the harvesting of light their primary function? *Gene* 258:1–8

58. Montane MH, Tardy F, Kloppstech K, Havaux M. 1998. Differential control of xanthophylls and light-induced stress proteins, as opposed to light-harvesting chlorophyll *a/b* proteins, during photosynthetic acclimation of Barley leaves to light irradiance. *Plant Physiol.* 118:227–35

59. Mou Z, Fan W, Dong X. 2003. Inducers of plant systemic acquired resistance regulate NPR1 function through redox changes. *Cell* 113:935–44

60. Niyogi KK. 1999. Photoprotection revisited: genetic and molecular approaches. *Annu. Rev. Plant Biol.* 50:333–59

61. Niyogi KK. 2000. Safety valves for photosynthesis. *Curr. Opin. Plant Biol.* 3:455–60

62. Oelmüller R, Levitan I, Bergfeld R, Rajasekhar VK, Mohr H. 1986. Expression of nuclear genes as affected by treatments acting on the plastids. *Planta* 168:482–92

63. Oelmüller R, Mohr H. 1986. Photooxidative destruction of chloroplast and its consequences for expression of nuclear genes. *Planta* 167:106–13

64. Ogawa K, Sun J, Taketani S, Nakajima O, Nishitani C, et al. 2001. Heme mediates derepression of Maf recognition element through direct binding to transcription repressor Bach1. *EMBO J.* 20:2835–43

65. op den Camp RGL, Przybyla D, Ochsenbein C, Laloi C, Kim C, et al. 2003. Rapid induction of distinct stress responses after the release of singlet oxygen in *Arabidopsis*. *Plant Cell* 15:2320–32

66. Oster U, Brunner H, Rudiger W. 1996. The greening process in cress seedlings. V. Possible interference of chlorophyll precursors, accumulated after thujaplicin treatment, with light-regulated expression of *Lhc* genes. *J. Photochem. Photobiol. B* 36:255–61

67. Oswald O, Martin T, Dominy PJ, Graham IA. 2001. Plastid redox state and sugars: interactive regulators of nuclear-encoded photosynthetic gene expression. *Proc. Natl. Acad. Sci. USA* 98:2047–52

68. Petracek ME, Dickey LF, Huber SC, Thompson WF. 1997. Light-regulated changes in abundance and polyribosome association of ferredoxin mRNA are dependent on photosynthesis. *Plant Cell* 9:2291–300

69. Petracek ME, Dickey LF, Nguyen TT, Gatz C, Sowinski DA, et al. 1998. Ferredoxin-1 mRNA is destabilized by changes in photosynthetic electron transport. *Proc. Natl. Acad. Sci. USA* 95:9009–13

70. Pfannschmidt T. 2003. Chloroplast redox signals: how photosynthesis controls its own genes. *Trends Plant Sci.* 8:33–41

71. Pfannschmidt T, Nilsson A, Allen JF. 1999. Photosynthetic control of chloroplast gene expression. *Nature* 397:625–28

72. Pfannschmidt T, Schutze K, Brost M, Oelmüller R. 2001. A novel mechanism of nuclear photosynthesis gene regulation by redox signals from the chloroplast during photosystem stoichiometry adjustment. *J. Biol. Chem.* 276:36125–30

73. Pontoppidan B, Kannangara CG. 1994. Purification and partial characterisation of barley glutamyl-tRNA(Glu) reductase, the enzyme that directs glutamate to chlorophyll biosynthesis. *Eur. J. Biochem.* 225:529–37

74. Puente P, Wei N, Deng XW. 1996. Combinatorial interplay of promoter elements constitutes the minimal determinants for light and developmental control of gene expression in *Arabidopsis*. *EMBO J.* 15:3732–43

75. Rapp JC, Mullet JE. 1991. Chloroplast transcription is required to express the nuclear genes *rbcS* and *cab*. Plastid DNA copy number is regulated independently. *Plant Mol. Biol.* 17:813–23

76. Reiß T, Bergfeld R, Link G, Thien W, Mohr H. 1983. Photooxidative destruction of chloroplast and its consequence for cytosolic enzyme levels and plant development. *Planta* 159:518–28

77. Richly E, Dietzmann A, Biehl A, Kurth J, Laloi C, et al. 2003. Covariations in the nuclear chloroplast transcriptome reveal a regulatory master-switch. *EMBO Rep.* 4:491–98

78. Rissler HM, Collakova E, DellaPenna D, Whelan J, Pogson BJ. 2002. Chlorophyll biosynthesis. Expression of a second *chl I* gene of magnesium chelatase in *Arabidopsis* supports only limited chlorophyll synthesis. *Plant Physiol* 128:770–79

79. Sherameti I, Nakamura M, Yamamoto YY, Pfannschmidt T, Obokata J, Oelmüller R. 2002. Polyribosome loading of spinach mRNAs for photosystem I subunits is controlled by photosynthetic electron transport. A crucial cis element in the spinach *PsaD* gene is located in the 5′-untranslated region. *Plant J.* 32:631–39

80. Shigeoka S, Ishikawa T, Tamoi M, Miyagawa Y, Takeda T, et al. 2002. Regulation and function of ascorbate peroxidase isoenzymes. *J. Exp. Bot.* 53:1305–19

81. Simpson J, Van Montagu M, Herrera-Estrella L. 1986. Photosynthesis-associated gene families: differences in response to tissue-specific and environmental factors. *Science* 233:34–38

82. Strand A. 2004. Plastid-to-nucleus signalling. *Curr. Opin. Plant Biol.* 7:621–25

83. Strand A, Asami T, Alonso J, Ecker JR, Chory J. 2003. Chloroplast to nucleus communication triggered by accumulation of Mg-protoporphyrinIX. *Nature* 421:79–83

84. Sullivan JA, Gray JC. 1999. Plastid translation is required for the expression of nuclear photosynthesis genes in the dark and in roots of the pea *lip1* mutant. *Plant Cell* 11:901–10

85. Susek RE, Ausubel FM, Chory J. 1993. Signal transduction mutants of *Arabidopsis* uncouple nuclear *CAB* and *RBCS* gene expression from chloroplast development. *Cell* 74:787–99

86. Taylor WC. 1989. Regulatory interactions between nuclear and plastid genomes. *Ann. Rev. Plant Physiol. Plant Mol. Biol.* 40:211–33

87. Terry MJ, Kendrick RE. 1999. Feedback inhibition of chlorophyll synthesis in the phytochrome chromophore-deficient *aurea* and *yellow-green-2* mutants of tomato. *Plant Physiol.* 119:143–52

88. Trebst A. 1980. Inhibitors in electron flow: tools for the functional and structural localization of carriers and energy conservation sites. In *Photosynthesis and Nitrogen Fixation–Part C.*, pp. 675–715. New York: Academic Press

89. Vorst O, Kock P, Lever A, Weterings B, Weisbeek P, Smeekens S. 1993. The promoter of the *Arabidopsis thaliana* plastocyanin gene contains a far upstream enhancer-like element involved in chloroplast-dependent expression. *Plant J.* 4:933–45

90. Vothknecht UC, Kannangara CG, von Wettstein D. 1996. Expression of catalytically active barley glutamyl tRNAGlu reductase in *Escherichia coli* as a fusion protein with glutathione S-transferase. *Proc. Natl. Acad. Sci. USA* 93:9287–91

91. Wagner D, Przybyla D, op den Camp R, Kim C, Landgraf F, et al. 2004. The genetic basis of singlet oxygen-induced stress responses of *Arabidopsis thaliana*. *Science* 306:1183–85

92. Wilde A, Mikolajczyk S, Alawady A, Lokstein H, Grimm B. 2004. The *gun4* gene is essential for cyanobacterial porphyrin metabolism. *FEBS Lett.* 571:119–23

93. Yabuta Y, Maruta T, Yoshimura K, Ishikawa T, Shigeoka S. 2004. Two distinct redox signaling pathways for cytosolic APX induction under photooxidative stress. *Plant Cell Physiol.* 45:1586–94

94. Yang D-H, Andersson B, Aro E-M, Ohad I. 2001. The redox state of the plastoquinone pool controls the level of the light-harvesting chlorophyll *a/b* binding protein complex II (LHC II) during photoacclimation. *Photosynth. Res.* 68:163–74

95. Zhang L, Hach A, Wang C. 1998. Molecular mechanism governing heme signaling in yeast: a higher-order complex mediates heme regulation of the transcriptional activator HAP1. *Mol. Cell Biol.* 18:3819–28

The Genetics and Biochemistry of Floral Pigments

Erich Grotewold

Department of Plant Cellular and Molecular Biology, Plant Biotechnology Center, Ohio State University, Columbus, Ohio 43210; email: grotewold.1@osu.edu

Annu. Rev. Plant Biol.
2006. 57:761–80

The *Annual Review of Plant Biology* is online at
plant.annualreviews.org

doi: 10.1146/
annurev.arplant.57.032905.105248

First published online as a
Review in Advance on
February 7, 2006

1543-5008/06/0602-
0761$20.00

Key Words

anthocyanins, betalains, carotenoids, pollination, flower color

Abstract

Three major groups of pigments, the betalains, the carotenoids, and the anthocyanins, are responsible for the attractive natural display of flower colors. Because of the broad distribution of anthocyanins (synthesized as part of the flavonoid pathway) among the flowering plants, their biosynthesis and regulation are best understood. However, over the past few years, significant progress has been made in understanding the synthesis and participation of carotenoids (derived from isoprenoids) and betalains (derived from tyrosine) in flower pigmentation. These three families of pigments play important ecological functions, for example in the attraction of pollinating animals. Anthocyanins in particular have also been the target of numerous biotechnological efforts with the objective of creating new, or altering the properties of existing, coloring compounds. The focus of this review is to examine the biosynthesis, regulation, and contribution to flower coloration of these three groups of pigments.

Contents

DOPA:
dihydroxyphenyl-
alanine

INTRODUCTION

Fruit and flower colors are of paramount importance in the ecology of plants and in their ability to attract pollinators and seed-dispersing organisms (43). In addition, plants also play an important aesthetic function by providing flowers with a broad spectrum of colors. Not surprisingly, ornamentals were among the first plants to be hybridized to alter specific color traits, and fruit and flower color have contributed to elucidating fundamental genetic principles. Today, the market for ornamental plants and cut flowers is rapidly expanding and totals over $70 billion in annual sales (5). Although increasing postharvest life, altering scent, and modifying flower shape are areas where progress is being actively pursued, much of the novelty in the cut flower industry continues to be targeted toward the generation of new colors (87). The high stakes associated with the development of new floral traits are best exemplified by the passions awaked in the seventeenth century by the unique pigmentation patterns of the "broken tulips," which led to the "tulipomania" for which records are preserved in many classical paintings (47). Florigene's Moonseries of genetically engineered carnations (**http://www.florigene.com/**), marketed in the United States, Australia, Canada, Japan, and some European countries, provide the first genetically engineered commercial flowers.

Three types of chemically distinct pigments, betalains, carotenoids, and anthocyanins are responsible for the colors of flowers (**Figure 1**). Of the three, the anthocyanins have been studied the most in the context of flower pigmentation, reflecting their broader distribution among the angiosperms. There are several excellent reviews documenting the complex biochemistry and distribution of flavonoid pigments (e.g., 16, 30, 32, 82) and their biosynthesis and regulation (e.g., 56, 70a, 101, 102). Much of the molecular information available on the regulation and biosynthesis of flower pigments derives from studies performed in model systems that include maize, *Arabidopsis*, petunia, and snapdragon. However, nonclassical plant models continue to provide unique insights into the ecophysiological regulation and functions of flower pigmentation. This review describes recent advances in our understanding of the biosynthesis, storage, and regulation of the different flower pigments.

BETALAINS

Biosynthesis

Betalains are water-soluble, nitrogen-containing compounds synthesized from tyrosine by the condensation of betalamic acid (**Figure 2**), a central intermediate in the formation of all betalains, with a derivative of dihydroxyphenylalanine (DOPA). This reaction results in the formation of the red to violet betacyanins, such as those found in red beets or in the flowers of portulaca (**Figure 1a**). The condensation of betalamic acid with an amino acid (e.g., Ser, Val, Leu, Iso, and Phe) or amino acid derivative

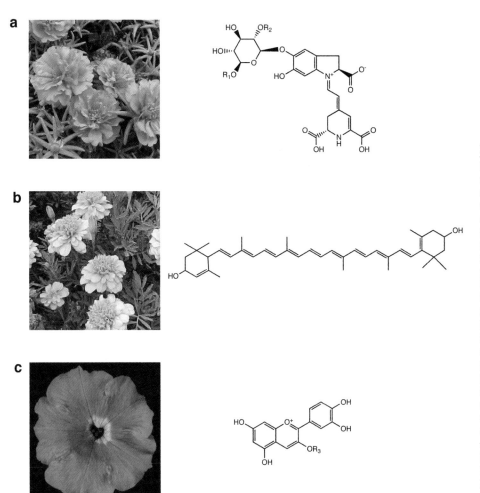

a

b

c

Figure 1

Flower displaying
the three major types
of pigments and the
corresponding
structures.
(*a*) Portulaca
(*Portulaca grandiflora*)
flowers accumulating
primarily the
betalain pigment,
betanin ($R_1 = R_2 =$
H). (*b*) Marigold
(*Tagetes patula*)
flowers accumulating
the carotenoid
pigment, lutein.
(*c*) Petunia (*Petunia
hybrida*) flower
accumulating an
anthocyanidin,
cyanidin. Pictures
were kindly provided
by the Missouri
Botanical
PlantFinder and F.
Quattrocchio.

(e.g., 3-methoxytyramine) (**Figure 2**) results in the formation of the yellow to orange betaxanthins. Betacyanins and betaxanthins can be further classified into several subclasses, based on the chemical characteristics of the betalamic acid conjugate (86). Recent advances in the separation and analysis of betalains, which are unstable under the acidic conditions normally used for Nuclear Magnetic Resonance (NMR) spectra analyses, are likely to shed additional light on the existence of novel conjugates (85). As is common for many other phytochemicals, light and hormones have a dramatic effect on the accumulation of betalains (70).

The conversion of tyrosine to DOPA (**Figure 2**) is carried out by a tyrosinase-type phenoloxidase (84), a group of copper-containing bifunctional enzymes involved in the hydroxylation of phenols to *o*-diphenols. In addition to participating in the formation of the betalamic acid core, the tyrosinase enzyme also oxidizes DOPA to dopaquinone, contributing to the biosynthesis of *cyclo*-DOPA, which conjugates with betalamic acid to form the chromophore of all betacyanins, betanidin (86). The formation of betalamic acid from DOPA requires the extradiol cleavage of the 4,5 bond carried out by a DOPA dioxygenase, first identified in the basidiomycete fly agaric (*Amanita muscaria*) (35). The plant

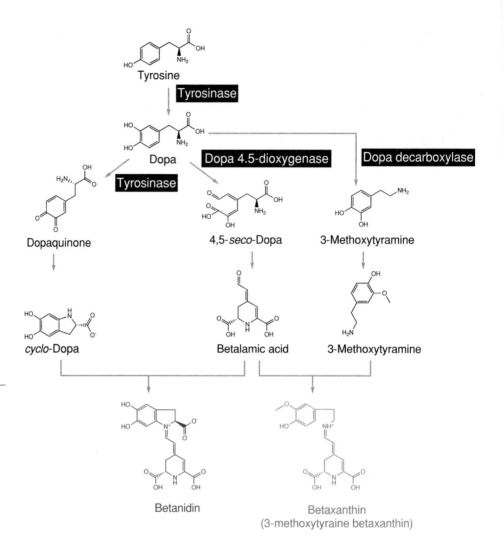

Figure 2

Schematic representation of the biosynthetic pathway of some betalain pigments. The known enzymes are indicated in black boxes and the compound names are shown.

enzyme was subsequently cloned by a subtractive cDNA approach using *Portulaca grandiflora* isogenic lines with different color phenotypes (7). The plant enzyme exhibits no obvious sequence or structural similarity with the fungal enzymes. Moreover, the plant enzyme displays regiospecific extradiol 4,5-dioxygenase (7), in contrast to the 2,3- and 4,5 dioxygenase activity of the *Amanita muscaria* enzyme (35). The 4,5-*seco*-DOPA is subsequently recyclized, a step likely to occur spontaneously (86). This different activity of the plant and fungal enzymes permits *Amanita muscaria* to accumulate muscaflavin, in addition to betalain, in the cuticle of the cap.

The introduction of the DOPA dioxygenase from *Amanita muscaria* into *Portulaca grandiflora* petals by particle bombardment resulted in the accumulation of various betalains, and also of muscaflavin, a pigment normally not found in plants (59), which is synthesized by the extradiol ring cleavage of the 2,3 bond followed by recyclization into the 6-atom, N-containing ring muscaflavin.

The next step in the biosynthesis of betalains involves the formation of an aldimine link between betalamic acid and *cyclo*-DOPA (to make betanidin) or an amino acid derivative (to make betaxanthin) (**Figure 2**). No enzyme capable of carrying out the aldimine reaction has yet been identified, opening the possibility that this step occurs spontaneously in vivo (86). It remains unclear how the spontaneous condensation of betalamic acid with various different DOPA or amino acid derivatives results in the specific patterns of betalains consistently obtained in the same plant.

As is the case with many other plant natural products (28), betalains are stored in the vacuole as glycosides. Glycosylation of betacyanins occurs both at the level of the *cyclo*-DOPA (74, 104) and by the glucosylation of betanidin (91, 92). The cloned *Dorotheanthus bellidiformis* 5- and 6-*O*-glucosyltranserases transfer glucose with similar efficiency from UDP-glucose to betanidin, to form betanin, and to several flavonoids (91, 92), raising the provocative possibility that there are evolutionary links between these two pathways (see below). Although yet to be tested for its ability to glycosylate flavonoids, the *cyclo*-DOPA 5-*O*-glucosyltransferase belongs to a group of enzymes very distinct from those involved in the phenylpropanoid pathway (75). Tyrosine feeding experiments suggest a strict compartmentalization for the betacyanin biosynthetic pathway, with the possibility of forming multienzyme complexes (83). However, it remains unknown whether there is a single or multiple pools of betalamic acid responsible for the formation of both betacyanins and betaxanthins, or how these compounds are transported to the vacuole, their ultimate site of accumulation.

Occurrence and the Mutual Exclusion with the Anthocyanins

Anthocyanin pigments are broadly distributed among the flowering plants (see below), but betalains are restricted to the order of the Caryophyllales. Within this order, betalains are absent in a couple of families including the Caryophyllaceae, which comprises genera such as *Lychnis* and *Dianthus* (e.g., carnations, *Dianthus caryophyllus*), widely used as ornamentals and cut flowers for their colorful anthocyanin pigmentation. Remarkably, anthocyanins are not present in any of the families accumulating betalains, an observation that has puzzled scientists for several decades, and which resulted in a model in which anthocyanins and betalains are mutually excluded (44, 48, 83). While this exclusion probably makes sense from a functional perspective, since both types of pigments have overlapping absorption spectra, and hence colors, the molecular basis of this exclusion is not clear. Plant-accumulating betalains express at least some of the flavonoid biosynthetic enzymes (e.g., 79) and can accumulate significant quantities of flavonols, other flavonoids, and in some cases even proanthocyanidins, suggesting that it might be the last step in the flavonoid pathway, the anthocyanidin synthase (ANS), the only enzyme "missing" in betalain-accumulating plants (83). The origin of the betalain biosynthetic pathway in just one order of the angiosperms is even more puzzling given that these pigments are also found in some basidiomycetes. One possibility is that the anthocyanin and betalain pigments have coexisted in ancestral plant species and that one of the two pigments has been selectively lost because of similar redundant pigmentation functions. Alternatively, the betalain biosynthetic pathway could have been acquired independently and more recently in the fungi and plants. The evolution of this pathway would have made unnecessary the presence of the anthocyanins, resulting in the observed exclusion of both pigments in the Caryophyllales. The paraphyletic relationship of the betanidin 5- and 6-*O*-glucosyltransferases from *Dorotheanthus bellidiformis* with other glucosyltransferases, together with their ability to utilize both betanidin and flavonoids as substrates (91, 92), was interpreted to indicate that these enzymes, originally involved in the glycosylation of flavonoids, were later recruited to glycosylate betacyanins. If so, these findings would suggest that betalains originated later in the evolution of plants than the anthocyanins. This model raises the question of how betalains appeared independently in the fungi, with a fungal betacyanin biosynthetic enzyme being able to function in the plants (59). An alternative model is that anthocyanins and betalains coexisted in an ancestral plant, and that during the evolution of the angiosperms, selective loss of ANS or of an enzyme necessary for betalain formation resulted in the current distribution. It remains to be established what selective advantage, if any, betalains provide over anthocyanins.

CAROTENOIDS

Functions

Carotenoids are plastid-synthesized and localized lipid-soluble C_{40} tetraterpenoids universally distributed in the plant kingdom. In contrast to the dispensable anthocyanins and betalains, carotenoids are essential for plant life, providing important photoprotective functions during photosynthesis and serving as precursors for the biosynthesis of the phytohormone abscisic acid (ABA) (11, 36). Carotenoids are also very significant nutraceutical components of the animal diet, serving, for example, as precursors for vitamin A biosynthesis and as antioxidants (17). Animals are unable to synthesize carotenoids de novo, yet recent studies indicate that plants and animals share multiple carotenoid-modifying enzymes (55). Birds, fish, and marine invertebrates frequently utilize carotenoids present in their diets for pigmentation purposes (78). For example, carotenoids color the red plumage of house finches and flamingos, and the keto-carotenoid astaxanthin is responsible for the orange color of salmon meat. Astaxanthin also provides the bluish color to lobster shells; the bathochromic shift from red to blue is the result of the binding of this carotenoid to the crustacyanin macromolecular complex (9). Boiling restores the red color by denaturing the β-crustacyanin protein and relaxing the proximity of the astaxanthin chromophore (90). The hue alteration resulting from the interaction of proteins and pigments remains to be exploited for the manipulation of flower color.

Beyond their essential biological activities, carotenoids have long been recognized as flower pigments (26). Carotenoids are responsible for most of the yellow to orange flower colors in ornamentals that include marigold (*Tagetes*) (**Figure 1b**), daffodil (*Narcissus*), *Freesia*, *Gerbera*, *Rosa*, *Lilium*, and *Calendula*. More important and less recognized is the ability of carotenoids to coexist with red or purple anthocyanins, resulting in brown and bronze hues that neither pigment would be able to provide by itself (16). From the more than 600 carotenoid structures known, the carotenes (hydrocarbons) and their oxygenated derivatives, the xanthophylls, are most commonly associated with flower pigmentation. Because of the many important functions that carotenoids have for plants and animals, most of the enzymes in the carotenoid biosynthetic pathway have been identified (11, 17, 103).

Biosynthesis

As is the case for other isoprenoids, isopentenyl diphosphate (IPP) provides the five-carbon building block for carotenoids. In the plastids, where carotenoid biosynthesis takes place, IPP is synthesized through the plastid-specific DOXP (1-deoxyxylulose 5-phosphate) pathway (47a). The first committed step in the carotenoid pathway is catalyzed by phytoene synthase (PSY), resulting in the condensation of two C_{20} geranylgeranyl diphosphate (GGPP) molecules to form phytoene (**Figure 3**). Four desaturation reactions, two each catalyzed by the membrane-associated phytoene desaturase (PDS) and ζ-carotene desaturase (ZDS), result in the formation of the pink lycopene from the colorless phytoene (**Figure 3**). In addition to the desaturases, the formation of lycopene (*trans* configuration) requires the action of the carotenoid isomerase (CRTISO) enzyme, cloned from the *tangerine* tomato mutant (41), which is responsible for converting

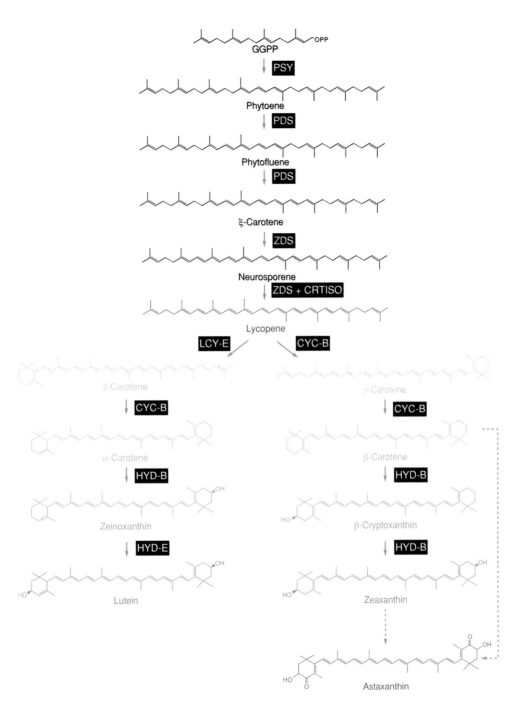

Figure 3

Schematic representation of the biosynthetic pathway of some major carotenoid pigments. The names of the compounds are indicated. GGPP corresponds to geranylgeranyl diphosphate. The enzyme names, in black boxes, are PSY, phytoene synthase; PDS, phytoene desaturase; ZDS, ζ-carotene desaturase; CRTISO, carotenoid isomerase; CYC-B, chromoplastic form of lycopene β-cyclase; LCY-E, lycopene ε-cyclase; HYD-B, carotenoid β-ring hydroxylases; HYD-E, carotenoid ε-ring hydroxylase.

poly-*cis*-lycopene (prolycopene) to lycopene. A single enzyme, phytoene desaturase (CRTI), carries out all four desaturation and isomerization reactions in bacteria and fungi. Although plant desaturases have no homology to CRTI, CRTISO does (41, 68). The cyclization of lycopene represents a branch point in the pathway, and two products can be formed depending on the position of the double bond on the cyclohexane ring. On one hand, lycopene β-cyclase, for which there are two forms in tomato, one specific to green tissues (LCY-B) and the other to chromoplasts (CYC-B), first produces γ-carotene containing one β-ring (**Figure 3**), which is subsequently converted to β-carotene by the same enzyme. On the other hand, lycopene ε-cyclase (LCY-E) produces δ-carotene. The formation of α-carotene, the precursor for lutein, involves formation of a β-ring on δ-carotene by lycopene β-cyclase (36).

The α- and β-carotenes are the precursors for the xanthophylls, which are oxygenated carotenoids generated by β- and ε-ring-specific hydroxylases. β-carotene is converted to zeaxanthin by the carotenoid β-ring hydroxylases (HYD-B), encoding a nonheme diiron enzyme (38) for which there are two genes in *Arabidopsis* (89). The hydroxylation of the ε-ring is carried out by the carotenoid ε-ring hydroxylase (HYD-E), a cytochrome P450 enzyme, CYP97C1, encoded by the *Arabidopsis LUT1* locus. In addition to displaying activity toward the ε-ring, LUT1 can also hydroxylate the β-ring (89). Hydroxylation of the β-ring of α-carotene is also mediated by a P450 enzyme (E. Wurtzel, personal communication). Lutein is the main carotenoid present in the petals of marigold, and the broad range of colors that characterize marigold flowers is due to the very different levels of this xanthophyll. Indeed, marigold varieties with very light flower color (e.g., French Vanilla) have a reduced expression of all the carotenoid biosynthetic genes, suggesting a regulatory mutation, rather than a defect in a single biosynthetic enzyme (54). Inter-estingly, however, the varieties with reduced xanthophyll accumulation in the petals display normal levels of carotenoids in the leaves, strengthening the notion that the "primary" role of carotenoids is independently regulated from their function as secondary metabolites.

The formation of ketocarotenoids, such as, for example, astaxanthin, requires the addition of keto groups in each β-ring of zeaxanthin (**Figure 3**). The initial engineering of astaxanthin in tobacco flowers was accomplished by the expression of the *CrtO* gene, encoding a β-carotene ketolase, from the algae *Haematococcus pluvialis* (49). Subsequently, the AdKeto enzyme was identified from *Adonis aestivalis* (summer pheasant's eye, Ranunculaceae), which is capable of desaturating the 3,4 positions of the β-ring followed by the 4-hydroxylation and the final keto-enol tautomerization, resulting in the formation of the blood-red pigment astaxanthin, abundantly present in the petals of this plant (12). The identification of AdKeto creates novel opportunities for the metabolic engineering of the commercially important ketocarotenoids from the abundant pools of β-carotenes present in many plants, offering alternatives to current approaches to manipulating the pathway involving the introduction of the 4,4′-oxygenase and 3,3′-hydroxylase from marine bacteria into plants (71).

ANTHOCYANINS

Biosynthesis

Anthocyanins are water-soluble pigments that occur in almost all vascular plants and excellent publications have extensively described their chemistry, distribution, and biosynthesis (16, 30, 82). The anthocyanin pigments are responsible for the majority of the orange, red, purple, and blue colors of flowers (**Figure 1c**). Anthocyanins are derived from a branch of the flavonoid pathway (**Figure 4**), for which chalcone synthase (CHS) provides the first committed step by condensing one molecule

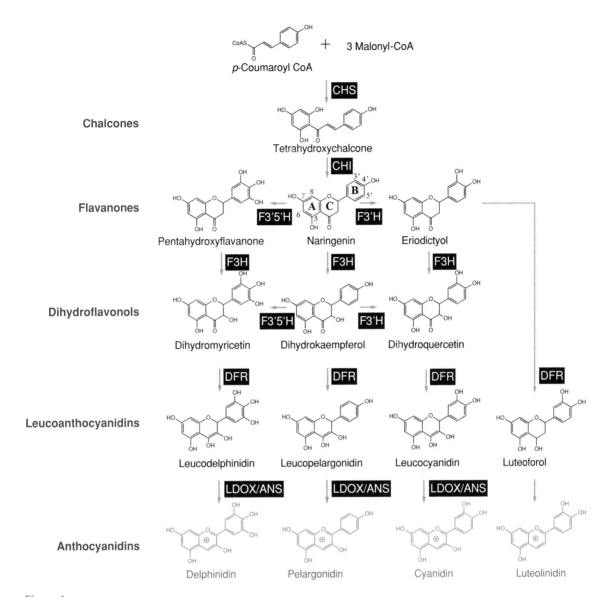

Chalcones

Tetrahydroxychalcone

Flavanones

Pentahydroxyflavanone Naringenin Eriodictyol

Dihydroflavonols

Dihydromyricetin Dihydrokaempferol Dihydroquercetin

Leucoanthocyanidins

Leucodelphinidin Leucopelargonidin Leucocyanidin Luteoforol

Anthocyanidins

Delphinidin Pelargonidin Cyanidin Luteolinidin

Figure 4

Schematic representation of the biosynthetic pathway of the most abundant anthocyanin pigments. The names of the compounds are indicated. The enzyme names, in black boxes, are CHS, chalcone synthase; CHI, chalcone isomerase; F3H, flavanone 3-hydroxylase; F3′H, flavanone 3′-hydroxylase; F3′5′H, flavanone 3′,5′-hydroxylase; DFR, dihydroflavonol 4-reductase; LDOX/ANS, leucoanthocyanidin dioxygenase/anthocyanidin synthase. The A-, B-, and C-rings with the carbon numbers are indicated in the structure corresponding to the flavanone naringenin.

of p-coumaroyl-CoA with three molecules of malonyl-CoA to produce tetrahydroxy-chalcone (a chalcone, **Figure 4**). CHS belongs to the family of polyketide synthases and the structure of this enzyme has been solved (2, 15). Chalcone provides the precursor for all classes of flavonoids, which include the flavones, flavonols, flavan-diols, flavan 4-ols, proanthocyanidins (condensed tannins), isoflavonoids, and anthocyanins. The closure of the C-ring, resulting in the formation of flavanones, is carried out by chalcone isomerase (CHI), an enzyme originally believed to have a structure unique to the plant kingdom (42), but which was also recently found in fungi and prokaryotes (20). In some bacteria, CHI-like enzymes contribute to the degradation of flavonoids by taking advantage of the reversible nature of the isomerization, which permits CHI to also convert flavanones to the corresponding chalcones (33). Flavanones (e.g., naringenin) provide a central branch point in the flavonoid pathway and can serve as substrates for enzymes that introduce –OH groups at the $3'$ and $5'$ positions of the B-ring (e.g., F3'H and F3'5'H), or for the hydroxylation of the C-ring by flavanone 3-hydroxylase (F3H), a soluble di-oxygenase. Dihydroflavonol 4-reductase (DFR) provides one entry step to the biosynthesis of anthocyanins, and depending on the plant species, it can utilize as a substrate any one or all three of the possible dihydroflavonols, dihydromyricetin, dihydrokaempferol, or dyhydroquercetin, resulting in the formation of the corresponding leucoanthocyanidins, providing structure to the anthocyanin biosynthetic grid (**Figure 4**). In some plant species, an activity that has sometimes been referred to as flavanone 4-reductase (FNR) reduces naringenin to the corresponding flavan 4-ol (e.g., apiferol). However, recent studies in maize suggest that DFR and FNR correspond to the same enzyme (29). The resulting 3-deoxy flavonoids, whose distribution is limited to some bryophytes, a few grasses (e.g., maize and sorghum), and the flowers of the Gesneriaceae (e.g., sinningia), can form 3-deoxyanthocyanin pigments (82), in contrast to the broadly distributed 3-hydroxyanthocyanins. The leucoanthocyanidins are converted into the corresponding anthocyanidins by the action of a leucoanthocyanidin dioxygenase/anthocyanidin synthase (LDOX/ANS). More than 17 different anthocyanidins have been described (31), and the major three are shown in **Figure 4**. Anthocyanidins also serve as substrates for antho-

cyanidin reductases (e.g., BANYLUS from *Arabidopsis*), key enzymes in the formation of proanthocyanidins (105).

The next step in the anthocyanin pathway is catalyzed by ANS. The structure of the *Arabidopsis* ANS enzyme has been solved (98). ANS, similar to F3H, flavone synthase I (FNSI), and flavonol synthase (FLS), is a member of the nonheme ferrous and 2-oxoglutarate (2OG)-dependent family of oxygenases, sufficient for the conversion of the leucoanthocyanidin (e.g., leucocyanidin) to the corresponding anthocyanidin (e.g., cyanidin) (60). Anthocyanidins, most often represented as the flavylium cation (red), can adopt multiple forms in solution in an equilibrium that primarily depends on the pH and the solvent. In aqueous solutions at pH of 3–6, conditions similar to those present in plant cells, the flavylium cation can be covalently hydrated at position 2, resulting in the corresponding colorless carbinol pseudobases (31). The colored flavylium ion is stabilized in the cell by inter- or intramolecular copigmentation (31). Intermolecular copigmentation involves the interaction of anthocyanins with other noncolored flavonoids (e.g., flavonols), phenylopropanoids, carotenoids, or metals (e.g., Mg^{2+} or Al^{3+}) (16, 31). Noncolored flavonoids provide "depth" to many white or cream flowers. In intramolecular copigmentation, the anthocyanin chromophores are covalently modified by organic acids, other flavonoids, or aromatic acyl groups. These modifications, together with the stacking of planar anthocyanins, add protection from nucleophilic water addition and result in increased anthocyanin pigmentation and hue changes.

Most of the currently known flavonoids are modified at one or several positions by methylation, acylation, or glycosylation. These modifications are often taxa specific and are believed to provide flavonoids with unique properties. For example, flavonoids found in the surface of leaves or flowers (surface flavonoids) are often methylated (67). Although these modifications occur after completion of the skeleton biosynthesis, the most common is the glycosylation at position 3 with one or multiple sugar residues, followed by acylation. Adding a sugar decoration to anthocyanidins results in a modest hypsochromic shift (to the blue) in the corresponding spectral maxima (31). The most studied glycosylation involves the addition of a glucose group by the UDP-3-*O*-glucosyltransferases (UFGT/3GT), and UFGT/3GT enzymes have been identified and cloned from numerous plant species. In addition to glucose, anthocyanins containing rhamnose and other sugars at the 5, 3′, and 7 positions are found in different plants. The 7GT have high similarity to the betanidin 5GT (92), and to the 3′GT from Gentian (*Gentiana triflora*), which glucosylates the 3′-OH group of delphinidin-type anthocyanins containing glucose groups at the 3′ and 5 positions (19). An interesting variation to the glycosylation of anthocyanidins by different glycosyltransferases in most plants is provided by recent findings in rose (*Rosa hybrida*), in which a single glucosyltransferase, RhGT1, sequentially catalyzes the addition of glucose at the 3-OH and 5-OH positions (65). In addition to glycosylations, anthocyanins can be acylated by a variety of organic acids by a group of enzymes collectively known as anthocyanin acyltransferases (60a). Acylation contributes to intermolecular and/or intermolecular stacking to increase anthocyanin stability and water solubility (81a).

Many of the enzymes in the *Arabidopsis* flavonoid biosynthetic pathway participate in the formation of multienzyme complexes, or metabolons, that may help direct flux into any of the multiple branches of the pathway that can coexist in a cell (3, 100). Although it has not been formally demonstrated for anthocyanin biosynthesis, channeling is involved in the biosynthesis of phenylpropanoids (1, 99). The flavonoid enzymes are associated with the cytoplasmic face of the endoplasmic reticulum (ER), anchored to the membrane through the cytochrome P450 proteins that participate in the pathway (e.g., F3′H) (37, 76, 82). The recent demonstration that several *Arabidopsis* flavonoid biosynthetic enzymes are also lo-

cated in the nucleus of some cell types (77) may provide clues on nuclear biosynthetic or regulatory activities not previously recognized.

Transport and Storage

Because of the visible phenotypes that result from defects in the proper sequestration of anthocyanins, some molecular components involved in the vacuolar trafficking of anthocyanins are starting to emerge (28). The *bz2* locus from maize encodes a glutathione *S*-transferase (GST), which was initially proposed to mediate the transfer of glutathione to cyanidine 3-glucoside (C3G) (51). However, rather than conjugating glutathione to C3G, BZ2 and the equivalent protein in petunia, AN9, appear to serve as carrier proteins, transporting C3G from the cytoplasm to the tonoplast (58), and delivering C3G to MRP3, a maize multidrug resistance-like protein that localizes to the vacuolar membrane (25). The *Arabidopsis TT19* locus also encodes a GST (45), and *tt19* mutants can be complemented by AN9 in their anthocyanin deficiency, but not in their inability to accumulate proanthocyanidins (condensed tannins) in the seed coat (discussed in Reference 46a). In addition to the participation of transporters, vesicles have been implicated in the transport of anthocyanins to the vacuole (28).

Several plant species store anthocyanins within vacuolar inclusions that have been loosely termed anthocyanoplasts, which initiate as vesicles in the cytoplasm and appear to be membrane bound (64, 69). More recently, the intravacuolar structures observed in the flower petals of various plants, including carnation and lisianthus, were termed anthocyanic vacuolar inclusions (AVIs) (50). These inclusions are likely membraneless proteinaceous matrixes that served as anthocyanin traps, preferentially for anthocyanidin 3,5-diglycosides (50) or acylated anthocyanins (10). The expression of the VP24 protein, first identified as encoded by a light-induced gene in sweet potato (*Ipomoea batata*)

AVI: anthocyanic vacuolar inclusions

AVI-containing cells, correlated with the accumulation of anthocyanins (63). Thus, the VP24 protein, a metalloprotease with aminopeptidase activity (62), likely participates in the transport or accumulation of anthocyanins to the vacuole (106).

Regulation

The regulation of anthocyanin biosynthesis continues to provide a paradigm for the combinatorial control of plant gene expression, providing one of the best-studied plant regulatory systems (40, 46, 56). Basic-helix-loophelix (bHLH) transcription factors, exemplified by members of the maize R/B family and the *Petunia* AN1 and JAF13 proteins, physically interact with R2R3 MYB proteins (e.g., maize C1 and Petunia AN2) (23) to activate all (in maize) or a subset (in *Petunia* and most other dicots) of the anthocyanin biosynthetic genes. Studies in maize have established that the bHLH-R2R3 MYB interaction serves two purposes: (*a*) it is essential for the activity of the R2R3 MYB partner, either by stabilizing the protein or permitting it to activate transcription, and (*b*) it provides enhanced activity on promoters containing a *cis*-regulatory element conserved in several anthocyanin biosynthetic genes (34). The *PAP1* gene, identified by the pigmentation provided by the enhanced expression in the *PAP1-D* activation-tagged line (2a), encodes the *Arabidopsis* functional ortholog of the maize C1 protein. A combination of RNA and metabolic profiling experiments in *PAP1-D* plants resulted in the identification of two new glycosyltransferases involved in anthocyanin modification in *Arabidopsis* (89a).

In addition to the R2R3 MYB and bHLH regulators, WD40 proteins, exemplified by the *Petunia* An11 (13), the *Arabidopsis* TTG1 (94), the maize PAC1 (4), and the *Perilla* PfWD (80) proteins, play a central role in the activity of the regulatory complex. This cooperation between R2R3 MYB, bHLH, and WD40 proteins is not limited to anthocyanin regulation, and is also involved in the control of multiple developmental processes (72). Little continues to be known on what regulates the regulators. Light and hormones play a central role in the expression of the anthocyanin biosynthetic genes, likely through the activation of the known transcription factors (57, 95).

CELLULAR ARCHITECTURE, pH, AND PIGMENTATION

Although the expression of the pigment biosynthetic genes and the proper subcellular localization of the corresponding pigments are essential, they may not be sufficient for providing the proper hue to flowers. Vacuolar pH plays an important function in coloring anthocyanin pigments. The vacuolar lumen in every cell type is more acidic than the surrounding cytoplasm. In petunia flowers, the acidification of the vacuole results in a red color of the flower and mutations affecting vacuolar pH regulation can be recognized because of the shift of the flower color toward blue. The opposite phenomenon is seen in flowers of *Ipomea*, where development of their normal blue color during petal maturation requires alkalinization of the vacuole by the PURPLE (PR) protein. PR is a putative Na^+/H^+ pump (18) believed to transport sodium ions into and protons out of the vacuole, resulting in the increased vacuolar pH and blue color. Screens have identified many loci in *Petunia* that, when mutated, are deficient in the acidification of the vacuole, and therefore result in hypsochromic shifts. Among them was *ph6* (8), which was an allele of the AN1 bHLH transcription factor (81). Thus, the regulators of the pathway also participate in establishing a vacuolar environment conducive to adequate pigmentation.

In addition to pH, cell shape has a dramatic impact on flower color. The snapdragon (*Antirrhinum majus*) MIXTA R2R3 MYB transcription factor is necessary for the formation of conical cells (61), a characteristic of the petals of many plants. Mutants in the *mixta* locus appear deficient in petal pigmentation, a consequence of the difference in the way the light is reflected by conical or flat cells (52). Beyond cell shape, the correct packing of anthocyanins in the vacuole is likely to also have a dramatic influence on hue. For example, flowers of the "Rhapsody in Blue" rose cultivar show a change in color induced by age, from red-purple to bluish-purple, and this variation is associated with a progressive accumulation of anthocyanins into AVI-like structures (24). *Lisianthus* flowers also show a correlation between the packaging of anthocyanins into AVIs, the presence of "blackish-purple" pigmentation at the base of the petal, and the reduction or absence of AVIs in the outer zones, associated with a lighter purple color of this region (50). Light affects the way in which anthocyanins are distributed among vacuolar and subvacuolar compartment in maize cells, providing interesting links between environmental signals and anthocyanin pigmentation (39).

FLOWER PIGMENTATION AS A VISUAL CUE

As Darwin noted, "Flowers rank among the most beautiful productions of nature; but they have been rendered conspicuous in contrast with the green leaves, and in consequence at the same time beautiful, so that they may be easily observed by insects. I have come to this conclusion from finding it an invariable rule that when a flower is fertilised by wind it never has a gaily-coloured corolla." Today, it is widely believed that the main function of flower pigments is to attract pollinators and to provide salient signals allowing them to learn the presence of food associated to these signals (53). The relationship between floral traits, among them pigmentation, and the behavior of pollinating animals has been an important factor in the coevolution of plants and the corresponding pollinators. Pollinators seek profitable rewards (e.g., quality and quantity of nectar or pollen) in their foraging visits, and their flower choice is based on a complex decision-making process that involves multiple factors (93). The different color visions of various pollinators make it tempting to speculate that there is a perfect correlation between the pigmentation of flowers and the spectra of colors that a particular pollinator can detect. It has been reported, for instance, that flower-naïve bees prefer hues that seem to be related to highly nectar-rewarding colors in nature in their first foraging flights (21). However, this correlation is far from being demonstrated for different ecosystems and floral varieties. There is a growing debate on whether the association between pollinator vision and flower pigmentation is as strong as believed (6). Indeed, multiple different pollinators can visit flowers with the same color, and it is not rare to find significant variations in flower pigmentation among populations. One possible aspect that needs to be considered is that flavonoids (88) and anthocyanins (27) play a number of important functions, unrelated to pollinator attraction, in vegetative tissues. Thus, the specific hue of a flower could be influenced by the accumulation of flavonoids elsewhere in the plant. On the other hand, our understanding of the specific cues perceived by pollinators in a total floral landscape is very rudimentary, and other factors, in addition to flower pigmentation, likely play a significant role. For example, achromatic cues such as the contrast provided by a corolla to the long-wave receptor type seem to be important for farthest floral detection (22). Also, floral symmetry is more important than color in the visitation preference of naïve bumblebees (73). In contrast, color has a priority over smell in the visitation preference of *Vanessa indica* butterflies (66).

The complexity of the interaction between pollinators and flower pigmentation is nicely illustrated by the phenomenon known as "floral color change," which is widespread in the plant kingdom and which occurs after pollinator visits to a given floral species (96). Floral color change occurs in fully opened, turgid flowers and independently of flower senescence. In some cases, such as in *Viola cornuta*, pollination triggers the accumulation of anthocyanins, changing the flower color from white to purple. The molecular signals involved in the induction of anthocyanin biosynthesis upon pollination are not known, but light plays a central role (14). In other cases, pigments disappear after pollination (97). Floral color change can involve any of the three types of flower pigments described here, although changes in anthocyanin pigmentation are the most-often recorded (97). It has been argued that color change results in a lost of chromaticity from the pollinator's perspective. This process would thus have an adaptive value, as insects would not need to pay attention to flowers that have been already exploited.

SUMMARY POINTS

1. Three groups of compounds, betalains, carotenoids and anthocyanins, constitute the majority of the flower pigments known.

2. While carotene pigments can coexist with anthocyanins and betalains, there is a mutual exclusion of the latter two.

3. The core biosynthetic pathways for these pigments are well established; only the regulation of anthocyanins is well understood today.

4. Significant biotechnological opportunities are available for additional modifications of the three types of pigments and for targeting them to particular subcellular compartments.

5. Although it is clear that flower pigmentation plays a central role in attracting pollinators, a unique pigment-pollinator relationship likely does not exist.

UNRESOLVED ISSUES AND FUTURE DIRECTIONS

1. There is a need to understand how the accumulation of carotenoids and betalains is regulated.

2. A better understanding of how the transport of these compounds occurs, and how their sequestration in plastid or vacuoles influences pigmentation, would provide unique opportunities for manipulating flower pigmentation.

3. A molecular explanation for the observed exclusion of anthocyanins and betalains is necessary.

ACKNOWLEDGMENTS

The author is thankful to Niloufer Irani, Brenda Shirley, Thomas Vogt, Elli Wurtzel and Martín Giurfa for helpful comments and suggestions on this review, and gratefully acknowledges the National Science Foundation (Grants MCB0130062 and MCB0210413) and the National Research Initiative of the USDA Cooperative State Research, Education and Extension Service (Grant 2003-35,318-13,689) for support on the research related to the regulation of anthocyanin pigmentation.

LITERATURE CITED

1. Achnine L, Blancaflor EB, Rasmussen S, Dixon RA. 2004. Colocalization of L-phenylalanine ammonia-lyase and cinnamate 4-hydroxylase for metabolic channeling in phenylpropanoid biosynthesis. *Plant Cell* 16:3098–109

2. Austin MB, Noel JP. 2003. The chalcone synthase superfamily of type III polyketide synthases. *Nat. Prod. Rep.* 20:79–110

2a. Borevitz JO, Xia Y, Blount J, Dixon RA, Lamb C. 2000. Activation tagging identifies a conserved MYB regulator of phenylpropanoid biosynthesis. *Plant Cell* 12:2383–94

3. Burbulis IE, Winkel BS. 1999. Interactions among enzymes of the *Arabidopsis* flavonoid biosynthetic pathway. *Proc. Natl. Acad. Sci. USA* 96:12929–34

4. Carey CC, Strahle JT, Selinger DA, Chandler VL. 2004. Mutations in the *pale aleurone color1* regulatory gene of the *Zea mays* anthocyanin pathway have distinct phenotypes relative to the functionally similar TRANSPARENT TESTA GLABRA1 gene in *Arabidopsis thaliana*. *Plant Cell* 16:450–64

5. Chandler S. 2003. Commercialization of genetically modified ornamental plants. *J. Plant Biotechnol.* 5:69–77

6. Chittka L, Spaethe J, Schmidt A, Hickelsberger A. 2001. Adaptation, constraint and chance in the evolution of flower color and pollinator color vision. In *Cognitive Ecology of Pollination: Animal Behavior and Evolution*, ed. L Chittka, JD Thomson, pp. 106–26. Cambridge, UK: Cambridge Univ. Press

7. Christinet L, Burdet FX, Zaiko M, Hinz U, Zryd JP. 2004. Characterization and functional identification of a novel plant 4,5-extradiol dioxygenase involved in betalain pigment biosynthesis in *Portulaca grandiflora*. *Plant Physiol.* 134:265–74

8. Chuck G, Robbins T, Nijjar C, Ralston E, Courtney-Gutterson N, Dooner HK. 1993. Tagging and cloning of a petunia flower color gene with the maize transposable element *Activator*. *Plant Cell* 5:371–78

9. Cianci M, Rizkallah PJ, Olczak A, Raftery J, Chayen NE, et al. 2002. The molecular basis of the coloration mechanism in lobster shell: beta-crustacyanin at 3.2Å resolution. *Proc. Natl. Acad. Sci. USA* 99:9795–800

10. Conn S, Zhang W, Franco C. 2003. Anthocyanic vacuolar inclusions (AVIs) selectively bind acylated anthocyanins in *Vita vinifera* L. (grapevine) suspension culture. *Biotech. Lett.* 25:835–39

11. Cunningham FX, Gantt E. 1998. Genes and enzymes of carotenoid biosynthesis in plants. *Annu. Rev. Plant Physiol. Plant. Mol. Biol.* 49:557–83

12. **Cunningham FX Jr, Gantt E. 2005. A study in scarlet: enzymes of ketocarotenoid biosynthesis in the flowers of *Adonis aestivalis*. *Plant J.* 41:478–92**

13. de Vetten N, Quattrocchio F, Mol J, Koes R. 1997. The *an11* locus controlling flower pigmentation in petunia encodes a novel WD-repeat protein conserved in yeast, plants, and animals. *Genes Dev.* 11:1422–34

14. Farzad M, Griesbach R, Weiss MR. 2002. Floral color change in *Viola cornuta* L. (Violaceae): a model system to study regulation of anthocyanin production. *Plant Sci.* 162:225–31

15. Ferrer JL, Jez JM, Bowman ME, Dixon RA, Noel JP. 1999. Structure of chalcone synthase and the molecular basis of plant polyketide biosynthesis. *Nat. Struct. Biol.* 6:775–84

16. Forkmann G. 1991. Flavonoids as flower pigments: the formation of the natural spectrum and its extension by genetic engineering. *Plant Breed.* 106:1–26

17. Fraser PD, Bramley PM. 2004. The biosynthesis and nutritional uses of carotenoids. *Prog. Lipid Res.* 43:228–65

This study provides the first plant enzyme that would permit manipulation of the accumulation of red ketocarotenoids from abundant precursors.

18. Fukada-Tanaka S, Inagaki Y, Yamaguchi T, Saito N, Iida S. 2000. Colour-enhancing protein in blue petals. *Nature* 407:581
19. Fukuchi-Mitzutani M, Okuhara H, Fukui Y, Nakao M, Katsumoto Y, et al. 2003. Biochemical and molecular characterization of a novel UDP-glucose: anthocyanin 3′-*O*-glucosyltransferase, a key enzyme for blue anthocyanin biosynthesis, from Gentian. *Plant Physiol.* 132:1652–63
20. Gensheimer M, Mushegian A. 2004. Chalcone isomerase family and fold: no longer unique to plants. *Protein Sci.* 13:540–44
21. Giurfa M, Nuñez JA, Chittka L, Menzel R. 1995. Colour preferences of flower-naïve honeybees. *J. Comp. Physiol.* 177:247–59
22. Giurfa M, Menzel R. 1997. Insect visual perception: complex abilities of simple nervous systems. *Curr. Opin. Neurobiol.* 7:505–13
23. Goff SA, Cone KC, Chandler VL. 1992. Functional analysis of the transcriptional activator encoded by the maize *B* gene: evidence for a direct functional interaction between two classes of regulatory proteins. *Genes Dev.* 6:864–75
24. Gonnet JF. 2003. Origin of the color of cv. Rhapsody in Blue rose and some other so-called "blue" roses. *J. Agric. Food Chem.* 51:4990–94
25. Goodman CD, Casati P, Walbot V. 2004. A multidrug resistance–associated protein involved in anthocyanin transport in *Zea mays*. *Plant Cell* 16:1812–26
26. Goodwin TW, Britton G. 1988. Distribution and analysis of carotenoids. In *Plant Pigments*, ed. TW Goodwin, pp. 61–132. San Diego: Academic
27. Gould KS. 2004. Nature's swiss army knife: the diverse protective roles of anthocyanins in leaves. *J. Biomed. Biotechnol.* 2004:314–20
28. Grotewold E. 2004. The challenges of moving chemicals within and out of cells: insights into the transport of plant natural products. *Planta* 219:906–9
29. Halbwirth H, Martens S, Wienand U, Forkmann G, Stich K. 2003. Biochemical formation of anthocyanins in silk tissues of *Zea mays*. *Plant Sci.* 164:489–95
30. Harborne JB. 1988. *The Flavonoids: Advances in Research Since 1980*. New York: Chapman and Hall
31. Harborne JB. 1988. The flavonoids: recent advances. In *Plant Pigments*, ed. TW Goodwin, pp. 299–343. San Diego: Academic
32. Harborne JB, Williams CA. 2000. Advances in flavonoid research since 1992. *Phytochemistry* 55:481–504
33. Herles C, Braune A, Blaut M. 2004. First bacterial chalcone isomerase isolated from *Eubacterium ramulus*. *Arch. Microbiol.* 181:428–34
34. Hernandez J, Heine G, Irani NG, Feller A, Kim M-G, et al. 2004. Mechanisms of cooperation between MYB and HLH transcription factors in the regulation of anthocyanin pigmentation. *J. Biol. Chem.* 279:48205–13
35. Hinz UG, Fivaz J, Girod PA, Zyrd JP. 1997. The gene coding for the DOPA dioxygenase involved in betalain biosynthesis in *Amanita muscaria* and its regulation. *Mol. Gen. Genet* 256:1–6
36. Hirschberg J. 2001. Carotenoid biosynthesis in flowering plants. *Curr. Opin. Plant Biol.* 4:210–18
37. Hrazdina G, Wagner GJ. 1985. Compartmentation of plant phenolic compounds; sites of synthesis and accumulation. *Ann. Proc. Phytochem.* 25:120–33
38. Inoue K. 2004. Carotenoid hydroxylation–P450 finally! *Trends. Plant Sci.* 9:515–17
39. Irani NG, Grotewold E. 2005. Light-induced morphological alteration in anthocyanin-accumulating vacuoles of maize cells. *BMC Plant Biol.* 5:7

40. Irani NG, Hernandez JM, Grotewold E. 2003. Regulation of anthocyanin pigmentation. *Rec. Adv. Phytochem.* 38:59–78

41. Isaacson T, Ronen G, Zamir D, Hirschberg J. 2002. Cloning of tangerine from tomato reveals a carotenoid isomerase essential for the production of beta-carotene and xanthophylls in plants. *Plant Cell* 14:333–42

42. Jez JM, Bowman ME, Dixon RA, Noel JP. 2000. Structure and mechanism of the evolutionarily unique plant enzyme chalcone isomerase. *Nat. Struct. Biol.* 7:786–91

43. Kevan PG, Baker HG. 1983. Insects as flower visitors and pollinators. *Annu. Rev. Entomol.* 28:407–53

44. Kimler L, Mears J, Mabry TJ, Roesler H. 1970. On the question of the mutual exclusivness of betalains and anthocyanins. *Taxon* 19:875–78

45. Kitamura S, Shikazono N, Tanaka A. 2004. TRANSPARENT TESTA 19 is involved in the accumulation of both anthocyanins and proanthocyanidins in *Arabidopsis. Plant J.* 37:104–14

46. Koes R, Verweij W, Quattrocchio F. 2005. Flavonoids: a colorful model for the regulation and evolution of biochemical pathways. *Trends Plant Sci.* 10:236–42

46a. Lepiniec L, Debeaujon I, Routaboul J-M, Baudry A, Pourcel L, et al. 2006. Genetics and biochemistry of seed flavonoids. *Annu. Rev. Plant Biol.* 57:405–430

47. Lesnaw JA, Ghabrial SA. 2000. Tulip breaking: past, present, and future. *Plant Dis.* 84:1052–60

47a. Lichtenthaler HK, Rohmer M, Schwender J. 1997. Two independent biochemical pathways for isopentenyl diphosphate and isoprenoid biosynthesis in higher plants. *Physiol. Plant* 101:643–52

48. Mabry TJ, Dreiding AS. 1968. The betalains. In *Recent Advances in Phytochemistry*, ed. TJ Mabry, RE Alstom, VC Runeckles. New York: Appleton-Century-Crofts

49. Mann V, Harker M, Pecker I, Hirschberg J. 2000. Metabolic engineering of astaxanthin production in tobacco flowers. *Nat. Biotechnol.* 18:888–92

50. Markham KR, Gould KS, Winefield CS, Mitchell KA, Bloor SJ, Boase MR. 2000. Anthocyanic vacuolar inclusions–their nature and significance in flower colouration. *Phytochemistry* 55:327–36

51. Marrs KA, Alfenito MR, Lloyd AM, Walbot V. 1995. A glutathione *S*-transferase involved in vacuolar transfer encoded by the maize gene *bronze-2. Nature* 375:397–400

52. Martin C, Bhatt K, Baumann K, Jin H, Zachgo S, et al. 2002. The mechanics of cell fate determination in petals. *Philos. Trans. Roy. Soc. London Ser. B Biol. Sci.* 357:809–13

53. Menzel R. 1985. Learning in honeybees in an ecological and behavioral context. In *Experimental Behavioral Ecology*, ed. B Hölldobler, M Lindauer, pp. 55–74. Stuttgart: Fisher

54. Moehs CP, Tian L, Osteryoung KW, DellaPenna D. 2001. Analysis of carotenoid biosynthetic gene expression during marigold petal development. *Plant Mol. Biol.* 45:281–93

55. Moise AR, von Lintig J, Palczewski K. 2005. Related enzymes solve evolutionarily recurrent problems in the metabolism of carotenoids. *Trends. Plant Sci.* 10:178–86

56. Mol J, Grotewold E, Koes R. 1998. How genes paint flowers and seeds. *Trends. Plant Sci.* 3:212–17

57. Mol J, Jenkins G, Schafer E, Weiss D. 1996. Signal perception, transduction, and gene expression involved in anthocyanin biosynthesis. *Crit. Rev. Plant Sci.* 15:525–57

58. Mueller LA, Goodman CD, Silady RA, Walbot V. 2000. AN9, a petunia glutathione *S*-transferase required for anthocyanin sequestration, is a flavonoid-binding protein. *Plant Physiol.* 123:1561–70

This review provides evidence that the way in which anthocyanins are packed influences the pigmentation provided by anthocyanins.

59. Mueller LA, Hinz U, Uze M, Sautter C, Zryd J-P. 1997. Biochemical complementation if the betalain biosynthetic pathway in *Portulaca grandiflora* by a fungal 3,4-dihydroxyphenylalanine dioxygenase. *Planta* 203:260–63

60. Nakajima J, Tanaka Y, Yamazaki M, Saito K. 2001. Reaction mechanism from leucoanthocyanidin to anthocyanidin 3-glucoside, a key reaction for coloring in anthocyanin biosynthesis. *J. Biol. Chem.* 276:25797–803

60a. Nakayama T, Suzuki H, Nishino T. 2003. Anthocyanin acyltransferases: specificities, mechanism, phylogenetics, and applications. *J. Mol. Catal. B Enzym.* 23:117–32

61. Noda K-I, Glover BJ, Linstead P, Martin C. 1994. Flower colour intensity depends on specialized cell shape controlled by a Myb-related transcription factor. *Nature* 369:661–64

62. Nozue M, Baba K, Kitamura S, Xu W, Kubo H, et al. 2003. VP24 found in anthocyanic vacuolar inclusions (AVIs) of sweet potato cells is a member of a metalloprotease family. *Biochem. Eng. J.* 14:199–205

63. Nozue M, Yamada K, Nakamura T, Kubo H, Kondo M, Nishimura M. 1997. Expression of a vacuolar protein (VP24) in anthocyanin-producing cells of sweet potato in suspension culture. *Plant Physiol* 115:1065–72

64. Nozzolillo C, Ishikura N. 1988. An investigation of the intracellular site of anthocyanoplasts using isolated protoplasts and vacuoles. *Plant Cell Rep.* 7:389–92

65. Ogata J, Kanno Y, Itoh Y, Tsugawa H, Suzuki M. 2005. Plant biochemistry: anthocyanin biosynthesis in roses. *Nature* 435:757–58

66. Omura H, Honda K. 2005. Priority of color over scent during flower visitation by adult *Vanessa indica* butterflies. *Oecologia* 142:588–96

67. Onyilagha JC, Grotewold E. 2004. The biology and structural distribution of surface flavonoids. *Recent Res. Dev. Plant Sci.* 2:53–71

68. Park H, Kreunen SS, Cuttriss AJ, DellaPenna D, Pogson BJ. 2002. Identification of the carotenoid isomerase provides insight into carotenoid biosynthesis, prolamellar body formation, and photomorphogenesis. *Plant Cell* 14:321–32

69. Pecket CR, Small CJ. 1980. Occurrence, location and development of anthocyanoplasts. *Phytochemistry* 19:2571–76

70. Piattelli M. 1981. The betalains: structure, biosynthesis, and chemical taxonomy. In *The Biochemistry of Plants*, ed. EE Conn, pp. 557–75. New York: Academic

70a. Quattrocchio F, Baudry A, Lepiniec L, Grotewold E. 2006. *The Regulation of Flavonoid Biosynthesis*, ed. E Grotewold, pp. 97–122. New York: Springer

71. Ralley L, Enfissi EM, Misawa N, Schuch W, Bramley PM, Fraser PD. 2004. Metabolic engineering of ketocarotenoid formation in higher plants. *Plant J.* 39:477–86

72. Ramsay NA, Glover BJ. 2005. MYB-bHLH-WD40 protein complex and the evolution of cellular diversity. *Trends Plant Sci.* 10:63–70

73. Rodriguez I, Gumbert A, Hempel de Ibarra N, Kunze J, Giurfa M. 2004. Symmetry is in the eye of the beeholder: innate preference for bilateral symmetry in flower-naive bumblebees. *Naturwissenschaften* 91:374–77

74. Sasaki N, Adachi T, Koda T, Ozeki Y. 2004. Detection of UDP-glucose:cyclo-DOPA 5-*O*-glucosyltransferase activity in four o'clocks (*Mirabilis jalapa* L.). *FEBS Lett.* 568:159–62

75. Sasaki N, Wada K, Koda T, Kasahara K, Adachi T, Ozeki Y. 2005. Isolation and characterization of cDNAs encoding an enzyme with glucosyltransferase activity for cyclo-dopa from four o'clocks and feather cockscombs. *Plant Cell Physiol.* 46:666–70

76. Saslowsky D, Winkel BS. 2001. Localization of flavonoid enzymes in *Arabidopsis* roots. *Plant J.* 27:37–48

77. Saslowsky DE, Warek U, Winkel BS. 2005. Nuclear localization of flavonoid enzymes in *Arabidopsis. J. Biol. Chem.* 280:23735–40

78. Shahidi F, Metusalach, Brown JA. 1998. Carotenoid pigments in seafoods and aquaculture. *Crit. Rev. Food Sci. Nutr.* 38:1–67

79. Shimada S, Takahashi K, Sato Y, Sakuta M. 2004. Dihydroflavonol 4-reductase cDNA from non-anthocyanin-producing species in the Caryophyllales. *Plant Cell Physiol.* 45:1290–98

80. Sompornpailin K, Makita Y, Yamazaki M, Saito K. 2002. A WD-repeat-containing putative regulatory protein in anthocyanin biosynthesis in *Perilla frutescens. Plant Mol. Biol.* 50:485–95

81. **Spelt C, Quattrocchio F, Mol J, Koes R. 2002. ANTHOCYANIN1 of petunia controls pigment synthesis, vacuolar pH, and seed coat development by genetically distinct mechanisms. *Plant Cell* 14:2121–35**

81a. Springob K, Nakajima J-i, Yamazaki M, Saito K. 2003. Recent advances in the biosynthesis and accumulation of anthocyanins. *Nat. Prod. Rep.* 20:288–303

82. Stafford HA. 1990. *Flavonoid Metabolism.* Boca Raton, Florida: CRC Press

83. Stafford HA. 1994. Anthocyanins and betalains: evolution of the mutually exclusive pathways. *Plant Sci.* 101:91–98

84. Steiner U, Schliemann W, Boehm H, Strack D. 1999. Tyrosinase involved in betalain biosynthesis of higher plants. *Planta* 208:114–24

85. Stintzing FC, Conrad J, Klaiber I, Beifuss U, Carle R. 2004. Structural investigations on betacyanin pigments by LC NMR and 2D NMR spectroscopy. *Phytochemistry* 65:415–22

86. Strack D, Vogt T, Schliemann W. 2003. Recent advances in betalain research. *Phytochemistry* 62:247–69

87. Tanaka Y, Katsumoto Y, Brugliera F, Mason J. 2005. Genetic engineering in floriculture. *Plant Cell Tiss. Org. Cult.* 80:1–24

88. Taylor LP, Grotewold E. 2005. Flavonoids as developmental regulators. *Curr. Opin. Plant Biol.* 8:317–23

89. Tian L, Magallanes-Lundback M, Musetti V, DellaPenna D. 2003. Functional analysis of beta- and epsilon-ring carotenoid hydroxylases in *Arabidopsis. Plant Cell* 15:1320–32

89a. Tohge T, Nishiyama Y, Hirai MY, Yano M, Nakajima J, et al. 2005. Functional genomics by integrated analysis of metabolome and transcriptome of Arabidopsis plants over-expressing an MYB transcription factor. *Plant J.* 42:218–35

90. van Wijk AA, Spaans A, Uzunbajakava N, Otto C, de Groot HJ, et al. 2005. Spectroscopy and quantum chemical modeling reveal a predominant contribution of excitonic interactions to the bathochromic shift in alpha-crustacyanin, the blue carotenoprotein in the carapace of the lobster *Homarus gammarus. J. Am. Chem. Soc.* 127:1438–45

91. Vogt T. 2002. Substrate specificity and sequence analysis define a polyphyletic origin of betanidin 5- and 6-*O*-glucosyltransferase from *Dorotheanthus bellidiformis. Planta* 214:492–95

92. Vogt T, Grimm R, Strack D. 1999. Cloning and expression of a cDNA encoding betanidin 5-*O*-glucosyltransferase, a betanidin- and flavonoid-specific enzyme with high homology to inducible glucosyltransferases from the Solanaceae. *Plant J.* 19:509–19

93. Waddington KD. 2001. Subjective evaluation and choices behavior by nectar- and pollen-collecting bees. In *Cognitive Ecology of Pollination: Animal Behavior and Evolution*, ed. L Chittka, JD Thomson, pp. 41–60. Cambridge, UK: Cambridge Univ. Press

94. Walker AR, Davison PA, Bolognesi-Winfield AC, James CM, Srinivasan N, et al. 1999. The *TRANSPARENT TESTA GLABRA1* locus, which regulates trichome differentiation

This study opens fundamental questions regarding the possibility that pigment biosynthetic enzymes have other functions in the nucleus.

This is the first evidence that the regulators of a metabolic pathway may also play a role in providing the proper conditions for storing the resulting pigments.

and anthocyanin biosynthesis in Arabidopsis, encodes a WD40 repeat protein. *Plant Cell* 11:1337–49

95. Weiss D. 2000. Regulation of flower pigmentation and growth: multiple signaling pathways control anthocyanin synthesis in expanding petals. *Physiol. Plant.* 110:152–57

96. Weiss MR. 1991. Floral colour changes as cues for pollinators. *Nature* 354:227–29

97. Weiss MR. 1995. Floral color change: a widespread functional convergence. *Am. J. Bot.* 82:167–85

98. Wilmouth RC, Turnbull JJ, Welford RW, Clifton IJ, Prescott AG, Schofield CJ. 2002. Structure and mechanism of anthocyanidin synthase from *Arabidopsis thaliana*. *Structure (Cambridge)* 10:93–103

99. Winkel BSJ. 2004. Metabolic channeling in plants. *Annu. Rev. Plant Biol.* 55:85–107

100. Winkel BSJ. 1999. Evidence of enzyme complexes in the phenylpropanoid and flavonoid pathways. *Physiol. Plant.* 107:142–49

101. Winkel BSJ. 2001. Flavonoid biosynthesis. A colorful model for genetics, biochemistry, cell biology and biotechnology. *Plant Physiol.* 126:485–93

102. Winkel BSJ. 2001. It takes a garden. How work on diverse plant species has contributed to an understanding of flavonoid metabolism. *Plant Physiol* 127:1399–404

103. Wurtzel ET. 2004. Genomics, genetics, and biochemistry of maize carotenoid biosynthesis. In *Recent Advances in Phytochemistry*, ed. J Romeo, pp. 85–110. Oxford, UK: Elsevier

104. Wyler H, Meuer U, Bauer J, Stravs-Mombelli L. 1984. Cyclo-dopa glucoside and its occurrence in red beet (*Beta vulgaris* var. *rubra* L.). *Helv. Chim. Acta* 67:1348–55

105. Xie D, Sharma S, Paiva N, Ferreira D, Dixon R. 2003. Role of anthocyanidin reductase, encoded by *BANYULS* in plant flavonoid biosynthesis. *Science* 299:396–99

106. Xu W, Moriya K, Yamada K, Nishimura M, Shioiri H, et al. 2000. Detection and characterization of a 36-kDa peptide in C-terminal region of a 24-kDa vacuolar protein (VP24) precursor in anthocyanin-producing sweet potato cells in suspension culture. *Plant Sci.* 160:121–28

This study provides evidence for an unexpected link between the biosynthesis of anthocyanins and condensed tannins (proanthocyanidins).

Transcriptional Regulatory Networks in Cellular Responses and Tolerance to Dehydration and Cold Stresses

Kazuko Yamaguchi-Shinozaki[1,2,4] and Kazuo Shinozaki[3,4]

[1] Laboratory of Plant Molecular Physiology, Graduate School of Agricultural and Life Sciences, University of Tokyo, Tokyo 113-8657, Japan; email: akys@mail.ecc.u-tokyo.ac.jp

[2] Biological Resources Division, Japan International Research Center for Agricultural Sciences (JIRCAS), Ibaraki 305-8686, Japan

[3] RIKEN Plant Science Center, Yokohama 203-0045, Japan

[4] CREST, Japan Science and Technology Corporation (JST), Japan

Annu. Rev. Plant Biol. 2006. 57:781–803

The *Annual Review of Plant Biology* is online at plant.annualreviews.org

doi: 10.1146/ annurev.arplant.57.032905.105444

First published online as a Review in Advance on March 3, 2006

1543-5008/06/0602-0781$20.00

Key Words

gene expression, *cis*-element, transcription factor, stress tolerance

Abstract

Plant growth and productivity are greatly affected by environmental stresses such as drought, high salinity, and low temperature. Expression of a variety of genes is induced by these stresses in various plants. The products of these genes function not only in stress tolerance but also in stress response. In the signal transduction network from perception of stress signals to stress-responsive gene expression, various transcription factors and *cis*-acting elements in the stress-responsive promoters function for plant adaptation to environmental stresses. Recent progress has been made in analyzing the complex cascades of gene expression in drought and cold stress responses, especially in identifying specificity and cross talk in stress signaling. In this review article, we highlight transcriptional regulation of gene expression in response to drought and cold stresses, with particular emphasis on the role of transcription factors and *cis*-acting elements in stress-inducible promoters.

Contents

INTRODUCTION

Drought, high salinity, and low temperature are all environmental conditions that have an adverse effect on the growth of plants and the productivity of crops. Plants have adapted to respond to these stresses at the molecular and cellular levels as well as at the physiological and biochemical levels, thus enabling them to survive. Expression of a variety of genes is induced by these stresses in various plants (39, 103, 114). The products of these genes function not only in stress tolerance but also in the regulation of gene expression and signal transduction in stress responses (5, 104, 125).

Abscisic acid (ABA) is produced under water-deficit conditions and plays an impor-tant role in the tolerance response of plants to drought and high salinity. Exogenous application of ABA also induces a number of genes that respond to dehydration and cold stress (104, 136). Nevertheless, the role of ABA in cold stress-responsive gene expression is not clear. Several reports have described genes that are induced by dehydration and cold stresses but that do not respond to exogenous ABA treatment (104, 132, 136). This suggests the existence of ABA-independent, as well as ABA-dependent, signal transduction cascades between the initial stress signal and the expression of specific genes. The molecular mechanisms regulating gene expression in response to dehydration and cold stresses have been studied by analyzing the *cis-* and *trans-*acting elements that function in ABA-independent and ABA-responsive gene expression during the stresses in *Arabidopsis* (104, 132).

In this review article, we focus on transcriptional regulation of gene expression in response to dehydration and cold stresses, with particular emphasis on the role of transcription factors and *cis-*acting elements in stress-inducible promoters. The signal transduction pathways controlling abiotic stress responses are very complex, and many excellent review articles in this area were recently published (5, 9, 15, 126).

FUNCTION OF OSMOTIC- AND COLD-INDUCIBLE GENES

Transcriptome analysis using microarray technology is a powerful technique, which has proven very useful for discovering many stress-inducible genes involved in stress response and tolerance (96, 104). Numerous genes that are induced by various abiotic stresses have been identified using various microarray systems (12, 22, 52, 62, 72, 87, 93, 94, 121). Recently, more stress-inducible genes were identified using the Affimetrix 22K Gene Chip ATH1, and the data obtained are now avilable from TAIR URL (**http://www.arabidopsis.org/**).

Genes induced during stress conditions function not only in protecting cells from stress by producing important metabolic proteins, but also in regulating genes for signal transduction in the stress response. Thus, these gene products are classified into two groups (22, 62, 94). The first group includes proteins that probably function in stress tolerance, such as chaperones, LEA (late embryogenesis abundant) proteins, osmotin, antifreeze proteins, mRNA-binding proteins, key enzymes for osmolyte biosynthesis such as proline, water channel proteins, sugar and proline transporters, detoxification enzymes, enzymes for fatty acid metabolism, proteinase inhibitors, ferritin, and lipid-transfer proteins. Some of these stress-inducible genes that encode proteins, such as key enzymes for osmolyte biosynthesis, LEA proteins, and detoxification enzymes have been overexpressed in transgenic plants and produce stress-tolerant phenotypes in the transgenic plants (19, 36). These results indicate that the gene products of the stress-inducible genes really function in stress tolerance.

The second group contained protein factors involved in further regulation of signal transduction and gene expression that probably function in stress response. They included various transcription factors, suggesting that various transcriptional regulatory mechanisms function in the drought-, cold-, or high-salinity-stress signal transduction pathways (95). These transcription factors could regulate various stress-inducible genes cooperatively or separately, and may constitute gene networks. Functional analysis of these stress-inducible transcription factors should provide more information on the complex regulatory gene networks that are involved in responses to drought, cold, and high-salinity stresses. The others were proteins kinases, protein phosphatases, enzymes involved in phospholipids metabolism, and other signaling molecules such as calmodulin-binding protein and 14-3-3 proteins. At present, the functions of most of these genes are not fully understood. Some of these stress-inducible regulatory genes that encode proteins such as transcription factors have been overexpressed in transgenic plants and generate stress-tolerant phenotypes in the transgenic plants (113, 120, 135).

REGULATION OF GENE EXPRESSION BY OSMOTIC AND COLD STRESSES

The expression patterns of genes induced by drought, high-salinity, and cold stresses in *Arabidopsis* were analyzed by northern blot analyses and recently by microarray and quantitative Polymerase Chain Reaction (PCR)

(22, 62, 94, 121). Through this work more than 300 genes have been identified as being stress-inducible. Among these genes, more than half of the drought-inducible genes are also induced by high salinity, indicating the existence of significant cross talk between the drought and high-salinity responses. By contrast, only 10% of the drought-inducible genes were also induced by cold stress (94).

Results also indicate broad variations in the timing of induction of theses genes and that there are at least two groups showing different expression profiles. In one group gene expression was rapid and transient in response to drought, high-salinity, and cold stresses, reached a maximum at several hours, and then decreased. Most of these genes encode regulatory protein factors such as zinc-finger protein, SOS2-like protein kinase PKS5, bHLH transcription factor, DREB1A, DREB2A, AP2/ERF domain-containing protein RAP2, and growth factor-like protein. In the other group, gene expression slowly and gradually increased after stress treatment within 10 h. Most of these genes encode functional proteins such as LEA proteins, detoxification enzymes, and enzymes for osmoprotectant synthesis. On the other hand, some these stress-inducible genes respond to ABA, whereas others do not. ABA-deficient mutants were used to analyze cold-inducible and drought-inducible genes that respond to ABA (102, 104). Several genes were induced by exogenous ABA treatment, but they were also induced by cold or drought in ABA-deficient (aba) or ABA-insensitive (abi) *Arabidopsis* mutants. These results indicate that there are not only ABA-dependent pathways but also ABA-independent pathways involved in the abiotic stress response (**Figure 1**).

A MAJOR ABA-INDEPENDENT GENE EXPRESSION UNDER OSMOTIC AND COLD STRESSES

The *Arabidipsis RD29A/COR78/LTI78* gene is induced by drought, cold, and ABA. However, this gene is induced in *aba* or *abi* mutants

by both drought and cold stresses, which indicates that it is governed by both ABA-dependent and ABA-independent regulation under drought and cold conditions (130). Analyses of this promoter have shown that a 9-bp conserved sequence, TACCGACAT, named the DRE, is an essential *cis*-element for regulating *RD29A* induction in the ABA-independent response to dehydration and cold (131). DRE is also found in the promoter regions of many drought- and cold-inducible genes (103, 114). Similar *cis*-acting elements, named C-repeat (CRT) and low-temperature-responsive element (LTRE), both containing an A/GCCGAC motif that forms the core of the DRE sequence, regulate cold-inducible promoters (4, 46, 109, 114). The cDNAs encoding DRE-/CRT-binding proteins, *CBF/DREB1* (C-repeat Binding Factor/DRE Binding protein 1), and *DREB2*, were isolated using yeast one-hybrid screening (68, 109). These proteins contained the conserved DNA-binding domain found in the ERF (etheylene-responsive element-binding factor) and AP2 proteins. These proteins specifically bind to the DRE/CRT sequence and activate the transcription of genes driven by the DRE/CRT sequence (**Figure 2**).

In *Arabidopsis*, three genes encoding DREB1/CBF lie in tandem on chromosome 4 in the following order: DREB1B/CBF1, DREB1A/CBF3, and DREB1C/CBF2. There are two DREB2 proteins, DREB2A and DREB2B (25). Expression of the *DREB1/CBF* genes is induced by cold, but not by dehydration and high-salinity stresses (68, 105). By contrast, expression of the *DREB2* genes is induced by dehydration and high-salinity stresses but not by cold stress (68, 79). Later, Sakuma et al. (90) reported three novel *DREB1/CBF*-related genes and six novel *DREB2*-related genes that were not expressed at high levels under various stress conditions. The three DREB1 proteins are probably major transcription factors involved in cold-induced gene expression and the DREB2A and DREB2B proteins are involved

Time course

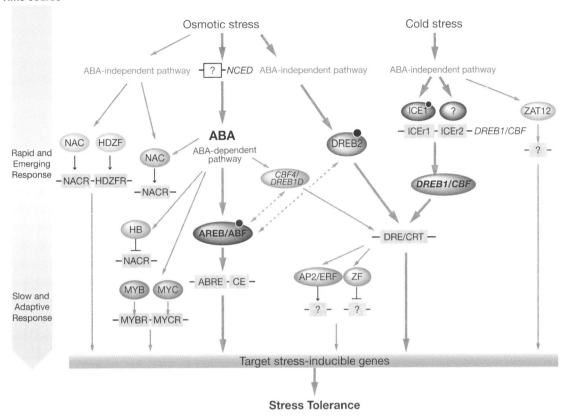

Figure 1

Transcriptional regulatory networks of *cis*-acting elements and transcription factors involved in osmotic- and cold-stress-responsive gene expression in *Arabidopsis*. Transcription factors controlling stress-inducible gene expression are shown in colored ellipses. *cis*-acting elements involved in stress-responsive transcription are shown in boxes. Small filled circles reveal modification of transcription factors in response to stress signals for their activation, such as phosphorylation. Regulatory cascade of stress-responsive gene expression is shown from top to bottom. Early and emergency responses of gene expression are shown in the upper part, and late and adaptive responses in the bottom. Thick gray arrows indicate the major signaling pathways and these pathways regulate many downstream genes. Broken arrows indicate protein-protein interactions.

in high-salinity- and drought-induced gene expression. However, the expression of one of the *CBF/DREB1* genes, *CBF4/DREB1D*, is induced by osmotic stress (31) and the other two CBF/DREB1 genes, DDF1/DREB1F and DDF2/DREB1E, are induced by high-salinity stress (71), suggesting the existence of cross talk between the CBF/DREB1 and the DREB2 pathways.

DREB1/CBFs: Major Transcription Factors that Regulate Many Cold-Inducible Genes Involved in Stress Tolerance

Transgenic *Arabidopsis* plants overexpressing *CBF1/DREB1B* under control of the cauliflower mosaic virus (CaMV) 35S promoter showed a high tolerance to freezing stress (44). Overexpression of the

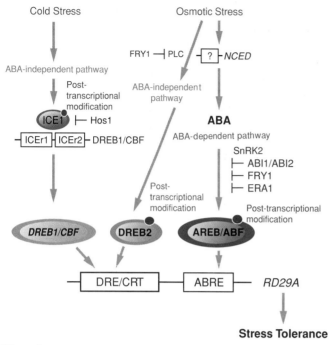

Figure 2

A model of the induction of the *RD29A/cor78/lti78* gene. The *RD29* gene contains both ABRE and DRE/DRT *cis* elements in its promoter. Two different DRE/CRT-binding proteins, DREB1/CBF and DREB2, distinguish two different signal transduction pathways in response to cold and drought stresses, respectively (68). A transcriptional activator, ICE1 (Inducer of CBF Expression 1), functions upstream of the DRE/DREB regulon (14). HOS1 functions as a negative regulator of ICE1 (64). FRY1 functions as a negative regulator of drought, cold, and ABA responses (124). SnRK2 is involved in ABA signaling. ABI1, ABI2, and ERA1 function as negative regulators for ABA signaling.

drate metabolism-related proteins, LEA proteins, KIN (cold-inducible) proteins, osmoprotectant biosynthesis protein, and protease inhibitors, function against stresses and are probably responsible for the stress tolerance of the transgenic plants. The downstream genes also included genes for transcription factors such as C2H2 zinc-finger-type and AP2/ERF-type transcription factors, suggesting the existence of further regulation of gene expression downstream of the DRE/DREB regulon (72, 89). The product of one such downstream gene, *STZ*, functions as a transcriptional repressor, and its overexpression retards growth and induces tolerance to drought stress (89). The target downregulated genes of STZ might promote plant tolerance and inhibit plant growth under stress conditions. Conserved sequences in the promoter regions of the genes directly downstream of *DREB1A* were analyzed, and A/GCCGACNT was found in their promoter regions between –51 and –450 as a consensus DRE (72). The recombinant DREB1A/CBF3 protein bound to A/GCCGACNT more efficiently than to A/GCCGACNA/G/C. Thus, analysis of promoter regions of direct target genes of a transcription factor allows the accurate elucidation of a *cis*-acting element that functions in plants.

Recently, Vogel et al. (121) reported analysis of the upregulated and downregulated genes of CBF2/DREB1C using the Affymetrix GeneChip containing probe sets for approximately 24,000 *Arabidopsis* genes. This analysis revealed that the CBF2/DREB1A-regulated genes included a significant portion (28%) of these cold-induced genes. Additionally, the changes that occur in the *Arabidopsis* metabolome in response to cold were examined and the role of the CBF/DREB1 cold-response pathway were assessed (18). When the metabolite profiles for nonacclimated and cold-acclimated wild-type plants were compared with nonacclimated CBF3/DREB1C overexpression plants and the data were subjected to hierarchical clustering, the results indicated

DREB1A/CBF3 under the control of the CaMV 35S promoter also increased the tolerance to drought, high-salinity, and freezing stresses (28, 50, 68). These transgenic plants also caused growth retardation under normal growth conditions. Use of the stress-inducible *RD29A* promoter instead of the constitutive CaMV 35S promoter for the overexpression of DREB1A/CBF3 minimizes the negative effects on plant growth (50).

More than 40 genes downstream of DREB1/CBF have been identified through the use of both cDNA and GeneChip microarrays (22, 72, 94, 121). Many of their protein products, such as RNA-binding proteins, sugar transport proteins, desaturase, carbohy-

that the metabolome of the nonacclimated CBF3/DREB1C overexpressor was more similar to that of cold-acclimated than to that of nonacclimated wild-type plants. Thus, DREB1/CBF regulates many stress-inducible genes and has a prominent role in the cold-responsive gene expression in *Arabidopsis*.

The DREB/DRE Regulons in Plants Other Than *Arabidopsis*

DRE/CRT functions in gene expression in response to stress in tobacco plants, which suggests the existence of similar regulatory systems in tobacco and other crop plants (131). The DRE/CRT-related motifs have been reported in the promoter region of cold-inducible *Brassica napus* and wheat genes (46, 84). However, the orthologous genes of DREB1/CBF have been isolated in many plant species such as wheat, *B. napus*, rice, barley, maize, and cherry (17, 20, 26, 43, 54, 86, 100, 101, 119, 128). Overexpression of the *Arabidopsis DREB1/CBF* genes in transgenic *B. Napus* or tobacco plants induced expression of orthologs of *Arabidopsis* CBF/DREB1-targeted genes and increased the freezing and drought tolerance of transgenic plants (43, 51). Constitutive overexpression of CBF1/DREB1B in transgenic tomato increased drought, chilling, and oxidative stress tolerance (37, 38, 135).

In rice, four DREB1/CBF homologous-genes and one DREB2 homologous gene, OsDREB1A, OsDREB1B, OsDREB1C and OsDREB1D, and OsDREB2A, respectively, have been isolated (20). Overexpression of OsDREB1A in transgenic *Arabidopsis* resulted in improved high-salinity and freezing stress tolerance. A DREB1/CBF-type transcription factor, ZmDREB1A, was also identified in maize (86). The ZmDREB1A protein was shown to be involved in cold-responsive gene expression, and the overexpression of this gene in *Arabidopsis* resulted in improved stress tolerance to drought and freezing. These transgenic plants also showed growth retardation. These results

indicate that similar regulatory systems are conserved in monocots as well as dicots. Pellegrineschi et al. (85) showed that overexpression of DREB1A/CBF3 driven by the stress-inducible *RD29A* promoter in transgenic wheat improved drought stress tolerance. Oh et al. (82) reported that constitutive overexpression of DREB1A using the 35S promoter in transgenic rice resulted in increased stress tolerance to drought and high salinity. These observations suggest that the DRE/DREB regulon can be used to improve the tolerance of various kinds of agriculturally important crop plants to drought, high-salinity, and freezing stresses by gene transfer.

Cis-Acting Regulatory Elements and Transcription Factors that Function Upstream of CBF3/DREB1A

A gene for a transcription factor, Inducer of CBF Expression 1 (ICE1), was identified through the map-based cloning of the *Arabidopsis ice1* mutation. The *ice1* mutation affects the expression of the *CBF3/DREB1A* promoter::*LUC* transgene (14). *ICE1* encodes a MYC-like bHLH protein that regulates the expression of *CBF3/DREB1A* but not that of other *CBF/DREB1* genes, indicting that there are different expression mechanisms among the three *CBF/DREB1* genes. Molecular analysis of the *DREB1C/CBF2* promoter identified multiple *cis*-acting elements involved in cold-responsive gene expression (105, 134; Y. Imura, unpublished information). Zarka et al. (134) reported two promoter sequences, designated *ICEr1* and *ICEr2*, that function cooperatively to induce gene expression under cold conditions. *ICEr1* contains the sequence CACATG, which includes a consensus recognition site for bHLH proteins, CANNTG (73). Therefore, *ICEr1* is a potential binding site for the ICE1 protein. However, ICE1 does not regulate the expression of *CBF2/DREB1C*. Thus, the transcription factors that bind to these *cis*-acting elements remain to be identified. A DNA-binding protein that interacts with

ICEr1 of the DREB1C/CBF promoter has been isolated using yeast one-hybrid screening and shown to be a MYC-like bHLH protein that is different from ICE1 (Y. Imura, unpublished information). These results suggest the redundant involvement of MYC-type bHLH transcription factors in the cold-responsive expression of DREB1/CBF genes.

Novillo et al. (81) reported that the *cbf2* mutant, in which the CBF2/DREB1C gene has been disrupted, has higher capacity to tolerate freezing, dehydration, and salt stresses. They found that CBF/DREB1-regulated genes showed stronger and more sustained expression in the *cbf2* plants, which results from increased expression of CBF1/DREB1B and CBF3/DREB1A in the mutant. Thus, CBF2/DREB1C functions as a negative regulator of *CBF1/DREB1B* and *CBF3/DREB1A* expression in *Arabidopsis*, indicating complex regulation of *DREB1/CBF* gene expression.

The DREB2 Proteins Function in Osmotic Stress-Responsive Gene Expression

The DREB2A protein has a conserved ERF/AP2 DNA-binding domain and recognizes the DRE sequence like DREB1A (68). Among the eight DREB2-type proteins, DREB2A and DREB2B are major transcription factors that function under dehydration and high-salinity stress conditions (79, 90). However, overexpression of DREB2A in transgenic plants neither caused growth retardation nor improved stress tolerance, suggesting that the DREB2A protein requires post-translational modification such as phosphorylation for its activation (68). Nevertheless, the activation mechanism of the DREB2A protein has not yet been elucidated. Domain analysis of DREB2A using *Arabidopsis* protoplasts revealed that a negative regulatory domain exists in the central region of DREB2A and deletion of this region transforms DREB2A to a constitutive active form. Overexpression of the constitutive active form of DREB2A resulted in growth

retardation in transgenic *Arabidopsis* plants. These transgenic plants revealed significant tolerance to drought stress but only slight tolerance to freezing. Microarray analyses of the transgenic plants revealed that DREB2A regulates expression of many dehydration-inducible genes. However, some genes downstream of DREB2A are not downstream of DREB1A, which also recognizes DRE/CRT but functions in cold-stress-responsive gene expression (Y. Sakuma, unpublished information). The genes downstream of DREB2A play an important role in drought stress tolerance, but alone are not sufficient to withstand freezing stress.

OTHER ABA-INDEPENDENT GENE EXPRESSION UNDER OSMOTIC AND COLD STRESSES

There are several dehydration-inducible genes that do not respond to either cold or ABA treatment, suggesting the existence of another ABA-independent pathway in the dehydration stress response. These genes include early response to dehydration1 (*ERD1*), which encodes a Clp protease regulatory subunit, ClpD (78). *ERD1* is not only induced by dehydration, but also upregulated during natural senescence and dark-induced senescence (106). Promoter analysis of *ERD1* in transgenic plants indicates that the *cis*-acting elements responsible for gene expression during dehydration and etiolation are separately located in two discrete portions of the *ERD1* promoter. Moreover, two different novel *cis*-acting elements, a MYC-like sequence (CATGTG) and a 14-bp *rps1* site 1-like sequence, are involved in induction by dehydration stress (106). Recently, three cDNAs encoding MYC-like sequence-binding proteins—ANAC019, ANAC055, and ANAC072—were isolated by the yeast one-hybrid screening method (115). Microarray analysis of transgenic plants overexpressing either *ANAC019*, *ANAC055*, or *ANAC072* revealed that several stress-inducible genes were upregulated in the transgenic plants, and the plants showed significantly increased drought tolerance. However, *ERD1* was not upregulated in the transgenic plants. cDNAs for the transcription factor that binds to the 14-bp *rps1* site 1-like sequence was isolated by using one-hybrid screening. These cDNAs encoded zinc-finger homeodomain (ZFHD) proteins and one of these genes, ZFHD1, was shown to function as a transcriptional activator in response to dehydration stress (L.-S. P. Tran, unpublished information). Overproduction of both the NAC and ZFHD proteins increased expression of *ERD1*, indicating that both *cis*-acting elements are necessary for expression of *ERD1*. The NAC proteins function as transcription activators in cooperation with the ZFHD proteins or alone.

Several genes for transcription factors are also induced under cold conditions. One such gene, *ZAT12*, was overexpressed under the control of the CaMV 35S promoter in transgenic *Arabidopsis* plants, and upregulated genes in the plants were analyzed using microarray. More than 20 cold-inducible genes were upregulated in the transgenic plants and these transgenic plants showed a small, but reproducible, increase in freezing tolerance, indicating that ZAT12 functions in cold-responsive gene expression and plays an important role in cold acclimation (121).

A MAJOR ABA-RESPONSIVE GENE EXPRESSION UNDER OSMOTIC STRESSES

ABA plays an important role in the adaptation of vegetative tissues to abiotic stresses such as drought and high salinity, as well as in seed maturation and dormancy (11, 104). ABA promotes stomatal closure in guard cells, mediating by solute efflux, and regulates the expression of many genes that may function in dehydration tolerance in both vegetative tissues and seeds (33). Many ABA-inducible genes contain a conserved, ABA-responsive, *cis*-acting element named ABRE (ABA-responsive element; PyACGTGGC) in

their promoter regions. The ABRE functions as a *cis*-acting DNA element involved in ABA-regulated gene expression. This sequence was first identified in the wheat *Em* gene, which functions mainly in seeds during late embryogenesis (30), and in the rice *RAB16* gene, which is expressed in both dehydrated vegetative tissues and maturating seeds (76). ABRE is a major *cis*-acting element in ABA-responsive gene expression.

However, a number of environmentally induced genes other than ABA contain a similar conserved *cis*-acting element called the G-box (CACGTGGC) (74). Deletion and mutational analyses of promoters responsive to light, UV radiation, and coumaric acid have also shown that disruption of the G-box compromises the ability of each promoter to respond to its respective stimulus. All of these promoters require at least one *cis*-acting element in addition to the G-box for appropriate transcriptional activation. For ABA-responsive transcription, a single copy of ABRE is not sufficient. ABRE and coupling elements such as CE1 and CE3 constitute an ABA-responsive complex in the regulation of wheat *HVA1* and *HVA22* genes (98, 99). Two ABRE sequences are necessary for the expression of *Arabidopsis RD29B* in seeds and for the ABA-responsive expression of *RD29B* in vegetative tissue (117). One of these ABRE sequences might function as a coupling element. Most of the known coupling elements have similarity with ABREs and contain an A/GCGT motif (35). Either additional copies of the ABRE or coupling elements are necessary for ABA-responsive gene expression.

Arabidopsis cDNAs encoding the bZIP transcription factors referred to as ABRE-binding (AREB) proteins or ABRE-binding factors (ABFs) were isolated using the yeast one-hybrid screening method (16, 117). Among these AREB/ABF proteins, expression of AREB1/ABF2, AREB2/ABF4, and ABF3 was upregulated by ABA, dehydration, and high-salinity stresses. They function as *trans*-acting activators through transient expression studies in protoplasts (117). Their activities were reduced in the ABA-deficient *aba2* mutant and in the ABA-insensitive *abi1* mutant, but were enhanced in the ABA-hypersensitive *era1* mutant (60, 61, 117). In the *Arabidopsis* genome, 75 distinct bZIP transcription factors exist and 13 members are classified as a homologous subfamily of AREBs that contain three N-terminal (C1, C2, C3) and one C-terminal (C4) conserved domains (6, 45, 111). Most of the AREB subfamily proteins are involved in ABA-responsive signal transduction pathways in vegetative tissues or seeds (16, 21, 69, 117). *Arabidopsis AREB1/ABF2, AREB2/ABF4*, and *ABF3* were mainly expressed in vegetative tissues but not in seeds (16, 117), whereas *Arabidopsis ABI5* and *EEL* were expressed during seed maturation and/or germination (6, 21, 69). Rice homolog TRAB1 and barley homolog HvABI5 also activate ABA-responsive gene expression in seeds (13, 34). It is possible that redundancy and tissue-specific expression of these genes may be important for their function.

Kang et al. (49) reported that overexpression of ABF3 and ABF4/AREB2 resulted in ABA-hypersensitive phenotypes in germination and seedling growth stages in *Arabidopsis*. These transgenic plants also showed improvement of drought stress tolerance and the expression of some ABA-responsive genes, such as LEA class genes (*RD29B, rab18*), cell cycle regulator genes (*ICK1*), and protein phosphatase 2C genes (*ABI1* and *ABI2*), suggesting that AREB/ABF proteins are involved in ABA response and stress tolerance in plants. Moreover, ABF2/AREB1 was shown to be an essential component of glucose signaling, and its overexpression also improved stress tolerance to drought (53). However, AREB1/ABF2 and AREB2/ABF4 require ABA for their maximum activation, as shown by their low transactivation abilities in protoplasts prepared from the ABA-deficient *aba2* mutant (117). ABA-responsive 42-kDa kinase activities phosphorylate conserved regions of AREB/ABFs, which suggests that ABA-dependent phosphorylation may be in-

volved in activation of the AREB subfamily proteins (117). In rice, TRAB1 was also shown to be phosphorylated rapidly in response to ABA (48).

Phosphorylation-/dephosphorylation-regulated events play important roles in ABA signaling. Several type-2 SNF1-related protein kinases (SnRK2-type) such as AAPK (ABA activated protein kinase) in *Vicia faba* (67) and OST1/SRK2E in *Arabidopsis* (77, 133) were reported as ABA-activated protein kinases, and were shown to mediate the regulation of stomatal aperture and function upstream of ABA-responsive expression. In *Arabidopsis*, 9 of 10 SnRK2 are activated by hyperosmolarity and 5 of the 9 SnRK2 are activated by ABA (8). Recently, ABA-activated SnRK2 protein kinases were shown to phosphorylate the conserved regions of AREB/ABFs (25). These kinases might phosphorylate and activate the AREB/ABF-type proteins in *Arabidopsis*. In rice, 10 SnRK2 protein kinases were reported. All family members are activated by hyperosmotic stress and three of them are also activated by ABA (57). These rice ABA-activated SnRK2 can phosphorylate an ABRE-binding factor TRAB1 (58). Dominant negative mutations of both *ABI1* and *ABI2* encoding type 2C protein phosphatase cause the ABA-insensitive mutants *abi1* and *abi2* (65, 66, 75). Because null mutations of ABI1 and ABI2 resulted in ABA hypersensitivity, ABI1 and ABI2 are thought to negatively regulate ABA-dependent responses (29).

Overexpression of AREB1/ABF2 in transgenic plants is not sufficient to activate its downstream genes such as *RD29B*. Domain analysis of AREB1 using *Arabidopsis* protoplasts revealed that an activation domain exists in the N-terminal region of AREB1. To overcome the masked transactivation activity of AREB1, a constitutive active form of AREB1 was created using the N-terminal activation and bZIP DNA-binding domains. Transgenic *Arabidopsis* plants overexpressing the active form of AREB1 showed ABA hypersensitivity and enhanced drought tolerance, and eight genes in two groups were upregulated: LEA-class genes and ABA- and dehydration-stress-inducible regulatory genes such as linker histone H1 and AAA ATPase. In the promoter region of each gene, two or more ABRE motifs were found. By contrast, an *areb1* null mutant and a dominant loss-of-function mutant of AREB1 with a repression domain exhibited ABA insensitivity and some of the upregulated genes were downregulated (24). Thus, AREBs/ABFs regulate ABA-mediated ABRE-dependent gene expression that enhances drought tolerance in vegetative tissues, and phosphorylation/dephosphorylation plays an important role in the activation of the AREB/ABF proteins.

OTHER TYPES OF ABA-DEPENDENT GENE EXPRESSION UNDER DEHYDRATION STRESS

ABRE-like motifs are not involved in the ABA regulation of some stress-inducible genes such as *RD22*. Induction of the dehydration-inducible *RD22* is mediated by ABA and requires protein biosynthesis for its ABA-dependent expression (1). MYC and MYB recognition sites in the *RD22* promoter function as *cis*-acting elements in the dehydration-inducible expression of *RD22* (2). A MYC transcription factor, AtMYC2 (rd22BP1), and a MYB transcription factor, AtMYB2, bind these *cis*-elements in the *RD22* promoter and cooperatively activate the expression of *RD22*. These two transcription factors are synthesized after the accumulation of endogenous ABA, indicating that they play roles in a late stage of the plant's response to different stresses. Transgenic plants overproducing MYC and MYB had higher sensitivity to ABA and revealed osmotic stress tolerance (2). Microarray analysis of the transgenic plants indicated the presence of several target genes such as ABA-inducible genes, including an *AtADH* gene, and jasmonic-acid (JA)-inducible genes (2). By contrast, an At-MYC2 mutant was less sensitive to ABA and

showed significantly decreased ABA-induced gene expression of *RD22* and *AtADH1*. Recently, AtMYC2 was also reported as a transcription factor that functions in JA and JA-ethylene-regulated defense responses in *Arabidopsis* (3, 7, 70). Cross talk occurs on AtMYC2 between ABA- and JA-responsive gene expression at the MYC recognition sites in the promoters. In addition, genetic analysis of *AtMYC2* suggests that it acts as a negative regulator of blue-light-mediated photomorphogenic growth (129). AtMYC2 might be a common transcription factor of ABA, JA, and light-signaling pathways in *Arabidopsis*.

Arabidopsis RD26 encodes a NAC protein and is induced not only by dehydration but also by ABA. Transgenic plants overexpressing *RD26* were highly sensitive to ABA, whereas *RD26*-repressed plants were insensitive (23). Microarray analysis showed that ABA- and stress-inducible genes were upregulated in *RD26*-overexpressing plants and repressed in *RD26*-repressed plants, indicating that a *cis*-regulatory factor, the NAC recognition site, may function in ABA-dependent gene expression under stress conditions.

The homeodomain-containing transcription factor ATHB6 binds to an AT-rich *cis*-acting element CAATTATTG and interacts with ABI1. The interaction between ATHB6 and ABI1 is positively correlated with the PP2C activity of the ABI1 catalytic domain. Transgenic *Arabidopsis* plants that constitutively express *ATHB6* revealed ABA insensitivity in a subset of ABI1-dependent responses. Thus, ATHB6 functions as a negative regulator downstream of ABI1 in the ABA signal transduction pathway (32). AtERF7 binds to a *cis*-acting element, a GCC-box, and acts as a repressor of GCC-box-mediated transcription. AtERF7 interacts with the protein kinase PKS3, which is a global regulator of ABA responses and can be phsphorylated by PKS3. Overexpression of *AtERF7* in transgenic *Arabidopsis* plants reduced ABA responses in guard cells and decreased drought tolerance, whereas reductions in *AtERF7* expression caused ABA hypersensitivity in guard cells, seed germination, and seedling growth. AtERF7 may bind to the GCC-box of ABA-induced genes and repress further gene expression. The DNA-binding and/or transcriptional repressor activity of AtERF7 may be regulated by PKS3 via phosphorylation (108).

Maize ERF/AP2-type transcription factors DBF1 and DBF2 can bind the DRE/CRT sequence of a maize *rab17* gene. However, these proteins were grouped into a different subfamily from those of DREB1A/CBF and DREB2A. DBF1 was shown to be an activator of the ABA-dependent expression of the *rab17* gene, whereas DBF2 overexpression reduced promoter activity in either control or ABA-induced conditions (55). Various kinds of transcription activators and repressors function in ABA-dependent transcription in plants.

REGULATION OF ABA BIOSYNTHESIS AND DEGRADATION DURING DEHYDRATION AND REHYDRATION

ABA is synthesized de novo during dehydration, and degraded during rehydration after dehydration. Recently, many genes involved in ABA biosynthesis during dehydration were identified based on genetic and molecular approaches, especially in *Arabidopdis* (80). Among them, AtNCED3 for 9-*cis*-epoxycarotenoid dioxygenase (42), AAO3 for abscisic aldehyde oxidase (97), AtABA3 for MoCo sulfurase (123), and AtZEP (121) for zeaxanthin epoxidase are upregulated by dehydration, but AtABA2 is not. NCED is a key enzyme of ABA biosynthesis, and *AtNCED3* is most strongly induced by dehydration and high salinity. Overexpression of *AtNCED3* improved dehydration stress tolerance in transgenic plants and its knockout mutant showed a dehydration-sensitive phenotype (42). This indicates that AtNCED3 must have an important role in ABA accumulation during dehydration. The regulation of *AtNCED3* gene expression is important

in the dehydration-induced biosynthesis of ABA; however, this theory has yet to be fully demonstrated.

ABA is catabolized to inactive form by oxidation or conjugation (80). Recently, a major regulatory step in the oxidative pathway of ABA catabolism was shown to be ABA 8′-hydroxylase, a kind of cytochrome P450, and its gene was determined to be CYP707As (63, 88). CYP707As are strongly induced by exogenous ABA treatment, dehydration, and rehydration. Among the 4 CYP707As, CYP707A3 is the major ABA-catabolizing enzyme and is mainly expressed in vegetative tissues. Its expression is controlled by dehydration/rehydration (63, 116). The expression profile of *CYP707A3* in response to rehydration is very rapid compared with that of the rehydration-inducible gene, proline dehydrogenase ProDH (83, 116). Regulation of *CYP707A3* gene expression may be regulated by a novel regulatory system in response to rehydration.

REGULATION OF GENE EXPRESSION DURING REHYDRATION AFTER DEHYDRATION

Many genes that are regulated during rehydration after dehydration have been identified using microarray analysis (83). These rehydration-inducible genes function in recovery from stress conditions. Among them, gene expression for proline dehydrogenase ProDH has been extensively studied during dehydration and rehydration. ProDH functions in proline catabolism during rehydration. The ProDH promoter has been extensively analyzed to show that ACTCAT is an important *cis*-acting element in rehydration-responsive gene expression (91). Many rehydration-inducible gene promoters contain the ACTCAT motif that functions in rehydration-responsive gene expression (83). Recently, ACTCAT-binding proteins were identified as ATB2-type bZIP transcription factors (ATB2/AtbZIP11,

AtbZIP2, AtbZIP44, and AtbZIP53) based on the binding specificity (92). The ATB2 subgroup of bZIP proteins specifically bind to ACTCAT and transactivate the ACTCAT-containing promoter in transient expression using protoplasts. ATB2 subgroup bZIP transcription factors function in hypoosmolarity-inducible gene expression.

GENETIC ANALYSIS OF SIGNAL TRANSDUCTION IN RESPONSE TO DEHYDRATION AND COLD STRESSES

A unique mutant screening system in transgenic *Arabidopsis* plants using a firefly luciferase reporter gene (*LUC*) under the control of the *RD29A* promoter was developed to screen *Arabidopsis* mutants with altered induction of stress-responsive genes by dehydration, high salinity, cold, and ABA. Using this system, many *Arabidopsis* mutants have been isolated that exhibit altered expression of the *RD29A::LUC* gene at constitutive (*cos*), high (*hos*), or low (*los*) levels in response to various abiotic-stress or ABA treatments (40). The mutated genes function not only upstream of *RD29A* induction in signal transduction pathways but also in post-transcriptional regulation of the activation of the DREB1/CBF, DREB2, and/or AREB/ABF transcription factors.

The occurrence of mutations with differential responses to dehydration, high salinity, cold, and/or ABA reveals complex cross talk among signaling pathways in dehydration, high-salinity, and cold-stress responses, and suggests that stress-signaling pathways are not completely independent. Recently, many genes were identified using map-based cloning such as *fiery1* (*fly1*)/*hos2*, *fry2*, *hos1*, *hos9*, *hos10*, *los1*, *los2*, *los4*, *los5*/*aba3*, *los6*/*aba1*, and *sad1* (126). Some of the products of these genes function directly in the regulation of transcription. The *hos1* mutation causes enhanced induction of the CBF/DREB1 transcription factors by low temperature as well as of their downstream cold-responsive genes

(41). HOS1 encodes a novel protein that contains a RING-finger motif, which may function in the degradation of the ICE protein (14, 64). *Hos1* is ubiquitously expressed in all plant tissues and the HOS1 protein resides in the cytoplasm at normal growth temperatures. However, in response to low-temperature treatments, it accumulates in the nucleus. FRY2/CBL1 functions as a transcriptional repressor and contains a region homologous to the catalytic domain of RNA polymerase II C-terminal domain phosphatases found in yeast and animals (59, 126). FLY2/CPL1 also contains two double-stranded RNA-binding domains that may function in mRNA processing.

The *hos9* mutation occurs in a homeodomain transcription factor gene that affects gene expression and freezing tolerance without changing the expression of *CBF/DREB1* genes. Mutation of *HOS9* also alters several developmental characteristics including growth rate, flowering time, and trichome density. *HOS9* may control freezing tolerance mainly through constitutive pathways separate from the CBF/DREB1 regulon (137). The *hos10* mutants are extremely sensitive to freezing temperatures, completely unable to acclimate to the cold, and hypersensitive to salinity. Induction of *NCED3* (a gene encoding the rate-limiting enzyme in ABA biosynthesis) by dehydration and ABA accumulation are reduced by this mutation. *HOS10* encodes a putative R2R3-type MYB transcription factor that is localized to the nucleus. HOS10 is essential for cold acclimation and may affect dehydration stress tolerance in plants by controlling stress-induced ABA biosynthesis (138).

The *fly 1* mutation results in superinduction of ABA- and stress-responsive genes. FLY1 encodes an inositol polyphosphate 1-phosphatase, which functions in the catabolism of inositol 1, 4, 5-trisphosphate (IP3). *Fly1* mutant plants accumulate more IP3 than do the wild-type plants in both control and ABA-treated plants (124). FLY1 is a general negative regulator that controls cold, osmotic stress, and ABA signal

Table 1 Transcription factors that function in osmotic- and cold-stress-responsive gene expression and their binding sites in the promoter regions of the stress-inducible *Arabidopsis* genes

Transcription factor name	Transcription factor type	*cis* element	Gene	Stress condition	References
DREB1A/CBF3	AP2/ERF	DRE/CRT	*RD29A, Cor15A*	Cold	(27, 68)
DREB1B/CBF1	AP2/ERF	DRE/CRT	*RD29A, Cor15A*	Cold	(68, 108)
DREB1C/CBF2	AP2/ERF	DRE/CRT	*RD29A, Cor15A*	Cold	(27, 68)
CBF4/DREB1D	AP2/ERF	DRE/CRT		Dehydration	(31)
DREB2A	AP2/ERF	DRE	*RD29A*	Dehydration	(68)
DREB2B	AP2/ERF	DRE	*RD29A*	Dehydration	(68)
DDF1/DREB1F	AP2/ERF			High salinity	(71)
DDF2/DREB1E	AP2/ERF			High salinity	(71)
ICE1	bHLH	ICEr1?	*CBF2/DREB1C*	Cold	(14)
ANAC019	NAC	NACR	*ERD1*	Dehydration	(115)
ANAC055	NAC	NACR	*ERD1*	Dehydration	(115)
ANAC072/RD26	NAC	NACR	*ERD1*	Dehydration	(23, 115)
ZFHD1	ZFHD	rps1 site	ERD1	Dehydration	(115)
ZAT12	Zinc finger			Cold	(121)
STZ	Zinc finger			Cold, dehydration	(89)
AREB1/ABF2	bZIP	ABRE	*RD29B*	ABA, dehydration	(16, 117)
AREB2/ABF4	bZIP	ABRE	*RD29B*	ABA, dehydration	(16, 117)
ABF3	bZIP	ABRE		ABA, dehydration	(16)
AtMYB2	MYB	MYBR	*RD22*	ABA, dehydration	(118)
AtMYC2	bHLH	MYCR	*RD22*	ABA, dehydration	(1)
ATHB6	Homeodomain	At rich		ABA	(32, 107)
AtERF7	ERF/AP2	GCC-box		ABA	(108)
ATB2/AtbZIP11	bZIP	ACTCAT	*ProDH*	Rehydration	(92)
AtbZIP2	bZIP	ACTCAT	*ProDH*	Rehydration	(92)
AtbZIP44	bZIP	ACTCAT	*ProDH*	Rehydration	(92)
AtbZIP53	bZIP	ACTCAT	*ProDH*	Rehydration	(92)
HOS9	Homeodomain			Cold	(137)
HOS10	MYB			ABA, dehydration	(138)

transduction, and provides genetic evidence that phosphoinositols play an important role in ABA and stress-related signal transduction in plants (127). Biochemical analysis has shown that phospholipase C functions upstream of *RD29A* expression in osmotic stress signaling (112), which may be negatively regulated by FLY1.

Five freezing-sensitive [sensitivity to freezing (*sfr*)] *Arabidopsis* mutants were isolated on the basis of their inability to survive freezing after cold acclimation and their chromo-some positions were mapped on the *Arabidopsis* genome (122). Among these mutants, sfr6 plants were deficient in the expression of cold-inducible genes such as *KIN1*, *COR15A*, and *LTI78/RD29A* (56). Microarray analysis indicates that the *sfr6* mutation specifically affects the expression of genes containing the DRE/CRT motif under cold and osmotic stress conditions (10). As the expression level of *DREB1/CBF* or *DREB2* is not reduced in this mutant, the failure to express CRT/DRE-regulated genes correctly may involve the interaction of DREB1/CBF and DREB2 transcription factors with the CRT/DRE promoter element (10).

CONCLUSIONS AND FUTURE PERSPECTIVES

Many plant genes are regulated in response to abitoic stresses, such as dehydration and cold, and their gene products function in stress response and tolerance. In the signal transduction network from perception of stress signals to stress-responsive gene expression, various transcription factors and *cis*-acting elements in the stress-responsive promoters function not only as molecular switches for gene expression but also as terminal points of stress signals in the signaling processes (**Figure 1**; **Table 1**). Timing of stress-responsive gene expression is regulated by a combination of transcription factors and *cis*-acting elements in stress-inducible promoters (**Figure 1**). DRE/CRT and ABRE are major *cis*-acting elements in abiotic stress-inducible gene expression. DRE/CRT functions in the early process of stress-responsive gene expression whereas ABRE functions after the accumulation of ABA during dehydration and high-salinity stress response. There are many ABA-inducible transcription factors that function downstream of ABA responses and stress responses. These transcription factors are involved mainly in late and adaptive processes during stress responses.

Different promoter *cis*-acting elements are involved in the cross talk between different stress signals that regulate gene expression. DRE/CRT is a major *cis*-acting element in cold-inducible gene expression. Thus, DRE/CRT functions in cross talk between dehydration/salinity stress response and cold stress response. Combinations of *cis*-acting elements and transcription factors are important to determine cross talk in stress signaling pathways. DRE is one of the coupling elements of ABRE, which results in cross talk at the promoter level between ABA-independent and ABA-dependent pathways.

Abiotic stresses affect plant growth and development, such as flowering time and cell growth. This indicates cross talk between environmental stress signals and plant growth. Plant hormones are involved in these cross talk events. Transcription is important in regulating plant development and environmental interactions, which may be affected by cross talk in transcriptional regulatory networks. Cross talk between signal transduction pathways will be an important subject in the near future.

Negative regulation as well as positive regulation are important for gene expression. The degradation of transcription factor proteins plays an important role in the negative regulation of gene expression. Specific F-box proteins are involved in stabilizing some transcription factors in stress response (64). Recently, RNA interference or mRNA degradation were suggested to function in stress-responsive gene expression (47, 110). Complex regulation of gene expression may cause complex and flexible responses of plants to abiotic stresses.

ACKNOWLEDGMENTS

We thank Dr. Sean Simpson for critical review of the manuscript. Research in our laboratories is supported by the Program for Promotion of Basic Research Activities for Innovative Biosciences (BRAIN), project grants from the Ministry of Agriculture, Forestry and Fisheries, Japan, and Grants-in-Aid from the Ministry of Education, Culture, Sports, Science and Technology of Japan.

LITERATURE CITED

1. Abe H, Yamaguchi-Shinozaki K, Urao T, Iwasaki T, Hosokawa D, et al. 1997. Role of Arabidopsis MYC and MYB homologs in drought- and abscisic acid-regulated gene expression. *Plant Cell* 9:1859–68

2. Abe H, Urao T, Ito T, Seki M, Shinozaki K, et al. 2003. Arabidopsis AtMYC2 (bHLH) and AtMYB2 (MYB) function as transcriptional activators in abscisic acid signaling. *Plant Cell* 15:63–78

3. Anderson JP, Badruzsaufari E, Schenk PM, Manners JM, Desmond OJ, et al. 2004. Antagonistic interaction between abscisic acid and jasmonate-ethylene signaling pathways modulates defense gene expression and disease resistance in Arabidopsis. *Plant Cell* 16:3460–79

4. Baker SS, Wilhelm KS, Thomashow MF. 1994. The 5′-region of *Arabidopsis thaliana cor15a* has *cis*-acting elements that confer cold-, drought- and ABA-regulated gene expression. *Plant Mol. Biol.* 24:701–13

5. Bartels D, Sunkar R. 2005. Drought and salt tolerance in plants. *Crit. Rev. Plant Sci.* 24:23–58

6. Bensmihen S, Rippa S, Lambert G, Jublot D, Pautot V, et al. 2002. The homologous ABI5 and EEL transcription factors function antagonistically to fine-tune gene expression during late embryogenesis. *Plant Cell* 14:1391–403

7. Boter M, Ruiz-Rivero O, Abdeen A, Prat S. 2004. Conserved MYC transcription factors play a key role in jasmonate signaling both in tomato and Arabidopsis. *Genes Dev.* 18:1577–91

8. Boudsocq M, Barbier-Brygoo H, Lauriere C. 2004. Identification of nine sucrose non-fermenting 1-related protein kinases 2 activated by hyperosmotic and saline stresses in *Arabidopsis thaliana*. *J. Biol. Chem.* 279:41758–66

9. Boudsocq M, Lauriere C. 2005. Osmotic signaling in plants: multiple pathways mediated by emerging kinase families. *Plant Physiol.* 138:1185–94

10. Boyce JM, Knight H, Deyholos M, Openshaw MR, Galbraith DW, et al. 2003. The sfr6 mutant of Arabidopsis is defective in transcriptional activation via CBF/DREB1 and DREB2 and shows sensitivity to osmotic stress. *Plant J.* 34:395–406

11. Bray E, Bailey-Serres J, Weretilnyk E. 2000. Responses to abiotic stresses. In *Biochemistry and Molecular Biology of Plants*, ed. BB Buchanan, W Gruissem, RL Jones. pp. 1158–203. Rockville, MD: Amer. Soc. Plant Physiol.

12. Bray EA. 2004. Genes commonly regulated by water-deficit stress in *Arabidopsis thaliana*. *J. Exp. Bot.* 55:2331–41

13. Casaretto J, Ho TH. 2003. The transcription factors HvABI5 and HvVP1 are required for the abscisic acid induction of gene expression in barley aleurone cells. *Plant Cell* 15:271–84

14. Chinnusamy V, Ohta M, Kanrar S, Lee BH, Hong X, et al. 2003. ICE1: a regulator of cold-induced transcriptome and freezing tolerance in *Arabidopsis*. *Gene Dev.* 17:1043–54

15. Chinnusamy V, Schumaker K, Zhu JK. 2004. Molecular genetic perspectives on cross-talk and specificity in abiotic stress signalling in plants. *J. Exp. Bot.* 55:225–36

16. Choi H, Hong J, Ha J, Kang J, Kim SY. 2000. ABFs, a family of ABA-responsive element binding factors. *J. Biol. Chem.* 275:1723–30

17. Choi DW, Rodriguez EM, Close TJ. 2002. Barley *Cbf3* gene identification, expression pattern, and map location. *Plant Physiol.* 129:1781–87

18. Cook D, Fowler S, Fiehn O, Thomashow MF. 2004. A prominent role for the CBF cold response pathway in configuring the low-temperature metabolome of Arabidopsis. *Proc. Natl. Acad. Sci. USA* 101:15243–48

19. Cushman JC, Bohnert HJ. 2000. Genome approaches to plant stress tolerance. *Curr. Opin. Plant Biol.* 3:117–24

20. Dubouzet JG, Sakuma Y, Ito Y, Kasuga M, Dubouzet EG, et al. 2003. OsDREB genes in rice, *Oryza sativa* L., encode transcription activators that function in drought-, high-salt- and cold-responsive gene expression. *Plant J.* 33:751–63

21. Finkelstein RR, Lynch TJ. 2000. The Arabidopsis abscisic acid response gene ABI5 encodes a basic leucine zipper transcription factor. *Plant Cell* 12:599–609

22. Fowler S, Thomashow MF. 2002. Arabidopsis transcriptome profiling indicates that multiple regulatory pathways are activated during cold acclimation in addition to the CBF cold response pathway. *Plant Cell* 14:1675–90

23. Fujita M, Fujita Y, Maruyama K, Seki M, Hiratsu K, et al. 2004. A dehydration-induced NAC protein, RD26, is involved in a novel ABA-dependent stress-signaling pathway. *Plant J.* 39:863–76

24. Fujita Y, Fujita M, Satoh R, Maruyama K, Parvez MM, et al. 2005. AREB1 is a transcription activator of novel ABRE-dependent ABA-signaling that enhances drought stress tolerance in Arabidopsis. *Plant Cell* 17:3470–88

25. Furihata T, Maruyama K, Fujita Y, Umezawa T, Yoshida R, et al. 2006. ABA-dependent multisite phosphorylation regulates the activity of a transcription activator AREB1. *Proc. Natl. Acad. Sci. USA.* 103:1988–93

26. Gao MJ, Allard G, Byass L, Flanagan AM, Singh J. 2002. Regulation and characterization of four CBF transcription factors from *Brassica napus*. *Plant Mol. Biol.* 49:459–71

27. Gilmour SJ, Zarka DG, Stockinger EJ, Salazar MP, Houghton JM, et al. 1998. Low temperature regulation of *Arabidopsis* CBF family of AP2 transcriptional activators as an early step in cold-induced COR gene expression. *Plant J.* 16:433–42

28. Gilmour SJ, Sebolt AM, Salazar MP, Everard JD, Thomashow MF. 2000. Overexpression of the Arabidopsis CBF3 transcriptional activator mimics multiple biochemical changes associated with cold acclimation. *Plant Physiol.* 124:1854–65

29. Gosti F, Beaudoin N, Serizet C, Webb AA, Vartanian N, et al. 1999. ABI1 protein phosphatase 2C is a negative regulator of abscisic acid signaling. *Plant Cell* 11:1897–910

30. Guiltinan MJ, Marcotte WR, Quatrano RS. 1990. A plant leucine zipper protein that recognizes an abscisic acid response element. *Science* 250:267–71

31. Haake V, Cook D, Riechmann JL, Pineda O, Thomashow MF, et al. 2002. Transcription factor CBF4 is a regulator of drought adaptation in Arabidopsis. *Plant Physiol.* 130:639–48

32. Himmelbach A, Hoffmann T, Leube M, Hohener B, Grill E. 2002. Homeodomain protein ATHB6 is a target of the protein phosphatase ABI1 and regulates hormone responses in *Arabidopsis*. *EMBO J.* 21:3029–38

33. Himmelbach A, Yang Y, Grill E. 2003. Relay and control of abscisic acid signaling. *Curr. Opin. Plant Biol.* 6:470–79

34. Hobo T, Kowyama Y, Hattori T. 1999. A bZIP factor, TRAB1, interacts with VP1 and mediates abscisic acid-induced transcription. *Proc. Natl. Acad. Sci. USA* 96:15348–53

35. Hobo T, Asada M, Kowyama Y, Hattori T. 1999. ACGT-containing abscisic acid response element (ABRE) and coupling element 3 (CE3) are functionally equivalent. *Plant J.* 19:679–89

36. Holmberg N, Bulow L. 1998. Improving stress tolerance in plants by gene transfer. *Trends Plant Sci.* 3:61–66

37. Hsieh TH, Lee JT, Yang PT, Chiu LH, Charng YY, et al. 2002. Heterology expression of the Arabidopsis C-repeat/dehydration response element binding factor 1 gene confers elevated tolerance to chilling and oxidative stresses in transgenic tomato. *Plant Physiol.* 129:1086–94

38. Hsieh TH, Lee JT, Charng YY, Chan MT. 2002. Tomato plants ectopically expressing Arabidopsis CBF1 show enhanced resistance to water deficit stress. *Plant Physiol.* 130:618–26

39. Ingram J, Bartels D. 1996. The molecular basis of dehydration tolerance in plants. *Annu. Rev. Plant Physiol. Plant Mol. Biol.* 47:377–403

40. Ishitani M, Xiong L, Stevenson B, Zhu JK. 1997. Genetic analysis of osmotic and cold stress signal transduction in Arabidopsis: interactions and convergence of abscisic acid-dependent and abscisic acid-independent pathways. *Plant Cell* 9:1935–49

41. Ishitani M, Xiong L, Lee H, Stevenson B, Zhu JK. 1998. HOS1, a genetic locus involved in cold-responsive gene expression in Arabidopsis. *Plant Cell* 10:1151–61

42. Iuchi S, Kobayashi M, Taji T, Naramoto M, Seki M, et al. 2001. Regulation of drought tolerance by gene manipulation of 9-*cis*-epoxycarotenoid dioxygenase, a key enzyme in abscisic acid biosynthesis in *Arabidopsis*. *Plant J.* 27:325–33

43. Jaglo KR, Kleff S, Amundsen KL, Zhang X, Haake V, et al. 2001. Components of the Arabidopsis C-repeat/dehydration-responsive element binding factor cold-response pathway are conserved in *Brassica napus* and other plant species. *Plant Physiol.* 127:910–17

44. Jaglo-Ottosen KR, Gilmour SJ, Zarka DG, Schabenberger O, Thomashow MF. 1998. *Arabidopsis* CBF1 overexpression induces *cor* genes and enhances freezing tolerance. *Science* 280:104–06

45. Jakoby M, Weisshaar B, Droge-Laser W, Vicente-Carbajosa J, Tiedemann J, et al. 2002. bZIP transcription factors in Arabidopsis. *Trends Plant Sci.* 7:106–11

46. Jiang C, Iu B, Singh J. 1996. Requirement of a CCGAC *cis*-acting element for cold induction of the *BN115* gene from winter *Brassica napus*. *Plant Mol. Biol.* 30:679–84

47. Jones-Rhoades MW, Bartel DP. 2004. Computational identification of plant microRNAs and their targets, including a stress-induced miRNA. *Mol. Cell* 14:787–99

48. Kagaya Y, Hobo T, Murata M, Ban A, Hattori T. 2002. Abscisic acid-induced transcription is mediated by phosphorylation of an abscisic acid response element binding factor, TRAB1. *Plant Cell* 14:3177–89

49. Kang JY, Choi HI, Im MY, Kim SY. 2002. *Arabidopsis* basic leucine zipper proteins that mediate stress-responsive abscisic acid signaling. *Plant Cell* 14:343–57

50. Kasuga M, Liu Q, Miura S, Yamaguchi-Shinozaki K, Shinozaki K. 1999. Improving plant drought, salt, and freezing tolerance by gene transfer of a single stress-inducible transcription factor. *Nat. Biotechnol.* 17:287–91

51. Kasuga M, Miura S, Shinozaki K, Yamaguchi-Shinozaki K. 2004. A combination of the Arabidopsis *DREB1A* gene and stress-inducible rd29A promoter improved drought- and low-temperature stress tolerance in tobacco by gene transfer. *Plant Cell Physiol.* 45:346–50

52. Kawasaki S, Borchert C, Deyholos M, Wang H, Brazille S, et al. 2001. Gene expression profiles during the initial phase of salt stress in rice. *Plant Cell* 13:889–905

53. Kim S, Kang JY, Cho DI, Park JH, Kim SY. 2004. ABF2, an ABRE-binding bZIP factor, is an essential component of glucose signaling and its overexpression affects multiple stress tolerance. *Plant J.* 40(1):75–87

54. Kitashiba H, Ishizaka T, Isuzugawa K, Nishimura K, Suzuki T. 2004. Expression of a sweet cherry DREB1/CBF ortholog in Arabidopsis confers salt and freezing tolerance. *J Plant Physiol.* 161:1171–76

55. Kizis D, Pages M. 2002. Maize DRE-binding proteins DBF1 and DBF2 are involved in rab17 regulation through the drought-responsive element in an ABA-dependent pathway. *Plant J.* 30:679–89

56. Knight H, Veale EL, Warren GJ, Knight MR. 1999. The sfr6 mutation in Arabidopsis suppresses low-temperature induction of genes dependent on the CRT/DRE sequence motif. *Plant Cell* 11:875–86

57. Kobayashi Y, Yamamoto S, Minami H, Kagaya Y, Hattori T. 2004. Differential activation of the rice sucrose nonfermenting1-related protein kinase2 family by hyperosmotic stress and abscisic acid. *Plant Cell* 16:1163–77

58. Kobayashi Y, Murata M, Minami H, Yamamoto S, Kagaya Y, et al. 2005. Abscisic acid-activated SNRK2 protein kinases function in the gene-regulation pathway of ABA signal transduction by phosphorylating ABA response element-binding factors *Plant J.* 44:939–49

59. Koiwa H, Barb AW, Xiong L, Li F, McCully MG, et al. 2002. C-terminal domain phosphatase-like family members (AtCPLs) differentially regulate *Arabidopsis thaliana* abiotic stress signaling, growth, and development. *Proc. Natl. Acad. Sci. USA* 99:10893–98

60. Koornneef M, Reuling G, Karssen CM. 1984. The isolation and characterization of abscisic acid-insensitive mutants of *Arabidopsis thaliana*. *Physiol. Plant.* 61:377–83

61. Koornneef M, Jorna ML, Brinkhorst-van der Swan DLC, Karssen CM. 1992. The isolation of abscisic acid (ABA)-deficient mutants by selection of induced revertants in non-germinating gibberellin sensitive lines of *Arabidopsis thaliana* (L.) Heynh. *Theor. Appl. Genet.* 61:385–93

62. Kreps JA, Wu Y, Chang HS, Zhu T, Wang X, et al. 2002. Transcriptome changes for Arabidopsis in response to salt, osmotic, and cold stress. *Plant Physiol.* 130:2129–41

63. Kushiro T, Okamoto M, Nakabayashi K, Yamagishi K, Kitamura S, et al. 2004. The Arabidopsis cytochrome P450 CYP707A encodes ABA 8′-hydroxylases:key enzymes in ABA catabolism. *EMBO J.* 23:1647–56

64. Lee H, Xiong L, Gong Z, Ishitani M, Stevenson B, et al. 2001. The Arabidopsis *HOS1* gene negatively regulates cold signal transduction and encodes a RING finger protein that displays cold-regulated nucleo–cytoplasmic partitioning. *Genes Dev.* 15:912–24

65. Leung J, Bouvier-Durand M, Morris PC, Guerrier D, Chefdor F, et al. 1994. Arabidopsis ABA response gene *ABI1*: features of a calcium-modulated protein phosphatase. *Science* 264:1448–52

66. Leung J, Merlot S, Giraudat J. 1997. The Arabidopsis *ABSCISIC ACID-INSENSITIVE2* (*ABI2*) and *ABI1* genes encode homologous protein phosphatases 2C involved in abscisic acid signal transduction. *Plant Cell* 9:759–71

67. Li J, Wang XQ, Watson MB, Assmann SM. 2000. Regulation of abscisic acid-induced stomatal closure and anion channels by guard cell AAPK kinase. *Science* 287:300–3

68. Liu Q, Kasuga M, Sakuma Y, Abe H, Miura S, et al. 1998. Two transcription factors, DREB1 and DREB2, with an EREBP/AP2 DNA binding domain separate two cellular signal transduction pathways in drought- and low-temperature-responsive gene expression, respectively, in *Arabidopsis*. *Plant Cell* 10:1391–406

69. Lopez-Molina L, Chua NH. 2000. A null mutation in a bZIP factor confers ABA-insensitivity in *Arabidopsis thaliana*. *Plant Cell Physiol.* 41:541–47

70. Lorenzo O, Chico JM, Sanchez-Serrano JJ, Solano R. 2004. JASMONATE-INSENSITIVE1 encodes a MYC transcription factor essential to discriminate between different jasmonate-regulated defense responses in Arabidopsis. *Plant Cell* 16:1938–50

71. Magome H, Yamaguchi S, Hanada A, Kamiya Y, Oda K. 2004. Dwarf and delayed-flowering 1, a novel Arabidopsis mutant deficient in gibberellin biosynthesis because of overexpression of a putative AP2 transcription factor. *Plant J.* 37:720–29

72. Maruyama K, Sakuma Y, Kasuga M, Ito Y, Seki M, et al. 2004. Identification of cold-inducible downstream genes of the *Arabidopsis* DREB1A/CBF3 transcriptional factor using two microarray systems. *Plant J.* 38:982–93

73. Massari ME, Murre C. 2000. Helix-loop-helix proteins: regulators of transcription in eucaryotic organisms. *Mol. Cell Biol.* 20:429–40

74. Menkens AE, Schindler U, Cashmore AR. 1995. The G-box: a ubiquitous regulatory DNA element in plants bound by the GBF family of bZIP proteins. *Trends Biochem. Sci.* 20:506–10

75. Meyer K, Leube MP, Grill E. 1994. A protein phosphatase 2C involved in ABA signal transduction in *Arabidopsis thaliana*. *Science* 264:1452–55

76. Mundy J, Yamaguchi-Shinozaki K, Chua NH. 1990. Nuclear proteins bind conserved elements in the abscisic acid-responsive promoter of a rice rab gene. *Proc. Natl. Acad. Sci. USA* 87:1406–10

77. Mustilli AC, Merlot S, Vavasseur A, Fenzi F, Giraudat J. 2002. *Arabidopsis* OST1 protein kinase mediates the regulation of stomatal aperture by abscisic acid and acts upstream of reactive oxygen spieces production. *Plant Cell* 14:3089–99

78. Nakashima K, Kiyosue T, Yamaguchi-Shinozaki K, Shinozaki K. 1997. A nuclear gene, erd1, encoding a chloroplast-targeted Clp protease regulatory subunit homolog is not only induced by water stress but also developmentally upregulated during senescence in *Arabidopsis thaliana*. *Plant J.* 12:851–61

79. Nakashima K, Shinwari ZK, Sakuma Y, Seki M, Miura S, et al. 2000. Organization and expression of two Arabidopsis *DREB2* genes encoding DRE-binding proteins involved in dehydration and high-salinity-responsive gene expression. *Plant Mol. Biol.* 42:657–65

80. Nambara E, Marion-Poll A. 2005. Abscisic acid biosynthesis and catabolism. *Annu. Rev. Plant Biol.* 56:165–85

81. Novillo F, Alonso JM, Ecker JR, Salinas J. 2004. CBF2/DREB1C is a negative regulator of CBF1/DREB1B and CBF3/DREB1A expression and plays a central role in stress tolerance in Arabidopsis. *Proc. Natl. Acad. Sci. USA* 101:3985–90

82. Oh SJ, Song SI, Kim YS, Jang HJ, Kim SY, et al. 2005. Arabidopsis CBF3/DREB1A and ABF3 in transgenic rice increased tolerance to abiotic stress without stunting growth. *Plant Physiol.* 138:341–51

83. Oono Y, Seki M, Nanjo T, Narusaka M, Fujita M, et al. 2003. Monitoring expression profiles of *Arabidopsis* gene expression during rehydration process after dehydration using *ca.* 7000 full-length cDNA microarray. *Plant J.* 34:868–87

84. Ouellet F, Vazquez-Tello A, Sarhan F. 1998. The wheat wcs120 promoter is cold-inducible in both monocotyledonous and dicotyledonous species. *FEBS Lett.* 423:324–28

85. Pellegrineschi A, Reynolds M, Pacheco M, Brito RM, Almeraya R, et al. 2004. Stress-induced expression in wheat of the *Arabidopsis thaliana DREB1A* gene delays water stress symptoms under greenhouse conditions. *Genome* 47:493–500

86. Qin F, Sakuma Y, Li J, Liu Q, Li YQ, et al. 2004. Cloning and functional analysis of a novel DREB1/CBF transcription factor involved in cold-responsive gene expression in *Zea mays* L. *Plant Cell Physiol.* 45:1042–52

87. Rabbani MA, Maruyama K, Abe H, Khan MA, Katsura K, et al. 2003. Monitoring expression profiles of rice genes under cold, drought, and high-salinity stresses and abscisic acid application using cDNA microarray and RNA gel-blot analyses. *Plant Physiol.* 133:1755–67

88. Saito S, Hirai N, Matsumoto C, Ohigashi H, Ohta D, et al. 2004. Arabidopsis CYP707As encode (+)-abscisic acid 8′-hydroxylase, a key enzyme in the oxidative catabolism of abscisic acid. *Plant Physiol.* 134(4):1439–49

89. Sakamoto H, Maruyama K, Sakuma Y, Meshi T, Iwabuchi M, et al. 2004. *Arabidopsis* Cys2/His2-type zinc-finger proteins function as transcription repressors under drought-, cold-, and high-salinity-stress conditions. *Plant Physiol.* 136:2734–46

90. Sakuma Y, Liu Q, Dubouzet JG, Abe H, Shinozaki K, et al. 2002. DNA-binding speci-ficity of the ERF/AP2 domain of Arabidopsis DREBs, transcription factors involved in dehydration- and cold-inducible gene expression. *Biochem. Biophys. Res. Commun.* 290:998–1009

91. Satoh R, Nakashima K, Seki M, Shinozaki K, Yamaguchi-Shinozaki K. 2002. ACTCAT, a novel cis-acting element for proline- and hypoosmolarity-responsive expression of the *ProDH* gene encoding proline dehydrogenase in Arabidopsis. *Plant Physiol.* 130:709–19

92. Satoh R, Fujita Y, Nakashima K, Shinozaki K, Yamaguchi-Shinozaki K. 2004. A novel subgroup of bZIP proteins function as transcriptional activators in hypoosmolarity-responsive expression of the *ProDH* gene in *Arabidopsis*. *Plant Cell Physiol.* 45:309–17

93. Seki M, Narusaka M, Abe H, Kasuga M, Yamaguchi-Shinozaki K, et al. 2001. Monitoring the expression pattern of 1300 Arabidopsis genes under drought and cold stresses by using a full-length cDNA microarray. *Plant Cell* 13:61–72

94. Seki M, Narusaka M, Ishida J, Nanjo T, Fujita M, et al. 2002. Monitoring the expression profiles of 7000 Arabidopsis genes under drought, cold and high-salinity stresses using a full-length cDNA microarray. *Plant J.* 31:279–92

95. Seki M, Kamei A, Yamaguchi-Shinozaki K, Shinozaki K. 2003. Molecular responses to drought, salinity and frost: common and different paths for plant protection. *Curr. Opin. Biotechnol.* 14:194–99

96. Seki M, Satou M, Sakurai T, Akiyama K, Iida K. et al. 2004. RIKEN Arabidopsis full-length (RAFL) cDNA and its applications for expression profiling under abiotic stress conditions. *J. Exp. Bot.* 55:213–23

97. Seo M, Peeters AJ, Koiwai H, Oritani T, Marion-Poll A, et al. 2000. The Arabidopsis aldehyde oxidase 3 (AAO3) gene product catalyzes the final step in abscisic acid biosyn-thesis in leaves. *Proc. Natl. Acad. Sci. USA* 97:12908–13

98. Shen Q, Ho TH. 1995 Functional dissection of an abscisic acid (ABA)-inducible gene reveals two independent ABA-responsive complexes each containing a G-box and a novel *cis*-acting element. *Plant Cell* 7:295–307

99. Shen Q, Zhang P, Ho TH. 1996. Modular nature of abscisic acid (ABA) response com-plexes: composite promoter units that are necessary and sufficient for ABA induction of gene expression in barley. *Plant Cell* 8:1107–19

100. Shen YG, Zhang WK, He SJ, Zhang JS, Liu Q, et al. 2003a. An EREBP/AP2-type protein in *Triticum aestivum* was a DRE-binding transcription factor induced by cold, dehydration and ABA stress. *Theor. Appl. Genet.* 106:923–30

101. Shen YG, Zhang WK, Yan DQ, Du BX, Zhang JS, et al. 2003b. Characterization of a DRE-binding transcription factor from a halophyte *Atriplex hortensis*. *Theor. Appl. Genet.* 107:155–61

102. Shinozaki K, Yamaguchi-Shinozaki K. 1997. Gene expression and signal transduction in water-stress response. *Plant Physiol.* 115:327–34

103. Shinozaki K, Yamaguchi-Shinozaki K. 2000. Molecular responses to dehydration and low temperature: differences and cross-talk between two stress signaling pathways. *Curr. Opin. Plant Biol.* 3:217–23

104. Shinozaki K, Yamaguchi-Shinozaki K, Seki M. 2003. Regulatory network of gene expression in the drought and cold stress responses. *Curr. Opin. Plant Biol.* 6:410–17

105. Shinwari ZK, Nakashima K, Miura S, Kasuga M, Seki M, et al. 1998. An *Arabidopsis* gene family encoding DRE/CRT binding proteins involved in low-temperature-responsive gene expression. *Biochem. Biophys. Res. Commun.* 250:161–70

106. Simpson SD, Nakashima K, Narusaka Y, Seki M, Shinozaki K, et al. 2003. Two different novel *cis*-acting elements of *erd1*, a *clpA* homologous *Arabidopsis* gene function in induction by dehydration stress and dark-induced senescence. *Plant J.* 33:259–70

107. Soderman E, Hjellstrom M, Fahleson J, Engstrom P. 1999. The HD-Zip gene *ATHB6* in Arabidopsis is expressed in developing leaves, roots and carpels and up-regulated by water deficit conditions. *Plant Mol. Biol.* 40:1073–83

108. Song CP, Agarwal M, Ohta M, Guo Y, Halfter U, et al. 2005. Role of an Arabidopsis AP2/EREBP-type transcriptional repressor in abscisic acid and drought stress responses. *Plant Cell* 17:2384–96

109. Stockinger EJ, Gilmour SJ, Thomashow MF. 1997. *Arabidopsis thaliana CBF1* encodes an AP2 domain-containing transcription activator that binds to the C-repeat/DRE, a *cis*-acting DNA regulatory element that stimulates transcription in response to low temperature and water deficit. *Proc. Natl. Acad. Sci. USA* 94:1035–40

110. Sunkar R, Zhu JK. 2004. Novel and stress-regulated microRNAs and other small RNAs from Arabidopsis. *Plant Cell* 16:2001–19

111. Suzuki M, Ketterling MG, Li QB, McCarty DR. 2003. Viviparous1 alters global gene expression patterns through regulation of abscisic acid signaling. *Plant Physiol.* 132:1664–77

112. Takahashi S, Katagiri T, Hirayama T, Yamaguchi-Shinozaki K, Shinozaki K. 2001. Hyperosmotic stress induces a rapid and transient increase in inositol 1,4,5-trisphosphate independent of abscisic acid in Arabidopsis cell culture. *Plant Cell Physiol.* 42:214–22

113. Tester M, Bacic A. 2005. Abiotic stress tolerance in grasses. From model plants to crop plants. *Plant Physiol.* 137:791–93

114. Thomashow MF. 1999. Plant cold acclimation: freezing tolerance genes and regulatory mechanisms *Annu. Rev. Plant Physiol. Plant Mol. Biol.* 50:571–99

115. Tran LSP, Nakashima K, Sakuma Y, Simpson SD, Fujita Y, et al. 2004. Functional analysis of *Arabidopsis* NAC transcription factors controlling expression of *erd1* gene under drought stress. *Plant Cell* 16:2482–98

116. Umezawa T, Okamoto M, Kushiro T, Nambara E, Oono Y, et al. 2006. CYP707A3, a major ABA 8′-hydroxylase involved in dehydration and rehydration response in *Arabidopsis thaliana*. *Plant J.* In press

117. Uno Y, Furihata T, Abe H, Yoshida R, Shinozaki K, et al. 2000. *Arabidopsis* basic leucine zipper transcription factors involved in an abscisic acid-dependent signal transduction pathway under drought and high-salinity conditions. *Proc. Natl. Acad. Sci. USA* 97:11632–37

118. Urao T, Yamaguchi-Shinozaki K, Urao S, Shinozaki K. 1993. An Arabidopsis myb homolog is induced by dehydration stress and its gene product binds to the conserved MYB recognition sequence. *Plant Cell* 5:1529–39

119. Vagujfalvi A, Galiba G, Cattivelli L, Dubcovsky J. 2003. The cold-regulated transcriptional activator Cbf3 is linked to the frost-tolerance locus Fr-A2 on wheat chromosome 5A. *Mol. Genet. Genomics* 269:60–67

120. Vinocur B, Altman A. 2005. Recent advances in engineering plant tolerance to abiotic stress: achievements and limitations. *Curr. Opin. Biotechnol.* 16:123–32

121. Vogel JT, Zarka DG, Van Buskirk HA, Fowler SG, Thomashow MF. 2005. Roles of the CBF2 and ZAT12 transcription factors in configuring the low temperature transcriptome of Arabidopsis. *Plant J.* 41:195–211

122. Warren G, McKown R, Marin AL, Teutonico R. 1996. Isolation of mutations affecting the development of freezing tolerance in *Arabidopsis thaliana* (L.) Heynh. *Plant Physiol.* 111:1011–19

123. Xiong L, Ishitani M, Lee H, Zhu JK. 2001. The Arabidopsis LOS5/ABA3 locus encodes a molybdenum cofactor sulfurase and modulates cold stress- and osmotic stress-responsive gene expression. *Plant Cell* 13:2063–83

124. Xiong L, Lee Bh, Ishitani M, Lee H, Zhang C, et al. 2001. FIERY1 encoding an inositol polyphosphate 1-phosphatase is a negative regulator of abscisic acid and stress signaling in Arabidopsis. *Genes Dev.* 15:1971–84

125. Xiong L, Lee H, Ishitani M, Zhu JK. 2002. Regulation of osmotic stress-responsive gene expression by the LOS6/ABA1 locus in Arabidopsis. *J. Biol. Chem.* 277:8588–96

126. Xiong L, Schumaker KS, Zhu JK. 2002. Cell signaling during cold, drought, and salt stress. *Plant Cell* 14(Suppl.):S165–83

127. Xiong L, Lee H, Huang R, Zhu JK. 2004. A single amino acid substitution in the Arabidopsis FIERY1/HOS2 protein confers cold signaling specificity and lithium tolerance. *Plant J.* 40:536–45

128. Xue GP. 2003. The DNA-binding activity of an AP2 transcriptional activator HvCBF2 involved in regulation of low-temperature responsive genes in barley is modulated by temperature. *Plant J.* 33: 373–83

129. Yadav V, Mallappa C, Gangappa SN, Bhatia S, Chattopadhyay S. 2005. A basic helix-loop-helix transcription factor in Arabidopsis, MYC2, acts as a repressor of blue light-mediated photomorphogenic growth. *Plant Cell* 17:1953–66

130. Yamaguchi-Shinozaki K, Shinozaki K. 1992. A novel Arabidopsis DNA binding protein contains the conserved motif of HMG-box proteins. *Nucleic Acids Res.* 20:6737

131. Yamaguchi-Shinozaki K, Shinozaki K. 1994. A novel *cis*-acting element in an *Arabidopsis* gene is involved in responsiveness to drought, low temperature, or high-salt stress. *Plant Cell* 6:251–64

132. Yamaguchi-Shinozaki K, Shinozaki K. 2005. Organization of cis-acting regulatory elements in osmotic- and cold-stress-responsive promoters. *Trends Plant Sci.* 10:88–94

133. Yoshida R, Hobo T, Ichimura K, Mizoguchi T, Takahashi F, et al. 2002. ABA-activated SnRK2 protein kinase is required for dehydration stress signaling in *Arabidopsis*. *Plant Cell Physiol.* 43:1473–83

134. Zarka DG, Vogel JT, Cook D, Thomashow MF. 2003. Cold induction of *Arabidopsis* CBF genes involves multiple ICE (inducer of CBF expression) promoter elements and a cold-regulatory circuit that is desensitized by low temperature. *Plant Physiol.* 133:910–18

135. Zhang JZ, Creelman RA, Zhu JK. 2004. From laboratory to field. Using information from Arabidopsis to engineer salt, cold, and drought tolerance in crops. *Plant Physiol.* 135:615–21

136. Zhu J. 2002. Salt and drought stress signal transduction in plants. *Annu. Rev. Plant Biol.* 53:247–73

137. Zhu J, Shi H, Lee BH, Damsz B, Cheng S, et al. 2004. An *Arabidopsis* homeodomain transcription factor gene, *HOS9*, mediates cold tolerance through a CBF-independent pathway. *Proc. Natl. Acad. Sci. USA* 101:9873–78

138. Zhu J, Verslues PE, Zheng X, Lee BH, Zhan X, et al. 2005. HOS10 encodes an R2R3-type MYB transcription factor essential for cold acclimation in plants. *Proc. Natl. Acad. Sci. USA* 102:9966–71

Pyrimidine and Purine Biosynthesis and Degradation in Plants

Rita Zrenner,[1] Mark Stitt,[1] Uwe Sonnewald,[2] and Ralf Boldt[3]

[1] Max Planck Institute of Molecular Plant Physiology, 14476 Potsdam OT Golm, Germany; email: zrenner@mpimp-golm.mpg.de, mstitt@mpimp-golm.mpg.de

[2] Friedrich-Alexander-Universität Erlangen-Nürnberg, Lehrstuhl für Biochemie, 91058 Erlangen, Germany; email: usonne@biologie.uni-erlangen.de

[3] University of Rostock, Institute of Bioscience, Department of Plant Physiology, 18059 Rostock, Germany; email: ralf.boldt@biologie.uni-rostock.de

Annu. Rev. Plant Biol. 2006. 57:805–36

The *Annual Review of Plant Biology* is online at plant.annualreviews.org

doi: 10.1146/ annurev.arplant.57.032905.105421

Abstract

Nucleotide metabolism operates in all living organisms, embodies an evolutionarily ancient and indispensable complex of metabolic pathways and is of utmost importance for plant metabolism and development. In plants, nucleotides can be synthesized de novo from 5-phosphoribosyl-1-pyrophosphate and simple molecules (e.g., CO_2, amino acids, and tetrahydrofolate), or be derived from preformed nucleosides and nucleobases via salvage reactions. Nucleotides are degraded to simple metabolites, and this process permits the recycling of phosphate, nitrogen, and carbon into central metabolic pools. Despite extensive biochemical knowledge about purine and pyrimidine metabolism, comprehensive studies of the regulation of this metabolism in plants are only starting to emerge. Here we review progress in molecular aspects and recent studies on the regulation and manipulation of nucleotide metabolism in plants.

Contents

INTRODUCTION

Nucleotides are some of the most crucial cellular components for plant growth, development, and metabolism. The vital processes of plant purine and pyrimidine metabolism are required for primary metabolism, secondary metabolism, and gene expression and underpin the majority of the fundamental cellular and biochemical processes that are required for cell growth.

Purine and pyrimidine nucleotides play an essential role in information storage and retrieval in dividing and elongating tissues by acting as building blocks of DNA in the nucleus or DNA-synthesizing organelles and as components of transcripts (109). Ribosomal and transfer RNA are also essential components of the protein synthesis machinery. Nucleotides also serve as direct precursors for the synthesis of B-class vitamins such as riboflavin, thiamine, and folates (32, 54, 56) as well as several essential coenzymes like nicotinamide adenine dinucleotide (NAD), flavin adenine dinucleotide (FAD), and S-adenosylmethionine (SAM). During the fundamental energetic processes of photosynthesis and respiration, the purine nucleotide ATP is produced from ADP and phosphate as the major triphosphate for general chemical energy conservation. ATP is the major energy donor in most metabolic reactions and is also used to generate activated precursors for the synthesis of many macromolecules, including AMP-activated amino acids for protein synthesis and ADP-glucose for starch synthesis. In plants the pyrimidine nucleotides also have important functions as co-substrates. UTP and UDP are directly involved in the synthesis and degradation of sucrose, and the energy-rich nucleotide sugar UDP-glucose is the precursor for the synthesis of cellulose and additional polysaccharides, glycoproteins, and phospholipids; UDP-glucose also acts as a glucosyl donor in the derivatization of secondary metabolites and hormones in a wide range of reactions catalyzed by the enormous protein family of UDP-glucose glycosyltransferases (77).

The pathways of nucleotide metabolism are presented in more detail later. Broadly, nucleotide metabolism can be divided into (i) de novo synthesis, (ii) nucleotide degradation, (iii) salvage pathways that recycle nucleosides and free bases, and (iv) phosphotransfer reactions that convert mono- and dinucleotides to the triphosphate form and equilibrate different pools of nucleotides. In addition, specific nucleotides are modified (for example, to deoxynucleotides for DNA synthesis), or by addition of side chains to produce unusual nucleotides that are components of tRNA. Individual nucleotides and intermediates are also precursors for the synthesis of secondary metabolites and hormones. This fact makes nucleotide metabolism considerably more complicated than amino acid metabolism, which consists essentially of anabolic and catabolic reactions.

This fact also raises questions why, in addition to de novo synthesis, scavenging reactions are so widely distributed. Salvage reactions recycle nucleosides and free bases that are formed in the first steps of the degradation pathways: 5'-Nucleotidases remove the 5'-phosphate from nucleotides to form nucleosides, and nucleosidases remove the ribose sugar groups to release free bases (see below for a more detailed account of these pathways). Whereas de novo synthesis of nucleotides is very energy consuming (see below), the strategy to reuse preformed nucleosides and bases through these salvage reactions needs less energy than de novo synthesis of nucleotides. It is often assumed that the large demand for nucleotides in growing and dividing cells is met by de novo synthesis, whereas nongrowing cells may be able to maintain their pools of nucleotides by salvaging preformed nucleosides, perhaps supplemented to a certain degree with newly synthesized nucleotides to balance degradation processes. However, this assumption begs the question why significant amounts of nucleosides and free bases are formed in the first place.

A further potentially important distinction between amino acid and nucleotide metabolism is that, whereas amino acids contain carbon, nitrogen and in some cases sulphur, nucleotides contain carbon, nitrogen, and phosphate. Indeed, the initial incorporation of phosphate into organic compounds occurs almost entirely via the conversion of ADP to ATP in oxidative or photosynthetic ATP synthesis or substrate level phosphorylation. Nucleotides also play a unique role in transferring phosphate into macromolecules like nucleic acids and phospholipids. One of the early changes in response to inorganic phosphate (Pi)-deprivation or readdition is a decrease and increase, respectively, in the levels of nucleotides (93). It can be anticipated that there will be an intimate relation between nucleotide and phosphate metabolism.

The basic research on nucleotide metabolism was carried out using animals and microorganisms (22, 94, 151). Medical applications like anticancer drug development and the investigation of hereditary diseases have motivated much research on nucleotide metabolism in human systems. Research on nucleotide metabolism in higher plants is gaining momentum, which is reflected in a series of excellent reviews that comprehensively summarize the physiology and biochemistry of purine and pyrimidine biosynthesis, salvage, and degradation (82, 115, 119), the genomic organization in *Arabidopsis thaliana* (19), the role of purine metabolism in the synthesis of caffeine (9), the function of purine biosynthesis in the primary nitrogen metabolism in tropical legumes (113), and the function of purine salvage enzymes in cytokinine interconversion (106). In addition, emerging information about the functional characterization of nucleotide, nucleoside, and nucleobase transport proteins (24, 39, 48, 76, 104, 143) is providing a deeper insight in the interaction and the inter- and intracellular localization of different parts of nucleotide metabolism.

It is now evident that molecular and enzymatic organization, control mechanisms, and subcellular localization of proteins involved in nucleotide metabolism in plants show distinct differences to those found in other organisms. In this article we give a summary of nucleotide metabolism by first providing a brief overview of the functions and levels of different nucleotides in plant cells and then focusing on the molecular aspects of pyrimidine and purine biosynthesis and degradation, including the genomic organization and the subcellular organization of these complex pathways (**Figures 1** and **2**). We then discuss recent studies on the manipulation of nucleotide metabolism in plants and consider the possible role and interactions of the de novo synthesis and scavenging pathways.

COMPARTMENTALIZATION AND LEVELS OF NUCLEOTIDES IN PLANT CELLS

Adenine and uridine nucleotides are present at much higher levels than guanine and cytosine nucleotides (134); this fact reflects the

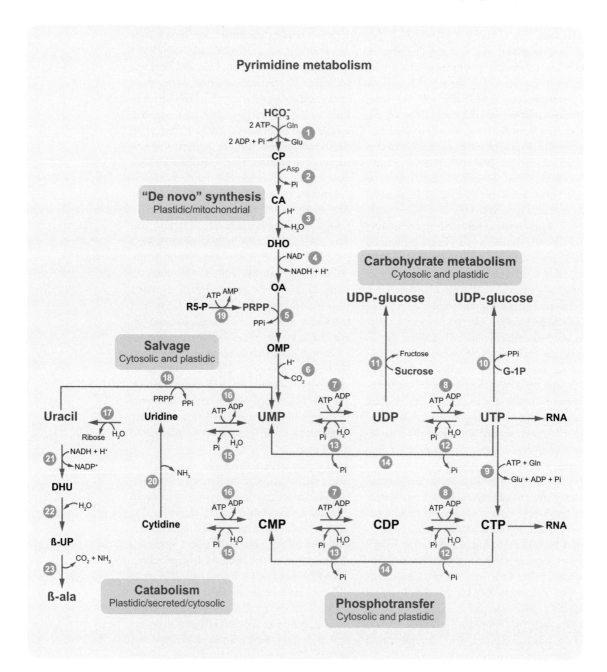

more general role of adenine and uridine nucleotides as cofactors in metabolism as well as in the synthesis of nucleic acids. All nucleotides are strongly compartmentalized between the cytosol, plastids, and mitochondria of plant cells.

The main nucleotides for energy metabolism, the adenine nucleotides, have significant pools in at least three cellular compartments; approximately 45% of adenine nucleotides in leaves is found in the plastid, 46% in the cytosol, and 9% in the mitochondria (121, 122). Specific transporters catalyze the counter-exchange of ATP and ADP between the mitochondrial lumen and the cytosol (44) and the exchange between the cytosol and plastid stroma (97). The picture is similar in nonphotosynthetic tissues like potato tubers (128). In an aerobic cell, the ATP/ADP ratios are high in the cytosol (121, 128) and considerably lower in the plastid, even in a chloroplast in the light, and even more so in the dark or in plastids in nonphotosynthetic tissues.

In plant cells, a large proportion of the total free uridine nucleotide pool consists of nucleoside diphosphate sugars. They are needed for the synthesis of transport forms of carbohydrates like sucrose, cellulose, most cell wall matrix polysaccharides, and the sugar components of glycoproteins. UDP-sugars comprise up to 55% of the total nucleotide content (134). In spinach leaves and potato tubers the major proportion of the nucleotides UTP and UDP are located in the cytoplasm (33, 43). The UTP/UDP ratio in the cytosol is similar to the ATP/ADP ratio; this similarity indicates efficient equilibration between these two energy couples. Over 90% of the UDP-glucose is located in the cytosol (121). This pool includes that found in the lumen of the endomembrane system, into which UDP-glucose is transported by a small family of UDP-sugar/UMP exchangers (89). Almost all UDP-sugars are made from UDP-glucose. There are basically two routes for the production of UDP-glucose in the cytosol of a plant cell. These routes differ in their need for nucleotide cosubstrates: Whereas UDP-glucose pyrophosphorylase catalyzes the interconversion of glucose 1-phosphate and the pyrimidine nucleotide UTP to UDP-glucose and pyrophosphate (71), sucrose synthase catalyzes the reversible interconversion of sucrose and UDP to UDP-glucose and fructose (142).

To adjust the nucleotide pools to differing needs during metabolism, regulatory mechanisms are required that coordinate the absolute and relative levels of purines to pyrimidines in the various cells and subcellular compartments, as well as the relative levels of the mono-, di-, and triphosphate forms. The importance of such regulation is illustrated by the observations (a) that uridine nucleotide levels decline rapidly after detachment of a growing tuber from the mother

---

Figure 1

General schematic overview of plant pyrimidine metabolism. Enzymes involved in pyrimidine metabolism are numbered and correspond to those listed in **Table 1**. To simplify matters, no deoxynucleotide metabolism and no subcellular compartmentation and transporters are shown. The metabolic components shown are: 1. 5-phosphoribosyl-1-pyrophosphate (*PRPP*), 2. ribose-5-phosphate (*R5-P*), 3. glutamine (*Gln*), 4. glutamate (*Glu*), 5. adenosine triphosphate (*ATP*), 6. adenosine diphosphate (*ADP*), 7. inorganic phosphate (*Pi*), 8. carbamoyl phosphate (*CP*), 9. carbamoyl aspartate (*CA*), 10. dihydro-orotate (*DHO*), 11. orotic acid (*OA*), 12. orotidine 5′-monophosphate (*OMP*), 13. uridine monophosphate (*UMP*), 14. uridine diphosphate (*UDP*), 15. uridine triphosphate (*UTP*), 16. uridine diphosphoglucose (*UDP-glucose*), 17. cytosine monophosphate (*CMP*), 18. cytosine diphosphate (*CDP*), 19. cytosine triphosphate (*CTP*), 20. dihydrouracil (*DHU*), 21. β-ureidopropionate (*β-UP*), 22. β-alanine (*β-ala*), 23. pyrophosphate (*PPi*), 24. glucose-1-phosphate (*G-1P*), 25. aspartate (*Asp*), and 26. adenosine monophosphate (*AMP*).

potato plant, and (*b*) that the levels of uridine nucleotides can be restored by feeding orotate (an intermediate in the pyrimidine biosynthesis pathway) to tuber slices. Feeding orotate to potato tubers leads to a general stimulation of sucrose mobilization, starch synthesis, and cell-wall synthesis (78). Similarly, external orotate leads to increased levels of uridine nucleotides and a stimulation of sucrose mobilization and lipid synthesis in *Arabidopsis* and rape seeds (P. Geigenberger, unpublished observations).

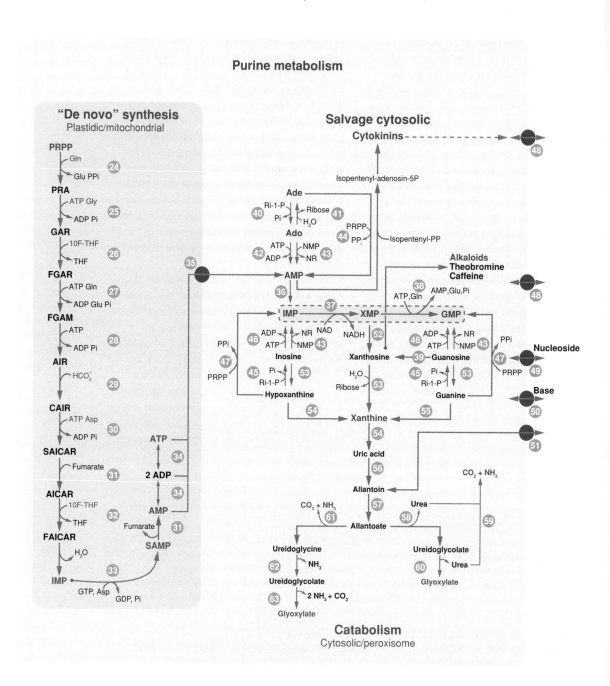

PYRIMIDINE METABOLISM

Molecular Analysis of Pyrimidine de novo Synthesis

De novo pyrimidine nucleotide biosynthesis is evolutionarily conserved in all species examined and is defined as the formation of UMP from carbamoylphosphate (CP), aspartate, and 5-phosphoribosyl-1-pyrophosphate (PRPP); de novo pyrimidine nucleotide biosynthesis is also referred to as the orotate pathway. Pyrimidine nucleotide biosynthesis consists of six enzymatic steps (**Figure 1**). Carbamoylphosphate synthase (CPSase) produces CP from a combination of carbonate, ATP, and an amino group. CP is used not only in pyrimidine de novo synthesis, but also as a precursor for arginine biosynthesis. The next step, in which aspartate transcarbamoylase (ATCase) catalyzes the condensation of CP with aspartate to form carbamoylaspartate (CA), is specific for pyrimidine biosynthesis. Cyclization of the carbamoylaspartate to produce the pyrimidine ring is catalyzed by the enzyme dihydroorotase (DHOase). Subsequently, dihydroorotate (DHO) is oxidized by dihydroorotate dehydrogenase (DHODH) to yield orotate (OA). Orotate is condensed with PRPP to orotidine 5′-monophosphate (OMP) by orotate phosphoribosyltransferase (OPRTase), which is then decarboxylated by orotidylate decarboxylase (ODCase) to form uridine-5′-monophosphate (UMP).

Although pyrimidine de novo synthesis is conserved, it shows distinct differences between bacteria, yeast, and higher eukaryotes (86). In *Escherichia coli* and other bacteria, each enzymatic step is catalyzed by a different protein that is encoded by a different gene (88). In plants, the first three steps are catalyzed by three separate proteins (40), whereas in mammals all three steps are carried out by a single multifunctional protein called CAD (Carbamoylphosphate synthase-Aspartate transcarbamoylase-Dihydroorotase) (60). In mammals and plants (137), the last two steps are catalyzed by distinct domains of a bi-functional protein called UMP synthase (UMPSase). From a phylogenetic viewpoint, the organization of the pathway in plants is chimeric: The CPSase subunits cluster in the cyanobacteria clade, DHOase in proteobacteria, ATCase in eukaryotes, and DHODH and UMP synthase in the clade of higher eukaryotes (86).

The first complete plant genome sequence (127) together with biochemical studies (139) reveal that higher plants, like *E. coli*, possess a single form of CPSase that supplies CP to both the pyrimidine and the arginine pathway. Most other higher eukaryotes have two types of CPSase. CPSaseI is specific for ammonia, is located in mitochondria, and contributes to arginine biosynthesis, whereas CPSaseII preferentially uses glutamine, is located in the cytosol, and contributes to pyrimidine biosynthesis. Plant CPSase consists of

---

Figure 2

General schematic overview of plant purine metabolism. Enzymes involved in purine metabolism are numbered and correspond to those listed in **Table 2**. The cytosolic part of purine de novo synthesis is boxed. Metabolic components shown are: 1. 5-phosphoribosyl-1-pyrophosphate (*PRPP*), 2. glutamine (*Gln*), 3. glutamate (*Glu*), 4. 5-phosphoribosylamine (*PRA*), 5. pyrophosphate (*PPi*), 6. glycine (*Gly*), 7. glycinamide ribonucleotide (*GAR*), 8. 10-formyl tetrahydrofolate (*10F-THF*), 9. formylglycinamide ribonucleotide (*FGAR*), 10. formylglycinamidine ribonucleotide (*FGAM*), 11. 5-aminoimidazole ribonucleotide (*AIR*), 12. 4-carboxy aminoimidazole ribonucleotide (*CAIR*), 13. aspartate (*Asp*), 14. N-succinyl-5-aminoimidazole-4-carboxamide ribonucleotide (*SAICAR*), 15. 5-aminoimidazole-4-carboxamide ribonucleotide (*AICAR*), 16. 5-formaminoimidazole-4-carboxamide ribonucleotide (*FAICAR*), 17. inosine monophosphate (*IMP*), 18. adenylosuccinate (*SAMP*), 19. adenosine monophosphate (*AMP*), 20. xanthosine monophosphate (*XMP*), 21. guanosine monophosphate (*GMP*), 22. adenine (*Ade*), and 23. adenosine (*Ado*).

two subunits. The small subunit exhibits a glutamine-amidotransferase activity and provides ammonia to the large subunit. The large subunit catalyzes the CPSase reaction and possesses regulatory properties. Cloning and characterization of the respective subunit cDNAs from various plants revealed that the subunits are encoded by individual genes (NCBI accession numbers U73175 and U40341, respectively) (47). There is a report of a plant CPSase cDNA with bicistronic organization in *Medicago* (NCBI accession number AF191301). The amino acid sequences deduced from these cDNAs suggest that the plant proteins are synthesized as precursors that contain chloroplast-transit peptides. This finding is consistent with biochemical (112) and immunological evidence (R. Zrenner, unpublished observations), in which proteins of 125 kDa for the large subunit and of 45 kDa for the small subunit have been detected in chloroplasts.

Sequences encoding proteins with ATCase activity have been characterized from various plants (47, 87, 140). The amino acid sequences deduced from these cDNAs suggest that the plant ATCase is synthesized as precursor containing a chloroplast-transit peptide. This finding is consistent with biochemical (41) and immunological evidence (15) that shows that a 36 kDa protein is detected in chloroplasts.

Sequences encoding proteins with DHOase activity have been characterized from *Arabidopsis* and potato (*Solanum tuberosum*) (AF000146 for *Arabidopsis* and AX093580 for potato) (47). The amino acid sequences deduced from these cDNAs suggest that the plant DHOase is synthesized as precursor containing an N-terminal transit peptide, but do not indicate whether the protein would be located in plastids or mitochondria. However, biochemical (41) and immunological evidence (R. Zrenner, unpublished observations) reveal that the 42 kDa protein is located in chloroplasts.

Sequences encoding proteins with DHODH activity have been characterized

from *Arabidopsis* and tobacco (*Nicotiana tabacum*) (47, 81). All plant DHODHs sequenced to date belong to the membrane-bound family 2 of dihydroorotate dehydrogenases, which are flavoproteins. The deduced amino acid sequences suggest that the plant protein is synthesized as precursor containing an N-terminal transit peptide for mitochondrial targeting. Biochemical (41) and immunological evidence (130) confirm that the 45 kDa protein is located on the outer surface of the inner mitochondrial membrane, as has been shown in mammals (30). The activity of the *Arabidopsis* enzyme shows significant differences in substrate specificity and inhibition from the animal enzyme (130).

Sequences encoding proteins with UMPSase activity have been characterized from various plants (87, 100). The deduced amino acid sequences indicate that the plant protein is synthesized as precursor containing an N-terminal transit peptide. Biochemical evidence (41) confirms that the protein is located in chloroplasts.

In contrast to other pathways in primary plant carbon metabolism where usually more than one gene encodes a single enzymatic function, the pyrimidine biosynthetic pathway has a simple genomic organization. In the plant species analyzed so far, each species has only one gene for each enzymatic function (47). This general picture is confirmed by inspection of the full genome sequence of *Arabidopsis thaliana* (19). One exception is rice, in which more than one gene for UMPSase has been found (AF210323, AF210324, AF210325). Another well-known exception is ATCase of pea, for which three different cDNAs have been characterized. Screening of all available EST sequence information for soybean also reveals two putatively different isoforms of ATCase. It can be speculated that the presence of multiple ATCase genes in legumes might be due to the additional functions of nucleotides in the nitrogen fixation processes in the symbiosis of legumes. The full genome sequencing projects currently running for *Lotus japonicus* and *Medicago trunculata* will reveal if the presence of multiple ATCase genes is a general feature of nitrogen-fixing legumes. So far, however, only one ATCase has been found in the *Medicago* sequencing project.

In contrast to its rather simple genomic organization, the reactions in the de novo synthesis pathway take place in a number of different subcellular locations. Whereas the first three steps of the pathway take place in the plastid, the dehydrogenase reaction takes place at the outer surface of the inner mitochondrial membrane and is coupled to the respiratory chain; the last two steps, catalyzed by UMPSase, again take place in the plastids (see above). Therefore, to produce UMP, DHO must leave the plastid and access the outer surface of the inner mitochondrial membrane, where it is converted to OA. Subsequently the OA must move back across the outer membrane of the mitochondria and re-enter the plastids, where it is converted to UMP. Until now, no transport proteins for these intermediates have been described. A specialized transport system is almost certainly required for movement between the plastid and cytosol. Whereas movement of low-molecular weight metabolites across the outer membrane of the mitochondria has previously been thought to occur via nonspecific porins, there is increasingly evidence that such proteins can exhibit a certain degree of specificity (20). This finding expands the possibility for regulatory access because transport processes across several membranes have to be involved in the de novo pyrimidine biosynthesis.

Regulation of Pyrimidine de novo Biosynthesis

Transcriptional control of genes of the pyrimidine de novo biosynthesis seems not to be strongly pronounced in plants, except for some changes of expression along developmental gradients (47). AtGenExpress data of the expression atlas of *Arabidopsis* development (103) and Genevestigator analysis (154)

of *Arabidopsis* array hybridization databases confirm this assumption, although not all genes of this pathway are represented on the *Arabidopsis* ATH1 full genome array (95). As the de novo synthesis of nucleotides represents a basic cellular function, it is not surprising that the expression of all involved genes is correlated with plant growth. Even when mitotic and expansion activity has completely stopped, however, there is still a considerable amount of steady-state mRNA detectable from the genes (47). This observation may reflect the role of pyrimidine nucleotides in providing energy-rich precursors for sucrose and cell wall biosynthesis, as well as in cell division and expansion.

Transcriptional control is also found during phosphate limitation or after feeding the metabolic inhibitor 5-fluoroorotic acid. Upon phosphate starvation, transcripts for UMPSase and ATCase in *Arabidopsis* roots rise, together with transcripts for genes of the salvage pathway; this observation indicates coordinate transcriptional control of UMP formation (58). Induction of a thymine-starvation phenotype by feeding the metabolic inhibitor 5-fluoroorotic acid to tobacco cell cultures increases expression of UMPSase (99).

Regulation of the whole pathway is exerted on enzyme activity level via feedback and feed-forward loops acting on CPSase and ATCase. The responses of these enzymes were first elucidated in microbes and represent classic examples of allosteric regulation. Allosteric regulation of plant CPSase by feedback inhibition with UMP and feed-forward activation with PRPP has been described (65, 91). Allosteric inhibition of CPSase by UMP can be overcome by ornithine, presumably to allow CP to be produced for arginine biosynthesis independently of the requirement for CP in pyrimidine nucleotide synthesis (90). In mammals, the CPSase large subunit domain of the CAD protein is subject to regulation via phosphorylation by protein kinase A (27) and MAP kinase (51). These putative phosphorylation sites are conserved within the plant protein, but phosphorylation of the plant CPSase has not been analyzed until now. Activity of plant ATCase can also be decreased in vitro by binding of UMP to a putative pyrimidine-binding site of the enzyme (31).

As pointed out before, the enzymatic steps of the pyrimidine de novo synthesis pathway are typically encoded by single genes, none of which appear to be functionally redundant. This fact may explain why no mutants of the pyrimidine biosynthesis are known. So far, only the establishment of tobacco cell cultures with reduced UMPSase activity has been reported (100, 101). Screening of the available *Arabidopsis* T-DNA insertion lines for each step of the de novo synthesis pathway yielded only heterozygous T-DNA insertion lines, presumably because the homozygote mutant genotype was lethal (R. Zrenner, unpublished observations).

For this reason, metabolic inhibitors or transgenic plants with a partial inhibition or increase of expression are potent tools for functional analysis of this pathway. *Arabidopsis* seedlings grown in the presence of the ATCase inhibitor *N*-(phosphonacetyl)-L-aspartate (PALA) (16) show a general reduction in growth and development, and this reduction is accompanied by chlorosis. A complete functional analysis of the pyrimidine de novo synthesis pathway has recently been performed by using antisense and co-suppression strategies to create plants with reduced expression of each single gene involved (107). A stepwise reduction of the abundance of ATCase or DHOase protein resulted in an inhibition of growth with no further obvious pleiotropic effects on the visual appearance or even on the levels of pyrimidine nucleotides in the mature source organs. The major reason for the reduced organ size was a decreased cell number per organ; this observation indicates that reduced pyrimidine de novo synthesis is compensated for by reduced growth rates (107).

Another very interesting compensatory mechanism was found by organ-specific reduction of the expression of UMPSase (46).

Here, tuber-specific silencing of UMPSase lead to a decreased pyrimidine de novo synthesis that was accompanied by a stimulation of the less-energy-consuming salvage pathway. This stimulation leads to overcompensation, even higher pyrimidine levels in the tubers as compared to untransformed wild-type plants, and, subsequently, to a higher starch content in the tubers.

For the sake of completeness, CTP synthase, which catalyzes the amination of UTP to CTP in an energy consuming reaction, and thymidylate synthase, which produces dTMP, are also listed in **Table 1**. CTP synthases have not been analyzed in plants so far. Thymidylate synthase together with dihydrofolate reductase are located on a bi-functional protein found in *Arabidopsis* (74) and carrot (*Daucus carota*) (79). This organization is rather unusual when compared to microorganisms or the majority of higher eukaryotes.

Molecular Analysis of Pyrimidine Catabolism

Pyrimidine nucleotides are catabolized to pyrimidine nucleosides by removal of the phosphate group in a reaction catalyzed by 5'-nucleotidases [e.g., uridine monophosphate hydrolase (UMPH)]. The nucleosides are then converted to free pyrimidine bases by removal of the ribose group, in a reaction catalysed by nucleosidases [e.g., uridine nucleosidase (URH)]. As plants and animals do not possess cytosine deaminase, the nucleoside cytidine is deaminated by cytidine deaminase (CDA) to uridine, and the latter is then metabolized to uracil. The pyrimidine bases uracil and thymine are then degraded by a reductive pathway (138) in three sequential reactions catalyzed by dihydrouracil dehydrogenase (PYD1), dihydropyrimidinase (PYD2), and β-ureidopropionase (PYD3). Alternatively, uracil and the three nucleosides can be converted back to nucleotides via the salvage pathways (see below).

Chemically, the degradative pathway is a reversion of the de novo synthesis pathway

Table 1 Summary of enzymes involved in pyrimidine metabolism and experimental evidence of gene function

Number	Enzyme	Abbreviation	EC-Number	Refs.
1	Carbamoylphosphate synthase	CPSase	EC 6.3.5.5	—
2	Aspartate transcarbamoylase	ATCase	EC 2.1.3.2	(47, 87)
3	Dihydroorotase	DHOase	EC 3.5.2.3	(47)
4	Dihydroorotate dehydrogenase	DHODH	EC 1.3.99.11	(81, 130)
5	Orotate phosphoribosyltransferase	OPRTase	EC 2.4.2.10	(87)
6	Orotidine 5′-phosphate decarboxylase	ODCase	EC 4.1.1.23	(87)
7	Uridylate/cytidylate kinase	UMK	EC 2.7.4.4	(151)
8	Nucleoside diphosphate kinase	NDK	EC 2.7.4.6.	(148)
9	CTP synthase	—	EC 6.3.4.2	—
10	UDP-glucose pyrophosphorylase	UGPase	EC 2.7.7.9	(80)
11	Sucrose synthase	SuSy	EC 2.4.1.13	(14)
12	Nucleoside triphosphate phosphatase	NTPase	EC 3.6.1.15	—
13	Nucleoside diphosphate phosphatase	NDPase	EC 3.6.1.6	—
14	Apyrase	Apy	EC 3.6.1.5	(141)
15	Pyrimidine specific 5′-nucleotidase	UMPH	EC 3.1.3.5	—
16	Uridine/cytidine kinase	UK	EC 2.7.1.48	—
17	Uridine nucleosidase	URH	EC 3.2.2.3	—
18	Uracil phosphoribosyltransferase	UPRT	EC 2.4.2.9	—
19	PRPP synthase	PRS	EC 2.7.6.1	(73)
20	Cytidine deaminase	CDA	EC 3.5.4.5	(42, 133)
21	Dihydrouracil dehydrogenase	PYD1	EC 1.3.1.2	—
22	Dihydropyrimidinase	PYD2	EC 3.5.2.2	(50)
23	ß-ureidopropionase	PYD3	EC 3.5.1.6	(136)

and leads to the formation of β-alanine or β-aminobutyrate through the release of NH_3 and CO_2. It has been proposed that uracil degradation might be an important source of β-alanine as a precursor for pantothenate of coenzyme A (136). Pyrimidines (like purines, see below) can also be metabolized to secondary plant products with specific functions in defense. This latter metabolic pathway was recently summarized for pyrimidines by Kafer (64) and is not discussed in this review.

The entire *Arabidopsis* genome contains only one gene with homology to humans UMPH-1. However, cDNAs encoding proteins with UMPH activity have not yet been cloned and characterized from plants. Indeed, to date, plant 5′-nucleotidase activity has only been demonstrated for purine nucleotidases

(23, 52). Similarly, no cDNAs coding proteins with uridine nucleosidase activity have been cloned and characterized in plants. Analysis of the *Arabidopsis* genome reveals five different genes with high homology to inosine-uridine-preferring nucleoside hydrolase of *Leishmania major*. Activity of plant uridine nucleosidases was demonstrated in mung bean (1).

Two different cDNAs coding for cytidine deaminase activity have been cloned and characterized in *Arabidopsis* (42, 133). In the *Arabidopsis* genome, nine different genes have been found with high homology to CDAs, and transcription of these genes has been confirmed. The predicted mature proteins share higher homology with the *E. coli* enzyme than with the respective cytidine deaminases of other eukaryotes. Whether all these enzymes are involved in nucleotide degradation or whether any of these cytidine deaminases is involved in the RNA-editing process of plant mitochondria and chloroplasts is still unknown (126).

Plant cDNAs that code for proteins that potentially have dihydropyrimidine dehydrogenase activity have been identified by sequence homology to the human dihydropyrimidine dehydrogenase gene, PYD1. The proteins encoded by PYD1-homologous cDNAs from *Arabidopsis* (AF545062) and tomato (*Lycopersicon esculentum*; Accession number AF545063) together with the PYD1-homologous cDNAs of *Homo sapiens* (Accession number U09178), *Drosophila melanogaster* (Accession number U65491), and *Caenorhabditis elegans* (Accession number U39742) are phylogenetically related to the de novo biosynthetic DHODH enzymes (86). The amino acid sequences suggest that the plant protein is synthesized as precursor containing an N-terminal chloroplast-transit peptide. The predicted mature protein shares high homology with the enzyme of other eukaryotes, but the plant enzyme lacks the N-terminal domain harboring the NADPH binding site. This observation suggests that in plants another interacting protein is needed for complete function. Screening all commonly available expression data for coexpressed genes (120; see **http://csbdb.mpimp-golm.mpg.de**) containing a NADPH binding site and a predicted chloroplast localization signal did not reveal an obvious candidate for this putative gene.

A single PYD2 cDNA coding for dihydropyrimidinase has been characterized from plants (50). The deduced amino acid sequence suggests that the plant protein is synthesized as precursor containing an N-terminal signal peptide. Comparisons of the *Arabidopsis* cDNA with sequences of various other organisms indicates that PYD2 is phylogenetically related to the de novo biosynthetic DHOase enzymes (50).

Walsh et al. (136) have cloned and characterized the first plant cDNA encoding PYD3 from *Arabidopsis*. The predicted mature protein shares 55% homology with the enzyme of other eukaryotes. The deduced amino acid sequences suggest that the plant protein is located in the cytosol. The activity of maize (*Zea mays*) PYD3 has also been characterized (136), and it was shown that β-ureidopropionate (derived from uracil) and β-ureidoisobutyrate (derived from thymine) are both substrates.

The genomic organization of the uracil degradation is as simple as that of the de novo synthesis pathway: Single genes code for PYD1 to PYD3. The simple genomic organization is again superimposed by a rather complicated putative subcellular distribution, in which plastids, endoplasmic reticulum, and the cytosol host the mature proteins. Therefore, membrane transport of uracil degradation products has to be considered. AtGenExpress data of the expression atlas of *Arabidopsis* development (103) shows highly coordinated expression pattern of all three PYD genes, with a strong increase of expression in senescing leaves.

In contrast to the case with the de novo synthesis pathway, homozygous knockout mutants of the genes encoding for the three steps of uracil degradation can be isolated from *Arabidopsis*. These plants are no longer able to degrade uracil, but show no phenotypic difference to wild-type plants when grown under standard growth conditions in the greenhouse (R. Zrenner, unpublished observations). These results imply that the uracil degradation pathway is of minor importance in *Arabidopsis* under nonstress conditions.

Molecular Analysis of Pyrimidine Salvage

As we discuss above, nucleotides are catabolized to pyrimidine nucleosides and free bases by sequential action of 5′-nucleotidases (e.g., UMPH) and nucleosidases (e.g., URH). As de novo synthesis of nucleotides is very energy consuming (see above), cells have developed a strategy to reuse preformed nucleosides and nucleobases through salvage reactions. The nucleosides uridine/cytidine and thymidine are salvaged to their respective nucleotides by specific nucleoside kinases [uridine kinase (UK) and thymidine kinase (TK)] and uracil is directly salvaged with PRPP into UMP via uracil phosphoribosyltransferase (UPRT).

Most plant tissues analyzed so far contain much higher activity of UK than UPRT (8). Although UK activity has been repeatedly characterized in plants (37, 38), to date no plant cDNA has been functionally characterized. Two cDNAs coding for putative UK activity have been identified in the *Arabidopsis* genome, and their transcription is confirmed by expression data of commonly available sources (103, 146). So far no TK activity or plant cDNAs have been functionally characterized. Two *Arabidopsis* cDNAs coding for putative TK activity are identified in the *Arabidopsis* genome, and their transcription has been confirmed by expression data of commonly available sources (103, 146).

From the pyrimidine bases, only uracil is directly salvaged into UMP, in a PRPP-dependent reactin catalyzed by UPRT (21). So far only one cDNA from *Arabidopsis* has been cloned (Accession number AF116860). This UPRT is structurally similar to phosphoribosyltransferases of other organisms and is presumably located in the cytosol. The completion of the *Arabidopsis* genome sequence revealed that PRPP synthetase and UPRT are encoded by small gene families, and that different members may be located in the cytosol or the plastid. Expression data of commonly available sources (103, 146) confirm that all isoforms are differentially expressed. From this finding it is assumed that salvage of pyrimidines may occur in the cytosol and the plastids.

Salvage pathways may also play an important role in providing nucleobases to cells, which are unable to synthesize sufficient amounts for their needs. Recently the physiological substrates of the homologues of the ureide permease (UPS) transporters in *Arabidopsis* have been identified as being uracil and potentially other nucleobases (104). It has also been demonstrated that the gene family of equilibrative nucleoside transporters (ENT) encodes proteins that transport purine and pyrimidine nucleosides with the same specificity (62). So far no mutant in the pyrimidine salvage pathway is known.

PURINE METABOLISM

Molecular Analysis of Purine de novo Synthesis

Purine nucleotides are synthesized de novo from small molecules like the amino acids glycine, glutamine, and aspartate, the activated ribose precursor PRPP, 10-formyl tetrahydrofolate, and carbon dioxide. The basic biochemical and molecular analysis of purine biosynthesis has been done in microorganisms (94, 150, 151) and animals (22). Detailed molecular and biochemical studies (61, 82, 113, 132), the complete *Arabidopsis* genome (19, 127), and the available sequence information from the rice genome (e.g., **http://rice.tigr.org**) reveal that plants synthesize IMP, AMP, and GMP using similar reactions to those found in microorganisms and animals. The 14 enzymatic reactions of the pathway of the purine biosynthesis are summarized in **Figure 2** and **Table 2**.

The purine biosynthesis starts with the formation of phosphorybosylamine (PRA) from PRPP and glutamine. This first and initial reaction of the purine biosynthesis is catalyzed by PRPP amidotransferase (ATase). GAR synthetase catalyzes the ATP dependent formation of glycine amide ribonucleotide (GAR) by attaching glycine via an amide bond to PRA. GAR is subsequently transformylated by the enzyme GAR transformylase (GART) using 10-formyltetrahydrofolate (10F-THF) to form formylglycinamide ribonucleotide (FGAR). The next step is catalyzed by formylglycinamidine ribonucleotide (FGAM) synthetase (FGAMS), consumes ATP and glutamine, and leads to the formation of FGAM. FGAM then undergoes ring closure to form 5-aminoimidazole

Table 2 Summary of enzymes involved in purine metabolism and experimental evidence of gene function

Number	Enzyme/Transporter	Abbreviation	EC/TC-Number	Refs.
24	PRPP amidotransferase	ATase	EC 2.4.2.14	(70, 132)
25	GAR synthase	GARS	EC 6.3.4.13	(105)
26	GAR transformylase	GART	EC 2.1.2.2	(105)
27	FGAM synthase	FGAMS	EC 6.3.5.3	—
28	AIR synthase	AIRS	EC 6.3.3.1	(110)
29	AIR carboxylase	AIRC	EC 4.1.1.21	(28)
30	SAICAR synthase	SAICARS	EC 6.3.2.6	(109)
31	Adenylosuccinate lyase	ASL	EC 4.3.2.2	—
32	AICAR transformylase/IMP cyclohydrolase	ATIC	EC 2.1.2.3 EC 3.5.4.10	(17)
33	Adenylosuccinate synthase	ASS	EC 6.3.4.4	(45)
34	Adenylate kinase	AMK	EC 2.7.4.3	(68)
35	StBT1 adenine nucleotide uniporter	StBT1		(76)
36	AMP deaminase	AMPD	EC 3.5.4.6	(144)
37	IMP dehydrogenase	IMPDH	EC 1.1.1.205	(25, 108)
38	GMP synthase	GMPS	EC 6.3.5.2	—
39	Guanosine deaminase	—	EC 3.5.4.15	—
40	Adenosine phosphorylase	Ade Pase	EC 2.4.2.1	—
41	Adenosine nucleosidase	Ado Nase	EC 3.2.2.1	—
42	Adenosine kinase	Ado kinase	EC 2.7.1.20	(82)
43	Nucleoside phosphotransferase	NPT	EC 2.7.1.77	—
44	Adenine phosphoribosyltransferase	APT	EC 2.4.2.7	(3)
45	Inosine–guanosine phosphorylase	PNPase	EC 2.4.2.1	—
46	Inosine–guanosine kinase	InoK	EC 2.7.1.73	—
47	Hypoxanthine–guanine phosphoribosyltransferase	HGRT	EC 2.4.2.8	—
48	PUP purine permease transporters		TC 2.A.7.14	(24)
49	ENT equilibrative nucleoside transporters		TC 2.A.57	(143)
50	NAT nucleobase transportes, xanthine-uracil permeases		TC 2.A.40	(2)
51	UPS ureide permeases, allantoine transporters			(104)
52	5′(tm) nucleotidase	NMPase	EC 3.1.3.5	—
53	Inosine-guanosine nucleosidase	Ino Nase	EC 3.2.2.2	—
54	Xanthine dehydrogenase	XDH	EC 1.1.1.204	(57, 149)
55	Guanine deaminase	GuaD	EC 3.5.4.15	—
56	Uricase	—	EC 1.7.3.3	(125)
57	Allantoinase, allantoin amidohydrolase	ALNase	EC 3.5.2.5	(147)
58	Allantoicase, allantoate amidohydrolase	—	EC 3.5.3.4	—
59	Urease	—	EC 3.5.1.5	—
60	Ureidoglycolate lyase	—	EC 4.3.2.3	—
61	Allantoin deaminase	—	EC 3.5.3.9	—
62	Ureidoglycine amidohydrolase	—		—
63	Ureidoglycolate hydrolase	—	EC 3.5.3.19	—

ribonucleotide (AIR) by consuming an additional molecule of ATP. This reaction is catalyzed by AIR-synthase (AIRS). To build the second ring of the purine skeleton CO_2, aspartate, and a second molecule 10F-THF are inserted. AIR is carboxylated by AIR carboxylase to 4-carboxy aminoimidazole ribonucleotide (CAIR). Adding aspartate and using a further molecule ATP, N-succinyl-5-aminoimidazole-4-carboxamide ribonucleotide (SAICAR) is formed. This step is catalyzed by SAICAR synthase. Fumarate is released to build 5-aminoimidazole-4-carboxamide ribonucleotide (AICAR), catalyzed by adenylosuccinate lyase (ASL). The last two steps to form the first complete purine molecule IMP are catalyzed by the bifunctional enzyme 5-aminoimidazole-4-carboxamide ribonucleotide formyltransferase/inosine monophosphate cyclohydrolase (ATIC). In the first part of this reaction the final carbon of the purine ring is provided by 10F-THF to form 5-formaminoimidazole-4-carboxamide ribonucleotide (FAICAR). FAICAR undergoes dehydration and ring closure to form IMP.

After IMP, the purine biosynthesis divides in two branches. Adenosine monophosphate is synthesized by replacing the carboxyl group at C6 by an amino group. This amino group is provided by aspartate and guanosine triphosphate (GTP) is the donor for the energy rich phosphate bond to form adenylosuccinate (SAMP). This reaction is catalyzed by the enzyme SAMP synthase (ASS). The removal of fumarate to form AMP is catalyzed by ASL. The second branch to GMP is initiated by the oxidation of IMP followed by the insertion of an amino group that is provided by glutamine. Xanthosine monophosphate (XMP) is formed by IMP dehydrogenase (IMPDH) using NAD as the hydrogen acceptor. The final step to form GMP is catalyzed by GMP synthase (GMPS).

As we discuss above for pyrimidine biosynthesis, the genomic and pathway organization of purine biosynthesis differs from that in microorganisms and higher eukaryotes (19). Prokaryotes harbor single genes encoding monofunctional proteins (except for the bifunctional ATIC), whereas other higher eukaryotes contain single genes encoding mono-, bi-, and trifunctional proteins (113); these are probably organized as enzyme complexes in mammals (30). The organization of the purine biosynthesis pathway in plants is more similar to prokaryotes, with monofunctional proteins, except for the bifunctional enzymes AIRC and ATIC (**Figure 2**).

In *Arabidopsis*, most of the enzymes involved in purine biosynthesis are encoded by single copy genes, with the exception of *Arabidopsis* (At) *PURF* (encoding ATase) and *AtPURB* (ASL). *AtPURF* is encoded by a small gene family of three members and the *AtPURB* (ASL) is encoded by two genes (19). Likewise, the AIR carboxylase that catalyzes the sixth step of the purine biosynthesis is encoded by two potentially redundant genes.

Cloning of the *PUREK* gene from *Vigna aconitifolia* revealed that plant AIR-carboxylases are derived from a fusion of PURK and PURE-like proteins, with both domains encoded by a single gene (28). In *Arabidopsis* one locus, *AtPUREK1* (At2g37690), has been annotated as a complete *PUREK* gene. A second locus (*AtPurEK2*) is annotated as encoding only the PurE domain (At2g05140), but contains further upstream sequence fragments homologous to a PurK domain but with a large deletion; this observation indicates *AtPUREK2* may be a nonfunctional cDNA or a pseudogene.

cDNAs encoding ATase were first isolated from *Arabidopsis* (63) and functionally characterized by complementation of an purine auxotroph *E.coli* mutant in *G. max* and *V. aconitifolia* (69). The in planta function was demonstrated by complementation of an *Arabidopsis* T-DNA insertional mutant (132). The *Araibidopsis* genome contains three genes encoding ATases in *Arabidopsis*. In *N. tabacum*, only one ATase isoform could be isolated to date (132).

The reaction catalyzed by ATase involves the conversion of PRPP to PRA, using glutamine as the source for the amide group. This reaction is carried out by two separate catalytic domains: Ammonia is released at the glutaminase domain and channelled to the PRPP binding site in the phosphoribosyltransferase domain (150). Both catalytic domains are conserved in plant ATases. As described for microorganisms (94, 150) and other higher eukaryotes, plant ATases are subjected to feedback regulation by the final products of the purine biosynthesis and the purine salvage pathways (98). Plant ATases so far analyzed display the typical conserved protein structures of type I ATases, containing a propeptide preceding the first cysteine and four conserved cysteine residues that are ligands to a [4Fe-4S] cluster and crucial for catalytic activity and feedback regulation (63, 69, 70).

Complementation of purine auxotrophic *E. coli* and/or yeast mutants has been taken as a strategy to clone and functionally verify the genes encoding the second (*GARS*) and third (*GART*) steps of the pathway from *A. thaliana*, *G. max*, and *S. tuberosum* (105, 132), the genes encoding the fifth (*AIRS*), sixth (*AIRC*), and seventh (*SAICARS*) from *Arabidopsis* and *Vigna* (28, 109, 110), and the gene encoding the bifunctional enzyme that catalyzes the last steps in IMP synthesis (*ATIC*) from *N. tabacum* (17), as well as the gene catalyzing the first reaction in the synthesis of AMP (*ASS*) from *Arabidopsis*, *Zea mays*, and *Triticum aestivum* (45) (summarized in **Table 2**). Special features of the *Arabidopsis* genes have recently been reviewed by Moffatt and Ashihara (82).

All of the genes encoding enzymes required for the ten-step synthesis of IMP (**Figure 2**) contain sequences that are predicted to encode N-terminal plastid-transit peptides. This observation indicates a chloroplast localization of this portion of the purine biosynthesis. Experimental evidence for a chloroplastic localization has been provided for the *Arabidopsis* ATases (61) and for AIRS from the tropical legume *V. unguiculata* (Cowpea) (114). For the other enzymes, the proposed subcellular localization has not been experimentally confirmed.

The situation may be more complex in specialized nitrogen-fixing tropical legumes. Here, biochemical evidence shows that at least part of the pathway leading to IMP occurs in mitochondria as well as plastids (12). One case has been established in which an enzyme of the purine biosynthesis is dually targeted to either chloroplasts or mitochondria. In the tropical legume *V. unguiculata* the AIR synthase is encoded by a single copy gene (113). The enzyme was immunolocalized in chloroplasts and mitochondria and separately purified from both organelles. Amino acid sequencing of both isoforms revealed a five-amino-acids-longer N terminus for the mitochondrial AIR synthase; this observation indicates a different processing, due to N-terminal signal sequences that contain elements of a plastidic and a mitochondrial targeting sequence (49). However, so far there is no evidence for dual targeting of the other nine enzymes required for IMP synthesis in cowpea, nor has dual targeting been shown for any of the proteins in other plant species.

The cDNAs encoding the enzymes for AMP synthesis from IMP, ASL, and ASS were cloned from different plant sources (45, 132) and shown to contain putative plastid transit sequences; this observation indicates that the AMP branch point pathway is located in chloroplasts. In contrast, the genes encoding IMPDH and GMPS, which are involved in the branch of the purine biosynthesis pathway leading to GMP (25, 132), do not contain N-terminal transit peptides; this observation indicates that the synthesis of XMP and GMP may occur in the cytosol. Experimental evidence for this assumption is missing. A cytosolic localization of GMP synthesis via IMP and XMP receives indirect support from biochemical tracer experiments. When [8-^{14}C]-hypoxanthine is supplied to soybean embryo axes or Jerusalem artichoke shoots (4, 75), it selectively labels the guanine nucleotide pool rather than the adenine nucleotide pool. This observation is consistent with the transformation of hypoxanthine via the cytosolic purine salvage pathway into IMP, which preferentially enters the GMP synthesis branch of purine metabolism but is compartmented from the plastidic pathway that converts IMP into AMP.

The occurrence of IMPDH in the cytosol implies that de novo synthesized IMP has to cross the plastid envelope membranes. There are only limited data (111) to support this idea, and more research is required to understand how de novo synthesized IMP enters the cytosolic pathway. Similar questions arise for the export of AMP after its synthesis in the plastid. The recent discovery of a novel plastidic adenine nucleotide uniporter from *S. tuberosum* (76) might help to resolve these issues. The StBT1 uniporter resides in the inner plastid envelope and exports the adenine nucleotides AMP, ADP, and ATP with high substrate specificities and apparent K_m values of 350 μM from the chloroplast and might supply the cytosol with purine nucleotides (76). De novo synthesized IMP in the plastid could be converted to AMP via the plastidic branch of purine biosynthesis, exported into the cytosol (**Figure 2**), and then converted back into IMP via AMP deaminase in order to feed the cytosolic branch of the purine synthesis pathway.

Regulation of Purine de novo Biosynthesis

Following initial studies of genes involved in purine biosynthesis in N-fixing tropical legumes (113), all the genes involved in purine biosynthesis have now been isolated and partially characterized in non-N-fixing plants like *Arabidopsis*, *N. tabacum* (Nt), and *S. tuberosum* (19, 61, 82, 132). These genes include the recently cloned genes *AtPURL* and *NtPURL* (which encode FGAMS) *NtGUAA* (which encodes GMPS) and *NtPURH* (which encodes ATIC) (17, 132).

Earlier expression analyses (109), particularly of the *Arabidopsis PURC* gene encoding SAICARS, revealed that purine biosynthesis genes are basically expressed in mitotically active tissues and are primarily involved in the process of cell division. The expression of the complete pathway has now been analyzed in *N. tabacum* (132). In *N. tabacum*, all genes of the purine biosynthesis show their strongest expression in ovaries; this observation implicates their function in cell division. Most of those genes are expressed at lower levels in a constitutive manner; this observation indicates housekeeping functions for these genes. In contrast, the genes encoding GMPS, SAICAS, and IMPDH were specifically expressed in *N. tabacum* sink leaves and floral organs. Different expression patterns could also be observed for the *NtPURF*, *NtPURL*, and *NtPURH* genes during flower development (132). This expression analysis clearly showed transcriptional regulation of purine biosynthesis genes during plant development and, furthermore, indicates that the expression of purine biosynthesis genes is not solely confined to meristematic tissues.

As we describe above, PRPP aminotransferase is encoded by a small gene family in *Arabidopsis*. The genes encoding *Arabidopsis* ATase1-3 isoforms are differently expressed (18, 61): *AtATase1* is specifically expressed in roots and flower organs but absent in leaves, *AtATase2* is rather constitutively expressed, whereas *AtATase3* is weakly expressed but is highest in flowers (18). Those expression patterns could be verified by using microarray data (103).

In association with investigations of cyst nematode resistance two genes encoding FGAMS were isolated from soybean (131). Both genes show high sequence homologies on the nucleotide and deduced amino acid level. The promoters of both genes were isolated and truncated versions were fused to green fluorescent protein (GFP) and β-glucuronidase (GUS). It was shown that both genes are nematode inducible; in addition, it was shown that FGAMS1 exhibits basically housekeeping functions and was found responsive whereas FGAMS2 may respond to specific environmental stimuli. A specific nematode responsive *cis*-regulatory element could not be detected in either of the FGAM promoters (131).

The organization of the *Arabidopsis* ATases as a small gene family raises the question of whether individual members of this family fulfil specialized functions. To tackle this question, reverse and forward genetic strategies have been followed to study their respective physiological functions in transgenic and mutant plants.

Recently transgenic tobacco plants with reduced *NtATase* transcript and reduced Atase activity and *Arabidopsis* T-DNA insertional mutants for *AtAtase1* and *AtAtase2* [e.g., *Atatd2* (aminotransferase deficient)] as well as an EMS mutant called *Atcia1* (chloroplast import apparatus) were isolated (61, 132). The *cia1* mutant was isolated in a transgene based screening to isolate *Arabidopsis* mutants defective in chloroplast import. Positional cloning of the *CIA1* locus revealed that it encodes AtATase2 (61, 123). The transgenic tobacco plants as well as the *atd2* and *cia1* mutants revealed a similar phenotype, which is characterized by strong growth retardation and chlorotic leaves; however the plants grow and set seed. A special feature of the *Arabidopsis atd2* and *cia1* is the formation of green cotyledons but chlorotic leaves. Furthermore, it was observed that the *atd2* mutant did not form an organized thylakoid membrane structure. First biochemical analysis showed reduced adenine and guanine nucleotide levels in the *cia1* mutant (61) and reduced ATase activity in transgenic tobacco plants (132). Complementation experiments were done genetically and biochemically. The *AtATase2* cDNA under the control of the 35S constitutive promoter complements both the *atd2* and *cia1* mutants' phenotype (61, 132). Interestingly, the *AtATase1* cDNA fused to the 35S promoter and transformed in the *cia1* mutant background can completely restore the phenotype; this observation indicates that AtATase1 can functionally substitute AtATase2. Localization experiments (61) clearly demonstrate that both isoforms are localized exclusively in the chloroplasts of *Arabidopsis* leaves. An *AtATase1* knockout mutant appeared wild type, and a double mutant of *ATase1/cia1* was indistinguishable from *cia1*. The expression profile of the *AtAtase* genes and the mutant analysis showed that ATase2 is clearly the major isoenzyme for plant growth (61).

This molecular and functional analysis of the ATase isozyme system (61, 132) provided conclusive evidence for the strong impact of the ATase isoforms on plant growth and development and indicates the central function of ATases in plant purine biosynthesis. Furthermore, the dramatic effects of the *atd2* and *cia1* mutations on chloroplast development and the chloroplast import machinery link purine biosynthesis and chloroplast development. The underlying mechanisms still have to be resolved.

Molecular Analysis of Purine Catabolism

Purine catabolism plays a central role in plant nitrogen metabolism. Animals and other higher primates lack the enzyme uricase, and the final product of the purine catabolism is uric acid, which is excreted as the main source of waste nitrogen. Plants depend on an effective nitrogen utilization, and store rather than excrete nitrogen (113). In most plants the purine nucleotides are oxidatively degraded via uric acid and allantoin to CO_2 and NH_3, which is then reassimilated via the glutamine oxoglutarate aminotransferase (GOGAT) pathway (108, 129). All enzymes biochemically detected in the plant purine catabolism and the respective characterized genes are summarized in **Figure 2** and **Table 2**.

Following the conversion of AMP to IMP by AMP deaminase (AMPD), there are two possible routes for the subsequent catabolism of adenine nucleotides. IMP is either dephosphorylated to inosine by 5'-nucleotidases or phosphatases, subsequently hydrolyzed to hypoxanthine by inosine/guanine nucleosidase

(13), and further transformed to xanthine via xanthine dehydrogenase (XDH); alternatively, IMP is transformed to XMP by IMPDH and further metabolized by 5′-nucleotidases to xanthosine, which is then transformed to xanthine by inosine/guanine nucleosidase (**Figure 2**). The latter route seems to be specific for tropical legumes like soybean (108). Both routes of adenine nucleotide degradation depend on AMPD, as plants do not contain adenine deaminase (145) and adenosine deaminase (75, 82, 115). In contrast to adenine and adenosine deaminase, guanosine deaminase could be detected in plants; this observation indicates that guanine nucleotides are degraded by dephosphorylation yielding guanosine, which is then deaminated to xanthosine or transformed to guanine by inosine/guanine nucleosidase leading to xanthine. These pathways converge on xanthine, which is a central metabolite in purine degradation prior to purine ring cleavage (10, 115).

The subsequent degradation of the purine base xanthine is performed by xanthine dehydrogenase and leads to the formation of uric acid. Uricase then converts uric acid to allantoin, which is subsequently converted to allantoate by the enzyme allantoinase (115). The ureides allantoin and allantoate are important nitrogen storage and transport compounds in tropical legumes (113). Allantoic acid is transformed to either ureidoglycolate or ureidoglycine, which are further metabolized to produce the final products of the purine catabolism NH_3, CO_2, and glyoxylate. Those end products may be reused in photosynthesis (CO_2) or reassimilated by the photorespiratory glycolate and GOGAT cycle.

In addition to recycling carbon and nitrogen, the purine catabolic pathways have an important and essential function in the synthesis of the alkaloids theobromine and caffeine (6, 9). These methylated xanthine derivatives play a role in the defense of young leaf tissues against insect grub or are released into the soil to inhibit the germination of seeds from other plant species. Furthermore, these derivatives

are interesting candidates for the biotechnological manipulation of crop plants to produce decaffeinated beverages (9).

Recently molecular analyses on purine catabolism enzymes and genes emerged for AMPD, XDH, uricase and allantoinase. AMPD previously has been viewed as a central enzyme of purine catabolism (115). As the AtAMPD amino acid sequence does not contain an N-terminal transit peptide, the protein is expected to accumulate in the cytosol. A crucial role for AMPD in plant development was recently emphasized by the characterization of the embryogenic factor 1 (FAC1) in *Arabidopsis* (144). FAC1 was identified by screening an EMS-mutagenized *Arabidopsis* population and by positional cloning of the respective locus. The gene encodes AMPD and, when mutagenized, causes a zygote-lethal embryonic phenotype. An *Arabidopsis* T-DNA insertional mutant also showed this phenotype (144). Furthermore, AMPD was identified as a potent herbicide target (34). The microbial compound carbocyclic conformycin in its phosphorylated form is a strong inhibitor of the AMP deaminase, and, when applied to plants, leads to rapid death (34). This observation may indicate that AMPD operates as a crucial intersection for cytosolic purine biosynthesis and catabolism.

XDH catalyzes the oxidation of hypoxanthine to xanthine and uric acid and is a metallo-flavo enzyme requiring FAD and the molybdenum cofactor sulfurase. In *Arabidopsis*, two isoforms were recently discovered and characterized at the molecular and biochemical level (57, 149). In *Arabidopsis*, XDH is encoded by two genes that are orientated in tandem and separated by 704 bp on chromosome 4 in the *Arabidopsis* genome. Both XDHs are expressed differently. Whereas *AtXDH2* is expressed constitutively, *AtXDH1* transcription is induced by drought, salt, and abscisic acid (ABA) treatment; this observation indicates that AtXDH1 is the major component in hypoxanthine oxidation. Heterologous overexpression of XDHA1 protein shows it forms a homodimer with subunits of 150 KDa and utilizes hypoxanthine and xanthine as main substrates. The activity of XDH1 is strongly inhibited by allopurinol known to be a strong inhibitor of XDHs. XDH belongs to the class of xanthine oxidoreductases, which in mammals exist as xanthine dehydrogenases or as O_2-dependant xanthine oxidases. The *Arabidopsis* XDHs are strict dehydrogenases, but produce superoxide radicals; this observation indicates that plant XDHs might also be involved in stress responses that require reactive oxygen species (57). The production of reactive oxygen species and the upregulation of *Arabidopsis* and tomato XDHs transcripts by ABA treatment or water stress indicate that this enzyme reaction might be an additional and novel source of reactive oxygen species (57, 149).

Uricase catalyzes the formation of allantoin and has been intensively investigated in nitrogen fixing legumes. In these studies it was discovered as a nodule-specific gene from soybean and designated as Nod-35 (125). In soybean, which is a specialized symbiotic species, uricase plays an important role to produce ureides as nitrogen storage and transport intermediates and may have a function in the process of plant microbe interaction (56).

The next reactions in purine degradation are performed by allantoinase, which converts allantoin into allantoate (115). Allantoinases from tropical legumes (108) and more recently from *Arabidopsis* (147) have been characterized at the biochemical and molecular level. In *Arabidopsis* the single copy gene and the corresponding cDNA have been characterized. The encoded polypeptide contains an N-terminal signal peptide for the secretory pathway, and this observation corresponds to biochemical results that locate allantoinase activity to peroxisomes or the endoplasmatic reticulum (53). The functional analysis was done by complementation of a yeast mutant deficient in allantoin hydrolysis and isolation of a T-DNA insertion mutant, which was characterized as incapable to grow on minimal media supplemented with allantoine (147). The further metabolization of ureides may follow one of two possible routes (**Figure 2**) yielding either ureidoglycine or ureidoglycolate, which are further decomposed to glyoxylate and urea that is transformed to ammonia and carbondioxide by the enzyme urease. When analyzing the *Arabidopsis* genome as a non-N-fixing plant only one gene could be found with homologies to uricase and urease. Immunolocalization and in situ hybridization experiments indicate peroxisomes as the ureide-producing organelle in N-fixing legumes (125). The subcellular localization of the purine catabolic enzymes seems to be in the cytosol and in peroxisomes. However, experimental evidence in non-legume plant species still has to be provided.

Molecular Analysis of the Purine Salvage Pathway

Whereas the de novo pathway has a high demand for energy and uses five nucleotides to produce AMP or seven to synthesize GMP, the purine salvage pathway preserves energy by using just one ATP. The salvage pathway or cycle serves to regenerate the plant nucleotide pools by inter-converting purine bases, nucleosides, and nucleotides that are derived from plant cell metabolism and catabolism (e.g., nucleic acid turnover, adenine, and adenosine release during methionine and ethylene synthesis) (82, 106).

The interconversion of purines is summarized in **Figure 2** and includes the action of several enzymes. The purine bases adenine and guanine can be converted to the respective monophosphates by adenine and hypoxanthine/guanine phosphoribosyltransferases (APT and HGPT, respectively) using PRPP as the source of ribose phosphate. Another route to recycle purine bases is catalyzed by adenine or inosine/guanosine phosphorylases. The conversion of adenosine, inosine, and guanosine to IMP, XMP, and GMP can be catalyzed by adenosine and inosine/guanine kinases or nucleoside phosphotransferases. Additionally, Ado deaminase, guanosine deaminase, and Ado nucleosidase contribute to the purine salvage reactions (**Figure 2**). The occurrence of Ado deaminase in plant is still a matter of debate, as the activity of this enzyme could not unambiguously be demonstrated in plants. In the *Arabidopsis* genome one gene (At4g04880) is annotated as a putative Ado deaminase, and its expression could be verified (106).

A comprehensive biochemical and molecular analysis for the central salvage enzymes, adenine phosphoribosyltransferases (APT) and Ado kinases, has been carried out in *Arabidopsis* (82). APT is represented by a multigene family encoding five isoenzymes. None of the AtAPTs contain N-terminal signal sequences, and by immunolocalization it could be demonstrated that APT1, APT2, and APT3 are localized in the cytosol (3). The *Arabidopsis* Ado kinase, which phosphorylates Ado to AMP, is encoded by two genes. Microarray analyses indicate that Ado kinase may function in transmethylation reactions involved in cell-wall biosynthesis and seed filling (106). ADK1 and ADK2 are constitutively expressed, which classifies the ADKs as housekeeping enzymes (3, 82). In contrast to the well-established adenine recycling, investigations on the guanine/guanosine salvage are restricted to biochemical evidences of activities for HGPT, guanosine nucleosidase, and guanosine deaminase in diverse plant species (5).

The purine salvage enzymes adenine phosphoribosyltranserases (APTs) and Ado kinase also play a crucial role in the interconversion of cytokinins (82). The naturally occurring cytokinins are N^6-substituted adenine derivatives. These derivatives are generally synthesized by the addition of isopentenyl to AMP to yield isopentenyladenosine monophosphate. The isoprenoid derivative side chain is then modified to lead to the formation of the different cytokinin derivatives. An alternative pathway, synthesizing cytokinins directly from AMP, has been described recently for *Arabidopsis* (11). It is generally assumed that the free base and the riboside derivatives are the biological active forms of the cytokinins (11); therefore, an interconversion of free base cytokinins to nucleoside and nucleotide cytokinins seems to be necessary. In vitro assays with APTs (3) and adenosine kinase (83) showed the crucial role of these adenine salvage enzymes for cytokinin metabolism.

MOLECULAR ANALYSIS OF NUCLEOTIDE PHOSPHOTRANSFER

The levels of the respective purine and pyrimidine nucleoside mono-, di-, and triphosphates are equilibrated in cells and also subcellular compartments (see above). This process of nucleotide phosphotransfer is catalyzed by mono- and diphosphate kinases, specific for the respective purine and pyrimidine nucleotides. The reversible transphosphorylation reaction interconverting ADP to ATP and AMP is catalyzed by adenylate kinases (AMK). This reaction is considered a key step in energy metabolism (92) and is essential to recycle AMP and ADP that are formed in reactions where ATP donates energy to drive reactions in intermediary metabolism. Distinct nucleoside mono- and diphosphate kinases are involved in the transfer of energy from the adenine into the uridine and other nucleotide systems. For example, UMP is the end product of the pyrimidine de novo synthesis pathway. It is further phosphorylated to UDP and UTP in two ATP consuming reactions catalyzed by uridine monophosphate kinase (UMK) and nucleoside diphosphate kinase (NDK), respectively. These reactions are also required to recycle UMP and UDP that are formed in reactions that consume UTP or UDP-sugars or formed after degradation of nucleic acids.

cDNAs encoding AMKs have been cloned from a wide range of plant species, and the specificity of the adenylate kinase reaction has been demonstrated for one cDNA of rice (68). In the complete *Arabidopsis* genome, seven genes can be found that belong to this type of kinase. The sequence shows a distant relationship to the three genes coding for the eukaryotic type of UMK (see below). Soluble adenylate kinase isoforms occur in different subcellular compartments including plastids, mitochondria, and the cytosol (102). The deduced amino acid sequences of the seven expressed genes suggest that some of the plant proteins are synthesized as precursors containing either chloroplast or mitochondrial transit peptides.

One *Arabidopsis* cDNA coding for UMK activity has been cloned and characterized (152, 153). It has been demonstrated that this plant enzyme equally accepts UMP and CMP as substrate and is insensitive to UTP and GTP. The complete *Arabidopsis* genome contains three differentially expressed genes that encode the eukaryotic type of UMK. In addition, plants also contain another type of uridylate kinases belonging to the amino acid kinase protein family; these kinases have very high homology to uridylate kinases of *Lactococcus lactis*. Two genes of this type of uridylate kinase can be found in *Arabidopsis*. Although one of these two genes is much higher expressed than the eukaryotic type, it has not yet be shown whether the encoded proteins are functional plant uridylate kinases.

The nucleoside diphosphate kinases are highly conserved between all species analyzed. The substrate specificity of NDKs is rather unspecific; therefore the reaction of a nucleoside diphosphate kinase can be generalized as follows: $NDP + ATP \rightarrow NTP + ADP$. NDKs are classified in three types: Type I NDKs contain no targeting sequence and are located in the cytosol, type II have an N-terminal extension targeting GFP fusion proteins into the chloroplast stroma, and type III are localized to the intermembrane space in plant mitochondria (124), where they interact with the adenine nucleotide transporter (72).

In striking contrast to the genes involved in the de novo synthesis and catabolism, those which encode the phosphotransfer enzymes comprise small gene families of three to seven family members. UMK, AMK, and

NDK isoforms are located in the plastids and in the cytosol, whereas in mitochondria only AMK and NDK are present (55, 102; R. Zrenner, unpublished observations). One prokaryotic type UMK is also found in the nucleus (R. Zrenner, unpublished observations). Whether this fact is of regulatory importance needs to be analyzed.

AtGenExpress data of the expression atlas of *Arabidopsis* development (103) shows distinct expression patterns for each of the family members that are represented on the ATH1 full genome array (95). A screen of all commonly available expression data sets for coexpressed genes (120; **http://csbdb.mpimpgolm.mpg.de**) reveals that none of the genes is coexpressed with the de novo synthesis pathway. Considering leaf developmental processes only, a developmental gradient, found for most genes of the de novo synthesis pathway, was also found for one AMK, one UMK and three of the NDK genes.

The activity of NDKs is very high in plants (59), and the enzymes are not known to be regulated allosterically. However, most of the molecular research has concentrated on the possible involvement of NDKs in signal transduction pathways. Plant NDKs have protein kinase activity (135), and it was shown that they are autophosphorylating (84). In humans, NDK was identified as the tumor suppressor nm23 (35). It has been shown that plant NDK2 specifically interacts with two H_2O_2- activated, mitogen-activated kinases (85). It has also been suggested that NDK isoforms in *Arabidopsis* are involved in phytochrome B response (29) and UV-B light signaling (155).

It is assumed that AMK is important to keep the adenine nucleotides in a homeostatic status in living cells (see above). In this case, reduced expression or inhibition of gene activity should be detrimental. The surprising results of two studies indicate that specific AMKs may also have other roles, or that the relation between the recycling of AMP and metabolism is more complicated than previously suspected. Regierer et al. (96) found that tuber-specific reduction of a plastid AMK leads to an observable increase in the total adenylate pool as well as improved starch content in transgenic potato plants (96). Carrari et al. (26) recently reported that *Arabidopsis* mutants with a knockout of the most homologous AMK isoform showed elevated amino acid biosynthesis and enhanced growth, but unaltered starch content in leaves and reduced starch content in roots. Taken together, these results suggest a role for plastid AMK in the coordination of metabolism and growth in a tissue-dependant manner. Another possibility may be that the increased AMP levels or changed ATP/ADP ratios may actually favor certain processes in plants.

For completeness, (*a*) guanylate kinase (GMK), which catalyzes the transfer of a phosphoryl group from ATP to GMP to GDP, and (*b*) thymidylate kinase, which produces dTDP form dTMP, are listed here. Neither enzyme has been analyzed in plants so far.

INTERACTION OF THE DE NOVO AND SALVAGE PATHWAYS THROUGHOUT PLANT DEVELOPMENT

Different types of plant systems have been used in the past to study the physiological aspects of pyrimidine metabolism; these systems range from unsynchronized cell suspension cultures to whole plants. The changes in nucleotide metabolism in various cell cultures during the different growth phases have been summarized in References 134 and 115. Using ^{14}C-labeled-precursor feeding experiments it was shown that, in the initial lag phase of growth, nucleotides are produced mainly by salvaging of nucleosides and nucleobases. During further growth of the cell cultures, this process is replaced by the de novo synthesis of nucleotides during the cell division phase (8, 66). Further analysis of the different processes during the individual phases of the cell cycle in a synchronized cell culture might be very informative but has not yet been performed.

During the process of seed germination, a comparable behavior is found. The first phase of seed germination is characterized by high enzyme activity of the pyrimidine salvage reactions (116, 117), which are replaced by the de novo synthesis pathway later in development (5). In contrast, in developing embryos of *Pices glauca*, the de novo pathway is very active, whereas there is also a reasonable active salvage pathway operating (7). Specific alterations in the balance of pyrimidine nucleotide synthesis were also found during induction of programmed cell death in BY-2 cells and include a decreased rate of salvage activity of uracil and uridine and increased salvage activity of thymidine (118).

In recent years potato tubers have been used as a system to study nucleotide metabolism in storage organs. As already demonstrated for leaves (47), there is also developmentally-controlled expression of the de novo nucleotide biosynthesis genes through the life cycle of potato tubers (R. Zrenner, unpublished observations). It was demonstrated by Loef et al. (78) that increased levels of pyrimidine nucleotides through feeding of precursors of de novo synthesis and salvage pathway stimulate the conversion of sucrose to starch. By feeding labeled nucleotide precursors the occurrence of active nucleotide de novo synthesis and highly active salvage pathways were shown in potato tuber discs (67). Together, these results indicate that de novo synthesis and salvage may both contribute to the maintenance of nucleotides for storage compound synthesis.

These results indicate that de novo synthesis is essential at a whole plant level and presumably in specific cells and tissues or developmental stages. But it is also obvious that in many tissues or conditions the transport of free bases or nucleosides and the subsequent salvage pathway may provide an alternative source of nucleotides. Indirect evidence of this hypothesis has recently been shown in Reference 46, in which the tuber-specific inhibition of UMPSase activity leads to an increased nucleotide content and salvage activity.

Most investigations of nucleotide metabolism in plants have studied either the levels of nucleotides or the expression of genes involved in nucleotide metabolism. To gain deeper insights into the coordination of nucleotide synthesis and use, it will be necessary to integrate studies of the expression of proteins involved in nucleotide metabolism with measurements of the levels of nucleotides, nucleosides and free bases, and of fluxes between these pools. These studies will reveal whether nucleosides are present at small amounts and immediately recycled via salvage pathways, or if they accumulate to significant levels relative to those of the nucleotides themselves. In microbes, the salvage pathway probably evolved to facilitate utilization of nucleosides and free bases in the medium. In highly compartmented cells and especially in multicellular organisms, nucleosides and free bases may be more suited for transport than the phosphorylated, highly polar nucleotides. In this context, it is noteworthy that the first advances are being made in characterizing nucleoside and base transporters, including the ENT family, in higher plants (143). A further aspect that requires research is the possible role of nucleosides and free bases as metabolically-inactive storage forms of nucleotides. Quantitative studies of the levels of the whole spectrum of metabolites in nucleotide metabolism in combination with studies of the rates of de novo synthesis and salvaging (67, 116) could provide new insights into the regulation and integration of nucleotide metabolism during the cell cycle, cellular growth, and during transitions in the carbon, nitrogen, or phosphate supply.

ACKNOWLEDGMENTS

We gratefully acknowledge the funding of our research by the Bundesministerium für Bildung und Forschung, (BMBF, fellowship number 0311626) to U.S. and M.S., the Deutsche Forschungsgemeinschaft (DFG, fellowship number Bo1236/3 and Zr3/2) as a part of The *Arabidopsis* Functional Genomics Network to R.B. and R.Z., and the BASF AG.

LITERATURE CITED

1. Achar BS, Vaidyanathan CS. 1967. Purification and properties of uridine hydrolase from mung-bean (*Phaseolus radiatus*) seedlings. *Arch. Biochem. Biophys.* 119:356–62
2. Agyrou E, Sophianopoulou V, Schultes N, Diallinas G. 2001. Functional characterization of a maize purine transporter by expression in Aspergillus nidulans. *Plant Cell* 13:953–64
3. Allen M, Qin WS, Moreau F, Moffatt B. 2002. Adenine phosphoribosyltransferase isoforms of Arabidopsis and their potential contribution to adenine and cytokinin metabolism. *Physiol. Plant.* 115:56–68
4. Anderson JD. 1979. Purine nucleotide metabolism of germinating soybean embryonic axes. *Plant Physiol.* 63:100–4
5. Ashihara H. 1977. Changes in the activities of the de novo and salvage pathways of pyrimidine nucleotide biosynthesis during germination of black gram (*Phaseolus mungo*) seeds. *Z. Pflanzenphysiol.* 81:199–211
6. Ashihara H, Crozier A. 1999. Biosynthesis and metabolism of caffeine and related purine alkaloids in plants. *Adv. Bot. Res.* 30:118–205
7. Ashihara H, Loukanina N, Stasolla C, Thorpe TA. 2001. Pyrimidine metabolism during somatic embryo development in white spruce (*Picea glauca*). *J. Plant Physiol.* 158:613–21
8. Ashihara H, Stasolla C, Loukanina N, Thorpe TA. 2000. Purine and pyrimidine metabolism in cultured white spruce (*Picea glauca*) cells: metabolic fate of ^{14}C-labeled precursors and activity of key enzymes. *Physiol. Plant.* 108:25–53

9. Ashihara H, Suzuki T. 2004. Distribution and biosynthesis of caffeine in plants. *Front. Biosci.* 9:1864–76

10. Ashihara H, Takasawa Y, Suzuki T. 1997. Metabolic fate of guanosine in higher plants. *Physiol. Plant.* 100:909–16

11. Astot C, Dolezal K, Nordstrom A, Wang Q, Kunkel T, et al. 2000. An alternative cytokinin biosynthesis pathway. *Proc. Natl. Acad. Sci. USA* 26:14778–83

12. Atkins CA, Smith PMC, Storer P. 1997. Reexamination of untracellular localization of de novo purine synthesis in cowpea nodules. *Plant Physiol.* 113:127–35

13. Atkins CA, Storer PJ, Shelp BJ. 1989. Purification and properties of purine nucleosidase from N2-fixing nodules of cowpea (Vigna uniguiculata). *J. Plant. Physiol.* 134:447–52

14. Barratt DH, Barber L, Kruger NJ, Smith AM, Wang TL, et al. 2001. Multiple, distinct isoforms of sucrose synthase in pea. *Plant Physiol.* 127:655–64

15. Bartlett TJ, Aibangbee A, Bruce IJ, Donovan PJ, Yon RJ. 1994. Endogenous polypeptide-chain length and partial sequence of aspartate transcarbamoylase from wheat, characterised by immunochemical and cDNA methods. *Biochim. Biophys. Acta* 1207:187–93

16. Bassett EV, Bouchet BY, Carr JM, Williamson CL, Slocum RD. 2003. PALA-mediated pyrimidine starvation increases expression of aspartate transcarbamoylase (pyrB) in *Arabidopsis* seedlings. *Plant Physiol. Biochem.* 41:695–703

17. Boldt R, Kunze G, Lerchl J, Lein W, Sonnewald U. 2001. Cloning and molecular characterization of Nicotiana tabacum purH cDNA encoding 5-aminoimidazole-4-carboxamide ribonucleotide formyltransferase/inosine monophosphate cyclohydrolase. *J. Plant Physiol.* 158:1591–99

18. Boldt R, Messutat S. 2003. Nucleotide metabolism in higher plants. The purine and pyrimidine phosphoribosyltransferase gene family in *A. thaliana*. In *Proc. 12th Int. Congr. Genes, Gene Fam. Isozymes*, ed. B Wittmann-Liebold, C Schnarrenberger, pp. 229–34. Berlin: Medimond Int. Proc.

19. Boldt R, Zrenner R. 2003. Purine and pyrimidine biosynthesis in higher plants. *Physiol. Plant.* 117:297–304

20. Bolter B, Soll J. 2001. Ion channels in the outer membranes of chloroplasts and mitochondria: open doors or regulated gates? *EMBO J.* 20:935–40

21. Bressan RA, Murray MG, Gale JM, Ross CW. 1978. Properties of pea seedling uracil phsophoribosyltransferase and its distribution in other plants (pinto beans, soybeans, cereals). *Plant Physiol.* 61:442–46

22. Buchanan JM, Hartmann SC. 1959. Enzymatic reactions in the synthesis of the purines. *Adv. Enzymol. Relat. Areas Mol. Biol.* 21:199–216

23. Burch LR, Stuchbury T. 1986. Metabolism of purine nucleotides in the tomato plant. *Phytochemistry* 25:2445–49

24. Bürkle L, Cedzich A, Döpke C, Stransky H, Okumoto S, et al. 2003. The transport of cytokinins mediated by purine transporters of the PUP family expressed in phloem, hyddathodes, and pollen of *Arabidopsis. Plant J.* 34:13–26

25. Cao Y, Schubert RK. 2001. Molecular cloning and characterization of a cDNA encoding soybean nodule IMP dehydrogenase. *Biochim. Biophys. Acta* 1520:242–46

26. Carrari F, Coll-Garcia D, Schauer N, Lytovchenko A, Palacios-Rojas N, et al. 2005. Deficiency of plastidial anenylate kinase in *Arabidopsis* results in elevated photosynthetic amino acid biosynthesis and enhanced growth. *Plant Physiol.* 137:70–82

27. Carrey EA, Hardie DG. 1988. Mapping of catalytic domains and phosphorylation sites in the multifunctional pyrimidine-biosynthetic protein CAD. *Eur. J. Biochem.* 171:583–88

28. Chapman KA, Delauney AJ, Kim JH, Verma DP. 1994. Structural organization of de novo purine biosynthesis enzymes in plants: 5-aminoimidazole ribonucleotide carboxy-lase and 5- aminoimidazole-4-N-succinocarboxamide ribonucleotide synthetase cDNAs from *Vigna aconitifolia*. *Plant Mol. Biol.* 24:389–95

29. Choi G, Yi H, Lee J, Kwon YK, Soh MS, et al. 1999. Phytochrome signalling is mediated through nucleoside diphosphate kinase 2. *Nature* 401:610–13

30. Christopherson RI, Szabados E. 1997. Nucleotide biosynthesis in mammals. In *Channelling in Intermediary Metabolism*, ed. L Agius, HSA Sherratt, pp. 315–35. London: Portland Press

31. Cole SC, Yon RJ. 1984. Ligand-mediated conformational changes in wheat-germ aspartate transcarbamoylase indicated by proteolytic susceptibility. *Biochem. J.* 221:289–96

32. Crozier A, Kamiya Y, Bishop G, Yokota T. 2000. Biosynthesis of hormones and elicitor molecules. In *Biochemistry and Molecular Biology of Plants*, ed. BB Buchanan, W Gruissem, RL Jones, pp. 850–929. Rockville, MA: Am. Soc. Plant Physiol.

33. Dancer J, Neuhaus EH, Stitt M. 1990. Subcellular compartmentation of uridine nucleotides and nucleoside-5′-diphosphate kinase in leaves. *Plant Physiol.* 92:637–41

34. Dancer JE, Hughes RG, Lindell SD. 1997. Adenosine-5′-phosphate deaminase. A novel herbicide target. *Plant Physiol.* 114:119–29

35. De La Rosa A, Williams RL, Steeg PS. 1995. Nm23/nucleoside diphosphate kinase: toward a structural and biochemical understanding of its biological functions. *BioEssays* 17:53–62

36. Deleted in proof

37. Deng QI, Ives DH. 1972. Modes of nucleoside phosphorylation in plants: studies on the apparent thymidine kinase and true uridine kinase of seedlings. *Biochim. Biophys. Acta* 277:235–44

38. Deng QI, Ives DH. 1975. Non-allosteric regulation of the uridine kinase from seeds of *Zea mays*. *Biochim. Biophys. Acta* 377:84–94

39. Desimone M, Catoni E, Ludewig U, Hilpert M, Schneider A, et al. 2002. A novel superfamily of transporters for Allantoin and other oxo derivatives of nitrogen heterocyclic compounds in Arabidopsis. *Plant Cell* 14:847–56

40. Doremus DH. 1986. Organization of the pathway of de novo pyrimidine nucleotide biosynthesis in pea (*Pisum sativum* L. cv. Progress No. 9) leaves. *Arch. Biochem. Biophys.* 250:112–19

41. Doremus DH, Jagendorf AT. 1985. Subcellular localisation of the pathway of de novo pyrimidine nucleotide biosynthesis in pea leaves. *Plant Physiol.* 79:856–61

42. Faivre-Nitschke SE, Grienenberger JM, Gualberto JM. 1999. A prokaryotic-type cytidine deaminase from *Arabidospis thaliana*. gene expression and functional characterization. *Eur. J. Biochem.* 263:896–903

43. Farre EM, Tiessen A, Roessner U, Geigenberger P, Trethewey RN, et al. 2001. Analysis of the compartmentation of glycolytic intermediates, nucleotides, sugars, organic acids, amino acids, and sugar alcohols in potato tubers using a nonaqueous fractionation method. *Plant Physiol.* 127:685–700

44. Fiore C, Trezeguet V, Le Saux A, Roux P, Schwimmer C, et al. 1998. The mitochondrial ADP/ATP carrier: structural, physiological and pathological aspects. *Biochimie* 80:137–50

45. Fonne-Pfister R, Chemla P, Ward E, Girardet M, Kreuz KE, et al. 1996. The mode of action and the structure of a herbicide in complex with its target: binding of activated hydantocidin to the feedback regulation site of adenylosuccinate synthase. *Proc. Natl. Acad. Sci. USA* 93:9431–36

46. Geigenberger P, Regierer B, Nunes-Nesi A, Leisse A, Urbanczyk-Wochniak E, et al. 2005. Inhibition of de novo pyrimidine synthesis in growing potato tubers leads to a compensatory stimulation of the pyrimidine salvage pathway and a subsequent increase in biosynthetic performance. *Plant Cell* 17:2077–88

47. Giermann N, Schröder M, Ritter T, Zrenner R. 2002. Molecular analysis of de novo pyrimidine synthesis in solanaceous species. *Plant Mol. Biol.* 50:393–403

48. Gillissen B, Bürkle L, Andre B, Kühn C, Rentsch D, et al. 2000. A new family of high-affinity transporters for adenine, cytosine, and purine derivatives in *Arabidopsis. Plant Cell* 12:291–300

49. Goggin DE, Lipscombe R, Fedorowa E, Millar AH, Mann A, et al. 2003. Dual intracellular localization and targeting of aminoimidazole ribonucleotide synthetase in cowpea. *Plant Physiol.* 131:1033–41

50. Gojkovic Z, Rislund L, Andersen B, Sandrini MPB, Cook PF, et al. 2003. Dihydropyrimidine amidohydrolases and dihydroorotases share the same origin and several enzymatic properties. *Nucleic Acids Res.* 31:1683–92

51. Graves LM, Guy HI, Kozlowski P, Huang M, Lazarowski E, et al. 2000. Regulation of carbamoyl phosphate synthetase by MAP kinase. *Nature* 403:328–31

52. Gupta A, Sharma CB. 1996. Purification to homogeneity and characterization of plasma membrane and Golgi apparatus-specific 5′-adenosine monophosphatases from peanut cotyledons. *Plant Sci.* 117:65–74

53. Hanks JF, Tolbert NE, Schubert KR. 1981. Localization of enzymes of ureide biosynthesis in peroxisomes and microsomes of nodules. *Plant Physiol.* 68:65–69

54. Hanson AD, Gregory JF. 2002. Synthesis and turnover of folates in plants. *Curr. Opin. Plant Biol.* 5:244–49

55. Hasunuma K, Yabe N, Yoshida Y, Ogura Y, Hamada T. 2003. Putative functions of nucleoside diphosphate kinase in plants and fungi. *J. Bioenerg. Biomembr.* 35:57–65

56. Herz S, Eberhard S, Bacher A. 2000. Biosynthesis of riboflavin in plants. The *ribA* gene of *Arabidopsis thaliana* specifies a bifunctional GTP cyclohydrolase II/3,4-dihydroxy-2-butanone 4-phosphat synthase. *Phytochemistry* 53:723–31

57. Hesberg C, Hänsch R, Mendel RR, Bittner F. 2004. Tandem orientation of duplicated xanthine dehydrogenase genes from Arabidopsis thaliana. *J. Biol. Chem.* 279:13547–54

58. Hewitt MM, Carr JM, Williamson CL, Slocum RD. 2005. Effects of phosphate limitation on expression of genes involved in pyrimidine synthesis and salvaging in *Arabidopsis. Plant Physiol. Biochem.* 43:91–99

59. Hirose F, Ashihara H. 1984. Changes in activity of enzymes involved in purine "salvage" and nucleic acid degradation during the growth of *Catharanthus roseus* cells in suspension culture. *Physiol. Plant.* 60:532–38

60. Hiroyuki I, Miwa F, Setsuko I, Maki K, Maki M, et al. 1996. Molecular cloning of a human cDNA encoding a trifunctional enzyme of carbamoyl-phosphate synthetase-aspartate transcarbamoylase-dihydroorotase in de novo pyrimidine synthesis. *Biochem. Biophys. Res. Commun.* 219:249–55

61. Hung WF, Chen LJ, Boldt R, Sun CW, Li HM. 2004. Characterization of Arabidopsis glutamine phosphoribosyl pyrophosphate amidotransferase-deficient mutants. *Plant Physiol.* 135:1314–23

62. Hyde RJ, Cass CE, Young JD, Baldwin SA. 2001. The ENT family of eukaryote nucleoside and nucleobase transporters: recent advances in the investigation of structure/function relationships and the identification of novel isoforms. *Mol. Membr. Biol.* 18:53–63

63. Ito T, Shiraishi H, Okada K, Shimura Y. 1994. Two amidophosphoribosyltransferase genes of *Arabidopsis thaliana* expressed in different organs. *Plant Mol. Biol.* 26:529–33

64. Kafer C, Zhou L, Santose D, Guirgis A, Weers B, et al. 2004. Regulation of pyrimidine metabolism in plants. *Front. Biosci.* 9:1611–25

65. Kanamori I, Ashihara H, Komamine A. 1980. Subcellular distribution and activity of enzymes involved in uridine-5′-monophosphate synthesis in *Vinca rosea* cells in suspension cultures. *Z. Pflanzenphysiol.* 93:437–48

66. Kanamori-Fukuda I, Ashihara H, Komamine A. 1981. Pyrimidine nucleotide biosynthesis in *Vinca rosea* cells: Changes in the activity of de novo and salvage pathways during growth in a suspension culture. *J. Exp. Bot.* 32:69–78

67. Katahira R, Ashihara H. 2002. Profiles of pyrimidine biosynthesis, salvage and degradation of disks of potato (*Solanum tuberosum* L.) tubers. *Planta* 215:821–28

68. Kawai M, Kidou S-I, Kato A, Uchimiya H. 1992. Molecular characterization of cDNA encoding for adenylate kinase of rice (*Oryza sativa* L.). *Plant J.* 2:845–54

69. Kim JH, Delauney AJ, Verma DPS. 1995. Control of de novo purine biosynthesis genes in ureide producing legumes: induction of glutamine phosphoribosylpyrophosphate amidotransferase gene and characterizatioin of ist cDNA from soy bean and Vigna. *Plant J.* 7:77–86

70. Kim JH, Krahn JM, Tomchick DR, Smith JL, Zalkin H. 1996. Structure and function of the glutamine phosphoribosylpyrophosphate amidotransferase glutamine site and communication with the phosphoribosylpyrophosphate site. *J. Biol. Chem.* 271:15549–57

71. Kleczkowski LA, Geisler M, Ciereszko I, Johansson H. 2004. UDP-glucose pyrophosphorylase. An old protein with new tricks. *Plant Physiol.* 134:912–18

72. Knorpp C, Johansson M, Baird AM. 2003. Plant mitochondrial nucleoside diphosphate kinase is attached to the membrane through interaction with the adenine nucleotide translocator. *FEBS Lett.* 555:363–66

73. Krath BN, Hove-Jensen B. 1999. Organellar and cytosolic localization of four phosphoribosyl diphosphate synthase isozymes in spinach. *Plant Physiol.* 119:497–505

74. Lazar G, Zhang H, Goodman HM. 1993. The origin of the bifunctional dihydrofolate reductase-thymidylate synthase isogenes of *Arabidopsis thaliana*. *Plant J.* 3:657–68

75. Le Floch F, Lafleuriel J, Guillot A. 1982. Interconversion of purine nucleotides in Jerusalem artichocke shoots. *Plant Sci. Lett.* 27:309–16

76. Leroch M, Kirchberger S, Haferkamp I, Wahl M, Neuhaus HE, et al. 2005. Identification and characterization of a novel plastidic adenine nucleotide uniporter from *Solanum tuberosum*. *J. Biol. Chem.* 280:17992–18000

77. Lim E-K, Bowles DJ. 2004. A class of plant glycosyltransferases involved in cellular homeostasis. *EMBO J.* 23:2915–22

78. Loef I, Geigenberger P, Stitt M. 1999. Orotate leads to a specific increase in uridine nucleotide levels and a stimulation of sucrose degradation and starch synthesis in discs from growing potato tubers. *Planta* 209:314–23

79. Luo M, Piffanelli P, Rastelli L, Cella R. 1993. Molecular cloning and analysis of a cDNA coding for the bifunctional dihydrofolate reductase-thymidylate synthase of *Daucus carota*. *Plant Mol. Biol.* 22:427–35

80. Martz F, Wilczynska M, Kleczkowski LA. 2002. Oligomerization status, with the monomer as active species, defines catalytic efficiency of UDP-glucose pyrophosphorylase. *Biochem. J.* 367:295–300

81. Minet M, Dufour ME, Lacroute F. 1992. Complementation of *Saccharomyces cerevisiae* auxotrophic mutants by *Arabidopsis thaliana* cDNAs. *Plant J.* 2:417–22

82. Moffatt BA, Ashihara H. 2002. Purine and pyrimidine nucleotide synthesis and metabolism. In *The Arabidopsis Book*, ed. CR Somerville, EM Meyerowitz. Rockville, MD: Am. Soc. Plant Biol. doi/10.1199/tab.0018. **http://www.aspb.org/publications/arabidopsis/**

83. Moffatt BA, Wang L, Allen MS, Stevens YY, Qin WS, et al. 2000. Adenosine kinase of Arabidopsis. Kinetic properties and gene expression. *Plant Physiol.* 124:1775–85

84. Moisyadi S, Dharmasiri S, Harrington H, Lukas T. 1994. Characterization of a low molecular mass autophosphorylating protein in cultured sugarcane cells and its identification as a nucleoside diphosphate kinase. *Plant Physiol.* 104:1401–9

85. Moon H, Lee B, Choi G, Shin D, Prasad TD, et al. 2003. NDP kinase 2 interacts with two oxidative stress-activated MAPKs to regulate cellular redox state and enhances multiple stress tolerance in transgenic plants. *Proc. Natl. Acad. Sci. USA* 100:358–63

86. Nara T, Hshimoto T, Aoki T. 2000. Evolutionary implications of the mosaic pyrimidine-biosynthetic pathway in eukaryotes. *Gene* 257:209–22

87. Nasr F, Bertauche N, Dufour ME, Minet M, Lacroute F. 1994. Heterospecific cloning of *Arabidopsis thaliana* cDNAs by direct complementation of pyrimidine auxotrophic mutants of *Saccharomyces cerevisiae*. I. Cloning and sequence analysis of two cDNAs catalysing the second, fifth and sixth steps of the de novo pyrimidine biosynthesis pathway. *Mol. Gen. Genet.* 244:23–32

88. Neuhard J, Nygaard P. 1987. Purines and pyrimidines. In *Escherichia coli* and *Salmonella typhimurium: Cellular and Molecular Biology*, ed. FC Neidhardt, JL Ingraham, BK Low, B Magasanik, M Schaechter, HE Umbarger, pp. 445–73. Washington, DC: ASM Press

89. Norambuena L, Marchant L, Berninsone P, Hirschberg CB, Silva H, et al. 2002. Transport of UDP-galactose in plants. Identification and functional characterization of AtUTr1, an Arabidopsis thaliana UDP-galactose/UDP-glucose transporter. *J. Biol. Chem.* 277:32923–29

90. O'Neal TD, Naylor AW. 1976. Some properties of pea leaf carbamoyl phosphate synthetase of Alaska pea (*Pisum sativum* L. cv. Alaska). *Plant Physiol.* 57:23–28

91. Ong BL, Jackson JF. 1972. Pyrimidine nucleotide biosynthesis in *Phaseolus aureus*. Enzymatic aspects of the control of carbamoyl phosphate synthesis and utilization. *Biochem. J.* 129:583–93

92. Pradet A, Raymond P. 1983. Adenine-nucleotide ratios and adenylate energy-charge in energy-metabolism. *Annu. Rev. Plant Physiol.* 34:199–224

93. Raghothama KG. 1999. Phosphate acquisition. *Annu. Rev. Plant Physiol. Plant Mol. Biol.* 50:665–93

94. Rebora K, Desmoucelles C, Borne F, Pinson B, Daignan-Fornier B. 2001. Yeast AMP pathway respond to adenine trough regulated synthesis of a metabolic intermediate. *Mol. Cell Biol.* 21:7901–12

95. Redman JC, Haas BJ, Tanimoto G, Town CD. 2004. Development and evaluation of an *Arabidopsis* whole genome Affymetrix probe array. *Plant J.* 38:545–61

96. Regierer B, Fernie AR, Springer F, Perez-Melis A, Leisse A, et al. 2002. Starch content and yield increase as a result of altering adenylate pools in transgenic plants. *Nat. Biotechnol.* 20:1256–60

97. Reiser J, Linka N, Lemke L, Jeblick W, Neuhaus HE. 2004. Molecular physiological analysis of the two plastidic ATP/ADP transporters from *Arabidopsis*. *Plant Physiol.* 136:3524–36

98. Reynolds P, Blevins D, Randall D. 1984. 5-Phosphorybosylpyrophosphate amidotransferase from soybean root nodules: Kinetic and regulatory properties. *Arch. Biochem. Biophys.* 299:623–31

99. Santoso D, Thornburg RW. 1998. Uridine 5′-monophosphate synthase is transcriptionally regulated by pyrimidine levels in *Nicotiana plumbaginifolia*. *Plant Physiol.* 116:815–21

100. Santoso D, Thornburg RW. 1992. Isolation and characterization of UMP synthase mutants from haploid cell suspensions of *Nicotiana tabacum*. *Plant Physiol.* 99:1216–25

101. Santoso D, Thornburg RW. 2000. Fluoroorotic acid-selected *Nicotiana plumbaginifolia* cell lines with a stable thymine starvation phenotype have lost the thymine-regulated transcriptional program. *Plant Physiol.* 123:1517–24

102. Schlattner U, Wagner E, Greppin H, Bonzon M. 1993. Adenylate kinase in tobacco cell cultures: separation and localization of different activities. *Plant Physiol. Biochem.* 31:815–25

103. Schmid M, Davison TS, Henz SR, Pape UJ, Demar M, et al. 2005. A gene expression map of *Arabidopsis thaliana* development. *Nat. Genet.* 37:501–6

104. Schmidt A, Su YH, Kunze R, Warner S, Hewitt M, et al. 2004. UPS1 and UPS2 from *Arabidopsis* mediate high affinity transport of uracil and 5-fluorouracil. *J. Biol. Chem.* 279:44817–24

105. Schnorr KM, Laloue M, Hirel B. 1996. Isolation of cDNAs encoding two purine biosynthetic enzymes of soybean and expression of the corresponding transcripts in roots and root nodules. *Plant Mol. Biol.* 32:751–57

106. Schoor S, Moffatt BA. 2004. Applying high throughput techniques in the study of adenosine kinase in plant metabolism and development. *Front. Biosci.* 9:1771–81

107. Schröder M, Giermann N, Zrenner R. 2005. Functional analysis of the pyrimidine de novo synthesis pathway in solanaceous species. *Plant Physiol.* 138:1926–38

108. Schubert KR, Boland MJ. 1990. The urides. In *The Biochemistry of Plants*, ed. PK Stump, EE Conn, 16:197–282. San Diego: Academic

109. Senecoff JF, McKinney EC, Meagher RB. 1996. De novo purine synthesis in *Arabidopsis thaliana*. II. The PUR7 gene encoding 5′-phosphoribosyl-4-(N-succinocarboxamide)-5-aminoimidazole synthetase is expressed in rapidly dividing tissues. *Plant Physiol.* 112:905–17

110. Senecoff JF, Meagher RB. 1993. Isolating the *Arabidopsis thaliana* genes for de novo purine synthesis by suppression of *Escherichia coli* mutants. I. 5′-phosphoribosyl-5-aminoimidazole synthetase. *Plant Physiol.* 102:387–99

111. Shelp BJ, Atkins CA, Storer PJ, Canvin DT. 1983. Cellular and subcellular organization of pathways of ammonia assimilation and ureide synthesis in nodules of cowpea (vigna unguiculata L.Walp). *Arch. Biochem. Biophys.* 224:429–41

112. Shibata H, Ochiai H, Sawa Y, Miyoshi S. 1986. Localization of carbamoylphosphate synthetase and aspartate carbamoyltransferase in chloroplasts. *Plant Physiol.* 80:126–29

113. Smith PMC, Atkins CA. 2002. Purine biosynthesis. Big in cell division, even bigger in nitrogen assimilation. *Plant Physiol.* 128:793–802

114. Smith PMC, Mann AJ, Goggin DE, Atkins CA. 1998. Air synthetase in coepea nodules: a single gene product targeted to two oganelles. *Plant Mol. Biol.* 36:811–20

115. Stasolla C, Katahira R, Thorpe TA, Ashihara H. 2003. Purine and pyrimidine nucleotide metabolism in higher plants. *J. Plant Physiol.* 160:1271–95

116. Stasolla C, Loukanina N, Ashihara H, Yeung EC, Thorpe TA. 2001. Changes in pyrimidine nucleotide biosynthesis during germination of white spruce (*Picea glauca*) somatic embryos. *In Vitro Cell Dev. Biol. Plant.* 37:285–92

117. Stasolla C, Loukanina N, Ashihara H, Yeung EC, Thorpe TA. 2002. Pyrimidine nucleotide biosynthesis and nucleic acid metabolism in embryos and megagametophytes of white spruce (*Picea glauca*) during germination. *Physiol. Plant.* 115:155–65

118. Stasolla C, Loukanina N, Yeung EC, Thorpe TA. 2004. Alterations in pyrimidine nucleotide metabolism as an early signal during the execution of programmed cell death in tobacco BY-2 cells. *J. Exp. Bot.* 55:2513–22

119. Stasolla C, Thorpe TA. 2004. Purine and pyrimidine synthesis and degradation during in vitro morphogenesis of white spruce (*Picea glauca*). *Front. Biosci.* 9:1506–19

120. Steinhauser D, Usadel B, Luedemann A, Thimm O, Kopka J. 2004. CSB.DB: a comprehensive syntems-biology database. *Bioinformatics* 20:3647–51

121. Stitt M, Lilley RM, Gerhardt R, Heldt HW. 1989. Metabolite levels in specific cells and subcellular compartments of plant leaves. *Methods Enzymol.* 174:518–50

122. Stitt M, Lilley RM, Heldt HW. 1982. Adenine nucleotide levels in the cytosol, chloroplast, and mitochondria of wheat leaf protoplasts. *Plant Physiol.* 70:971–77

123. Sun CW, Chen LJ, Lin LC, Li HM. 2001. Leaf specific up regulation of chloroplast translocon genes by a CCT motif-containing protein, CIA2. *Plant Cell* 13:2053–61

124. Sweetlove LJ, Mowday B, Hebestreit HF, Leaver CJ, Millar AH. 2001. Nucleoside diphosophate kinase III is localized to the inter-membrane space in plant mitochondria. *FEBS Lett.* 508:272–76

125. Tajima S, Nomura M, Kouchi H. 2004. Ureide biosynthesis in legume nodules. *Front. Biosci.* 9:1374–81

126. Takenaka M, Brennicke A. 2003. In vitro RNA editing in pea mitochondria requires NTP or dNTP, suggesting involvement of an RNA helicase. *J. Biol. Chem.* 278:47526–53

127. The *Arabidopsis* Genome Initiative. 2000. Analysis of the genome sequence of the flowering plant *Arabidopsis thaliana*. *Nature* 408:796–815

128. Tiessen A, Hendriks JH, Stitt M, Branscheid A, Gibon Y, et al. 2002. Starch synthesis in potato tubers is regulated by post-translational redox modification of ADP-glucose pyrophosphorylase: a novel regulatory mechanism linking starch synthesis to the sucrose supply. *Plant Cell* 14:2191–213

129. Todd CD, Polacco JC. 2004. Soybean cultivars "Williams 82" and "Maple Arrow" produce both urea and ammonia during ureide degradation. *J. Exp. Bot.* 55:867–77

130. Ullrich A, Knecht W, Piskur J, Löffler M. 2002. Plant dihydroorotate dehydrogenase differs significantly in substrate specificity and inhibition from the animal enzymes. *FEBS Lett.* 529:346–50

131. Vaghchhipawala ZE, Schlueter JA, Shoemaker RC, Mackenzie SA. 2004. Soybean FGAM synthase promoters direct ectopic nematode feeding site activity. *Genome* 47:404–11

132. van der Graaff E, Hooykaas P, Lein W, Lerchl J, Kunze G, et al. 2004. Molecular analysis of the de novo purine biosynthesis in solanaceous species and in *Arabidopsis thaliana*. *Front. Biosci.* 9:1803–16

133. Vincenzetti S, Cambi A, Neuhard J, Schnorr K, Grelloni M, Vita A. 1999. Cloning, expression, and purification of cytidine deaminase from *Arabidopsis thaliana*. *Protein Expr. Purif.* 15:8–15

134. Wagner KG, Backer AI. 1992. Dynamics of nucleotides in plants studied on a cellular basis. *Int. Rev.Cytol.* 134:1–84

135. Wagner PD, Vu N-D. 1995. Phosphorylation of ATP-citrate lyase by nucleoside diphosphate kinase. *J. Biol. Chem.* 270:21758–64

136. Walsh TA, Green SB, Larrinua IM, Schmitzer PR. 2001. Characterisation of plant β-ureidopropionase and functional over expression in *Escherichia coli*. *Plant Physiol.* 125:1001–11

137. Walther R, Wald K, Glund K, Tewes A. 1984. Evidence that a single polypeptide catalyses the two step conversion of orotate to UMP in cells from a tomato suspension culture. *J. Plant Physiol.* 116:301–11

138. Wasternack C. 1978. Degradation of pyrimidines - enzymes, localization and role in metabolism. *Biochem. Physiol. Pflanz.* 173:467–99

139. Wasternack C. 1982. Metabolism of pyrimidines and purines. In *Encyclopedia of Plant Physiology*, (New Ser.), ed. A Pirson, MH Zimmermann, 14B:263–301. Berlin: Springer-Verlag

140. Williamson CL, Slocum RD. 1994. Molecular cloning and characterization of the pyrB1 and pyrB2 genes encoding aspartate transcarbamoylase in pea (*Pisum sativum* L.). *Plant Physiol.* 105:377–84

141. Windsor B, Roux SJ, Lloyd A. 2003. Multiherbicide tolerance conferred by AtPgp1 and apyrase overexpression in *Arabidopsis thaliana*. *Nat. Biotechnol.* 21:428–33

142. Winter H, Huber SC. 2000. Regulation of sucrose metabolism in higher plants: localization and regulation of activity of key enzymes. *Crit. Rev. Biochem. Mol. Biol.* 35:253–89

143. Wormit A, Traub M, Flörchinger M, Neuhaus HE, Möhlmann T. 2004. Characterization of three novel members of the *Arabidopsis thaliana* equilibrative nucleoside transporter (ENT) family. *Biochem J.* 383:19–26

144. Xu J, Zhang HY, Xie CH, Xue HW, Dijkhuis P, Liu CM. 2005. Embryonic factor 1 encodes an AMP deaminase and is essential for zygote to embryo transition in Arabidopsis. *Plant J.* 42:743–58

145. Yabuki N, Ashihara H. 1991. Catabolism of adenine nucleotides in suspension-cultured plant cells. *Biochem. Biophys. Acta* 1073:474–80

146. Yamada K, Lim J, Dale JM, Chen H, Shinn P, et al. 2003. Empirical analysis of transcriptional activity in the *Arabidopsis* genome. *Science* 302:842–46

147. Yang J, Han KH. 2004. Functional characterization of allontoinase genes from Arabidopsis and a nonureide type legume black locust. *Plant Physiol.* 134:1039–49

148. Yano A, Umeda M, Uchimiya H. 1995. Expression of functional proteins of cDNA encoding rice nucleoside diphosphate kinase (NDK) in *Escherichia coli* and organ-related alteration of NDK activities during rice seed germination (*Oryza sativa* L.). *Plant Mol. Biol.* 27:1053–58

149. Yesbergenova Z, Yang GH, Oron E, Soffer D, Fluhr R, Sagi M. 2005. The plant Mo-hydroxylases aldehyde oxidase and xanthine dehydrogenase have distinct reactive oxygen species signatures and are induced by drougt and abscisic acid. *Plant J.* 42:862–76

150. Zalkin H, Dixon JE. 1992. De novo purine nucleotide biosynthesis. *Prog. Nucleic Acid Res.* 42:259–86

151. Zalkin H, Nygaard PP. 1996. Biosynthesis of purine nucleotides. In *Escherichia coli and Salmonella: Cellular and Molecular Biology*, ed. FC Neidhardt, R Curtiss III, JL Ingraham, ECC Lin, KB Low, et al, pp. 561–79. Washington, DC: ASM Press

152. Zhou L, Lacroute F, Thornburg R. 1998. Cloning, expression in *Escherichia coli* and characterization of *Arabidopsis thaliana* uridine 5'-monophosphate/cytidine 5'-monophosphate kinase. *Plant Physiol.* 117:245–53

153. Zhou L, Thornburg R. 1998. Site specific mutagenesis of conserved residues in the phosphate binding loop of the *Arabidopsis* UMP/CMP kinase alter ATP and UTP binding. *Arch. Biochem. Biophys.* 358:297–302

154. Zimmermann P, Hirsch-Hoffmann M, Hennig L, Gruissem W. 2004. GENEVESTI-GATOR. *Arabidopsis* microarray database and analysis toolbox. *Plant Physiol.* 136:2621–32

155. Zimmermann S, Baumann A, Jaekel K, Marbach I, Engelberg D, et al. 1999. UV-responsive genes of *Arabidopsis* revealed by similarity to the Gcn4-mediated UV response in yeast. *J. Biol. Chem.* 274:17017–24

Phytochrome Structure and Signaling Mechanisms

Nathan C. Rockwell, Yi-Shin Su, and J. Clark Lagarias

Section of Molecular and Cellular Biology, University of California, Davis, California 95616; email: jclagarias@ucdavis.edu

Annu. Rev. Plant Biol. 2006. 57:837–58

The *Annual Review of Plant Biology* is online at plant.annualreviews.org

doi: 10.1146/ annurev.arplant.56.032604.144208

First published online as a Review in Advance on February 7, 2006

1543-5008/06/ 0602-0837$20.00

Key Words

phytochrome, biochemistry, biliprotein, photoreceptor, light signaling, photochemistry

Abstract

Phytochromes are a widespread family of red/far-red responsive photoreceptors first discovered in plants, where they constitute one of the three main classes of photomorphogenesis regulators. All phytochromes utilize covalently attached bilin chromophores that enable photoconversion between red-absorbing (P_r) and far-red-absorbing (P_{fr}) forms. Phytochromes are thus photoswitchable photosensors; canonical phytochromes have a conserved N-terminal photosensory core and a C-terminal regulatory region, which typically includes a histidine-kinase-related domain. The discovery of new bacterial and cyanobacterial members of the phytochrome family within the last decade has greatly aided biochemical and structural characterization of this family, with the first crystal structure of a bacteriophytochrome photosensory core appearing in 2005. This structure and other recent biochemical studies have provided exciting new insights into the structure of phytochrome, the photoconversion process that is central to light sensing, and the mechanism of signal transfer by this important family of photoreceptors.

Contents

R: red light

FR: far-red light

Cph1, Cph2:
phytochrome
subfamilies named
after cyanobacterial
phytochromes 1
and 2

GENERAL INTRODUCTION

Phytochrome was first discovered in plants in 1959 as the photoreceptor that mediates plant growth and development in response to long-wavelength visible light (9). Phytochrome measures the ratio of red light (R) to far-red light (FR), thereby allowing the plant to as-

sess the quantity of photosynthetically active light and trigger shade avoidance responses (89). Phytochromes are found in all flowering plants and cryptophytes, and this important family of developmental regulators constitutes one of the three major classes of photoreceptors in higher plants, with the others being cryptochromes and phototropins (3, 8, 91).

More recently, phytochrome-related proteins have been isolated from other taxa. The first such protein to be discovered was the cyanobacterial chromatic adaptation sensor RcaE (51). Since this initial discovery, R/FR-sensing phytochromes have been discovered in cyanobacteria (Cph1/CphA, Cph2, and CphB/BphP), nonoxygenic bacteria (bacteriophytochromes or BphPs), and even fungi (Fphs), demonstrating that this class of photosensors is not limited to photosynthetic organisms (49). The true extent of the phytochrome family is only now becoming apparent with the advent of genome sequencing. **Supplemental Table 1** lists currently known (or suspected) phytochromes and phytochrome-related proteins, and a sequence alignment of more than 120 of these proteins is shown in **Supplemental Figure 1**. (Follow the Supplemental Material link from the Annual Reviews home page at **http://www.annualreviews.org**.)

Although microbial phytochromes have proven amenable systems for biochemical and spectroscopic analyses, much remains to be determined about the function of many of these molecules in vivo. The BphPs from *Rhodopseudomonas palustris* regulate the biosynthesis of the photosynthetic apparatus in this organism (32, 33), and BphPs regulate pigment biosynthesis in *Deinococcus radiodurans* and *Rhodospirillum centenum* (14, 45). The phytochrome from the filamentous fungus *Aspergillus nidulans* was recently implicated in sexual development (5). These functions are thus conceptually analogous to functions of plant Phys: Phytochromes regulate the metabolic response of the organism to its light environment.

PHYTOCHROMES ARE BILIPROTEIN PHOTOSWITCHES

Photoconversion: The "Central Dogma" of Phytochromes

An early key in defining the action of phytochrome in plant biology was the observation that both the spectrum of phytochrome preparations and the action spectrum of many plant responses were reversibly altered by illumination (89). Illuminating dark-grown tissues with R converts phytochrome from the R-absorbing P_r form to the FR-absorbing P_{fr} form, which triggers photomorphogenesis (**Figure 1a**). This change is reversible, with FR illumination restoring P_r, and involves both primary photochemistry and subsequent thermal steps. For a detailed review of the microscopic steps involved in the phytochrome photocycle, we refer the reader to References 36 and 94.

R/FR photoreversibility, the hallmark of plant Phys, is rarely observed in other organisms, because higher fluences or continuous light are typically required to maintain a threshold P_r/P_{fr} ratio for light responsiveness (91). This reflects a thermal process known as dark reversion, in which P_{fr} phytochrome is slowly converted to P_r phytochrome in the absence of light. While dark reversion is an intrinsic property of all phytochromes, plant phytochromes have apparently evolved to exhibit slower dark reversion (31). Interestingly, BphPs that possess far-red absorbance maxima in the thermal ground state with photoconversion to P_r-like species were recently described (32, 48, 100). Whether this spectral inversion proceeds via a reverse of the normal dark reversion pathway or via some other mechanism is not yet clear for any of these bathyBphPs. However, despite these spectral variations, it is clear that the biological outputs from phytochromes reflect the ratio of the P_r and P_{fr} forms, and that this ratio is determined by the light environment, by the forward and reverse rates of photoconversion,

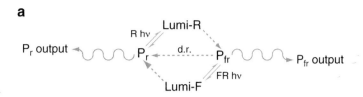

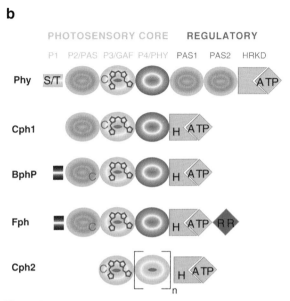

Figure 1

Domain structure and chromophores of phytochromes. (*a*) The phytochrome photocycle. Illumination of P_r phytochrome with red light (R) produces lumi-R as the primary photoproduct. This is subsequently converted to P_{fr} via multiple light-independent steps. P_{fr} can be converted into P_r either by illumination with far-red light (FR), producing lumi-F and then P_r via subsequent thermal steps, or by an entirely thermal process known as dark reversion (d.r., *center*). The ratio between P_r and P_{fr} (and hence between the two physiological outputs) is thus determined by the light environment and by the rate of dark reversion. (*b*) Domain architecture of the extended phytochrome family. The five classes of phytochromes possess an N-terminal photosensory core region and typically share regulatory output domains related to those found on two-component histidine kinases (HKRD). The P3/GAF domain is associated with the bilin chromophore and is highly conserved. All phytochromes except those found in the Cph2 subfamily share P2/PAS domains, whereas P4/PHY photosensory domains are specific to phytochromes and are thought to have folds similar to GAF domains (69). Plant phytochromes (Phys) possess two additional PAS domains within the regulatory region. Fungal phytochromes (Fphs) have a domain structure similar to those of the cyanobacterial phytochrome 1 (Cph1) and bacteriophytochrome (BphP) families, except for an additional C-terminal response regulator receiver domain (RR) extension and variable N-terminal extensions.

and by the rates for thermal interconversion between these forms.

The Modular Domain Architecture of Phytochromes

The large and steadily growing number of phytochrome sequences now known permit classification into subfamilies (**Supplemental Table 1**) (50, 69) and delineation of conserved sequences and domains that are either ubiquitous among phytochromes or conserved in different subfamilies (**Figure 1***b*; **Supplemental Figure 1**). Plant Phys, Cph1s, and most BphPs share a common architecture consisting of an N-terminal photosensory region with three conserved domains (termed P2 or PAS domain, P3 or GAF domain, and P4 or PHY domain) and a C-terminal regulatory histidine kinase or histidine kinase-related domain (HKRD). Plant Phys have an additional N-terminal extension termed P1 known to inhibit dark reversion (102) and two additional regulatory PAS domains important for nuclear localization (13). Fungal Fphs have distinct N-terminal extensions and additional C-terminal response regulator domains (RR/REC) (5, 29). The other class of cyanobacterial phytochromes, the Cph2s, lack the N-terminal P2/PAS domain, but have other GAF domains duplicated C terminal to the P4/PHY domain.

Canonical phytochromes thus consist of a PAS-GAF-PHY N-terminal photosensory module typically combined with a C-terminal HKRD module. PAS and GAF domains are present in other signaling molecules; for example, the photosensory LOV domains of the phototropins are PAS domains (19, 37), whereas GAF domains have been implicated as regulators of cyclic nucleotide metabolism in organisms as diverse as cyanobacteria and mammals (62, 63). Although there is not yet experimental structural information about the PHY domain, P4/PHY domains typically exhibit low similarity to GAF domains. It has

therefore been proposed that this domain also assumes a GAF fold (69). The concatenation of PAS, GAF, and PHY domains attached to HKRD modules typify all classes of phytochromes and phytochrome-related proteins.

Phytochrome Chromophore Structure

The characteristic absorbance spectra and photoconversion of phytochromes reflect their association with a linear tetrapyrrole bilin chromophore, which is normally covalently attached via a thioether linkage (**Figure 2***a*). Photoconversion involves a *Z*–*E* isomerization about the C15–C16 double bond of the bilin, as apophytochrome neither photoconverts nor exhibits a typical phytochrome absorbance spectrum (36, 94). The exact nature of this chromophore varies for different subfamilies of phytochromes: Plant Phys use phytochromobilin (PΦB) (**Figure 2***a*), and Cph1s and Cph2s use phycocyanobilin (PCB). Both bilins are covalently attached at $C3^1$ to a conserved Cys in the P3/GAF domain of the photosensory core (56, 59, 80, 105). In contrast, BphPs and Fphs incorporate biliverdin IXα (BV) chromophores (**Figure 2***a*). In these proteins, the more oxidized BV (see Sidebar) is attached to a conserved Cys upstream of the P2/PAS domain, apparently via a $C3^2$ linkage (58, 103). This linkage appears less stable in BphPs than the $C3^1$ linkage to PCB, based on recent evidence for its reversibility (86). Covalent attachment does not appear to be a prerequisite for photoconversion; indeed, a mutant BphP lacking the nucleophilic Cys residue functions as an enzyme for producing C15–C16 *E* bilins (60). Covalent attachment likely provides a more stable holoprotein that is better suited to reversible photoswitching. Phytochromes are thus photoswitchable photosensors that utilize bilin chromophores.

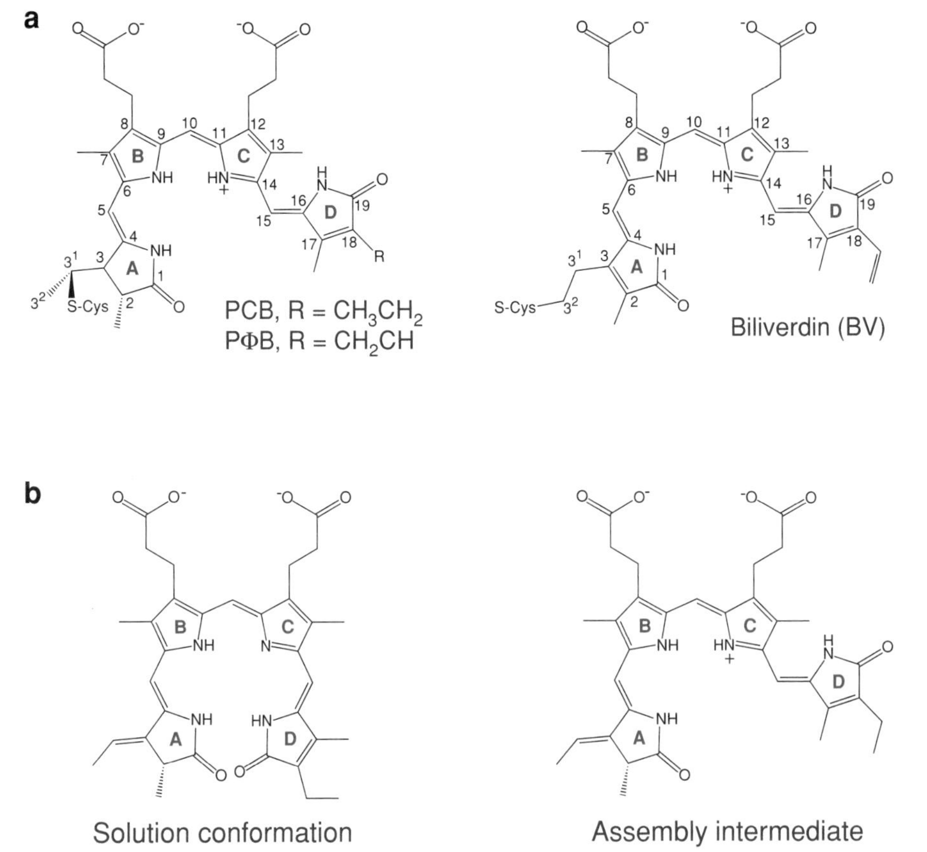

a

PCB, R = CH₃CH₂
PΦB, R = CH₂CH

Biliverdin (BV)

b

Solution conformation

Assembly intermediate

Figure 2

Chromophore structure and assembly. (*a*) The structures of the bilin chromophores utilized by known phytochromes are shown. Left: Phycocyanobilin (PCB) and phytochromobilin (PΦB) chromophores share a reduced A-ring and differ only at the C18 side chain. These chromophores are utilized by plant and algal Phys and cyanobacterial Cph1s and Cph2s. Right: The BphPs and Fphs instead utilize biliverdin (BV) as chromophore. All chromophores are shown in the C5–*Z,syn* C10–*Z,syn* C15–*Z,anti* configuration adopted in the P$_r$ state (103). (*b*) Conformations of PCB thought to be present during the assembly reaction with Cph1 are shown (6). The cyclic, porphyrin-like C15–*Z,syn* species (*left*) is the most stable in solution at neutral pH and initially binds to apoCph1. After binding, the B-/C-ring system becomes protonated, driving adoption of a C15–*Z,anti* conformation (*right*), which is characterized by enhanced, red-shifted long-wavelength absorbance. This species then becomes covalently attached to Cys259 of Cph1 to give the P$_r$ structure shown in (*a*). BV is bound to a different Cys upstream of the P2/PAS domain of BphPs (58, 103).

THE STRUCTURE AND FUNCTION OF THE PHYTOCHROME PHOTOSENSORY CORE

Phytochromes are Bilin Lyases

Because the bilin precursor of the Cph1 and Cph2 phytochrome chromophores are identical to those used in assembly of the cyanobacterial phycobiliprotein antennae complexes, it was expected that phytochromes would also require bilin lyases for assembly of holoprotein. Surprisingly, plant, bacterial, and fungal apophytochromes can all self-ligate to appropriate bilins in vitro in the absence of other proteins or cofactors. This intrinsic

HKRD: histidine kinase related domain

P2/PAS: the PAS domain in the phytochrome photosensory core

P4/PHY: the PHY domain in the phytochrome photosensory core

Bilin: a linear tetrapyrrole, metabolically derived from heme

PΦB: phytochromobilin

PCB: phycocyanobilin

PHYTOCHROMES AS SENSORS OF OXYGEN-DEPENDENT HEME CATABOLISM

The bilin chromophores incorporated by all phytochromes are synthesized from heme in two steps. First, a heme oxygenase converts heme into BV, which is directly incorporated as the chromophore of BphP and Fph phytochromes. In plants and cyanobacteria, however, BV is further reduced to yield PΦB in higher plants and PCB in cyanobacteria and green algae. Conversion of BV to PΦB is carried out by HY2 in the chloroplast, whereas reduction of BV to yield PCB is instead carried out by PcyA. Both HY2 and PcyA belong to a conserved family of ferredoxin-dependent bilin reductases.

The kinase activity and regulatory signaling state of many phytochromes are regulated not only by light but by the presence or absence of chromophore. The synthesis of chromophore depends on the heme metabolism of the cell, because chromophore will only be produced sparingly if cells are starved for heme or oxygen. Hence, phytochrome signaling is sensitive to heme metabolism and oxygen levels. Phytochromes therefore integrate both the light environment and the metabolic state of the cell to affect a single signaling readout. Bilin metabolism was recently reviewed (26).

P3/GAF: the GAF domain in the phytochrome photosensory core

bilin lyase activity has been mapped to the P3/GAF domain by truncation analysis, with the P2/PAS and P4/PHY domains important for tuning the spectroscopic properties of the bound bilin (105). Although removal of the P4/PHY domain permits bilin assembly for Phys, Cphs, and BphPs, such truncated phytochromes typically exhibit reduced efficiency of photoconversion and enhanced dark reversion (50, 77, 81, 105). The P4/PHY domain thus seems to play an accessory role in reducing both unproductive modes of de-excitation and dark reversion. In contrast, deleting either the P2/PAS or P3/GAF domains typically yielded unstable or misfolded protein; indeed, AphA, a Cph1 from *Anabaena* sp. PCC7120, absolutely requires a small extension N terminal to the P2/PAS domain for bilin assembly (108). However, because the cyanobacterial Cph2 phytochromes lack a P2/PAS domain, it was possible to express a Cph2 P3/GAF domain alone and demonstrate formation of a

covalent PCB adduct (105). The bilin lyase activity of phytochromes thus wholly resides in the P3/GAF domain.

The assembly reaction of Cph1 with PCB was recently examined by stopped-flow absorbance spectroscopy (6). PCB rapidly binds noncovalently in a cyclic, porphyrin-like conformation with *Z,syn* geometry at C5, C10, and C15, which is the most stable configuration in solution (18) (**Figure 2b**). A second intermediate with a red-shifted long-wavelength absorbance maximum and enhanced long-wavelength absorbance intensity appears soon after, followed by a blue shift of the long-wavelength absorbance maximum concomitant with thioether bond formation. The second intermediate exhibits the spectral signature of a bilin in a more extended conformation with all four nitrogens protonated (18, 34, 35). ^{15}N-NMR characterization of the P_r state in Cph1 corroborates this interpretation (97). Recent studies have isolated point mutations in the P3/GAF domain of Cph1 that form covalent PCB or PΦB adducts exhibiting a porphyrin-like conformation; one of these forms a covalent adduct with an endogenous porphyrin (21). The extended chromophore configuration is thus not necessary for covalent attachment, and indeed this work raises the intriguing possibility that porphyrins or metalloporphyrins may also modulate phytochrome function.

The Crystal Structure of the DrBphP Photosensory Core

A major breakthrough in understanding the photochemistry and structure of phytochrome was the unveiling of a 2.5 Å crystal structure for the BV-bound P2/PAS and P3/GAF domains of DrBphP, the BphP from *Deinococcus radiodurans*, in the P_r state (103). This structure confirms that the P2 and P3 domains adopt PAS and GAF folds, as expected (**Figure 3a**). Gaps and insertions within these domains in the extended phytochrome family largely fall outside of secondary structure elements, as would be expected for a conserved fold, and both domains exhibit conserved cores (**Figure 3a**). Consistent with biochemical studies, the BV chromophore is covalently attached to Cys24, apparently by linkage to $C3^2$ rather than $C3^1$ as in Phys or Cph1 (**Figure 2a**), and is deeply buried within a conserved pocket in the P3/GAF domain.

Unexpectedly, the interface between the PAS and GAF domains is formed by a deep trefoil knot (**Figure 3b**). Such knots have only been recognized relatively recently, so known examples are relatively few (76, 101). Phytochrome biosynthesis thus holds the promise of providing new insight into knot formation. The phytochrome knot is formed from sequence lying between Cys24 and the P2/PAS domain proper, which passes through a "lasso" formed by P3/GAF sequence between the fourth and fifth strands of the central GAF β sheet (103). The trefoil knot is centered on the conserved Ile35, which lies within the N-terminal sequence element required for bilin assembly of AphA (108), and also contains Arg254, a conserved residue directly interacting with the B-ring carboxylate of the biliverdin chromophore. It is therefore highly likely that this architecture will be conserved among other phytochromes. Additional N-terminal extensions such as the P1 region in plant phytochrome or the large N-terminal extensions of Fphs must either be largely unstructured or else could be proteolytically removed to facilitate this folding process. The potential regulatory role of such extensions is an interesting topic for future investigation.

Mutations in the PAS and GAF domains of plant phytochromes that result in altered function in vivo (**Supplemental Table 2**) have been mapped onto the DrBphP structure (**Figure 3a**). Although several loss-of-function mutations cluster about the chromophore-binding pocket as expected, others occur in residues at the interface between the PAS domain and the trefoil knot, such as Gly118, Ser134, and Ile208 in *Arabidopsis* PhyB (**Supplemental Table 2**). Such mutations might well affect the proper folding of these domains. Both loss-of-function and

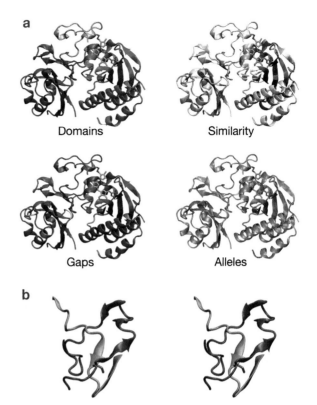

Figure 3

Conservation of the PAS and GAF domains of phytochromes. The 2.5 Å crystal structure of DrBphP P2/PAS and P3/GAF domains (PDB code 1ZTU; Reference 103) is shown with bound BV chromophore covalently attached to Cys24 (*bronze*) colored by domains (*top left*), similarity (*top right*), gaps (*bottom left*), and known alleles of plant Phys (*bottom right*). The DrBphP structure colored by domains (*top left*) uses the following color scheme: PAS, blue; GAF, red; N-terminal knot interface, green; GAF insert knot interface, purple; N terminus, gray. The DrBphP structure colored by similarity (*top right*) uses a normalized BLOSUM62 matrix (38) and the alignment of 122 phytochromes presented in **Supplemental Figure 1**. A continuous color scale is used, ranging from dark blue (100% conserved) to bright red (variable). The DrBphP structure colored by length of gaps (*bottom left*) uses the alignment in **Supplemental Figure 1**. A continuous color scale ranges from light blue (no gaps) to bright red (gaps ≥5 amino acids long), with a gap defined as a position where any phytochrome has insertions relative to DrBphP. The DrBphP structure colored by the location of alleles in plant phytochromes (*bottom right*) shows alleles that have been reported within the PAS/GAF domains of DrBphP against a gray background (see **Supplemental Table 2**). Loss-of-function alleles are colored red, gain-of-function alleles are colored blue, positions with multiple phenotypes are colored yellow, and silent alleles are colored green. **Figures 3** and **4** were prepared using VMD (40), Tachyon (96), STRIDE (28), and homolmapper (N. C. Rockwell & J. C. Lagarias, unpublished results). (*b*) Stereoview of the conserved trefoil knot at the interface between the PAS and GAF domains by residues 27–43 (*green*, upstream of the PAS domain and the first beta strand of the PAS domain) and 227–257 (*purple*). Ile35 (*blue*) is at the center of the knot.

BV: biliverdin IXα

FT-IR: Fourier transform infrared spectroscopy

gain-of-function alleles have been isolated in the "back-side" helices of the GAF domain, which lie on the other side of the central β sheet from the chromophore-binding pocket (e.g., mutation of *Arabidopsis* PhyA Glu229 and pea PhyB Val238). It is thus conceivable that these helices play a role in signal transduction via light-mediated regulation of either intramolecular interactions (with the P4/PHY domain, C-terminal regulatory domains, or plant Phy P1 sequence) or direct intermolecular interactions with downstream signaling components.

The BV chromophore of DrBphP is unequivocally bound in the C5–Z,*syn* C10–Z,*syn* C15–Z,*anti* configuration in the P_r state (**Figure 4**), ending a controversy which has lasted for some time. The chromophore is deeply buried in the GAF domain, and both the carboxylate side chains and the tetrapyrrole ring system are excluded from bulk solvent. The B-ring carboxylate forms a tight, bidentate association with Arg254, while the C-ring carboxylate is associated with His260, Ser272, and Ser274 (**Figure 4a**).

The chromophore ring system is on one side packed onto the highly conserved motif formed by Asp207, Ile208, and Pro209, and on the other closely apposed to His260. Assuming that this structure reflects a protonated BV species, as seems likely based on spectral characterization of the crystals, the positive charge that is delocalized across the B- and C-ring NH moieties is sandwiched between the backbone carbonyl oxygen of Asp207 and the side chain of His260. The charge of the ring system is thus closely associated with the partial negative charges of the His260 δ1 nitrogen and the backbone carbonyl oxygen of Asp207, which together should suffice to stabilize the charged, protonated BV-ring system.

Although DrBphP was crystallized without the PHY domain, this crystal structure nevertheless provides unique insight into the photoconversion process. The BV A-ring is sandwiched between secondary structure elements of the GAF domain and is covalently

attached to Cys24. The C10 methine bridge is tightly packed by the B- and C-rings of chromophore as well as by the conserved Asp207, Ile208, Pro209, Ala212, Tyr216, and His260 (**Figure 4b**). C10 is thus held tightly in place, so photochemistry cannot occur about this position, explaining the lack of photoconversion and the intense fluorescence observed upon assembly of apophytochrome with a bilin containing a saturated C15 bridge (71). In contrast, the D-ring is in a looser environment that would sterically permit more ready rotation. The D-ring pocket is also lined with highly conserved residues (**Figure 4c**), at least one of which is critical for normal photochemistry (20, 21). This structure thus provides strong evidence that the conversion of P_r to P_{fr} proceeds with rotation of the D-ring and only the D-ring of the chromophore.

THE PHYTOCHROME PHOTOCYCLE AND DARK REVERSION

The "Forward" Reaction: P_r to P_{fr} Phototransformation

The DrBphP crystal structure is in the P_r state, so the exact structure of P_{fr} must await future investigation. However, in combination with other data, this structure provides a new basis for more directed speculation about the photochemical pathway than was possible without any experimental structure. Several Resonance Raman studies have led to proposal of a C15–E,*anti* geometry for the P_{fr} chromophore, although without any consensus as to the structure of the P_r chromophore (1, 22, 54, 66, 67, 70). Examination of both Phys and Cph1 by FT-IR spectroscopy provides evidence that the primary photoproduct formed upon irradiation of P_r, lumi-R, has a P_{fr}-like configuration (23–25). The subsequent dark reactions leading to P_{fr} have been proposed to involve a further rotation about C15 to generate a C15–E,*syn* conformation (2), but the crystal structure of DrBphP indicates that this conformer would be

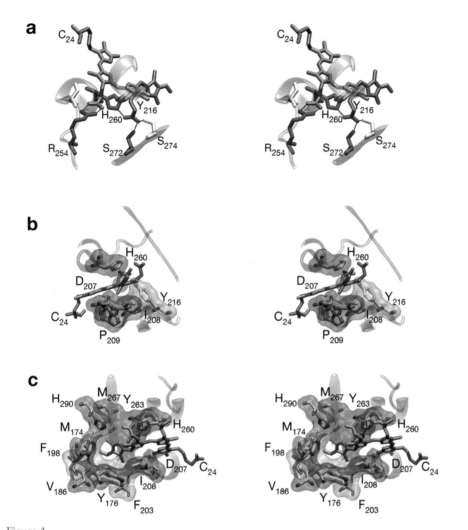

Figure 4

Chromophore-protein interactions in DrBphP are conserved. (*a*) Interaction of the buried carboxylate side chains of BV (*bronze*) with DrBphP (103). The B-ring carboxylate interacts with the conserved Arg254, which is part of the trefoil knot, whereas the C-ring carboxylate interacts with conserved Ser272 and His260. All protein residues within 3.5 Å of the carboxylate oxygens are shown colored by similarity as in **Figure 2**. Secondary structure elements are shown in transparent gray for residues 214–218, 254–262, and 271–275 for reference. (*b*) Environment of the C10 bridging carbon (*bronze sphere*). This atom is held in place by the B- and C-rings of biliverdin along with the conserved Asp207, Ile208, Tyr216, His260, and Pro209 (*sticks* colored by atom type and solvent-accessible surface colored by similarity as in **Figure 2**). (*c*) Environment of the D-ring. Residues within 5 Å of the chromophore D-ring and/or C15 methine bridge are shown as sticks and surface as in part (*b*).

sterically disfavored (103). A recent study utilizing synthetic bilins that are unable to rotate about C15 (44) demonstrated that only the C15–*E,anti* BV analog yielded a BphP adduct with properties similar to those of P_{fr} (**Figure 5***a*). This approach also correctly identified the C15–*Z,anti* conformation of the P_r chromophore (44). Taken together with the crystal structure, these data provide good evidence that conversion of P_r to P_{fr} is best described by a single photochemical isomerization of the chromophore about the C15–C16

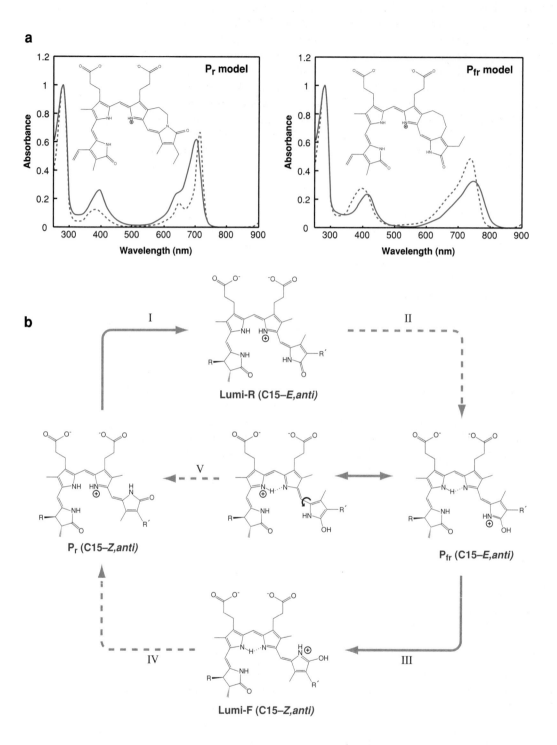

a

Pr model

Pfr model

b

I

II

Lumi-R (C15–*E,anti*)

V

Pr (C15–*Z,anti*)

Pfr (C15–*E,anti*)

III

IV

Lumi-F (C15–*Z,anti*)

double bond, with both the lumi-R primary photoproduct and P_{fr} adopting a C15–E,anti conformation (**Figure 5b**).

Unlike P_r, the P_{fr} state is not stable in solution and can only be observed within its native protein matrix (88). The substantial red shift of P_r relative to P_{fr} (**Figure 5a**) indicates either a much more extended conformation, which is not the case for the proposed C15–E,anti configuration, or greater electron density on the D-ring that extends the effective length of the conjugated system and red shifts the resulting spectrum. Such electron density could readily result from the hypothetical P_{fr} structure shown in **Figure 5b**, which would arise from two proton transfers between the chromophore and the protein. The greater electron density on the D-ring is consistent with the observed red shift of P_{fr}. The O-protonated P_{fr} species proposed in **Figure 5b** would explain the instability of the P_{fr} chromophore upon denaturation (87), because it is not significantly populated in solution (18). A recent nuclear magnetic resonance (NMR) study of Cph1 presented evidence that all four nitrogens were protonated in the P_{fr} state (97), but it is unclear whether these technically challenging experiments would have been able to distinguish between such a model and one in which one proton is shared between the B- and C-ring nitrogens, particularly in light of the apparently weak NMR intensities seen for deprotonated bilin nitrogens (18).

The proposed P_{fr} structure in **Figure 5b** would be stabilized in the chromophore-binding pocket through the action of a proton acceptor (taking a proton from the B-/C-ring NH moieties) and a proton donor (transferring a proton to the D-ring carbonyl oxygen). Recently, the pK_a of the chromophore ring system in holoprotein was estimated at ~9.5, suggesting that conserved Tyr or Cys residues could be viable proton donors in addition to conserved His, Asp, or Glu residues (101a). It should now be possible to test this model and others by mutagenizing candidate proton donors and acceptors based on the DrBphP crystal structure.

In this proposed model, the photoconversion of P_r to P_{fr} proceeds via initial photoisomerization of the C15–C16 double bond followed by proton transfers and conformational changes of the protein matrix. The P_{fr} state is much less fluorescent than the P_r state, and the proposed structure in **Figure 5b** provides a possible explanation for this: Excited chromophore molecules that do not undergo photochemistry could readily undergo proton transfer either via tunneling between the B- and C-rings or at the D-ring carbonyl, leading to spectrally silent de-excitation.

Figure 5

Chemical delineation of the phytochrome photocycle. (a) Structures and spectra for synthetic, sterically locked bilins (44) assembled with the bacteriophytochrome Agp1 from *Agrobacterium tumefaciens*. (*left*) Spectra for the C15–Z,anti locked bilin (*dashed*) and P_r biliverdin (*solid*) adducts. (b) Spectra for the C15–E,anti locked bilin (*dashed*) and P_{fr} biliverdin (*solid*) adducts. Spectra in (a) and (b) are courtesy of Drs. Tilman Lamparter and Katsuhiko Inomata. (c) Proposed photocycle for phytochromes utilizing PCB or PΦB. The P_r conformation is assigned based on the crystal structure of DrBphP, the locked bilin data presented in part (a), and the known stereochemistry of the three stereocenters in these molecules. Illumination with red light (R) triggers photoisomerization about the C15–C16 double bond (I) to give the C15–E,anti primary photoproduct lumi-R, which is subsequently converted to P_{fr} in several light-independent steps (II). As discussed in the text, the proposed P_{fr} is hypothetical but would account for the observed instability of the P_{fr} chromopeptide, the red-shifted P_{fr} absorbance maximum, and the observed P_{fr} dark reversion. Illumination of P_{fr} with far-red light (FR) (III) triggers the reverse photoisomerization to yield the C15–Z,anti lumi-F primary photoproduct, which is subsequently converted to P_r in a series of light-independent steps (IV). Dark reversion would proceed through the P_{fr} resonance form with single-bond character about C15–C16, which would readily undergo thermal rotation about this bond and then convert to P_r (V).

The "Reverse" Reaction: P_{fr} to P_r Phototransformation

The conversion of P_{fr} to P_r proceeds via a distinct pathway from that of conversion from P_r to P_{fr} (36). For at least one phytochrome, recent FT-IR data provide evidence that the lumi-F primary photoproduct adopts a P_r-like configuration, which would imply a C15–Z,anti configuration, but this may not be universal (24). Although the P_{fr} structure proposed in **Figure 5b** is hypothetical and is presented here as a conceptual aid, one can see that the reverse reaction from this species would indeed proceed via a different pathway with a different primary photoproduct. Subsequent thermal relaxation of lumi-F to P_r would entail a different pathway of proton transfers and protein conformational changes, with the residue donating a proton to the D-ring in the P_{fr} state again becoming protonated and the proton acceptor returning the proton to the B-/C-ring system. Additional structural information about the P_{fr} state will be needed before a more informed description of the photochemical reverse reaction can be attained.

Dark Reversion

The P_{fr} state is also thermally unstable in most phytochromes, with restoration of the P_r state over time in a process known as dark reversion. It has long been known that multiple factors are capable of modulating the rate of dark reversion, such as changes in pH, ionic strength, reducing agents, or metal ion concentration (27). By definition, this process cannot be triggered by spectral techniques, so it is much less amenable to study than photoconversion. The proposed P_{fr} structure suggests a mechanism for dark reversion via an alternate resonance form with single-bond character about C15–C16 that could therefore thermally rotate to the C15–Z,anti configuration of P_r (**Figure 5b**, center). Reversion of this intermediate to P_r via a series of steps reminiscent of the photochemical process can

then be envisaged. Although dark reversion is not yet well characterized, it makes an important contribution to the balance between P_r and P_{fr} and hence to determining the output state of a given phytochrome. Indeed, evidence that dark reversion of plant Phys is fluence rate dependent (39) and can be reduced by interaction with other proteins (99) or enhanced by missense mutations (16) suggests that regulation of dark reversion may play a significant role in Phy signal output.

Phytochrome after Dark: From Photochemistry to Signaling

In view of the diversity of regulatory domains associated with a conserved bilin-binding GAF domain of phytochromes, the molecular mechanisms of signal output are expected to vary widely. Phytochromes with histidine kinase(-related) regulatory domains are the most widespread—an observation that strongly suggests that plant phytochromes evolved from a two-component sensor precursor with a tetrapyrrole-binding pocket (69). Indeed, prokaryotic phytochromes of the Cph1 and BphP families are predominantly ATP-dependent histidine kinases that mediate phosphotransfer to aspartate residues of their cognate response regulators, which are often encoded within the same operon (50). Despite the nature of the output domain, it is well accepted that phytochrome signaling involves light-mediated changes in interactions between photosensory and regulatory domains that are best understood for plant phytochromes (79).

Molecular Mechanisms of Prokaryotic Phytochrome Signaling

Signal transfer by prokaryotic phytochromes most frequently utilizes the two-component signaling paradigm, i.e., ligand-dependent histidine kinase activation and phosphotransfer to a response regulator that directly regulates transcription or motility (82). Phosphotransfer is both bilin and light modulated for Cph1s and BphPs, a result consistent with the regulation of photoreceptor homodimerization and substrate interaction dynamics by these input signals (69, 78). Bilin binding stimulates kinase activity for Cph1s, whereas R inhibits both autophosphorylation and response regulator phosphorylation in a mechanistic interpretation depicted in **Figure 6** (17, 43, 59, 107). Although some BphPs show photoregulation similar to Cph1 (33, 43, 61), other BphPs exhibit a reversal in polarity with P_{fr} being more active than P_r (4, 48), whereas others show no effect of light on autophosphorylation (100). Unfortunately, the structural basis of this diversity in biochemical signal output is not readily revealed by comparison of the protein sequences; we expect that compensatory changes in both the photosensory and regulatory domains will be responsible.

Molecular Mechanisms of Plant Phytochrome Signaling

Our understanding of plant phytochrome signaling has benefited from extensive genetic, biochemical, and cell biological investigations going back many years (7, 10, 11, 30, 42, 68, 73, 83, 84, 90, 95). For this reason, the following discussion is limited to recent data that most directly impinge on the molecular basis of phytochrome signaling. As depicted in **Figure 1b**, the structure of plant phytochromes (Phys) has been remarkably preserved throughout evolution (69). In contrast with Cph1s and BphPs, plant phytochromes are obligate dimers consisting of two ~120-kDa subunits with both regulatory PAS and HKRD subdomains contributing to the high-affinity subunit-subunit interaction (47). Small-angle X-ray scattering and electron microscopy (EM) analysis indicates that the phytochrome holoprotein has similar overall dimensions to mammalian immunoglobulin Gs (46, 74, 75). Encoded by small gene families in angiosperms (64), phytochromes fall into two classes—those that are light labile (phyAs) and those that are

light stable (phyB-F). Although phyAs are mostly homodimeric, recent studies reveal that light-stable phytochromes are also found as tightly bound heterodimers (92). Based on this structural property, it is clear that light-regulated subunit-subunit dissociation cannot be the signaling mechanism used by plant phytochromes.

The recent discovery that the P1-P3 photosensory core domains of plant phytochrome are fully sufficient for phytochrome signaling as long as the truncated polypeptide is targeted to the plant cell nucleus as a homodimeric holoprotein was another paradigm-shifting observation in the field of phytochrome research (65, 77). This work, along with a plethora of other studies using green fluorescent protein-(GFP-) labeled phytochromes (reviewed in 68, 72, 73) and cytoplasm-anchored phytochrome (41), indicates that phytochrome signaling requires dynamic cytoplasm-to-nuclear relocalization following its photoactivation. Because the nuclear localization signal (NLS) has been localized to the C-terminal PAS domains (13), the regulatory domains must play a dual role in phytochrome signaling to maintain the homodimer and to target the photoreceptor to the nucleus. The evidence that plant phytochromes are serine/threonine kinases suggests that ATP-binding and/or protein phosphorylation mediated by the regulatory domains also play a role in light signaling (106).

Phytochrome phosphorylation contributes to desensitization of the light signal (52, 53). However, the hypothesis that light-regulated protein phosphorylation is the trigger enabling the photoreceptor to uncouple itself from a cytoplasmic anchor, thereby exposing the NLS, remains a viable one (90). In this signaling model depicted in **Figure 6**, photoconversion of P_r to P_{fr} with R effects a conformational change that facilitates phosphotransfer to a bound anchoring molecule (X). The P_{fr}(ADP):X-P complex dissociates upon ATP-ADP exchange, enabling exposure of the PAS-localized NLS

EM: electron microscopy

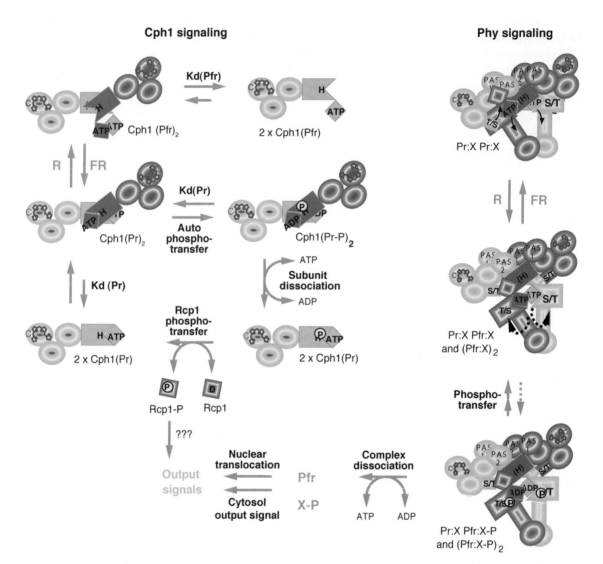

Figure 6

Hypothetical signaling mechanisms for prokaryote and eukaryote phytochromes. Homodimerization of the prokaryote phytochrome [Cph1] is dynamic and light dependent (*upper left*) because autophosphorylation is favored by the formation of homodimers in the P_r form [Cph1(P_r)$_2$] and inhibited by conversion to P_{fr} [Cph1(P_{fr})$_2$] which dissociates to an inactive monomer [(Cph1(P_{fr})]. Exchange of bound ADP with ATP, a process that promotes dissociation of the phosphorylated P_r dimer [Cph1(P_r-P)$_2$] by inhibiting reassociation of the phosphorylated P_r monomer [Cph1(P_r-P)], stimulates histidine to aspartate phosphotransfer to Cph1's substrate Rcp1. The dephosphorylated P_r monomer [Cph1(P_r)] reassociates to form the active homodimer [Cph1(P_r)$_2$]. Eukaryote phytochromes (Phys) are obligate dimers that are associated with a cytosolic anchoring protein X in an ATP-dependent protein complex (*upper right*). Photoconversion yields a P_r-P_{fr} heterodimer/P_{fr}-P_{fr} homodimer mixture [P_r:X P_{fr}:X & (P_{fr}:X)$_2$], which results in activation of the Ser/Thr kinase activity and the stimulation of phosphotransfer to anchoring protein X. The exchange of bound ADP with ATP favors dissociation of the P_{fr}:X complexes, enabling free P_{fr} to move to the nucleus and phosphorylated X to mediate a cytosolic output signal.

and P_{fr} migration to the nucleus where the N-terminal photosensory domain can interact with regulatory transcription factors (42). The altered activity of the putative anchoring molecule(s) X-P is envisaged to initiate a cytoplasmic output signal. Little is presently known about the cytoplasmic signaling pathway; candidate phytochrome-interacting cytoplasmic substrates have been identified (90). Once in the nucleus, P_{fr} accumulates in subnuclear foci or speckles whose appearance are correlated with the output signal (12). Speckles are thought to represent sites of transcription factor degradation, although other hypotheses have been proposed (11). Speckle formation requires the intact C terminus, i.e., both PAS and HKRD domains, suggesting this region plays an additional signaling role in the nucleus (77). P_{fr} autophosphorylation and/or subsequent dark reversion are envisaged to complete the phytochrome signaling cycle, whereupon free phosphorylated forms of phytochrome are degraded (phyA) or recycled (PhyB-E).

Through isolation of missense alleles of phytochromes, genetic approaches have provided valuable insight into the molecular basis of phytochrome signaling. Such mutant alleles can be categorized into two classes: hyposensitive (loss-of-function) and hypersensitive (gain-of-function) alleles (**Supplemental Table 2**). Although a large majority of the loss-of-function mutations fall within the regulatory PAS domains (85), loss-of-function mutations also occur throughout the photosensory region. Where tested, the molecular bases for loss-of-function phenotypes include increased dark reversion, reduced nuclear targeting, and altered subnuclear localization. Known gain-of-function mutations

are rare (15, 55, 104), with some falling in the photosensory core (**Figure 3a**). These mutations could enhance the translocation of P_{fr} to the nucleus or inhibit nuclear turnover of phytochrome (104). The accumulation of additional mutant alleles, together with x-ray crystallographic analysis, will be a powerful combination to assess the molecular basis of phytochrome signaling in the future.

Phytochrome Signaling Mechanisms Are Still Evolving

There are a number of BphPs that lack HKRDs altogether, and other catalytic/regulatory domains have been inserted in their place during evolution (32, 50). This type of exchange appears to have occurred many times in the past, but the probability that the new phytochrome chimera remained functional is small because few such phytochromes exist (outside the cyanobacteria). Domain exchange is likely responsible for the emergence of the plant phytochrome lineage because their regulatory PAS and HKRD modules appear evolutionarily distinct from HKRDs found on the extant prokaryotic phytochromes (64). Domain exchange has occurred more recently in primitive plants to yield the neochromes, which are functional chimeras of a plant phytochrome photosensory P1-P4 domain and a blue-light-sensing phototropin (98). It is clear that the most extensive phytochrome evolution took place in the cyanobacteria, which probably reflects the abundance of multiple bilin ligands and the need of these photosynthetic bacteria to adapt to light environments that are enriched in blue, green, or red wavelengths (57).

SUMMARY POINTS

1. Phytochromes photoconvert between P_r and P_{fr} states, and the ratio of these states determines the signaling state of phytochrome.

2. Phytochromes have a modular domain architecture with a conserved N-terminal photosensory core and a C-terminal regulatory region.

3. Phytochromes utilize bilin chromophores that photoisomerize during the conversion between P_r and P_{fr}.

4. The conserved N-terminal photosensor of phytochromes can be fused to a variety of regulatory domains, which can act in bacterial two-component pathways or in more complex pathways in plants.

5. Recent structural breakthroughs and biochemical results have defined the P_r state of the chromophore and provide new insight into the structure of the P_{fr} state.

FUTURE DIRECTIONS

1. Further data are needed to better understand the structural changes associated with photoisomerization.

2. It will also be critical to examine how those changes alter the function of the regulatory domains to trigger signaling.

3. Another interesting challenge is understanding the biological functions of phytochromes in nonphotosynthetic microbes and of divergent, phytochrome-related molecules in plants and cyanobacteria.

ACKNOWLEDGMENTS

We gratefully acknowledge Drs. Katrina Forest and Richard Vierstra for supplying the coordinates for the DrBphP structure prior to publication. The authors also thank Drs. Katsuhiko Inomata and Tilman Lamparter for providing the raw spectral data for Agp1. Our work was supported by grants from the National Institutes of Health (GM068552) and from the National Science Foundation Center for Biophotonics Science and Technology PHY-0120999.

LITERATURE CITED

1. Andel F, Lagarias JC, Mathies RA. 1996. Resonance Raman analysis of chromophore structure in the lumi-R photoproduct of phytochrome. *Biochemistry* 35:15997–6008

2. Andel F, Murphy JT, Haas JA, McDowell MT, van der Hoef I, et al. 2000. Probing the photoreaction mechanism of phytochrome through analysis of resonance Raman vibrational spectra of recombinant analogues. *Biochemistry* 39:2667–76

3. Batschauer A, ed. 2003. *Photoreceptors and Light Signaling*, Vol. 3. Cambridge, UK: Roy. Soc. Chem. 388 pp.

4. Bhoo SH, Davis SJ, Walker J, Karniol B, Vierstra RD. 2001. Bacteriophytochromes are photochromic histidine kinases using a biliverdin chromophore. *Nature* 414:776–79

5. Blumenstein A, Vienken K, Tasler R, Purschwitz J, Veith D, et al. 2005. The *Aspergillus nidulans* phytochrome FphA represses sexual development in red light. *Curr. Biol.* 15:1833–38

6. Borucki B, Otto H, Rottwinkel G, Hughes J, Heyn MP, Lamparter T. 2003. Mechanism of Cph1 phytochrome assembly from stopped-flow kinetics and circular dichroism. *Biochemistry* 42:13684–97

This study examines the assembly reaction of Cph1 with PCB in real time using stopped-flow techniques.

7. Briggs WR, Rice HV. 1972. Phytochrome: chemical and physical properties and mechanism of action. *Annu. Rev. Plant Physiol.* 23:293–334

8. Briggs WR, Spudich JA, eds. 2005. *Handbook of Photosensory Receptors.* Weinheim: Wiley VCH. 473 pp.

9. Butler WL, Norris KH, Seigelman HW, Hendricks SB. 1959. Detection, assay, and preliminary purification of the pigment controlling photoresponsive development of plants. *Proc. Natl. Acad. Sci. USA* 45:1703–8

10. Casal JJ, Luccioni LG, Oliverio KA, Boccalandro HE. 2003. Light, phytochrome signalling and photomorphogenesis in Arabidopsis. *Photochem. Photobiol. Sci.* 2:625–36

11. Chen M, Chory J, Fankhauser C. 2004. Light signal transduction in higher plants. *Annu. Rev. Genet.* 38:87–117

12. Chen M, Schwabb R, Chory J. 2003. Characterization of the requirements for localization of phytochrome B to nuclear bodies. *Proc. Natl. Acad. Sci. USA* 100:14493–98

13. Chen M, Tao Y, Lim J, Shaw A, Chory J. 2005. Regulation of phytochrome B nuclear localization through light-dependent unmasking of nuclear-localization signals. *Curr. Biol.* 15:637–42

14. Davis SJ, Vener AV, Vierstra RD. 1999. Bacteriophytochromes: phytochrome-like photoreceptors from nonphotosynthetic eubacteria. *Science* 286:2517–20

15. Dieterle M, Bauer D, Buche C, Krenz M, Schäfer E, Kretsch T. 2005. A new type of mutation in phytochrome A causes enhanced light sensitivity and alters the degradation and subcellular partitioning of the photoreceptor. *Plant J.* 41:146–61

16. Elich TD, Chory J. 1997. Biochemical characterization of Arabidopsis wild-type and mutant phytochrome B holoproteins. *Plant Cell* 9:2271–80

17. Esteban B, Carrascal M, Abian J, Lamparter T. 2005. Light-induced conformational changes of cyanobacterial phytochrome Cph1 probed by limited proteolysis and autophosphorylation. *Biochemistry* 44:450–61

18. Falk H. 1989. *The Chemistry of Linear Oligopyrroles and Bile Pigments.* Vienna: Springer-Verlag. 621 pp.

19. Fedorov R, Schlichting I, Hartmann E, Domratcheva T, Fuhrmann M, Hegemann P. 2003. Crystal structures and molecular mechanism of a light-induced signaling switch: the Phot-LOV1 domain from *Chlamydomonas reinhardtii. Biophys. J.* 84:2474–82

20. Fischer AJ, Lagarias JC. 2004. Harnessing phytochrome's glowing potential. *Proc. Natl. Acad. Sci. USA* 101:17334–39

21. Fischer AJ, Rockwell NC, Jang AY, Ernst LA, Waggoner AS, et al. 2005. Multiple roles of a conserved GAF domain tyrosine residue in cyanobacterial and plant phytochromes. *Biochemistry* 44:15203–15

22. Fodor SPA, Lagarias JC, Mathies RA. 1990. Resonance Raman analysis of the Pr and Pfr forms of phytochrome. *Biochemistry* 29:11141–46

23. Foerstendorf H, Benda C, Gärtner W, Storf M, Scheer H, Siebert F. 2001. FTIR studies of phytochrome photoreactions reveal the C=O bands of the chromophore: consequences for its protonation states, conformation, and protein interaction. *Biochemistry* 40:14952–59

24. Foerstendorf H, Lamparter T, Hughes J, Gärtner W, Siebert F. 2000. The photoreactions of recombinant phytochrome from the cyanobacterium Synechocystis: a low-temperature UV-Vis and FT-IR spectroscopic study. *Photochem. Photobiol.* 71:655–61

25. Foerstendorf H, Mummert E, Schäfer E, Scheer H, Siebert F. 1996. Fourier-transform infrared spectroscopy of phytochrome—difference spectra of the intermediates of the photoreactions. *Biochemistry* 35:10793–99

This work demonstrates that the PAS repeat domains of plant Phys contain a cryptic NLS that is key for light-mediated signaling.

This classic work covers the chemistry of bilins and provides invaluable information on how bilin chromophores behave in solution.

26. Frankenberg NF, Lagarias JC. 2003. Biosynthesis and biological function of bilins. In *The Porphyrin Handbook. Chlorophylls and Bilins: Biosynthesis Structure and Degradation*, ed. KM Kadish, KM Smith, R Guilard, pp. 211–35. New York: Academic

27. Franklin B. 1972. Biosynthesis and dark transformations of phytochrome. In *Phytochrome*, ed. K Mitrakos, W Shropshire, pp. 195–225. New York: Academic

28. Frishman D, Argos P. 1995. Knowledge-based protein secondary structure assignment. *Proteins* 23:566–79

29. Froehlich AC, Noh B, Vierstra RD, Loros J, Dunlap JC. 2005. Genetic and molecular analysis of phytochromes from the filamentous fungus *Neurospora crassa*. *Eukaryotic Cell* 4:2140–52

30. Furuya M. 1993. Phytochromes—their molecular species, gene families, and functions. *Annu. Rev. Plant Physiol. Plant Mol. Biol.* 44:617–45

31. Furuya M, Schäfer E. 1996. Photoperception and signalling of induction reactions by different phytochromes. *Trends Plant Sci.* 1:301–7

32. Giraud E, Fardoux J, Fourier N, Hannibal L, Genty B, et al. 2002. Bacteriophytochrome controls photosystem synthesis in anoxygenic bacteria. *Nature* 417:202–5

33. Giraud E, Zappa S, Vuillet L, Adriano JM, Hannibal L, et al. 2005. A new type of bacteriophytochrome acts in tandem with a classical bacteriophytochrome to control the antennae synthesis in *Rhodopseudomonas palustris*. *J. Biol. Chem.* 280:32389–97

34. Goller AH, Strehlow D, Hermann G. 2001. Conformational flexibility of phycocyanobilin: an AM1 semiempirical study. *Chemphyschem.* 2:665–71

35. Goller AH, Strehlow D, Hermann G. 2005. The excited-state chemistry of phycocyanobilin: a semiempirical study. *Chemphyschem.* 6:1259–68

36. Gärtner W, Braslavsky SE. 2003. The phytochromes: spectroscopy and function. In *Photoreceptors and Light Signalling*, ed. A Batschauer, pp. 136–80. Cambridge, UK: Roy. Soc. Chem.

37. Harper SM, Neil LC, Gardner KH. 2003. Structural basis of a phototropin light switch. *Science* 301:1541–44

38. Henikoff S, Henikoff JG. 1992. Amino acid substitution matrices from protein blocks. *Proc. Natl. Acad. Sci. USA* 89:10915–19

39. Hennig L, Schäfer E. 2001. Both subunits of the dimeric plant photoreceptor phytochrome require chromophore for stability of the far-red light-absorbing form. *J. Biol. Chem.* 276:7913–18

40. Humphrey W, Dalke A, Schulten K. 1996. VMD: visual molecular dynamics. *J. Mol. Graph.* 14:33–38

41. Huq E, Al-Sady B, Quail PH. 2003. Nuclear translocation of the photoreceptor phytochrome B is necessary for its biological function in seedling photomorphogenesis. *Plant J.* 35:660–64

42. Huq E, Quail PH. 2005. Phytochrome signaling. In *Handbook of Photosensory Receptors*, ed. WR Briggs, JA Spudich, pp. 151–70. Weinheim: Wiley VCH

43. Hübschmann T, Jorissen HJ, Börner T, Gärtner W, Tandeau de Marsac N. 2001. Phosphorylation of proteins in the light-dependent signalling pathway of a filamentous cyanobacterium. *Eur. J. Biochem.* 268:3383–89

44. Inomata K, Hammam MAS, Kinoshita H, Murata Y, Khawn H, et al. 2005. Sterically locked synthetic bilin derivatives and phytochrome Agp1 from *Agrobacterium tumefaciens* form photoinsensitive Pr- and Pfr-like adducts. *J. Biol. Chem.* 280:24491–97

This study uses novel synthetic bilins unable to rotate about the C15 methine bridge to delineate the geometry of P_r and P_{fr}.

45. Jiang ZY, Swem LR, Rushing BG, Devanathan S, Tollin G, Bauer CE. 1999. Bacterial photoreceptor with similarity to photoactive yellow protein and plant phytochromes. *Science* 285:406–9

46. Jones A, Erickson H. 1989. Domain structure of phytochrome from *Avena sativa* visualized by electron microscopy. *Photochem. Photobiol.* 49:479–83

47. Jones AM, Edgerton MD. 1994. The anatomy of phytochrome, a unique photoreceptor in plants. *Semin. Cell Biol.* 5:295–302

48. Karniol B, Vierstra RD. 2003. The pair of bacteriophytochromes from *Agrobacterium tumefaciens* are histidine kinases with opposing photobiological properties. *Proc. Natl. Acad. Sci. USA* 100:2807–12

49. Karniol B, Vierstra RD. 2006. Structure, function, and evolution of microbial phytochromes. In *Photomorphogenesis in Plants and Bacteria: Function and Signal Transduction Mechanisms (3rd Edition)*, ed. E Schäfer, F Nagy. Dordrecht, The Netherlands: Springer

50. Karniol B, Wagner JR, Walker JM, Vierstra RD. 2005. Phylogenetic analysis of the phytochrome superfamily reveals distinct microbial subfamilies of photoreceptors. *Biochem. J.* 392:103–16

51. Kehoe DM, Grossman AR. 1996. Similarity of a chromatic adaptation sensor to phytochrome and ethylene receptors. *Science* 273:1409–12

52. Kim JI, Park JE, Zarate X, Song PS. 2005. Phytochrome phosphorylation in plant light signaling. *Photochem. Photobiol. Sci.* 4:681–87

53. Kim JI, Shen Y, Han YJ, Park JE, Kirchenbauer D, et al. 2004. Phytochrome phosphorylation modulates light signaling by influencing the protein-protein interaction. *Plant Cell* 16:2629–40

54. Kneip C, Schlamann W, Braslavsky SE, Hildebrandt P, Schaffner K. 2000. Resonance Raman spectroscopic study of the tryptic 39-kDa fragment of phytochrome. *FEBS Lett.* 482:252–56

55. Kretsch T, Poppe C, Schäfer E. 2000. A new type of mutation in the plant photoreceptor phytochrome B causes loss of photoreversibility and an extremely enhanced light sensitivity. *Plant J.* 22:177–86

56. Lagarias JC, Rapoport H. 1980. Chromopeptides from phytochrome. The structure and linkage of the Pr form of the phytochrome chromophore. *J. Am. Chem. Soc.* 102:4821–28

57. Lamparter T. 2004. Evolution of cyanobacterial and plant phytochromes. *FEBS Lett.* 573:1–5

58. Lamparter T, Carrascal M, Michael N, Martinez E, Rottwinkel G, Abian J. 2004. The biliverdin chromophore binds covalently to a conserved cysteine residue in the N-terminus of *Agrobacterium* phytochrome Agp1. *Biochemistry* 43:3659–69

59. Lamparter T, Esteban B, Hughes J. 2001. Phytochrome Cph1 from the cyanobacterium *Synechocystis* PCC6803—purification, assembly, and quaternary structure. *Eur. J. Biochem.* 268:4720–30

60. Lamparter T, Michael N. 2005. Agrobacterium phytochrome as an enzyme for the production of ZZE bilins. *Biochemistry* 44:8461–69

61. Lamparter T, Michael N, Mittmann F, Esteban B. 2002. Phytochrome from *Agrobacterium tumefaciens* has unusual spectral properties and reveals an N-terminal chromophore attachment site. *Proc. Natl. Acad. Sci. USA* 99:11628–33

62. Martinez SE, Bruder S, Schultz A, Zheng N, Schultz JE, et al. 2005. Crystal structure of the tandem GAF domains from a cyanobacterial adenylyl cyclase: modes of ligand binding and dimerization. *Proc. Natl. Acad. Sci. USA* 102:3082–87

This paper presents the first description of a phytochrome from a bacterial system.

This paper demonstrates the nature of covalent attachment for phytochromes that utilize BV as chromophore.

63. Martinez SE, Wu AY, Glavas NA, Tang XB, Turley S, et al. 2002. The two GAF domains in phosphodiesterase 2A have distinct roles in dimerization and in cGMP binding. *Proc. Natl. Acad. Sci. USA* 99:13260–65

64. Mathews S, Sharrock RA. 1997. Phytochrome gene diversity. *Plant Cell Environ.* 20:666–71

65. Matsushita T, Mochizuki N, Nagatani A. 2003. Dimers of the N-terminal domain of phytochrome B are functional in the nucleus. *Nature* 424:571–74

66. Matysik J, Hildebrandt P, Schlamann W, Braslavsky SE, Schaffner K. 1995. Fourier-transform resonance Raman spectroscopy of intermediates of the phytochrome photocycle. *Biochemistry* 34:10497–507

67. Mizutani Y, Tokutomi S, Kitagawa T. 1994. Resonance Raman spectra of the intermediates in phototransformation of large phytochrome - deprotonation of the chromophore in the bleached intermediate. *Biochemistry* 33:153–58

68. Moller SG, Ingles PJ, Whitelam GC. 2002. The cell biology of phytochrome signalling. *New Phytol.* 154:553–90

69. Montgomery BL, Lagarias JC. 2002. Phytochrome ancestry. Sensors of bilins and light. *Trends Plant Sci.* 7:357–66

70. Mroginski MA, Murgida DH, von Stetten D, Kneip C, Mark F, Hildebrandt P. 2004. Determination of the chromophore structures in the photoinduced reaction cycle of phytochrome. *J. Am. Chem. Soc.* 126:16734–35

71. Murphy JT, Lagarias JC. 1997. The Phytofluors: a new class of fluorescent protein probes. *Curr. Biol.* 7:870–76

72. Nagatani A. 2004. Light-regulated nuclear localization of phytochromes. *Curr. Opin. Plant Biol.* 7:708–11

73. Nagy F, Schäfer E. 2002. Phytochromes control photomorphogenesis by differentially regulated, interacting signaling pathways in higher plants. *Annu. Rev. Plant Biol.* 53:329–55

74. Nakasako M, Iwata T, Inoue K, Tokutomi S. 2005. Light-induced global structural changes in phytochrome A regulating photomorphogenesis in plants. *FEBS J.* 272:603–12

75. Nakasako M, Wada M, Tokutomi S, Yamamoto KT, Sakai J, et al. 1990. Quaternary structure of pea phytochrome-I dimer studied with small-angle X-ray scattering and rotary-shadowing electron microscopy. *Photochem. Photobiol.* 52:3–12

76. Nureki O, Shirouzu M, Hashimoto K, Ishitani R, Terada T, et al. 2002. An enzyme with a deep trefoil knot for the active-site architecture. *Acta Crystallogr. D Biol. Crystallogr.* 58:1129–37

77. Oka Y, Matsushita T, Mochizuki N, Suzuki T, Tokutomi S, Nagatani A. 2004. Functional analysis of a 450-amino Acid N-terminal fragment of phytochrome B in Arabidopsis. *Plant Cell* 16:2104–16

78. Otto H, Lamparter T, Borucki B, Hughes J, Heyn MP. 2003. Dimerization and inter-chromophore distance of Cph1 phytochrome from *Synechocystis*, as monitored by fluorescence homo and hetero energy transfer. *Biochemistry* 42:5885–95

79. Park CM, Bhoo SH, Song PS. 2000. Inter-domain crosstalk in the phytochrome molecules. *Semin. Cell Dev. Biol.* 11:449–56

80. Park CM, Kim JI, Yang SS, Kang JG, Kang JH, et al. 2000. A second photochromic bacteriophytochrome from *Synechocystis* sp PCC 6803: spectral analysis and down-regulation by light. *Biochemistry* 39:10840–47

81. Park CM, Shim JY, Yang SS, Kang JG, Kim JI, et al. 2000. Chromophore-apoprotein interactions in *Synechocystis* sp PCC6803 phytochrome Cph1. *Biochemistry* 39:6349–56

82. Parkinson JS. 1993. Signal transduction schemes of bacteria. *Cell* 73:857–71
83. Pratt LH. 1982. Phytochrome: the protein moiety. *Annu. Rev. Plant Physiol.* 33:557–82
84. Quail PH. 1991. Phytochrome—a light-activated molecular switch that regulates plant gene expression. *Annu. Rev. Genet.* 25:389–409
85. Quail PH, Boylan MT, Parks BM, Short TW, Xu Y, Wagner D. 1995. Phytochromes: photosensory perception and signal transduction. *Science* 268:675–80
86. Quest B, Gärtner W. 2004. Chromophore selectivity in bacterial phytochromes: dissecting the process of chromophore attachment. *Eur. J. Biochem.* 271:1117–26
87. Rüdiger W, Brandlmeier T, Blos I, Gossauer A, Weller JP. 1980. Isolation of the phytochrome chromophore. The cleavage reaction with hydrogen bromide. *Z. Naturforsch.* 35c:763–69
88. Rüdiger W, Thümmler F, Cmiel E, Schneider S. 1983. Chromophore structure of the physiologically active form (Pfr) of phytochrome. *Proc. Natl. Acad. Sci. USA* 80:6244–48
89. **Sage LC. 1992. *Pigment of the Imagination: A History of Phytochrome Research*. San Diego: Academic. 562 pp.**
90. Schepens I, Duek P, Fankhauser C. 2004. Phytochrome-mediated light signalling in Arabidopsis. *Curr. Opin. Plant Biol.* 7:564–69
91. Schäfer E, Nagy F, eds. 2006. *Photomorphogenesis in Plants and Bacteria: Function and Signal Transduction Mechanisms (3rd Edition)*. Dordrecht, The Netherlands: Springer. 662 pp.
92. Sharrock RA, Clack T. 2004. Heterodimerization of type II phytochromes in Arabidopsis. *Proc. Natl. Acad. Sci. USA* 101:11500–5
93. Deleted in proof
94. Sineshchekov VA. 1995. Photobiophysics and photobiochemistry of the heterogeneous phytochrome system. *Biochimica Biophysica Acta-Bioenergetic* 1228:125–64
95. Smith H. 1995. Physiological and ecological function within the phytochrome family. *Annu. Rev. Plant Physiol. Plant Mol. Biol.* 46:289–315
96. Stone J. 1998. *An Efficient Library for Parallel Ray Tracing and Animation*. Masters thesis. Univ. Missouri-Rolla. 89 pp.
97. Strauss HM, Hughes J, Schmieder P. 2005. Heteronuclear solution-state NMR studies of the chromophore in cyanobacterial phytochrome Cph1. *Biochemistry* 44:8244–50
98. Suetsugu N, Mittmann F, Wagner G, Hughes J, Wada M. 2005. A chimeric photoreceptor gene, NEOCHROME, has arisen twice during plant evolution. *Proc. Natl. Acad. Sci. USA* 102:13705–9
99. Sweere U, Eichenberg K, Lohrmann J, Mira-Rodado V, Baurle I, et al. 2001. Interaction of the response regulator ARR4 with phytochrome B in modulating red light signaling. *Science* 294:1108–11
100. Tasler R, Moises T, Frankenberg-Dinkel N. 2005. Biochemical and spectroscopic characterization of the bacterial phytochrome of *Pseudomonas aeruginosa*. *FEBS J.* 272:1927–36
101. Taylor WR. 2000. A deeply knotted protein structure and how it might fold. *Nature* 406:916–19
101a. van Thor JJ, Borucki B, Crielaard W, Otto H, Lamparter T, et al. 2001. Light-induced proton release and proton uptake reactions in the cyanobacterial phytochrome Cph1. *Biochemistry* 40:11460–71
102. Vierstra RD. 1993. Illuminating phytochrome functions. *Plant Physiol.* 103:679–84
103. **Wagner JR, Brunzelle JS, Forest KT, Vierstra RD. 2005. A light-sensing knot revealed by the structure of the chromophore binding domain of phytochrome. *Nature* 438: 325–31**

This interesting popular work provides a unique perspective on the early years of phytochrome research.

This paper presents a pivotal breakthrough: the first crystal structure of a phytochrome photosensory core.

This paper describes a series of truncation experiments demonstrating that the P3/GAF domain is sufficient for covalent attachment of chromophore.

This paper demonstrates that the prokaryotic phytochrome Cph1 functions as a light-regulated protein kinase.

104. Weller JL, Batge SL, Smith JJ, Kerckhoffs LH, Sineshchekov VA, et al. 2004. A dominant mutation in the pea *PHYA* gene confers enhanced responses to light and impairs the light-dependent degradation of phytochrome A. *Plant Physiol.* 135:2186–95

105. **Wu SH, Lagarias JC. 2000. Defining the bilin lyase domain: lessons from the extended phytochrome superfamily.** *Biochemistry* **39:13487–95**

106. Yeh KC, Lagarias JC. 1998. Eukaryotic phytochromes: light-regulated serine/threonine protein kinases with histidine kinase ancestry. *Proc. Natl. Acad. Sci. USA* 95:13976–81

107. **Yeh KC, Wu SH, Murphy JT, Lagarias JC. 1997. A cyanobacterial phytochrome two-component light sensory system.** *Science* **277:1505–8**

108. Zhao KH, Ran Y, Li M, Sun YN, Zhou M, et al. 2004. Photochromic biliproteins from the cyanobacterium *Anabaena* sp. PCC 7120: lyase activities, chromophore exchange, and photochromism in phytochrome AphA. *Biochemistry* 43:11576–88

RELATED RESOURCE

Kehoe D, Gutu A. 2006. Responding to color: the regulation of complementary chromatic adaptation. *Annu. Rev. Plant Biol.* 57:127–50

Microtubule Dynamics and Organization in the Plant Cortical Array

David W. Ehrhardt[1] and Sidney L. Shaw[2]

[1] Department of Plant Biology, Carnegie Institution, Stanford, California 94020;
email: ehrhardt@stanford.edu

[2] Department of Biology, Indiana University, Bloomington, Indiana 47405;
email: sishaw@Indiana.edu

Annu. Rev. Plant Biol.
2006. 57:859–75

The *Annual Review of
Plant Biology* is online at
plant.annualreviews.org

doi: 10.1146/
annurev.arplant.57.032905.105329

1543-5008/06/
0602-0859$20.00

Key Words

polymer bundling, polymer treadmilling, nucleation,
self-organization

Abstract

Live-cell studies have brought fresh insight into the organizational
activities of the plant cortical array. Plant interphase arrays organize in the absence of a discrete microtubule organizing center,
having plus and minus ends distributed throughout the cell cortex. Microtubule nucleation occurs at the cell cortex, frequently followed by minus-end detachment from origin sites. Microtubules
associate tightly with the cell cortex, resisting lateral and axial
translocation. Slow, intermitant loss of dimers from minus ends, coupled with growth-biased dynamic instability at the plus ends, results
in the migration of cortically attached microtubules across the cell
via polymer treadmilling. Microtubule-microtubule interactions, a
direct consequence of treadmilling, result in polymer reorientation
and creation of polymer bundles. The combined properties of microtubule dynamics and interactions among polymers constitute a
system with predicted properties of self-organization.

Contents

INTRODUCTION

The microtubule cytoskeleton is an engine for cellular organization. The diverse roles that microtubules play in guiding cell growth, morphogenesis, and cell division depend on their arrangement in space and time. To understand cytoskeletal function, it is therefore necessary to understand the organizational mechanisms that create and maintain these arrangements. Although the organizational properties of astral arrays, formed with the aid of centrosomes or spindle pole bodies, are well characterized (31, 32), our understanding of how noncentrosomal arrays are built is considerably less advanced. The interphase cortical arrays of plant cells are striking examples of noncentrosomal microtubule arrays and provide an excellent model system for investigating how these arrays are created, organized, and maintained.

In fungal and animal cells, the spindle pole body or centrosome plays a dominant role in creating the functional architecture of the interphase microtubule array. These organelles nucleate microtubules, gather the minus ends into a centralized location, and stabilize the array by discouraging subunit removal from the tethered minus ends (14, 16, 62). The microtubule plus ends exhibit dynamic instability (45), characterized by stochastic episodes of subunit addition and loss. The random switching is driven in part by cycles of GTP binding and hydrolysis that condition the binding affinity of free dimers with the polymer end (4). Polymer nucleation and the rates of polymerization and switching determine the dimensions and uniformity of the aster (46). Microtubules also interact with other cellular components, including vesicles and organelles, via microtubule-associated proteins including motors and end-binding proteins. Together, these activities create a radial array designed to support the shape of the mechanically plastic animal cell. Furthermore, the intrinsic polarity of the astral array facilitates processes such as the polar transport of material from sites of synthesis near the cell's center to the cell cortex, and the delivery of materials from the cell cortex to the cell's center. (**Figure 1**)

Higher plant cells have a fundamentally different internal architecture from that in fungal and animal cells, consisting of a thin layer of cytosol at the cell cortex surrounding a large central vacuole. Organelles and other cellular contents are widely dispersed and are constantly redistributed through the action of actin-/myosin-based cytoplasmic streaming. This change in cytoarchitecture is accompanied by an equally large difference in cytoskeletal organization. Microtubules positioned just under, and parallel with, the plasma membrane constitute the majority of the plant interphase array (23, 26, 33). The arrangement of polymers within this cortical array varies with cell type and developmental state, often showing striking coalignment and smoothly shifting patterns of organization from cell to cell. A classic example is the expanding root epidermal cell. Cortical microtubules are randomly arranged after cell division but organize into a banded pattern that slowly changes from transverse to longitudinal as the cell reaches maturity (reviewed in Reference 1). The commonly observed oblique pattern of microtubules in growing cells takes on a helical arrangement when viewed in three dimensions, forming a coil-like architecture about the periphery of the cell (35, 38) (**Figure 1**). Cells with more complicated morphologies show more complicated array patterns. Vascular cells, for example, show superaggregates of cortical microtubules that correlate with patterns of cell wall thickening (23, 24, 35). Another example is that the puzzle piece–shaped pavement cells in the leaf epidermis show a relatively random pattern on the exposed cell face, but an increasing density and tendency to be parallel to each other in the invaginations along the suture with neighboring cells (17, 60).

As cells approach mitosis, the plant cortical cytoskeleton undergoes a remarkable transformation. Microtubules become progressively depopulated at the cortex, leaving a circumferential band of polymers that gradually narrows to a tight ring (49). This preprophase band (PPB) of microtubules forms in dividing cells, independent from the previous interphase organization, and predicts the site of later cytokinesis. The PPB disappears at prophase, leaving little trace of the cortical array until cell division is complete, when the array begins to reassemble.

The discovery of interphase microtubules was stimulated by the observation that the mitotic spindle-disrupting drug colchicine caused giant algal cells to swell in a radial pattern. Green was inspired to ask if the orientation of structural polymers in the algal cell wall, as revealed by polarization microscopy, was also affected by this treatment.

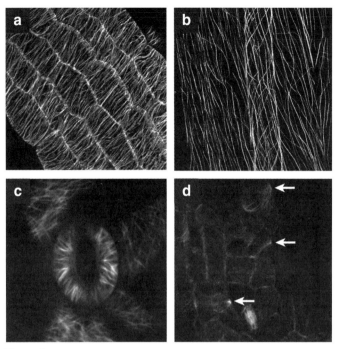

Figure 1

Cortical arrays of microtubules in Arabidopsis cells. Plant cells display a diversity of cortical array patterns, including (*a*) transverse arrays in elongating cells (epidermal cells in the hypocotyl), (*b*) longitudinal arrays of long polymers in cells that have ceased growing (hypocotyl epidermal cells in a six-day-old etiolated seedling), (*c*) highly parallel and transverse arrays in mature guard cells, and (*d*) preprophase bands in dividing cells (petiole epidermal cells, arrows indicate PPBs). Images are projections of confocal Z stacks (*a*, *b*, and *d*) or a time series (*c*). Microtubules are labeled with either EYFP::TUA5 (*a*, *d*) (56), MAP4::GFP (*b*) (40), or EB1::GFP (*b*) (41).

When he observed evidence that the cell wall polymers were becoming randomized by the colchicine treatment, he proposed that linear, colchicine-sensitive structures subtending the plasma membrane might guide the deposition of the cell wall polymers (20, 20a). The hypothesized linear structures would therefore order the deposition of wall fibers, creating the observed material anisotropy in the cell wall leading to anisotropic cell growth. Two years later, microtubules were discovered in higher plant cells by using transmission electron microscopy (33). The authors noted that these microtubules laid parallel to and just under the plasma membrane. In subsequent studies, these authors and others observed that cell wall fibers in growing cells tended to be parallel to, and were often coincident with, the subjacent microtubules (26, 39), providing compelling support for Green's hypothesis.

Together, structural studies, pharmacological disruption of microtubules, and genetic analyses support a functional relationship between the cortical cytoskeleton and growth pattern of the cell wall. However, to date no direct biochemical or cell biological evidence has been presented that explains the mechanism by which microtubules direct cell wall deposition, expansion, and determination of the site of cell plate insertion. It is also clear that the relationship between the cortical microtubules and cell morphogenesis is more complicated than early models predicted. For example, it is possible to observe uncoupling of microtubule and cellulose orientation, and to see order appear in one array when the other array is experimentally disrupted (for reviews, see References 1 and 68).

The astral interphase arrays in animal and yeast cells act through their architecture, facilitating vesicle, organelle, and mRNA traffic among other activities. The functions of the plant cortical array, with its acentrosomeal organization, remain ill characterized. Understanding these functions, and how the cortical microtubule cytoskeleton guides plant cell morphogenesis requires understanding the mechanisms of array organization. Here we review how live-cell imaging experiments provide insight into how discreet polymer activities contribute to microtubule array creation, maintenance, and rearrangement in this acentrosomal system.

Molecular Behaviors of Cortical Microtubules

A microtubule array arises from the collective behavior of individual polymers. Observations made from imaging and biochemistry studies suggest at least four classes of polymer activities contributing to cortical array organization in higher plant cells. New microtubules are created via nucleation complexes and through severing of ex-

isting microtubules. A strong cortical association restricts microtubule activities to a two-dimensional environment subtending the plasma membrane. The polymerization properties of the microtubules, including dimer addition, dimer loss, and the switching between states, occur at both ends of cortical microtubules, giving rise to a remarkable degree of dynamism in array organization. Lastly, microtubules in plant cells tend to self-associate, forming superstructures and bundles at the cell cortex. Together, these molecular behaviors create a degree of self-organization, driven by the dynamic properties of the ends and constrained by the attachment to the cell cortex and bundling interactions.

Creating New Cortical Microtubules

The distributed nature of plant cell microtubules led Mazia to postulate the presence of a distributed or flexible centrosome (8, 42). Although the core proteins used for microtubule nucleation have been discovered in plants (15, 34, 50, 57), genes encoding other centrosomal proteins appear to be largely missing (1). Hence, plant cells likely specify both the location and timing of microtubule nucleation differently than a centrosomally based system. The core proteins used to nucleate microtubules contitute the gamma-tubulin ring complex (g-TuRC), which acts to lower the energetic barrier to nucleation (29). The demonstration of g-TuRC components in plant cells and their localization to the nuclear surface, spindle, and cell cortex supports a role in plant cell nucleation events (14a, 15, 34, 55).

Microtubule initiation has been observed in living cells both at the nuclear surface and at the cell cortex (5, 47, 56). Nucleation has also been biochemically reconstituted at the surface of isolated plant nuclei (46a) and on cortical microtubules in protoplast ghosts (15). There is evidence for initiation from cortical sites that are both attached (47) and unattached (5, 56) to existing microtubules, and for microtubules playing a role in the distribution of these potential nucleation sites (5). Determination of the total number and general distribution of initiation sites has been hampered by the difficulty of detecting newly initiating microtubules within cortical microtubule bundles. Although evidence of intrabundle nucleation has been reported (66), the prevalence of these events is unknown.

Microtubule severing, through the action of katanin proteins, may also increase the number of cortical microtubules (43, 61). Cleaving long microtubules into smaller polymers, or severing the minus end of new microtubules from nucleation sites, would result in an increase in total microtubule number, without requiring de novo initiation (2, 3).

Association with the Cell Cortex During Interphase

The first published electron micrographs of vascular plant microtubules showed distinct localization to the cortex of the cell (25, 33). Together with the apparent stability of microtubules relative to cytoplasmic streaming, these observations suggested physical attachment to the plasma membrane or cortical actin cytoskeleton. Interphase microtubules not associated with the cell cortex are also routinely observed, but little is known about their dynamic properties.

Visualization of cortical microtubules in live cells indicates a relatively strong cortical attachment (5, 12, 56, 67). Microtubules in close association with the cell cortex do not appear to slide either laterally or axially (56). Additionally, no evidence has been found for intrabundle sliding (56, 66). Rare untethering of microtubule plus ends from the cell cortex results in rapid contortions of the polymer as it is buffeted by the streaming cytoplasm, often leading to depolymerization (56). Lack of such contortions when microtubule ends polymerize over other polymers suggests that newly synthesized polymer is coupled rapidly to the cortex during growth. These data demonstrate a tight, near continuous association of

microtubules with the cell cortex during interphase.

The molecular mechanism of cortical association remains unclear. Phospholipase-D (PLD) plays a role in microtubule association with the cell cortex (18) and agents inhibiting normal PLD activity result in a loss of cortical association (12). Whether PLD interacts directly with the microtubule, indirectly through a complex, or signals for the dissociation has not been established. Other proteins known to function in the interphase array, such as MOR1 (65, 71, 75), or membrane proteins that cortical microtubules may associate with, such as cellulose synthase, are also candidates for providing connection to the plasma membrane.

Dynamics of Cortical Interphase Microtubules

Tradescantia cells, injected with fluorescently labeled animal tubulin, provided the first quantitative measurements of plant cortical array dynamics (28). Although single microtubules were not resolved, measurements of fluorescence recovery after photobleaching (FRAP) revealed a three- to four-times faster recovery time for plant microtubules when compared with animal interphase cells. The rapid return of fluorescence, attributable to polymerization of new polymer, suggested that plant microtubules were rapidly and constantly polymerizing (5, 28, 36).

Observations of single microtubules using fluorescent protein tags and confocal microscopy revealed that the plus ends of plant microtubules exhibit dynamic instability (11, 56, 67). Interestingly, the rates of plus-end polymerization (3–5 μm/min) and depolymerization (5–9 μm/min) for single plant microtubules are typically slower than average values observed in animal cells by a factor greater than threefold (67), a result that was not predicted by the more rapid recovery of photobleaching in plant cells. The average time spent in each dynamic phase for plant and animal cells shows that plant interphase microtubules pause only about 10% of the time (56), whereas microtubules in some animal tissue culture cells pause nearly 60% of the time (53 and references therein). The more continuous dynamics of the plant microtubules help account for the faster FRAP time; however, a further examination of the dynamics reveals a more probable explanation.

Observation of both ends of single microtubules in the *Arabidopsis* cortical array revealed that many minus ends also exhibited dynamic behaviors (5, 56), a phenomenon rarely observed in cells containing defined microtubule organizing centers (51, 70). The possibility that the minus ends of cortical microtubules might be dynamic was suggested by the observation that many polymers appeared to move unidirectionally across the cortex of *Arabidopsis* epidermal cells. Marks created by photobleaching on these migrating microtubules remained stationary as the microtubule moved, demonstrating that microtubules do not physically translocate, but rather reposition through the addition of dimers to the plus end with concomitant loss at the minus end, a mechanism termed treadmilling. In the *Arabidopsis* epidermal cells studied, the minus ends showed persistently slow depolymerization and pausing whereas the plus ends exhibited dynamic instability biased toward growth (56). Because the patterns of polymerization activity at the two polymer ends are different, i.e., one end displays dynamic instability and the other does not, the resulting behavior constitutes a hybrid treadmilling mechanism. The constant loss from the minus ends provides free dimers for biasing the plus dynamic instability toward net growth, a possible mechanism to account for the increased rate of fluorescence recovery in the photobleaching experiments.

Microtubule-Microtubule Interactions

The constant treadmilling movement of microtubules, and restriction of this movement to the two-dimensional surface of the cell cortex, leads to physical interactions among polymers. The growing plus end of a treadmilling microtubule travels in a straight line or slight arc until it encounters another polymer (13, 56). Time-lapsed observations indicate several possible outcomes from the microtubule-microtubule interaction. In general, the growing microtubule end either crosses over the encountered polymer, or its trajectory is redirected to coalign with the encountered polymer. The decision to coalign or cross over shows a steep dependence on the angle of the interaction. If the angle is greater than 30–40°, the plus end typically crosses over in Arabidopsis cells, and in tobacco tissue culture cells may show an increased tendency to depolymerize (13). Encounters at angles less than 30–40° result in coalignment, and an abrupt change in growth direction an uncommon event for free microtubules (**Figure 2**). This behavior strongly suggests a direct interaction between microtubules or associated microtubule-binding proteins.

Treadmilling plays a specific role in the creation of plant microtubule bundles. As the plus end encounters a second polymer and begins to coalign, the minus end depolymerizes until the entire length of the polymer becomes aligned. This interaction results in the formation of a coherent polymer bundle, where the stray ends have been erased by minus-end depolymerization and the single polymer has taken a new growth direction (56). If microtubules were not dismantled from the minus end, plus end-mediated interactions would tend to create a meshwork of polymers, hindering the formation of a parallel array.

The observations of bundling in live cells likely represent the microtubule cross-bridging observed in electron micrographs, attributed principally to the family of MAP65-related proteins (6, 58). Purified plant MAP65 protein, when added to purified animal tubulin, creates 24-nm bridges between microtubules, in good agreement with microtubule spacings measured in plant cells (6). Recent investigations of the MAP65 family (nine genes in *Arabidopsis*) suggest functional specificity

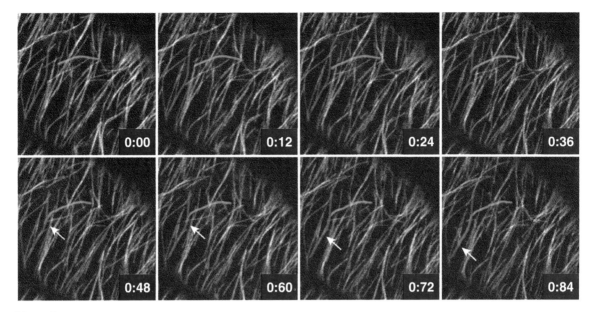

Figure 2

Polymer treadmilling and bundling. Time series of confocal images acquired at the cortex of an
Arabidopsis hypocotyl cell expressing EYFP::TUA5. One treadmilling polymer (*green*) encounters and
bundles with a second polymer (*red*), changing both its position on the cortex and its angular orientation.
Images are shown at 12-second intervals.

and localized binding preferences within the cell for MAP65 isoforms (5, 7, 59, 66, 72). Interestingly, the MAP65-1 protein appears to bind and unbind microtubules faster than the rate of growth (7), an unexpected result for a protein expected to stabilize microtubule-microtubule interactions. MOR1, which is required for interphase microtubule array construction (71), may be able to bundle microtubules (75), although limitations in expressing or isolating the >200-kD protein have precluded biochemical attributions of activity.

CORTICAL ARRAY ORGANIZATION

Array order and organization can be difficult to define in developing cells and mutants. In general terms, arrays have been characterized as "organized" if the microtubules have some degree of coalignment with either themselves or a cellular axis (e.g., epidermal root cells in the growth zone or guard cells). However, this is only a partial description of array order. Identifying and quantifying more complete and subtle aspects of order will be important both for understanding cellular morphogenesis and for discovering mechanisms related to array organization (48, 63). The problem of describing array order becomes particularly apparent when comparing mutant phenotypes to the progression of array organization in wild-type cells. For example, alleles of Mor1(71) ,Ton1 and 2 (3a, 42a, 64a), and katanin P60 (2, 3, 43, 61) cause gross array disorganization. The descriptions of general loss of array organization in these mutants demonstrate important requirements for array construction but leave in question what specific roles these proteins might play in directing microtubule spacing and organization (71). Similarly, mutations in Spr1 and tubulin (lefty) can cause changes in the pitch of helical arrays in root and hypocotyl cells (48, 54, 63). Although the pitch change has been described, there may be other important changes in polymer that may accompany this change.

Determining to what degree a microtubule array is ordered, developing criteria for ranking the severity of patterning defects, or defining what aspects of order typically change have not been rigorously explored and require an accounting of several array properties. Each microtubule in the cell has unit properties of length and of bending (curvature) over its length. The microtubule also has properties measured relative to the cell, including an angle of orientation to the cell axis and both X and Y positions on the cell cortex. Each property will have a defined distribution for the microtubule population in a given cell. For example, the length distribution for all microtubules in a cell could be described as Gaussian, multimodal, exponential, or even uniform if all polymers were the same length. Similarly, the X and Y positions, curvatures, and relative distribution of orientations can deviate from random to highly ordered.

Array order increases as each of the property distributions (length, curvature, X position, Y position, angular orientation) becomes less random. Nonrandom distributions have properties of dispersion, characterized by attraction (clustering) and repulsion (maximum equidistant spacing). An array spaced at equal intervals on the Y axis, and maintaining exactly 90° in orientation to the cell axis, constitutes a highly ordered system (**Figure 3a**). Placing these microtubules at the same distance from the Y axis creates a pattern reminiscent of a preprophase band (**Figure 3b**). Both patterns are ordered to the same extent but differ in their distribution properties. Randomly distributing the Y axis positions of these microtubules results in a less ordered system, even though the microtubules remain co-oriented with the X axis (**Figure 3c**). The concept of dispersion also applies to angular orientation. By selecting polymers that have the same position on the Y axis and ordering the angles in repulsion instead of attraction, a pattern is created that resembles a two-diminsional aster instead of a band (**Figure 3d**).

The distributions of polymer properties have important interdependencies with regard to the total degree of order in the system. For example, the relative importance of position and angle depend on the polymer length distribution. From the preprophase band example above, reordering longer polymers along the band has little impact on pattern (**Figure 3e**), whereas changing the angle of those longer polymers abruptly disrupts the organization (**Figure 3d**). On the other hand, if the band were composed of short microtubules, changing the relative angles produces less disruption to the overall banding pattern (**Figure 3d, e**). This property becomes more evident if we consider longer microtubules as spatially coordinated assemblies of smaller polymers. The position and angle of each subpolymer is then constrained by the average angle of orientation and the curvature of the relatively stiff polymer. One hundred polymers, 1 micron long, can be patterned in many more ways than a single 100-micron polymer with limited curvature. Hence, the length and curvature distributions place limits on the degrees of freedom available for spatial and angular displacements.

Microtubules Organization and Polymer Polarity

Microtubules typically direct activities of other proteins through orientation of their inherently polarized structure. The dynamics of polymerization differ strikingly at the two ends, and the lattice orientation contains information for the directionality of motor protein movement and for the binding orientation of microtubule-associated proteins. Limitation of most nucleation to the microtubule organizing center in interphase animal and fungal cells generates an inherent polarity in these astral arrays, with plus ends at the cell periphery and minus ends interior to the cell. The orientation of polar filaments in the nonastral plant cortical array is distinctly

X axis

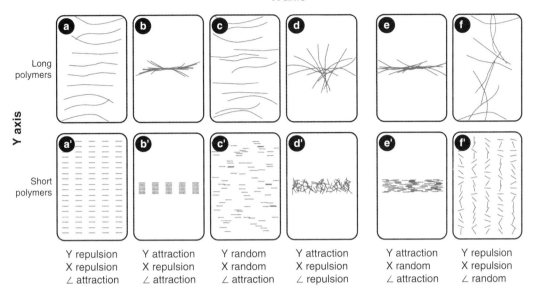

Y repulsion	Y attraction	Y random	Y attraction	Y attraction	Y repulsion
X repulsion	X repulsion	X random	X repulsion	X random	X repulsion
∠ attraction	∠ attraction	∠ attraction	∠ repulsion	∠ attraction	∠ random

Figure 3

Aspects of cortical microtubule organization. Distribution of long (*a–f*) and short (*a'–f'*) polymers with relation to cell axes and angular orientation. Microtubules show repulsive (*a* and *a'*) or attractive (*b* and *b'*) dispersion along the X and Y axes and angular co-orientation to the X axis. Randomizing spatial distribution, with retention of angular co-orientation (*c* and *c'*), results in a less ordered array. Ordering the angular orientation in repulsion has dramatic consequences for longer microtubules (*d*), with less impact on shorter microtubules (*d'*). Note that total polymer mass is equivalent for arrays of long and short microtubules. The relative importance of angular orientation and spatial positioning on two axes depends on polymer length. Randomizing position along the axis of angular orientation (*e*) shows little effect on the pattern for longer microtubules (*e* and *b*), but can be significant for shorter polymers (*e'* and *b'*). Conversely, shorter polymers can be patterned with respect to both X and Y axes, nearly independently from angular orientation (*f'*), whereas patterns for longer polymers are more difficult to construct using only X and Y axis spacing (*f*).

different. Current evidence (1, 56) shows that the long microtubules in transversely aligned arrays do not have uniform polarity (i.e., there are microtubules aligned in both directions). The highly ordered arrays in guard cells may be an exception given the concentrated localization of gamma-tubulin on the aperture side of the cells, potentially giving rise to a polarized array (44, 76). The lack of oriented microtubule polarity in most epidermal cells suggests that plant cortical arrays play a fundamentally different role in vesicle targeting than that characterized for animal interphase arrays. If vesicles translocate on microtubules at the cell cortex, the pattern and polarity of the array would promote distribution, but would not easily support targeted transport based on the directionality of motor protein movement.

MICROTUBULE BEHAVIORS AND CORTICAL ARRAY ORGANIZATION

Observing single microtubules in living cells has shed new light on the mechanisms of cortical array organization. Most prior studies have concluded with a general view that either microtubules slide from one position to another, or they are polymerized directly into new positions (9, 36, 69). The dynamic spring hypothesis, proposed by Lloyd based on ideas of

Green, was an exception, offering a mechanistic model for microtubule orientation based on lateral plasma membrane attachment and the telescoping of polymers via molecular motors (39). Recent studies, involving the direct visualization of microtubules, indicate little or no lateral sliding and no intrabundle sliding of polymers, suggesting that mechanisms that require such sliding, including the dynamic spring hypothesis, are not likely to play a significant role in organizing cortical arrays (19, 30, 56, 74, 77). The notion of microtubules being polymerized directly into a pattern does not appear to agree with the observed initiations of microtubules in live cells (5, 47, 56), or with the observations of gamma-tubulin/Spc98 localization (15, 34, 57), with one special exception (see below).

Integration of Microtubule Behaviors

The picture that is emerging from newer studies is that a variety of polymer behaviors act together to create a degree of self-organization, and the regulation of these behaviors in a spatially defined context may influence the local or more global organizational patterns.

The nucleation and retention of microtubules within the two-dimensional plane of the cell cortex contribute directly to array organization. This dimensional limitation prevents the formation of three-dimensional arrangements, such as spherical asters, and increases the probability that polymers will interact and coalign. Furthermore, positioning of cortical nucleation sites with reference to cellular geometry can have a defining influence on array organization. For example, the extremely regular, transverse alignment of microtubules in mature guard cells (**Figure 1**) likely arises in part through the concentration of gamma-tubulin-containing nucleation sites adjacent to the stomatal aperture (44). However, the observable nucleation sites in other cell types, such as hypocotyl or tissue culture cells (5, 47, 56), show little indication of positional grouping or angular pattern with

reference to the cell axis, suggesting that new cortical microtubules either change direction or become destabilized to achieve orientation with respect to the cell axis.

Regardless of where a polymer is initiated, minus-end detachment and dynamics prevent the microtubule from being anchored to the site of origin. Polymer treadmilling combined with cortical association allows microtubules to migrate across the cortex. This remarkable behavior reorganizes microtubule positions and angles. As the plus end explores space, the initial angle of polymerization can change either gradually, producing shallow curvature of the growing polymer, or abruptly, either by interaction with other polymers or by detachment from the cell cortex and reattachment at a new angle. As subunit loss gradually consumes the minus end, the older portions of the polymer are erased, resulting in a complete angular reorientation of the microtubule. Treadmilling motility thus alters polymer position and orientation, uncoupled from the site of initiation and without requiring de novo nucleation in the array.

ROLE OF POLYMERIZATION DYNAMICS

Array organization depends directly on the polymerization dynamics of the microtubules. Maintaining a steady-state array of treadmilling polymers requires that the total amount of dimer binding to the plus ends be equal to the amount of dimer liberated from the minus ends. Cellular control of the system is likely exerted through as yet unidentified accessory proteins, but the system is ultimately responsive to the concentration of free tubulin dimer. Hence, if any single rate changes, compensating adjustments will occur to other rates, with compounding effects on microtubule number, length distribution, and possibly the polymer-to-dimer ratio. For example, a sudden increase in the catastrophe frequency would produce shorter microtubules on average, but the resulting liberation of dimer would then promote nucleation, eventually increasing the total number of polymers in the cell. The increased catastrophe rate would also affect the balance of plus- and minus-end activities that produce treadmilling motility. Thus, altering polymerization dynamics will have consequences for treadmilling, the length distribution of polymers, and the roles they both play in array organization.

A special contribution to array organization and dynamics will also be made through the control of polymer detachment from the initiation site, the behavior that gives rise to treadmilling microtubules. If the mean time to polymer detachment is increased, growth at plus ends will, on average, produce more polymer before the minus ends become active, thereby producing a population of longer treadmilling microtubules that have a greater chance of moving to new positions before extinction. The ratio of polymer mass to free ends also influences the dynamics of array turnover. If most of the tubulin is held in a few long polymers, it will take longer to disassemble and reassemble the array than if the same amount of assembled tubulin was distributed into many smaller polymers, with lots of exposed ends.

Microtubule Interactions and Self-Organization

One of the most notable outcomes of polymer treadmilling is the promotion of microtubule interactions that lead to formation of microtubule bundles. If a growing plus end contacts another cortical microtubule at a sufficiently shallow angle, the resulting interaction aligns new polymer growth with the contacted microtubule. Loss of dimers at the minus end removes the older polymer, resulting in a reorientation to the position and angle of the encountered polymer. This remarkable interaction has the properties of a self-templating process, providing a means to associate and coalign polymers with each other to create an ordered arrangement.

The microtubule bundles created by this process have important organizational and functional properties. Bundles of polymers are predicted to have greater positional and angular stability than do single, unassociated microtubules. Because more than one polymer occupies the position at the cell cortex, the chance that at least one polymer is present at that position and angle at any point in time is significantly greater than can be the case for a single treadmilling microtubule. For biochemical activities that may require cytoskeletal support for longer than a few minutes, such as cell wall biosynthesis, the increased positional stability of the microtubule bundles may provide needed structure over an appropriate timescale. Observations in root cells have shown that transversly orientated polymers are more stable than polymers in other orientations (64). In this study it was not possible to distinguish between single and bundled fibers. It will be interesting to determine if the increased stablity of transverse polymers is due to their orientation alone or to their degree of polymer bundling.

Due to their stability, bundles, along with long polymers, act as positional traps for single treadmilling microtubules. Once microtubules associate into bundles, they remain dynamic (56, 66), but rarely depart from the sides of the bundle or show cortical detachment (S.L. Shaw & D.W. Ehrhardt, unpublished observations). The polymer interaction therefore confines the plus end of the captured microtubule to the track already defined by the bundle, preventing the microtubule from exploring cortical space and creating a new organization. By trapping locally initiated polymers, a bundle tends to deplete the immediate area of polymers with discordant orientations and also discourages the formation of new bundles that might intersect at less than the 30° bundling acceptance angle. This relatively simple act of microtubule bundling, heavily promoted by restriction of microtubules to the cortex, will therefore lead to the formation of array pattern. Thus, we can view the cortical array as a dynamic system with locally acting, self-organizing properties.

Forming local arrangements of stable polymer bundles raises a fundamental question regarding cytoskeletal function—how the cell balances the need to create stable structures with the need to reorganize in response to developmental and environmental cues. A recent study by Murata and colleagues (47) describes another type of polymer interaction that provides a possible means to change bundle organization. These investigators observed that many nucleation events occur in association with the walls of previous microtubules. Intriguingly, new microtubules grew at these sites in a narrow range of angles with a mean of about $40°$. If enough new polymers initiate by this mechanism, it would break up stable patterns of bundles, potentially leading to a new pattern of organization, oriented with respect to the original array. Thus, new polymers may be polymerized in a fixed orientation to help generate array organization, but in reference to the polymer orientation rather than to the axis of the cell. There is also evidence for initiation of new polymers along the axis of existing bundles (66), potentially reinforcing the existing array pattern. It will be important to determine if the angle of nucleation events associated with microtubule walls is a point of array regulation.

Self-Organization and Cellular Patterning

How much of the observed patterning in cortical arrays arises through the random association of treadmilling polymers? The self-organizing properties of cortical microtubules act with reference to other microtubules and have not been studied in the context of cellular geometry. Even if cortically associated polymers eventually formed a coaligned array through treadmilling and bundling interactions, the bundles still require orientation to the cell axis to be useful. Creating specific regions of the cell cortex with different

microtubule-related properties may provide the means to relate self-organizational mechanisms to the reference frame of the cell.

One source for such a cellular influence on self organization may be the cell wall itself. Although microtubules have been postulated to direct the deposition of the cell wall, cellulose microfibrils may also feed back on microtubule organization. Oriented cellulose microfibrils may help to create fine-scale organization of microtubule interaction sites at the cortex. Linear arrays of microtubule association sites could possibly stabilize polymers that have preferred orientations, or guide the direction of polymerization of the plus end (13, 27, 64). By providing a bias to individual polymer behavior relative to the frame of the cell, the self-organizing behavior of the system of interacting polymers may be influenced to achieve a particular orientation. Larger-scale, regional patterns of microtubule regulation could also influence self-organizing behavior. For example, if the poles of cylindrical cells retard cortical association or promote catastrophe, creation of longitudinally organized arrays would be strongly inhibited and transverse arrays promoted. Obvious examples of direct regional influence of array organization include the clustering of nucleation sites in guard cells already described, and the selective depopulation of cortical microtubules during preprophase band construction.

Recent studies by Yang and colleagues provide exciting insight into how regional differences in microtubule properties and their effect on cell growth may be determined (17). Small GTPases are involved in identifying cellular domains (21, 22). Yang's group found that a dominant gain-of-function ROP2, or loss of ROP2 function, both cause reduced pavement cell interdigitation (lobing) and promote formation of transverse microtubule arrays throughout the cell. Pavement cells typically only have local patches of parallel microtubules, located in the sinuses of the lobes, with a random pattern of cortical polymers elsewhere. ROP2 distribution is concentrated at the lobe apices for wild-type cells. RIC1, a novel ROP2-interacting protein (73), binds microtubules in a ROP2-dependent manner (17). The overexpression of RIC1 in wild-type plants dramatically reduced cell lobing and caused formation of highly parallel and transverse cortical arrays, similar to ROP2 manipulation. Taken together, these data suggest that ROP2 defines regions of the cortex and modifies microtubule activity through the action of RIC1. The microtubule activity(s) affected by ROP2/RIC1 action has not yet been defined. Curiously, highly oriented transverse arrays are created when ROP2 is both hyper- and hypoactive, suggesting that the array assumes a default condition, possibly through simple self-organization, when GTPase activity can not specify regional domains.

Our ability to learn about function from mutants and other genetic manipulations is limited by the detail with which we can understand phenotype. By observing and measuring the behaviors of individual microtubules and other molecules in living plant cells, understanding of mutant phenotypes is refined from a general description of a disorganized or disassembled cytoskeleton to molecular phenotypes that lie much closer to the point of action for these gene products. These data will lead to more mechanistically detailed hypotheses for cortical array organization and function.

LITERATURE CITED

1. Baskin TI. 2001. On the alignment of cellulose microfibrils by cortical microtubules: a review and a model. *Protoplasma* 215:150–71
2. Bouquin T, Mattsson O, Naested H, Foster R, Mundy J. 2003. The Arabidopsis lue1 mutant defines a katanin p60 ortholog involved in hormonal control of microtubule orientation during cell growth. *J. Cell Sci.* 116:791–801
3. Burk DH, Liu B, Zhong R, Morrison WH, Ye ZH. 2001. A katanin-like protein regulates normal cell wall biosynthesis and cell elongation. *Plant Cell* 13:807–27
3a. Camilleri C, Azimzadeh J, Pastuglia M, Bellini C, Grandjean O, Bouchez D. 2002. The Arabidopsis *TONNEAU2* gene encodes a putative novel protein phosphatase 2A regulatory subunit essential for the control of the cortical cytoskeleton. *Plant Cell* 14:833–45
4. Caplow M, Fee L. 2003. Concerning the chemical nature of tubulin subunits that cap and stabilize microtubules. *Biochemistry* 42:2122–26
5. Chan J, Calder GM, Doonan JH, Lloyd CW. 2003. EB1 reveals mobile microtubule nucleation sites in Arabidopsis. *Nat. Cell Biol.* 5:967–71
6. Chan J, Jensen CG, Jensen LC, Bush M, Lloyd CW. 1999. The 65-kDa carrot microtubule-associated protein forms regularly arranged filamentous cross-bridges between microtubules. *Proc. Natl. Acad. Sci. USA* 96:14931–36
7. Chang HY, Smertenko AP, Igarashi H, Dixon DP, Hussey PJ. 2005. Dynamic interaction of NtMAP65-1a with microtubules in vivo. *J. Cell Sci.* 118:3195–201
8. Clayton L, Black CM, Lloyd CW. 1985. Microtubule nucleating sites in higher plant cells identified by an auto-antibody against pericentriolar material. *J. Cell Biol.* 101:319–24
9. Cyr RJ. 1994. Microtubules in plant morphogenesis: role of the cortical array. *Annu. Rev. Cell Biol.* 10:153–80
10. Cyr RJ, Palevitz BA. 1995. Organization of cortical microtubules in plant cells. *Curr. Opin. Cell Biol.* 7:65–71
11. Dhonukshe P, Gadella TW Jr. 2003. Alteration of microtubule dynamic instability during preprophase band formation revealed by yellow fluorescent protein-CLIP170 microtubule plus-end labeling. *Plant Cell* 15:597–611

12. Dhonukshe P, Laxalt AM, Goedhart J, Gadella TW, Munnik T. 2003. Phospholipase d activation correlates with microtubule reorganization in living plant cells. *Plant Cell* 15:2666–79

13. Dixit R, Cyr R. 2004. Encounters between dynamic cortical microtubules promote ordering of the cortical array through angle-dependent modifications of microtubule behavior. *Plant Cell* 16:3274–84

14. Doxsey S, McCollum D, Theurkauf W. 2005. Centrosomes in cellular regulation. *Annu. Rev. Cell Dev. Biol.* 21:411–34

14a. Drykova D, Cenklova V, Sulimenko V, Volc J, Draber P, Binarova P. 2003. Plant gamma-tubulin interacts with alphabeta-tubulin dimers and forms membrane-associated complexes. *Plant Cell* 15:465–80

15. Erhardt M, Stoppin-Mellet V, Campagne S, Canaday J, Mutterer J, et al. 2002. The plant Spc98p homologue colocalizes with gamma-tubulin at microtubule nucleation sites and is required for microtubule nucleation. *J. Cell Sci.* 115:2423–31

16. Fant X, Merdes A, Haren L. 2004. Cell and molecular biology of spindle poles and NuMA. *Int. Rev. Cytol.* 238:1–57

17. Fu Y, Gu Y, Zheng Z, Wasteneys G, Yang Z. 2005. Arabidopsis interdigitating cell growth requires two antagonistic pathways with opposing action on cell morphogenesis. *Cell* 120:687–700

18. Gardiner JC, Harper JD, Weerakoon ND, Collings DA, Ritchie S, et al. 2001. A 90-kD phospholipase D from tobacco binds to microtubules and the plasma membrane. *Plant Cell* 13:2143–58

19. Granger CL, Cyr RJ. 2001. Spatiotemporal relationships between growth and microtubule orientation as revealed in living root cells of Arabidopsis thaliana transformed with green-fluorescent-protein gene construct GFP-MBD. *Protoplasma* 216:201–14

20. Green PB. 1962. Mechanism for plant cell morphogensis. *Science* 138:1404

20a. Green PB. 1963. On mechanisms of elongation. In *Cytodifferentiation and Macromolecular Synthesis*, ed. M. Locke. pp. 203–34. New York: Academic Press

21. Gu Y, Wang Z, Yang Z. 2004. ROP/RAC GTPase: an old master regulator for plant signalling. *Curr. Opin. Plant Biol.* 7:527–36

22. Hall A. 1992. Ras-related GTPases and the cytoskeleton. *Mol. Biol. Cell* 3:475–79

23. Hardham AR, Gunning BE. 1978. Structure of cortical microtubule arrays in plant cells. *J. Cell Biol.* 77:14–34

24. Hardham AR, Gunning BE. 1979. Interpolation of microtubules into cortical arrays during cell elongation and differentiation in roots of Azolla pinnata. *J. Cell Sci.* 37:411–42

25. Hepler PK, Newcomb EH. 1964. Microtubules and fibrils in the cytoplasm of coleus cells undergoing secondary wall deposition. *J. Cell Biol.* 20:529–32

26. Hepler PK, Palevitz BA. 1974. Microtubules and microfilaments. *Annu. Rev. Plant Physiol.* 25:309–62

27. Himmelspach R, Williamson RE, Wasteneys GO. 2003. Cellulose microfibril alignment recovers from DCB-induced disruption despite microtubule disorganization. *Plant J.* 36:565–75

28. Hush JM, Wadsworth P, Callaham DA, Hepler PK. 1994. Quantification of microtubule dynamics in living plant cells using fluorescence redistribution after photobleaching. *J. Cell Sci.* 107(Pt. 4):775–84

29. Job D, Valiron O, Oakley B. 2003. Microtubule nucleation. *Curr. Opin. Cell Biol.* 15:111–17

30. Katsuna N, Hasezawa S. 2002. Dynamic organization of vacuolar and microtuule structures during cell cycle progression in synchronized tobacco BY-2 cells. *Plant Cell Physiol.* 43:965–73

31. Kellogg DR. 1994. Centrosome and cellular organization. *Annu. Rev. Biochem.* 63:639–74

32. Komarova YA, Vorobjev IA, Borisy GG. 2002. Life cycle of MTs: persistent growth in the cell interior, asymmetric transition frequencies and effects of the cell boundary. *J. Cell Sci.* 115:3527–39

33. Ledbetter MC, Porter KR. 1963. A "microtubule" in plant cell fine structure. *J. Cell Biol.* 19:239–50

34. Liu B, Joshi HC, Wilson TJ, Silflow CD, Palevitz BA, Snustad DP. 1994. gamma-Tubulin in Arabidopsis: gene sequence, immunoblot, and immunofluorescence studies. *Plant Cell* 6:303–14

35. Lloyd C. 1984. Toward a dynamic helical model for the influence of microtubules on wall patterns in plants. *Int. Rev. Cyt.* 86:1–51

36. Lloyd C. 1994. Why should stationary plant cells have such dynamic microtubules? *Mol. Biol. Cell* 5:1277–80

37. Lloyd C, Chan J. 2002. Helical microtubule arrays and spiral growth. *Plant Cell* 14:2319–24

38. Lloyd C, Seagull RW. 1985. A new spring for plant cell biology: microtubules as dynamic helices. *TIBS* 476–8

39. Lloyd CW, Clayton L, Dawson PJ, Doonan JH, Hulme JS, et al. 1985. The cytoskeleton underlying side walls and cross walls in plants: molecules and macromolecular assemblies. *J. Cell Sci. Suppl.* 2:143–55

40. Marc J, Granger CL, Brincat J, Fisher DD, Kao T, et al. 1998. A *GFP-MAP4* reporter gene for visualizing cortical microtubule arrangements in living epidermal cells. *Plant Cell* 10:1927–40

41. Mathur J, Mathur N, Kernebeck B, Srinivas BP, Hulskamp M. 2003. A novel localization pattern for an EB1-like protein links micortubules dynamics to endomembarne organization. *Curr. Biol.* 13:1991–97

42. Mazia D. 1984. Centrosomes and mitotic poles. *Exp. Cell Res.* 153:1–15

42a. McClinton RS, Sung ZR. 1997. Organization of cortical microtubules at the plasma membrane in *Arabidopsis. Planta* 201:252–26

43. McClinton RS, Chandler JS, Callis J. 2001. cDNA isolation, characterization, and protein intracellular localization of a katanin-like p60 subunit from Arabidopsis thaliana. *Protoplasma* 216:181–90

44. McDonald AR, Liu B, Joshi HC, Palevitz BA. 1993. Gamma-tubulin is associated with a cortical-microtubule-organizing zone in the developing guard cells of Allium cepa L. *Planta* 191:357–61

45. Mitchison T, Kirschner M. 1984. Dynamic instability of microtubule growth. *Nature* 312:237–42

46. Mitchison TJ, Kirschner MW. 1987. Some thoughts on the partitioning of tubulin between monomer and polymer under conditions of dynamic instability. *Cell Biophys* 11:35–55

46a. Mizuno K. 1993. Microtubule-nucleation sites on nuclei of higher plant cells. *Protoplasma* 173:77–85

47. Murata M, Sonobe S, Baskin TI, Hyodo S, Hasezawa S, et al. 2005. Microtubule-dependent microtubule nucleation based on recruitment of gamma-tubulin in higher plants. *Nat. Cell Biol.* 19:961–68

48. Nakajima K, Furutani I, Tachimoto H, Matsubara H, Hashimoto T. 2004. SPIRAL1 encodes a plant-specific microtubule-localized protein required for directional control of rapidly expanding Arabidopsis cells. *Plant Cell* 16:1178–90

49. Pickett-Heaps JD. 1969. Preprophase microtubule bands in some abnormal mitotic cells of wheat. *J. Cell Sci.* 4:397–420

50. Renzaglia KS, Maden AR. 2000. Microtubule organizing centers and the origin of centrioles during spermatogenesis in the pteridophyte Phylloglossum. *Microsc. Res. Tech.* 49:496–505

51. Rodionov VI, Borisy GG. 1997. Microtubule treadmilling in vivo. *Science* 275:215–18

52. Roudier F, Fernandez AG, Fujita M, Himmelspach R, Borner GH, et al. 2005. COBRA, an Arabidopsis extracellular glycosyl-phosphatidyl inositol-anchored protein, specifically controls highly anisotropic expansion through its involvement in cellulose microfibril orientation. *Plant Cell* 17:1749–63

53. Rusan NM, Fagerstrom CJ, Yvon AM, Wadsworth P. 2001. Cell cycle-dependent changes in microtubule dynamics in living cells expressing green fluorescent protein-alpha tubulin. *Mol. Biol. Cell* 12:971–80

54. Sedbrook JC, Ehrhardt DW, Fisher SE, Scheible WR, Somerville CR. 2004. The Arabidopsis *sku6/spiral1* gene encodes a plus end-localized microtubule-interacting protein involved in directional cell expansion. *Plant Cell* 16:1506–20

55. Seltzer V, Pawlowski T, Campagne S, Canaday J, Erhardt M, et al. 2003. Multiple microtubule nucleation sites in higher plants. *Cell Biol. Int.* 27:267–69

56. Shaw SL, Kamyar R, Ehrhardt DW. 2003. Sustained microtubule treadmilling in Arabidopsis cortical arrays. *Science* 300:1715–18

57. Shimamura M, Brown RC, Lemmon BE, Akashi T, Mizuno K, et al. 2004. Gamma-tubulin in basal land plants: characterization, localization, and implication in the evolution of acentriolar microtubule organizing centers. *Plant Cell* 16:45–59

58. Smertenko A, Saleh N, Igarashi H, Mori H, Hauser-Hahn I, et al. 2000. A new class of microtubule-associated proteins in plants. *Nat. Cell Biol.* 2:750–53

59. Smertenko AP, Chang HY, Wagner V, Kaloriti D, Fenyk S, et al. 2004. The Arabidopsis microtubule-associated protein AtMAP65-1: molecular analysis of its microtubule bundling activity. *Plant Cell* 16:2035–47

60. Smith LG, Oppenheimer DG. 2005. Spatial control of cell expansion by the plant cytoskeleton. *Annu. Rev. Cell Dev. Biol.* 21:271–95

61. Stoppin-Mellet V, Gaillard J, Vantard M. 2003. Plant katanin, a microtubule severing protein. *Cell Biol. Int.* 27:279

62. Tassin AM, Bornens M. 1999. Centrosome structure and microtubule nucleation in animal cells. *Biol Cell* 91:343–54

63. Thitamadee S, Tuchihara K, Hashimoto T. 2002. Microtubule basis for left-handed helical growth in Arabidopsis. *Nature* 417:193–96

64. Tian GW, Smith D, Gluck S, Baskin TI. 2004. Higher plant cortical microtubule array analyzed in vitro in the presence of the cell wall. *Cell Motil. Cytoskel.* 57:26–36

64a. Traas J, Bellini C, Nacry P, Kronenberger J, Bouchez D, Caboche M. 1995. Normal differentiation patterns in plants lacking microtubular preprophase bands. *Nature* 375:676–67

65. Twell D, Park SK, Hawkins TJ, Schubert D, Schmidt R, et al. 2002. MOR1/GEM1 has an essential role in the plant-specific cytokinetic phragmoplast. *Nat. Cell Biol.* 4:711–14

66. Van Damme D, Van Poucke K, Boutant E, Ritzenthaler C, Inze D, Geelen D. 2004. In vivo dynamics and differential microtubule-binding activities of MAP65 proteins. *Plant Physiol* 136:3956–67

67. Vos JW, Dogterom M, Emons AM. 2004. Microtubules become more dynamic but not shorter during preprophase band formation: a possible "search-and-capture" mechanism for microtubule translocation. *Cell Motil. Cytoskel.* 57:246–58

68. Wasteneys GO. 2004. Progress in understanding the role of microtubules in plant cells. *Curr. Opin. Plant Biol.* 7:651–60

69. Wasteneys GO, Galway ME. 2003. Remodeling the cytoskeleton for growth and form: an overview with some new views. *Annu. Rev. Plant Biol.* 54:691–722

70. Waterman-Storer CM, Salmon ED. 1997. Actomyosin-based retrograde flow of microtubules in the lamella of migrating epithelial cells influences microtubule dynamic instability and turnover and is associated with microtubule breakage and treadmilling. *J. Cell Biol.* 139:417–34

71. Whittington AT, Vugrek O, Wei KJ, Hasenbein NG, Sugimoto K, et al. 2001. MOR1 is essential for organizing cortical microtubules in plants. *Nature* 411:610–13

72. Wicker-Planquart C, Stoppin-Mellet V, Blanchoin L, Vantard M. 2004. Interactions of tobacco microtubule-associated protein MAP65-1b with microtubules. *Plant J* 39:126–34

73. Wu G, Gu Y, Li S, Yang Z. 2001. A genome-wide analysis of Arabidopsis Rop-interactive CRIB motif-containing proteins that act as Rop GTPase targets. *Plant Cell* 13:2841–56

74. Wymer CL, Fisher DD, Moore RC, Cyr RJ. 1996. Elucidating the mechanism of cortical microtubule reorientation in plant cells. *Cell Motil. Cytoskel.* 35:162–73

75. Yasuhara H, Muraoka M, Shogaki H, Mori H, Sonobe S. 2002. TMBP200, a microtubule bundling polypeptide isolated from telophase tobacco BY-2 cells is a MOR1 homologue. *Plant Cell Physiol.* 43:595–603

76. Yu R, Huang RF, Wang XC, Yuan M. 2001. Microtubule dynamics are involved in stomatal movement of Vicia faba L. *Protoplasma* 216:113–18

77. Yuan M, Shaw PJ, Warn RM, Lloyd CW. 1994. Dynamic reorientation of cortical microtubules, from transverse to longitudinal, in living plant cells. *Proc. Natl. Acad. Sci. USA* 91:6050–53

Subject Index

ADF/cofilin
actin cytoskeleton in plant cell growth and, 114–15
Adonis aestivalis
floral pigments and, 768
tocopherol and carotenoid synthesis, 721
Aequoria victoria
quantitative fluorescence microscopy and, 92
Aerial tissues
seasonal control of tuberization in potato and, 158–60
Aesculus hippocastanum
leaf hydraulic conductance and, 369
Aging
chlorophyll degradation during senescence and, 55, 57–69
leaf hydraulic conductance and, 372
AGO genes
microRNAs and, 22–23, 31–34, 38–39, 41, 43
Agriculture
tocopherol and carotenoid synthesis, 720–21
Agrobacterium tumefaciens
cytokinins and, 431–32, 437–39
phloem long-distance macromolecular trafficking and, 219
quantitative fluorescence microscopy and, 88–89
AHP genes
meiotic prophase I and, 288
AIP1 protein
actin cytoskeleton in plant cell growth and, 115
Aldehyde oxidase
molybdenum cofactor and molybdenum enzymes, 623–38
Aldoximes
glucosinolates and, 308–10
Algae
history of research, 6–8, 13–14, 16
microtubules and plant cortical array, 861
molybdenum cofactor and molybdenum enzymes, 625, 630, 634
plastid-to-nucleus retrograde signaling and, 742–44, 746–47
protein degradation machineries in plastids and, 602
Allelopathy
root exudates and rhizosphere interactions, 233, 236–39
Allium spp.
meiotic prophase I and, 281
root exudates and rhizosphere interactions, 240
Aloina aloides

mosses in metabolism and developmental studies, 503
Alternaria spp.
glycosyltransferases of lipophilic small molecules and, 584
uncoupling proteins and, 396
AM1 gene
meiotic prophase I and, 267, 274–76, 278, 290
Amanita muscaria
floral pigments and, 763–64
Anisotropy
microtubules and plant cortical array, 861
Annotation
bioinformatics and, 346–47
microRNAs and, 29
Antheridia
mosses in metabolism and developmental studies, 500
Anthocyanidins
glycosyltransferases of lipophilic small molecules and, 578–80
Anthocyanins
floral pigments and, 761, 765–66, 768–72
Antimicrobials
root exudates and rhizosphere interactions, 233, 248–49
Antioxidants
tocopherol and carotenoid synthesis, 711–29, 738
Antirrhinum spp.
seed flavonoids and, 413–14, 418
Aocectangium thomsonii
mosses in metabolism and developmental studies, 501
AOP genes
glucosinolates and, 311–12
AP1 gene
seasonal control of tuberization in potato and, 168
Apical cells
mosses in metabolism and developmental studies, 497–513
Apoptosis
chlorophyll degradation during senescence and, 55, 63–64, 67–68
Aquaporins
leaf hydraulics and, 361
Aquaspirillum spp.
root exudates and rhizosphere interactions, 251
Arabidopsis thaliana
actin cytoskeleton in plant cell growth and, 111, 113–14, 116

chlorophyll degradation during senescence
and, 60–65, 67, 69
cytokinins and, 433–42
floral pigments and, 762, 768, 770–72
global gene expression in specific cell types
and, 451, 457, 459–67
glucosinolates and, 303–4, 306–13, 315–18,
320–23
glycosyltransferases of lipophilic small
molecules and, 568, 570, 573–77, 582–85
laser microdissection and, 186, 188, 190–93
leaf hydraulic conductance and, 364
leaf-shape determination mechanism and,
477–90
meiotic prophase I and, 267–68, 270–92
microRNAs and, 21–44
microtubules and plant cortical array, 861,
864–65
molybdenum cofactor and molybdenum
enzymes, 625, 628, 630, 634–38
mosses in metabolism and developmental
studies, 505
peptide hormones and, 654–56, 658, 660–61,
663–64, 666
phloem long-distance macromolecular
trafficking and, 212, 221
photosystems I and II, 531, 545
phytochrome structure and signaling
mechanisms, 843–44
plastid-to-nucleus retrograde signaling and,
744–45, 750–53
protein degradation machineries in plastids
and, 599–612
pyrimidine/purine biosynthesis and
degradation, 810, 812–27
quantitative fluorescence microscopy and,
88–89, 94–95
root exudates and rhizosphere interactions,
235, 239, 244, 248–49, 253
seasonal control of tuberization in potato and,
159, 161, 164–69, 171–72
seed flavonoids and, 405–20
sugar sensing and signaling, 675, 684–99
tocopherol and carotenoid synthesis, 711,
714–29
transcriptional regulatory networks in
dehydration and cold stresses, 783–94
uncoupling proteins and, 386, 388, 391–96
Aralia spp.
glycosyltransferases of lipophilic small
molecules and, 586
Archegonia

mosses in metabolism and developmental
studies, 500
Aromatic headgroups
tocopherol and carotenoid synthesis, 723–25
Arp2/3 complex
actin cytoskeleton in plant cell growth and,
112–13
arpc1-rnai complex
mosses in metabolism and developmental
studies, 512
Artifactual Ca^{2+} oscillations
quantitative fluorescence microscopy and, 96
ASA1 gene
glucosinolates and, 313
Asparagus officinalis
root exudates and rhizosphere interactions, 238
Aspergillus nidulans
molybdenum cofactor and molybdenum
enzymes, 624, 633
phytochrome structure and signaling
mechanisms, 838
Athalia rosae
glucosinolates and, 320
atr4 gene
glucosinolates and, 316
Atrichum spp.
mosses in metabolism and developmental
studies, 503–4
Autoinhibition
root exudates and rhizosphere interactions, 238
Autotoxicity
root exudates and rhizosphere interactions, 239
Autumnal leaf coloration
chlorophyll degradation during senescence
and, 59
Auxins
glycosyltransferases of lipophilic small
molecules and, 574–75
mosses in metabolism and developmental
studies, 497, 501–2, 510–11
Avena barbata
root exudates and rhizosphere interactions, 247
Axial translocation
microtubules and plant cortical array, 859
Azospirillum spp.
root exudates and rhizosphere interactions, 247

B

Bacillus subtilis
protein degradation machineries in plastids
and, 606

root exudates and rhizosphere interactions, 235, 253

Bacteriophytochrome
phytochrome structure and signaling mechanisms, 837

BANYULS gene
seed flavonoids and, 410, 417

Barbed end
actin cytoskeleton in plant cell growth and, 111

BCRP1 protein
chlorophyll degradation during senescence and, 63

BEL genes
seasonal control of tuberization in potato and, 161–62

Bellis perennis
glycosyltransferases of lipophilic small molecules and, 578–79

Benzylaminopurine
mosses in metabolism and developmental studies, 511

Betalains
floral pigments and, 761–66
glycosyltransferases of lipophilic small molecules and, 571–72, 580

Beta vulgaris
glycosyltransferases of lipophilic small molecules and, 580
root exudates and rhizosphere interactions, 248

bHLH protein
seed flavonoids and, 405, 418–21

Bilin lyases
phytochrome structure and signaling mechanisms, 841–42

Biloprotein photoswitches
phytochrome structure and signaling mechanisms, 839–41

Bi-molecular fluorescence complementation (BiFC)
quantitative fluorescence microscopy and, 83, 90–91

Bioinformatics
annotations, 346–47
applications, 345–46
cellular localization, 351
computational proteomics, 342–43
computational systems biology, 350–51
conclusions, 351–52
databases, 347–50
electrophoresis analysis, 342
emerging areas, 350–51
gene finding, 337–38

genomics, 337–38
introduction, 336–37
mass spectrometry, 342–43
metabolic flux, 344–45
metabolomics, 344
microarray analysis, 340–41
microRNAs and, 23–25
ontologies, 345–47
peptide mass fingerprinting, 343
regulatory sequence analysis, 341–42
semantic web, 351
sequence analysis, 337–39
sequence comparison, 338–39
software, 346–47
spatially resolved data, 351
tandem mass spectrometry, 343
text mining, 350
tilling arrays, 341
transcriptome analysis, 340–42

Biological invasions
root exudates and rhizosphere interactions, 239–40

Bioluminescence resonance energy transfer (BRET)
quantitative fluorescence microscopy and, 83, 90

Biosensors
quantitative fluorescence microscopy and, 79, 83, 93–94, 97
sugar sensing and signaling, 675–700

Biotic compounds
glycosyltransferases of lipophilic small molecules and, 584

Bixa orellana
tocopherol and carotenoid synthesis, 719

Bouquet
meiotic prophase I and, 267, 274, 279–81

Bovine serum albumin (BSA)
uncoupling proteins and, 385

Bradyrhizobium japonicum
root exudates and rhizosphere interactions, 234, 245

Brassica napus
chlorophyll degradation during senescence and, 61
glucosinolates and, 306, 310, 312–13, 318
glycosyltransferases of lipophilic small molecules and, 576
root exudates and rhizosphere interactions, 243
transcriptional regulatory networks in dehydration and cold stresses, 787

Brassica spp.

glucosinolates and, 304–5, 311, 317

    meiotic prophase I and, 283

    peptide hormones and, 657

Brassinosteroids

    glycosyltransferases of lipophilic small
        molecules and, 575

BRCA2 gene

    meiotic prophase I and, 267, 275, 286–87

Brevicoryne brassicae

    glucosinolates and, 320

Bundling

    actin cytoskeleton in plant cell growth and,
        111, 116

    leaf hydraulic conductance and, 365–66

    microtubules and plant cortical array, 859, 862,
        865, 869–70

C

Ca^{2+}

    mosses in metabolism and developmental
        studies, 502

    quantitative fluorescence microscopy and,
        93–94, 96

Caenorhabditis elegans

    actin cytoskeleton in plant cell growth and, 112

    meiotic prophase I and, 289–90

    pyrimidine/purine biosynthesis and
        degradation, 816

    root exudates and rhizosphere interactions,
        235, 252

    uncoupling proteins and, 384, 391, 393–94

Calendula spp.

    floral pigments and, 766

Calothrix spp.

    complementary chromatic adaptation and, 128

Camalexin

    glucosinolates and, 313, 317–18

Cameleon probes

    quantitative fluorescence microscopy and, 79,
        83, 93–96

Cancer

    glucosinolates and, 306

    laser microdissection and, 193

Candidate genes

    meiotic prophase I and, 273

CAP protein

    actin cytoskeleton in plant cell growth and,
        115–16

Capsicum annum

    tocopherol and carotenoid synthesis, 717

Carbon

    pyrimidine/purine biosynthesis and
        degradation, 805

    sugar sensing and signaling, 675

Carbon dioxide (CO_2)

    pyrimidine/purine biosynthesis and
        degradation, 805

Carduus nutans

    root exudates and rhizosphere interactions, 240

β-Carotene

    tocopherol and carotenoid synthesis, 717

Carotenoids

    floral pigments and, 761, 766–68

    tocopherol and carotenoid synthesis, 714–21

Cascade

    committmentmeiotic prophase I and, 276–77

Catabolism

    chlorophyll degradation during senescence
        and, 55, 62–65

    phytochrome structure and signaling
        mechanisms, 842

    pyrimidine/purine biosynthesis and
        degradation, 814–16, 822–24

Catalytic triad

    protein degradation machineries in plastids
        and, 604

Catastrophe rate

    microtubules and plant cortical array, 869–70

Caulenemata

    mosses in metabolism and developmental
        studies, 499–500, 508–10

Cavitation

    leaf hydraulic conductance and, 361, 371

Cdc42/Rac-interactive binding protein (CRIB)

    actin cytoskeleton in plant cell growth and,
        117–18

CDPK-SnRK

    sugar sensing and signaling, 694–95

Cell death

    chlorophyll degradation during senescence
        and, 55, 63–64, 67–68

Cell identity regulator

    global gene expression in specific cell types
        and, 451, 458

Cell plate factors

    glycosyltransferases of lipophilic small
        molecules and, 584

Cell-specific expression analysis

    global gene expression in specific cell types
        and, 451–68

Cell surface receptors

    sugar sensing and signaling, 688–89

Cell-type atlases

laser microdissection and, 192

Centaurea spp.
    root exudates and rhizosphere interactions,
        236, 238–39, 244, 251

Ceratodon purpureus
    mosses in metabolism and developmental
        studies, 497, 505–9

Cercidiphyllum japonicum
    chlorophyll degradation during senescence
        and, 60–61

cgi genes
    complementary chromatic adaptation and,
        140–41

Chalcones
    floral pigments and, 769

Chaperones
    phloem long-distance macromolecular
        trafficking and, 209
    protein degradation machineries in plastids
        and, 599, 605

Chenopodium spp.
    sugar sensing and signaling, 690

Chiasmata resolution
    meiotic prophase I and, 289–90

Chilide
    chlorophyll degradation during senescence
        and, 58

Chlamydomonas reinhardtii
    chlorophyll degradation during senescence
        and, 62, 64
    molybdenum cofactor and molybdenum
        enzymes, 625, 630, 634
    photosystems I and II, 525, 531, 546
    plastid-to-nucleus retrograde signaling and,
        742–44, 746–47
    root exudates and rhizosphere interactions, 250

Chlamydomonas spp.
    history of research, 6–7
    protein degradation machineries in plastids
        and, 606

Chloramphenicol
    plastid-to-nucleus retrograde signaling and,
        741

Chlorella spp.
    sugar sensing and signaling, 690

Chloronemata
    mosses in metabolism and developmental
        studies, 499–500, 508–10

Chlorophyll
    photosystems I and II, 524
    plastid-to-nucleus retrograde signaling and,
        739–53

Chlorophyll degradation
    during senescence
        autumnal leaf coloration, 59
        catabolic mutants, 64–65
        catabolite transporters, 62–63
        cell death, 67–68
        chlorophyll cycle, 58–59
        chlorophyllase, 57–58, 63, 65
        chlorophyllide, 58
        conclusions, 69
        degradation pathway, 57–62
        demethylation, 61–62
        genes, 63–65
        green pigments, 57–59
        introduction, 56
        Mg dechelation, 58
        mutations, 63–65
        NCCs, 60–62
        nitrogen economy, 68–69
        pFCCs, 60–61
        pheophorbide *a* oxygenase, 59, 63–67
        red Chl catabolite reductase, 59–60, 64, 67
        significance, 65–69
        summary points, 69
        tautomerization, 62
        topology, 62–63

Chloroplasts
    history of research, 7–13, 16
    photosystems I and II, 521–47
    protein degradation machineries in plastids
        and, 599–613
    tocopherol and carotenoid synthesis, 711

Chromatin
    laser microdissection and, 192–93
    meiotic prophase I and, 277–79

Chromobacterium violaceum
    root exudates and rhizosphere interactions, 250

Chromophores
    phytochrome structure and signaling
        mechanisms, 840–41

Chromosomes
    laser microdissection and, 192
    meiotic prophase I and, 267–92

Chrysomonas spp.
    root exudates and rhizosphere interactions, 251

cia genes
    pyrimidine/purine biosynthesis and
        degradation, 822

Cibacron Blue 3GA
    uncoupling proteins and, 385

cis-acting elements

plastid-to-nucleus retrograde signaling and,
746–47
seed flavonoids and, 416–17
transcriptional regulatory networks in
dehydration and cold stresses, 781, 787–88
Citrus spp.
chlorophyll degradation during senescence
and, 65
Cleavage
meiotic prophase I and, 290
microRNAs and, 29, 33
tocopherol and carotenoid synthesis, 718–19
CLE genes
peptide hormones and, 660–61
Climacteric fruits
uncoupling proteins and, 386
Cloning
microRNAs and, 21–22
uncoupling proteins and, 391
Clp protease
protein degradation machineries in plastids
and, 599, 604–6
CLV3 gene
peptide hormones and, 658–61
cnx genes
molybdenum cofactor and molybdenum
enzymes, 626–28, 630–33
CO genes
seasonal control of tuberization in potato and,
151, 164–67, 169, 172
Cohesion
meiotic prophase I and, 267, 276–78, 289–90
Colchicine
microtubules and plant cortical array, 861
Cold stress
transcriptional regulatory networks in
dehydration and cold stresses, 781–95
Color
complementary chromatic adaptation and,
127–44
Commelina commensis
quantitative fluorescence microscopy and,
94–95
Committment
meiotic prophase I and, 274–77
Community-scale interactions
root exudates and rhizosphere interactions,
239–40
Compartmentalization
pyrimidine/purine biosynthesis and
degradation, 808–10
seed flavonoids and, 412–13

Compensated cell enlargement
leaf-shape determination mechanism and, 477,
485–89
Complementary chromatic adaptation
cellular responses, 131–33
Cgi system, 140–41
concept, 128–31
conclusions, 143–44
coordination, 142–43
development, 132–33
DNA-binding activities, 142–43
evolution, 140–41
gene activation, 141–43
gene expression, 131–32
green light, 141–43
introduction, 128
morphology, 132–33
nutrient limitation, 132
photoreceptors, 134–40
phycobilisomes, 131–32
posttranscriptional control, 135–36
promoter studies, 142–43
Rca system, 136–41
red light, 142–43
redox, 134–35
regulation, 134–43
summary points, 144
transcriptional control, 135–36
Computational proteomics
bioinformatics and, 335, 342–43
Computational systems biology
bioinformatics and, 350–51
Condensation
chromatin
meiotic prophase I and, 277–79
Confident annotation
microRNAs and, 29
Confocal scanning laser microscopy
quantitative fluorescence microscopy and, 79
root exudates and rhizosphere interactions, 253
Conserved elements
seasonal control of tuberization in potato and,
151–72
Conserved mechanisms
sugar sensing and signaling, 675–700
Conserved structures
uncoupling proteins and, 386–88
Coordination
complementary chromatic adaptation and,
142–43
meiotic prophase I and, 288–90
Copper

molybdenum cofactor and molybdenum
    enzymes, 631–32
Coregulation
    seed flavonoids and, 416
Core structure
    glucosinolates and, 308–11
Coronilla varia
    root exudates and rhizosphere interactions, 250
Cortical array
    microtubule dynamics and organization,
    859–71
Coumarins
    glycosyltransferases of lipophilic small
    molecules and, 571–72, 580
cox3 gene
    mosses in metabolism and developmental
    studies, 507
Crocus sativus
    glycosyltransferases of lipophilic small
    molecules and, 581
    tocopherol and carotenoid synthesis, 719
Crossover formation
    meiotic prophase I and, 282–90
Cross talk
    transcriptional regulatory networks in
    dehydration and cold stresses, 781–95
CRTISO gene
    tocopherol and carotenoid synthesis, 714–16,
    720
CrtO gene
    floral pigments and, 768
Cryptochromes
    seasonal control of tuberization in potato and,
    164
C-terminal regulatory region
    phytochrome structure and signaling
    mechanisms, 837
cu-3 genes
    peptide hormones and, 654
Cucumis sativa
    root exudates and rhizosphere interactions, 238
Cucurbita maxima
    phloem long-distance macromolecular
    trafficking and, 208, 210
Cyan fluorescent protein (CFP)
    quantitative fluorescence microscopy and,
    88–89, 93–94, 96
Cyanidin
    floral pigments and, 769
Cyanidioschyzon merolae
    protein degradation machineries in plastids
    and, 602

Cyanobacteria
    photosystems I and II, 521–47
    tocopherol and carotenoid synthesis, 721–27
Cyanogenic glucosides
    glucosinolates and, 310–11
    glycosyltransferases of lipophilic small
    molecules and, 572, 582–83
Cyclic hydroxamic acids
    glycosyltransferases of lipophilic small
    molecules and, 572, 583
Cyclic pyranopterin monophosphate (cPMP)
    molybdenum cofactor and molybdenum
    enzymes, 628–29
Cyclins
    meiotic prophase I and, 276–77
CYP genes
    glucosinolates and, 308–11, 313, 316–18,
    320–21
Cytochalasin D
    mosses in metabolism and developmental
    studies, 512
Cytochrome b_6f complex
    photosystems I and II, 521, 545–46
Cytochrome P450 monooxygenase
    cytokinins and, 431, 438
Cytokinins
    Agrobacterium, 438–39
    aromatic, 439
    biological activity, 433–34
    biosynthesis, 434–40
    determinants, 436
    future research, 443
    glycosylation, 436
    glycosyltransferases of lipophilic small
    molecules, 575
    homeostasis, 434–36
    hormones, 439–40
    hydroxylation, 438
    intracellular traffic, 442
    introduction, 432–33
    isoprenoids, 435, 437–38
    local signal, 440
    long-range signal, 440
    metabolism, 434–40
    mosses in metabolism and developmental
    studies, 497, 502–4
    nitrogen supply, 440
    nucleoside transport, 441–42
    regulation, 439–40
    seasonal control of tuberization in potato and,
    163
    spatial expression, 439

structural diversity, 433
summary points, 442–43
translocation, 440–42
trans-zeatin, 438
tRNA degradation, 439
Cytoplasmic streaming
actin cytoskeleton in plant cell growth and, 110
Cytoskeleton
actin cytoskeleton in plant cell growth and, 109, 116–19
mosses in metabolism and developmental studies, 497–513

D

Dark reversion
phytochrome structure and signaling mechanisms, 844–49
Data curation
bioinformatics and, 349–50
Daucus carota
pyrimidine/purine biosynthesis and degradation, 814
Day length
seasonal control of tuberization in potato and, 151–72
DCL genes
microRNAs and, 19, 21–23, 25, 27, 29–31, 34, 36, 38–39, 43–44
def-1 gene
peptide hormones and, 651
Defense compounds
glucosinolates and, 303–23
Deg proteases
protein degradation machineries in plastids and, 611
Degradation
chlorophyll degradation during senescence and, 55, 57–69
cytokinins and, 439
glucosinolates and, 303, 313–16
molybdenum cofactor and molybdenum enzymes, 623
protein degradation machineries in plastids and, 599–613
pyrimidine/purine biosynthesis and degradation, 805–28
sugar sensing and signaling, 695–96
transcriptional regulatory networks in dehydration and cold stresses, 792–93
Dehydration
leaf hydraulic conductance and, 369–71

Dehydration and cold stresses
transcriptional regulatory networks and
abscisic acid, 784–85, 788–92
Arabidopsis, 787
cis-acting elements, 787–88
cold-inducible genes, 783, 785–87
cold stress, 783–85, 793–95
conclusions, 795
degradation, 792–93
dehydration stress, 791–95
DREB1/CBF, 785–89
future research, 795
gene expression, 783–84, 788–92
introduction, 782–83
osmotic-inducible genes, 783
osmotic stress, 783–85
perspectives, 795
regulation, 783–87, 792–93
rehydration, 792–93
signal transduction, 793–95
stress tolerance, 785–87
transcription factors, 785–88
upstream function, 787–88
Deinococcus radiodurans
phytochrome structure and signaling mechanisms, 838, 842
Delisea pulchra
root exudates and rhizosphere interactions, 250
Delphinidin
floral pigments and, 769
Demethylation
chlorophyll degradation during senescence and, 61–62
Desaturation
tocopherol and carotenoid synthesis, 714–17
Detoxification
glycosyltransferases of lipophilic small molecules and, 567–88
Development
complementary chromatic adaptation and, 132–33
glycosyltransferases of lipophilic small molecules and, 567
leaf hydraulic conductance and, 361, 372
meiotic prophase I and, 272
microRNAs and, 19–45
mosses in metabolism and developmental studies, 497, 501–13
phloem long-distance macromolecular trafficking and, 203, 206
quantitative fluorescence microscopy and, 92–93

seasonal control of tuberization in potato and, 168–71

sugar sensing and signaling, 681–86

uncoupling proteins and, 397

DF119L gene

glucosinolates and, 312–13

Dicer-like enzyme

microRNAs and, 19, 21–23, 25, 27, 29–31, 34, 36, 38–39, 43–44

Dictyostelium discoideum

cytokinins and, 436–37

uncoupling proteins and, 384

N,N′-Dicyclohexylcarbodiimide

uncoupling proteins and, 385

DIF1 gene

meiotic prophase I and, 273–75, 278

Differentiation

global gene expression in specific cell types and, 451

seasonal control of tuberization in potato and, 151–72

seed flavonoids and, 417–18

Dihydroflavonols

floral pigments and, 769

Dihydroxyphenylalanine (DOPA)

floral pigments and, 762–65

Dimer loss

microtubules and plant cortical array, 859, 862, 869

Dimethylallyl diphosphate (DMAPP)

cytokinins and, 436–37

Diothiolates

molybdenum cofactor and molybdenum enzymes, 629–30

Diphyscium foliosum

mosses in metabolism and developmental studies, 503

Diploidy

mosses in metabolism and developmental studies, 511

Diurnal rhythms

leaf hydraulic conductance and, 372

seasonal control of tuberization in potato and, 151–72

Diversity

cytokinins and, 433

leaf-shape determination mechanism and, 477

DMC1 gene

meiotic prophase I and, 273, 275–76, 284–86

DNA binding

complementary chromatic adaptation and, 142–43

Dorotheanthus bellidiformis

floral pigments and, 765

glycosyltransferases of lipophilic small molecules and, 580

Double-stranded breaks (DSBs)

meiotic prophase I and, 269, 284–87

Downstream separation

global gene expression in specific cell types and, 458

Dracunculus spp.

uncoupling proteins and, 393

DrBphP photosensory core

phytochrome structure and signaling mechanisms, 842–44

DREB1/CBF genes

transcriptional regulatory networks in dehydration and cold stresses, 785–89

Drosophila melanogaster

actin cytoskeleton in plant cell growth and, 112

meiotic prophase I and, 268, 287

molybdenum cofactor and molybdenum enzymes, 624, 633

pyrimidine/purine biosynthesis and degradation, 816

tocopherol and carotenoid synthesis, 718

Drought

leaf hydraulic conductance and, 369

molybdenum cofactor and molybdenum enzymes, 638

transcriptional regulatory networks in dehydration and cold stresses, 781–95

Drypetes spp.

glucosinolates and, 304, 310

Dunaliella spp.

plastid-to-nucleus retrograde signaling and, 752–53

tocopherol and carotenoid synthesis, 720

DVL1 gene

peptide hormones and, 663–64

Dynamic spring hypothesis

microtubules and plant cortical array, 867–68

E

EB1::GFP

microtubules and plant cortical array, 861

Ecological plant-microbe interactions

root exudates and rhizosphere interactions, 251

Effectors

actin cytoskeleton in plant cell growth and, 117–18

EGY1/EGY2 proteases

protein degradation machineries in plastids
and, 611

Electrochemical proton potential
uncoupling proteins and, 383–84, 388, 394–97

Electron microscopy
history of research, 4, 6–17
microtubules and plant cortical array, 861

Electron transfer
photosystems I and II, 521–47

Electron transport
plastid-to-nucleus retrograde signaling and,
739, 742, 748–52

Electrophoresis analysis
bioinformatics and, 342

Elong gene
glucosinolates and, 312

Elytrigia repens
root exudates and rhizosphere interactions,
241–42

Embolism
leaf hydraulic conductance and, 361

Empetrum hermaphroditum
root exudates and rhizosphere interactions, 240

Endoplasmic reticulum
history of research, 13–14

Endosymbionts
eukaryotic
history of research, 13–14

ENOD40 gene
peptide hormones and, 661–62

ENT genes
cytokinins and, 442

Epidermal cell differentation
seed flavonoids and, 417–18

Epithiospecifer protein (ESP)
glucosinolates and, 314–15

Erwinia uredorva
tocopherol and carotenoid synthesis, 720

Erythrosin B
uncoupling proteins and, 385

Escherichia coli
chlorophyll degradation during senescence
and, 60
cytokinins and, 434
glucosinolates and, 307, 311
glycosyltransferases of lipophilic small
molecules and, 570, 575
molybdenum cofactor and molybdenum
enzymes, 624, 627–28, 630–31
protein degradation machineries in plastids
and, 599–600, 602–7, 610–11

pyrimidine/purine biosynthesis and
degradation, 811, 819–20
sugar sensing and signaling, 698
tocopherol and carotenoid synthesis, 726
uncoupling proteins and, 386

Esculetin
glycosyltransferases of lipophilic small
molecules and, 573

Ethyl vinyl acetate film
laser microdissection and, 183–84, 194

Euglena gracilis
history of research, 8, 13

Evaporation
leaf hydraulic conductance and, 361–62,
365–66

Evolution
complementary chromatic adaptation and,
140–41
glucosinolates and, 303, 310–11
glycosyltransferases of lipophilic small
molecules and, 573
microRNAs and, 24–28
phloem long-distance macromolecular
trafficking and, 203–4
photosystems I and II, 521, 526–28, 536,
543–44
phytochrome structure and signaling
mechanisms, 851
pyrimidine/purine biosynthesis and
degradation, 805
seasonal control of tuberization in potato and,
151–72
seed flavonoids and, 420–21
sugar sensing and signaling, 675–700
uncoupling proteins and, 383, 386–88, 391,
394

Exitation transfer
photosystems I and II, 536–37, 544–45

Exocytosis
actin cytoskeleton in plant cell growth and, 110

Export
microRNAs and, 29–31

Expressed sequence tags (ESTs)
global gene expression in specific cell types
and, 451
microRNAs and, 25, 27–28
mosses in metabolism and developmental
studies, 506
phloem long-distance macromolecular
trafficking and, 220

EYFP::TUA5
microtubules and plant cortical array, 861, 865

F

F-ATPase
  photosystems I and II, 521
Fatty acids
  uncoupling proteins and, 383–98
F-box proteins
  microRNAs and, 19
Ferredoxin
  photosystems I and II, 526, 535
Festuca spp.
  chlorophyll degradation during senescence
    and, 65
  root exudates and rhizosphere interactions, 251
Filaments
  actin cytoskeleton in plant cell growth and,
    109, 116–19
  mosses in metabolism and developmental
    studies, 497–513
Fingerprinting
  bioinformatics and, 343
Flatness
  leaf-shape determination mechanism and, 477,
    486
Flavanone
  glycosyltransferases of lipophilic small
    molecules and, 580
Flavonoids
  floral pigments and, 761, 765–66, 768–72
  glycosyltransferases of lipophilic small
    molecules and, 571–72, 577–80
  seed flavonoids and, 405–21
Flavonols
  glycosyltransferases of lipophilic small
    molecules and, 577–78
  seed flavonoids and, 405, 408–10
Flavonones
  floral pigments and, 769
Floral pigments
  anthocyanins, 765–66, 768–72
  betalains, 762–66
  biosynthesis, 762–70
  carotenoids, 766–68
  cellular architecture, 772–73
  functions, 766
  future research, 774
  introduction, 762
  mutual exclusion, 765–66
  occurence, 765–66
  pH, 772–73
  regulation, 772
  storage, 771–72
  summary points, 774

transport, 771–72
  unresolved issues, 774
  visual cues, 773–74
Florigen
  phloem long-distance macromolecular
    trafficking and, 212–13
Flowering response
  phloem long-distance macromolecular
    trafficking and, 212–13
  seasonal control of tuberization in potato and,
    151, 164–66
Fluorescence-activated sorting (FAS)
  global gene expression in specific cell types
    and, 457
Fluorescence correlation spectroscopy (FCS)
  quantitative fluorescence microscopy and, 84,
    90
Fluorescence in situ hybridization (FISH)
  quantitative fluorescence microscopy and, 81
Fluorescence recovery after photobleaching
    (FRAP)
  microtubules and plant cortical array, 863–64
  quantitative fluorescence microscopy and, 84,
    91
Fluorescence resonance energy transfer (FRET)
  quantitative fluorescence microscopy and, 83,
    89, 97
Fluorescent chlorophyll catabolite (FCC)
  chlorophyll degradation during senescence
    and, 56, 58, 60–61
Fluorescent protein fusions
  quantitative fluorescence microscopy and, 85
Flux
  bioinformatics and, 344–45
  leaf hydraulic conductance and, 368–69
Formins
  actin cytoskeleton in plant cell growth and, 113
Forward genetics
  meiotic prophase I and, 271–73
"Forward" reaction
  phytochrome structure and signaling
    mechanisms, 844–47
Free fatty acids
  uncoupling proteins and, 383–98
Freesia spp.
  floral pigments and, 766
Fremyella diplosiphon
  complementary chromatic adaptation and,
    128–40, 142–43
FT genes
  seasonal control of tuberization in potato and,
    151, 155, 164–67, 169, 172

FtsH protease
  protein degradation machineries in plastids
    and, 599, 606–10
Fumaria spp.
  cytokinins and, 433
  mosses in metabolism and developmental
    studies, 497, 501–4, 507–8, 510
Functional genomics
  phloem long-distance macromolecular
    trafficking and, 220–21
Fungi
  glycosyltransferases of lipophilic small
    molecules and, 583
  microtubules and plant cortical array, 866
  molybdenum cofactor and molybdenum
    enzymes, 624, 626, 633
  phytochrome structure and signaling
    mechanisms, 838
Fusarium oxysporum
  glucosinolates and, 320
  glycosyltransferases of lipophilic small
    molecules and, 584

G

Gaeumannomyces graminis
  glycosyltransferases of lipophilic small
    molecules and, 581
gai genes
  seasonal control of tuberization in potato and,
    159–61, 171
Gaillardia aristata
  root exudates and rhizosphere interactions, 251
Gametophores
  mosses in metabolism and developmental
    studies, 499–500, 511
Gametophytes
  mosses in metabolism and developmental
    studies, 497–513
Gamma-tubulin ring complex (g-TuRC)
  microtubules and plant cortical array, 862,
    867–68
Gas exchange
  leaf hydraulic conductance and, 367–68, 372
Gastritis
  glucosinolates and, 306
Gelsolin
  actin cytoskeleton in plant cell growth and, 113
Genetic engineering
  tocopherol and carotenoid synthesis, 720–21
Genetic redundancy
  global gene expression in specific cell types
    and, 463

Genome-wide expression analysis
  sugar sensing and signaling, 690–92
Genomics
  bioinformatics and, 337–38
  global gene expression in specific cell types
    and, 451, 459–67
  glucosinolates and, 303
  laser microdissection and, 181
  microRNAs and, 21–31
  mosses in metabolism and developmental
    studies, 497, 500
  phloem long-distance macromolecular
    trafficking and, 220–21
  tocopherol and carotenoid synthesis, 711,
    722–23
Genotype
  seasonal control of tuberization in potato and,
    153–54
Gentiana triflora
  floral pigments and, 771
  glycosyltransferases of lipophilic small
    molecules and, 578–79
Gephyrin
  molybdenum cofactor and molybdenum
    enzymes, 626–27
Gerbera spp.
  floral pigments and, 766
Germination
  sugar sensing and signaling, 681–84
Gerontoplasts
  chlorophyll degradation during senescence
    and, 56
Geum spp.
  root exudates and rhizosphere interactions, 240
Gibberellin
  seasonal control of tuberization in potato and,
    151, 155, 157–62
Gibbs SP, 1–17
Gigaspora margarita
  root exudates and rhizosphere interactions, 247
GI genes
  seasonal control of tuberization in potato and,
    164–65, 167, 169, 171
gin genes
  sugar sensing and signaling, 682, 684, 686–87
Global gene expression
  cell-specific expression analysis and
    amplification methods, 459
    author's note, 468
    cell cycle, 466
    cell specificity, 462, 465–66
    contributions of specific cell types, 456–59

downstream separation, 458
fluorescence-activated sorting, 457
functional patterns at cell level, 463–65
gene duplicates, 462–63
genomics, 459–67
high-throughput RT-PCR, 456
hybridization, 454, 455
identification of specific cell types, 458–59
introduction, 452–53
laser capture microdissection, 457–58
localized hormone responses, 465
microarray technology, 453–55
microRNAs, 465–66
microsampling, 458
Northern analysis, 455–56
phenotypes, 462
prior physical separation, 456–57
prospects, 467
purification, 456–57
sampling sequence information in RNA
    populations, 456
summary points, 468
transcriptome, 459–62
Glucose
  sugar sensing and signaling, 675, 686–88
Glucosinolates
  aldoximes, 308–10
  amino acid chain elongation, 306–8
  biochemistry, 315–16
  biological function, 319–21
  biosynthesis, 306–13
  chemical structure, 304–5
  core structure, 308–11
  cyanogenic glucosides, 310–11
  degradation, 313–16
  evolutionary link, 310–11
  future research, 323
  glycosyltransferases of lipophilic small
      molecules, 572, 582–83
  humans, 305–6
  hydrolysis, 304–5, 313–15
  indole-3-acetic acid, 316–17
  indole compounds, 316–17
  introduction, 304–6
  metabolic engineering, 320–22
  metabolic links, 316–17
  myrosinases, 315–16
  perspective, 322
  physiology, 315–16
  regulation, 311–12
  secondary transformations, 311–12
  summary points, 322–23

thiohydroxymic acids, 309–10
transport, 317–18
Glutathione-S-transferase (GST)
  glucosinolates and, 318
Glycine max
  pyrimidine/purine biosynthesis and
      degradation, 819–20
  root exudates and rhizosphere interactions,
      245, 250
Glycosylation
  cytokinins and, 436
Glycosyltransferases
  of lipophilic small molecules
    abiotic compounds, 584–85
    abscisic acid, 575
    acceptors of family 1 plant
        glycosyltransferases, 574–85
    anthocyanidins, 578–80
    applications, 585–87
    auxins, 574–75
    betalains, 580
    biotic compounds, 584
    brassinosteroids, 575
    cell plate factors, 584
    conclusions, 587
    coumarins, 580
    cyanogenic glucosides, 582–83
    cyclic hydroxamic acids, 583
    cytokinins, 575
    flavanone, 580
    flavonoids, 577–80
    flavonols, 577–78
    glucosinolates, 582–83
    hormones, 574–76
    introduction, 568–69
    organic/inorganic pollutants, 584–85
    pathogen toxins, 584
    phenylpropanoids, 576–77
    root factors, 583–84
    salicylic acid, 575–76
    secondary metabolites, 576–83
    sequence, 569–74
    steroids, 581–82
    structure, 569–74
    substrate recognition, 569–74
    summary points, 587–88
    terpenoids, 581–82
    undefined plant acceptors, 583–84
Graft union
  phloem long-distance macromolecular
      trafficking and, 207
Green algae

history of research, 13
molybdenum cofactor and molybdenum
    enzymes, 625, 630, 634
plastid-to-nucleus retrograde signaling and,
    742–44, 746–47
Green fluorescent protein (GFP)
    actin cytoskeleton in plant cell growth and, 116
    laser microdissection and, 193–94
    meiotic prophase I and, 276–77
    microtubules and plant cortical array, 861
    mosses in metabolism and developmental
        studies, 505–6
    phloem long-distance macromolecular
        trafficking and, 208–9, 219
    protein degradation machineries in plastids
        and, 604, 607, 610
    pyrimidine/purine biosynthesis and
        degradation, 821
    quantitative fluorescence microscopy and, 79,
        81–82, 84–92
Green light
    complementary chromatic adaptation and,
        141–43
Green pigments
    chlorophyll degradation during senescence
        and, 57–59
Growth
    actin cytoskeleton in plant cell growth and,
        109, 116–19
    leaf hydraulic conductance and, 372–73
    sugar sensing and signaling, 681–86
GS genes
    glucosinolates and, 312
GTPases
    microtubules and plant cortical array, 870–71
gtrA gene
    mosses in metabolism and developmental
        studies, 509
Guanosine triphosphate (GTP)
    molybdenum cofactor and molybdenum
        enzymes, 628–29
Guard cells
    stomatal
        quantitative fluorescence microscopy and,
            95–96
gun genes
    plastid-to-nucleus retrograde signaling and,
        739, 743–45, 747
GUS reporter gene
    glucosinolates and, 315
    meiotic prophase I and, 276

mosses in metabolism and developmental
    studies, 501, 505
Gypsophila paniculata
    root exudates and rhizosphere interactions, 251

H

Haematococcus pluvialis
    floral pigments and, 768
    tocopherol and carotenoid synthesis, 720
Haploidy
    mosses in metabolism and developmental
        studies, 497–513
Helicobacter pylori
    glucosinolates and, 306
Helicodiceros muscivorus
    uncoupling proteins and, 392, 395
Heme
    phytochrome structure and signaling
        mechanisms, 842
HEN1 gene
    microRNAs and, 22, 30
Heterodera trifolii
    root exudates and rhizosphere interactions, 252
Heterodimeric capping protein (HCP)
    actin cytoskeleton in plant cell growth and,
        113–14
Hexokinase
    seasonal control of tuberization in potato and,
        170
    sugar sensing and signaling, 675, 686–88
High-throughput RT-PCR
    global gene expression in specific cell types
        and, 456
Histidine phosphotranspher (HPt) domain
    complementary chromatic adaptation and, 139
Histones
    meiotic prophase I and, 279
Homeostasis
    cytokinins and, 434–36
    glycosyltransferases of lipophilic small
        molecules and, 567–88
Homogentisic acid
    tocopherol and carotenoid synthesis, 725–26
Homology recognition
    meiotic prophase I and, 277–82
HOP1 gene
    meiotic prophase I and, 275, 283
Hordeum vulgare
    chlorophyll degradation during senescence
        and, 61
    meiotic prophase I and, 279

plastid-to-nucleus retrograde signaling and, 741

root exudates and rhizosphere interactions, 241–42

Hormones

cytokinins and, 431–43

global gene expression in specific cell types and, 451, 465

glycosyltransferases of lipophilic small molecules and, 567–88

mosses in metabolism and developmental studies, 501–3

peptide hormones and, 649–67

seasonal control of tuberization in potato and, 162–63

sugar sensing and signaling, 682–84

HST genes

microRNAs and, 30–31

Hybridization

global gene expression in specific cell types and, 454–55

Hydrolysis

glucosinolates and, 304–5, 313–15

Hydroxylation

cytokinins and, 438

Hydroxymethylbutenyl diphosphate (HMBDP)

cytokinins and, 436–37

HYL1 gene

microRNAs and, 30

I

IDA genes

peptide hormones and, 663

Idioblasts

glucosinolates and, 315

Index

leaf-shape determination mechanism and, 477, 481–84

Indole-3-acetaldoxime (IAOx)

glucosinolates and, 309, 317–18

Indole-3-acetic acid (IAA)

glucosinolates and, 316–17

glycosyltransferases of lipophilic small molecules and, 572, 574

molybdenum cofactor and molybdenum enzymes, 638

Induced herbivore resistance

root exudates and rhizosphere interactions, 241–42

Information macromolecules

phloem long-distance macromolecular trafficking and, 203–23

Integrative plant biology

microtubules and plant cortical array, 868

phloem long-distance macromolecular trafficking and, 203–23

seasonal control of tuberization in potato and, 167–68

Intercalary growth

actin cytoskeleton in plant cell growth and, 111

Interphase arrays

microtubules and plant cortical array, 859–67

Intrinsically fluorescent proteins (IFPs)

quantitative fluorescence microscopy and, 80–98

Introgression

chlorophyll degradation during senescence and, 65

Ion/metabolite imaging

quantitative fluorescence microscopy and, 93–97

Ipomoea spp.

floral pigments and, 771

glycosyltransferases of lipophilic small molecules and, 578–79

Irradiance

leaf hydraulic conductance and, 361, 363, 371–72

Isomerization

tocopherol and carotenoid synthesis, 714–17

Isoprenoids

cytokinins and, 435, 437–38

floral pigments and, 761, 766–68

tocopherol and carotenoid synthesis, 712–13

Isothiocyanates

glucosinolates and, 303–23

J

Jasmonic acid

seasonal control of tuberization in potato and, 162–63

Juglans nigra

root exudates and rhizosphere interactions, 236, 238

K

Kalanchoë spp.

leaf hydraulic conductance and, 365

Katanin

microtubules and plant cortical array, 863, 865

Kinases

peptide hormones and, 649, 654

sugar sensing and signaling, 675, 694–97

pyrimidine/purine biosynthesis and
degradation, 815
Lens spp.
root exudates and rhizosphere interactions, 245
Lesion mimic mutants
chlorophyll degradation during senescence
and, 67
Leucine-rich repeat receptor-like kinase
(LRR-RLK)
peptide hormones and, 654
Leucoanthocyanidins
floral pigments and, 769
Life cycle
mosses in metabolism and developmental
studies, 498–99
Ligand-receptor interaction
peptide hormones and, 649, 657–58
Light-harvesting complexes (LHCs)
chlorophyll degradation during senescence
and, 65
complementary chromatic adaptation and, 127
photosystems I and II, 521, 524–26, 528–33,
536–37, 544–46
plastid-to-nucleus retrograde signaling and,
741
protein degradation machineries in plastids
and, 602
Light receptors
seasonal control of tuberization in potato and,
155–57
Light regulation
complementary chromatic adaptation and,
127–44
Lilium spp.
floral pigments and, 766
meiotic prophase I and, 281
quantitative fluorescence microscopy and, 95
Linear unmixing
quantitative fluorescence microscopy and, 87
Linoleic acid
uncoupling proteins and, 388, 390
Linolenic acid
uncoupling proteins and, 388
Lipophilic small molecules
glycosyltransferases and, 567–88
Lipophis erysimi
glucosinolates and, 320
Liquidambar spp.
chlorophyll degradation during senescence
and, 61
Lithospermum erythrorbizon
root exudates and rhizosphere interactions, 248

Lobing
microtubules and plant cortical array, 870
Localization
quantitative fluorescence microscopy and,
84–85
Lolium spp.
chlorophyll degradation during senescence
and, 65
Long days
seasonal control of tuberization in potato and,
153, 155–57, 160–61, 164–67, 172
Long-distance transport
phloem long-distance macromolecular
trafficking and, 203–23
Lon protease
protein degradation machineries in plastids
and, 599, 610
Lotus japonicus
pyrimidine/purine biosynthesis and
degradation, 813
root exudates and rhizosphere interactions, 246
Low-molecular weight genetically encoded tags
quantitative fluorescence microscopy and, 87
Lupinus alba
root exudates and rhizosphere interactions, 243
Lutein
tocopherol and carotenoid synthesis, 717–18
Luteolinidin
floral pigments and, 769
Lychnis spp.
floral pigments and, 765
Lycopersicon esculentum
pyrimidine/purine biosynthesis and
degradation, 816
root exudates and rhizosphere interactions, 250
uncoupling proteins and, 392

M

MAM genes
glucosinolates and, 307–8, 320
Mangifera indica
uncoupling proteins and, 392
Manihot esculenta
glucosinolates and, 321
Mannitol
uncoupling proteins and, 385
MAP4::GFP
microtubules and plant cortical array, 861
MAP65 protein
microtubules and plant cortical array,
864–65

Margin
    leaf-shape determination mechanism and, 477,
        484–86
Mass spectrometry
    bioinformatics and, 342–43
MBW complex
    seed flavonoids and, 418–21
Medicago sativa
    root exudates and rhizosphere interactions,
        235, 243, 246
Medicago trunculata
    glycosyltransferases of lipophilic small
        molecules and, 569, 582
    phloem long-distance macromolecular
        trafficking and, 217
    pyrimidine/purine biosynthesis and
        degradation, 812–13
    root exudates and rhizosphere interactions,
        250, 252
Meiotic prophase I
    acquisition of mutants, 273–74
    AM1, 274–76
    approaches, 271–74
    Arabidopsis, 272
    bouquet, 280–81
    candidate genes, 273
    chiasmata resolution, 289–90
    chromatin condensation, 277–79
    chromosome structure, 277–82
    committment, 274–77
    coordination, 288–90
    crossover formation, 282–90
    developmental mutants, 272
    forward genetics, 271–73
    future research, 291
    gene expression, 273
    histone modifications, 279
    homology recognition, 277–82
    introduction, 268–69
    maize, 272
    meiosis overview, 269–71
    meiotic mutants, 272
    model plants, 271–74
    outlook, 290
    pairing, 280–82, 288
    primary screen, 271–72
    recombination, 282–90
    reverse genetics, 273–74
    secondary screen, 272
    sequence identity, 273
    sister chromatid cohesion, 277–90
    sterility, 271–72

summary points, 290–91
SWI1, 274–76
synapsis, 282–90
synaptonemal complex, 282–84
Melilotus spp.
    root exudates and rhizosphere interactions, 245
Meloidogyne incognita
    root exudates and rhizosphere interactions, 252
"Melt-stick-pull off" strategy
    laser microdissection and, 183
MER3 gene
    meiotic prophase I and, 267, 275, 285, 289, 291
Mercaptoethanol
    leaf hydraulic conductance and, 371
Meristem
    phloem long-distance macromolecular
        trafficking and, 203–23
    seasonal control of tuberization in potato and,
        151, 161–62
Mesophyll
    leaf hydraulic conductance and, 365–66
Messenger RNA (mRNA)
    phloem long-distance macromolecular
        trafficking and, 203, 210, 221
Metabolic engineering
    glucosinolates and, 303–23
    tocopherol and carotenoid synthesis, 711
Metabolism
    bioinformatics and, 344–45
    cytokinins and, 434–40
    glucosinolates and, 316–17
    glycosyltransferases of lipophilic small
        molecules and, 567–88
    mosses in metabolism and developmental
        studies, 497, 500–1
    pyrimidine/purine biosynthesis and
        degradation, 805–28
    quantitative fluorescence microscopy and,
        93–97
    seed flavonoids and, 405–21
    sugar sensing and signaling, 675
    uncoupling proteins and, 383, 394–95
Metabolite profiling
    laser microdissection and, 181, 189, 193–94
    quantitative fluorescence microscopy and,
        97–98
Metabolomics
    bioinformatics and, 344
Metabolons
    seed flavonoids and, 412
    sugar sensing and signaling, 687–88
Metal chelating substance (MCS)

diothiolate sulfurs, 629–30
future research, 638–39
genetics, 624–26
GTP, 628–29
insertion, 630–31
introduction, 624
maturation, 633–34
metal-insertion reaction, 631–33
molybdenum enzymes, 634–38
nitrate reductase, 634–36
storage, 634
sulfite oxidase, 636–37
summary points, 638
transfer, 634
uptake, 630–31
xanthine dehydrogenase, 637
MOR1 protein
microtubules and plant cortical array, 863, 865
Morphogenesis
actin cytoskeleton in plant cell growth and, 109, 116–19
complementary chromatic adaptation and, 132–33
mosses in metabolism and developmental studies, 507
quantitative fluorescence microscopy and, 92–93
Mosses
cytokinins and, 433
microRNAs and, 25
as model systems for study of metabolism and development
abscisic acid, 503–5
auxin, 501–2
cytokinin, 502–3
cytoskeleton, 511–13
developmental studies, 501–13
future research, 513
gametophore, 511
hormones, 501–3
introduction, 498–99
life cycle, 498–99
metabolic studies, 500–1
morphogenesis, 507
organelles, 505–7
polar axis, 507–10
protonemal patterning, 510–11
related resources, 513
sporophyte, 511
summary points, 513
unresolved issues, 513
sugar sensing and signaling, 681, 697

Movement proteins
phloem long-distance macromolecular trafficking and, 211–12
MRE11 gene
meiotic prophase I and, 267, 284
MSH4 gene
meiotic prophase I and, 267, 285, 289, 291
Multichannel imaging
quantitative fluorescence microscopy and, 87
Murgantia bistrionica
glucosinolates and, 320
Mutual exclusion
floral pigments and, 765–66
MYB protein
seed flavonoids and, 405, 418–21
Mycorrhizal associations
root exudates and rhizosphere interactions, 246–47
Myosins
mosses in metabolism and developmental studies, 513
Myristic acid
uncoupling proteins and, 388
Myrosinases
glucosinolates and, 303, 315–16

N

Nalidixic acid
plastid-to-nucleus retrograde signaling and, 741
1-Naphthalene acetic acid
molybdenum cofactor and molybdenum enzymes, 638
mosses in metabolism and developmental studies, 511
Narcissus spp.
floral pigments and, 766
Neoxanthin
tocopherol and carotenoid synthesis, 717
Neurospora crassa
glycosyltransferases of lipophilic small molecules and, 583
molybdenum cofactor and molybdenum enzymes, 626
Nicotiana spp.
chlorophyll degradation during senescence and, 61
laser microdissection and, 193
leaf hydraulic conductance and, 364
molybdenum cofactor and molybdenum enzymes, 625

plastid-to-nucleus retrograde signaling and, 746

pyrimidine/purine biosynthesis and degradation, 812, 819–21

quantitative fluorescence microscopy and, 88–89, 95

Night break

seasonal control of tuberization in potato and, 153, 155–57

nit genes

glucosinolates and, 317

molybdenum cofactor and molybdenum enzymes, 626

Nitrate reductase

molybdenum cofactor and molybdenum enzymes, 623–25, 632, 634–36

Nitriles

glucosinolates and, 303–23

Nitrogen

chlorophyll degradation during senescence and, 55, 68–69

cytokinins and, 440

pyrimidine/purine biosynthesis and degradation, 805

nod genes

root exudates and rhizosphere interactions, 245–46

Nodulation

root exudates and rhizosphere interactions, 245–46

Non-cell-autonomous proteins (NCAPs)

phloem long-distance macromolecular trafficking and, 206–9

Noncoding RNAs

microRNAs and, 19–45

Nonfluorescent chlorophyll catabolites (NCCs)

chlorophyll degradation during senescence and, 55, 60–62

Norflurazon

plastid-to-nucleus retrograde signaling and, 741

Northern analysis

global gene expression in specific cell types and, 455

Nostoc spp.

complementary chromatic adaptation and, 131

N-terminal photosensory core

phytochrome structure and signaling mechanisms, 837

Nuclear genes

plastid-to-nucleus retrograde signaling and, 739, 742, 751

Nucleation

actin cytoskeleton in plant cell growth and, 109, 112

microtubules and plant cortical array, 859, 862, 866, 868, 870

Nucleomorphs

history of research, 14

Nucleoside transport

cytokinins and, 441–42

Nucleotide metabolism

pyrimidine/purine biosynthesis and degradation, 805–28

Nucleus

quantitative fluorescence microscopy and, 81–83

Nutrient limitation

complementary chromatic adaptation and, 132

Nutrient signaling

phloem long-distance macromolecular trafficking and, 216–18

O

O_2 evolution

photosystems I and II, 521, 526–28, 543–44

Ochromonas danica

history of research, 8, 13

Oleic acid

uncoupling proteins and, 388

Olisthodiscus luteus

history of research, 16

Ontology

bioinformatics and, 345–47

Organ development

uncoupling proteins and, 397

Organic acids

root exudates and rhizosphere interactions, 243

Orobanche spp.

root exudates and rhizosphere interactions, 241

Orthologs

microRNAs and, 24

Oryza sativa

global gene expression in specific cell types and, 451

meiotic prophase I and, 283–84

microRNAs and, 21, 24–26, 28–29, 35–38

root exudates and rhizosphere interactions, 236, 238, 250

seasonal control of tuberization in potato and, 165–69

uncoupling proteins and, 392

Oscillations

glycosyltransferases of lipophilic small
molecules and, 575
root exudates and rhizosphere interactions, 242
Phenotype
chlorophyll degradation during senescence
and, 55
global gene expression in specific cell types
and, 462
microRNAs and, 21–22
microtubules and plant cortical array, 871
molybdenum cofactor and molybdenum
enzymes, 626
mosses in metabolism and developmental
studies, 511
protein degradation machineries in plastids
and, 609
Phenylpropanoids
glycosyltransferases of lipophilic small
molecules and, 571–72, 576–77
Pheophorbide *a* oxygenase (PAO)
chlorophyll degradation during senescence
and, 55–56, 58–59, 63–67
Phloem long-distance macromolecular trafficking
conduit for macromolecule delivery, 206–7
developmental domains, 206
endogenous macromolecules, 207–9
exogenous macromolecules, 210–12
florigen, 212–13
flowering, 212–13
functional genomics, 220–21
future research, 222–23
introduction, 204–6
leaf architecture, 218–19
mRNA, 210–11, 221
nutrient signaling, 216–18
pathogen defense, 219–20
"phloemics", 220–21
phloem proteins, 207–9
plasmodesmata, 206
protein trafficking, 206
proteomics, 221–22
resource allocation, 215–16
RNA viruses, 211–12
SE-CC complex, 206–7
small RNA, 210, 221
summary points, 222–23
transcriptome, 221–22
tuberigen, 213–15
tuberization, 213–15
vascular genomics, 220–21
vascularization, 206–7
viroids, 210–11

whole-plant function, 207
whole-plant signaling, 212–20
PHOR1 gene
seasonal control of tuberization in potato and,
159
Phormidium spp.
complementary chromatic adaptation and, 130
Phosphate
pyrimidine/purine biosynthesis and
degradation, 805
Phospholipase D
microtubules and plant cortical array, 863
5-Phosphoribosyl-1-pyrophosphate
pyrimidine/purine biosynthesis and
degradation, 805
Phosphorus
root exudates and rhizosphere interactions, 243
Phosphorylation
uncoupling proteins and, 383, 395–96
Photoactivation
quantitative fluorescence microscopy and, 84,
91–92
Photobleaching
quantitative fluorescence microscopy and, 91
Photoconversion
phytochrome structure and signaling
mechanisms, 839–40
quantitative fluorescence microscopy and, 84
Photomorphogenesis regulators
phytochrome structure and signaling
mechanisms, 837–52
Photoperiodicity
seasonal control of tuberization in potato and,
151–72
Photoreceptors
complementary chromatic adaptation and, 127,
134–40
phytochrome structure and signaling
mechanisms, 837–52
Photosensory core
phytochrome structure and signaling
mechanisms, 841–44
Photoswitching
phytochrome structure and signaling
mechanisms, 839–41
quantitative fluorescence microscopy and, 84
Photosynthesis
complementary chromatic adaptation and,
127–44
leaf hydraulic conductance and, 361, 371
mosses in metabolism and developmental
studies, 504

photosystems I and II, 521–47

plastid-to-nucleus retrograde signaling and, 739, 742, 748–52

protein degradation machineries in plastids and, 599, 607

sugar sensing and signaling, 675

tocopherol and carotenoid synthesis, 711

Photosystem II

chlorophyll degradation during senescence and, 65

mosses in metabolism and developmental studies, 504

protein degradation machineries in plastids and, 602, 608, 610–11

Photosystems I and II

biochemistry, 526

conclusions, 547

cyclic electron transport, 545–47

electron acceptors, 536

electron donors, 531–33

electron transport, 533–36, 541–43, 545–47

excitation transfer, 536–37, 544–45

higher-order interactions, 525–26

introduction, 522

light harvesting, 536–37, 544–45

molecular biology, 545–47

O_2 evolution, 526–28, 543–44

P700-containing complexes, 526

photosystem I, 528–33

photosystem II, 526–28, 537–45

physiology, 545–47

state transitions, 545–47

structural studies, 528–45

supercomplexes, 524–25

thylakoid membrane-protein complexes, 523–24

thylakoid membranes, 522–23

Phragmoplasts

global gene expression in specific cell types and, 452

PHS1 gene

meiotic prophase I and, 267, 274–75, 278, 285–88

Phycobilisomes

complementary chromatic adaptation and, 128–29, 131–32

Phyllotreta spp.

glucosinolates and, 319

Phylogeny

uncoupling proteins and, 391–94

Physcomitrella patens

global gene expression in specific cell types and, 466

microRNAs and, 25

mosses in metabolism and developmental studies, 497–513

sugar sensing and signaling, 681, 697

Phytochromes

complementary chromatic adaptation and, 127, 131

seasonal control of tuberization in potato and, 155–57

structure and signaling mechanisms

bilin lyases, 841–42

biloprotein photoswitches, 839–41

"central dogma," 839–40

chromophores, 840–41

crystal structure, 842–44

dark reversion, 844–49

DrBphP photosensory core, 842–44

evolution, 851

"forward" reaction, 844–47

future research, 852

introduction, 838

modular domains, 840

molecular mechanisms, 848–51

oxygen-dependent heme catabolism, 842

photoconversion, 839–40

photocycle, 844–49

photosensory core, 841–44

"reverse" reaction, 848

signaling, 848–51

summary points, 851–52

Phytophthora spp.

root exudates and rhizosphere interactions, 234, 248

Phytosiderophores

root exudates and rhizosphere interactions, 242–43

Phytosulfokines

peptide hormones and, 655–56

Phytyl tails

tocopherol and carotenoid synthesis, 726

Pices glauca

pyrimidine/purine biosynthesis and degradation, 827

Pichia angusta

molybdenum cofactor and molybdenum enzymes, 635–36

Pieris rapae

glucosinolates and, 319–20

Pigments

floral pigments and, 761–74

Potato
  seasonal control of tuberization in, 151–72
POTH1 gene
  seasonal control of tuberization in potato and,
    161–62
POTLX-1 gene
  seasonal control of tuberization in potato and,
    163
POTM1 gene
  seasonal control of tuberization in potato and,
    163
Pottia intermedia
  mosses in metabolism and developmental
    studies, 497
Ppbb7 gene
  mosses in metabolism and developmental
    studies, 502
Predator attraction
  root exudates and rhizosphere interactions, 242
Prenylation
  tocopherol and carotenoid synthesis, 725
Preprophase band
  microtubules and plant cortical array, 861, 866,
    870
Primary screen
  meiotic prophase I and, 271–72
pri-miRNAs
  microRNAs and, 29
Proanthocyanidins
  seed flavonoids and, 405, 408–12
Prochlorococus marinus
  tocopherol and carotenoid synthesis, 717
Profilin
  actin cytoskeleton in plant cell growth and, 114
Programmed cell death
  chlorophyll degradation during senescence
    and, 55, 63–64, 67–68
Promoters
  complementary chromatic adaptation and,
    142–43
  quantitative fluorescence microscopy and, 85
  seed flavonoids and, 416–17
  sugar sensing and signaling, 692–93
  transcriptional regulatory networks in
    dehydration and cold stresses, 781
Prophase I
  meiotic, 267–92
Proteases
  protein degradation machineries in plastids
    and, 599–613
Protein concentration controls
  quantitative fluorescence microscopy and, 86

Proteomics
  bioinformatics and, 335, 342–43
  laser microdissection and, 181, 189, 192
  phloem long-distance macromolecular
    trafficking and, 203, 221–22
  protein degradation machineries in plastids
    and, 609
Protonemal stage
  mosses in metabolism and developmental
    studies, 497–513
Protonophores
  uncoupling proteins and, 385, 388, 390
Provitamin A
  tocopherol and carotenoid synthesis, 711–29,
    738
Pseudomonas spp.
  root exudates and rhizosphere interactions,
    235, 247–48, 250–51, 253
Psilotum nudum
  leaf-shape determination mechanism and,
    478–79
PSK genes
  peptide hormones and, 655
Pterins
  molybdenum cofactor and molybdenum
    enzymes, 623–39
ptr genes
  mosses in metabolism and developmental
    studies, 509
PUMP proteins
  uncoupling proteins and, 386–97
Purine degradation
  molybdenum cofactor and molybdenum
    enzymes, 623
Purine nucleotides
  uncoupling proteins and, 390–91
Purine permease
  cytokinins and, 441
Pyrenoids
  history of research, 7
Pyrimidines and purines
  biosynthesis and degradation
    compartmentalization, 808–10
    introduction, 806–8
    nucleotide levels in plant cells, 808–10
    purine catabolism, 822–24
    purine de novo biosynthesis, 817–21,
      827–28
    purine metabolism, 817–22
    purine salvage, 824–25, 827–28
    pyrimidine catabolism, 814–16

chlorophyll degradation during senescence
and, 55–56, 58–60, 64, 67
Red/far-red responsive receptors
phytochrome structure and signaling
mechanisms, 837–52
Red light
complementary chromatic adaptation and,
142–43
Redox signaling
complementary chromatic adaptation and, 127,
133–35
plastid-to-nucleus retrograde signaling and,
739, 748–53
sugar sensing and signaling, 695
Regulatory sequence analysis
bioinformatics and, 341–42
Rehydration
transcriptional regulatory networks in
dehydration and cold stresses, 792–93
Repression
microRNAs and, 33–34
Reproductive development
sugar sensing and signaling, 684–85
Resistance
leaf hydraulic conductance and, 361–63,
366–67
Resource allocation
phloem long-distance macromolecular
trafficking and, 215–16
Respiratory chain
uncoupling proteins and, 384
Retrograde signaling
plastid-to-nucleus retrograde signaling and,
739–53
Reverse genetics
meiotic prophase I and, 273–74
"Reverse" reaction
phytochrome structure and signaling
mechanisms, 848
Rhizobium spp.
phloem long-distance macromolecular
trafficking and, 217
root exudates and rhizosphere interactions,
245–46, 250
Rhizoctonia solani
root exudates and rhizosphere interactions, 252
Rhizosphere
root exudates and rhizosphere interactions,
233–55
Rhizotron
root exudates and rhizosphere interactions, 255
Rhodanese-like domain (RLD)

molybdenum cofactor and molybdenum
enzymes, 630
Rhodopseudomonas palustris
phytochrome structure and signaling
mechanisms, 838
Rhodospirillum spp.
history of research, 8
phytochrome structure and signaling
mechanisms, 838
Ribonucleoprotein (RNP) complex
phloem long-distance macromolecular
trafficking and, 206
RIC genes
actin cytoskeleton in plant cell growth and,
117–18
microtubules and plant cortical array, 871
Ricinus spp.
phloem long-distance macromolecular
trafficking and, 207, 210
Rieske center
chlorophyll degradation during senescence
and, 58
RNA-induced silencing complex (RISC)
microRNAs and, 31–32
RNA interference (RNAi)
microRNAs and, 19, 23, 29, 31
mosses in metabolism and developmental
studies, 497, 512
RNA viruses
phloem long-distance macromolecular
trafficking and, 211–12
Root exudates
rhizosphere interactions and
allelopathy, 236–39
antimicrobial effects, 248–49
biological invasions, 239–40
community-scale interactions, 239–40
conclusions, 255
ecological plant-microbe interactions, 251
induced herbivore resistance, 241–42
introduction, 234–35
methods for studying, 253–55
micronutrients, 242–43
molecular interactions, 243–44
mycorrhizal associations, 246–47
nematodes, 252–53
nodulation of legumes by rhizobia, 245–46
organic acids, 243
parasitic plant-host interactions, 240–41
phosphorus, 243
phytosiderophores, 242–43
plant growth-promoting bacteria, 247–48

unresolved issues, 421

Selaginella spp.
    microRNAs and, 25
    sugar sensing and signaling, 698

Self-incompatibility response
    peptide hormones and, 657–58

Self-organization
    microtubules and plant cortical array, 859,
        869–71

Self-pruning
    seasonal control of tuberization in potato and,
        167

Semantic web
    bioinformatics and, 351

Senescence
    chlorophyll degradation and, 55–69
    sugar sensing and signaling, 685–86

Sequestration
    actin cytoskeleton in plant cell growth and, 114

Serratia marcescens
    root exudates and rhizosphere interactions, 248

Shoot apical meristem
    phloem long-distance macromolecular
        trafficking and, 203–23

Shoots
    cytokinins and, 431–43

Short days
    seasonal control of tuberization in potato and,
        151, 153, 155–67, 169, 172

sid genes
    chlorophyll degradation during senescence
        and, 65

Sieve tube system
    phloem long-distance macromolecular
        trafficking and, 206

Signaling
    actin cytoskeleton in plant cell growth and,
        109, 116–19
    complementary chromatic adaptation and, 127
    cytokinins and, 431–43
    peptide hormones and, 649–67
    phloem long-distance macromolecular
        trafficking and, 203–23
    phytochrome structure and signaling
        mechanisms, 837–52
    plastid-to-nucleus retrograde signaling and,
        739–53
    seasonal control of tuberization in potato and,
        151–72
    sugar sensing and signaling, 675–700
    transcriptional regulatory networks in
        dehydration and cold stresses, 781–95

Silencing complex
    microRNAs and, 31–32

Silene spp.
    laser microdissection and, 192–93

Sinapis alba
    glycosyltransferases of lipophilic small
        molecules and, 584

Sink cells
    sugar sensing and signaling, 675, 679–80

Sinorhizobium meliloti
    root exudates and rhizosphere interactions,
        235, 245, 250, 252

Sister chromatid cohesion
    meiotic prophase I and, 267, 276–90

Size control
    leaf-shape determination mechanism and, 477,
        486–89

Small interfering RNA (siRNAs)
    microRNAs and, 21
    phloem long-distance macromolecular
        trafficking and, 210

Small RNAs (sRNAs)
    phloem long-distance macromolecular
        trafficking and, 210, 221

snf genes
    mosses in metabolism and developmental
        studies, 501
    sugar sensing and signaling, 675, 678, 684,
        694–97

SOC1 gene
    seasonal control of tuberization in potato and,
        172

Soil
    root exudates and rhizosphere interactions,
        242–43

Solanum spp.
    glucosinolates and, 311, 321
    glycosyltransferases of lipophilic small
        molecules and, 582
    pyrimidine/purine biosynthesis and
        degradation, 812, 820–21
    seasonal control of tuberization in potato and,
        151–72
    uncoupling proteins and, 392

Sorghum spp.
    root exudates and rhizosphere interactions,
        236, 238, 241

Source cells
    sugar sensing and signaling, 675, 679–80

Spatial factors
    bioinformatics and, 351
    cytokinins and, 439

Specificity
global gene expression in specific cell types
and, 465–66
microtubules and plant cortical array, 864
seed flavonoids and, 406–10
transcriptional regulatory networks in
dehydration and cold stresses, 781–95
Spectral analysis
complementary chromatic adaptation and, 131
quantitative fluorescence microscopy and, 87,
96–97
Sphagnum spp.
mosses in metabolism and developmental
studies, 497
Spinacia oleracea
chlorophyll degradation during senescence
and, 61
Split-root studies
phloem long-distance macromolecular
trafficking and, 216
SPO genes
meiotic prophase I and, 273, 275, 284, 286
Sporophytes
mosses in metabolism and developmental
studies, 499, 511
spr genes
microtubules and plant cortical array, 865
peptide hormones and, 652
Starvation
sugar sensing and signaling, 686
State transitions
photosystems I and II, 545–47
Stem cell niche
global gene expression in specific cell types
and, 462
Sterility
meiotic prophase I and, 271–72
Steroids
glycosyltransferases of lipophilic small
molecules and, 572, 581–82
Stevia rebaudiana
glycosyltransferases of lipophilic small
molecules and, 581
Stolon meristem
seasonal control of tuberization in potato and,
151, 161–62
Stomata
leaf hydraulic conductance and, 361, 363,
366–67, 372
quantitative fluorescence microscopy and,
95–96
Storage

floral pigments and, 771–72
molybdenum cofactor and molybdenum
enzymes, 634
Streptomyces spp.
root exudates and rhizosphere interactions, 249
Stress response
glycosyltransferases of lipophilic small
molecules and, 567–88
molybdenum cofactor and molybdenum
enzymes, 623, 638
plastid-to-nucleus retrograde signaling and,
752
sugar sensing and signaling, 685–86
transcriptional regulatory networks in
dehydration and cold stresses, 781–95
uncoupling proteins and, 383, 396
Striga spp.
root exudates and rhizosphere interactions, 241
Structural genes
seed flavonoids and, 416–18
Structural studies
photosystems I and II, 528–45
Structure/function relationships
leaf hydraulic conductance and, 367–69
Substrate recognition
glycosyltransferases of lipophilic small
molecules and, 567, 569
Sucrose
seasonal control of tuberization in potato and,
170–71
sugar sensing and signaling, 675, 680
Sugar sensing and signaling
CDPK-SnRK, 694–95
cell surface receptors, 688–89
conclusions, 699–700
development, 681–86
enzymatic activity, 695–96
gene expression, 689–90, 696
genome-wide expression analyses, 690–92
growth, 681–86
hexokinase glucose sensor, 686–88
hormone signaling, 682–84
introduction, 676–77
molecular mechanisms, 689–94
perspectives, 699–700
plants, 679–81
promoter elements, 692–93
protein degradation, 695–96
protein stability, 694
regulation, 689–90, 696–97
reproductive development, 684–85
seed development and germination, 681–84

plastid-to-nucleus retrograde signaling and, 739–53

Text mining
    bioinformatics and, 350

Thermogenesis
    uncoupling proteins and, 383, 394–95

Thermosynechococcus spp.
    photosystems I and II, 527

Thiocyanates
    glucosinolates and, 303–23

Thioglucosidases
    glucosinolates and, 303–23

Thiohydroximic acids
    glucosinolates and, 309–10

Thylakoid membranes
    photosystems I and II, 521–47
    protein degradation machineries in plastids and, 599–613

Tic translocon
    protein degradation machineries in plastids and, 606

Tilling arrays
    bioinformatics and, 341

Tissue/organ development
    uncoupling proteins and, 397

Tocopherol and carotenoid synthesis
    abscicic acid, 718
    agriculture, 720–21
    appendix, 738
    aromatic headgroups, 723–25
    biochemical genomics, 722–23
    β-carotene, 717
    carotenoids, 714–21
    cleavage products, 718–19
    compound abbreviations, 738
    cyanobacteria, 721–27
    desaturation, 714–17
    enzyme abbreviations, 738
    future research, 729
    genetic engineering, 720–21
    homogentisic acid, 725–26
    human health, 720–21
    isomerizations, 714–17
    isoprenoids, 712–13
    lutein, 717–18
    methyltransferases, 726–27
    neoxanthin, 717
    nongreen plastids, 719–20
    phytyl tails, 726
    plants, 721–27
    plastids, 712–13, 719–20
    prenylation, 725

    summary points, 728–29
    tocochromanols, 721–27
    tocopherol cyclase, 727–28
    tocopherol functions, 728
    unresolved issues, 729
    violaxanthin, 717
    vitamin E, 721–23
    zeaxanthin, 717

Tolypothrix spp.
    complementary chromatic adaptation and, 128–30, 136

Topology
    chlorophyll degradation during senescence and, 62–63

Tortula ruralis
    mosses in metabolism and developmental studies, 504

Tradescantia spp.
    microtubules and plant cortical array, 863

Trafficking
    cytokinins and, 442
    phloem long-distance macromolecular trafficking and, 203–23

trans-acting siRNA (ta-siRNA)
    microRNAs and, 27–29

Transcript analysis
    laser microdissection and, 181, 190–92

Transcriptional regulation
    complementary chromatic adaptation and, 135–36
    microRNAs and, 28–29
    seed flavonoids and, 419–20
    sugar sensing and signaling, 690, 693

Transcriptional silencing
    microRNAs and, 34–35

Transcription factors
    microRNAs and, 19
    sugar sensing and signaling, 692–93
    transcriptional regulatory networks in dehydration and cold stresses, 781, 785–88

Transcriptome
    bioinformatics and, 335, 340–42
    global gene expression in specific cell types and, 451, 459–62
    phloem long-distance macromolecular trafficking and, 203, 221–22

Transfer RNA (tRNA) degradation
    cytokinins and, 439

Transit peptides
    protein degradation machineries in plastids and, 602, 610

Translation

glycosyltransferases of lipophilic small
molecules and, 575
meiotic prophase I and, 267–68, 270–76,
278–79, 281, 283–84, 286, 289, 292
pyrimidine/purine biosynthesis and
degradation, 820
root exudates and rhizosphere interactions,
239, 251
uncoupling proteins and, 392, 394
Zeatins
cytokinins and, 431–35, 438

Zeaxanthin
tocopherol and carotenoid synthesis, 717
Zinc-binding motifs
protein degradation machineries in plastids
and, 604, 611
Zinnia spp.
global gene expression in specific cell types
and, 460
peptide hormones and, 655
ZIP1 gene
meiotic prophase I and, 267, 273

Cumulative Indexes

Contributing Authors, Volumes 47–57

Cuccovia I, 57:383–404
Cunningham FX Jr, 49:557–83
Curie C, 54:183–206
Curran AC, 51:433–62
Cushman JC, 50:305–32

D

Darvill AG, 55:109–39
Davenport RJ, 53:67–107
Davies JP, 51:141–66
Dawe RK, 49:371–95
Day DA, 48:493–523
Dean DR, 52:269–95
Debeaujon I, 57:405–30
Deeks MJ, 57:109–25
de Godoy Maia I, 57:383–404
Delhaize E, 52:527–60
DellaPenna D, 50:133–61;
    57:711–38
Delmer DP, 50:245–76
Demidchik V, 53:67–107
Deng X-W, 47:215–43;
    54:165–82
Dennis ES, 49:223–47
Denyer K, 48:67–87
de Souza MP, 51:401–32
Dewitte W, 54:235–64
Dickerson J, 57:335–59
Dietrich MA, 49:501–23
Dietz K-S, 54:93–107
Diner BA, 53:551–80
Dixon RA, 48:251–75;
    55:225–61
Douce R, 51:17–47
Drake BG, 48:609–39
Drew MC, 48:223–50
Dreyfuss BW, 49:25–51
Drozdowicz YM, 49:727–60
Durnford DG, 47:685–714

E

Edwards GE, 55:173–96
Ehrhardt DW, 57:859–75
Elliott KA, 53:131–58
Elthon TE, 55:23–39
Emes MJ, 51:111–40
Epstein E, 50:641–64
Evans LT, 54:1–21, 307–28
Evans MMS, 48:673–701
Evans TC Jr, 56:375–92

Evron Y, 51:83–109

F

Facchini PJ, 52:29–66
Fagard M, 51:167–94
Falciatore A, 53:109–30
Ferl RJ, 47:49–73
Feussner I, 53:275–97
Finnegan EJ, 49:223–47
Fischer RL, 56:327–51
Fletcher JC, 53:45–66
Flint-Garcia SA, 54:357–74
Flügge U-I, 50:27–45;
    56:133–64
Forde BG, 53:203–24
Fox TC, 49:669–96
Foyer CH, 49:249–79
Franceschi VR, 55:173–96;
    56:41–71
Fricker M, 57:79–107
Fromm H, 56:435–66
Frommer WB, 55:341–71
Fujioka S, 54:137–64
Fukayama H, 52:297–314
Fukuda H, 47:299–325
Furbank RT, 52:297–314
Furumoto T, 55:69–84
Furuya M, 55:1–21

G

Galbraith DW, 57:451–75
Galili G, 53:27–43
Galway ME, 54:691–722
Gandotra N, 57:181–201
Gang DR, 56:301–25
Gantt E, 49:557–83
García-Mata C, 54:109–36
Gasser C, 49:1–24
Gatz C, 48:89–108
Gelvin SB, 51:223–56
Genger RK, 49:233–47
Gershenzon J, 57:303–33
Ghoshroy S, 48:27–50
Gibbs M, 50:1–25
Gibbs SP, 57:1–17
Gilroy S, 48:165–90; 57:233–66
Giordano M, 56:99–131
Giovannoni J, 52:725–49
Giraudat J, 49:199–222
Golden SS, 48:327–54

Goldsbrough P, 53:159–82
Gonzalez-Carranza ZH,
    53:131–58
González-Meler MA, 48:609–39
Graziano M, 54:109–36
Green BR, 47:685–714
Greenberg JT, 48:525–45
Grossman A, 52:163–210
Grossniklaus U, 54:547–74
Grotewold E, 57:761–80
Grusak MA, 50:133–61
Guan C, 53:421–47
Gubler F, 55:197–223
Guerinot ML, 49:669–96
Gutu A, 57:127–50

H

Halkier BA, 57:303–33
Hamant O, 57:267–302
Hammond-Kosack KE,
    48:575–607
Hankamer B, 48:641–71
Hanson AD, 52:119–37
Harberd NP, 52:67–88
Hardie DG, 50:97–131
Harmon A, 55:263–88
Harper JF, 51:433–62;
    55:263–88
Harries P, 57:497–520
Harris EH, 52:363–406
Harrison MJ, 50:361–89
Hasegawa PM, 51:463–99
Hauser B, 49:1–24
Hedden P, 48:431–60
Henderson JHM, 52:1–28
Henikoff S, 54:375–401
Hepler PK, 48:461–91
Herrera-Estrella L, 49:525–55
Herrmann KM, 50:473–503
Hetherington AM, 55:401–27
Hirt H, 55:373–99
Hoekenga OA, 55:459–93
Holbrook NM, 57:361–81
Holstein SE, 56:221–51
Hörtensteiner S, 50:67–95;
    57:55–77
Horton P, 47:655–84
Hsieh T-F, 56:327–51
Huang D, 47:477–508
Huber JL, 47:431–44
Huber SC, 47:431–44

Hudson A, 51:349–70
Hugouvieux V, 52:627–58
Huner NPA, 54:329–55
Hussey PJ, 57:109–25
Hwang I, 51:433–62

I

Iba K, 53:225–45
Ingram J, 47:377–403
Ishii T, 55:109–39
Ishiura M, 48:327–54
Isogai A, 56:467–89
Izui K, 55:69–84

J

Jacquot J-P, 51:371–400
Jaworski JG, 48:109–36
Job D, 51:17–47
John P, 47:245–71
Johnson CH, 48:327–54
Johnson EA, 51:83–109
Jones DL, 52:527–60
Jones JDG, 48:575–607
Jones-Rhoades MW,
    57:19–53
Jung H, 57:739–59
Jürgens G, 56:281–99

K

Kader J-C, 47:627–54
Kagawa T, 54:455–68
Kai Y, 55:69–84
Kakimoto T, 54:605–27
Kamiya Y, 48:431–60
Kaplan A, 50:539–70
Kato N, 55:537–54
Kehoe DM, 57:127–50
Kerfeld CA, 49:397–425
Kessler A, 53:299–328
Ketelaar T, 57:109–25
Kieber JJ, 48:277–96
King KE, 52:67–88
King RW, 54:307–28
Kinney AJ, 52:335–61
Koch KE, 47:509–40
Kochian L, 55:459–93
Koltunow AM, 54:547–74
Komeda Y, 55:521–35
Kondo T, 48:327–54

Koornneef M, 49:345–70;
    55:141–72
Kotani H, 49:151–71
Koussevitzky S, 57:739–59
Krogmann DW, 49:397–425
Kwak JM, 52:627–58
Kyozuka J, 53:399–419

L

Lagarias J, 57:837–58
Lalonde S, 55:341–71
Lam E, 55:537–54
Lam H-M, 47:569–93
Lamattina L, 54:109–36
Lamb C, 48:251–75
Larkin JC, 54:403–30
Lartey R, 48:27–50
Leigh RA, 50:447–72
Leon P, 49:453–80
Lepiniec L, 57:405–30
Leuchtmann A, 55:315–40
Leung J, 49:199–222
Leustek T, 51:141–66
Leyser O, 53:377–98; 56:353–74
Li Z-S, 49:727–60
Liang F, 51:433–62
Lichtenthaler HK, 50:47–65
Lim E, 57:567–97
Lin C, 54:469–96
Liu T, 57:181–201
Loewus FA, 52:437–67
Long SP, 48:609–39; 55:557–94
Lough TJ, 57:203–32
Lu Y-P, 49:727–60
Luan S, 54:63–92
Lucas WJ, 57:203–32
Lukaszewski KM, 49:481–500

M

Ma H, 56:393–434; 57:267–302
MacKay JJ, 49:585–609
Mackenzie S, 49:453–80
MacMillan J, 47:1–21
Maeshima M, 52:469–97
Maliga P, 55:289–313
Mandoli DF, 49:173–98
Marion-Poll A, 56:165–85
Marks MD, 48:137–63
Marrs KA, 47:127–58
Martin C, 48:67–87

Martin GB, 54:23–61
Martin MN, 51:141–66
Martinez SE, 47:477–508
Martinoia E, 49:727–60
Masson PH, 53:421–47
Matsubayashi Y, 57:649–74
Matile P, 50:67–95
Matsumura H, 55:69–84
Matsuoka M, 52:297–314
Maurel C, 48:399–429
McAndrew RS, 52:315–33
McCarty RE, 51:83–109
McClung CR, 52:139–62
McCourt P, 50:219–43
McCully ME, 50:695–718
McCurdy DW, 54:431–54
McIntosh L, 48:703–34
McSteen P, 56:353–74
Meijer HJG, 54:265–306
Melo-Oliveira R, 47:569–93
Mendel RR, 57:623–47
Merchant S, 49:25–51
Meyer P, 47:23–48
Miernyk JA, 53:357–75
Miller AJ, 52:659–88
Miyao M, 52:297–314
Mok DWS, 52:89–118
Mok MC, 52:89–118
Møller IM, 52:561–91
Mooney BP, 53:357–75
Moore G, 51:195–222
Moore I, 57:79–107
Morell MK, 54:207–33
Mudgett M, 56:509–31
Mullet JE, 48:355–81
Munnik T, 54:265–306
Murata N, 47:541–68
Murphy AS, 56:221–51
Murray JAH, 54:235–64

N

Nagy F, 53:329–55
Nakata PA, 56:41–71
Nambara E, 56:165–85
Nelson N, 57:521–65
Nelson T, 57:181–201
Nesi N, 57:405–30
Neuhaus HE, 51:111–40
Nielsen K, 52:785–816
Nishida I, 47:541–68
Niyogi KK, 50:333–59

Noctor G, 49:249–79
Nott A, 57:739–59

O

Oaks A, 51:1–16
Offler CE, 54:431–54
Ohlrogge JB, 48:109–36
Okita TW, 47:327–50
O'Leary MH, 47:273–98
Oliveira IC, 47:569–93
Olsen O-A, 52:233–67
O'Neill MA, 55:109–39
Oparka KJ, 51:323–47
Öquist G, 54:329–55
Ort DR, 55:557–94
Osteryoung KW, 52:315–33

P

Pagnussat G, 54:109–36
Palmgren MG, 52:817–45
Pantoja O, 47:159–84
Patrick JW, 48:191–222;
    54:431–54
Peacock WJ, 49:223–47
Peer WA, 56:221–51
Peeters AJM, 49:345–70
Peltier G, 53:523–50
Perry LG, 57:233–66
Pilon-Smits E, 56:15–39
Piñeros MA, 55:459–93
Plaxton WC, 47:185–214
Pogson B, 57:711–38
Ponomarev M, 47:477–508
Poppenberger B, 57:567–97
Post-Beittenmiller D,
    47:405–30
Pourcel L, 57:405–30
Pradhan S, 56:375–92
Prat S, 57:151–80
Prescott AG, 47:245–71

Q

Quatrano R, 57:497–520

R

Rademacher W, 51:501–31
Raghothama KG, 50:665–93

Ralph J, 54:519–46
Randall DD, 53:357–75
Rappaport F, 53:551–80
Raskin I, 49:643–68
Rasmusson AG, 55:23–39
Ratcliffe RG, 52:499–526
Raven JA, 56:99–131
Rea PA, 49:727–60
Reinhold L, 50:539–70
Rhee SY, 57:335–59
Richards DE, 52:67–88
Roberts JA, 53:131–58
Robertson D, 55:495–519
Rockwell NC, 57:837–58
Rodríguez-Falcón M, 57:151–80
Rogers A, 55:557–94
Rogers JC, 47:327–50
Roje S, 52:119–37
Rolland F, 57:675–709
Routaboul J, 57:405–30
Ruban AV, 47:655–84
Runions J, 57:79–107
Ryan PR, 52:527–60

S

Sack L, 57:361–81
Saedler H, 47:23–47
Sakagami Y, 57:649–74
Sakakibara H, 57:431–49
Sakamoto W, 57:599–621
Salt DE, 49:643–68
Salvucci ME, 53:449–75
Santa Cruz S, 51:323–47
Sasse JM, 49:427–51
Sato Y, 54:455–68
Schaefer DG, 53:477–501
Schäfer E, 53:329–55
Schardl CL, 55:315–40
Scheres B, 50:505–37
Schiefelbein J, 54:403–30
Schnell DJ, 49:97–126
Schroeder JI, 52:627–58
Schuler MA, 54:629–67
Schumaker KS, 49:501–23
Schürmann P, 51:371–400
Schwacke R, 56:133–64
Schwarz G, 57:623–47
Schwechheimer C, 49:127–50
Sederoff RR, 49:585–609
Seefeldt LC, 52:269–95
Sentenac H, 54:575–603

Serino G, 54:165–82
Sessa G, 54:23–61
Shachar-Hill Y, 52:499–526
Shalitin D, 54:469–96
Shanklin J, 49:611–41
Sharkey TD, 52:407–36
Shaw SL, 57:859–75
Sheen J, 50:187–217;
    57:675–709
Sheng J, 48:27–50
Shimamoto K, 53:399–419
Shinozaki K, 57:781–803
Simpson CG, 49:77–95
Sinha N, 50:419–46
Smalle J, 55:555–90
Smeekens S, 51:49–81
Smirnoff N, 52:437–67
Smith AM, 48:67–87; 56:73–97
Smith JL, 47:477–508
Smith RD, 47:101–25;
    49:643–68
Smith SM, 56:73–97
Snedden WA, 56:435–66
Sonnewald U, 57:805–36
Soole KL, 55:23–39
Soppe W, 49:345–70
Soriano GM, 47:477–508
Spiering MJ, 55:315–40
Spreitzer RJ, 53:449–75
Staiger CJ, 51:257–88
Starlinger P, 56:1–13
Stenmark P, 54:497–517
Steudle E, 52:847–75
Stitt M, 57:805–36
Su Y, 57:837–58
Sugiura M, 48:383–98
Sun T-p, 55:197–223
Sung S, 56:491–508
Sussex I, 49:xiii–xxii
Sussex IM, 47:351–76
Sze H, 51:433–62
Szymkowiak EJ, 47:351–76

T

Tabata S, 49:151–71
Takahashi H, 52:163–210
Takayama S, 56:467–89
Talbot MJ, 54:431–54
Tanner W, 47:595–626
Tarun AS, 51:401–32
Tausta SL, 57:181–201

Taylor LP, 48:461–91
Terry N, 51:401–32
Tester M, 53:67–107
Thomas H, 50:67–95
Thomashow MF, 50:571–99
Thornsberry JM, 54:357–74
Tolbert NE, 48:1–25
Tomos AD, 50:447–72
Trapp S, 52:689–724
Tsukaya H, 57:477–96

U

Udvardi MK, 48:493–523

V

Vaistij FE, 57:567–97
Vanlerberghe GC, 48:703–34
Vaucheret H, 51:167–94
Vercesi A, 57:383–404
Verma DPS, 52:751–84
Véry A-A, 54:575–603
Vidal J, 47:273–98
Vierstra RD, 55:555–90
Vivanco JM, 57:233–66

Voelker T, 52:335–61
von Arnim A, 47:215–43
Voznesenskaya EE, 55:173–96
Vreugdenhil D, 55:141–72

W

Wada M, 54:455–68
Walker JC, 47:101–25
Walters RG, 47:655–84
Waner D, 52:627–58
Wang X, 52:211–31
Wasteneys GO, 54:691–722
Wasternack C, 53:275–97
Watanabe K, 55:537–54
Weaver LM, 50:473–503
Weber APM, 56:133–64
Weber H, 56:253–79
Weckwerth W, 54:669–89
Weir TL, 57:233–66
Werck-Reichhart D, 54:629–67
Whetten RW, 49:585–609
Williams LE, 52:659–88
Winkel BSJ, 55:85–107
Wipf D, 55:341–71
Wobus U, 56:253–79

X

Xiong J, 53:503–21
Xu D, 57:335–59
Xu M-Q, 56:375–92

Y

Yamaguchi-Shinozaki K,
    57:781–803
Ye Z-H, 53:183–202
Yeh S, 52:407–36
Yellin A, 56:435–66
Yocum CF, 57:521–65
Yokota T, 54:137–64

Z

Zayed AM, 51:401–32
Zeeman SC, 56:73–97
Zhang H, 47:477–508
Zhu J-K, 51:463–62;
    53:247–73
Zielinski RE, 49:697–725
Zourelidou M, 49:127–50
Zrenner R, 57:805–36

Chapter Titles, Volumes 47–57

ANNUAL REVIEWS
Intelligent Synthesis of the Scientific Literature

Annual Reviews – Your Starting Point for Research Online
http://arjournals.annualreviews.org

- Over 900 Annual Reviews volumes—more than 25,000 critical, authoritative review articles in 31 disciplines spanning the Biomedical, Physical, and Social sciences— available online, including all Annual Reviews back volumes, dating to 1932

- Current individual subscriptions include seamless online access to full-text articles, PDFs, Reviews in Advance (as much as 6 months ahead of print publication), bibliographies, and other supplementary material in the current volume and the prior 4 years' volumes

- All articles are fully supplemented, searchable, and downloadable — see http://arplant.annualreviews.org

- Access links to the reviewed references (when available online)

- Site features include customized alerting services, citation tracking, and saved searches

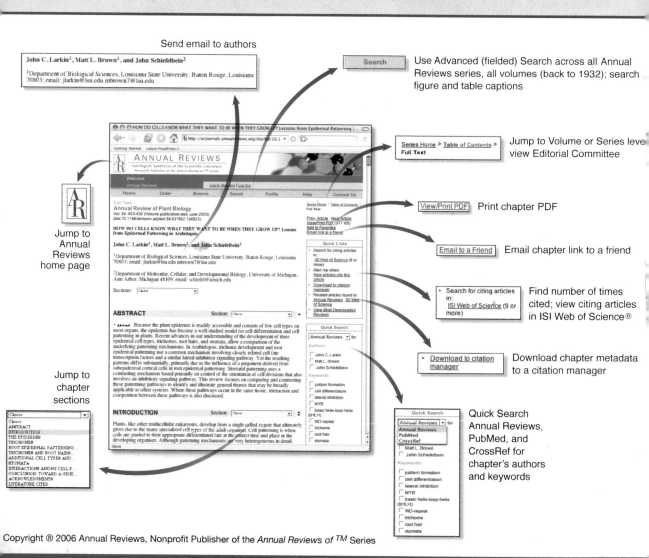

Send email to authors

Use Advanced (fielded) Search across all Annual Reviews series, all volumes (back to 1932); search figure and table captions

Jump to Volume or Series level view Editorial Committee

Print chapter PDF

Jump to Annual Reviews home page

Email chapter link to a friend

Find number of times cited; view citing articles in ISI Web of Science®

Download chapter metadata to a citation manager

Jump to chapter sections

Quick Search Annual Reviews, PubMed, and CrossRef for chapter's authors and keywords